MCAT®

Science Workbook

2016 Edition

Contributors and Acknowledgments

Original course materials edited for production by Judene Wright, M.S., M.A.Ed., National Content Director for the TPR MCAT Program, who would like to thank all of the TPR MCAT science developers, including Alison Baxter, Bethany Blackwell, M.S.; Chris Burgess, Psy.D.; Erika C. Castro, B.A.; Maria S. Chushak, M.S.; Guenevieve O. Del Mundo, B.A., B.S., C.C.S.; William Ewing, Ph.D.; Cara Fabre, Ph.D.; Chris Fortenbach, B.S.; Jon Fowler, M.A.; Michelle E. Fox, B.S.; K. Beth Hollingsworth; Nadia Johnson, M.A., M.S.; Sarah Kass, Ph.D., Brandon T. Kelley, Ph.D.; Tom Kurtovic; Ali Landreau, B.A.; Heather Liwanag, Ph.D.; Toni Lupro, B.A.; Mike Matera, B.A.; Douglas K. McLemore, B.S.; Jonathan Nasrallah, B.A., Jason Osman, Ph.D., Chris Pentzell, M.S.; Steve Rines, Ph.D.; Shalom Shapiro; Andrew Snyder, M.S.; Laurie Stickney, M.S.; Felicia Tam, Ph.D.; Jenkang Tao, B.S., B.A., Alexandra Vinson, Chelsea K. Wise, M.S.; Sarah Woodruff, B.S., B.A.

Special thanks to all former contributors, including James Patrick Abulencia, Ph.D.; Jes Adams, Ph.D.; Peter J. Alaimo, Ph.D.; John Bahling, M.D.; Garrett T. Biehle, Ph.D.; Kendra Bowman, Kristen Brunson, Ph.D.; Clay Cauthen, M.D.; Glenn E. Croston, Ph.D.; Douglas S. Daniels, Ph.D.; Joshua Dilworth, M.D., Ph.D.; Frank Gibson, Ph.D.; Scott C. Johnson, Najeeb Khan, Matthew D. Kohler, Ph.D.; Stefan Loren, Ph.D.; Allen Nicol, Ph.D.; Daniel J. Pallin, M.D.; Matthew Patterson, M.D.; Karen Salazar, Ph.D.; Carolyn Shiau, M.D.; Kirk Tanner, and Christopher M. Volpe, Ph.D.

The Princeton Review would also like to thank all of the following:
Terese Alban, Kyle Alexander, Trevor Andrews, Hillary Anger, Salman Baig, Donna Barba, Nancy Beth Barr, Tom Barry, Elizabeth Barrekette, Jinhee Bae, John Bergdahl, Steve Borstelman, Jessica Brockington, Kristin Brown, Ian Carleton, Alex Carney, Joe Cavallaro, Cecelia Chao, Mina Chong, Kasia Clark, Peggy Cloutier, Lyndall Culbertson, Patrick Darby, Shannon Daugherty, Joseph Deltoro, Ray Dykeman, Leland Elliot, Fritz Engebrethsen, Alicia Ernst, Jen Ewart, Mary Favier, Alan Feinberg, Julie Fisher, Doug French, Michael Gamerl, Jay Glick, Nell Goddin, Mitchell Golden, Joe Goy, Kalee Gregory, Even Gross, Deborah Guest, Russell Haddock, Michael Haile, Julian Ham, Clayton Harding, Ken Howard, Adam Hurwitz, Sara Hymowitz, Norm Issa, Justin Jackson, Brett Jaffe, Sora Jun, Peter Jung, Andrew Kagan, Sara Kane, Jason Kasin, David Kaufman, Jeff Kelley, Bill Kerr, Meher Khambata, Robert Y. Kim, Julie Lapp, Laura Lee, Warren Leung, Lila Kal, Martha Link, John Litter, Karen Lurie, Illeny Maaza, Lisa Mack, Mark Malanowsky, Tom Meltzer, Andre Manitiu, Steve Menzies, Colin Morley, Elahe Mostaghel, Joe Mrus, Bryan Natinsky, Ray Nazzario, Jeff Newman, Jeff Nichols, Mike Nunley, Orestes O'Brien, Richard Onishi, John Orsay, John Pak, Karl Pankratz, Dinica Quesada, Andrea Paykin, Laurice Pearson, Gillian Perrone, Seijen Ra, Josh Rabinovich, Ken Riley, Grace Roegner, Jenny Robbins, Lisa Ruyter, Sharjeel H. Sabir, Eric Schroeder, Christopher D. Scott, Marc Seiden, Nilanjan Sen, Jason Shave, Kelly Shrago, Jonathan Silver, Leonard Silver, Carol Slominski, Kristine Smart, Carrie Smith, Susan Stroud, Michael Stuart, John Sun, Aaron Sylvan, Rob Tallia, Johnny Tang, Linda Tarleton, Chris Thomas, Jeff Thompson, Sam Tomasello, Gary Ulaner, Kirsten Ulve, Ed Urbansky, Todd Weiser, Taylor Weiss, Eric Wertzer, Rick Westreich, Joanna Whiteley, Susan Wilcox, Barry Witner, Rose Wong, David Wright, Gail Zarick, Jordan Zaretsky, and Rob Zopf.

Special thanks to Paul Foglino, Kim Magloire, Paul Maniscalco, and John Mariani.

PrincetonReview.com

Contents

Periodic Table of the Elements

1																	2
H 1.0																	**He** 4.0
3 **Li** 6.9	4 **Be** 9.0											5 **B** 10.8	6 **C** 12.0	7 **N** 14.0	8 **O** 16.0	9 **F** 19.0	10 **Ne** 20.2
11 **Na** 23.0	12 **Mg** 24.3											13 **Al** 27.0	14 **Si** 28.1	15 **P** 31.0	16 **S** 32.1	17 **Cl** 35.5	18 **Ar** 39.9
19 **K** 39.1	20 **Ca** 40.1	21 **Sc** 45.0	22 **Ti** 47.9	23 **V** 50.9	24 **Cr** 52.0	25 **Mn** 54.9	26 **Fe** 55.8	27 **Co** 58.9	28 **Ni** 58.7	29 **Cu** 63.5	30 **Zn** 65.4	31 **Ga** 69.7	32 **Ge** 72.6	33 **As** 74.9	34 **Se** 79.0	35 **Br** 79.9	36 **Kr** 83.8
37 **Rb** 85.5	38 **Sr** 87.6	39 **Y** 88.9	40 **Zr** 91.2	41 **Nb** 92.9	42 **Mo** 95.9	43 **Tc** (98)	44 **Ru** 101.1	45 **Rh** 102.9	46 **Pd** 106.4	47 **Ag** 107.9	48 **Cd** 112.4	49 **In** 114.8	50 **Sn** 118.7	51 **Sb** 121.8	52 **Te** 127.6	53 **I** 126.9	54 **Xe** 131.3
55 **Cs** 132.9	56 **Ba** 137.3	57 ***La** 138.9	72 **Hf** 178.5	73 **Ta** 180.9	74 **W** 183.9	75 **Re** 186.2	76 **Os** 190.2	77 **Ir** 192.2	78 **Pt** 195.1	79 **Au** 197.0	80 **Hg** 200.6	81 **Tl** 204.4	82 **Pb** 207.2	83 **Bi** 209.0	84 **Po** (209)	85 **At** (210)	86 **Rn** (222)
87 **Fr** (223)	88 **Ra** 226.0	89 **†Ac** 227.0	104 **Rf** (261)	105 **Db** (262)	106 **Sg** (266)	107 **Bh** (264)	108 **Hs** (277)	109 **Mt** (268)	110 **Ds** (281)	111 **Rg** (272)	112 **Cn** (285)	113 **Uut** (286)	114 **Fl** (289)	115 **Uup** (288)	116 **Lv** (293)	117 **Uus** (294)	118 **Uuo** (294)

*Lanthanide Series:

58 **Ce** 140.1	59 **Pr** 140.9	60 **Nd** 144.2	61 **Pm** (145)	62 **Sm** 150.4	63 **Eu** 152.0	64 **Gd** 157.3	65 **Tb** 158.9	66 **Dy** 162.5	67 **Ho** 164.9	68 **Er** 167.3	69 **Tm** 168.9	70 **Yb** 173.0	71 **Lu** 175.0

†Actinide Series:

90 **Th** 232.0	91 **Pa** (231)	92 **U** 238.0	93 **Np** (237)	94 **Pu** (244)	95 **Am** (243)	96 **Cm** (247)	97 **Bk** (247)	98 **Cf** (251)	99 **Es** (252)	100 **Fm** (257)	101 **Md** (258)	102 **No** (259)	103 **Lr** (260)

MCAT General Chemistry
Passages

Passage 1 (Questions 1-5)

The transition metals are characterized by valence electrons that lie within the d subshell. Those positioned in the third period of the periodic table, like chromium and iron, undergo serial filling of orbitals in the $3d$ subshell and have the general electron configuration [Ar] $4s^x 3d^y$ where [Ar] represents the electron configuration for the noble gas argon, x is the number of electrons in the $4s$ subshell and y is the number of electrons in the $3d$ subshell.

For iron in the +3 oxidation state (Fe^{3+}) the electron configuration is [Ar] $3d^5$. In transforming from a neutral to a +3 state, the iron atom first loses two electrons from the $4s$ subshell and then an electron from the $3d$ subshell.

In general, transition metals may assume multiple oxidation states. Although metals tend to form basic oxides (e.g., Na_2O) and nonmetals tend to form acidic oxides (e.g., SO_3), transition metal oxides may be acidic or basic depending on the oxidation state of the metal. For example, Mn_2O_7 is highly acidic while MnO is basic.

This behavior of the oxides, or anhydrides as they are also known, may be better understood in terms of the elemental hydroxides. Reaction of the two manganese oxides above with water takes place as follows:

$$Mn_2O_7 + H_2O \rightarrow 2\,H^+ + 2\,MnO_4^-$$
$$MnO + H_2O \rightarrow Mn^{2+} + 2\,OH^-$$

The difference in behavior between the two oxides and their hydroxides results from the relative sizes of the M–O electronegativity difference ($\Delta\chi_{M-O}$). When $\Delta\chi_{M-O}$ is less than $\Delta\chi_{O-H}$, the O–H bond has ionic character, and the proton may dissociate; consequently, the metal hydroxide is an acid. This type of behavior is observed in metal anhydrides in which the metal has a high oxidation state (usually greater than +5).

On the other hand, $\Delta\chi_{M-O}$ is greater than $\Delta\chi_{O-H}$, the M–OH bond has ionic character, and the hydroxide may dissociate; accordingly, the metal hydroxide is basic. Generally, metal anhydrides are basic when the oxidation state of the metal is less than or equal to +4.

1. Knowing that the transition metal chromium may assume the oxidation states +2, +3, +4, +5, or +6, a researcher attempted to identify the oxidation state of chromium in an oxide of unknown formula: Cr_mO_n. The compound was completely dissolved in water and the pH of the resulting solution was measured to be 6.0. Among the following, the formula for the experimental Cr_mO_n molecule is most likely:

   6 = acidic

   A. CrO_2.
   B. CrO_3.
   C. CrO_4.
   D. Cr_2O.

2. The electronic configuration [Ar] $4s^2 3d^5$ corresponds to a neutral atom of the element:

   A. manganese.
   B. technetium.
   C. chromium.
   D. vanadium.

3. Based upon closed-shell and half-closed shell considerations, which of the following metals is the LEAST reactive?

   A. Li(s)
   B. K(s)
   C. Mg(s)
   D. Cu(s)

4. Compounds I and II, two oxides of the same transition metal, are placed separately into two vessels of aqueous media. Compound I produces an acidic solution, and Compound II produces a basic solution. It can be concluded that the metal–oxide bonding in:

   A. Compounds I and II are nonpolar.
   B. Compound I is more polar than is the bonding in Compound II.
   C. Compound I is more ionic, and the bonding in Compound II is more covalent.
   D. Compound I is more covalent, and the bonding in Compound II is more ionic.

5. Which of the following would NOT be predicted to be paramagnetic based on the electronic configurations given?

   A. Sc^{2+} — [Ar] $3d^1$
   B. Mn^{2+} — [Ar] $3d^5$
   C. Co^{3+} — [Ar] $3d^6$
   D. Zn^{2+} — [Ar] $3d^{10}$

Passage 2 (Questions 1-6)

The unique electronic structure of an atom determines all of its chemical properties. One of the most exploited properties of an atom is stimulated photon emission through the use of heat.

Laboratory Bunsen burners have flames that are hot enough for many atoms and ions to absorb sufficient energy to promote one of their valence electrons into the next higher energy level, thus becoming excited. Once excited, the atom or ion will eventually relax into the ground state, whereby the excited electron drops back down to its original valence orbital. In order for the atom or ion to return to the ground state, the excited electron must emit the same amount of energy it absorbed (the energy difference between excited and ground states) in the form of a photon of light. Hence, atoms and ions can impart characteristic colors to flames, as the emitted photons often correspond to specific wavelengths in the visible spectrum.

Emitted energy is unique for every element and ion and thereby serves as a fingerprint. The energetic spacing of the electron orbitals can be determined by examining the emission photons of an atom or ion. Although the vast majority of atoms and ions emit photons of higher energy, some ions emit photons in the visible region of the spectra and can be seen by human eyes as glowing a particular color.

The following table lists a few ions that emit bright colors when strongly heated; these are the ions that are added to a flame to produce beautiful and entertaining fireworks.

Ion	Observed color when heated
lithium	red
strontium	red
sodium	yellow
barium	green
potassium	violet
copper(I)	blue

Table 1

1. Which of the following ions from Table 1 has the greatest energy of excitation?

    A. Sodium
    B. Barium
    C. Potassium
    D. Copper(I)

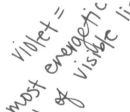

2. There is a direct correlation with atomic size and emission spectra/color between atoms or ions that have the same valence structure. Based on the information above, heated radium ions might appear:

    A. red.
    B. yellow.
    C. green.
    D. violet.

3. Magnesium metal burns in air with a brilliant white flame. Why?

    A. Magnesium's excited state corresponds to the energy of white photons.
    B. Magnesium is undergoing several different electronic transitions at the same time.
    C. Oxygen atoms always emit UV light during combustion.
    D. When heated, magnesium emits x-rays, which appear white to the human retina.

4. What color might a tube of heated cesium ions glow?

    A. Blue
    B. Orange
    C. Green
    D. The emitted radiation is not in the visible region.

5. The reduction of any of the ions in Table 1 with a single electron would result in a species that is:

    A. negatively charged.
    B. paramagnetic.
    C. diamagnetic.
    D. radioactive.

6. What is a possible electronic structure for an excited Cu(I) ion?

    A. [Ar] $4s^1 3d^{10}$
    B. [Ar] $3d^{10}$
    C. [Ar] $4s^2 3d^9$
    D. [Ar] $3d^9 4p^1$

Passage 3 (Questions 1-4)

The static x-ray has been the principal diagnostic tool used by physicians to provide comprehensive images of internal anatomy. Only recently have non-destructive diagnostic techniques, such as magnetic resonance imaging (MRI), been widely available to most physicians.

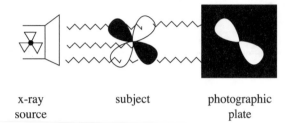

| x-ray | subject | photographic |
| source | | plate |

In a conventional x-ray device, the subject is placed between an x-ray source and a photographic plate. A high voltage cathode tube is used to produce a burst of x-rays traveling at 3.0×10^8 m/sec that irradiate the subject. High energy photons (x-rays and γ-rays) easily travel through matter because atoms are mostly empty space. Only collisions with the innermost electrons deflect or absorb x-rays. The remainder of the photons—those that pass cleanly through the subject—strike the photographic film.

Photographic film consists of AgBr and AgI crystals fixed on a transparent plastic resin. All photons with energy greater than those of infrared cause electrons to cluster in crevices on the surface of the crystals. Later, when the film is processed, metallic silver is deposited at these sites. Deposited silver is so finely divided that it appears black, not metallic. The final product, called a negative image, has dark areas where the film has been exposed to light, and transparent areas where no light reached the film.

1. A warning tag containing photographic film would not indicate exposure to:

    A. x-rays.
    B. microwaves.
    C. ultraviolet light.
    D. gamma rays.

2. Which one of the following elements should be the most opaque to x-rays?

    A. Hydrogen
    B. Lead
    C. Uranium
    D. Calcium

3. Ionizing forms of energy such as x-rays and nuclear radiation cause cellular dysfunction at the location of absorbance. Extreme exposure to x-rays might result in a dramatic increase in the risk of developing:

    A. bone marrow cancer.
    B. thyroid cancer.
    C. lung cancer.
    D. lymphogenous leukemia.

4. Following exposure to a burst of γ-rays, a pure sample of sodium chloride began to exhaust a small amount of argon. What process did the gamma rays initiate in the salt?

    A. α decay of sodium
    B. α decay of chloride
    C. β^- decay of chloride
    D. β^+ decay of chloride

Cons = BGR

Passage 4 (Questions 1-6)

Vision is facilitated by specialized cells called *rods* and *cones* which line the human retina. While rod cells serve as the primary photosensor in the eye, color perception is the sole function of cone cells. Cone cells come in either blue, green, or red types as determined by the color-sensitive molecule present. In other words, blue cones contain only blue-sensitive pigment, green cones contain only green-sensitive pigment, and red cones contain only red-sensitive pigment.

Color-sensing pigments are organic molecules that undergo electronic excitation when exposed to a narrow range of photon energy. Although each pigment has a maximum sensitivity to one particular wavelength of light, all three pigments have some sensitivity towards photons within 50 to 100 nanometers of this sensitivity maximum wavelength, as shown by the curves below:

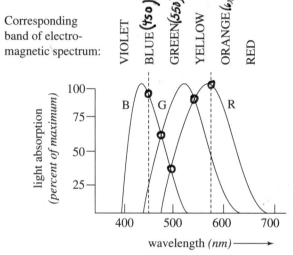

BLUE cone = B,   GREEN cone = G,   RED cone = R

Color is nothing more than the brain's interpretation of the relative ratio of the levels of excitation of the blue, green, and red cones. The brain maintains a library of possible cone excitation ratios and the colors that are to be assigned to them.

For example, based upon the table above, if a photon of light excites the blue cone to 90% and the green cone to 15%, then the brain indicates that the color blue is observed. Likewise, if a photon of light excites the red cone 100% and the green cone 50%, the color is perceived as being orange. These examples are highlighted by the dotted lines in the figure above.

If no message from any cone is received, the brain interprets the image as being gray, while if all three types of cones are excited to an equivalent degree, the brain interprets this as being white.

1. Which of the following light-sensing pigments has the greatest energy of excitation?

   A. Blue-sensitive pigment
   B. Green-sensitive pigment
   C. Red-sensitive pigment
   D. Cannot be determined from the information given

2. What is the approximate ratio of the energy of a photon with the sensitivity maximum wavelength for the red cone to that for the blue cone?

   A. 1:2
   B. 2:1
   C. 2:3
   D. 3:2

   600 : 450   Energy is inversely prop. to wavelength

3. A blinking light which first emits photons that stimulate the red and green cones equally and then emits photons that stimulate the blue and green cones equally would appear:

   A. red followed by blue.
   B. yellow followed by green.
   C. orange followed by blue.
   D. white all the time.

4. Which of the following statements is FALSE?

   A. The sensitivity maximum wavelengths of the blue, green, and red cones do not necessarily correspond to the colors blue, green, and red.
   B. Using an external light source, it is physically impossible to exclusively stimulate green cones in the presence of red and blue cones in the human eye.
   C. The chemical structure of the red and blue cones is more similar than that of the red and green cones.
   D. No individual photon can excite all three types of cones equally, hence, no single wavelength of light can be perceived as being white.

5. Neglecting the participation of rod cells, the color that should appear the most intense (i.e., the brightest) to the human eye is:

   A. red.
   B. yellow.
   C. blue.
   D. violet.

6. Which one of the following statements is true?

   A. Violet light has a longer wavelength than red light, so it must have a higher energy.
   B. Orange photons have a higher frequency than green photons.
   C. If the $n = 4$ to $n = 3$ electronic transition of an element generates yellow photons, then the $n = 3$ to $n = 2$ transition could generate green photons.
   D. The electronic transition from $n = 0$ to $n = 1$ is an emission process, while the transition from $n = 1$ to $n = 0$ is an absorption process.

Passage 5 (Questions 1-6)

Protons and neutrons, collectively known as nucleons, are bound together to form nuclei by the strong nuclear force. Although this force acts over very short distances only, it is much stronger than the electromagnetic force, so nuclei are held together despite the electrical repulsion of its constituent protons.

The number of protons in a nucleus is called the atomic number, denoted by Z; the number of neutrons is denoted by N; and the total number of protons and neutrons, $Z + N$, is called the mass number, denoted by A. Stable nuclei with low values of Z tend to have the same (or a slightly greater) number of neutrons than protons, while stable nuclei with large values of Z have $N > Z$. In both cases these excess neutrons help to stabilize the Coulomb repulsion of the protons, but when $Z \geq 26$ they can contribute to instability since too many neutrons makes the nucleus susceptible to beta decay.

It has been determined that certain values of Z and/or N can confer extra stability to a nucleus. These special values are called *magic numbers*, the first seven of which are

2, 8, 20, 28, 50, 82, and 126

A nucleus that has a magic number of protons or a magic number of neutrons is said to be *magic* and is tightly bound and usually quite stable. If a nucleus has a magic number of protons *and* a magic number of neutrons, it's said to be *doubly magic*, and is very tightly bound, stable, and abundant.

Just as an atom's electrons occupy quantized energy states, the *nuclear shell model*—proposed by the Nobel laureates Maria Goeppert Mayer and J. H. D. Jensen—says that nucleons also occupy quantized energy states as they orbit within the confines of a nucleus. Like electrons in atoms, nucleons fill states in the nucleus which depend on quantum numbers for energy, angular momentum, and spin.

The quantum numbers for a nucleon are n, J, and m_J. The principal quantum number, n, which relates to energy, can take on positive whole number values only: $n = 1, 2, 3$, etc. J is the total angular momentum quantum number and is equal to $L + S$, where L is the orbital angular momentum ($L = 0, 1, 2,...n - 1$) and S is the nucleon's spin [$S = +1/2$ (spin-up) or $-1/2$ (spin-down)]. As in atomic chemistry, spectroscopic notation is also used for nucleon quantum numbers, so $L = 0$ is denoted by s, $L = 1$ by p, $L = 2$ by d, $L = 3$ by f, $L = 4$ by g, and so on.

Because $J = L + S$, we see that J can only equal $L + 1/2$ or $L - 1/2$. The allowed values of the magnetic quantum number, m_J, are from $-J$ through $+J$, in integer steps, giving a total of $2J + 1$ possibilities. For example, for the state $3d_{J=5/2}$, we can have $m_J = -5/2, -3/2, -1/2, 1/2, 3/2$, or $5/2$, so this state may hold 6 protons or 6 neutrons. For a given nucleus, therefore, the $3d_{J=5/2}$ states may contain 12 nucleons. A proton and a neutron may share the same set of quantum numbers, since they are distinct particles and thus not subject to the Pauli exclusion principle.

Nucleons form spin-up/spin-down pairs; even–even nuclei (that is, nuclei with Z even and N even) always form such pairs and are very stable. If one of the numbers Z or N is even and the other is odd, the total nuclear spin (the sum of the nucleons' spins) is equal to the spin of the unpaired nucleon, and the nucleus is rather stable. Stable odd–odd nuclei are very rare; in fact, there are only four: ^2H, ^6Li, ^{10}B, and ^{14}N.

Figure 1 shows the sequence of the first seventeen energy levels in the nuclear shell model—that is, the order in which the highest energy levels of the nucleus are filled—including the relative magnitudes of the separation between adjacent energy levels. The numbers on the right in the figure give the total capacity (number of protons or neutrons) of the level up to and including the indicated level. Notice how the levels tend to bunch into groups separated by unusually large gaps when the number of protons or neutrons is equal to a magic number. For this reason, these separations are called *magic gaps*.

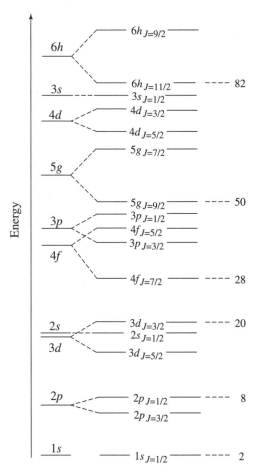

Figure 1

1. Which of the following nuclei are magic or doubly magic?

   I. Oxygen-15
   II. Lead-208
   III. Iron-50

   A. I only
   B. I and II only
   C. I and III only
   D. II and III only

2. What is the total nuclear spin of an oxygen-16 nucleus?

   A. 0
   B. 1/2
   C. 4
   D. 8

3. All of the following nuclides—except one—are radioactive, with a half-life of between 1 and 10 seconds. Which one is NOT radioactive?

   A. ^8Li
   B. ^{15}N
   C. ^{20}F
   D. ^{26}Na

4. Based on information given in the passage, what is the maximum total number of nucleons that can exist in the $5g_{J=7/2}$ nuclear states in a given nucleus?

   A. 8
   B. 11
   C. 16
   D. 22

5. In a laboratory experiment, each of the nuclei listed below—all isotopes of molybdenum—absorbed enough energy to raise a neutron to the next highest nuclear energy level. Which one likely required the most energy?

   A. ^{91}Mo
   B. ^{92}Mo
   C. ^{93}Mo
   D. ^{94}Mo

6. Which one of the following nucleon energy levels is higher than $3p_{J=1/2}$?

   A. $3d_{J=3/2}$
   B. $3p_{J=3/2}$
   C. $3s_{J=1/2}$
   D. $4f_{J=5/2}$

Passage 6 (Questions 1-6)
ADVANCED PASSAGE

If an atom is irradiated with enough energy, electrons can be promoted to higher energy levels or ejected from the atom entirely. An example of this latter phenomenon—electron ejection—is the photoelectric effect.

If a metal surface is illuminated with light of sufficient energy, an electron may absorb enough energy to free it from the metal entirely. An electron ejected in this manner is called a photoelectron. The kinetic energy of a photoelectron is equal to the energy of the absorbed photon minus the energy required to displace the electron from the atom. The minimum amount of energy required to liberate an electron from the surface of a metal is called the metal's photoelectric work function, denoted ϕ. Thus, the maximum amount of kinetic energy of the ejected electrons is equal to the difference between the energy of the irradiating photons, hf, and the metal's work function:

$$KE_{max} = hf - \phi$$

Equation 1

Different metals have different work functions, typically on the order of a few electron volts (eV); see Table 1. The threshold frequency, f_0, is the frequency of the irradiating light below which no photoelectrons are produced. The equation $\lambda_0 f_0 = c$ determines the threshold wavelength, that is, the wavelength of the irradiating light above which no photoelectrons are produced. It is easy to show that $\lambda_0 = (1240 \text{ eV-nm})/\phi$.

Metal	ϕ (eV)	λ_0 (nm)
Cesium (Cs)	1.94	639
Rubidium (Rb)	2.13	582
Potassium (K)	2.25	551
Sodium (Na)	2.29	541
Lithium (Li)	2.46	504
Copper (Cu)	4.70	264

Table 1 Work Functions and Threshold Wavelengths

Electrons that are not provided with enough energy to be either elevated to a higher energy level or ejected remain in their ground state. That is, an electron cannot absorb a quantum of energy unless it is large enough to produce one of the two above effects. For atoms in the gas phase, ϕ is the first ionization energy, I_1. (Note: Planck's constant $= h = 4.1 \times 10^{-15}$ eV-s $= 6.6 \times 10^{-34}$ J-s, and 1 eV $= 1.6 \times 10^{-19}$ J.)

1. Which one of the following graphs best illustrates the relationship between the maximum kinetic energy of a photoelectron and the frequency of the radiation that illuminates the metal?

   A.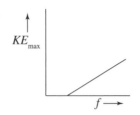
   B.

   C.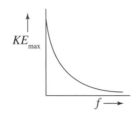
   D.

2. A sample of cesium is illuminated by a source of monochromatic light. If the electrons that are ejected from the sample have a maximum kinetic energy of 0.11 eV, what is the frequency of the incident light?

   A. 4.0×10^{14} Hz
   B. 5.0×10^{14} Hz
   C. 4.0×10^{16} Hz
   D. 5.0×10^{16} Hz

3. A sample containing a mixture of rubidium and cesium is irradiated with light of wavelength of approximately 550 nm. Which of the following best explains the effect?

   A. No electrons are expelled from either metal because the incoming radiation has insufficient energy.
   B. Electrons are expelled from both metals and have equivalent kinetic energies.
   C. Electrons are expelled from both metals, but those originating in the rubidium have greater kinetic energy.
   D. Electrons are expelled from both metals, but those originating in the cesium have greater kinetic energy.

4. Which of the following best explains why the work function for sodium is less than that for lithium?

   A. Sodium is more electronegative than lithium.
   B. The threshold frequency for sodium is greater than that for lithium.
   C. The valence electron of lithium is less tightly bound than that of sodium due to decreased nuclear shielding in the lithium atom.
   D. The valence electron of sodium is less tightly bound than that of lithium due to increased nuclear shielding in the sodium atom.

5. Based on the work functions given in Table 1, it can be inferred that which one of the following elements is the most reactive?

   A. Copper
   B. Potassium
   C. Cesium
   D. Lithium

6. In a photoelectric-effect experiment, a sample of copper is illuminated with ultraviolet light of wavelength 250 nm, and x photoelectrons per second are emitted. If the copper is instead illuminated with green light of wavelength 500 nm, how many photoelectrons should be emitted per second?

   A. 0
   B. $\frac{1}{2}x$
   C. x
   D. $2x$

Passage 7 (Questions 1-5)

Atoms are the building blocks of molecules and they consist of electrons surrounding a nucleus composed of neutrons and protons. The identity of an atom depends on how many protons it contains. The stability and/or reactivity of an atom often depends on how many neutrons and electrons it contains.

Nucleons themselves are composed of elementary particles known as quarks. Quarks are held together by the *strong force* to generate composite particles referred to as *hadrons*. This strong force, sometimes called the *nuclear force*, is also responsible for holding protons and neutrons together in the nucleus and overcomes other forces that may be present. *Baryons*, which are hadrons containing three quarks, form a charged nucleon when two up quarks and one down quark combine and uncharged nucleons when one up quark combines with two down quarks. *Mesons*, which are the other family of hadrons, are unstable particles composed of one quark and one antiquark.

1. An atom contains 29 hadrons comprised of two down quarks and one up quark and 28 hadrons comprised of two up quarks and one down quark. Which one of the following is the identity of the atom?

    A. Iron-57
    B. Nickel-57
    C. Copper-57
    D. Nickel-58

2. An excited electron drops down to its ground state and in the process a photon of light with a wavelength of 525 nm is emitted. Which of the following types of electromagnetic radiation could the photon be?

    A. Infrared
    B. Visible light
    C. X-ray
    D. Cannot be determined from the information given

3. A scientist in a laboratory observes a nucleon composed of three quarks with charges of $+2/3\ e$, $-1/3\ e$, and $-1/3\ e$ respectively. Which of the following best describes the nucleon?

    A. The particle is a neutron and it contains two down quarks.
    B. The particle is a proton and it contains two down quarks.
    C. The particle is a neutron and it contains one down quark.
    D. The particle is a proton and it contains one down quark.

4. The first, second, and third ionization energies for strontium are 549.5 kJ/mol, 1064.2 kJ/mol, and 4138 kJ/mol respectively. Why is the third ionization energy so much higher than the first two ionization energies?

    A. The third electron is being removed from a completely full subshell.
    B. The third electron has a larger mass than the first two electrons being removed.
    C. The third electron being removed is less attracted to the nucleus than the first two electrons.
    D. The third electron is at a higher energy level than the first two electrons.

5. Particles with opposite charges attract one another and particles with like charges repel. How can protons, which are positively charged, coexist in the nucleus?

    A. The neutrons in the nucleus prevent the protons from touching one another.
    B. The nuclear force is stronger than the repulsive forces between protons.
    C. Hadrons do not experience forces with one another.
    D. The surrounding cloud of electrons generates an opposing force.

_____

Passage 8 (Questions 1-6)

The size of an atom or ion depends upon the domain of the outermost valence electrons. Advancing through the periodic table, atoms increase in size as new electronic shells begin to be filled; however, the orbital extent of subshells within the *same* shell are approximately equal. Therefore, filling the *np* or *nd* after the *ns* has been filled does not increase the size of the atom, but placing electrons in the *n+1* shell [(*n+1*)*s*, (*n+1*)*p*, *etc.*] would substantially increase the size of the atom.

Since subshells in the same electronic shell have the same orbital domain, atomic sizes in a given periodic row would be expected to remain relatively constant, with increasing electron-electron repulsion swelling the atom slightly. Yet on the contrary, elements in the same period decrease in size proceeding from left to right since the increasing nuclear charge draws the electrons closer to the nucleus.

The addition or removal of electrons from a neutral atom has a drastic effect upon the final size of the ion.

Anions have more electrons than protons. Consequently, each electron experiences less nuclear charge, hence can orbit further away from the nucleus. The addition of an electron to an atom can increase its final size by as much as sixty percent.

On the other hand, cations have more protons than electrons, and therefore the electrons experience more nuclear charge and are reeled in closer to the nucleus. The diameter of a singly-charged cation is typically forty percent smaller than that of the corresponding neutral atom.

Removal (or addition) of a second electron from (or to) an ionic species will affect the previous ionic size in the same manner as did the removal (or addition) of the first electron. As such, highly charged ions are either very large or very small.

1. Cellular membranes are selective towards sodium and potassium ions. Given that transmembrane channels (which are sensitive to ionic size) can discriminate between these ions, thereby actively transporting or excluding these ions at will, which one of the following statements is true?

    A. Due to their smaller size, it is more difficult to prevent potassium ions from passing across the membrane than sodium ions.
    B. Chloride ions are often mistaken for sodium ions because they have similar sizes.
    C. Since membranes are less permeable to larger ions, sodium ions will leak through the membrane faster than potassium ions.
    D. Calcium ions are larger than either sodium or potassium ions.

2. Based on the information in the passage, which one of the following atoms has the smallest radius?

    A. Oxygen
    B. Lithium
    C. Fluorine
    D. Helium

3. A sulfur atom has a radius of about 1.0 angstrom (Å). If every additional electron increases the previous atomic/ionic size by thirty percent, what is the size of a sulfide ion?

    A. 1.3 Å
    B. 1.6 Å
    C. 1.7 Å
    D. 2.0 Å

4. Based upon the fact that the diffusion rate of ions through a cell membrane is inversely proportional to the size of the ion, which one of the following ions would passively pass through a cell membrane most easily?

    A. Ca^{2+}
    B. Cl^-
    C. H^+
    D. Ba^{2+}

5. Identify the graph that best illustrates the trend of atomic size based upon atomic number, Z.

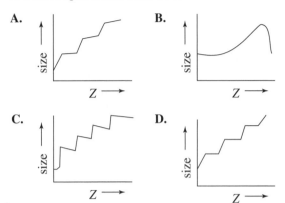

A.

B.

C.

D.

6. Some toothpastes include strontium nitrate as an active ingredient because strontium ions can competitively bind to enzymes crucial for transmittance of sensory nerve impulses. These toothpastes therefore reduce the pain associated with sensitive gums. The ion that strontium is mimicking in the enzymatic cleft is:

- **A.** H^+.
- **B.** Ca^{2+}.
- **C.** acetylcholine.
- **D.** F^-.

Passage 9 (Questions 1-5)

An isolated atom can undergo one of two processes: either the removal of or the capture of, an additional valence electron. Both *ionization* and *electron capture* are energetically favorable when either of these processes would result in the formation of a closed-shell configuration. Alternatively, these processes are energetically costly when pre-existing closed-shell stability is compromised. Ionization is always an endothermic process:

$$atom + energy \rightarrow cation + e^-$$

Ionization energy is primarily a function of atomic size. However, variations in shell stability of the initial versus ionized species have second-order effects.

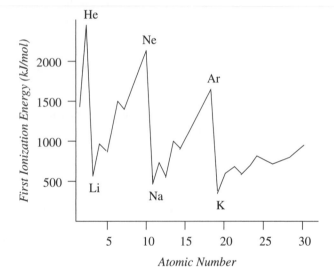

The energies required to ionize successive electrons in a single atom are more difficult to predict. Atoms no longer obey the periodicity displayed above after the first ionization energy. However, it becomes more and more difficult to remove successive electrons due to the increasingly stronger electrostatic attraction of the nucleus.

In contrast to ionization, the initial capture of *one* additional valence electron is usually an exothermic process:

$$atom + e^- \rightarrow anion + energy$$

The energy associated with this capture is referred to as the *electron affinity* of that atom. Electron affinity follows the same general trend as ionization energy. As with ionization energy, periodicity is obscured with successive additions of electrons to an anion.

Successive Ionization Energies (kJ/mol)					
	1	2	3	4	5	6
H	1310					
He	2370	5220				
Li	520	7300	11,810			
Be	900	7150	14,850	21,000		
B	800	2430	3660	25,020	32,820	
C	1090	2350	4620	6220	37,820	47,260

Table 1

Electron Affinity (kJ/mol)		
	first e^-	second e^-
H	−72	large positive
O	−142	+844
F	−344	large positive

Table 2

As Table 2 indicates, the addition of *successive* electrons can completely contrast the initial capture and become an endothermic process.

1. What is the periodic trend of ionization energies for the elements?

    A. Decreases to the right, increases downwards.
    B. Increases to the right, increases upwards.
    C. Increases to the left, decreases upwards.
    D. Increases to the right, increases downwards.

2. Which one of the following atoms has the least tendency to gain another electron?

    A. Helium
    B. Oxygen
    C. Fluorine
    D. Hydrogen

3. Given that the electron configuration of nickel is [Ar] $4s^2 3d^8$, what would be the electron configuration of the Ni$^-$ ion?

    A. [Ar] $4s^2 3d^9$
    B. [Ar] $4s^2 3d^8 4p^1$
    C. [Ar] $4s^2 3d^{10}$
    D. [Ar] $4s^1 3d^{10}$

4. Which one of the following species has the most negative electron affinity?

    A. K$^+$
    B. Be^{3+}
    C. O$^-$
    D. O^{2-}

5. Why is the ionization energy of fluorine greater than that of lithium?

    A. The valence $2d$ electrons of fluorine are more stable (have less energy) than the $2s$ electrons of lithium.
    B. The fluorine electrons have more energy levels to reach before n = infinity than do the lithium electrons.
    C. The valence electrons of lithium are farther from the nucleus than are the valence electrons of fluorine.
    D. All of the above.

Passage 10 (Questions 1-5)

Simple organic molecules may differ significantly in their cohesive properties. The table below lists properties of some organic molecules.

Substance	Mass (amu)	Dipole Moment*	Boiling Point**
Propane, $CH_3CH_2CH_3$	44	0.0 D	231 K
Dimethyl ether, CH_3OCH_3	46	1.3	249
Methyl chloride, CH_3Cl	50	2.0	259
Acetaldehyde, CH_3CHO	44	2.7	293
Acetonitrile, CH_3CN	41	3.9	355

*Dipole moment increases with increasing charge separation and/or distance between charges.
**Determined at 1 atm pressure

Table 1

At room temperature, propane exists as a gas and has a molecular structure which shows freedom of rotation about the two carbon–carbon bonds.

Propane is a three-carbon member of the group of alkane hydrocarbons. Alkanes with fewer than three carbons have boiling points lower than –44°C. Alkanes with more than three carbons demonstrate increasing boiling point temperatures with each added carbon atom.

1. Compared to propane, nonane (a nine-carbon alkane) is:

    A. less likely to be a liquid at room temperature because of the increased freedom of rotation about carbon–carbon bonds.
    B. less likely to be a liquid at room temperature because of its longer carbon chain.
    C. more likely to be a liquid at room temperature because of the increased freedom of rotation about carbon–carbon bonds.
    D. more likely to be liquid at room temperature because of its longer carbon chain.

2. Under which condition is the normal boiling point of dimethyl ether determined?

    A. An external pressure below 760 torr
    B. An external pressure at 760 torr
    C. An external pressure above 760 torr
    D. A temperature below 249 K

3. Which of the following statements best applies to the compounds listed in Table 1?

    A. Increasing dipole moment is associated with increasing boiling point.
    B. Increasing molecular mass is associated with increasing boiling point.
    C. Decreasing dipole moment is associated with increasing molecular mass.
    D. Decreasing molecular mass is associated with decreasing dipole moment.

4. The central oxygen in dimethyl ether (CH_3OCH_3) most likely demonstrates:

    A. hydrophobic bonding to saturated alkanes.
    B. covalent bonding between two of its sp^3 orbital electrons and two hydrogen electrons.
    C. covalent bonding between two of its sp^3 orbital electrons and two sp^3 carbon electrons.
    D. covalent bonding between two of its d orbital electrons and two sp carbon electrons.

5. Propane gas collected over water at room temperature does not exert fully 100% of the gas pressure in the collecting tube, because part of the contribution to gas pressure in the tube:

    A. is lost in the form of CO_2.
    B. is lost through propane vaporization.
    C. derives from the liquid phase of propane.
    D. derives from the vapor pressure of water.

_____

Passage 11 (Questions 1-4)

Oxygen transport in multicellular animals is facilitated by specialized oxygen-bearing proteins. One feature common to all oxygen-bearing proteins is the utilization of transition metal ions in the protein binding site. Some transition metal ions have a unique ability to form weak covalent bonds with molecular oxygen. Oxygen-metal covalent bonds must be weak to ensure the reversibility of binding. Other molecules, like cyanide and carbon monoxide, form strong covalent bonds with transition metal ions. As a result, exposure to CN^- or CO is often fatal for anaerobic organisms.

Hemerythrin is an oxygen-storage protein found in marine invertebrates. The protein active site consists of a pair of iron ions which are bridged by an oxygen atom and two carboxylate groups.

deoxyhemerythrin   *oxyhemerythrin*

The metal ions are coordinated to five histidine residues, and in this way, are anchored to the parent protein.

Hemocyanin is another oxygen-storage protein that is found in insects. Although it is similar to hemerythrin in gross structure, hemocyanin utilizes a pair of copper ions in its binding site. In the *oxy* form, molecular oxygen bridges the copper ions.

deoxyhemocyanin   *oxyhemocyanin*

Amino acid structures:

1. When oxygen is binding to the iron atom in hemerythrin, it is acting as a(n):

   A. Lewis acid.
   B. Lewis base.
   C. oxidant.
   D. reductant.

2. Which of the following amino acid residues CANNOT form a coordinate covalent bond with a transition metal ion in a protein?

   A. tyrosine

   B. cysteine

   C. phenyl alanine

   D. serine

3. Which one of the following statements is NOT true?

   A. Hydrogen bonding helps to bind O_2 in hemerythrin.
   B. The O to O bond distance decreases when O_2 is bound to hemocyanin.
   C. Carbon dioxide doesn't destroy metalloproteins.
   D. The charge distribution in the carboxylate group COO^- is distributed evenly between both oxygens.

4. Identify the most reasonable resonance structure for carbon monoxide:

   A. $:C=O:^+$

   B. $:C=\ddot{O}:$

   C. $^+:C-\ddot{O}:^-$

   D. $:C\equiv O:$

Passage 12 (Questions 1-6)

Urea is a metabolic waste product of protein oxidation in mammals.

Urea (Structure A)

In humans, urea is removed from the body while dissolved in urine and perspiration. Urea has little metabolic use to mammals because it has a low amount of usable bond energy. Internal resonance is responsible for the molecule's low energy and high stability.

Urea (Structure B)   *Urea* (Structure C)

Nitrogen has the ability to donate its pair of nonbonding electrons to the formation of a fourth covalent bond. In urea, these electrons give rise to a second covalent bond (π bond) with the carbon atom. Simultaneously, the oxygen atom withdraws the π electrons in the C=O bond and places them within a third nonbonding orbital.

1. What are the charges of the oxygen and π-bonded nitrogen, respectively, in Structure C?

   A. $-1, 0$
   B. $-1, +1$
   C. $+1, -1$
   D. $+1, 0$

2. What is the hybridization of the oxygen atom in Structures A and B?

   A. sp and sp
   B. sp and sp^2
   C. sp^2 and sp^3
   D. sp^3 and sp^4

3. The shape of urea is:

   A. trigonal planar.
   B. trigonal pyramid.
   C. tetrahedral.
   D. always changing.

4. A theoretical chemist once postulated that urea existed entirely as Structure A, and that Structures B and C never occurred. Later, an experimental chemist disproved this suggestion by measuring the actual bond lengths in urea. What did the experimentalist find?

   A. The carbon–oxygen and carbon–nitrogen bonds were shorter than those predicted by the theoretical chemist.
   B. The carbon–oxygen bond was shorter, and the carbon–nitrogen bond was longer, than those predicted by the theoretical chemist.
   C. The carbon–oxygen and carbon–nitrogen bonds were longer than those predicted by the theoretical chemist.
   D. None of the above

5. Urea represents the oxidized fragment of a(n):

   A. carbohydrate.
   B. lipid.
   C. fatty acid.
   D. amino acid.

6. What is the mass percent of carbon in urea?

   A. 15%
   B. 20%
   C. 25%
   D. 33%

Passage 13 (Questions 1-6)

Aromatic compounds, such as benzene, are susceptible to attack from atoms or molecules having some positive charge (called *electrophiles*). For example, benzene reacts with a mixture of nitric acid and sulfuric acid to form the initial product nitrobenzene:

The reaction intermediate is stabilized by resonance; the three resonance structures for the intermediate are:

For more complex molecules, electrophilic substitution to a functionalized benzene system is strongly influenced by the nature of the ring substituent; the location of electrophilic attack (regioselectivity) and rate of substitution depend upon the type of ring substituent. For example, the presence of the hydroxy group in phenol provides a fourth resonance structure to the reaction intermediate. As a result, when present, the OH group activates the ring to further substitution.

resonance structures

However, the fourth resonance structure is only accessible when the addition is to the 2 (*ortho*) or 4 (*para*) position.

Other groups strongly inhibit electrophilic addition by destabilizing the resonant intermediates. In nitro benzene, the nitro group deactivates the ring to further addition. The presence of the deactivating group has the least effect upon the 3 (*meta*) position, so whenever addition does occur, it occurs with this regioselectivity.

1. Identify the molecule which is responsible for attacking benzene to make nitrobenzene.

   A. NO_3^-
   B. NO_2^-
   C. NO_2^+
   D. SO_3^+

2. What is the shape of the nitrate ion?

   A. Trigonal planar
   B. Trigonal pyramid
   C. Tetrahedral
   D. Bent

3. Most often, *ortho-para* directing groups have an atom with nonbonding electrons directly attached to the aromatic ring. Based upon this trend, which one of the following benzene derivatives is *meta*-directing?

   A. H₂N   NH₂
   B. HO   F
   C. H₃CHN   CH₃
   D. HOOC   COOH

4. Which one of the following is NOT a legitimate resonance structure for benzoic acid, C_6H_5COOH?

   A.
   B.
   C.
   D.

5. Which one of the following statements correctly explains why *ortho*-nitrophenol has a lower melting point than *para*-nitrophenol?

    A. *Ortho*-nitrophenol experiences less intramolecular hydrogen bonding because the hydroxy and nitro group are on opposite sides of the ring.

    B. *Ortho*-nitrophenol experiences less intermolecular forces because the hydroxy and nitro groups do not interact via intramolecular hydrogen bonds.

    C. *Ortho*-nitrophenol experiences less intermolecular forces because the hydroxy and nitro groups have a strong intramolecular hydrogen bond.

    D. Neither molecule can experience hydrogen bonding.

6. During an electrophilic substitution reaction, what are the initial, the intermediate, and the final hybridizations of the ring carbon that is being attacked?

    A. sp^2, sp^2, sp^2
    B. sp^2, sp^2, sp^3
    C. sp^2, sp^3, sp^2
    D. sp^3, sp^3, sp^3

Passage 14 (Questions 1-6)

Several different toxic substances can be found under the average kitchen sink. Oven cleaners and clogged-drain cleansers are effective at dissolving organic matter such as oven grease (which is just fat), hair, and skin because they contain concentrated sodium hydroxide. Just like all aqueous strong bases, sodium hydroxide hydrolyzes the peptide and ester linkages present in proteins and fats.

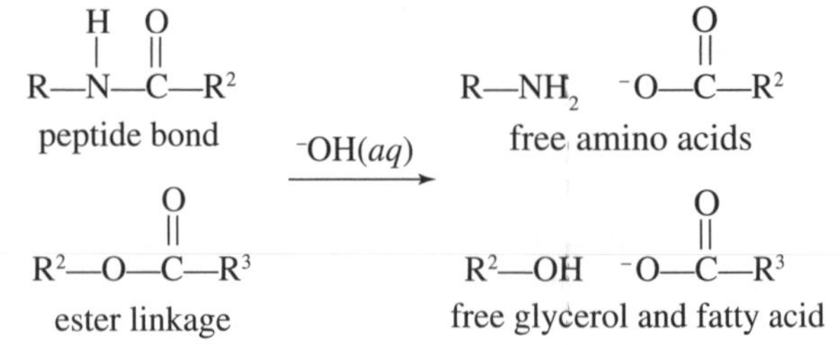

Household bleach is a 5% by mass solution of sodium hypochlorite (NaClO) and water. The hypochlorite ion is a mild oxidizing agent and toxic when taken internally. Low concentrations of chlorine gas may also be found dissolved in bleach solutions.

Ammonia, a gas at room temperature, can be highly toxic when inhaled because of its basic properties. In addition, it is a strong ligand capable of displacing diatomic oxygen from hemoglobin in a manner similar to that of carbon monoxide.

$$4\,NH_3(g) + Hb\cdot4\,O_2(aq) \longrightarrow 4\,O_2(g) + Hb\cdot4\,NH_3(aq)$$

Yet most household deaths that involve chemicals are due to the toxic gases formed when bleach and ammonia are mixed together. Highly insidious vapors, seeded with hydrazine: H_2NNH_2, chloroamine: $ClNH_2$, and hydrogen chloride: HCl, are released from the solution.

$$n\text{NaOCl}(aq) + n\text{NH}_3(aq)$$
$$\downarrow$$
$$H_2NNH_2(aq) + ClNH_2(aq) + HCl(aq)$$

1. Based upon the passage, which one of the following statements is INCORRECT?

    A. If each iron ion in hemoglobin can only bind to one ligand at a time, every hemoglobin molecule must contain four iron centers.
    B. Peptide bonds link together amino acids.
    C. An ester is composed of a fatty acid part and an amine part.
    D. Fat and protein hydrolysis can occur in the presence of water.

2. An experiment demonstrates that chloroamine is a stronger ligand than ammonia. Why might this be so?

    A. The electron density around nitrogen is reduced in chloroamine compared to ammonia.
    B. Chlorine donates electron density to the nitrogen atom in chloroamine.
    C. Chlorine acts as the Lewis base in chloroamine.
    D. Since chlorine atoms are much larger than hydrogen atoms, ammonia experiences less steric hindrance in coordination complexes.

3. Ammonium chloride is also formed when bleach and ammonia are mixed together. What is the phase of pure ammonium chloride at room temperature?

    A. Solid
    B. Liquid
    C. Gas
    D. Plasma

4. Which one of the following statements is true?

    A. Oxygen is a better Lewis base than either ammonia or CO.
    B. Hydrazine experiences dipole interactions, not hydrogen bonds.
    C. Hydrazine cannot act as a ligand.
    D. At room temperature, the vapor pressure of ammonia is greater than 760 torr.

5. The shapes of ammonia and chloroamine are identical. Which one of the following molecules will also have a trigonal pyramid shape?

    A. HOCl
    B. HCl
    C. $AlCl_3$
    D. H_3O^+

6. The formal charges of the atoms in the hypochlorite ion ClO^- are:

    A. +1 for chlorine, –2 for oxygen.
    B. –1 for chlorine, 0 for oxygen.
    C. 0 for chlorine, –1 for oxygen.
    D. –1/2 for both atoms.

_____

Passage 15 (Questions 1-6)

Many of the most essential proteins in humans employ transition metal complexes in their active sites. Iron, as the ferrous ion iron(II), is the predominant transition metal used in human proteins. In fact, higher organisms have evolved a class of unusual ligands called *porphyrins* to enhance the versatility of iron's chemistry.

One example of a ferroprotein is *hemoglobin*. The oxygen binding site in hemoglobin is a heme unit consisting of a porphyrin ligand, *protoporphyrin IX*, bound to a ferrous ion:

protoporphyrin IX

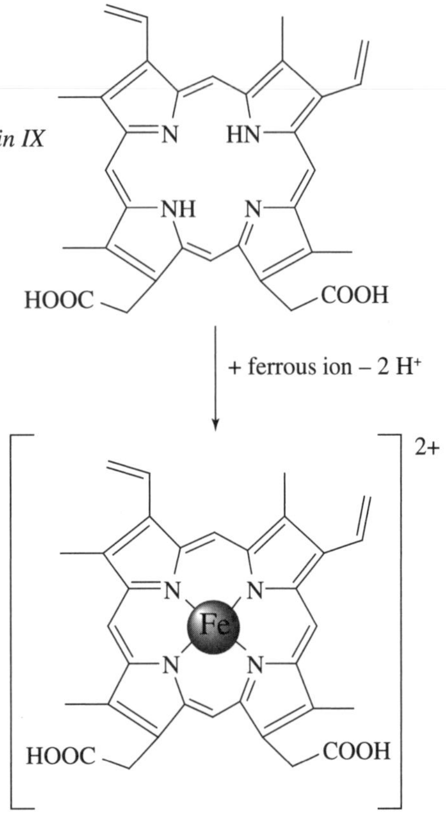

+ ferrous ion – 2 H⁺

heme unit

In hemoglobin, each heme unit is nestled in a parent protein to which it is anchored by a single coordinated histidine residue; oxygen binding occurs at the sixth open coordination site.

The chemistry of the porphyrins is unusual. Porphyrins are fully-conjugated, flat tetradentate ligands. Their extensive conjugation allows them to undergo electronic transitions at visible wavelengths that give porphyrins intense color. The heme unit strongly absorbs green light ($\lambda = 550$ nm) and is responsible for the coloration of the blood. Colors come in opposite pairs, *red-green*, *orange-blue*, and *yellow-violet*. Depletion of one of the colors in a pair will intensify the perception of the other color in the pair.

1. Protoporphyrin IX has three absorbances in the visible region, with the most intense one at $\lambda = 405$ nm. What color is protoporphyrin IX?

   A. Green
   B. Blue
   C. Violet
   D. Yellow

2. The ferrous ion fits snugly inside protoporphyrin's "donut hole". Among the following four, identify the ion that cannot form a protoporphyrin-metal complex due to excessive size.

   A. K^+
   B. Fe^{3+}
   C. Cu^{2+}
   D. Mg^{2+}

3. A laboratory technician prepared 0.10 gram of heme solution from protoporphyrin IX and ferrous nitrate, as illustrated in the passage. If the initial pH of the solution was 6, what was the final pH of the solution?

   A. Less than 6
   B. Equal to 6
   C. Greater than 6
   D. Cannot be determined

4. Classify the reaction type between a ferrous ion and protoporphyrin IX.

   A. Precipitation reaction
   B. Lewis acid–base reaction
   C. Oxidation–reduction reaction
   D. Single displacement reaction

5. Another important heme protein is *catalase*, an enzyme which oxidizes oxygen atoms in highly reactive compounds. Which of the following reactions could be catalyzed by catalase?

   A. $O_2 \rightarrow 2\ H_2O$
   B. $O_2 \rightarrow 2\ O^{2-}$
   C. $H_2O_2 \rightarrow O_2$
   D. $H_2O_2 \rightarrow 2\ H_2O$

6. Some evidence indicates that while coordinated with the iron in the heme unit, diatomic oxygen is also being held in the protein through a hydrogen-bonding interaction with an amino acid residue protruding from the parent protein. Which one of the following amino acid residues is a possible candidate?

   A. Phenylalanine
   B. Alanine
   C. Cysteine
   D. Tyrosine

Passage 16 (Questions 1-5)

Radicals are a class of chemical species that have an odd number of electrons. As their name implies, radicals are extremely reactive due to chemical tendencies driven by their unpaired electron. In humans, enzymes have been discovered that actually produce radicals for cellular defense and neural transmission. Yet even with this discovery, the preponderance of *in vivo* radicals are unwanted toxins produced as a by-product of everyday cellular metabolism.

Most frequently produced *in vivo* free radicals:

nitric oxide, NO
hydroxyl radical, OH
peroxyradical, HO_2
nitrogen dioxide, NO_2

Radicals readily react with atoms or molecules having lone pairs of electrons or extensive π (double-bond) systems.

Most cancerous cells are believed to arise when radical species inadvertently attack and disable the gene that limits cell replication. Once this gene is turned off, the cell reproduces uncontrollably and loses all useful function for the parent organism. So in some respects, the term *carcinogen* is analogous to the term *radical-maker*.

However, healthy cells are equipped with enzymes and molecules that can quench radicals before they do any harm. One class of molecules, called *carotenoids* are adept at reacting with radicals to form much less reactive species.

A carotenoid (vitamin A)

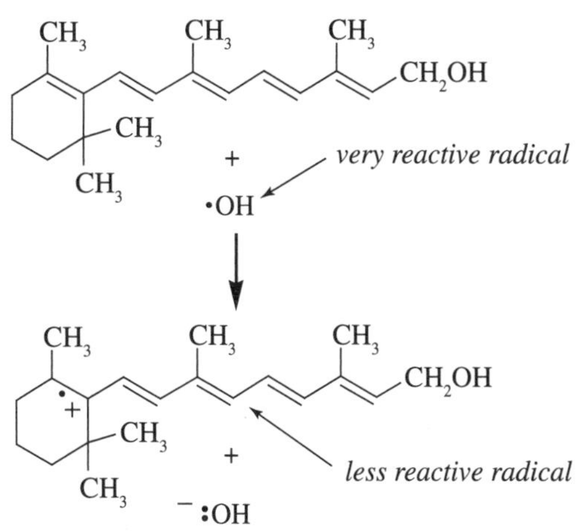

1. Which one of the following molecules is a free radical?

    A. N_2O
    B. OCl_2
    C. H_2O_2
    D. BrO_3

2. If all the bond angles in $\cdot CH_3$ are 120°, what is the hybridization of the carbon atom?

    A. sp
    B. sp^2
    C. sp^3
    D. none of the above

3. Why are radical species very reactive?

    A. Radicals have atoms that are highly charged.
    B. Radicals always involve highly electronegative atoms.
    C. Radicals have an atom without an octet.
    D. The net electron magnetic spin in a radical is zero.

4. According to the passage, radicals can also be classified as strong:

    A. reductants.
    B. oxidants.
    C. electrolytes.
    D. Lewis bases.

5. Why is the vitamin A radical so much more stable than the hydroxyl radical?

    A. The hydroxyl radical has less energy than the vitamin A radical.
    B. The hydroxyl radical has a greater molecular mass.
    C. The hydroxyl radical is not stabilized by internal resonance.
    D. The hydroxyl radical is not very soluble in the aqueous medium within cells.

Passage 17 (Questions 1-4)

Upon solidification, the molecules of a few substances do not align themselves into a regular, crystalline arrangement, but instead remain disorganized. Compounds of this type are called *amorphous solids*, an example of which is silica glass.

Ideally, silica glass may be obtained from melting quartz sand, SiO_2, and then allowing the melt to solidify. However, in practice, glass is not made in this fashion because the melting point of quartz sand is nearly 2000 K. Instead, a variety of inorganic salts may be added to silica to reduce its melting point to a more manageable 1000 K.

Glass type	Additives
soda-lime-silica	Na_2CO_3, $CaCO_3$
lead crystal	PbO
borosilicate	B_2O_3
Vycor®	(very few)

The most inexpensive and widely produced glass is soda-lime-silica (SLS) glass. While soda ash (Na_2O) and lime (CaO) are not additives in SLS glass, they are produced, *in situ*, by the thermal decomposition of sodium and calcium carbonate when the glass is molten. One of the limitations of SLS glass is that this material expands and cools unevenly. Therefore, when exposed to sudden temperature fluctuations, SLS glass tends to shatter. Alternative glasses are used in these situations. Glasses such as borosilicate glass (Pyrex®) and Vycor® experience minimal deformation with temperature change and are extremely resistant to the stresses associated with heating and cooling.

Glass type	Expandability relative to pure silica glass
soda-lime-silica	15.0
lead crystal	16.0
borosilicate	6.1
Vycor®	1.4

Transition metal oxides may be added to a glass to give it color. Most transition metals are vividly colored because they contain partially filled *d* orbitals whose electrons undergo transitions at visible wavelengths. Stained glass windows are among the most technologically advanced and durable art forms of the millennium.

1. What is the shape of the carbonate ion, CO_3^{2-}?

   A. Linear
   B. Trigonal planar
   C. Trigonal pyramid
   D. Tetrahedral

2. Silica glass is resistant to all common acids except hydrofluoric acid (HF), which reacts with the glass to form H_2O and a film of SiF_4. Silicon tetrafluoride is:

   A. a polar molecule.
   B. a coordination complex.
   C. an ionic compound.
   D. nonpolar.

3. Which one of the following transition metal oxides is NOT colored?

   A. CuO
   B. FeO
   C. TiO_2
   D. Mn_2O_3

4. A gas is produced during the production of SLS glass. What is it?

   A. $O_2(g)$
   B. $N_2(g)$
   C. $H_2(g)$
   D. $CO_2(g)$

Passage 18 (Questions 1-6)

Transition metal complexes have unique chemical and physical properties. One of the most obvious is that of color. With the exception of highly conjugated organic molecules, nearly all other chemical compounds have no color. Color is just one consequence of the effect of six ligands upon the electronic structure of a transition metal ion.

In an octahedral coordination complex, the electron clouds of the bonding ligands repel the metal ion's d orbitals, driving the energy of some d orbitals (the d_{z2} and d_{x2-y2}) higher and the energy of the other d orbitals (the d_{xy}, d_{yz}, and d_{xz}) lower. The repulsion exercised by the ligands' electron clouds, called the *crystal field*, makes the d orbitals nondegenerate.

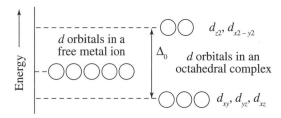

The energy gap between the two sets of d orbitals, Δ_0, is called the *crystal field splitting energy*. Unlike the first electronic transition of other compounds (which corresponds to UV photons), Δ_0 corresponds to photons of visible wavelengths.

The magnitude of Δ_0 is proportional to both the electron density of the ligands and the positive character of the metal ion. The *spectrochemical series* is a ranking of ligands based upon their ability to influence Δ_0; ligands on the left are strong crystal field ligands that give large Δ_0:

Spectrochemical series:

$$^-CN > NH_3 > H_2O > {}^-OH > F^- > I^-$$

Note that colors are classified in opposite pairs: *red–green*, *orange–blue*, and *yellow–violet*. A deficiency in one of these colors intensifies the appearance of the other pair-member. For example, a complex with a Δ_0 corresponding to a photon whose wavelength is 420 nm (violet) appears yellow.

1. The term *degenerate* means:

   A. to be too small.
   B. to be too large.
   C. to have equal potential energy.
   D. to have equal charge.

2. Apparently, the formation of a coordination complex makes the d_{z2} and d_{x2-y2} orbitals of the metal:

   A. have less energy.
   B. more stable.
   C. less stable.
   D. have less energy and less stability.

3. The fluoride ion is a stronger crystal field ligand than the iodide ion because the fluoride ion:

   A. has a greater charge.
   B. has a greater charge density.
   C. has more valence electrons.
   D. is a weaker base.

4. Which one of the following has the greatest crystal field energy?

   A. $Cr(H_2O)_6^{2+}$
   B. $Cr(NH_3)_6^{2+}$
   C. CrF_6^{3-}
   D. $Cr(NH_3)_6^{3+}$

5. A blue transition metal complex has a Δ_0 that corresponds to:

   A. red photons.
   B. orange photons.
   C. green photons.
   D. blue photons.

6. Sodium-vapor street lights are bright yellow. This means that the majority of photons being emitted by the lamps are:

   A. red.
   B. yellow.
   C. green.
   D. violet.

Passage 19 (Questions 1-6)

Cells exist in a chemically regulated envelope of electrolytic fluid delineated by the cell membrane. The cell membrane acts as a semi-permeable barrier, allowing only the smallest compounds to passively pass through. A schematic cross-section of a region of a typical eukaryotic cellular membrane is presented below:

Schematic cross-section of eukaryotic cell membrane

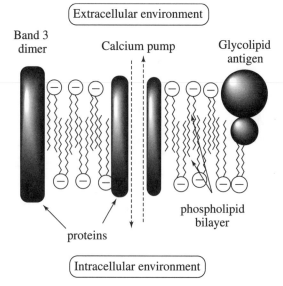

The bulk constituency of the cell membrane is a phospholipid bilayer. These molecules assume a bilayer conformation due to the hydrophilic nature of the fluid inside and outside the cell; they are not covalently cross-linked.

General structure of a phospholipid

Therefore, cell membranes may disintegrate in organic solvents and in solutions containing high concentrations of surfactants (detergents). However, the rigidity of the membrane is enhanced by the presence of an internal network of anchoring proteins (spectrin and ankyrin) which are not shown in this schematic.

Proteins, glycoproteins, and glycolipids are embedded within the bilayer to serve as cellular recognition sites, extracellular chemical sensors, and selective transmembrane channels. The transmembrane channels selectively facilitate the transport of ions and nutrients across the membrane.

1. What is responsible for holding together the long, aliphatic hydrocarbon chains in the bilayer?

    A. Hydrophobic force
    B. Hydrophilic force
    C. van der Waals forces
    D. Both A and C

2. The function of the glycolipid labeled in the schematic CANNOT be one of:

    A. cell recognition.
    B. chemical recognition.
    C. intercellular anchoring.
    D. active transport.

3. Although the shape (called secondary and tertiary structure) of the calcium pump protein is highly complex, it would be logical to assume that an amino acid residue present within the channel might be:

    A. phenyalanine

    $R-CH_2-$⬡

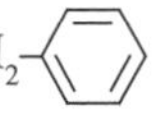

    B. lysine

    $R-(CH_2)_4-\overset{+}{N}H_3$

    C. glutamic acid
    $R-(CH_2)_2-COO^-$

    D. cysteine
    $R-CH_2-SH$

4. Which of the following ions would have the greatest rate of transmembrane diffusion?

    A. H^+
    B. K^+
    C. Mg^{2+}
    D. Ti^{3+}

5. What is the oxidation state of the phosphorous in a phospholipid?

    A. +3
    B. +4
    C. +5
    D. +6

6. Which one of the following statements is correct?

    A. Due to their charge, deprotonated phosphate groups should cluster together in a stable arrangement.
    B. A high concentration of cations should be found near the surface of the cell membrane.
    C. Transmembrane proteins should be entirely composed of hydrophilic amino acid residues.
    D. The only force which maintains a hydrous shell around the phosphate ion is hydrogen bonding.

Passage 20 (Questions 1-6)

Quantum mechanics dictates that the probability of finding an electron is greatest in one of an infinite number of energy levels. For example, the electronic energy levels for a Bohr atom are:

The electron pair in a covalent bond is also quantized and thus found in one of an infinite number of molecular electronic energy levels. Yet all bonding electrons exercise another mode of motion called *vibration*. Covalent bonds are not rigid; they oscillate and vibrate to and fro with quantized frequencies. Therefore *each* electronic energy level of a bond is actually composed of an infinite number of closely spaced vibrational energy levels:

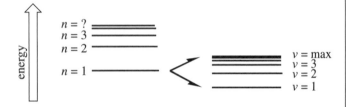

Vibrational energy levels are most often illustrated based upon their relationship to the stretching, bending, and contraction of a covalent bond. These diagrams are called Morse potential diagrams:

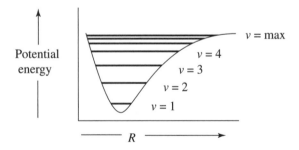

where R is the covalent bond length. The *bond dissociation energy* is the energy required to go from the occupied vibration energy level to $v = $ max.

1. If the electronic transition of the bonding electrons in HCl corresponds to UV photons, then the vibrational transition of HCl corresponds to:

   A. x-rays.
   B. UV photons.
   C. infrared photons.
   D. photons of infinite energy.

2. The vibrational transition $v = 2$ to $v = 1$ does NOT:

   A. reduce the energy of the molecule.
   B. increase the stability of the molecule.
   C. decrease the amount of additional energy required to break the bond.
   D. emit energy to the surroundings.

3. According to the Morse potential diagrams, which one of the following statements is true?

   A. The stability of a bond is inversely proportional its energy.
   B. The change in the length of an oscillating bond decreases with increasing energy.
   C. The change in energy between adjacent vibrational energy levels increases at higher energies.
   D. A catalyst increases the heat produced when a bond is broken.

4. How would the Morse potential diagram of a C=O bond differ from that of a C–O bond?

   A. The dissociation energy of C=O is smaller than for C–O.
   B. The average R for each vibrational energy level would be smaller for C=O than for C–O.
   C. The $v = 1$ to $v = $ max transition for C=O is smaller than for C–O.
   D. The C=O bond does not vibrate, while the C–O bond does.

5. Which one of the following gases will have no vibrational modes?

   A. H_2
   B. Ne
   C. O_2
   D. UF_6

6. N_2O is a gas with several complex vibrational modes (that is, it is not symmetric). What is the Lewis dot structure of nitrous oxide?

A. 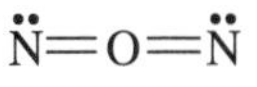 $\ddot{N}=O=\ddot{N}$

B. 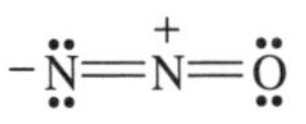 $-\ddot{\ddot{N}}=\overset{+}{N}=\ddot{\ddot{O}}$

C. 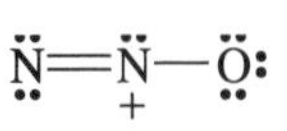 $\ddot{\ddot{N}}=\overset{+}{\ddot{N}}-\ddot{\ddot{O}}:$

D.

Passage 21 (Questions 1-6)
ADVANCED PASSAGE

Molecules are not rigid, unchanging structures. Their atoms are in constant motion even relative to each other, ceaselessly oscillating around their average bond lengths and bond angles. For instance, in non-linear triatomic molecules there are three possible modes of vibration. There is the symmetric stretch in which both bonds in the molecule lengthen and contract in unison. In the asymmetric stretch, one bond lengthens while the other contracts. Finally, there is the bend in which the bond angle alternately widens and narrows.

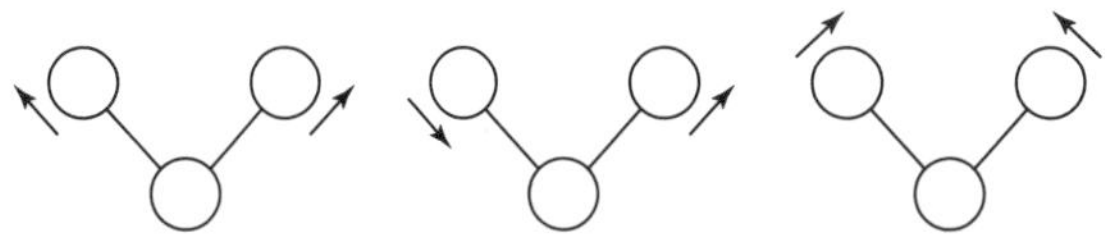

Symmetric   Asymmetric   Bend
Stretch   Stretch

Figure 1   Vibrations of a Triatomic Molecule

More generally, each atom in a molecule is capable of moving in three distinct directions, often represented by x, y and z. In a molecule with N atoms, there will be $3N$ possible atomic movements. However, if all the atoms in a molecule move in the same direction, translational movement and not vibration will result. Likewise, there are some combinations of atomic motions that result in rotation of the molecule and not vibration. Taking this into account, in a molecule containing N atoms there will be $3N - 6$ normal modes of vibration in non-linear molecules and $3N - 5$ normal modes of vibration in linear molecules.

If we make the rough approximation that atoms in a molecule are harmonic oscillators, then the energy of their vibration is given by:

$$E = \left(v + \frac{1}{2}\right)\left(\frac{h}{2\pi}\right)\sqrt{\frac{k}{u}} \text{ for } v = 0, 1, 2, \ldots$$

where v is the quantum vibrational number, h is Planck's constant, k is the force constant of the bond which increases with bond strength, and u is the reduced mass of the molecule. Changes in the vibrational quantum state are associated with energies similar to infrared photons. Thus, IR spectroscopy is the study of the energetics of a molecule's vibrational quantum states. However, only those normal modes of vibration that induce a change in the dipole moment of a molecule can be excited with IR light.

Molecule	Bond Energy (kJ/mol)
H_2	436
N_2	946
O_2	497
F_2	155

Table 1 Bond Energies of Select Diatomic Elements

1. Which of the following molecules has nine normal modes of vibration?

   A. NI_3
   B. CH_4
   C. PF_5
   D. SCl_6

2. A change in which of the following combinations of molecular movement can never produce a peak in an IR spectrum?

   A. Translation and rotation
   B. Stretching and bending
   C. Vibration and translation
   D. Rotation and bending

3. Assuming their reduced masses are the same, which molecule will have the highest energy of vibration in the $v = 0$ state?

   A. N_2
   B. O_2
   C. F_2
   D. Cannot be determined from the information given.

4. All of the following molecules will display absorption peaks in an IR spectrum EXCEPT

   A. $HClO_4$
   B. SO_3
   C. CO
   D. O_2

5. For a diatomic molecule, the reduced mass is given by $u = (m_1 \times m_2)/(m_1 + m_2)$ where m_1 and m_2 are the atomic weights of the two bonded atoms. What will be the ratio of the ground state vibration energies of D_2 to H_2 assuming the force constant k is the same for both?

   A. 0.5
   B. 0.7
   C. 1.4
   D. 2.0

6. Nitrate is best described by a resonance average of three structures:

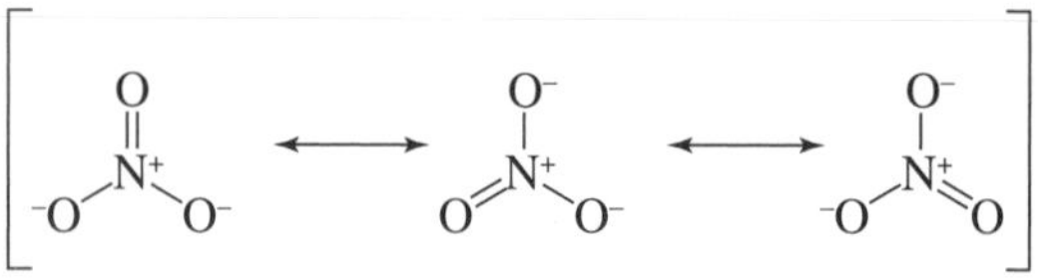

   What best describes the peaks in an IR spectrum that result from the three N—O bond stretches?

   A. One peak at the double bond N=O stretch frequency and two peaks at the single bond N—O stretch frequency
   B. One peak at the double bond N=O stretch frequency and one peak at the single bond N—O stretch frequency
   C. One peak at the double bond N=O stretch frequency and one peak between the single N—O and double bond N=O stretch frequencies
   D. One peak between the single N—O and double bond N=O stretch frequencies

Passage 22 (Questions 1-4)

Imines are formed from the condensation of a primary or secondary amine and a ketone or aldehyde. One example of an imine condensation is the reaction between propylamine and cyclohexanone:

$$CH_3CH_2CH_2NH_2 \quad + \quad \text{(cyclohexanone)}$$

$$\updownarrow H^+$$

$$CH_3CH_2CH_2N= \text{(cyclohexane)} \quad + \quad H_2O$$

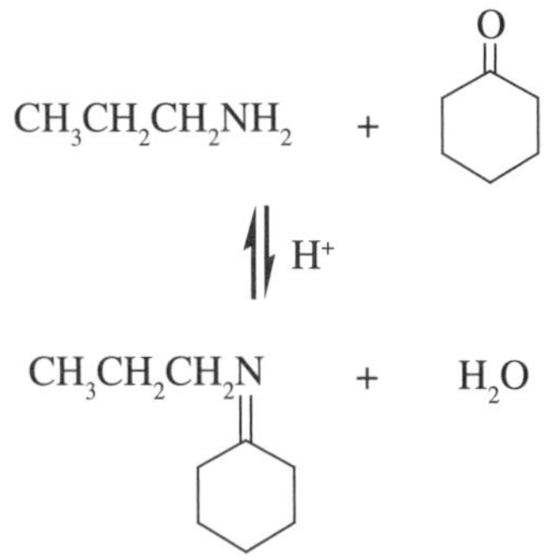

Imine condensation reactions are catalyzed by acid. Typical equilibrium constants for these reactions have values between 1 and 10, depending on the nature of the reactants and products. These reactions are most often carried out at temperatures between 40°C and 100°C.

The yield of imine product can be maximized by using an excess of the reactants and/or removing the products as they are formed. The data for the variability of product yield as a function of reactant concentrations are given below:

moles of propylamine	moles of cyclohexone	yield of imine
1	5	90%
1	10	95%
2	1	78%
2	5	815

Table 1

All reactions were carried out at 90°C in 250 mL of toluene. (*Note*: The BP of toluene is 110.6°C at 760 torr.)

1. How many grams of water are produced in the reaction between 2 moles of propylamine and 1 mole of cyclohexanone?

   A. 5
   B. 10
   C. 14
   D. 18

2. The theoretical yield of a reaction depends upon the:

   A. concentration of the reagent in excess.
   B. number of catalytic sites.
   C. amount of product recovered.
   D. concentration of the limiting reagent.

3. Which one of the following statements is FALSE?

   A. At 110°C, the vapor pressure of pure toluene is less than that of pure water.
   B. Both propylamine and cyclohexanone may hydrogen bond with water.
   C. Since toluene is a hydrocarbon, it will not be water soluble.
   D. None of the above

4. The imine product has all of the following EXCEPT:

   A. nonbonding electrons.
   B. intermolecular van der Waals forces.
   C. intermolecular dipole forces.
   D. intermolecular hydrogen bonds.

Passage 23 (Questions 1-6)

Coal is a major source of energy that can be converted from its solid, raw form to a gaseous phase of fuel. This is accomplished by the *water gas reaction*:

$$C(s) + H_2O(g) \rightleftharpoons CO(g) + H_2(g)$$

Solid carbon reacts with steam to produce a mixture of carbon monoxide and hydrogen gas. This mixture is what is called *water gas*. Table 1 lists the standard heats of formation, free energies of formation, and standard absolute entropies of each of the four compounds in the water gas reaction.

Compound	ΔH_f°(kJ/ mol)	ΔG_f°(kJ/ mol)	S°(J/K mol)
$C(s)$	0.0	0.0	5.7
$H_2O(g)$	−241.8	−228.6	188.7
$CO(g)$	−110.5	−137.1	197.6
$H_2(g)$	0.0	0.0	130.6

Table 1 Thermodynamic Data for Reactants and Products in Water Gas Reaction

1. What is ΔH° for the water gas reaction when one mole of $C(s)$ is reacted with an excess of $H_2O(g)$ to completion?

    A. −352.3 kJ
    B. −131.3 kJ
    C. 131.3 kJ
    D. 352.3 kJ

2. Water gas is a desirable product because its components are combustible with oxygen.

    $$CO(g) + \tfrac{1}{2}O_2(g) \rightarrow CO_2(g) \quad \Delta H^\circ = -283.0 \text{ kJ}$$
    $$H_2(g) + \tfrac{1}{2}O_2(g) \rightarrow H_2O(g) \quad \Delta H^\circ = -241.8 \text{ kJ}$$

    If 2 moles of $C(s)$ are consumed in the water gas reaction, what is the approximate amount of heat released when the final products undergo complete combustion as shown above?

    A. 262 kJ
    B. 483 kJ
    C. 525 kJ
    D. 1050 kJ

3. The pressure of the reaction chamber at equilibrium is suddenly increased by compressing the chamber. It is expected that the water gas reaction will move:

    A. in the forward direction, resulting in an increase in entropy.
    B. in the reverse direction, resulting in a decrease in entropy.
    C. in the forward direction, resulting in a decrease in entropy.
    D. in the reverse direction, resulting in an increase in entropy.

4. The potential energy diagram below illustrates a reaction that is:

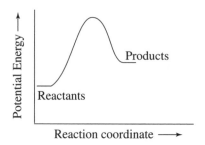

    A. catalyzed.
    B. uncatalyzed.
    C. exothermic.
    D. endothermic.

5. What is ΔS° for the water gas reaction?

    A. −268 J/K mol
    B. −134 J/K mol
    C. 0 J/K mol
    D. 134 J/K mol

6. Which of the following is most likely to affect ΔG° of the water gas reaction?

    A. The addition of a catalyst
    B. Changing the temperature of the reaction
    C. Changing the pathway of the reaction
    D. The rate at which the reaction occurs

Passage 24 (Questions 1-5)

A scientist conducted a series of experiments with the intent of finding the optimum rocket propellant: one that produces the most energy per gram of reactants. The scientist chose propellant candidates based upon calculated standard Gibbs free energy of formation of each compound:

molecule	$\Delta G_f°(kJ\cdot mol^{-1})$
$CH_4(g)$	+209.0
$CO_2(g)$	−386.0
$HF(g)$	−273.0
$H_2O(g)$	−228.6
$N_2H_4(l)$	+149.4

Since rocket engines operate at very high temperatures and pressures, the scientist attempted to simulate these conditions in the laboratory and then measure the heats of reactions for the candidate propellants. She measured the heat evolved by 1.0 gram of reactants in each of the following reactions by using a bomb (air-tight) calorimeter. The scientist's results are as follows:

ΔT represents the change in temperature of the calorimeter:

$$\Delta T = T_{final} - T_{initial}$$

Set 1. Oxidizing agent: oxygen

(1) $2 H_2(g) + O_2(g) \rightarrow 2 H_2O(g)$ $\Delta T = 36°C$
(2) $CH_4(g) + 2 O_2(g) \rightarrow CO_2(g) + 2 H_2O(g)$ $\Delta T = 23°C$
(3) $N_2H_4(l) + O_2(g) \rightarrow N_2(g) + 2 H_2O(g)$ $\Delta T = 17°C$

Set 2. Oxidizing agent: fluorine

(4) $H_2(g) + F_2(g) \rightarrow 2 HF(g)$ $\Delta T = 42°C$

1. Which one of the following statements is NOT true?

   A. Gases typically have more entropy than solids.
   B. Cooling any substance to 0.0 K will reduce the entropy of that substance to 0.
   C. Under standard conditions, pure elements in their natural phase have $H_f°$ and $G_f°$ of zero.
   D. STP and standard conditions do not describe the same conditions.

2. Based upon the table in the passage, what is $\Delta G°_{rxn}$ for the reaction of two moles of hydrogen gas with one mole of oxygen gas (at standard conditions)?

   A. −457.2 kJ·mol^{-1}
   B. −228.6 kJ·mol^{-1}
   C. +228.6 kJ·mol^{-1}
   D. +457.2 kJ·mol^{-1}

3. A molecule that has two or more highly electronegative atoms covalently bonded to one another will always be an oxidizing agent. Which one of the following is an oxidizing agent?

   A. KBr
   B. NH_3
   C. H_2O_2
   D. BH_3

4. What is the oxidation state of each nitrogen atom in hydrazine, N_2H_4?

   A. 0
   B. −1
   C. −2
   D. −3

5. Consider the reaction between hydrogen and bromine vapor at standard conditions:

   $$H_2(g) + Br_2(g) \rightarrow 2 HBr(g)$$

   Given that the $H_f°$ of HBr is −36 kJ·mol^{-1}, what is the ΔH_{rxn} for this reaction?

   A. −36 kJ·mol^{-1}
   B. −72 kJ·mol^{-1}
   C. +72 kJ·mol^{-1}
   D. Cannot be determined without more information

Passage 25 (Questions 1-6)

A chemist performed a systematic experiment in order to determine the extent to which transition metal complexes can be used as dyes in stain glass windows. Her only guide throughout the analysis was the fact that the color of a transition complex is a function of the strength of the metal-ligand *coordinate bond*. Specifically, the strength of the coordinate bond is proportional to the energy of the photon absorbed by that complex. Moreover, the chemist was careful not to confuse the solution's apparent color with the wavelength of light that was actually being absorbed. She realized that the observed color is actually the opposing color of the absorbed light; for example, a green solution is green because it is absorbing red light.

Opposing colors are illustrated in a **color wheel**.

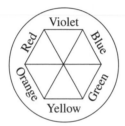

The chemist tested a host of transition metals and ligands, acquiring the following data:

Metal	Ligand	Color
Cu	H_2O	blue
Cu	CN^-	yellow
Ni	H_2O	green
Cr	H_2O	violet
Cr	CN^-	yellow
Cr	Cl^-	green
Cr	I^-	green
Cr	NH_3	orange
Fe	H_2O	orange

Notes: All metal cations are in the +3 oxidation state (except Cu, which is +2). All solutions are aqueous. Unlike the other ligands, high concentrations of haloacids had to be added before the Cr(III) solution turned from violet to green.

1. What is the oxidation state of the carbon atom in the cyanide ion?

    A.   0
    B.   +1
    C.   +2
    D.   +3

2. Based upon what limited data is available, which ligand has the strongest crystal field (that is, which forms the strongest coordinate covalent bond)?

    A. CN^-
    B. H_2O
    C. Cl^-
    D. NH_3

3. Which one of the following statements best explains why the chemist has a more difficult time forming the chromium halide complexes?

    A.   Due to their negative charge, halide anions are much stronger ligands than is water.
    B.   Haloacids are insoluble in water.
    C.   Chloride and iodide cannot act as Lewis bases.
    D.   High concentrations of halides are required to displace coordinated water molecules which are better ligands.

4. Identify the correct molecular formula for the hexamine copper(II) complex.

    A. $[Cu(NH_3)_6]$
    B. $[Cu(NH_3)_6]^+$
    C. $[Cu(NH_3)_6]^{2+}$
    D.   None of the above

5. Ligation is an example of a:

    A.   redox reaction.
    B.   Lewis acid–base reaction.
    C.   precipitation reaction.
    D.   Brønsted–Lowry acid–base reaction.

6. Which of the following metal complexes absorbs the longest wavelength of light?

    A. $[Cr(H_2O)_6]^{3+}$
    B. $[Fe(H_2O)_6]^{3+}$
    C. $[Cu(H_2O)_6]^{2+}$
    D. $[Cu(CN)_6]^{4-}$

Passage 26 (Questions 1-6)

Common laboratory liquids often display unique phase-related properties. Table 1 below lists two such properties for several of these liquids: enthalpy of vaporization (ΔH_{vap}) and boiling point (BP).

Substance	Formula	ΔH_{vap}	BP (at 1 atm)
Benzene	C_6H_6	30.8	80.2°C
Ethanol	C_2H_5OH	39.2	78.3
Diethyl Ether	$C_2H_5OC_2H_5$	26.0	34.6
Mercury	Hg	59.3*	356.9
Methane	CH_4	10.4	−164
Water	H_2O	40.7	100

*Mercury has a lower heat of vaporization per gram than does water, but a higher heat of vaporization per mole.

Table 1

The boiling point of water, normally calculated at standard atmospheric pressure, is nearly 0°C when the external pressure is reduced to zero.

Both ethanol and diethyl ether exhibit lower boiling point temperatures under lower pressure conditions. While ether shows a 0°C boiling point between 170 and 200 mmHg, the boiling point of ethanol is still above 40°C in this pressure range. The vaporization of water absorbs much more heat than does the melting of ice. Under standard conditions, the heat of fusion for water is 6 kJ/mol. The heat of vaporization for water under these conditions is almost seven times greater (40.7 kJ/mol).

1. On what basis does water have a higher heat of vaporization than mercury?

    A. On a per mole basis
    B. In terms of enthalpy of condensation
    C. In terms of enthalpy of vaporization
    D. On a per gram basis

2. At 1 atm of pressure, the temperature of ethanol gas is reduced from 100°C to 78°C. Which of the following events is most likely to occur?

    A. Ethanol will undergo a phase change to form a liquid.
    B. Ethanol will undergo a phase change to form a gas.
    C. Ethanol molecules will exhibit greater average kinetic energy.
    D. Ethanol molecules will exert a greater total vapor pressure.

3. Which of the following best illustrates the relationship between temperature (T) and vapor pressure (P) for ethanol and for diethyl ether?

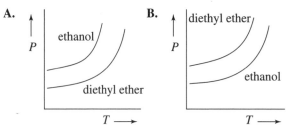

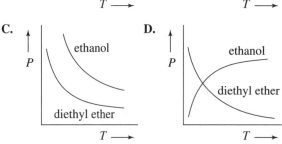

4. Which of the following best explains why the boiling point of water decreases with increasing altitude?

    A. Increasing altitude is accompanied by an increase in pressure.
    B. Increasing altitude is accompanied by an increase in escape velocity.
    C. Increasing altitude is accompanied by a decrease in temperature.
    D. Increasing altitude is accompanied by a decrease in pressure.

5. According to the passage, the vaporization of water requires more heat than does the melting of ice. The most likely explanation for this is that:

 A. ice has a smaller heat capacity than does steam.
 B. ice has a larger heat capacity than does steam.
 C. melting requires that only a fraction of intermolecular forces be broken while vaporization requires complete separation of molecules.
 D. the temperature of ice must be raised less than does the temperature of water to achieve a phase change.

6. Diethyl ether has a lower boiling point than does ethanol because:

 A. ethanol has a greater molecular weight than diethyl ether.
 B. ethanol undergoes hydrogen bonding, while diethyl ether only experiences van der Waals attractions.
 C. ethanol undergoes hydrogen bonding, while diethyl ether experiences no intermolecular interactions.
 D. the central oxygen atom in diethyl ether causes it to be more polar than ethanol.

Passage 27 (Questions 1-6)

The phase diagram in Figure 1 describes the state of sulfur under various conditions of temperature and pressure. As shown in the phase diagram, sulfur may assume two different crystalline forms in the solid state: rhombic sulfur and monoclinic sulfur.

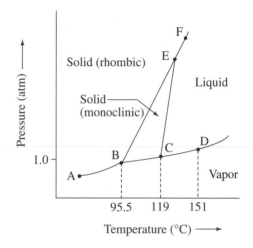

Figure 1 Phase diagram for sulfur (not to scale)

The stable form of sulfur at room temperature and 1 atm of pressure is rhombic sulfur, in which sulfur forms crystalline units characterized by rhombohedral geometrical symmetry. When heated slowly at constant pressure to a temperature above 95.5°C, rhombic sulfur is transformed to solid monoclinic sulfur, another crystal, stable under that set of conditions. The transformation between the two solid forms must be undertaken slowly. Rapid heating might produce incomplete transformation and melting.

The phase diagram for sulfur reveals three triple points corresponding to temperatures of 95.5°C, 119°C, and 151°C.

(Note: For sulfur, the heat of fusion, ΔH_{fus}, is 38.1 J/g, and the heat of vaporization, ΔH_{vap}, is 326 J/g.)

1. Which segments of the phase diagram represent the sublimation of sulfur?

 A. AB and BC
 B. BC and CD
 C. AB and CD
 D. CE and EF

2. How much heat is required to transform 50 g of mono-clinic sulfur to the liquid phase at 119°C and 1 atm?

   A. 76.2 J
   B. 652 J
   C. 1905 J
   D. 16,300 J

3. Which of the following describes the progression of phase changes undergone by sulfur held at a constant temperature of 100°C as the pressure is gradually increased from 0.25 atm to 3 atm?

   A. Vapor, liquid, monoclinic solid
   B. Vapor, liquid, rhombic solid
   C. Vapor, rhombic solid, monoclinic solid
   D. Vapor, monoclinic solid, rhombic solid

4. Based on the following thermochemical data,

   $$S(rhombic) + O_2(g) \rightarrow SO_2(g) \qquad \Delta H° = -297.0 \text{ kJ/M}$$
   $$S(monoclinic) + O_2(g) \rightarrow SO_2(g) \qquad \Delta H° = -297.1 \text{ kJ/M}$$

   where $\Delta H°$ is the standard heat of reaction, what is the enthalpy change in the transformation of S(rhombic) to S(monoclinic)?

   A. −594.1 kJ/mol
   B. −0.1 kJ/mol
   C. 0.1 kJ/mol
   D. 594.1 kJ/mol

5. Which one of the following is the most stable state of sulfur at STP?

   A. S(rhombic)
   B. S(monoclinic)
   C. S(liquid)
   D. S(vapor)

6. A sample of sulfur vapor at a temperature of 100°C exerts a pressure of 0.75 atm on the walls of its container. If a researcher raises the temperature in the container to 200°C while holding all other factors constant, what will be the resulting pressure in the container due to the sulfur vapor?

   A. 0.38 atm
   B. 0.77 atm
   C. 0.95 atm
   D. 1.50 atm

Passage 28 (Questions 1-5)

A physical chemist conducted the following experiments in order to study the relation between temperature changes and the resulting changes in vapor pressure of various substances.

Experiment 1

Water was placed in an insulated container. The temperature was increased from –10.1°C to 100°C, under various conditions of pressure. Results gave rise to the phase diagram shown in Figure 1.

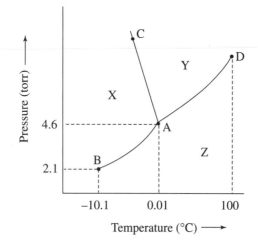

Figure 1   Phase diagram for water (not to scale)

Experiment 2

Experiment 1 was repeated using carbon dioxide and a temperature range of –78.5°C to 0°C. The results gave rise to the phase diagram shown in Figure 2.

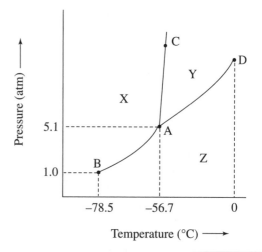

Figure 2 Phase diagram for carbon dioxide (not to scale)

Experiment 3

Various substances were heated in an insulated container to find their boiling points. These results are shown in Table 1.

Substance	Normal BP (°C)
H_2	–253
N_2	–196
O_2	–183
CO_2	–78 (sublimes)
NH_3	–33
H_2O	100

Table 1

1. The portion of Figure 1 that corresponds to the gas phase of water is denoted by:

    A. A.
    B. X.
    C. Y.
    D. Z.

2. A liquid situated in a gaseous medium reaches its boiling point when:

    A. its temperature equals that of the surrounding medium.
    B. its vapor pressure equals that of the surrounding medium.
    C. its density equals that of the surrounding medium.
    D. its heat capacity equals that of the surrounding medium.

3. A researcher adds 30 J of energy to a sample of water of 0°C and detects no change in temperature. Which of the following best explains this observation?

    A. The energy is dissipated by friction between the water and the walls of the container.
    B. The energy is used to decrease the entropy of the water.
    C. The energy is used to raise the Gibbs free energy associated with the water.
    D. The energy is used to break intermolecular forces between water molecules.

4. When temperature is increased and pressure is held fixed across phase changes in Experiment 2:

    A. ΔS is negative and ΔH is positive.
    B. ΔS is negative and ΔH is negative.
    C. ΔS is positive and ΔH is positive.
    D. ΔS is positive and ΔH is negative.

5. Which of the following could be used to explain why the segment AC in Figure 1 has a negative slope whereas AC in Figure 2 has a positive slope?

    A. Ice is less dense than liquid water in the vicinity of the liquid-solid equilibrium curve; this is not so for carbon dioxide.
    B. Carbon dioxide sublimes more easily than does water.
    C. Water is a linear molecule, whereas carbon dioxide has a bent structure.
    D. Water has a higher boiling point than carbon dioxide.

Passage 29 (Questions 1-6)

The Earth's atmosphere has several layers of gases with different characteristics and temperatures. The atmosphere has a total mass of 5×10^{18} kg, and is composed mainly of nitrogen, oxygen, argon, and carbon dioxide, as well as water vapor to a variable degree. Seventy-five percent of this mass is within 11 km from the Earth's surface. Although the limit between outer space and the atmosphere is not definite, the *Kármán Line*, approximately 100 km above sea level, is often taken as the boundary.

Gas	% of Dry Air
Nitrogen	78.1
Oxygen	20.9
Argon	0.93
Carbon dioxide	0.038

Table 1 Composition of atmosphere (dry)

The five main layers of atmosphere are the exosphere, thermosphere, mesosphere, stratosphere, and troposphere. The troposphere is the innermost layer, and extends to approximately 6 km above the Earth's surface at the poles and approximately 20 km above sea level at the equator. The next layer is the stratosphere. The ozone layer, which is considered to be a layer of its own because of its unique composition, is within the stratosphere. Approximately 90 percent of the O_3 in the atmosphere is found in the ozone layer, although the actual concentrations are quite low (2–8 ppm). This layer is very important as it absorbs much of the ultraviolet (UV) light emitted from the sun. The mesosphere is the middle layer of the atmosphere with a temperature of approximately –100°C. The thermosphere and exosphere in that order are the outermost layers.

The pressure, density, and temperature of the atmosphere vary with altitude. Both pressure and density decrease with increasing altitude. At sea level, the density of air is 1.2 kg/m³ and drops by approximately 50 percent every 5.5 km.

The atmosphere contains greenhouse gases, which absorb and emit thermal infrared radiation, leading to the greenhouse effect. Greenhouse gases include water vapor, methane, nitrous oxide, carbon dioxide, and ozone. These gases are needed to maintain the temperature of the earth, which would otherwise be much colder. However, it is thought that an increase in the amount of greenhouse gases in the atmosphere has contributed to the increase in average temperature in the twentieth century. Methane is a very potent greenhouse gas. It can be oxidized in the atmosphere to produce carbon dioxide and water, with a half-life of 7 years.

1. How long would it take for a 1 L sample of methane to decrease to 1 percent of its original amount from atmospheric oxidation?

    A. 38 years
    B. 42 years
    C. 47 years
    D. 50 years

2. What is the partial pressure of nitrogen gas in the atmosphere at sea level?

    A. 7.91×10^1 Pa
    B. 5.96×10^2 Pa
    C. 7.91×10^4 Pa
    D. 5.96×10^5 Pa

3. The summit of Mount Everest is 8.8 km above sea level. What is the approximate density of air at this point?

    A. 0.2 kg/m^3
    B. 0.4 kg/m^3
    C. 0.8 kg/m^3
    D. 1.0 kg/m^3

4. A sample of gas containing oxygen, nitrogen, argon, and carbon dioxide in equal molar proportions is in a closed container. Which of these gases would escape the fastest if a small hole were punctured in the container?

    A. Nitrogen
    B. Oxygen
    C. Argon
    D. Carbon dioxide

5. All of the following are true regarding the earth's atmosphere EXCEPT:

    A. the boundary between the atmosphere and outer space is indistinct.
    B. the ozone layer is primarily composed of ozone gas.
    C. more than 3.75×10^{18} kg of atmospheric gases is contained within an 11 km distance from the earth's surface.
    D. water vapor contributes to warmer atmospheric temperatures.

6. If a 20 L sample of gas at STP were cooled to mesosphere temperatures at a constant volume, what would the new pressure be?

    A. 64 kPa
    B. 84 kPa
    C. 96 kPa
    D. 128 kPa

_____

Passage 30 (Questions 1-5)

For a given substance, the solid phase may offer more than one form, that is, more than one *allotrope*. Separate allotropes differ in their interatomic or intermolecular arrangements and in the attractive forces among their atoms or molecules. For a given solid, an allotrope with stronger intermolecular forces tends to produce a harder, less easily disrupted sample. An allotrope with weaker intermolecular forces tends to produce a softer, more easily disrupted sample.

Carbon exists in several allotropic forms, including diamond, graphite, carbon black, and charcoal. In a sample of diamond, each carbon atom forms four sp^3 hybridized orbitals and a σ bond with each of four other carbon atoms. A sample of graphite, on the other hand, consists of many planar sheets of carbon atoms in which individual atoms are strongly bonded together.

Individual sheets are themselves held together by intermolecular forces. The intermolecular forces are stronger when the sheets are closer together and weaker when they are farther apart.

Carbon forms a wide variety of compounds, many of which are not in solid form at room temperature. For example, benzene (C_6H_6) is a highly volatile hydrocarbon with a boiling point of 80.1°C at 1 atm. Figure 1 shows the temperature of benzene plotted against the amount of heat added to the liquid. Table 1 sets forth data concerning various properties of benzene. When a small amount of a nonvolatile solute is added to benzene, the vapor pressure of the solution decreases slightly. The extent to which a nonvolatile solute lowers a solvent's vapor pressure is proportional to its concentration.

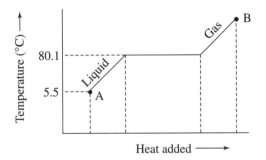

Figure 1

Properties of Benzene	
Density:	0.877 g/cm³
Specific heat of $C_6H_6(l)$:	0.415 cal/g°C
Specific heat of $C_6H_6(g)$:	0.249 cal/g°C
Heat of fusion:	30.4 cal/g
Heat of vaporization:	94.3 cal/g

Table 1

1. Which one of the following graphs best depicts the relationship between the strength of the intermolecular force, F, between graphite sheets and the distance, r, between them?

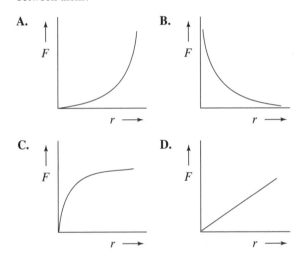

2. The most likely explanation for the fact that diamond is harder than graphite is that:

   A. all of the bonds in graphite are weak.
   B. the attraction between sheets of graphite is relatively weak.
   C. graphite has stronger interplanar hybrid bonds.
   D. all carbon atoms of graphite are more tightly bonded in a three-dimensional network.

3. At 1 atm, which will require more energy: raising the temperature of benzene from 25°C to 35°C, or from 75°C to 85°C?

A. 25°C to 35°C, because the heat of vaporization must also be added to the total energy required to raise the temperature
B. 25°C to 35°C, because it takes more energy to raise the benzene ten degrees at a lower temperature
C. 75°C to 85°C, because the intermolecular forces of benzene are stronger at lower temperatures
D. 75°C to 85°C, because the heat of vaporization must be added to the total energy required to raise the temperature

4. A sample of benzene undergoes a phase change from gas to liquid. The enthalpy change associated with this process is:

A. negative, because intermolecular forces are broken in the process.
B. negative, because intermolecular forces are formed in the process.
C. positive, because intermolecular forces are broken in the process.
D. positive, because intermolecular forces are formed in the process.

5. A chemist wishes to confirm the accuracy of the value reported in Table 1 for benzene's enthalpy of vaporization. She selects a sample of benzene, and at time 1 begins heating it. At time 2, the sample has reached a temperature of 80.1°C. At this point, the chemist should now:

A. stop heating and determine the quantity of heat consumed between times 1 and 2.
B. continue heating and determine the quantity of heat consumed between time 2 and the time at which the entire sample reaches the gas phase.
C. continue heating and determine the quantity of heat consumed between time 1 and the time at which the entire sample reaches the gas phase.
D. stop heating and determine the quantity of heat evolved as the sample cools to room temperature.

Passage 31 (Questions 1-6)

Rocket engines work on the simple principle that *momentum* is conserved in an explosion. For example, if a stationary (zero momentum) cannonball explodes, the total momentum of all the flying pieces of debris is still zero after the explosion.

stationary cannonball   outgoing fragments

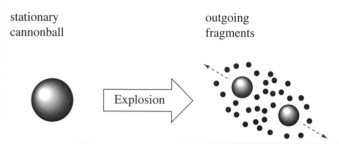

mass = m = 10 kg   mass = 3 kg + 3 kg
velocity = v = 0 m/s   velocity = –2 m/s + 2 m/s
momentum = p = mv = 0 total momentum = 0

In a chemical rocket engine, a mixture of gases are allowed to explosively react in a compartment with one open end. The hot gaseous products escape out the open end with great velocity (because they're hot) and propel the rocket in the opposite direction to conserve momentum.

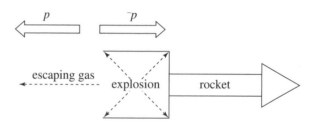

Hot gas escapes with momentum p, so the rocket is pushed with momentum $-p$.

The average kinetic energy of the atoms in a sample of matter is proportional to the absolute temperature of the sample. The kinetic energy (KE) of a particle is defined by the equation

$$KE = \tfrac{1}{2}mv^2$$

where m is the mass and v is the speed of the particle. Clearly, particles at rest have zero kinetic energy.

1. Identify the correct relationship between the kinetic energy (KE) and momentum (p) of a gas molecule.

A. $2 \times KE = p^{-1} \times \text{velocity}$
B. $2 \times KE = p \times \text{velocity}^{-1}$
C. $2 \times KE = p \times \text{velocity}$
D. $2 \times KE = (p \times \text{velocity})^{1/2}$

2. The space shuttle's liquid rockets use a fuel of liquid oxygen and hydrogen which react to give water vapor. The most efficient burn occurs when the ratio of hydrogen to oxygen gas is about 2 to 1. If one-fourth of the gas in the rocket nozzle is always water vapor, and the pressure in the nozzle is 10 atm, what H_2 partial pressure should be maintained for an efficient burn?

   A. 2.5 atm
   B. 5.0 atm
   C. 6.7 atm
   D. 7.5 atm

3. Given a mixture of equimolar amounts of hydrogen and oxygen gas under normal pressure, which one of the following statements is true?

   A. The kinetic energy of the oxygen molecules is less than that of the hydrogen molecules.
   B. The mole fraction of hydrogen is 0.5, and the mass fraction is 0.06.
   C. Due to its larger molecular size, oxygen gas occupies more volume than hydrogen gas.
   D. The momenta of oxygen and hydrogen molecules are equal.

4. If ten grams of each of the gases He and Ne were heated to 1000°C, which one would provide more rocket lift?

   A. He
   B. Ne
   C. They would provide the same lift.
   D. Unable to predict

5. The space shuttle's main tank storing the liquid hydrogen and oxygen fuel has microscopic cracks and holes which allow a very small amount of the liquid to vaporize and escape to the environment. Which one of the following statements is incorrect?

   A. Hydrogen gas will escape about four times faster than oxygen gas.
   B. The regions of escape will be colder than the surrounding tank.
   C. Escaped hydrogen gas will spontaneously explode upon contact with the air.
   D. The condensation of hydrogen and oxygen is an exothermic process.

6. Under what conditions does water vapor approach ideal behavior?

   A. Low pressure, low temperature
   B. Low pressure, high temperature
   C. High pressure, low temperature
   D. High pressure, high temperature

_____

Passage 32 (Questions 1-5)

Water has some unique physical characteristics. For example, on the Earth, water is the only substance to exist naturally in all three phases. Of all liquids, water has the lowest molecular weight. Furthermore, under ambient pressures, liquid water becomes *less* dense upon freezing, yet nearly all other substances are most dense in the solid phase. This unusual property is but another consequence of the strong hydrogen bonds that exist between water molecules. In ice, water molecules align themselves into a crystalline lattice.

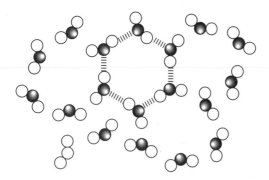

This arrangement leaves atomic-sized cavities between every six water molecules. It is these cavities that account for the lower density of the solid as compared with the liquid.

The phase of pure water is a function of temperature and pressure. The phase diagram for water illustrates these dependencies:

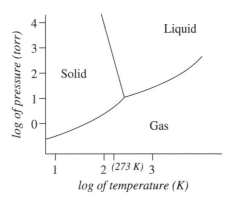

Moreover, the specific heat, heat of fusion, and heat of vaporization of water are among the highest found of any non-metallic substance:

	Specific heat*	Heat of fusion	Heat of vaporization
H_2O:	4.2 J g^{-1} K^{-1}	6.00 kJ mol^{-1}	40.7 kJ mol^{-1}

*for liquid water only

These thermal properties are a manifestation of the strong and extensive intermolecular forces between water molecules.

1. The phase of water at $-173°C$ and 10^2 torr pressure is:

    A. solid.
    B. liquid.
    C. gas.
    D. both solid and liquid

2. Which one of the following has the highest heat of vaporization?

    A. Methane
    B. Hydrogen sulfide
    C. Oxygen
    D. Methanol

3. What is the minimum amount of energy that must be added to 20 g of water at 75°C to convert it to steam at one atmosphere pressure?

    A. 20 kJ
    B. 30 kJ
    C. 40 kJ
    D. 50 kJ

4. The H–O–H bond in water has an angle:

    A. less than 90°.
    B. between 90° and 109.5°.
    C. equal to 109.5°.
    D. greater than 109.5°.

5. The densest phase of carbon is the solid phase. However, carbon has two allotropic forms as a solid: graphite and diamond, with the latter more dense than the former. Identify which of the following phase diagrams is that of elemental carbon.

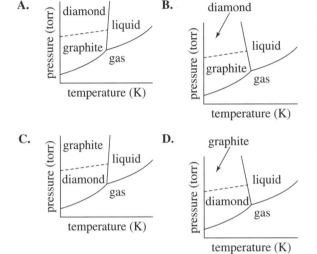

A.

B.

C.

D.

Passage 33 (Questions 1-5)

An athletic-shoe manufacturer decided to use a cushion of air to provide a comfortable, shock-absorbing sole for their next generation of basketball sneakers. The revolutionary cushion, which we will call the *rocket pocket* contains 25 cm³ of compressed air (5 atm pressure) sealed in an elastic rubber envelope.

Rocket pocket cushion

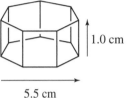

1.0 cm

5.5 cm

volume = 25 cc
horizontal cross-sectional area (top surface) = 25 cm²

Each sneaker will have a single *rocket pocket* unit, and tests show that approximately 98% of an individual's mass will rest directly upon the *rocket pocket* cushions.

Most current high-impact footwear utilizes the shock-absorbent, polymer foams. One limitation of these foams has been the loss of elasticity and flexibility when exposed to warm temperatures for prolonged periods of time. So it is hoped that the *rocket pocket* technology will increase the longevity of high-performance footwear.

1. One of the limitations of using a gas as a shock absorbing cushion is that under high pressures, the gas may liquefy and lose compressibility. Which of the following gases would be the best one to use in light of this concern?

  A. Carbon dioxide
  B. Water vapor
  C. Bromine gas
  D. Ammonia gas

2. The internal gas temperature of a *rocket pocket* was measured while a subject wore a pair of the experimental sneakers. Which plot reflects the measured temperature (*T*) when a subject who was first at rest jumped and then returned to rest?

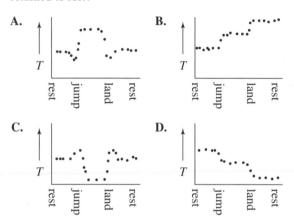

A.

B.

C.

D.

3. Which one of the following statements does NOT support the conclusion that water shouldn't be used instead of air for the *rocket pocket*?

   A. Water is nearly incompressible.
   B. Water is much denser than air.
   C. Water may freeze under high pressure.
   D. Water may freeze in cold weather.

4. Automotive safety air bags are inflated in less than one-hundredth of a second by (diatomic) nitrogen gas. The nitrogen is produced from sodium azide, NaN_3, which decomposes to sodium nitride, Na_3N, from the heat released in an exothermic reaction between rust and aluminum powder (called a *thermite* reaction). What volume of nitrogen, at STP, will be liberated if one mole of NaN_3 completely decomposes?

   A. Less than 22.4 L
   B. Equal to 22.4 L
   C. More than 22.4 L
   D. Unable to determine from the information given

5. What is the shape of the azide ion, N_3^-?

   A. Bent
   B. Linear
   C. Trigonal planar
   D. Three-membered ring

Passage 34 (Questions 1-5)

A biologist attempted to measure the concentration of dissolved ions (called *electrolytes*) in human lymphocytes. The experimental procedure consisted of immersing four groups of cells into four aqueous solutions (having different concentrations) for five minutes. The solutions were prepared by dissolving decreasing amounts of salt, NaCl, in 250 mL of water. The diameters of the lymphocytes, measured using an optical microscope before and after immersion, were carefully recorded.

Solution	change in cellular diameter
1	reduced by 34%
2	reduced by 8%
3	increased by 13%
4	*no cells were recovered
Solutions were labeled in order of concentration.	

In a second part of this experiment, the biologist extracted 10 mL of lymphocyte cytoplasm and measured its osmotic pressure using an osmometer.

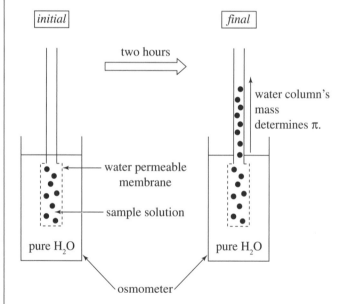

The osmotic pressure, π, is equal to the pressure exerted by the column of water in a capillary tube on the surface of the bulk solution in the osmometer. Osmotic pressure may also be calculated using the equation

$$\Pi = i \times \Delta M \times R \times T$$

where *i* is the ionizability factor, ΔM is the difference in the molarities of the solutions, *R* is the gas constant (= 0.0821 L atm mol⁻¹ K⁻¹), and *T* is the temperature.

1. Which one of the following statements is FALSE?

   A. The most dilute solution was Solution 1.
   B. Osmosis of water is responsible for the results in the first part of the experiment.
   C. The height of the water column on the capillary tube is proportional to the osmotic pressure.
   D. Glucose is not an electrolyte.

2. What is the most likely reason why no cells were recovered from Solution 4?

   A. The cells dissolved in the electrolytic solution.
   B. The cellular membranes ruptured in Solution 4.
   C. The cells shrank to a size undetectable to an optical microscope.
   D. The lymphocyte's cellular walls collapsed under the intense osmotic pressure of Solution 4.

3. Solution X and Solution Y are identical except for the fact that their temperatures are 15°C and 30°C respectively. The osmotic pressure of Solution Y is:

   A. half the osmotic pressure of Solution X.
   B. equal to the osmotic pressure of Solution X.
   C. twice the osmotic pressure of Solution X.
   D. None of the above

4. Which one of the following equations is equivalent to $\Pi = iMRT$?

   A. $\Pi V = iMRT$
   B. $\Pi V = inRT$
   C. $\Pi V = n^{-1}iRT$
   D. $\Pi V^{-1} = inRT$

5. Which one of the following statements is true?

   A. Water molecules do not pass through an osmotic membrane when the concentrations of solutes on the two sides are identical.
   B. The osmotic pressure of a solution is independent of the kinetic energy of the molecules in that solution.
   C. In osmosis, the direction of water flow is always into the solution of higher solute concentration.
   D. Osmotic pressure is responsible for forcing solvent molecules across a semipermeable membrane into the solution with greater solute concentration.

Passage 35 (Questions 1-5)
ADVANCED PASSAGE

The structure of a newly synthesized, organic liquid was elucidated by an analytical chemist. The compound was given the name *pandorium*, owing to the fact that this liquid violently explodes when in contact with atmospheric oxygen.

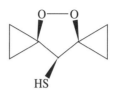

pandorium

A physical chemist attempted to construct a vapor pressure diagram for pandorium. The experimental procedure required that 5 grams of the liquid be placed under an inert atmosphere (760 torr pressure) in a sealed one-liter vessel. The liquid was then heated until it boiled. This temperature was recorded, and then a vacuum pump was used to slowly reduce the pressure above the boiling liquid. As the vacuum was gently applied, the decreasing temperature and pressure of the contents were recorded every two minutes. The experiment continued until the pressure inside the flask passed below 25 torr. The results of the experiment are graphed below:

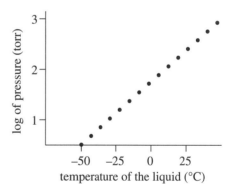

* = initial boiling point of liquid (34°C); no pressure reading taken—pressure was assumed to be 760 torr.

Two grams of the liquid remained, and its final temperature was –47°C.

1. Which one of the following gases could have served as the inert gas in this experiment?

   A. H_2
   B. N_2
   C. O_2
   D. F_2

2. The pressure at each data point is taken to be equal to the vapor pressure of the liquid at that temperature. Based upon these data, which of the following best describes the dependence of the vapor pressure (*VP*) of pandorium on its temperature (*T*)?

    A. $VP \propto T$
    B. $VP \propto T^{-1}$
    C. $VP \propto \log T$
    D. $VP \propto 10^{T}$

3. Later analysis showed that intermolecular interactions existed between the thiol (SH) hydrogen and the peroxy (O–O) bridge. These interactions would constitute:

    A. ionic interactions.
    B. hydrogen bonding.
    C. dipole interactions.
    D. London dispersion forces.

4. About how many moles of pandorium are in a 5-gram sample?

    A. 0.01
    B. 0.03
    C. 0.05
    D. 0.10

5. Which one of the following compounds is most likely to be a solid at room temperature?

A.

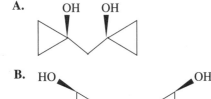

B.

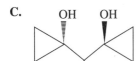

C.

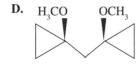

D.

H₃CO   OCH₃

Passage 36 (Questions 1-4)

All real gases depart from ideality because intermolecular forces cause molecules to attract and occupy slightly less volume than that predicted by the ideal gas law. This departure is most pronounced when gas molecules are densely packed, that is, under high pressure and low temperature.

Similarly, aqueous ionic solutions do not behave as if all of the ions were independent units. Some strong ion-ion interactions persist and draw the ions into small clusters even when the salt completely dissolves. In dilute solutions, clusters have little effect upon properties of the overall solution and are ignored. However, in very concentrated solutions (greater than 0.1 *M*), their contribution to the solution's properties becomes very significant.

Calcite ($CaCO_3$) is an insoluble ionic solid. The solubility expression of calcite ($K_{sp} = [Ca^{2+}] \cdot [CO_3^{2-}]$) only applies to dilute solutions. At higher concentrations, this expression is adjusted by multiplying each ionic concentration by an activity coefficient, γ. Therefore, the solubility expression becomes

$$K_{sp} = (\gamma_{Ca^{2+}} \cdot [Ca^{2+}])(\gamma_{CO_3^{2-}} \cdot [CO_3^{2-}])$$

Experiments have quantified the relationship between the solubility of calcite in various strengths of two different ionic solutions.

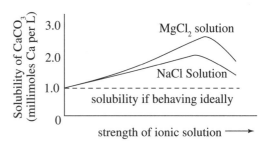

Keep in mind that the activity coefficient may be considered a correction factor that accounts for those ions that cluster with other ions and water molecules and no longer act as independent particles. An activity coefficient is a function of temperature, pressure, and concentration. Furthermore, over most concentrations, the activity coefficient varies inversely with the concentration of the solution, with typical values being less than one.

1. In very dilute solution, the values of all activity coefficients approach:

   A. 0.
   B. 0.5.
   C. 1.0.
   D. the absolute concentration of the ions.

2. According to the passage, what is the approximate value of the solubility constant for calcite in pure water?

   A. 10^{-2}
   B. 10^{-4}
   C. 10^{-6}
   D. 10^{-8}

3. Calcite will be least soluble in a solution of:

   A. $0.1\ M$ NaCl
   B. $0.1\ M$ $MgCl_2$
   C. $0.1\ M$ KCl
   D. $0.1\ M$ $CaCl_2$

4. One gram of a salt was added to 200 mL of pure water and completely dissolved. That salt could have been:

   A. AgCl.
   B. $PbSO_4$.
   C. $Cd(NO_3)_2$.
   D. $BaCO_3$.

Passage 37 (Questions 1-4)

The specific heat of a metal can be determined by a simple experiment. If a sample of metal of known mass and temperature is submerged into a water bath of known temperature and mass, the change in the temperature of the water will correspond to the heat capacity of the metal. The specific heat of the metal in this case may be expressed as:

$$C_p = \frac{-m_{water}(4.2\ J/g\text{-}°C)(T_{final} - T_{initial})_{water}}{B}$$

where

$$B = m_{metal}(T_{final} - T_{initial})_{metal}$$

and m is the mass (and assuming that the calorimeter itself does not absorb heat). Note that T_{final} and $T_{initial}$ for water and the metal will never be the same.

For example, a physicist used a coffee-cup calorimeter filled with 100 grams of water at room temperature to measure the heat capacity of four metals. A 20-gram sample of each metal was heated in a bath of boiling water for ten minutes and then transferred into the calorimeter. The temperatures of the system at thermal equilibrium are presented in Table 1.

	initial temperature of water bath	final temperature of water bath
metal #1	25.6°C	35.8°C
	25.4°C	35.4°C
metal #2	25.5°C	37.1°C
	25.5°C	37.6°C
metal #3	25.6°C	31.8°C
	25.5°C	31.7°C
metal #4	25.4°C	33.0°C
	25.3°C	31.7°C

Table 1

It should be mentioned that in each trial, the technician mixed the water bath with a thin metal spatula immediately after the hot metal was lowered into it. This was to ensure that the calorimeter's contents were thermally homogeneous.

1. What is the approximate specific heat of Metal #1?

   A. $3\ J\cdot(g\cdot K)^{-1}$
   B. $7\ J\cdot(g\cdot K)^{-1}$
   C. $10\ J\cdot(g\cdot K)^{-1}$
   D. $20\ J\cdot(g\cdot K)^{-1}$

2. Which one of the metals in Table 1 has the greatest specific heat?

    A. Metal #1
    B. Metal #2
    C. Metal #3
    D. Metal #4

3. A limitation of coffee-cup calorimeters is that they cannot be used to measure systems at:

    A. high pressure.
    B. very low pressure.
    C. very high temperature.
    D. all of the above

4. Which one of the following is the correct relationship between specific heat and heat capacity?

    A. Specific heat = (heat capacity) × temperature
    B. Specific heat = (heat capacity) / temperature
    C. Specific heat = (heat capacity) × mass
    D. Specific heat = (heat capacity) / mass

Passage 38 (Questions 1-6)

Over the last decade, atmospheric scientists have observed a substantial reduction in the concentration of stratospheric ozone directly attributable to the emission of chlorine-bearing man-made gases. Ozone reduction has been particularly acute over Antarctica, leading to an Antarctic "ozone hole" in the southern hemisphere winters. It is believed that this ozone hole is a consequence of the presence of polar stratospheric clouds (PSCs) that are formed from the crystallization of water vapor and gaseous nitric acid, a process that only occurs at very low temperatures.

$$T < 195 \text{ K}$$
$$HNO_3(g) + 3\ H_2O(g) \quad \rightarrow \quad HNO_3 \cdot 3\ H_2O(s)$$

Nitric acid trihydrate crystals, called NAT crystals, indirectly catalyze the destruction of $O_3(g)$ by producing chlorine gas.

$$Cl \cdot (g) + HNO_3 \cdot 3\ H_2O(s) \rightarrow HCl(g) + \cdot ONO_2 \cdot 3\ H_2O(s)$$

$$\cdot ONO_2 \cdot 3\ H_2O(s) + Cl \cdot (g) \rightarrow ClONO_2 \cdot 3\ H_2O(s)$$

$$HCl(g) + ClONO_2 \cdot 3\ H_2O(s) \rightarrow Cl_2(g) + HNO_3 \cdot 3\ H_2O(s)$$

In the presence of sunlight, $Cl_2(g)$ is rapidly photolyzed, initiating the chain reaction that leads to the loss of $O_3(g)$.

	Rate magnitude
$Cl_2(g) + hv \rightarrow 2\ Cl \cdot (g)$	seconds
$2 \cdot [Cl \cdot (g) + O_3(g) \rightarrow ClO \cdot (g) + O_2(g)]$	minutes
$ClO \cdot (g) + ClO \cdot (g) \rightarrow Cl_2O_2(g)$	hours
$Cl_2O_2(g) + hv \rightarrow 2\ Cl \cdot (g) + O_2(g)$	seconds

Once produced, $Cl \cdot$ can be recycled, destroying tens to hundreds of ozone molecules before being removed from the stratosphere.

Approximate σ bond energy between nonmetal atoms:

O–O	140 kJ·mol^{-1}
O–H	465 kJ·mol^{-1}
O–Cl	210 kJ·mol^{-1}
Cl–H	430 kJ·mol^{-1}
Cl–Cl	243 kJ·mol^{-1}

1. In the production of chlorine, NAT crystals serve as a:

   A. primary reactant.
   B. secondary reactant.
   C. homogeneous catalyst.
   D. heterogeneous catalyst.

2. Given that the energies of a red, green, and violet photon are 170 kJ/mol, 225 kJ/mol, and 290 kJ/mol, respectively, what is the longest wavelength of visible light than can *initiate* the catalytic destruction of ozone?

   A. Yellow
   B. Green
   C. Blue
   D. Ultraviolet

3. Determine ΔH_{rxn} for the third step in the chain destruction of ozone by chlorine.

   A. −280 kJ/mol
   B. −140 kJ/mol
   C. +140 kJ/mol
   D. +280 kJ/mol

4. Considering that the atmospheric pressure at stratospheric altitudes is about 8 torr, which one of the following statements must be true?

   A. Water would boil at a temperature lower than 100°C.
   B. The partial pressure of ozone at these altitudes is greater than 8 torr.
   C. Water will freeze at temperatures well above 100°C.
   D. Gaseous reactions cannot occur at these low pressures.

5. What is the rate law for the catalytic conversion of ozone to molecular oxygen?

   A. Rate = $k[Cl_2]$
   B. Rate = $k[Cl][O_3]$
   C. Rate = $k[ClO\cdot]^2$
   D. Rate = $k[ClO\cdot]^2 / [Cl_2O_2]$

6. Considering that chlorine can catalyze the destruction of O_3 in the stratosphere, which one of the following statements must NOT be true?

   A. Chlorine lowers the E_a of the rate-determining step.
   B. Chlorine does not affect the overall energy released during the destruction of ozone.
   C. The concentration of O_3 in the stratosphere is greater than it should be at equilibrium concentrations.
   D. None of the above

Passage 39 (Questions 1-6)
ADVANCED PASSAGE

A chemist used the following apparatus to measure some thermodynamic and kinetic characteristics of three systems of monatomic gases:

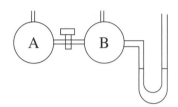

Some gas mixtures were expected to react while others were not. In each trial, Flask A was filled with 450 torr of Gas F. The pressure of the gas in Flask B varied with each trial and was measured *in situ* by an attached mercury manometer.

Experiments began when the valve separating the flasks was opened. In the first set of trials, the final equilibrium pressure of the mixture was measured with the manometer.

	test gas	initial pressure in flask B	final internal pressure of apparatus
test 1	M	240 mm Hg	132 mm Hg
test 2	N	620 mm Hg	535 mm Hg
test 3	O	450 mm Hg	148 mm Hg

The second phase of the experiment was designed to determine the rates of the following chemical reaction between Gases F and P:

$$2 F(g) + P(g) \rightarrow F_2P(g)$$

The same apparatus was used to measure the change in pressure as the reaction proceeded. Six trials were performed in hopes of elucidating the kinetic characteristics of each reaction component.

	initial pressure of F	initial pressure of P	$-(\Delta \text{pressure*})$
1	510 mm Hg	490 mm Hg	32 mm Hg·m^{-1}
2	630 mm Hg	422 mm Hg	34 mm Hg·m^{-1}
3	705 mm Hg	392 mm Hg	30 mm Hg·m^{-1}
4	528 mm Hg	301 mm Hg	8 mm Hg·m^{-1}
5	258 mm Hg	304 mm Hg	4 mm Hg·m^{-1}
6	263 mm Hg	599 mm Hg	16 mm Hg·m^{-1}

*Note: Here, Δpressure equals the pressure 60 seconds after the reaction began minus the initial pressure.

1. Considering the apparatus utilized in this experiment, if the height of the liquid in the left and right tubes of the manometer are Z and Z*, respectively, then the pressure inside Flask B equals:

    A. Z – Z*.
    B. Z* – Z.
    C. Z – Z* + 760 mm Hg.
    D. Z* – Z + 760 mm Hg.

2. This experiment assumes that:

    A. individual gas molecules exert equal pressures.
    B. the gases are not ideal.
    C. the pressure of a gas is proportional to its temperature.
    D. the volume of a gas is proportional to its temperature.

3. Given that Flasks A and B have the same volume, which of the following gas mixtures did not react?

    A. F and M
    B. F and N
    C. F and O
    D. None of the above

4. What is the rate law for the reaction of Gas F with Gas P?

    A. Rate = $k \cdot [F]$
    B. Rate = $k \cdot [P]$
    C. Rate = $k \cdot [F]^2 \cdot [P]$
    D. Rate = $k \cdot [F] \cdot [P]^2$

5. The rate constant of a reaction does NOT depend upon:

   A. the temperature of the reaction.
   B. the molecular shape of the reactants.
   C. the activation energy of the reactants.
   D. the free energy of the reaction.

6. The melting point of mercury metal is closest to:

   A. 250 K.
   B. 300 K.
   C. 350 K.
   D. 400 K.

Passage 40 (Questions 1-6)

Among the products formed by internal combustion engines are carbon monoxide (CO) and several oxides of nitrogen, such as nitrogen monoxide (NO) and nitrogen dioxide (NO_2). These gases enter the air and undergo a number of possible reactions.

For example, NO is a colorless gas which reacts spontaneously with oxygen to form NO_2, a reddish-brown gas. NO_2 can then react with H_2O to form nitric acid, thereby increasing the acidity of rain. At low temperatures, NO_2 molecules can also dimerize to form dinitrogen tetroxide (N_2O_4).

Another known atmospheric reaction is the following one between NO_2 and CO:

$$NO_2(g) + CO(g) \rightarrow NO(g) + CO_2(g)$$

Reaction 1

This reaction follows a two-step mechanism:

(1a) $\quad NO_2(g) + NO_2(g) \rightarrow NO_3(g) + NO(g) \qquad$ (slow)

(1b) $\quad NO_3(g) + CO(g) \rightarrow NO_2(g) + CO_2(g) \qquad$ (fast)

In addition, NO and CO are ozone-depleting compounds. Before the addition to the atmosphere of chemicals that react with ozone, the level of ozone present was in equilibrium, maintained by a photochemical process. Currently the dynamics of the ozone layer are disrupted by self-propagating chain reactions. One such mechanism is given below:

(2a) $\quad NO(g) + O_3(g) \rightarrow NO_2(g) + O_2(g)$

(2b) $\quad NO_2(g) + O(g) \rightarrow NO(g) + O_2(g)$

The net reaction is:

$$O_3(g) + O(g) \rightarrow 2\, O_2(g)$$

Reaction 2

1. A 1.00 L vessel at 400°C contains the following equilibrium concentrations: [NO] = 0.1 M, [CO_2] = 0.02 M, [NO_2] = 0.01 M, and [CO] = 0.1 M. What is the equilibrium constant of Reaction 1?

   A. 0.5
   B. 1.0
   C. 2.0
   D. 4.0

2. Reaction 1 is initially at equilibrium. A consequence of adding more $NO_2(g)$ is that:

    A. the equilibrium constant will increase.
    B. the equilibrium constant will decrease.
    C. the reaction will proceed in the forward direction.
    D. the reaction will proceed in the reverse direction.

3. Which of the following is true about Reaction 1?

    A. NO is an intermediary complex.
    B. Step 1a of the mechanism determines the overall rate of reaction.
    C. Step 1b of the mechanism is the rate-limiting step.
    D. The addition of a catalyst would increase the activation energy.

4. According to the passage, in the absence of ozone depleting chemicals, which of the following is necessary for maintenance of the ozone layer?

    A. Water vapor
    B. Nitrogen oxides
    C. Electromagnetic radiation
    D. Atmospheric pressure

5. Ozone-depleting reactions such as the one given in the passage are particularly nocuous because the destructive chemical:

    A. is produced in massive quantities.
    B. is more reactive than ozone.
    C. diffuses quickly into the upper atmosphere where the ozone layer is located.
    D. acts as a catalyst.

6. In order for the level of ozone to be maintained in dynamic equilibrium, the rate at which ozone-depleting processes occur must be:

    A. less than the rate at which ozone is formed.
    B. equal to the rate at which ozone is formed.
    C. greater than the rate at which ozone is formed.
    D. equal to zero.

Passage 41 (Questions 1-6)

One of the most studied reactions in the field of kinetics is the decomposition of hydrogen iodide, HI. In the absence of light, HI decomposes by a single elementary reaction:

$$2\,HI \rightarrow H_2 + I_2$$

Reaction 1

Reaction 1 is exothermic and, if uncatalyzed, has an activation energy of 184 kJ/mol. Various metal surfaces act as catalysts for this reaction. In the presence of gold and platinum catalysts, the activation energies for Reaction 1 are 105 kJ/mol and 59 kJ/mol, respectively.

The decomposition of HI becomes a photochemical reaction when exposed to light of wavelengths less than 327 nm. The HI molecule absorbs the photon's energy, hf (where h is Planck's constant and f is the frequency of the light). With this energy, the HI molecule dissociates in a three-step mechanism as shown in Reactions 2a, b, and c:

(2a) $HI + hf \rightarrow H\bullet + I\bullet$

(2b) $H\bullet + HI \rightarrow H_2 + I\bullet$

(2c) $2\,I\bullet \rightarrow I_2$

Reaction 2

In the laboratory, the photochemical decomposition of HI was studied by monitoring the mole percents of HI, I•, and I_2 during the course of the reaction. As shown in Figure 1, initially there was only HI present (and light of the appropriate wavelength).

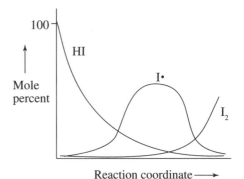

Figure 1

1. Using the experimental data below, which of the following is the proper rate law expression for Reaction 1?

Trial	$[HI]_{t=0}$	Initial Rate (M/s)
1	1.0	5.0×10^{-4}
2	2.0	2.0×10^{-3}
3	3.0	4.5×10^{-3}
4	4.0	8.0×10^{-3}

   A. Rate = k
   B. Rate = $k[HI]$
   C. Rate = $2k[HI]$
   D. Rate = $k[HI]^2$

2. Which one of the following graphs best illustrates the results of surface catalysts on the reaction profile of Reaction 1?

A.
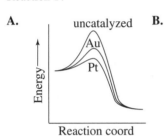

B.
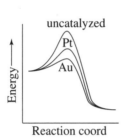

C.
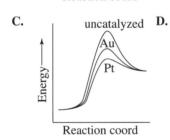

D.
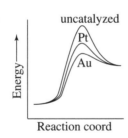

3. Assuming that Reaction 1 is reversible, increased temperature within the reaction system would most likely produce:

   A. increased initial rate of the forward reaction and increased equilibrium concentration of HI.
   B. increased initial rate of the forward reaction and increased equilibrium concentration of H_2 and I_2.
   C. decreased initial rate of the reverse reaction and decreased equilibrium concentration of HI.
   D. decreased initial rate of the reverse reaction and increased equilibrium concentration of H_2 and I_2.

4. Using the table below, what type of light would cause the photochemical decomposition of HI to occur?

Wavelength range (m)	Common name
1.0×10^{-3} down to 7.0×10^{-7}	Infrared
7.0×10^{-7} down to 6.3×10^{-7}	Red to orange
5.9×10^{-7} down to 4.8×10^{-7}	Yellow to green
4.8×10^{-7} down to 4.0×10^{-7}	Blue to violet
4.0×10^{-7} down to 5.0×10^{-8}	Ultraviolet

   A. Infrared
   B. Yellow light
   C. Violet light
   D. Ultraviolet

5. Which one of the following changes would cause a saturated solution of HI(aq) to drive off HI(g)?

   A. The addition of a catalyst
   B. An increase in temperature
   C. An increase in the atmospheric pressure
   D. The neutralization of HI(aq)

6. If the photochemical decomposition of HI were studied by monitoring the mole percents of HI, H, and H_2, as a function of reaction progress, which of the following graphs would best represent the results?

A.

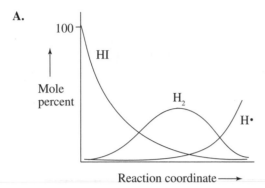

B.

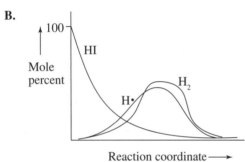

C.

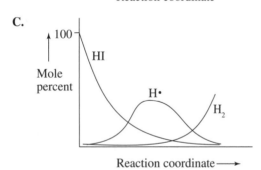

D.

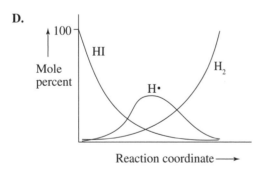

Passage 42 (Questions 1-6)

An atom is in the ground state if all of its electrons occupy orbitals that correspond to the lowest energy levels available to them. The ground state for oxygen, for example, is represented by $1s^2\,2s^2\,2p^4$ and that for sulfur is represented by $1s^2\,2s^2\,2p^6\,3s^2\,3p^4$.

When an atom in the ground state absorbs energy, an electron is elevated to a higher energy level, and a dark band appears on its absorption spectrum. When the excited electron returns to the ground state, a photon is emitted, producing a bright band on the emission spectrum. Absorption and emission spectra yield important information about the energy levels associated with the electrons of various atoms and ions.

Hydrochloric acid, for example, is created by combining hydrogen and chlorine gases as shown in Reaction 1:

$$H_2(g) + Cl_2(g) \rightleftharpoons 2\,HCl(g) \qquad \Delta H = -92.3 \text{ kJ/mol}$$

Reaction 1

In aqueous solutions of hydrochloric acid (HCl), the electron configuration of the conjugate base Cl^- may be ascertained by absorption spectroscopy. In the ground state, the chloride ion's additional electron occupies the last position in the $3p$ subshell, so that the configuration is identical to that of the inert gas, argon: $1s^2\,2s^2\,2p^6\,3s^2\,3p^6$.

An unknown hydrogen halide, HX was heated in a solution of the strong base NaOH. It was observed that on excitation, ions of the conjugate base revealed the electron configuration $1s^2\,2s^2\,2p^6\,3s^2\,3p^6\,4s^2\,3d^{10}\,4p^5\,5s^1$.

1. Which one of the following best represents the electron configuration of an oxygen atom in an excited state?

   A. $1s^2\,2s^2\,2p^4$
   B. $1s^2\,2s^2\,2p^5$
   C. $1s^2\,2s^2\,2p^3\,3s^1$
   D. $1s^2\,2s^2\,2p^1\,3s^2$

2. When the unknown conjugate base derived from the unknown hydrogen halide HX is excited, its absorption spectrum would most likely show:

   A. red shift.
   B. no absorption.
   C. bright bands.
   D. dark bands.

3. Based on the table below, which of the following conclusions can best be drawn regarding each of the listed hydrogen halides and the bonding between the associated hydrogen and halide atoms?

Hydrogen halide	Bond diss. energy of hybrid orbital (kJ/mol)	Radius of halide atom
HF	567	1.33 Å
HCl	431	1.81
HBr	366	1.96
HI	299	2.19

A. Stronger bonds are associated with smaller halide atoms.
B. Stronger bonds involve hybrids of greater lengths.
C. Smaller halide atoms display hybrids with greater lengths.
D. Smaller halide atoms are associated with weaker bonds.

4. For Reaction 1, K_{eq} is best expressed by which of the following?

A. $[H_2][Cl_2] / [HCl]$
B. $[H_2][Cl_2] / [HCl]^2$
C. $[HCl] / ([H_2][Cl_2])$
D. $[HCl]^2 / ([H_2][Cl_2])$

5. In a separate experiment, two additional hydrogen halides were studied. What can best be concluded about the ground state electron configurations of the two conjugate bases?

A. They have excited electrons.
B. They are missing electrons.
C. They are the configurations of two inert gases.
D. They are the configurations of two metals.

6. A chemist manufactures gaseous hydrogen chloride by combining hydrogen and chlorine in a closed container as shown in Reaction 1. When the reaction reaches equilibrium, an increase in the temperature of the reaction container would result in:

A. an increase in the concentration of hydrogen chloride due to the increased rate of reaction.
B. an increase in the concentration of hydrogen chloride due to the decrease in enthalpy associated with the forward reaction.
C. a decrease in the concentration of hydrogen chloride due to the increase in molar quantity of gas associated with the forward reaction.
D. a decrease in the concentration of hydrogen chloride due to the exothermic nature of the forward reaction.

Passage 43 (Questions 1-6)

Many caves trace their roots back to chemical principles. Some caves, called solutional caves, are formed as a result of acidic water flowing through rock such as limestone ($CaCO_3$, $K_{sp} = 3.4 \times 10^{-9}$ at 25°C). In this process limestone is dissolved, resulting in cave formation.

Solutional caves often contain spectacular rock formations. They are the products of equilibria involving water, carbon dioxide and limestone. The process begins when surface water flowing into the caves encounters soil with a higher P_{CO_2} than found in the atmosphere. This high CO_2 content is a result of CO_2 release from the earth's mantle, in a process called *outgassing*. Equation 1 describes the dissolution of CO_2 in water:

$$CO_2(g) + H_2O(l) \rightleftharpoons CO_2(aq) + H_2O(l)$$

Equation 1

Once solubilized, $CO_2(aq)$ causes the acidification of water via Equation 2:

$$CO_2(aq) + H_2O(l) \rightleftharpoons H_2CO_3(aq) \rightleftharpoons H_3O^+(aq) + HCO_3^-(aq)$$

Equation 2

The acidic water causes dissolution of limestone according to the following equilibrium:

$$CaCO_3(s) + H_3O^+(aq) \rightleftharpoons Ca^{2+}(aq) + HCO_3^-(aq) + H_2O(l)$$

Equation 3

When acidic solution finally flows through the roof and into the cave, it encounters ambient air with a lower P_{CO_2} than that in the soil. As such, dissolved $CO_2(aq)$ is released as a gas, eventually causing the precipitation of $CaCO_3(s)$. This precipitate forms *stalagmites*, an upward spike formed from water striking the ground in the cave, and *stalactites*, which are downward spikes created from water flowing down from the roofs toward the ground. Eventually, in a process that can take thousands of years, the two can meet to form a column in the cave.

1. A local factory accidentally pollutes groundwater supplies near a cave with $(NH_4)_2CO_3$. How would the cave most likely be affected?

   A. Stalagmite and stalactite formation would likely not be affected.
   B. Increased groundwater acidity would increase stalagmite and stalactite formation.
   C. Increased groundwater acidity would decrease stalagmite and stalactite formation.
   D. Cannot be determined from the information given.

2. As the ground temperature surrounding a cave increases, stalactite and stalagmite growth is found to decrease. What is the best explanation for this?

   A. Increased heat causes $CaCO_3$ to melt.
   B. Formation of stalactites and stalagmites is endothermic.
   C. Increasing temperature decreases the aqueous solubility of $CaCO_3$.
   D. The concentration of $CO_2(g)$ in water increases as temperature increases.

3. What is the approximate concentration of CO_3^{-2} when enough $CaCO_3(s)$ is dissolved in water to form a saturated solution?

   A. $2.5 \times 10^{-9}\ M$
   B. $5.0 \times 10^{-9}\ M$
   C. $6.0 \times 10^{-5}\ M$
   D. $1.0 \times 10^{-4}\ M$

4. Which of the following will form a buffer when combined with $CaCO_3(aq)$?

   A. $C_2H_4O_2$
   B. K_2CO_3
   C. $NaHCO_3$
   D. CO_2

5. The shape of the carbonate ion is:

   A. trigonal planar and the carbon atom is sp^3 hybridized.
   B. trigonal planar and the carbon atom is sp^2 hybridized.
   C. tetrahedral and the carbon atom is sp^2 hybridized.
   D. tetrahedral and the carbon atom is sp^3 hybridized.

6. A stalagmite in a cave suffers damage and researchers want it repaired naturally as quickly as possible. Which of the following will help this process?

   A. Adding $CaCl_2$ to groundwater.
   B. Adding chemical compounds in the cave that absorb CO_2 from the air.
   C. Increasing the pH of the groundwater supply.
   D. Spraying the stalagmite with compressed CO_2.

Passage 44 (Questions 1-6)

At low pH, a mixture of pure acetaldehyde and ethylene glycol undergoes a reversible condensation reaction forming a cyclic acetal.

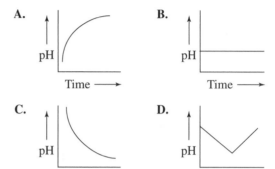

In an experiment, four mixtures containing different ratios of pure acetaldehyde and ethylene glycol (given below) were allowed to react in toluene (using 1.0 mL of sulfuric acid as a source of a catalytic amount of H⁺ to initiate the reaction) and come to equilibrium. Once at equilibrium, the amount of acetal was recorded. The complete listing of all data in this experiment follows:

CH₃CHO (mol)	HOCH₂CH₂OH (mol)	acetal yield (mol)
0.500	0.500	0.270
1.000	0.500	0.360
1.000	1.000	0.545
1.000	1.500	0.650

Note that in each case, a water bath was used to buffer the reaction temperature near 25°C. It was found that in the absence of the bath, the reaction vessel warmed significantly.

1. What is the equilibrium expression for the acetal reaction?

   A. $[CH_3CHO] \cdot [HOCH_2CH_2OH] / [acetal] \cdot [H_2O]$
   B. $[acetal] \cdot [H_2O] / [CH_3CHO] \cdot [HOCH_2CH_2OH]$
   C. $[acetal] / [CH_3CHO] \cdot [HOCH_2CH_2OH]$
   D. $[acetal] / [CH_3CHO] \cdot [HOCH_2CH_2OH] \cdot [H^+]$

2. If this reaction were heated, then the yield of acetal would:

   A. decrease.
   B. increase.
   C. remain the same.
   D. change, but there is not enough information to predict how.

3. The reaction would be shifted to the reactants by removing:

   A. water.
   B. acetal.
   C. ethylene glycol.
   D. acid.

4. The initial pH of a solution of sulfuric acid, acetaldehyde, and ethylene glycol was 1.3. Which one of the following plots illustrates how the pH of the solution changed as the solution was allowed to reach equilibrium as acetal and water were formed?

   A.
   [plot: pH vs Time — curve rising then leveling off]

   B.
   [plot: pH vs Time — flat horizontal line]

   C.
   [plot: pH vs Time — curve decreasing]

   D.
   [plot: pH vs Time — curve decreasing then increasing]

5. Increasing the pressure upon the equilibrated acetal reaction would:

   A. shift the reaction to the reactants.
   B. shift the reaction to the products.
   C. have no effect.
   D. cause the reaction to stop.

6. What are the geometries of the carbonyl carbon (the C=O carbon) in acetaldehyde and then in the acetal?

   A. Trigonal pyramid in acetaldehyde and trigonal pyramid in acetal
   B. Trigonal pyramid in acetaldehyde and tetrahedral in acetal
   C. Trigonal planar in acetaldehyde and trigonal pyramid in acetal
   D. Trigonal planar in acetaldehyde and tetrahedral in acetal

Passage 45 (Questions 1-5)

Many of the daughter elements of nuclear fission are particularly poisonous because many of these radioactive elements are actively absorbed by the human body. Radioactive isotopes are chemically indistinguishable from their stable cousins, and, as such, are absorbed by cells as if they were normal nutrients. For example, radioactive iodine, ^{131}I, is absorbed and concentrated in the thyroid gland.

$$^{131}I_{(environment)} \rightleftharpoons {}^{131}I_{(thyroid)}$$

Needless to say, chronic exposure to iodine-131 leads to a high risk of thyroid cancer.

Another potential threat is the absorption of strontium-90. While only trace amounts of strontium are required by the body, enzymes often mistake Sr for Ca and incorporate the Sr into the bone matrix. Once in the bone, strontium usually remains there until death due to the low solubility of strontium compounds.

strontium compound	K_{sp}
strontium fluoride	10^{-6}
strontium sulfate	10^{-7}
strontium carbonate	10^{-9}
strontium phosphate	10^{-28}

Radioactive cesium-137 is an additional hazard of nuclear waste. Unlike iodine and strontium, cesium is not concentrated in any specific tissue or organ. Instead, ^{137}Cs remains in the bloodstream and in intercellular fluids that are rich in other Group I metal ions until it is removed by passive diffusion by the kidneys. Internally, acute ^{137}Cs exposure is very deleterious. However, due to its chemical nature, chronic ^{137}Cs exposure can be effectively curtailed through proper treatment.

1. The Chernobyl catastrophe released tons of radioactive ^{131}I into the environment. What treatment could minimize the ingestion of ^{131}I on contaminated food?

   A. Have victims ingest soluble lead nitrate, because lead will precipitate out all halogens from solution.
   B. Inject victims with ^{131}I to prevent additional absorption.
   C. Have victims ingest solutions containing normal ^{127}I.
   D. To increase the decay rate of ^{131}I, boil all food before consuming it.

2. What is the approximate concentration of strontium ions in a saturated solution of strontium phosphate?

   A. $10^{-6}\ M$
   B. $10^{-10}\ M$
   C. $10^{-15}\ M$
   D. $10^{-30}\ M$

3. Which one of the following statements is true?

   A. In humans, Cs^+ can be expected to eventually precipitate out with Cl^-.
   B. In humans, Cs^+ can be expected to precipitate out with carbonate.
   C. Cs^+ will concentrate in vesicles rich in Mg^+.
   D. Cs^+ will concentrate in vesicles rich in K^+.

4. Kidney stones form over time as insoluble ionic compounds gradually precipitate out of solution. It has been found that these stones do not form in patients with more acidic urine. Which one of the following salts might be expected to compose a substantial mass of a kidney stone?

   A. NH_4Cl
   B. Na_2CO_3
   C. $CaCO_3$
   D. $Sr(NO_3)_2$

5. One gram of insoluble $Pb^{131}I_2$ containing only radioactive ^{131}I was added to 100 mL of water. Then one gram of soluble NaI (with ^{127}I) was added to the solution and completely dissolved. Which one of the following statements is correct?

   A. The addition of $Na^{127}I$ will decrease the amount of radioactive iodine in solution because of the common-ion effect.
   B. The addition of $Na^{127}I$ has no effect upon the solubility of $Pb^{131}I_2$.
   C. The $[^{131}I^-]$ dissolved in solution will increase after the addition of $Na^{127}I$ because of the dynamic equilibrium in solution.
   D. The addition of $Na^{127}I$ will make the solution reach critical mass and explode.

Passage 46 (Questions 1-6)
ADVANCED PASSAGE

Ammonia is one of the world's leading commercially produced (and consumed) chemicals. Today, ammonia is synthesized through a series of reactions (called the Haber–Bosch process) that take place between methane, air (which is four parts N_2, one part O_2), and potassium carbonate:

$$7 CH_4(g) + 8 N_2(g) + 2 O_2(g) + 17 H_2O(g) + 7 K_2CO_3(s) \rightleftharpoons$$
$$16 NH_3(g) + 14 KHCO_3(s)$$

Yet when production first began some eighty years ago, ammonia production relied upon the direct reaction between gaseous hydrogen and nitrogen called the Haber process:

$$3 H_2(g) + N_2(g) \rightleftharpoons 2 NH_3(g) \ \Delta H = -92.2 \ kJ$$

Even in the presence of a catalyst, the production of ammonia in this way is very inefficient at temperatures less than 200°C. Early experiments were carried out to determine the pressure and temperature sensitivities of the equilibria between hydrogen, nitrogen, and ammonia.

Mole percent of Ammonia at Equilibrium					
Temp (°C)	Pressure (atm)				
	10	50	100	500	1000
200	51	74	82	94	98
300	15	39	52	80	93
400	4	15	25	56	80
500	1.2	6	11	26	57

Experiments concluded that high pressures and high temperatures are required to sustain the Haber process.

1. The reaction between hydrogen and oxygen occurs at an explosive rate, while that of hydrogen and nitrogen is sluggish at all temperatures. Which of the following correctly accounts for this?

   A. At any given temperature, nitrogen molecules will have a lower velocity than oxygen molecules and thus collide with hydrogen less frequently.
   B. The ionization energy for atomic oxygen is less than that of atomic nitrogen.
   C. Molecular nitrogen lacks non-bonding electrons to interact with the hydrogen molecule directly.
   D. The bond dissociation energy of molecular nitrogen is greater than that of molecular oxygen.

2. Decreasing the temperature of an equilibrated reaction between hydrogen and nitrogen will:

   A. produce more ammonia.
   B. increase the velocity of the gas molecules.
   C. increase the kinetic energy of the gas molecules.
   D. have no effect.

3. Which one of the following energy diagrams illustrates the uncatalyzed (solid line) and catalyzed (dashed line) reaction of pure hydrogen and nitrogen?

   A. 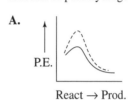   B.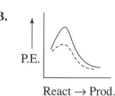

   C. 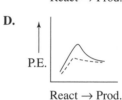   D.

4. A three-to-one mixture of hydrogen and nitrogen was rapidly pumped into a Haber apparatus until the internal pressure was 60 atm at 350°C. A catalyst was then added, and the system was allowed to reach equilibrium. The internal pressure was 45 atm. What was the partial pressure of the ammonia in the final mixture at 350°C?

   A. 2.0 atm
   B. 5.0 atm
   C. 7.5 atm
   D. 15.0 atm

5. The internal mixture of a Haber apparatus at equilibrium will be most dramatically affected by the reduction of:

   A. hydrogen by 50%.
   B. nitrogen by 60%.
   C. ammonia by 70%.
   D. the catalyst by 80%.

6. In the more complex Haber–Bosch process, the *in situ* production of trace amounts of carbon monoxide slowly poisons (binds to) the metal catalyst. Why does this occur?

    A. CO is a toxic molecule.
    B. CO is a strong Lewis acid.
    C. CO forms strong metallic bonds.
    D. CO is a strong ligand.

Passage 47 (Questions 1-6)

Microscopic droplets of H_2SO_4 play an important role in the distribution of trace gases in the stratosphere. One source of sulfuric acid droplets is the oxidation of carbonyl sulfide, COS, a gas produced by oceanic microorganisms. In the stratosphere COS is first converted to SO_2, either by direct photolysis by UV light,

Series 1:

$$COS + hf \rightarrow CO + S \qquad (1a)$$
$$S + O_2 \rightarrow SO + O \qquad (1b)$$
$$SO + O_2 \rightarrow SO_2 + O \qquad (1c)$$

or by oxidation with atomic oxygen, O, which itself comes from UV photolysis of ozone, O_3:

Series 2:

$$O_3 + hf \rightarrow O_2 + O \qquad (2a)$$
$$COS + O \rightarrow CO + SO \qquad (2b)$$
$$SO + O_2 \rightarrow SO_2 + O \qquad (2c)$$

Sulfur dioxide gas is further oxidized by the OH radical to ultimately yield $SO_3(g)$:

Series 3:

$$SO_2 + OH \rightarrow HSO_3 \qquad (3a)$$
$$HSO_3 + O_2 \rightarrow HO_2 + SO_3 \qquad (3b)$$

Since SO_3 is very water soluble, it readily combines with H_2O vapor to form H_2SO_4, which rapidly coalesces into droplets. The droplets then slowly rain out into the lower atmosphere.

1. In which of the following molecules is sulfur in the same oxidation state as in SO_3?

    A. S
    B. SO_2
    C. HSO_3
    D. H_2SO_4

2. Which one of the following is the correct Lewis dot structure for the radical intermediate HSO_3?

   A.

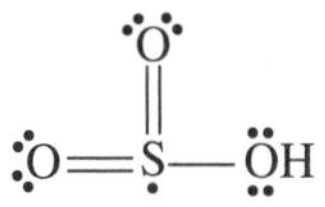

   B.

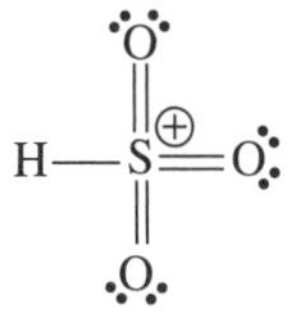

   C.

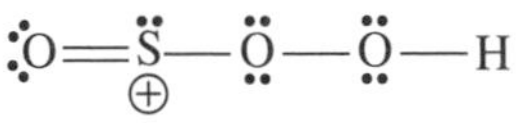

   D.

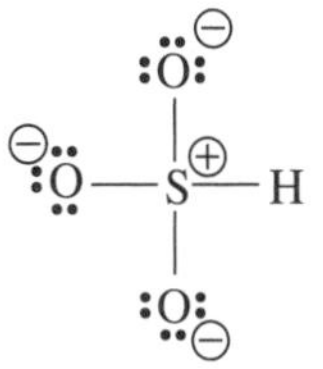

3. What are the signs of ΔH and ΔS for Reaction (3a), considering that during this reaction an S–O bond is formed and no bonds are broken?

   A. (–) and (–), respectively
   B. (–) and (+), respectively
   C. (+) and (–), respectively
   D. (+) and (+), respectively

4. If Reaction (1a) of Series 1 is slow relative to Reactions (1b) and (1c), then the rate of the Series 1 reactions would be affected *least* by:

   A. a drop in the flux of solar UV photons.
   B. the addition of a substance that weakens the C–S bond in COS.
   C. a decrease in the partial pressure of COS.
   D. an increase in the partial pressure of O_2.

5. Which of the following is supported by information in the passage?

   A. The density of sulfuric acid droplets is greater than the density of the surrounding air.
   B. Living organisms do not affect the composition of the atmosphere.
   C. The principal oxidizing agent in the atmosphere is SO_2.
   D. Oxidation of COS does not require UV light.

6. Given the dissolution equilibria for SO_2 and SO_3,

   $$SO_2(g) + H_2O(l) \rightleftharpoons H_2SO_3(aq) \qquad (1)$$
   $$SO_3(g) + H_2O(l) \rightleftharpoons H_2SO_4(aq) \qquad (2)$$

   why is SO_3 much more soluble in water than is SO_2?

   A. The complete dissociation of H_2SO_3 into H^+ and HSO_3^- drives Equilibrium (1) to the right.
   B. The complete dissociation of H_2SO_3 into H^+ and HSO_3^- drives Equilibrium (1) to the left.
   C. The complete dissociation of H_2SO_4 into H^+ and HSO_4^- drives Equilibrium (2) to the right.
   D. The complete dissociation of H_2SO_4 into H^+ and HSO_4^- drives Equilibrium (2) to the left.

Passage 48 (Questions 1-6)

Two theoretical chemists attempted to explain the observed trends of acidity by applying two interpretations of molecular orbital theory. Consider the pK_a's of some common acids listed along with each acids conjugate base:

acid	pK_a	conjugate base
H_2SO_4	< 0	HSO_4^-
H_2CrO_4	5.0	$HCrO_4^-$
H_3PO_4	2.1	$H_2PO_4^-$
HF	3.9	F^-
HOCl	7.8	ClO^-
HCN	9.5	CN^-
HIO_3	1.2	IO_3^-

Recall that acids with a $pK_a < 0$ are called strong acids, and those with a $pK_a > 0$ are called weak acids. The arguments of the chemists are given below.

Chemist #1:

"The acidity of a compound is proportional to the polarization of the H–X bond, where X is some nonmetal element. Complex acids, such as H_2SO_4, $HClO_4$, and HNO_3 are strong acids because the H–O bonding electrons are strongly drawn towards the oxygen. It is generally true that a covalent bond weakens as its polarization increases. Therefore, one can conclude that the strength of an acid is proportional to the number of electronegative atoms in that acid."

Chemist #2:

"The acidity of a compound is proportional to the number of stable resonance structures of that acid's conjugate base. H_2SO_4, $HClO_4$, and HNO_3 are all strong acids because their respective conjugate bases exhibit a high degree of resonance stabilization."

1. Which of the following is NOT a strong acid?

    A. Sulfuric acid
    B. Phosphoric acid
    C. Hydrochloric acid
    D. Hydroiodic acid

2. Perchloric, perbromic, and periodic acids are all potent oxyhalo-acids with the general empirical formula HXO_4. Which of the following does NOT explain why perfluoric acid, HFO_4, doesn't exist at all?

    A. Unlike the other halogens, fluorine cannot exceed an octet of valence electrons.
    B. Unlike the other halogens, fluorine has a greater electronegativity than oxygen.
    C. Unlike the other halogens, the fluoride ion is acidic.
    D. None of the above

3. Based upon Chemist #1's explanation, which one of the following organic acids should be the strongest?

    A. $HOOCCH_3$
    B. $HOOCCF_3$
    C. $HOOCCCl_3$
    D. $HOOCCBr_3$

4. Which one of the following acids would Chemist #2 expect to be the strongest?

    A. —OH
    B. CH_3CH_2OH
    C. —OH
    D. H_2O

5. Hydrochloric, hydrobromic, and hydroiodic acids are all strong acids, while hydrofluoric acid is only a weak acid. Which of the explanations listed above correctly predicts this trend?

    A. Chemist #1
    B. Chemist #2
    C. Both Chemist #1 and Chemist #2
    D. Neither Chemist #1 nor Chemist #2

6. The pH of a 1.0 M solution of H_2SO_4 should be:

    A. negative.
    B. exactly zero.
    C. positive.
    D. dependent upon the volume of the solution.

Passage 49 (Questions 1-6)

Nature abounds with fluids having a wide range of pHs. While most organisms can only survive in a narrow range of pH centered on neutrality, others only thrive in acidic or alkaline solutions. A few common liquids and their corresponding pH values are listed here:

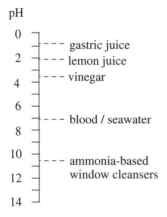

• The strong acidity of gastric juice is attributed to HCl which is produced by parietal cells present in the stomach lining.

• The principal acid in citrus fruits is citric acid:

$$\begin{array}{c} CH_2COOH \\ | \\ HO-CCOOH \\ | \\ CH_2COOH \end{array}$$

Citric acid is a weak, polyprotic acid having K_a's of 7.1×10^{-4}, 1.7×10^{-5}, and 4.0×10^{-7}, respectively.

• Vinegar is nothing more than a 2-3% solution of acetic acid.

• The pH of blood and seawater is primarily due to the presence of the bicarbonate ion, HCO_3^-, which is a weak base in solution.

• While ammonia is only a weak base, concentrated solutions of ammonia can be fairly basic. The pH of industrial ammonia-based cleansers can approach 12.

1. The [H⁺] is how many orders of magnitude greater in lemon juice than in seawater?

    A. 1
    B. 3
    C. 5
    D. 7

2. Heartburn is caused when gastric fluids leak above the cardiac sphincter into the lower esophagus. If a patient took an antacid that neutralized 99.9% of the HCl, the pH of the resulting solution would be:

    A. 4.
    B. 6.
    C. 7.
    D. greater than 7.

3. Which one of the following statements is true?

    A. HF is the conjugate base of F⁻.
    B. F⁻ is the conjugate acid of HF.
    C. A solution of NaF will have a higher pH than HF.
    D. None of the above

4. Which of the following ionic compounds will produce an acidic solution when dissolved in water?

    A. NaCl
    B. NaF
    C. NH₄Cl
    D. KOH

5. The pH of a solution produced when 10 mL of gastric juice and 10 mL of pure water are combined is about:

    A. 1.
    B. 3.
    C. 4.
    D. 7.

6. Hydrothermal vents on the ocean bottom expel mildly acidic solutions. The acidity of these solutions could be due to the presence of dissolved:

    A. CaCO₃.
    B. Na₂O.
    C. H₂S.
    D. CH₄.

Passage 50 (Questions 1-6)

Cellular membranes consist of a phospholipid bilayer speckled with transmembrane proteins. Transmembrane proteins, in turn, are anchored together by an internal network of filamentous structural polypeptides. Acidic and alkaline pH's are hazardous for the cell because the compositional members of the membrane—the proteins and phospholipids—are hydrolyzed in the presence of acids and bases. For example, the peptide bonds that are responsible for stringing amino acids together to form proteins are hydrolyzed by either H^+ or OH^-:

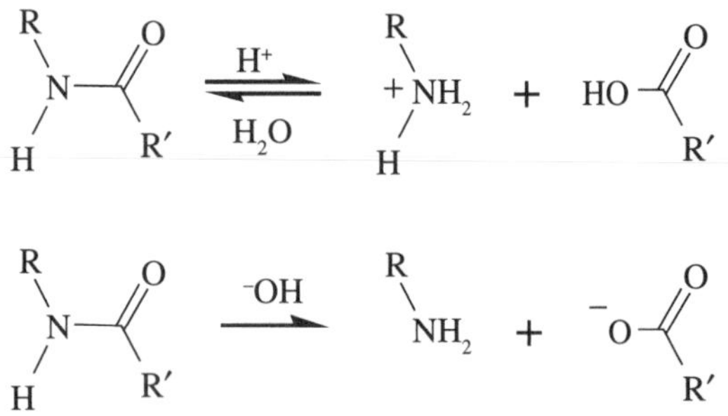

R = amino acid #1
R′ = amino acid #2

Likewise, the ester linkages that hold a pair of fatty acids and a phosphate group onto the glycerol (glycerin) backbone to form a phospholipid are also hydrolyzed in the presence of H^+ or OH^-:

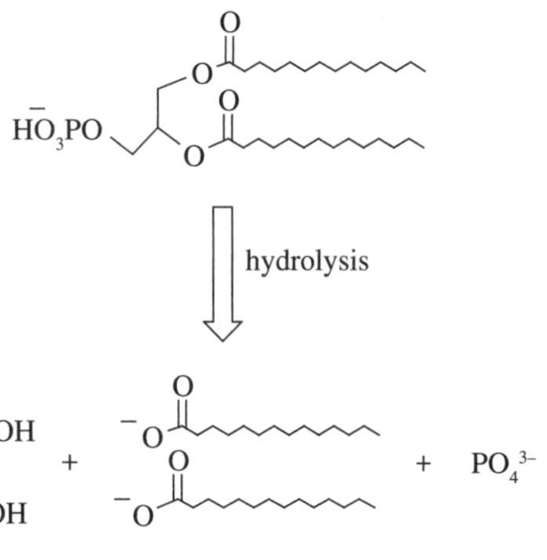

Since amino acids, glycerol, carboxylate ions, and the phosphate ion are all water soluble, once hydrolyzed, cellular proteins and phospholipids just dissolve away.

1. If the rate of acid hydrolysis of a protein is directly proportional to $[H^+]$, which one of the following solutions will digest a polypeptide the fastest?

   A. 0.1 M HF
   B. 0.1 M HNO_3
   C. 1.0 M $HC_2H_3O_2$
   D. 1.0 M H_3PO_4

2. Contact burns from strong bases are much more serious than those from equally potent strong acids. Speculate why.

   A. As opposed to acidic solutions, basic solutions irreversibly hydrolyze peptides and esters.
   B. H^+ is a better catalyst than OH^-.
   C. Due to its smaller size, the hydroxide ion diffuses through membranes with greater ease than the hydrogen ion.
   D. Sodium and potassium ions catalyze hydrolysis because these ions are strongly attracted to the positively charged carbonyl carbon atom.

3. Deprotonated carboxylic acids ($RCOO^-$) are much more soluble in water than the corresponding protonated acid (RCOOH) because:

   A. only the protonated acid can form hydrogen bonds.
   B. ion–dipole interactions are stronger than dipole–dipole interactions.
   C. the deprotonated molecule is more hydrophobic than the protonated one.
   D. the partial positive charge on each oxygen in water is attracted to the negative charge of the deprotonated acid.

4. Among the following, identify the compound with the highest melting point.

   A. CH_3COCH_3
   B. CH_3CH_2OH
   C. CH_3COOH
   D. $CH_3COO^-Na^+$

5. Identify the INCORRECT resonance structure for the dipeptide illustrated in the passage:

A.
B.
C.
D.

6. The phospholipid hydrolysis in the passage was performed in:

A. an acidic solution.
B. a basic solution.
C. a nonaqueous solution.
D. a pure water solution.

Passage 51 (Questions 1-5)

Ionic solids are compounds composed of ions of opposing charges which are held together by strong electrostatic attraction. They tend to be brittle and to have relatively high melting points. In the solid state, ionic substances are poor conductors, but in aqueous solutions, the ions are free to conduct electric current.

When ionic compounds are dissolved in water, an equilibrium between the solid phase and free ions is established. Ionic compounds that have low solubility in water are called slightly soluble salts. For example, solid silver chloride enters the following equilibrium:

$$AgCl(s) \rightleftharpoons Ag^+(aq) + Cl^-(aq)$$

Reaction 1

The dissolution of a salt is a thermodynamic process which is temperature dependent. At 25°C, the solubility constant of AgCl is 1.8×10^{-10}.

In an experiment, the identity of an unknown slightly soluble salt is studied. It is known that when it is dissolved in water, the salt forms a cation which is a weak acid, and which can therefore be titrated with a strong base. By adding aliquots of NaOH to an aqueous solution of the unknown salt, the titration curve shown in Figure 1 is obtained.

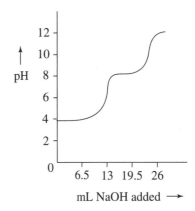

Figure 1

1. If the K_{sp} of AgCl is 1.8×10^{-10}, and the K_{sp} of AgI is 9.1×10^{-16}, which of the following statements is true?

A. The dissolution process of AgCl is more exothermic than the dissolution process of AgI.
B. AgI is more soluble than AgCl.
C. AgCl is more soluble than AgI.
D. The solvation of AgCl requires more energy than the solvation of AgI.

2. Based on the titration curve for the unknown salt shown in Figure 1, one would expect the unknown salt to be:

- **A.** amphoteric.
- **B.** monoprotic.
- **C.** diprotic.
- **D.** auto-ionized.

3. When 6.5 mL of NaOH have been added to the aqueous solution of the unknown salt, what is the hydrogen ion concentration?

- **A.** $1.0 \times 10^{-8} M$
- **B.** $1.0 \times 10^{-6} M$
- **C.** $1.0 \times 10^{-4} M$
- **D.** $1.0 \times 10^{-2} M$

4. The conjugate base of a monoprotic weak acid is titrated with a strong acid. Which of the following diagrams best illustrates this titration curve?

A.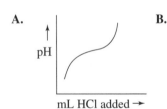

B.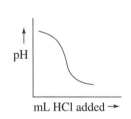

C.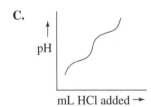

D.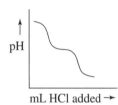

5. A solution of AgCl(*s*) is at equilibrium at 25°C. If NaCl is added to this solution, which of the following will occur?

- **A.** More AgCl(*s*) will form.
- **B.** More AgCl(*s*) will go into solution.
- **C.** The solubility constant increases.
- **D.** The solubility constant decreases.

Passage 52 (Questions 1-6)

Carbonic acid is formed when carbon dioxide is released by cells in the body as a metabolic by-product. Carbonic acid, in turn, dissociates to form hydrogen ions and bicarbonate ions:

$$CO_2(aq) + H_2O(l) \leftrightarrow H_2CO_3(aq) \leftrightarrow HCO_3^- (aq) + H^+(aq)$$

The conjugate acid-base pair, H_2CO_3/HCO_3^-, constitutes the principal buffer system in human blood plasma.

The carbonate buffer system works in conjunction with the respiratory apparatus to maintain normal hydrogen ion concentrations (pH of 7.4) in human blood.

When the respiratory rate increases, the partial pressure of CO_2 in the lungs decreases and carbon dioxide diffuses from the blood into the lungs. When the respiratory rate decreases, the partial pressure of CO_2 in the lungs increases and carbon dioxide diffuses from the lungs into the blood.

A buffer system is most effective when the concentrations of the acid and its conjugate base are equal. For that reason, the selection of an appropriate buffer is made on the basis of pK_a. The relationship between pH and pK_a is given by the Henderson–Hasselbalch equation:

$$pH = pK_a + \log \frac{[\text{conjugate base}]}{[\text{weak acid}]}$$

From the equation it is deduced that when concentrations of acid and conjugate base are equal, pH is equal to pK_a.

In Table 1, the K_a and pK_a values for several weak acids are listed in decreasing order of strength.

Name	Formula	K_a	pK_a
Phosphoric acid	H_3PO_4	7.5×10^{-3}	2.12
Formic acid	HCOOH	1.8×10^{-4}	3.74
Lactic acid	$CH_3CH(OH)COOH$	1.4×10^{-4}	3.86
Acetic acid	CH_3COOH	1.8×10^{-5}	4.74
Carbonic acid	H_2CO_3	4.3×10^{-7}	6.37
Dihydrogen phosphate ion	$H_2PO_4^-$	6.2×10^{-8}	7.21
Ammonium ion	NH_4^+	5.6×10^{-10}	9.26
Bicarbonate ion	HCO_3^-	5.6×10^{-11}	10.25
Hydrogen phosphate ion	HPO_4^{2-}	2.2×10^{-13}	12.66

Table 1

1. The bicarbonate ion (HCO_3^-) can react as an acid. Which of the following is the resulting species after the dissociation of bicarbonate?

   A. CO_3^{2-}
   B. HCO_3^{2-}
   C. CO_3^-
   D. HCO_3^-

2. Given that the normal pH of human bodily fluids is 7.4, which of the following conjugate acid-base pairs would make the most effective buffer system under physiological conditions?

   A. CH_3COOH / CH_3COO^-
   B. $HCOOH$ / $HCOO^-$
   C. $H_2PO_4^-$ / HPO_4^{2-}
   D. NH_4^+ / NH_3

3. The carbon in carbonic acid shares its valence electrons with oxygen atoms only. Therefore:

   A. carbon is single bonded to three oxygen atoms.
   B. carbon is single bonded to two oxygen atoms and double bonded to one oxygen atom.
   C. carbon is single bonded to one oxygen and double bonded to two oxygen atoms.
   D. carbon is double bonded to three oxygen atoms.

4. For the carbonate buffer system at pH 7.4, the concentration of carbonic acid is:

   A. greater than the concentration of bicarbonate.
   B. equal to the concentration of bicarbonate.
   C. less than the concentration of bicarbonate.
   D. equal to the concentration of hydrogen ions.

5. What volume of a 0.2 M solution of NaOH would be required to neutralize 0.5 L of a 0.1 M solution of HCl?

   A. 25 mL
   B. 50 mL
   C. 250 mL
   D. 500 mL

6. A child has ingested a bottle of aspirin pills and as a result has an abnormally high respiratory rate. What physiological changes will be observed in his blood?

   A. $[CO_2]$ increases, $[H^+]$ increases, pH decreases
   B. $[CO_2]$ decreases, $[H^+]$ decreases, pH increases
   C. $[CO_2]$ increases, $[H^+]$ decreases, pH decreases
   D. $[CO_2]$ decreases, $[H^+]$ increases, pH increases

Passage 53 (Questions 1-6)

Seawater and the blood plasma of mammals have very similar chemical constituencies. Both fluids have approximately the same partition and concentrations of major electrolytes.

	seawater	blood plasma
Na^+	106 ppt	142 ppt
Cl^-	180 ppt	103 ppt
K^+	5 ppt	4 ppt
HCO_3^-	12 ppt	28 ppt
Mg^{2+}	13 ppt	3 ppt
Ca^{2+}	4 ppt	5 ppt
* ppt = parts per thousand		

Not surprisingly, the pH of seawater and blood plasma are about the same: about 7.4. The pH dominating species in these solutions is the bicarbonate ion, HCO_3^-. Aqueous phase bicarbonate always strives to establish equilibrium concentrations with its conjugate acid, carbonic acid (H_2CO_3), and its conjugate base, the carbonate ion (CO_3^{2-}).

$$CO_3^{2-}(aq) + H^+(aq) \rightleftharpoons HCO_3^-(aq)$$

$$HCO_3^-(aq) + H^+(aq) \rightleftharpoons H_2CO_3(aq)$$

* Carbonic acid may dissociate into $CO_2(g)$ and H_2O.

K_a for HCO_3^- is 4.7×10^{-11}

K_b for HCO_3^- is 2.7×10^{-8}

The addition of an acid or a base to a solution containing the bicarbonate ion has a minimal effect upon the pH because bicarbonate serves in the capacity of a buffer. While other buffering ions, such as HPO_4^{2-}, are present in the ocean and blood, their contribution is secondary compared to that of HCO_3^-.

1. Adding hydrochloric acid to a saturated solution of sodium bicarbonate will NOT:

   A. lower the pH of the solution.
   B. produce carbon dioxide gas bubbles.
   C. shift the equilibria (given above) to the right.
   D. generate hydrogen gas.

2. What is the approximate pK_a for carbonic acid?

   A. 10
   B. 8
   C. 6
   D. 4

3. Considering that most of the carbon dioxide produced by cells is transported in the blood stream as bicarbonate then released in the lungs as CO_2, which one of the following statements is true under normal physiological conditions?

   A. The pH of the blood is greater in the lungs than in the tissues.
   B. The pH of the blood is greater in the tissues than in the lungs.
   C. The pH of the blood is the same in the tissues and the lungs.
   D. The pH of the blood is acidic throughout the body.

4. Which of the following functions of the kidney will contribute to raising plasma pH?

   A. Reabsorption of $H_2CO_3(aq)$
   B. Excretion of $NH_4^+(aq)$
   C. Reabsorption of $CO_2(g)$
   D. Excretion of $HCO_3^-(aq)$

5. Which of the following ions can buffer a solution against both acids and bases?

   A. Cl^-
   B. CO_3^{2-}
   C. $H_2PO_4^-$
   D. Ca^{2+}

6. Which one of the following statements is FALSE?

   A. The concentration of H^+ is less than that of OH^- in the blood.
   B. $Mg(OH)_2(s)$ is more soluble in the blood than in pure water.
   C. Respiratory arrest causes the pH of the blood to decrease.
   D. Carbonic acid is a weak electrolyte.

Passage 54 (Questions 1-5)

Several drums containing two unknown liquids were unearthed in an illegal landfill. Initial tests indicated that the liquids were aqueous-based solutions containing one solute each. An analytical chemist attempted to identify the solute in each of the solutions by employing classical laboratory techniques. The first set of analyses determined some basic physical characteristics (melting point, MP; boiling point, BP; density in grams per cc; and Q_e, the electrical conductivity of the solution relative to pure water) of 100 mL of each solution at standard pressure.

	Solution X	Solution Y
MP	−1.8°C	−3.9°C
BP	101.2°C	103.8°C
density	1.07	1.10
Q_e	1.51	8.54

The pH of Solutions X and Y were 10.7 and 0.6, respectively. Solution X was then titrated with aliquot 0.1 M HCl and Solution Y with 0.1 M NaOH. The results of these titrations are given below:

Solution X

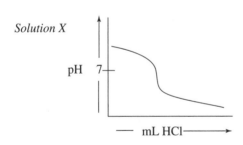

Solution Y

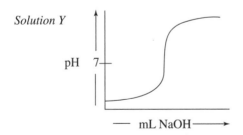

1. What is the identity of solute in Solution X?

    A. CH_3COOH
    B. CH_3CH_2OH
    C. NH_4NO_3
    D. $CH_3CH_2NH_2$

2. What is the identity of solute in solution Y?

    A. $HClO_4$
    B. $HClO_2$
    C. $HClO$
    D. HF

3. Which one of the following ionic compounds produces OH^- ions when dissolved in aqueous solution?

    A. $NaHSO_4$
    B. $Fe(NO_3)_2$
    C. NH_4I
    D. $NaClO_2$

4. What is the pK_a for the conjugate acid of the solute in Solution X?

    A. 1
    B. 2
    C. 6
    D. 9

5. Which one of the following statements is correct?

    A. Given that the K_a of the acid H_2X is 10^{-10}, then the K_b for H_2X must be 10^{-4} at 25°C.
    B. The K_w for water at 273 K is 10^{-14}.
    C. The solute in Solution X is a stronger electrolyte than the solute in Solution Y.
    D. At 100°C, the vapor pressure of Solution Y is less than Solution X.

Passage 55 (Questions 1-6)

At present, chemists employ a pH meter to electronically measure the instantaneous pH of a solution with high accuracy. In the past, however, titration chemists had to introduce an acid-sensitive dye into solution that would change color at a specific pH. These chemical indicators are nothing more than weak acids or bases. Protonation or deprotonation of these compounds induces a subtle change in the electronic structure of the molecules resulting in a change in their absorbance spectra.

For example, protonated methyl red is red in color while deprotonated methyl red is yellow:

protonated methyl red *(red)*

deprotonated methyl red *(yellow)*

The K_a for methyl red is about 10^{-5}. So in solution, methyl red exists in equilibrium between its protonated (HMr) and deprotonated (Mr$^-$) forms:

$$K_a = [H^+] \cdot [Mr^-] / [HMr]$$

At the half-equivalence point for methyl red, the concentrations of its protonated and deprotonated forms are the same. The expression above then reduces to

$$K_a = [H^+] \text{ or } pK_a = pH$$

Based upon this, the optimum indicator to use during a titration is one with a pK_a as close as possible to the pH of the anticipated equivalence point. In practice, the human eye will only detect the dominance of one of the color species when the concentration of one exceeds the other by an order of magnitude. Thus indicators are often used if their pK_a corresponds to ±1 of the anticipated equivalence point pH.

Name	pH Range	color change
methyl green	0.2 – 1.8	yellow to blue
methyl orange	3.2 – 4.4	red to yellow
methyl red	4.4 – 6.0	red to yellow
thymol blue	1.2 – 2.8	yellow to blue
phenolphthalein	8.2 – 10.0	clear to pink
clayton yellow	12.0 – 13.2	yellow to amber

1. If a student insisted on using much more indicator than was recommended by his laboratory supervisor, an error would be introduced into the titration because:

   A. the indicator would consume a significant amount of the titrant.
   B. the pK_a of the indicator would increase.
   C. the pK_a of the indicator would decrease.
   D. the indicator would begin to react with the glass beaker.

2. The K_a for thymol blue is approximately:

   A. 10^{-1}.
   B. 10^{-2}.
   C. 10^{-3}.
   D. 10^{-4}.

3. If R is neither an acidic nor basic organic fragment, then which one of the following compounds CANNOT be an acid–base indicator?

   A. R–COOH
   B. R–OSO$_3$H
   C. R–NH$_2$
   D. R–CH$_3$

4. A blue methyl green solution must have a ratio of protonated to unprotonated species of at least:

   A. 0.1.
   B. 1.
   C. 10.
   D. 100.

5. Which one of the following would be the best indicator to monitor the titration of a weak base having a pK_b of 8 with HCl?

A. Methyl green
B. Methyl orange
C. Phenolphthalein
D. Clayton yellow

6. The pH of pure ethanol is 7.1. A solution of 0.01 M methyl red in ethanol would have a pH of:

A. 1.0.
B. 3.5.
C. 5.0.
D. 8.5.

Passage 56 (Questions 1-6)

A solution that contains conjugate pairs of weak acids and bases will minimize the pH change resulting from the addition of a strong acid or strong base. Such a solution is called a buffer. Buffers are nothing more than the acid-base equivalent of Le Châtelier's principle and the common ion effect. Weak acids and bases exist in equilibria with their respective conjugates, and each equilibrium responds to perturbations accordingly.

For example, consider the buffering solution containing acetic acid and sodium acetate:

$$HC_2H_3O_2(aq) \rightleftharpoons H^+(aq) + C_2H_3O_2^-(aq)$$

Given that the K_a for acetic acid is about 10^{-5}, the equilibrium expression for the acetate system is

$$K_a = [H^+] \cdot [C_2H_3O_2^-] / [HC_2H_3O_2] = 10^{-5}.$$

Since it is useful to rearrange this expression in terms of $-\log[H^+]$, if we take the negative log of both sides, we get

$$pK_a = pH - \log([C_2H_3O_2^-] / [HC_2H_3O_2])$$

or

$$pH = pK_a + \log([C_2H_3O_2^-] / [HC_2H_3O_2])$$

This equation is an example of the Henderson–Hasselbalch relation, useful in determining the pH of buffered solutions following the addition of an acid or base.

K_a values for some common weak acids	
Weak acid	K_a
sulfurous acid	1.5×10^{-2}
hydrofluoric acid	6.8×10^{-4}
acetic acid	1.8×10^{-5}
carbonic acid	4.5×10^{-7}
ammonium ion	5.7×10^{-10}

1. What is the approximate pH of a solution containing 100 times more molecules of ammonia than ammonium at 25°C?

A. 4
B. 7
C. 11
D. Cannot be determined without knowing the volume of the solution.

2. Identify the buffering solution.

    A. HCl and NaCl
    B. H_2SO_3 and HSO_3^-
    C. HF and CH_3F
    D. NaOH and Na_2O

3. Adding sodium hydroxide to the acetic acid equilibrium system given in the passage will do all of the following EXCEPT:

    A. shift the equilibrium to the right.
    B. liberate heat.
    C. increase the electrical conductivity of the solution.
    D. decrease the pH.

4. The pK_a for sulfurous acid at 25°C is:

    A. less than 2.
    B. precisely 2.
    C. greater than 2.
    D. dependent upon the pH of the solution.

5. Given that HCl entirely dissolves in water to produce H_3O^+ and chloride ions, which one of the following statements is true?

    A. The pK_a for HCl is greater than for H_3O^+.
    B. The pK_a for H_2O must be less than for HCl.
    C. The pK_b for Cl$^-$ must be less than for H_2O.
    D. None of the above.

6. The pH of the solution that results after mixing 10 mL of 1.0 M HCl and 10 mL of 1.0 M NH_3 is the same as the pH of:

    A. a 0.5 M solution of NH_4Cl.
    B. a 1.0 M solution of NH_4Cl.
    C. a 2.0 M solution of NH_4Cl.
    D. pure water.

Passage 57 (Questions 1-5)

A laboratory assistant titrated an acid with 0.1 M KOH using a standard titration apparatus and a pH meter to measure instantaneous acid concentration.

The sample was titrated with 55 mL of the base. Eleven measurements of the solution's pH were recorded during the experiment.

Quantity of 0.1 M KOH added (in mL)	pH
0.0	1.3
10.0	2.0
15.0	2.5
18.0	3.1
21.0	7.7
29.0	8.0
37.0	8.9
40.0	11.2
42.0	11.9
48.0	12.1
55.0	12.3

These data points were used to construct the following titration diagram of the acid with 0.1 M KOH. The concentration of the initial acid sample was determined using the Henderson–Hasselbalch equation:

$$pH = pK_a - p([base]/[acid]).$$

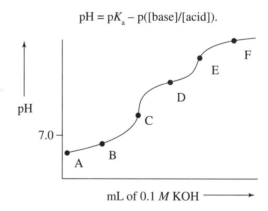

1. The acid analyzed in the passage is:

    A. monoprotic.
    B. diprotic.
    C. triprotic.
    D. none of the above.

2. The unknown acid could be:

A. H_2SO_4.
B. H_2SO_3.
C. H_3PO_4.
D. H_2O_2.

3. Points B, D, and E correspond to:

A. the pK_a of the first proton, the pK_a of the second proton, and the equivalence point for the second proton, respectively.
B. the pK_a of the first proton, the pK_b of the second proton, and the equivalence point for the second proton, respectively.
C. the equivalence point of the first proton, the equivalence point of the second proton, and the pK_b of the second proton, respectively.
D. none of the above.

4. The buffering capacity of the sample solution is maximum:

A. when the pK_a equals the pK_b.
B. when [conjugate base] equals [conjugate acid].
C. when the concentration of the solution is very low.
D. at or near pH 7.

5. Which one of the following compounds is a polyprotic base?

A. NH_4OH
B. Na_2O
C. NH_3
D. $SO_2(OH)_2$

Passage 58 (Questions 1-5)
ADVANCED PASSAGE

By definition, an amino acid is any molecule that has at least one carboxylic acid group (COOH) and one amino group (NH or NH_2). However, the amino acids found in living organisms are exclusively α-amino acids, that is, those in which the carboxylic acid and amino group are bonded to the same carbon atom.

Amino acids are amphoteric molecules, meaning they may behave as either acids or bases. In this way, the structure of an amino acid is very sensitive to the pH of its environment. For example, the pK_as of glycine are 2.3 and 9.6.

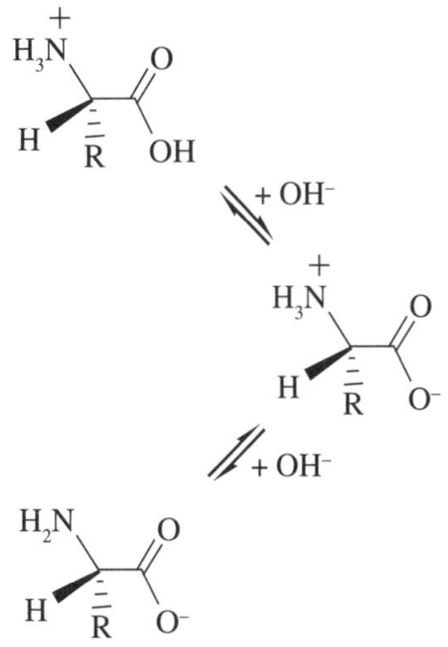

zwitterion

At a particular pH value, the total charge on glycine is zero. This is called the *zwitterion* form of glycine. The pH that corresponds to the maximum percent fraction of zwitterions that an amino acid may form is called the isoelectric point or pI point. For amino acids with one acid and one base group, the pI is nothing more than the average of the pK_as of these groups.

Table of amino acids pK_as			
Name	R	pK_{a1}	pK_{a2}
alanine	CH_3	2.3	9.6
asparagine	CH_2CONH_2	2.0	8.8
serine	CH_2OH	2.2	9.2
valine	$CH(CH_3)_2$	2.3	9.6

1. What is the isoelectric point for serine?

A. 2.2
B. 5.7
C. 6.2
D. 8.8

2. Electrophoresis is a process of separating molecules in an applied electric field. Which one of the following statements is true?

    A. In a solution of 1.0 *M* KOH, valine will not migrate in an electric field.
    B. Primary amides, $RCONH_2$, are acidic functional groups.
    C. When the pH = pI for an amino acid, it will migrate toward the cathode (positive plate).
    D. In 0.1 *M* HCl, amino acids will migrate toward the negative plate.

3. Given that the pK_as for cysteine are 1.8 (COOH), 8.3 (SH), and 10.8 (NH_3^+), what is the predominant structure for cysteine at pH 9.5?

    A. 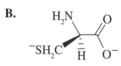   B.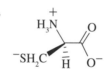

    C. 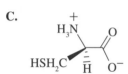   D.

4. Which one of the following statements is FALSE?

    A. At pH 2, half of the asparagine molecules have protonated carboxylic acids, and the other half are unprotonated.
    B. The hydroxy proton in serine is strongly acidic.
    C. Cysteine's thiol (SH) proton is more acidic than serine's hydroxy (OH) proton.
    D. The unprotonated amino group is a Lewis base.

5. If 90% of 1.0 *M* NaOH is neutralized during the dissolution of HCl gas, then the pH of the final solution is:

    A. 0.9.
    B. 7.0.
    C. 8.0.
    D. 13.0.

Passage 59 (Questions 1-6)

By definition, explosive chemical reactions are those that liberate vast amounts of gases and heat. Oxidation–reduction reactions are the most common class of chemical reactions that meet these criteria. Highly exothermic redox reactions result from reactions between strong oxidizing agents and strong reducing agents. The quantity of the heat evolved from these mixtures depends directly upon the strengths of the oxidant and the reductant.

Identification of oxidizing agents:

A compound containing a highly electronegative atom (e.g., O, N, Cl) with a nonnegative oxidation state will always be an oxidizing agent. An alternative way of stating this rule is that an oxidizing agent always has at least two highly electronegative elements covalently bonded together. Another class of good oxidizing agents is metals in anomalously high oxidation states. For strong metallic oxidizers the oxidation state is generally M(IV) or greater.

The strength of the oxidant is directly related to the electronegativity and oxidation state of the atom as mentioned above. Some common examples of *strong* oxidizing agents are H_2O_2, $KClO_4$, KNO_3, $KMnO_4$, and F_2.

Identification of reducing agents:

Reducing agents are compounds that contain an electropositive atom (e.g., C, H, metals) with a nonpositive oxidation state. Again, an interpretation of this rule is that a reducing agent is any compound in which at least two electropositive atoms are covalently bonded together.

The strength of a reductant is directly related to the electropositivity and the oxidation state of the atom, as mentioned above. Some common *mild* reducing agents are $H_2(g)$, $C(s)$, $S(s)$, metal powders, and propane.

Note that *strong* reducing agents, such as alkali metals, are infrequently used in explosives due to the constant difficulty of preventing the spontaneous detonation that would occur if they were exposed to atmospheric oxygen.

1. Sodium metal will not explode when mixed with:

    A. water.
    B. bromine liquid.
    C. oxygen gas.
    D. neon gas.

2. Household bleach is nothing more than 95% water, 5% mild oxidizing agent, and some fragrance. Mild oxidants contain electronegative atoms with a +1 or +2 oxidation state. Which of the following compounds is used in bleach?

   A. $NaIO_3$
   B. $NaClO$
   C. $NaClO_4$
   D. $NaCl$

3. Conventional gun powder, an explosive, consists of charcoal (pure carbon), elemental sulfur, and:

   A. iron filings.
   B. water.
   C. KNO_3.
   D. $CaCl_2$.

4. Which one of the following mixtures would violently detonate upon heating?

   A. H_2O_2 and Br_2
   B. CH_4 and NH_3
   C. $KMnO_4$ and Mn powder
   D. $LiCl$ and Cu powder

5. Hydrogen cyanate gas, HCNO, is not an oxidizing agent. Therefore, the structure of HCNO must be:

   A. H–N=C=O.
   B. H–C=O–N.
   C. H–N=O–C.
   D. H–O–N=C.

6. Although zinc metal is attacked by hydrochloric acid according to the reaction

   $$Zn(s) + 2\,HCl(aq) \rightarrow ZnCl_2(aq) + H_2(g)$$

   copper metal is unaffected by HCl. Why?

   A. Cl^- is a better oxidizing agent than zinc, but is not a better oxidizing agent than copper.
   B. Zinc is a better oxidant than copper.
   C. Zinc is a better oxidant than H^+.
   D. Cu^+ is a better oxidant than H^+.

Passage 60 (Questions 1-4)

All but the least important biochemical processes that occur in the cytoplasm require the cell to maintain its reducing interior. Failure to exclude oxidizing agents from the bulk cytoplasm leads to uncontrolled redox reactions damaging intracellular enzymes and glycoproteins, often culminating in metabolic collapse.

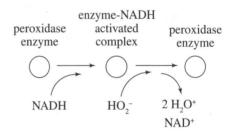

Oxidized site of NAD⁺   *Reduced site of NADH*

One of the prime responsibilities of the familiar reducing agents NADH and $FADH_2$ is to serve as *redox sentries*, protecting the cell by neutralizing any oxidant present in the cytoplasm via a self-sacrificing redox reaction. Eukaryotic cells maintain a battery of enzymes that enhance the oxidation of NADH and $FADH_2$. These enzymes are especially adept at reducing toxic oxidants often formed as by-products of cellular metabolism.

| | enzyme-NADH | |
| peroxidase enzyme | activated complex | peroxidase enzyme |

NADH HO_2^- $2\,H_2O^+$
                                    NAD^+

Disulfide bridges are one of the few biochemical structures that are actually more stable in an oxidizing environment. Therefore it is no surprise that proteins with disulfide linkages are primarily found in extracellular media.

1. What is the change in the oxidation state of the sulfur atoms of cysteine in going from the free thiol to the sulfide bridge?

   A. –2 to –1
   B. +1 to 0
   C. +2 to 0
   D. +2 to +1

2. During the oxidation of NADH, the lost electron density comes primarily from the:

- **A.** carbonyl (C=O) group.
- **B.** amido (NH_2) group.
- **C.** ring carbon opposite the ring nitrogen.
- **D.** aromatic nitrogen.

3. Respiration in humans often completely oxidizes all metabolites. Carbon dioxide and water are the ultimate oxidized by-products of carbohydrate metabolism. What is one of the ultimate oxidized products of *protein* metabolism?

- **A.**

    O
    ‖
    C
    H₂N   NH₂

- **B.** NH_3
- **C.** $C \equiv O$
- **D.** CH_4

4. The major energy production system in respiration requires the maintenance of a steep proton (H^+) gradient across the mitochondrial membrane. The transmembrane proteins which constitute the proton pump and maintain this gradient would be expected to have a:

- **A.** hydrophobic channel and be neutral.
- **B.** hydrophobic channel and be positively charged.
- **C.** hydrophilic channel and be negatively charged.
- **D.** hydrophilic channel and be positively charged.

Passage 61 (Questions 1-5)

The potentials of the oxidation and reduction half-reactions can be used to determine whether a particular oxidation–reduction reaction will occur spontaneously. A spontaneous oxidation–reduction reaction can be used to provide a constant voltage source for an electric circuit.

Some oxidation–reduction reactions are listed below, along with their associated potentials.

Reaction 1:

$$Cu(s) + 2\,H^+(aq) \rightarrow Cu^{2+}(aq) + H_2(g) \qquad E^\circ = -0.34 \text{ V}$$

Reaction 2:

$$Cl_2(g) + 2\,I^-(aq) \rightarrow 2\,Cl^-(aq) + I_2(s) \qquad E^\circ = +0.82 \text{ V}$$

Reaction 3:

$$Zn(s) + 2\,H^+(aq) \rightarrow Zn^{2+}(aq) + H_2(g) \qquad E^\circ = +0.76 \text{ V}$$

Reaction 4:

$$Mg(s) + Cl_2(g) \rightarrow Mg^{2+}(aq) + 2\,Cl^-(aq) \qquad E^\circ = +3.73 \text{ V}$$

1. Which of the following statements is true regarding Reaction 2?

- **A.** It is spontaneous because its potential is positive.
- **B.** It is spontaneous because its potential is negative.
- **C.** It is nonspontaneous because its potential is positive.
- **D.** It is nonspontaneous because its potential is negative.

2. Which of the reactions listed in the passage would most likely take place in an electrolytic cell?

- **A.** Reaction 1
- **B.** Reaction 2
- **C.** Reaction 3
- **D.** Reaction 4

3. As Reaction 3 progresses in the forward direction, which of the following changes would be expected to occur?

- **A.** The hydrogen ion concentration would increase, and the pH would decrease.
- **B.** The hydrogen ion concentration would increase, and the pH would increase.
- **C.** The hydrogen ion concentration would decrease, and the pH would decrease.
- **D.** The hydrogen ion concentration would decrease, and the pH would increase.

4. Reaction 3 and Reaction 4 are allowed to run to completion in separate galvanic cells. If the experiments start with equal molar quantities of zinc and magnesium and the two metals are the limiting reagents in their respective reactions, which reaction will generate more electrons for the electric circuit?

   A. Reaction 3, because it has a lower potential.
   B. Reaction 4, because it has a higher potential.
   C. Reaction 4, because it is more spontaneous.
   D. The two reactions will generate equal numbers of electrons.

5. Which of the reactions listed in the passage would be affected by a change in the pressure through a reduction in volume of the reaction vessel?

   A. None of them
   B. Reactions 1 and 3 only
   C. Reactions 2 and 4 only
   D. All of them

Passage 62 (Questions 1-5)

The voltage of a galvanic cell, E, will vary to some extent with changes in the concentrations of the reactants and products of the redox reaction used to generate the voltage, and can be calculated by using the Nernst equation:

$$E = E° - \frac{0.0592}{n} \log Q$$

Equation 1

Here, $E°$ is the standard cell voltage, n is the number of moles of electrons exchanged in the balanced equation, and Q is the reaction quotient (which takes the same form as K, but uses concentrations for a given moment rather than equilibrium concentrations).

As a reaction progresses in a galvanic cell, the voltage of the cell will change as reactants are consumed and products are generated.

Two oxidation–reduction reactions are listed below:

Reaction 1:

$$Fe^{2+}(aq) + Zn(s) \rightarrow Fe(s) + Zn^{2+}(aq) \qquad E° = +0.32 \text{ V}$$

Reaction 2:

$$2 Ag^+(aq) + Zn(s) \rightarrow 2 Ag(s) + Zn^{2+}(aq) \quad E° = +1.56 \text{ V}$$

1. As Reaction 1 proceeds from left to right in a galvanic cell, the voltage of the cell will:

   A. increase.
   B. decrease.
   C. increase, then decrease.
   D. decrease, then increase.

2. What is the value of n for Reaction 2?

   A. 0.5
   B. 1
   C. 2
   D. 4

3. For Reactions 1 and 2, what will be the effect on the voltage predicted by the Nernst equation if the molar quantity of solid zinc present in each cell is increased?

    A. Voltage will be increased.
    B. Voltage will be decreased.
    C. Voltage will be unaffected.
    D. Reaction 1 will show increased voltage, and Reaction 2 will show decreased voltage.

4. What is the voltage of the Reaction-2 cell at the moment when the concentrations of both species of ion in the cell are at 1.00 M?

    A. 1.50 V
    B. 1.53 V
    C. 1.56 V
    D. 1.59 V

5. Which of the following can be deduced from the Nernst equation about the value of E?

    A. E is always less than $E°$.
    B. E is always greater than $E°$.
    C. E is always equal to $E°$.
    D. E can be less than, greater than, or equal to $E°$.

Passage 63 (Questions 1-5)

In order to identify a metal, M, of unknown composition, a chemist conducted two experiments.

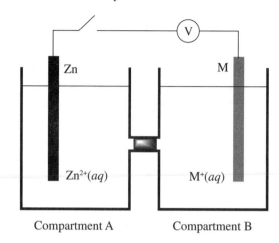

Figure 1

Experiment 1:

The chemist assembled a simple battery using zinc as one electrode and the unknown Metal M as the other (see Figure 1). The zinc electrode was immersed in Compartment A, which contained a 1.00 M solution of $Zn^{2+}(aq)$. The M electrode was immersed in Compartment B, which contained a 1.00 M solution of $M^+(aq)$. Spectator ions were present to maintain electrical neutrality.

Compartments A and B were joined by an opening plugged with glass wool to function as a salt bridge. The two electrodes were connected by a conducting wire, voltmeter, and switch. When the switch was closed, the voltmeter registered 1.28 V.

Table 1 lists several redox couples and their standard reduction potentials, $E°$.

Half-Reaction	$E°$
$Li^+(aq) + e^- \rightarrow Li(s)$	–3.05 V
$K^+(aq) + e^- \rightarrow K(s)$	–2.93 V
$Ca^{2+}(aq) + 2e^- \rightarrow Ca(s)$	–2.87 V
$Zn^{2+}(aq) + 2e^- \rightarrow Zn(s)$	–0.76 V
$Cu^+(aq) + e^- \rightarrow Cu(s)$	+0.52 V
$Ag^+(aq) + e^- \rightarrow Ag(s)$	+0.80 V

Table 1

Experiment 2:

Experiment 2 was identical to Experiment 1 except that the initial concentration of $Zn^{2+}(aq)$ in Compartment A was varied over five trials, and the voltage associated with each initial concentration was read from the voltmeter and recorded. The results are presented in Table 2.

Initial [$Zn^{2+}(aq)$]	E
0.01 M	1.34 V
0.10 M	1.31 V
0.50 M	1.29 V
1.00 M	1.28 V
5.00 M	1.26 V

Table 2

1. Which of the following statements best applies to Experiment 2?

   A. The cell is an electrolytic cell.
   B. The cell required an input of electric current to drive the redox reactions.
   C. The cell produced an electric current.
   D. The free energy of each of the reactions was large and positive.

2. In the apparatus used in Experiments 1 and 2, the negative electrode is:

   A. the cathode, where reduction takes place.
   B. the cathode, where oxidation takes place.
   C. the anode, where reduction takes place.
   D. the anode, where oxidation takes place.

3. Assume the direction of electron flow is from the Zn electrode to the M electrode. Based on Experiment 1 and Table 1, the identity of the unknown electrode is most likely:

   A. copper.
   B. calcium.
   C. lithium.
   D. potassium.

4. What is the expected sign of $\Delta G°$ and the expected value of the equilibrium constant, K, for the reactions associated with Experiment 2?

   A. $\Delta G°$ is positive, and K is less than 1.
   B. $\Delta G°$ is positive, and K is greater than 1.
   C. $\Delta G°$ is negative, and K is less than 1.
   D. $\Delta G°$ is negative, and K is greater than 1.

5. As the initial concentration of $Zn^{2+}(aq)$ increased in Experiment 2:

   A. the battery voltage increased, as expected for a concentration cell.
   B. the battery voltage decreased, as predicted by the Nernst equation.
   C. the voltmeter showed no detectable change in its reading since it is not sufficiently sensitive to detect such slight variations.
   D. the initial concentration of M^+ increased also.

Passage 64 (Questions 1-5)

In acidic aqueous solutions, vanadium can exist in four different oxidation states. In the two highest of these, vanadium(V) and vanadium(IV), it is present as the dioxovanadium ion, VO_2^+, and the vanadyl cation, VO^{2+}, respectively. In the two lowest states, vanadium(III) and vanadium(II), it simply occurs as the hydrated V^{3+} and V^{2+} cations. Each of these four species has a characteristic color in solution, and the oxidation state of vanadium in a given compound may often be deduced on that basis alone.

The dioxovanadium ion, VO_2^+, may be reduced chemically to lower oxidation states of vanadium. The standard electrode potentials associated with the reduction half-reactions of vanadium species are given below:

Reaction 1: $E°$

$$VO_2^+(aq) + 2\,H^+ + e^- \rightarrow VO^{2+}(aq) + H_2O \qquad +1.00\ V$$

Reaction 2:

$$VO^{2+}(aq) + 2\,H^+ + e^- \rightarrow V^{3+}(aq) + H_2O \qquad +0.36\ V$$

Reaction 3:

$$V^{3+}(aq) + e^- \rightarrow V^{2+}(aq) \qquad -0.26\ V$$

The oxidation state to which VO_2^+ is reduced in a redox reaction depends on the strength of the reducing agent, a stronger reducing agent being needed to bring about reduction to V(II) and V(III) than to V(IV).

An experiment is conducted in which equal volumes of a solution containing VO_2^+ ion are separately reduced using various reducing agents.

The state to which vanadium is reduced in each case can then be determined by comparing the volumes of standard permanganate solution needed to reoxidize the reduced vanadium species. Permanganate anion, MnO_4^-, is a very strong oxidizing agent. In acid solution it will convert any reduced vanadium species to the fully oxidized vanadium(V) state.

Reaction 4: $E°$

$$MnO_4^-(aq) + 8\,H^+(aq) + 5e^- \rightarrow Mn^{2+}(aq) + 4\,H_2O \qquad +1.51\ V$$

The amount of permanganate needed for a particular oxidation will be proportional to the change in oxidation state of the species being oxidized. For example, it would take twice as much permanganate to fully oxidize a sample of vanadium(III) as it would to oxidize an equivalent molar sample of vanadium(IV).

1. Which one of the following is the strongest oxidizing agent?

   A. VO_2^+
   B. VO^{2+}
   C. V^{2+}
   D. V^{3+}

2. If an extremely strong reducing agent is added to an aqueous solution of VO_2^+, the resulting species of vanadium will most likely be:

   A. vanadium(V), because it is the highest oxidation state.
   B. vanadium(V), because it is the lowest oxidation state.
   C. vanadium(II), because it is the highest oxidation state.
   D. vanadium(II), because it is the lowest oxidation state.

3. If 6 moles of permanganate anion are required to completely oxidize a sample of vanadium(II), how many moles of permanganate ion would be required to completely oxidize an equivalent molar sample of vanadium(IV)?

   A. 2
   B. 3
   C. 12
   D. 18

4. What is the standard electrode potential for the oxidation–reduction reaction between the vanadyl cation and the permanganate anion?

   A. 0.51 V
   B. 1.15 V
   C. 1.87 V
   D. 2.51 V

5. What is the oxidation state of manganese in the permanganate ion?

   A. +4
   B. +5
   C. +7
   D. +8

Passage 65 (Questions 1-5)

The exact amount of energy carried by an electron flow is dependent upon two fundamental properties of the flow—the voltage and the current.

The *voltage* of an electrochemical cell is the potential gradient which the electrons must flow across. Electrons spontaneously flow in a positive voltage (downhill gradient), thereby releasing energy. The voltage of a standard electrochemical cell is entirely determined by the chemical identity of the oxidant and the reductant; voltage is not a function of the size or shape of a cell.

The amount of charge that participates in the flow is called the *current*; that is, the current represents the number of electrons which comprise the flow. Electrical current is measured in units of *amperes*, the amount of charge which flows per second. Although there is a standard voltage defined for a given electrochemical cell, there is no standard current. The current produced by a cell is directly proportional to the surface area of the cathode and the anode; it is completely independent of the chemical nature of the cell. Therefore, regardless of a cell's voltage, the larger an electrochemical cell, the larger the output current.

Electrochemical cells may be wired in *series*, in which the anode of Cell A is wired to the cathode of Cell B, and the anode of Cell B is wired to the cathode of Cell C, etc. The following diagram shows three cells—A, B, and C—in series:

Cells that are wired in series produce an electron flow in which the currents (denoted by I) are the same in them all, and with a new voltage (V) which is the sum of these cells:

$$I_A = I_B = I_C$$

$$V_{total} = V_{Cell A} + V_{Cell B} + V_{Cell C}$$

In a similar fashion, the current of an electron flow may be increased. The amperage of a single cell may be enhanced by increasing the surface area of the internal electrodes. However, if this is not possible, several cells may be wired in parallel. In *parallel* wiring, all of the cathodes of the cells are wired together, and all of the anodes are wired together.

Identical cells that are wired in parallel produce a voltage equal to the initial voltage of any one of the separate cells, but with a current which is the sum of all of the cells:

$$I_{total} = I_{Cell A} + I_{Cell B} + I_{Cell C}$$

$$V_{total} = V_{individual cell}$$

In these ways, virtually any current or voltage can be easily produced from a small group of commercially available batteries.

Half-reactions (reductions)	E°_{red} (volts)
$F_2(g) + 2e^- \rightarrow 2\,F(aq)$	+2.87
$2\,H^+(aq) + 2e^- \rightarrow H_2(g)$	0.00
$Zn^{2+}(aq) + 2e^- \rightarrow Zn(s)$	–0.76

1. What is the voltage of three zinc–fluorine batteries wired in series?

   A. +2.11 V
   B. +3.63 V
   C. +10.89 V
   D. Cannot determine from the information given

2. The current of three zinc–fluorine batteries wired in series is:

   A. 1.2 amps.
   B. 1.6 amps.
   C. equal to that produced by a single Zn–F battery.
   D. indeterminable based upon this information.

3. Given that all of the following electrodes have a mass of one gram, which of these electrodes should be used to construct a high current battery?

   A. Solid cylinder electrode
   B. Thick plate electrode
   C. Spherical electrode
   D. Foil electrode

4. Which of the following statements is FALSE?

    A. The total output current over the entire lifetime of an electrochemical cell is only dependent upon the mass of the reacting electrodes, not on their shape.

    B. Given that the highest oxidation potential normally observed is +3.03 volts (lithium) and the highest reductive potential is +2.87 volts (fluorine), then any battery which has an output voltage of more that 5.90 volts must have several cells wired in series.

    C. Although there is no direct correlation between voltage and current, it is true that a redox reaction with a positive voltage will produce a positive current, and a redox reaction with a negative potential will produce a negative current.

    D. The voltage of a cell is independent of the size or shape of the electrodes.

5. In order for the total voltage of *three* batteries (each with potential *V*) to equal 3*V*:

    A. they must all be wired in series.

    B. they must all be wired in parallel.

    C. two should be wired in parallel, the combination in series with the third.

    D. two should be wired in series, the combination in parallel with the third.

Passage 66 (Questions 1-6)

Only the most inert metal surfaces are invulnerable to oxidizing agents. The reactions between iron and oxygen is a persistent problem; the rusting of iron significantly reduces the longevity of bridges, vehicles, and multi-story buildings, a problem enhanced by acid rain. Millions of dollars have been invested in trying to fully understand the electrochemical nature of corrosion. Metal corrosion is just an electrochemical cell which consumes the metal of interest. The following schematic holds for widely accepted mechanisms for the corrosion of iron.

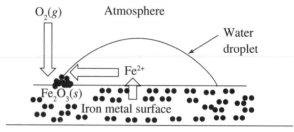

Rxn #1

$$Fe(s) + 2H_2O\ (l) \longrightarrow Fe^{2+}(aq) + H_2(g) + 2\ OH^-(aq)$$

Rxn #2

$$2\ Fe^{2+}(aq) + O_2(g) + H_2(g) + H_2O\ (l)$$

$$\downarrow$$

$$Fe_2O_3(s) + 4\ H^+(aq)$$

Reaction #1 may occur under anaerobic conditions because water is a mild oxidizing agent. The oxidation of ferrous ion to ferric ion in Reaction #2 requires a more powerful oxidizing agent such as oxygen gas.

One of the cheapest, most reliable ways of preventing corrosion is by insulating the metal surface from water and the atmosphere by using paint. However, over time, water can pervade even the most resilient metallic oxide paint.

Therefore, engineers protect metal surfaces which are in near constant contact with water or non alkaline soils, such as municipal pipes and ship hulls, by wiring them to a metal with a lower reduction potential such as magnesium or zinc. Because of its lower reduction potential, this "bait" metal serves as a *sacrificial anode*, becoming the site of oxidation in the corrosive cell instead of the structural metal.

1. With respect to the summation of Reaction #1 and Reaction #2, identify the cathode and the anode in the schematic above.

    A. The iron/atmosphere junction is the anode and the iron surface is the cathode.
    B. The iron/atmosphere/droplet junction is the cathode and the iron/droplet surface is the anode.
    C. The iron surface is the cathode and the water droplet is the anode.
    D. The atmosphere is the cathode and the iron metal is the anode.

2. A major deleterious side effect of road salts ($CaCl_2$ and $NaCl$) used to melt street ice during the winter is the fact that these salts dramatically increase the rate of corrosion of automobiles and bridges. Why does this occur?

    A. Cl^- is an oxidizing agent.
    B. Calcium and sodium ions can oxidize iron, forming Ca and Na metal.
    C. These salts are electrolytes, thereby enhancing electron transport between the cathode and the anode in a corrosive cell.
    D. $CaCl_2$ and $NaCl$ are mild acids and are efficient at stripping away the smooth layer of rust that protects the bulk metal surface.

3. Over a long period of time, the pH of a droplet that has been facilitating the corrosion of iron will:

    A. become more acidic.
    B. remain the same.
    C. become more basic.
    D. become less electrolytic.

4. Reactions #1 and #2 are:

    A. both redox reactions.
    B. a redox reaction and a precipitation reaction.
    C. an acid–base reaction and a redox reaction.
    D. an acid–base reaction and a precipitation reaction.

5. The Statue of Liberty consists of a copper shell internally supported by an iron framework. Until its renovation in the mid 1980s, the monument had sustained severe corrosion of the inner framework because the original insulating pads which prevented metal–metal contact at copper-iron interfaces had weathered away. Why is it important to prevent the copper and iron from making contact?

    A. Copper metal can oxidize iron metal over long periods of time.
    B. Iron is a better oxidizing agent than copper.
    C. Since iron is readily corroded in the moist marine air, copper had been serving as a sacrificial anode.
    D. Because copper metal is slowly oxidized in moist air, iron served as a sacrificial anode.

6. Aluminum metal has a lower electronegativity than iron, yet reacts very slowly with oxygen in moist air because of a hard, protective aluminum oxide coat that protects all exposed surfaces. Under which of the following conditions would aluminum be readily corroded?

    A. Immersed in a solution of HCl
    B. Immersed in a bath of hot sodium metal
    C. Immersed in a solution of NH_3
    D. Immersed in a solution of NaOH

Passage 67 (Questions 1-5)

Just as spontaneous redox reactions can be used to produce an electrical current, electricity may be used to drive a non-spontaneous redox reaction—a process called *electrolysis*. Electrolysis is utilized in the production of pure elements (such as electropositive metals and the halogens), the production of reagent grade chemicals, and in *electroplating*.

The configuration of an electrolytic cell is analogous to an electrochemical cell, except that the potential at the electrodes is applied by an outside electric source, not by reactions which occur on the electrodes' surfaces. This is an important point, because in electrolysis, the charge of the cathode and the anode are opposite those in an electrochemical cell.

Metals can be derived from the electrolysis of the pure, molten salts, typically group I or group II metal halide salts. During this process, cations are attracted to the negative terminal, and reduced by the excess electrons, while anions migrate to the positive terminal and are oxidized.

For example, the electrolysis of NaCl(l) forms sodium metal and chlorine gas.

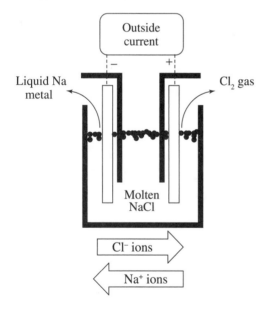

Electroplating, however, occurs in aqueous solution. A metal object serves as the negative electrode, and a mass of plating metal, typically silver, gold, or chromium, serves as the positive electrode. The atoms of the plating metal are oxidized, go into solution, and then migrate to the negative electrode. The plating ions are subsequently reduced on the surface of the object, forming a thin but complete plating film. Electroplating is often used on iron or steel objects to provide a corrosive-resistant surface of chromium or silver, or for aesthetic purposes, such as gold- or silver-plated cutlery, ornamental fixtures, and jewelry.

1. The most important industrial use for electrolysis is in the production of aluminum from the mineral bauxite, $Al_2O_3(s)$. For every mole of aluminum produced:

   A. 1/2 mole of oxygen gas is produced.
   B. 3/4 mole of oxygen gas is produced.
   C. 3/2 moles of oxygen gas is produced.
   D. 3 moles of oxygen gas is produced.

2. The electrolysis of water laced with some Na_2SO_4 produces one mole of pure oxygen for every two moles of pure hydrogen. Which one of the following statements is true?

   A. The oxygen in water is reduced to oxygen at the negative electrode.
   B. Because water molecules have a dipole moment, they have a net attraction to the positive electrode.
   C. Oxygen gas is produced half as fast as hydrogen because oxygen molecules have a double bond while the hydrogen molecule has a single bond.
   D. The presence of sodium sulfate increases the conductivity of the solution.

3. The product of the electrolysis of an aqueous solution of sodium chloride at the anode is most likely which of the following?

   A. Hydrogen gas
   B. Sodium metal
   C. Sodium hydroxide
   D. Chlorine gas

4. Which element has the ground state electron configuration $[Kr]5s^14d^5$?

   A. Nb
   B. Mo
   C. Tc
   D. This is not the ground state of any element.

5. Identify the compound which is not an electrolyte.

   A. LiI
   B. CaO
   C. HBr
   D. H_2O

Passage 68 (Questions 1-5)

A redox reaction can be used to produce an electrical current. Electrical currents are only produced when the oxidant and the reductant are physically separated and are bridged by a conducting media, such as a metal wire. An example of an electrochemical cell is the *galvanic cell* illustrated below.

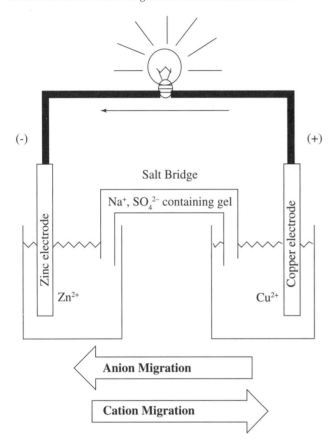

A standard *galvanic cell* utilizes a redox reaction between a 1.0 *M* aqueous solution of copper(II) ions and a zinc plate. The reactants are contained in two separate vessels, and are bridged only by a conducting copper wire and a salt bridge. A copper plate is used as a junction (called an electrode) between the wire and the copper solution, although any conducting, inert media such as platinum or graphite could be substituted for the copper plate. As the reaction proceeds, copper metal will be continuously deposited onto this electrode. In contrast, the zinc plate serves as both the reducing agent and its own electrode. Over time, the zinc electrode will erode away as Zn^{2+} ions are formed and dissolve into solution.

A *salt bridge* is typically a tube which contains a hydrous agar gel which is imbedded with dissolved salt. The main purpose of the salt bridge is to provide an ion conducting channel to facilitate ion migration, yet prevent copper ions from rapidly diffusing into the vessel containing the zinc electrode. The migration of copper ions is minimized by the competing migration of the ions already present in the gel.

If the oxidant and the reductant are allowed to come in physical contact with one another, electron flow through the wire will cease, and a substantial amount of heat will be liberated. When this occurs in a battery, the battery is said to be *shorted out*.

1. In the figure above, the arrow under the light bulb indicates the direction:

   A. of the electron flow.
   B. opposite to the electron flow.
   C. in which the copper atoms in the wire will migrate.
   D. Both A and C.

2. Any cell having a positive voltage must be powered by a reaction that is:

   A. in equilibrium.
   B. spontaneous.
   C. endothermic.
   D. both B and C.

3. What would NOT happen if a student accidentally placed the zinc electrode directly into the copper solution?

   A. The light bulb would go out.
   B. The zinc electrode would be immediately encrusted with a layer of copper metal.
   C. The copper electrode would be immediately encrusted with a layer of zinc metal.
   D. The solution would warm up.

4. Which of the following will not reduce the electrical current of a galvanic cell?

   A. Precipitate out the zinc ions.
   B. Let the solutions evaporate to dryness.
   C. Remove the salt bridge.
   D. Precipitate out the copper ions.

5. Which of the following materials is NOT a good conductor of electrons?

A. Platinum
B. Agar gel
C. Graphite
D. Zinc

Passage 69 (Questions 1-4)

Electrochemical cells are still the predominant source of portable electrical power. Although a whole spectrum of batteries have been designed to accommodate a range of specialized requirements, in principle, they all still depend on the electrical flow produced by a redox reaction. The voltage of a battery may be calculated if an adequate standard reduction potential table (see below) is available.

Half-reaction (reductions)	$E°$ (volts)
$F_2(g) + 2e^- \rightarrow 2\ F(aq)$	+2.87
$MnO_4^- + 4\ H^+ + 3e^- \rightarrow MnO_2(s) + 2\ H_2O$	+1.70
$MnO_2(s) + 4\ H^+ + 2e^- \rightarrow Mn^{2+}(aq) + 2\ H_2O$	+1.23
$NiO_2(s) + 2\ H_2O + 2e^- \rightarrow Ni(OH)_2(s) + 2\ OH^-(aq)$	+0.49
$2\ H^+(aq) + 2e^- \rightarrow H_2(g)$	0.00
$Zn^{2+}(aq) + 2e^- \rightarrow Zn(s)$	–0.44
$Cd(OH)_2(s) + 2e^- \rightarrow Cd(s) + 2\ OH^-(aq)$	–0.81

The most common, inexpensive battery is the *alkaline dry cell*. Dry cells come in a variety of shapes and sizes. All alkaline dry cells are powered by a Zn/MnO_2 reaction which occurs under basic conditions. The anode, which is nothing more than a zinc casing, serves as the negative terminal and the reductant itself. $MnO_2(s)$, which is suspended in a electrolytic paste, is reduced on a graphite cathode which is the positive terminal. The salt bridge which is present in an ordinary galvanic cell is replaced by an alkaline paste imbedded with MnO_2 and graphite powder. The paste is physically separated from the zinc can by a porous, paper shield.

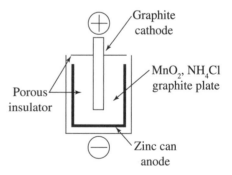

Most batteries have an output flow over their lifetime which resembles the plot below.

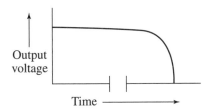

Output voltage is relatively constant for the most of the life of the battery. After 95% of the fuel has been consumed, the output voltage drops off rapidly until it reaches zero.

1. Based on the passage, the alkaline dry cell has an approximate potential of:

   A. 1.0 V.
   B. 1.4 V.
   C. 1.7 V.
   D. 2.1 V.

2. Why would an unused battery eventually die?

   A. Electrons slowly diffuse through the internal salt bridge.
   B. Conducted through the air, electrons travel from the cathode to the anode.
   C. Moisture in the air increases the electron flow along the surface of the battery from the cathode to the anode.
   D. Conducted through the air, cations travel from the anode to the cathode.

3. Which of the following equations could be used to calculate the output voltage, V_{out}, of an ordinary battery after its been in use for some length of time, T_{use}? (Note: K_e is a constant.)

   A. $V_{out} = E^o_{cell} + K_e T_{use}$
   B. $V_{out} = E^o_{cell} - K_e T_{use}$
   C. $V_{out} = E^o_{cell} - K_e / T_{use}$
   D. $V_{out} = E^o_{cell} - K_e (T_{use})^3$

4. Which one of the following statements about batteries is true?

   A. They are all rechargeable.
   B. Electrons always flow from the anode to the cathode.
   C. Oxidation occurs at the cathode.
   D. The cathode is consumed in the reaction.

Passage 70 (Questions 1-5)

A student follows the schematic below and sets up the following electrochemical cell at room temperature.

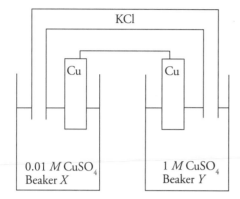

Figure 1 Schematic of an experimental electrochemical cell

The student fills Beaker X with a 0.01 M solution of $CuSO_4$ and Beaker Y with a 1 M solution of $CuSO_4$. Two copper plates serve as electrodes and a $KCl(aq)$ salt bridge is used. Because of the nonstandard conditions, the student uses the Nernst equation to calculate the expected potential of the cell:

$$E = E^\circ - \frac{RT}{nF} \ln Q$$

where E° is the standard cell voltage, R is the universal gas constant, T is the absolute temperature, n is the number of electron moles, F is Faraday's constant, and Q is the reaction quotient. Substituting in the constant variables and converting the natural logarithm, the student obtains the following formula:

$$E = E^\circ - \frac{0.0592}{n} \log Q \quad \text{at } 25^\circ \text{ C}$$

After setting up the half-cells, the student connects the two electrodes via a voltmeter and measures the initial cell potential.

Table 1 Standard reduction potentials for copper ions

Half-Reaction	E° (V)
$Cu^+ + e^- \rightarrow Cu(s)$	+0.52
$Cu^{2+} + 2e^- \rightarrow Cu(s)$	+0.34

1. What is the standard cell voltage, E°, of the cell used in the experiment?

   A. +0.52 V
   B. +0.34 V
   C. +0.18 V
   D. 0 V

2. Which of the following correctly describes the relationship between the movement of electrons and K^+ ions?

   A. K^+ ions and electrons both travel towards Beaker X.
   B. K^+ ions travel towards Beaker X and electrons travel towards Beaker Y.
   C. K^+ ions travel towards Beaker Y and electrons travel towards Beaker X.
   D. K^+ ions and electrons both travel towards Beaker Y.

3. Which of the following substances has the atom with the greatest oxidation state?

   A. CH_2F_2
   B. K_2O
   C. $S_4O_6^{2-}$
   D. Fe_2O_3

4. Which of the following best describes the cell used in the experiment?

   A. Beaker X contains the cathode that is negatively charged.
   B. Beaker Y contains the cathode that is negatively charged.
   C. Beaker X contains the anode that is negatively charged.
   D. Beaker Y contains the anode that is negatively charged.

5. What is the expected potential of the cell at the start of the experiment?

   A. +0.118 V
   B. +0.059 V
   C. −0.118 V
   D. −0.059 V

Passage 71 (Questions 1-6)
ADVANCED PASSAGE

A scientist performed an experiment which was designed to determine the effects of differing temperature, pressure, and concentration upon the output voltage of a galvanic cell. The scientist was attempting to reproduce an experiment performed some time earlier which produced results inconsistent with those predicated by the Nernst equation:

$$E_{cell} = E°_{cell} - \frac{2.303RT}{nF} \log\frac{[Zn^{2+}]}{[Cu^{2+}]}$$

Before the experiment began, the scientist constructed a standard state galvanic cell to serve as a control and let it completely discharge, all the while monitoring the voltage it produced.

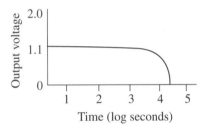

Control

The first step of the experiment involved repeating the control exercise, except the cell was forced to operate at 100°C. The output voltage of the cell decreased with time:

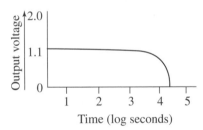

High Temperature

The second step of the experiment was a repeat of the control experiment under high pressures (10 atm). This experiment determined that increasing pressure had no effect on this cell.

The last part of the experiment involved constructing three galvanic cells in which the initial concentrations of copper and zinc ions varied. All three trials were monitored in the same fashion outlined above. A colorimeter was employed to accurately measure the concentration of copper ions during the course of these experiments. (A *colorimeter* is a device that detects the quantity of visible light that is absorbed by a colored

molecule in a solution.) A summary of the results are given below.

Note that only four measurements of voltage and copper concentration were performed for each trial. An initial sampling was taken for each trial (A), and three more samplings were taken 5 minutes (B), 10 minutes (C) and 15 minutes (D) after the cells were activated. Therefore, the dashed curves in the following figure are statistical extrapolations and are not composed of any data.

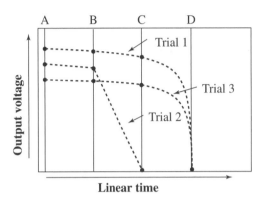

	A	B	C	D
Trial 1	12.6%	8.0%	3.8%	0.0%
Trial 2	11.3%	7.6%	5.9%	5.9%
Trial 3	10.5%	6.2%	3.0%	0.0%

Table 1 Colorimetric Absorbance at Different Points

Based upon Beer's law, the concentration of an optically active species, in this case Cu^{2+}, is directly proportional to the percent absorbance of a solution containing that species.

1. In the Nernst equation, what is the purpose of the factor 2.303?

   A. It represents the average number of transferred electrons.
   B. It is a conversion factor between natural and base ten logs.
   C. It is a conversion factor between calories and joules.
   D. It represents the ratio of electrical to mechanical potential.

2. If the properties of a cell are completely represented in the Nernst equation (not true in reality), what should be the initial voltage of the high temperature experiment?

   A. Less than the control, but negative
   B. Less than the control, but positive
   C. Equal to the control
   D. Greater than the control

3. E°_{cell} represents the potential at:

   A. 273 K, 760 torr.
   B. 273 K, 780 torr.
   C. 298 K, 760 torr.
   D. 298 K, 780 torr.

4. Colorimetry could only be used for determining copper ion concentrations, not zinc ions. Why?

   A. Unlike copper ions, zinc ions are colorless in solution.
   B. Once formed, zinc ions immediately precipitate out of solution.
   C. Colorimetry can only be used on clear solutions, not colored ones.
   D. None of the above

5. Based upon the results of Trials 1 through 3, trial 2 differed from Trials 1 and 3 because:

   A. the concentration of the copper ions was the limiting reagent for Trial 2.
   B. the concentration of zinc ions was the limiting reagent for Trial 2.
   C. the mass of the copper cathode was the limiting reagent for Trial 2.
   D. the mass of the zinc anode was the limiting reagent for Trial 2.

6. The voltage of a standard galvanic cell may be increased by:

   A. precipitating out all zinc ions as $ZnS(s)$ by bubbling $H_2S(g)$ through the anode solution.
   B. increasing the surface area of the cathode and anode.
   C. removing the salt bridge.
   D. replacing the copper cathode with a platinum electrode.

   _____

Passage 72 (Questions 1-6)

When an unstable nucleus spontaneously decomposes by emitting protons, neutrons, or electrons, it is said to have undergone radioactive decay.

The disappearance of radioactive isotopes in a sample is generally predicted by the half-life of the element in the sample. The half-life is the time it takes for half of the radioactive isotopes in the sample to disappear. The half-life of a radioactive element is independent of the size of the sample.

Two of the more common forms of radioactive decay are alpha decay, in which the nucleus emits two protons and two neutrons, and beta decay, in which the nucleus converts a neutron into a proton and emits a particle that is equivalent to an electron.

1. Which of the following graphs most closely represents the amount remaining of a sample undergoing radioactive decay over time?

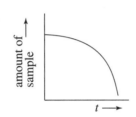

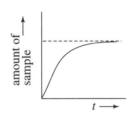

2. If a nucleus has undergone radioactive decay by emitting three alpha particles, by how much has its atomic number decreased?

   A. 3
   B. 6
   C. 9
   D. 12

3. As a result of a nuclear reaction, a nucleus undergoes a change in its charge. Which of the following is necessarily true?

   A. Atomic mass has increased.
   B. Atomic mass has decreased.
   C. Nuclear binding energy has increased.
   D. The atom has been transformed into a different element.

4. If an isotope of magnesium undergoes beta decay, then the daughter nuclide will be an isotope of:

   A. neon.
   B. sodium.
   C. aluminum.
   D. silicon.

5. How many half-lives would need to elapse before 87.5% of a given sample of a radioisotope has decomposed?

   A. 2.5
   B. 3
   C. 3.5
   D. 4

6. The difference between the actual mass of a nucleus and the sum of the masses of the protons and neutrons that form it is called the:

   A. mass defect.
   B. mass number.
   C. atomic weight.
   D. critical mass.

Passage 73 (Questions 1-6)

Technetium-99m is an unstable isotope used in medical imaging. The "m" stands for *metastable*, meaning the isotope has a short half-life, but can be isolated. ^{99m}Tc decays by a process known as isomeric transition. A nucleus undergoing isomeric transition rearranges to a lower energy state and, in doing so, emits a gamma ray:

$$^{99m}Tc \rightarrow {}^{99}Tc + \gamma$$

Equation 1

Technetium-99m has a half-life of 6.05 hours; therefore, it must be specially prepared before its use in a medical imaging study. Like all radioactive processes, the decay is first order and described by the following equation, where k is the rate constant:

$$N = N_0 e^{-kt}$$

Equation 2

A solution of ^{99m}Tc is injected intravenously into a patient about 3 hours before the intended imaging study. During this time, there is a pronounced uptake of the isotope at the target organs. A specific organ is targeted by the choice of ligand or ligands bound to the metal ion. In brain imaging, sodium pertechnetate-99m ($Na^{99m}TcO_4$) is used, while organic phosphonate complexes are used for the kidneys, liver, and other internal organs.

1. The half-life of ^{42}K is 12.1 hours, twice that of ^{99m}Tc. Compared to the rate constant of ^{99m}Tc, the rate constant of ^{42}K will be:

    A. smaller, by a factor of 2.
    B. smaller, but not by a factor of 2.
    C. larger, by a factor of 2.
    D. larger, but not by a factor of 2.

2. Which term best describes the process in Equation 1?

    A. Endothermic
    B. Equilibrium
    C. Exoergic
    D. Endoergic

3. Most of the ^{99m}Tc injected into the body is removed by glomerulonephrofiltration and excreted before it decays. What fraction of ^{99m}Tc has decayed after 5 half-lives have elapsed?

    A. 4/5
    B. 15/16
    C. 31/32
    D. 63/64

4. ^{99}Tc decays by β^- emission to a stable nuclide. What is the nuclide?

    A. ^{99}Ru
    B. ^{99}Mo
    C. ^{100}Tc
    D. ^{100}Ru

5. What is the oxidation state of technetium in sodium pertechnetate?

    A. +6
    B. +7
    C. +8
    D. +9

6. Sodium pertechnetate would be predicted to be:

    A. a weak electrolyte.
    B. a strong base.
    C. a reducing agent.
    D. an oxidizing agent.

Passage 74 (Questions 1-5)

To date an object with an age on the order of a billion years, one can examine the ratio of U-238 to Pb-206 contained in the object. U-238 decays to Pb-206 through a series of 13 intermediate nuclei. The rates at which these intermediate decays occur vary greatly. For example, the first decay, U-238 to Th-234 (Reaction 1 below), takes 4.47 billion years, while the third decay, Pa-234 to U-234, takes just 70 seconds. Overall, it would take 4.6 billion years for half a sample of U-238 to complete the series and decay to Pb-206.

In this series of decays, a total of eight alpha particles are emitted. An alpha particle (α) is composed of two neutrons and two protons. In the first decay in the series, U-238 is transformed into an isotope of thorium:

$$^{238}_{92}U \rightarrow {}^{234}_{90}Th + {}^{4}_{2}\alpha$$

Reaction 1

In addition to the eight alpha particles, six beta particles are also released in the decay series. A beta particle (β⁻) is an electron created in, and then ejected from, the nucleus. If a nucleus ejects a beta particle, it will lose one neutron and gain one proton. The parent nuclide of Pb-206 is Tl-206:

$$^{206}_{81}Tl \rightarrow {}^{206}_{82}Pb + {}^{0}_{-1}\beta$$

Reaction 2

Nuclear decay also produces gamma rays (γ), which are high-energy photons. These photons carry energy away from a nucleus, leaving it in a lower energy state.

(Note: proton mass = 1.0073 amu; electron rest mass = 9.1×10^{-31} kg 1 amu = 931 MeV; 1 eV = 1.6×10^{-19} J.)

1. Which of the following nuclear decay products would NOT be affected by a magnetic field?

   A. α particle
   B. β⁻ particle
   C. β⁺ particle
   D. γ ray

2. In the ^{238}U–^{206}Pb series, two alpha particles are emitted in the decay of ^{218}Po to ^{210}Pb. How many beta particles were emitted?

   A. 0
   B. 1
   C. 2
   D. 3

3. One half of an element will decay to lead in 4 seconds. How long would it take until only 1/10 of the original material remained?

   A. 10.8 sec
   B. 11.5 sec
   C. 13.3 sec
   D. 16.8 sec

4. Radium-228 can decay by emitting the following sequence of particles: alpha, alpha, alpha, beta, alpha, and beta. The resulting substance is an isotope of:

   A. Pb.
   B. Po.
   C. Rn.
   D. Th.

5. When measuring the mass of all particles involved in the fusion of two nuclei, 2.2×10^{-31} kg of mass is unaccounted for. Approximately how much energy must have been released?

   A. 6.6×10^{-23} J
   B. 4.6×10^{-21} J
   C. 2.0×10^{-14} J
   D. 1.4×10^{-12} J

Passage 75 (Questions 1-6)

Alpha, beta, and gamma particles are all biologically destructive to some degree because of their ability to ionize atoms they collide with. Ionization of compounds in biological systems inevitably results in some type of biochemical dysfunction, with the ionized molecule typically losing all useful activity. On the cellular level, limited exposure is rarely fatal because most damaged molecules can be readily replaced; however, DNA is an exception. If cellular DNA is struck by several decay particles, the sustained damaged is usually fatal for that cell. The destructiveness of ingested radioisotopes may be graded as: alpha > beta > gamma rays.

However, on occasion, a nonessential portion of the genetic code may be damaged, hence the genome of the cell is altered (mutated) without cell death. Note: If the damaged gene happened to restrict cell replication, the cell may become cancerous. Cancerous cells are basically human cells that replicate uncontrollably.

Hazards from external exposure differ drastically, with the potential biohazard proportional to the penetrability of the emitted particle. The following chart gives the average depth of penetration of alpha and beta particles and of gamma rays through various media.

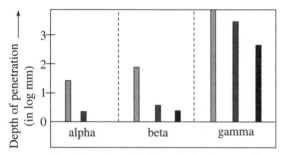

The first column is through air, the second column is through human tissue, and the third column is through lead. Note: Alpha particles do not penetrate lead.

The catastrophe at the Chernobyl nuclear power plant in 1986 released vast amounts of highly toxic radioisotopes such as cesium-137, strontium-90, and iodine-131 into the atmosphere. All are short-lived radioisotopes, with half-lives of 30 years, 28 years, and 8 days, respectively, and all are beta (β^-) emitters. As these radionuclides settled out of the atmosphere, they contaminated the water and soil of hundreds of thousands of square kilometers within the Ukraine and Scandinavia. Today, nearly one million citizens of the former Soviet Union may be suffering from some of the physiological effects associated with chronic radiation exposure.

1. What is the minimum thickness of a lead shield required to prevent all gamma ray penetration?

   A. 1 mm
   B. 3 mm
   C. 1 m
   D. 3 m

2. The daughter nucleus of ^{137}Cs is:

   A. ^{136}Xe.
   B. ^{137}Xe.
   C. ^{136}Ba.
   D. ^{137}Ba.

3. Which of the following is the best statement concerning the depth of penetration of radioactive decay products?

   A. As the mass of the particle increases, the penetration depth increases.
   B. As the mass of the particle increases, the penetration depth decreases.
   C. As the charge of the particle increases in magnitude, the penetration depth increases.
   D. As the charge of the particle decreases in magnitude, the penetration depth decreases.

4. Absorption of strontium-90 is responsible for the high occurrence of bone marrow cancer following the Chernobyl disaster. Why?

   A. Strontium is an essential component of hemoglobin, which is synthesized in the bone marrow.
   B. Strontium is chemically similar to beryllium, which is a major component of bone matrix.
   C. Strontium-90 decays into yttrium-90, which is a stable isotope. Yttrium, being a heavy metal, is then incorporated into bone matrix.
   D. Strontium is chemically similar to calcium and is incorporated into the bone matrix.

5. If you examined a patient who has received considerable radiation burns to their skin, throat, and lungs, you could conclude that this individual had just been exposed to high concentrations of:

 A. technetium-99, a gamma emitter.
 B. carbon-11, a positron emitter.
 C. radon-222, an alpha emitter.
 D. tellurium-123, which decays by electron capture.

6. How many times further does a gamma ray penetrate lead than does a beta particle?

 A. 2
 B. 3
 C. 10
 D. 100

Passage 76 (Questions 1-6)

Some very large nuclei are so unstable that normal radioactive mechanisms cannot release enough energy to sufficiently stabilize the nucleus. In these rare cases, the nucleus elects to follow a drastic course: it splits into smaller nuclei, a process termed *fission*, which produces two daughter nuclei of about the same mass, several free neutrons, and releases a tremendous amount of energy. Radionuclides that undergo fission are very short-lived; once a fissioning isotope is formed, it immediately undergoes fission.

Fission occurs extremely rapidly, yet the rate of production of the fissioning nuclei could be slow. For example, nuclear reactors maintain very low rates of fission by limiting the rate of formation of the *fissioning* isotope. Most nuclear reactors produce fissioning uranium-236 from *fissile* uranium-235, *in situ*, by neutron bombardment, with the neutrons coming from previously fissioned atoms. A fissile isotope is an isotope that will become a fissioning isotope following a single *neutron capture*. If neutron bombardment is low, the production of ^{236}U is low, thus ensuring that the fission rate is low.

Nuclear weapons, however, count on rapid, complete fission. A nuclear explosion results from the almost instantaneous conversion of all of the fissile isotope to fissioning isotope. For example, uranium-235 is used in nuclear devices. An initial source of neutrons converts a few ^{235}U into ^{236}U through neutron capture. Once formed, ^{236}U undergoes fission immediately, producing two daughter elements of roughly equivalent mass (krypton-94 and barium-139), lots of energy, and three neutrons. These new neutrons, in turn, are captured by another three ^{235}U, converting them into three new ^{236}U, which immediately undergo fission, producing more daughter elements, much more energy, and $3 \times 3 = 9$ more neutrons.

The process of neutron capture, fission, the release of more new neutrons, and so on, is called a *nuclear chain reaction* or *nuclear cascade*. This continues if there is enough fissile material packed tightly together. The minimum amount of fissile required to maintain a run-away nuclear cascade is called the *critical mass*.

1. If plutonium-239 captures a neutron, then the new, composite nucleus will instantaneously undergo fission. Based upon the passage, the most likely fission products would be:

 A. carbon-13, radium-225, and two neutrons.
 B. iodine-140 and niobium-99.
 C. xenon-138, zirconium-98, and four neutrons.
 D. uranium-236 and helium-4.

2. Which of the following graphs best illustrates the trend of the numbers of neutrons and protons in the nuclei of *stable* elements, where N is the number of neutrons and Z is the atomic number?

A.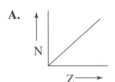

B.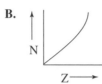

C.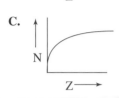

D.

3. Which of the following statements best explains why atomic devices produce a nuclear explosion but nuclear reactors do not?

   A. Nuclear reactors utilize different nuclear fuel than do atomic weapons.
   B. Nuclear reactors possess more concentrated fuel than do atomic devices.
   C. Atomic weapons use more fissionable material than do reactors.
   D. Atomic weapons allow their fuel to reach critical mass.

4. A free neutron is radioactive. It will decay via β^- emission with a half-life of 11 minutes. If a sample of contaminated air has a free neutron concentration of 1560 ppt/cc, approximately how many minutes would it take for the neutron concentration to decrease to 15% of its original value?

   A. 30
   B. 33
   C. 35
   D. 40

5. If thorium-233 is the only thorium isotope that spontaneously undergoes fission, which one of the following isotopes is a fissile?

   A. ^{232}Th
   B. ^{233}Th
   C. ^{234}Th
   D. ^{235}Th

6. In plutonium-240, the neutron/proton ratio is approximately 1.5. What is the approximate neutron/proton ratio of the two daughter products obtained by the fission of ^{240}Pu?

   A. 0.75
   B. 1.0
   C. 1.5
   D. 3.0

   _____

Passage 77 (Questions 1-5)

Unlike radioactive decay and fission, nuclear *fusion* involves combining two small nuclei to form a larger nucleus. Since the fusion of small nuclei to form larger ones inherently increases the total binding energy of the system, mass is converted to energy, and this energy is released to the environment. In fact, because fusion provides more energy per unit mass than fission does, intensive research is being conducted to develop the world's first fusion nuclear reactor.

Although fusion can occur between any two small nuclei, the fusion reaction currently being pursued is the following:

$$^3_1H + {}^2_1H \rightarrow {}^4_2He + {}^1_0n.$$

By definition, fusion occurs when two nuclei approach and bind to one another. However, the repulsive nature of the two positively-charged nuclei makes this very difficult. Temperatures in excess of one million degrees are required before the kinetic energy of the nuclei is sufficiently large to overwhelm this charge–charge repulsion. Production of such high temperatures is not very difficult, but their controlled containment is. At these temperatures, all known materials will completely vaporize into a plasma. Therefore, fusion reactors are being designed with magnetic walls, not material ones, with the hope that such containment bottles will be sufficiently strong to confine the fusing fuel safely.

The only fusion reactions that have occurred on Earth have been as H-bomb detonations ("H" stands for hydrogen). These thermonuclear devices are, in fact, two bombs in one: a small atomic bomb (fission device, fueled with ^{235}U or ^{239}Pu), encapsulated by several kilograms of lithium deuteride, the fusion fuel. Detonation of the fission device provides enough heat (several million degrees) to initiate the fusion of lithium and deuterium nuclei, which then increases the explosion's energy output by an order of magnitude.

1. Based on the passage, the ratio of the energy released by an H-bomb to that released by an atomic bomb is approximately:

   A. 2.
   B. 5.
   C. 10.
   D. 100.

2. Consider the following hypothetical fusion reaction:

   $$A + B \rightarrow C + energy.$$

   The exact mass of C must be:

   A. less than either A or B.
   B. less than A but more than B.
   C. less than A and B combined.
   D. more than A and B combined.

3. The sun is powered by fusion. The overall solar fusion reaction is:

   $$H + H + H + H \rightarrow {}^4He + 2 X + energy.$$

   Identify the missing particle type X.

   A. Alpha particle
   B. Electron
   C. Positron
   D. Neutron

4. The electrostatic repulsive force, F, is proportional to charge of the particles squared. If $F \propto T$ (temperature), which of the following graphs best illustrates the relationship between particle charge (Q) and minimum fusion temperature (T)?

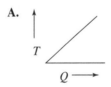

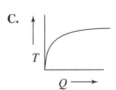
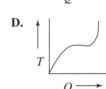

5. Unlike solar fusion, the fusion reaction currently being explored by scientists will produce free neutrons. These neutrons will be:

   A. unaffected by the magnetic field and convert the materials in the reactor walls to their heavier isotopes.
   B. unable to interact with any matter.
   C. effectively contained by the magnetic field.
   D. squeezed together to form large nuclei of pure neutrons.

Passage 78 (Questions 1-5)

A host of diagnostic tools conventionally utilized by radiologists expose patients to moderate levels of radiation and radionuclides. Techniques that employ potentially harmful types of radiation are termed *invasive*. A few commonly used invasive diagnostic techniques are listed below. Invasive techniques can be divided into two classes: *radiation exposing* and *radionuclide exposing*. The first two types given below are radiation exposing; the last three are radionuclide exposing.

Common X-ray. X-rays are generated by high-energy electron bombardment of a metal plate. Electron bombardment initiates electronic transitions within the atoms of the metal, generating x-rays. The x-ray burst is directed at the target. X-rays easily pass through soft tissue and clothing. Dense material such as metal, fibrous connective tissue, and bone will absorb, reflect, and refract x-rays. X-rays that pass through the target develop (i.e., darken) the colorless photographic film which lies behind the patient, producing a negative image.

CAT (Computerized Axial Tomography) Scan. CAT scans are similar to the common x-ray. The patient is irradiated with sheets of x-rays that give 2-D cross-sectional images after processing by an electronic detector. Several images can be combined to construct a 3-D image.

PET (Positron Emission Tomography) Scan. Prior to PET analysis, a metabolic nutrient, typically glucose or some amino acid, is injected into the patient's circulatory system and is allowed to permeate the body. The nutrients, which contain radionuclides such as ^{11}C, ^{13}N, or ^{15}O (all short-lived β^+ emitters), concentrate in active tissues. A gamma camera is used to detect outgoing gamma radiation (produced from the annihilation of the emitted β^+ with an electron) from the region of interest. In addition to a high resolution static image, this technique is useful in determining tissue activity.

Technetium-99m tracer. ^{99m}Tc, a gamma emitter, is administered intravenously and allowed to permeate the body. Although technetium is not a nutrient, it is concentrated in cells where high levels of plasma are being diffused through cellular membranes. Just as with PET, outgoing gamma rays are detected by a gamma camera.

Iodine-131 tracer. Positron emitter, analogous to PET.

Technique	Isotope	Half-life
PET Scan	^{11}C, ^{13}N, or ^{15}O	2–20 min
Technetium tracer	^{99m}Tc	6 hrs
Iodine tracer	^{131}I	8 days

Table 1   Radionuclide Exposing Techniques

1. A patient who has received several PET scans in a short period of time could have substantially elevated intravenous concentrations of:

   A. boron-11.
   B. nitrogen-14.
   C. oxygen-17.
   D. calcium-39.

2. Which of the following diagnostic techniques is the most appropriate for the detection of highly fluid abdominal tumors?

   A. X-ray
   B. CAT scan
   C. PET scan
   D. Iodine-131 tracer

3. Diagnostically, iodine-131 is primarily used to graphically represent thyroid function over several days. Which of the following graphs best depicts the intensity of the ^{131}I signal observed in a patient who ate shellfish (containing an ample quantity of ^{127}I) on the third day after ^{131}I was administered?

   A.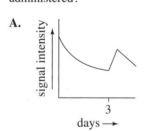
   B.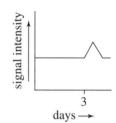
   C.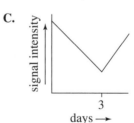
   D.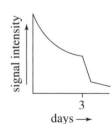

4. If a sample of ^{131}I was emitting 20 counts per second (c/sec) twenty days after being synthesized, what was the emission rate four days after being synthesized?

   A. 10 c/sec
   B. 80 c/sec
   C. 120 c/sec
   D. 240 c/sec

5. Which of the following systems would be best studied using intravenous technetium-99m tracking?

    A. Thyroid–pituitary
    B. Kidney–liver
    C. Stomach–intestine
    D. Heart–lungs

Passage 79 (Questions 1-6)

Nuclear reactors harness the nuclear energy released by fission and convert it into electrical energy through the use of steam turbines. Most reactors utilize diluted ^{235}U as their fuel. While producing vast amounts of energy, the fission of ^{235}U generates many different daughter elements, all of which are highly radioactive. Neutrons are also released during fission, most of which rapidly collide with and fuse to surrounding nuclei.

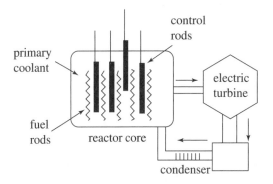

Control rods are present in the reactor in order to absorb free neutrons. Therefore the atoms which make up these control rods are gradually converted to heavier isotopes through neutron capture. These newly formed isotopes are often highly radioactive, and further add to the contamination of the reactor core.

Isotope	Half-life (if radioactive)
^1H	stable
^2H	stable
^3H	≈ 12 yr
^{12}C	stable
^{13}C	stable
^{14}C	≈ 5700 yr
^{19}F	stable
^{20}F	≈ 11 sec
^{27}Al	stable
^{28}Al	≈ 150 sec

Table 1

1. Based upon the table above, which material would be best suited for the prolonged neutron bombardment experienced by a control rod?

    A. Liquid deuterium
    B. ^{12}C
    C. ^{19}F
    D. ^{27}Al

2. Approximately how many minutes would it take for a 110 g sample of ^{28}Al to decay to only 25 g?

A. 3
B. 5
C. 8
D. 12

3. The fission of ^{235}U produces ^{142}Ba, three free neutrons, and one other nuclide. Identify this element.

A. Bromine
B. Krypton
C. Rubidium
D. Strontium

4. The size of a ^{235}U nucleus is about 10^{-14} m, and the size of the ^{235}U atom is approximately 10^{-10} m. Therefore, if the nucleus were the size of a marble (≈ 1.0 cm), the atom would be the size of:

A. a car.
B. an average house.
C. a sports stadium.
D. the Moon.

5. Vast deposits of ^{238}U in the desert southwest of the United States radioactively decay. One of the results of this decay is the production of helium gas in the atmosphere. What type of decay does ^{238}U undergo?

A. Alpha
B. Electron capture
C. Gamma
D. Positron emission

6. Which graph best illustrates the concentration of ^{235}U as a function of time due to its radioactive decay?

A.
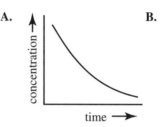

B.
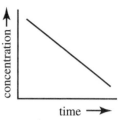

C.
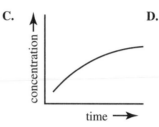

D.
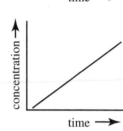

Passage 80 (Questions 1-4)

Electronic excitation is the process in which a molecule or an atom may absorb 1 to 1000 eV of energy, whether it is in the form of electromagnetic, thermal, or kinetic energy. During electronic excitation, a molecule (or atom) promotes an electron into a higher energy orbital, a process which destabilizes the molecule, and occasionally contorts the overall molecular structure. Hence, it should be no surprise that most molecular excited states usually have a very short lifetime: less than a second, with some as short as 10^{-14} second!

By definition, the process in which an excited molecule or atom emits one or more photons of light in order to return to its ground state is called fluorescence. Yet in practice, it is common to categorize molecules as fluorescent only when such molecules are emitting photons within visible wavelengths (400–700 nm).

The most common class of fluorescent molecules are conjugated, organic molecules which absorb UV photons (UV photons are invisible to the human eye), then emit several visible photons in order to expel energy in returning to their respective ground states. An example of one of these type of fluorescing molecules is fluorecein:

fluorecein

A fluorecein molecule may absorb a single UV photon through the excitation of one of its aromatic electrons into a more energetic molecular orbital. Once excited, the promoted electron decays back to its original ground state, liberating energy in a two-step process that emits a green and a yellow photon:

1. Which one of the following statements is true?

   A. Electronic transitions can only occur in conjugated molecules.
   B. Fluorescent molecules must emit photons of equal or shorter wavelength than that of the absorbed photons.
   C. Fluorescent molecules must emit photons of equal or greater energy than that of the absorbed photons.
   D. Fluorescent molecules must emit photons of equal or lower frequency than that of the absorbed photons.

2. How many sp^3 hybridized carbon atoms are there in the fluorecein molecule?

   A. 0
   B. 1
   C. 2
   D. 3

3. Identify the configuration of an excited oxygen atom prior to fluorescence.

   A. $1s^2 2s^2 2p^4$
   B. $1s^2 2s^2 2p^5$
   C. $1s^2 2s^2 2p^2 d^2$
   D. $1s^2 2s^2 2p^3 3s^1$

4. Which of the following processes cannot induce an atom in its ground state to fluoresce?

   A. Heating with a flame
   B. Exposure to x-rays
   C. Freezing with liquid nitrogen
   D. Irradiating with a laser

Passage 81 (Questions 1-6)

Two physicists proposed theoretical models to explain the structure of the atomic nucleus:

Physicist #1: "Just as with the extranuclear electrons, the nucleons that compose the nucleus may only exist in one of an infinite number of discrete energy levels. Therefore, the nucleus of an atom is quantized in both energy and rest mass."

Physicist #2: "Particles in a nucleus obey a different set of physical rules than electrons do. Nucleons may exist at any energy. Therefore, while the nucleus has a distinct rest mass, it is not quantized in energy."

Some time later, an experimentalist attempted to validate one of these models by measuring the energy of nuclear transitions. In the first part of the experiment, she measured the kinetic energy of alpha particles emitted by a sample of thorium-228:

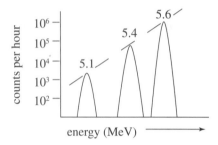

In the second part of the experiment, she measured the kinetic energy of β^- and β^+ particles emitted by a sample of copper-64:

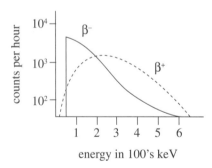

The particle detector she used had a sensitivity for particles with energies between 10 keV and 10 MeV.

1. Based upon the experimental data, which nuclear model is more valid?

    A. The first model
    B. The second model
    C. The data support elements of both models.
    D. The data are inconsistent with all elements of both models.

2. Which one of the following nuclides could not have been used as a source of alpha particles in the first part of the experiment?

    A. ^{3}H
    B. ^{44}Ca
    C. ^{222}Rn
    D. ^{238}U

3. The data from the second part of the experiment indicate that positrons, on average, have more energy than the emitted electrons because:

    A. positrons have less mass than electrons.
    B. positrons have greater mass than electrons.
    C. electrons are accelerated out of the nucleus by neutrons.
    D. positrons are accelerated out of the nucleus by protons.

4. What is the average kinetic energy of 0.1 mol of β^- particles emitted from a sample of ^{64}Cu?

    A. 100 keV
    B. 250 keV
    C. 350 keV
    D. 400 keV

5. Given that C is the number of detected alpha particles emitted by ^{228}Th and KE is their kinetic energy, then the equation for the dashed line superimposed on the first set of data should be of the form:

    A. $C \propto KE$.
    B. $C \propto KE^{-1}$.
    C. $C \propto \ln KE$.
    D. $C \propto e^{KE}$.

6. No β⁻ particles having less that 50 keV of energy were observed by the experimentalist. Why?

   A. The detector is not sensitive to particles having less than 100,000 eV of energy.
   B. β⁻ particles with less than 50 keV cannot escape from the positively charged nucleus.
   C. β⁻ particles of low energy react with electrons in a matter–antimatter reaction before escaping from the atom.
   D. β⁻ particles have zero mass at low velocities.

Passage 82 (Questions 1-6)

Nuclear power plants convert the heat generated by the nuclear fission of uranium-235 or plutonium-239 into electrical energy. While exact details vary from reactor to reactor, most nuclear power plants use a series of three liquid water coolant systems to transport large amounts of heat away from the core to electricity-generating turbines.

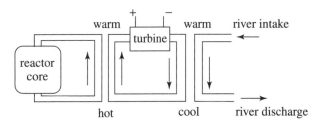

The *primary coolant* system circulates pressurized water through the reactor core itself. The water becomes superheated (i.e., it does not boil) reaching temperatures in excess of 250°C and is then pumped out of the core into a heat exchange area. In this heat exchange area, pipes containing the hot primary coolant and much cooler *secondary coolant* are wrapped around one another in order to facilitate heat transfer. The secondary coolant, which is not under very high pressure, absorbs heat and boils. This expanding steam spins the propeller-like blades of the electrical turbines, and electricity is produced.

Once through the turbine, the steam has to be condensed back to liquid water. The cool water (25°C) in the *tertiary coolant* system circulates through large condensing towers, absorbing heat from the secondary coolant. Unlike the primary and secondary coolant systems, the tertiary system is not closed. Tertiary water is simply pumped from a nearby body of water—a river or a lake—then released back into that body of water.

1. Based upon the passage, which one of the following statements is true?

   A. The conversion of heat to electrical energy is one-hundred percent efficient.
   B. The vapor pressure of the primary coolant often exceeds 760 torr.
   C. Heat is produced from the binding energy liberated by fusion.
   D. Electrical turbines convert electrical energy to mechanical energy.

2. Primary coolant water becomes highly radioactive with time due to its constant exposure to the core's neutron emissions. Which one of the nuclear reactions could NOT be a source of trace amounts of ^{15}N that build up in the system with time?

    A. Alpha decay of ^{19}F
    B. Beta emission of ^{14}C
    C. Positron emission of ^{15}O
    D. Electron capture by ^{15}O

3. As the primary coolant water is heated, its entropy increases because:

    A. the number of hydrogen bonds increases with increasing temperature.
    B. the spacing between water molecules decreases with increasing temperature.
    C. it boils.
    D. the average kinetic energy of the molecules increases with temperature.

4. Given that the reaction between H^+ and OH^- is highly exothermic and assuming that the primary coolant water is completely pure, what would be its pH?

    A. Less than 7
    B. Equal to 7, because K_w is independent of temperature
    C. Greater than 7
    D. Unknown, because pressure strongly affects K_w

5. Sodium-based Soviet nuclear submarines, i.e., those that used liquid sodium (MP = 98°C) as their primary coolant, suffered catastrophic disasters when ocean water would flood these systems because of the reaction:

    $$2\,Na(l) + H_2O(l) \rightarrow 2\,NaOH(aq) + H_2(g)$$

    This reaction is a(n):

    A. oxidation–reduction reaction.
    B. Lewis acid–base reaction.
    C. Brønsted acid–base reaction.
    D. combustion reaction.

6. If the temperature at the tertiary water intake was 23°C and the outflow water was 31°C, how much energy, in calories, has been absorbed by each liter of tertiary water?

    A. 8 cal
    B. 80 cal
    C. 800 cal
    D. 8000 cal

_____

MCAT
General
Chemistry
Solutions

Passage 1

1. **B** The question states that the permitted oxidation states of Cr are +2, +3, +4, +5, and +6. This eliminates choices C and D, for in these molecules, Cr would be in a +8 or +1 oxidation state, respectively. Since the passage states that the metal in an acidic transition metal oxide has an oxidation state greater than +5, the answer must be choice B (since in choice A, Cr is only in a +4 oxidation state, while in choice B, it's in a +6.)

2. **A** Count the number of electrons in the given configuration: [Ar] accounts for 18 electrons, $4s^2$ for 2 electrons, and $3d^5$ for 5 electrons. Since 18 + 2 + 5 = 25, the atom must be manganese (element number 25).

3. **D** Neither lithium nor potassium has a closed valence shell, so choices A and B are eliminated. While magnesium has a closed valence s subshell ([Ne]$3s^2$), copper has a closed valence d subshell ([Ar]$4s^1 3d^{10}$). This gives copper greater stabilization, making it much less reactive. (Note: This is why things like coins and water pipes are made from copper, not magnesium.)

4. **D** According to the passage, acidic compounds are those in which the MO–H bond is the ionic one; basic compounds are those in which the M–OH bond is ionic. Since Compound I is acidic and Compound II is basic, the metal–oxide bond in Compound I is not ionic (because the O–H bond is), but the metal–oxide bond in Compound II must be ionic.

5. **D** An atom/ion is paramagnetic if at least one electron is unpaired. Thus, an atom with an odd number of electrons must always be paramagnetic; this eliminates choices A and B. There are five d orbitals, and when filling them, 1 electron goes into each orbital before they start to pair up. Thus, the 6 d-orbital electrons in Co^{3+} are placed as follows: The first 5 electrons go one at a time into the five available d orbitals, and the sixth electron pairs up with the electron in the first d orbital, leaving the other four d orbitals with one (unpaired) electron. Since this ion has unpaired electrons, it is paramagnetic. Therefore, the answer is choice D; Zn^{2+} is not paramagnetic.

Passage 2

1. **C** The energy of excitation is equal to the energy of the emitted photon. Since violet is the most energetic band of visible light, the table tells us that potassium has the greatest energy of excitation.

2. **D** In order to answer this question, we must determine the atomic trend alluded to in the question. The description "same valence structure" is a complicated way of saying that the trend is based on atoms in the same family, i.e., column (atoms in the same family have identical valence structures). Since lithium is red, sodium is yellow, and potassium is violet, we conclude that as we go down a column, the emitted energy increases. Examining the second family (alkaline earth metals), we see that strontium is red and barium is green, so radium must emit photons of higher energy than green. Violet is therefore a possibility.

3. **B** Choice A is wrong because there is no such thing as a white photon. Choice C is partially true, but invisible UV light has nothing to do with white light. Choice D is wrong since x-rays are not produced by heated magnesium, and even if they were, they would also be invisible. (In fact, if you actually looked at a strong source of x-rays, the world would begin to look darker and darker as the x-rays obliterated your cones and rods.)

4. **D** This question is similar to question 2 above. Cesium is below potassium, so it must have a higher energy of excitation than violet, i.e., ultraviolet (UV). UV is not detectable by the retina, and no color would be observed. (Note: The same blinding would occur from higher-energy UV rays as from x-rays.)

5. **B** The addition of one electron (reduction) to any of the ions would result in a neutral atom or an ion with an odd number of electrons. Since at least one electron must be unpaired in these cases, the atom will be paramagnetic.

6. **D** The ground state for Cu is [Ar] $4s^13d^{10}$. Transition metals always lose their valence s electrons before any d electrons, so the ground-state electron configuration for Cu⁺ [(I) means +1] is [Ar] $3d^{10}$. The only plausible excited configuration for Cu⁺ must be [Ar] $3d^94p^1$. (Note: Since Cu⁺ has $29 - 1 = 28$ electrons, choices A and C are eliminated.)

Passage 3

1. **B** The passage indicates that silver-based photographic film will develop upon exposure to photons of greater energy than infrared. Microwaves (choice B) have less energy than infrared photons and will not develop the film.

2. **C** Since we are told that x-rays only significantly interact with the nuclei and inner electrons of large atoms, we are indirectly asked to choose the atom with the most inner electrons and the largest nucleus. Choose uranium.

3. **A** Chronic radiation exposure significantly increases the risk of cancers of the tissue where the maximum amount of radiation is absorbed. For instance:

   - Exposure to radioactive iodine (formed as nuclear waste) increases the risk of thyroid cancer because the thyroid concentrates iodine.

   - Exposure to radioactive gases (such as radon) cause cancers of the throat and lungs. Ingested radioactive heavy metals (such as strontium and plutonium) concentrate in the bone matrix leading to increases in the occurrence of bone marrow and myelogenous leukemia (cancer of white blood cells produced in the bone marrow).

   - X-rays are absorbed by bone, increasing the risk of developing bone marrow and myelogenous leukemia.

   The best choice is A. (Note that lymphogenous leukemia is cancer of white blood cells produced in the lymph nodes, not bone marrow.)

4. **C** According to the question, a nuclear reaction is producing argon gas. Since a sodium atom would need to gain 7 protons to become argon, it is unlikely that sodium transmutation is responsible for the production of argon (choice A is eliminated). More likely, a chlorine atom is undergoing a simple radioactive decay. So given the reaction

$$_{17}Cl \rightarrow {}_{18}Ar + {}_{?}?$$

and considering that charge (denoted by the subscripts) must be conserved, the emitted particle must have a charge of -1. We conclude that this particle is an electron (β^- particle), i.e., chlorine is undergoing β^- decay.

Passage 4

1. **A** Optical pigments are excited by a range of photons. The energy of excitation is equal to the energy of absorbed photons. Since blue light has higher energy than red or green light, the blue-sensitive pigment has a higher excitation energy.

2. **C** The maximum absorption for the red and blue cones (peak of the curves) are at about 600 nm and 400 nm, respectively. Therefore, in terms of wavelength, the ratio of the red and blue cones is 600 nm to 400 nm or 3:2. However, the energy of a photon of light is inversely proportional to its wavelength. So, in terms of photon energy, the correct ratio is the inverse of that for wavelength, or 2:3.

3. **B** Using the light absorption spectra for blue, green, and red cones, the wavelength of light that stimulates red and green cones equally (where the red and green cone lines intersect) corresponds to about 550 nm, or yellow light. Furthermore, the wavelength of light that stimulates green and blue cones equally (where the green and blue cone lines intersect) corresponds to about 480 nm.

4. **C** The sensitivity maximum of the blue, green, or red cones corresponds to the colors blue, yellow-green, and orange (choice A). Unlike the red and blue cones, the absorption spectrum of the green cone overlaps other spectra at every wavelength (choice B). While photons having a wavelength between 520 nm and 480 nm will excite all three cones, none of these photons excite all three cones to the same degree (choice D). The shape and maximum absorption energy of a molecule can be used as a tool for elucidating its structure. Similarities between two spectra often represent similarities between the structures of those molecules. By this argument, the spectra of the red and green cones are more similar in energy and shape than are the spectra of the red and blue cones, so choice C is false.

5. **B** Adding up all three sensitivity curves, one finds that the sensitivity to red is 50 (red cone only), to yellow is 160 (red cone plus green cone = 80 + 80), to blue is 100 (green cone plus blue cone = 20 + 80) and to violet is 50 (blue cone only). Therefore, the human eye has the maximum sensitivity to the color yellow, choice B, which is why signs and hazard labels are often painted yellow. (The fact that the human eye is most sensitive to yellow light shouldn't be too surprising. Humans evolved under the light of the Sun, and what color is the Sun?)

6   C   Violet light has a higher energy than red light, but the wavelength of violet light is less than that of red light, so choice A is wrong. Orange photons have less energy and a lower frequency than green photons, so choice B is wrong. There is no such thing as the $n = 0$ quantum level; the first level is always $n = 1$, so choice D is wrong. The energy spacing between adjacent orbitals decreases as the energy levels move further away from the nucleus. Therefore, the energy between the $n = 4$ and $n = 3$ shells is less than that between the $n = 3$ and $n = 2$ shells. Since the energy of absorbed or emitted photons is identical to the energy spacing, the transition from $n = 3$ to $n = 2$ must emit a higher energy photon than yellow, so green is a possibility: choice C.

Passage 5

1.   B   Oxygen-15 has 8 protons, so it is magic. Iron-50 has 26 protons and 24 neutrons, neither of which is magic. (Notice that $Z > N$ in iron-50, so this nucleus is very unstable.) Lead-208 has 82 protons and $208 - 82 = 126$ neutrons, so it is doubly magic.

2.   A   Oxygen-16 is an even–even nuclide (and doubly magic!), so all its nucleons will form spin-up/spin-down pairs. The sum of the spins in each such pair is $(+1/2) + (-1/2) = 0$. Since there is no unpaired nucleon, the total nuclear spin is 0.

3.   B   Choices A, C, and D are all odd–odd nuclides (^{8}Li has 3 protons and 5 neutrons, ^{20}F has 9 protons and 11 neutrons, and ^{26}Na has 11 protons and 15 neutrons). According to the passage, these odd–odd nuclides are not stable, so they must be radioactive. Choice B, ^{15}N, has a magic number of neutrons (namely, 8), so we expect it to be more stable than the other choices listed.

4.   C   For a given value of J, there are $2J + 1$ possible values for m_J. Since here we have $J = 7/2$, there are $2(7/2) + 1 = 8$ possible values for m_J, so the $5g_{J=7/2}$ state may hold 8 protons or 8 neutrons. Therefore, as illustrated by the example given in the passage, the $5g_{J=7/2}$ states may hold a total of $8 + 8 = 16$ nucleons.

5.   B   The principal difference between the choices is in the number of neutrons. Since $Z = 42$ for molybdenum (Mo), the numbers of neutrons in the given choices are 49, 50, 51, and 52. Is there anything special about one of these? Yes—50 is a magic number. The passage states that the quantized energy levels in the nuclear shell model are separated by unusually large gaps—magic gaps—when N (or Z) is a magic number. This fact is also depicted Figure 1. Our conclusion is that of the choices given, the isotope ^{92}Mo, the only one with a magic number of neutrons, will require the greatest amount of energy to raise it to the next allowed nuclear energy level.

6.   C   Looking at Figure 1, we see that of the choices listed, only the $3s_{J=1/2}$ level is higher than $3p_{J=1/2}$.

Passage 6

1. **B**   If the incident radiation has a frequency less than the threshold frequency f_0, no photoelectrons are produced. Thus, the graph of KE_{max} vs. f must start at $f = f_0$; it cannot start at $f = 0$. This eliminates choices A and D. The maximum kinetic energy of the electron is given by the equation $KE_{max} = hf - \phi$, which is linear in f. Thus, the graph cannot be the one in choice C.

2. **B**   From Table 1, $\phi = 1.94$ eV for cesium, so using Equation 1, the energy of the incident photons is $E = hf = \phi + KE_{max} = 1.94 + 0.11 = 2.05$ eV. Thus,

    $$f = E/h = (2.05 \text{ eV})/(4.1 \times 10^{-15} \text{ eV-s})$$

    $$= 5 \times 10^{14} \text{ Hz}$$

3. **D**   According to Table 1, light with a wavelength of 550 nm can eject electrons from both rubidium and cesium (since their threshold wavelengths are 582 nm and 639 nm, respectively); this eliminates choice A. Since the work function for Cs is less than that for Rb, electrons ejected from cesium atoms will have more kinetic energy than those ejected from rubidium atoms.

4. **D**   Statements A and C are false, and statement B contradicts Table 1 (since Na has a greater threshold wavelength than Li, it must have a lower threshold frequency).

5. **C**   Reactivity of an atom depends on how easily it can lose (or gain) electrons. According to Table 1, cesium has the lowest work function of the elements given, so it gives up electrons most easily.

6. **A**   Since copper has a threshold wavelength of 264 nm, light with a wavelength of 500 nm should eject no photoelectrons.

Passage 7

1. **B**   A hadron with two up quarks and one down quark is a charged nucleon or proton. Because the atom has 28 of these protons, it must be nickel, eliminating choices A and C. Furthermore, a hadron with two down quarks and one up quark is a neutron. The atom has 29 of these, so the atomic mass must be 28 + 29 = 57, eliminating choice D.

2. **B**   Visible light has a wavelength range of 450-700 nm. The photon falls in this range, so visible light must have been emitted.

3. **A**   The charges of the three quarks add up to 0, so the nucleon must be an uncharged neutron, eliminating choices B and D. The passage states that uncharged nucleons have two down quarks, eliminating choice C.

4. **A**   All electrons in an atom have the same mass, eliminating choice B. To remove three electrons from Sr, the first two electrons are removed from the $5s$ subshell and the third electron is removed from the $4p$ subshell, eliminating choice D. Since the third electron is at a lower energy level, it experiences less shielding and would be more attracted to the nucleus than the first two electrons removed, eliminating choice C. The third electron comes from the completely full $4p$ subshell and is much more difficult to remove, making choice A the best answer.

5. B   The passage describes the nuclear force as being responsible for holding the nucleons in the nucleus together and that it "overcomes other forces that may be present." Therefore, choice B is the best answer because it explains how protons are held together in close proximity despite having the same charge. The passage provides us with no indication that neutrons are preventing protons from touching one another, and particles need not physically touch in order to experience repulsion, eliminating choice A. The passage does describe how hadrons are held together by the strong force, eliminating choice C. The electron cloud surrounding the nucleus experiences an attractive force between the positive protons and the negative electrons. It is unlikely that this could generate an opposing force to prevent the repulsion of like-charged nucleons, eliminating choice D.

Passage 8

1. C   Choice A is incorrect because K^+ ions are larger than Na^+ ions. Choice B is wrong since Cl^- ions are much larger than Na^+ ions. And choice D should be eliminated since Ca^{2+} ions are smaller than either Na^+ or K^+ ions.

2. D   As one moves down the periodic table, size increases. As one moves from left to right across a row, size decreases. Therefore, the smallest atoms should be to the upper right, and that's where helium lives!

3. C   The passage and question both say that for multi-charged ions, each electron affects the size change by an equal percentage. So for a sulfide ion, S^{2-} (determining the charge is the first hurdle), each of the two added electrons will bloat the atom by the same percentage. The addition of the first electron to a sulfur atom of radius 1.0 Å will increase the size by 30%, giving 1.0 + (30% of 1.0) = 1.0 + 0.3 = 1.3 Å. Now the second electron will increase the ionic size by another 30%, so the radius of S^{2-} is 1.3 Å + (30% of 1.3 Å) = 1.3 + 0.4 = 1.7 Å.

4. C   The question tells us that the we must look for the smallest ion to find the greatest rate of diffusion. By far, H^+ has the smallest size—the H^+ ion is just a proton, there are no electrons. So while the calcium ion is small when compared to an ordinary atom—about half the size of a football stadium compared to the whole stadium—the exposed proton is the size of a marble on the fifty-yard line; H^+ wins, no contest. The mitochondria take advantage of the super-fast diffusion rate of the proton across semipermeable membranes to produce energy.

5. C   The passage indicated that size increases dramatically when going down the periodic table, but atomic size actually decreases a little when going from left to right. Therefore, as we move through the periodic table, sudden increases in size should occur when starting a new row (going from noble gas to alkali metal), but then gradually decrease as we proceed across the row.

6. B   Enzymatic active sites are uniquely constructed to complement the shape and charge of their substrates. Therefore, Sr must be acting as a competitive inhibitor for a substrate with similar size and charge. Based upon size considerations, chemical compatibility, and the ions that are important for nerve potentials, the best answer is Ca^{2+}. Ca and Sr are in the same periodic family.

Passage 9

1. B   The ionization energy table indicates the first-order (general) trend that ionization energy decreases with atomic number. Therefore ionization energy should decrease as one descends down a chemical family in the periodic table. Examining ionization energy more closely, it is evident that there is a second-order (periodic highs and lows) effect, where ionization energy increases gradually until peaking at the noble gas of each row. Therefore, ionization energy increases as one travels to the right in any given periodic row. The answer is choice B.

2. A   Helium, being a noble gas, would have the least tendency to gain another electron. The other three choices, all nonmetals, have negative electron affinities (meaning they gain electrons readily to become anions—fluorine especially).

3. D   One might expect that the extra electron would be accommodated into the partially filled $3d$ orbital, such that the Ni^- ion would have a configuration of $[Ar]4s^23d^9$. This line of thought is correct but incomplete. Just like the copper atom, the Ni^- ion will immediately take a $4s$ electron and use it to close the $3d$ subshell. So the configuration of Ni^- is in fact $[Ar]4s^13d^{10}$. Choices A and B are excited states of the Ni^-, and choice C has one too many electrons.

4. B   Choices C and D—being anions—will have positive electron affinities; the addition of an electron requires the input of energy (since the negative charge of the ion repels the negatively charged electron). Now, while the potassium ion does have a negative electron affinity, the Be^{3+} ion has an even more negative (more favorable) electron affinity (since a +3 charge will attract an electron more forcefully than a +1 charge will).

5. C   Since there is no such thing as a $2d$ orbital, choice A is eliminated. Since lithium and fluorine both reside in the $n = 2$ row of the periodic table, as far as the quantum number n, they are identical: They have to traverse the same number of energy levels to reach $n =$ infinity, so choice B is wrong. The answer is choice C. The lithium atom is larger than the fluorine atom. This translates into the fact that the valence electrons of lithium atom are, on average, farther away from the nucleus than are the valence electrons of fluorine.

Passage 10

1. D   The last sentence of the passage states that longer hydrocarbon molecules have higher boiling points. Therefore, nonane should have a higher boiling point than propane and be more likely to be a liquid at room temperature.

2. B   One of the footnotes to Table 1 states that the boiling point temperatures for all substances listed were determined at a pressure of 1 atm = 760 torr.

3. A   The data in the table support choice A: As the dipole moment increases, so does the boiling point temperature.

4. C   The oxygen and both carbons in dimethyl ether have four groups of electrons. Therefore, all of these atoms have sp^3 hybridization.

5. **D** In addition to the propane gas in the region above the liquid water surface, there is also water vapor, since water evaporates from the liquid surface due to its vapor pressure. Therefore, both the propane and the water vapor contribute to the total pressure of the gases.

Passage 11

1. **B** In almost all cases, when a nonmetal atom forms a covalent bond with a metal ion (more appropriately called a coordinate covalent bond), the nonmetal is acting as a ligand and a Lewis base by donating a pair of electrons to form the bond.

2. **C** The term chelator is analogous to the terms ligand and Lewis base. Therefore, an amino acid residue that cannot act as a chelator is one that cannot act as a Lewis base, i.e., cannot donate a pair of electrons. The phenyl alanine residue (choice C) cannot act a Lewis base because none of its atoms have a nonbonding pair of electrons. The phenolic oxygen in tyrosine (choice A), the alcoholic oxygen in serine (choice D), and the thiolic sulfur in cysteine (choice B) all have two lone pairs of electrons.

3. **B** According to the figure in the passage, hydrogen bonding does help to stabilize oxyhemerythrin, so choice A is a true statement. Choice C is also a true statement: CO_2 is not highly poisonous and does not destroy metal complexes. Finally, the carboxylate group constitutes a classic example of a resonant system; each oxygen bears a –0.5 charge, so the statement in choice D is also true. However, as far as bond lengths go, triple bonds are shorter than double bonds, and double bonds are shorter than single bonds. Therefore, when binding to hemocyanin, the O–O bond length increases, which means choice B is the correct answer.

4. **D** The number one rule in chemistry is that all atoms want an full valence shell (for most atoms, this means an octet of electrons). Choice A is an incorrect structure, since not enough valence electrons have been accounted for (CO has 4 + 6 = 10 electrons, not 8). Moreover, in choices B and C, the carbon atom does not have an octet. Therefore, choice D, where all valence electrons are accounted for and both atoms have an octet, is correct.

Passage 12

1. **B** The formal charge of an atom equals the number of valence electrons that element should have based upon the periodic table minus the number of valence electrons around that atom in this particular case—keeping in mind that each covalent bond counts as one electron. So in the case of oxygen, the formal charge is $6 - 7 = -1$, and in the case of nitrogen, the formal charge is $5 - 4 = +1$. The correct answer is choice B.

2. **C** The oxygen atom in Structure A has three groups of electrons (two nonbonding, one bonding; double bonds only count once), so it uses three orbitals—one s and two p's: its hybridization is sp^2. The oxygen atom in Structure B has four groups of electrons, so its hybridization is sp^3.

3. **A** The shape of urea is determined by the geometry of the central atom (carbon atom). Since the

carbon atom has three groups of bonding electrons, the geometry and shape of urea are trigonal planar.

4. D   Structures B and C give the C–O bond some single bond character (make it longer) and both C–N's double bond character (make them shorter). The correct answer is not listed, so the best answer is choice D.

5. D   The passage tells us that urea is a by-product of protein metabolism. Since proteins are nothing more than long chains of amino acids, the best answer is choice D. Furthermore, carbohydrates, lipids, and fatty acids are all molecules that contain few (or no) nitrogen atoms.

6. B   The mass percent of carbon equals the mass of carbon divided by the total mass of urea. Since the mass of carbon is 12 g/mol, and the total mass of urea is 60 g/mol, the mass percent of carbon in urea is 12/60 = 20%.

Passage 13

1. C   The passage tells us that these are all electrophilic substitutions and that the term "electrophilic" means an atom or molecule with some positive charge. So the species which is attacking the ring must have some positive character (this eliminates choices A and B). Since it was a NO_2 group which was substituted onto benzene, it must have been the nitronium ion, NO_2^+ which was responsible for the ring attack.

2. A   If you determine the Lewis structure for the nitrate ion, you should get

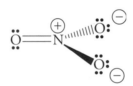

An atom that has three groups of atoms has a trigonal planar geometry—if all of the electron groups are bonding, then the shape and the geometry of a molecule are the same (choice A).

3. D   According to the rule of thumb alluded to in this question (which, by the way, works fine if you remember the most notable exception: hydrocarbon substituents are *ortho-para* directing even though they have no nonbonding electrons!), a *meta* directing group should have an atom with no nonbonding electrons directly attached to the ring. Since the nitrogen, oxygen, and fluorine atoms in all of these choices have nonbonding electrons, the correct answer must be phthalic acid, choice D—the carbon in a carboxylic functional group has no lone pairs.

4. D   Resonance structures are structures which only differ in the distribution of electrons, not in the location of atoms. So while choices A, B, and C all are resonance structure for benzoic acid, choice D represents a structural isomer of benzoic acid (an H has moved).

5. C   The fact that the *ortho* isomer has a lower melting point than the *para* isomer means that the

ortho isomer is experiencing fewer intermolecular interactions than the *para* isomer. The structures for these isomers are:

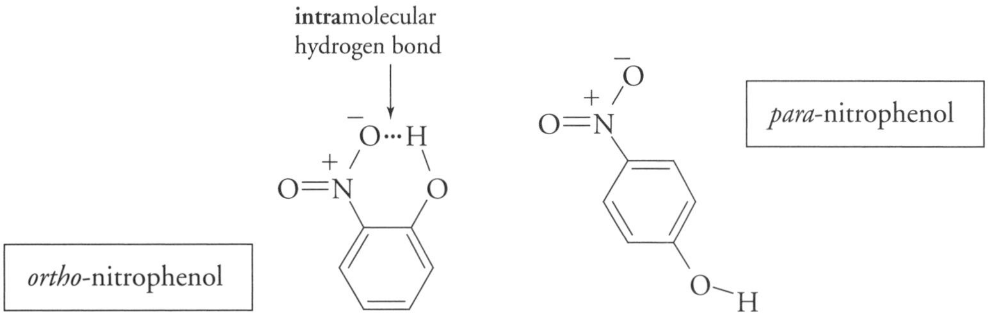

Due to their proximity in the *ortho* structure, the nitro and hydroxy groups of the *ortho* isomer spend a significant amount of their time interacting with one another, and not with the nitro and hydroxy group of other *ortho*-nitrophenol molecules.

6. **C**   The initial and final hybridizations of the carbon atom at the site of substitution is sp^2 because in these structures, the carbon atom has three groups of electrons (therefore, it needs to use three orbitals, $s + p + p$). However, in all of the intermediate structures, this carbon atom has four groups of electrons; the hybridization of an atom with four groups of electrons is $s + p + p + p = sp^3$.

Passage 14

1. **C**   Hemoglobin is a tetramer, meaning it consists of four individual protein chains clumped together. Each hemoglobin unit has one iron–oxygen binding site, so each hemoglobin macroprotein has four iron-oxygen binding sites (choice A is a correct statement and can be eliminated). Peptide bonds are amide bonds between amino acids (choice B is correct and can be eliminated). The term *hydrolysis* means, to cleave (*lysis*) with water (*hydro*). All types of hydrolysis require the presence of water (choice D is correct and can be eliminated). However, an ester bond exists between a carboxylic acid (like a fatty acid) and an alcohol; a fat is a molecule in which three fatty acids are linked to a molecule of glycerol (a triol alcohol, not an amine; choice C is wrong and the correct answer choice).

2. **B**   It is a general rule that the best ligands are those of nitrogen and carbon which have a excess of electron density (i.e., Lewis bases). The fact that chloroamine is a better ligand than ammonia tells us that the nitrogen atom in chloroamine must have more electron density than in ammonia. Choice A is the opposite of this idea. Choice C is incorrect because neutral halogens are very poor ligands. While the rationale used in choice D sounds good, it leads to the conclusion that ammonia should be a better ligand than chloroamine.

3. **A**   Ammonium chloride, NH_4Cl, is ionic, and at room temperature, all ionic compounds are solids.

4. **D**   Part of the danger associated with ammonia and carbon monoxide stems from the fact that these compounds are better ligands than O_2—that's why they replace oxygen in hemoglobin

(choice A is wrong). Molecules with N–H, O–H, or F–H bonds always experience hydrogen bonding (choice B is wrong). The nitrogen atoms in hydrazine have a lone pair of electrons, hence, hydrazine can be expected to be a good ligand like ammonia (choice C is wrong). The fact that ammonia is a gas at room temperature (as revealed by the passage) tells us that the vapor pressure of ammonia must be greater than atmospheric pressure (760 torr).

5. **D** A molecule which has a trigonal pyramid shape is one that has three groups of bonding electrons and one group of nonbonding electrons.

| bent | linear | trigonal planar | trigonal pyramid |

The correct answer is choice D.

6. **C** The electronegativity of the atoms determines the distribution of electrons in a molecule. Oxygen is more electronegative than chlorine, so it will never evenly share electron density with chlorine atoms (choice D is eliminated). Furthermore, if extra electron density is to be had in a bond with chlorine, oxygen will monopolize that electron density (choice B is eliminated). In the hypochlorite ion, oxygen has a –1 charge, and chlorine has no charge.

Passage 15

1. **D** No one expects you to memorize the wavelengths associated with each color (although it might come in handy). You have to be a little clever to get this one. Protoporphyrin IX has its maximum absorbance at 405 nm. The passage said that green light has a wavelength of 550 nm, so the color absorbed by protoporphyrin IX has a higher energy. There are only two colors that have more energy than green: blue and violet. Therefore, protoporphyrin IX will have the color opposite to either blue or violet—orange or yellow. Since only yellow appears as a choice, the correct answer must be choice D, and 405 nm must correspond to violet light.

2. **A** If the ferrous ion fits snugly into the porphyrin's donut hole, then larger ions will not fit inside and form stable complexes. Based upon the periodic trend of sizes of neutral atoms, atomic size increases as one moves down or to the left in the periodic table. However, there is a second consideration: For each electron an atoms loses, its size contracts. So we can say that the ion with the least positive charge, and the furthest to the left and bottom of the periodic table, should be the largest. Potassium ion must be the largest.

3. **A** When protoporphyrin IX chelates the ferrous ion, the two hydrogen atoms that are bonded to the nitrogen (called amino hydrogens) are lost as H^+ ions. The acidity of a solution is proportional to the concentration of hydrogen ions. Therefore, the pH of this solution decreases, and it becomes more acidic (choice A). (This question was just meant to start warming you up for the study of acids, bases, and buffers that lies ahead.)

4. **B** Whenever a metal ion forms coordinate covalent bonds with a ligand, this constitutes a Lewis acid–base reaction (choice B). No indication of precipitates was referred to in the passage (choice A). The iron ion has a charge of +2 before and after it is chelated, so choice C is eliminated. As for choice D, an argument can be made that the formation of heme is a double displacement reaction (two hydrogen ions are removed), yet examples of single and double displacement reactions are most often substitution reactions in organic chemistry such as S_N1 and S_N2 reactions.

5. **C** This is a lesson in keeping track of oxidation numbers. The problem says that catalase oxidizes (removes electrons from) oxygen atoms in certain compounds. So you have to find the reaction where the oxidation number of the oxygen atoms increases. In terms of oxidation numbers, oxygen in choice A goes from 0 to –2, in choice B it goes from 0 to –2, in choice C it goes from –1 to 0, and in choice D it goes from –1 to –2. So the answer is C. (Just a bit of info: Catalase is responsible for making oxygen gas from hydrogen peroxide. So the next time you cut yourself and you apply "peroxide," just remember that the fizzing and foaming is catalase's way of saying "hi.")

6. **D** Hydrogen bonds can only exist between N–H, O–H, F–H, and another N, O, or F. Therefore, since oxygen gas is providing the O, tyrosine with a hydroxyl group attached to a benzene ring, must provide the O–H (choice D).

Passage 16

1. **D** A radical has an odd number of electrons. Nitrous oxide (laughing gas) has 5 + 5 + 6 = 16 valence electrons (after all, that's why nitrous oxide is funny, not fatal), dichlorine oxide has 7 + 7 + 6 = 20, and hydrogen peroxide has 1 + 1 + 6 + 6 = 14, so none of these are radical species (choices A, B, and C are eliminated). Bromine trioxide, having 7 + 6 + 6 + 6 = 25 valence electrons, is a radical.

2. **B** A molecule with bond angles of 120° must be trigonal planar, and any trigonal planar molecule must have sp^2 hybridization:

3. **C** Radicals have atoms that violate the prime directive of chemistry, "All atoms want an octet." Radical species always have an atom which does not have a complete octet (choice C); this is why radicals remove electrons from other molecules. Radicals do not necessarily have to be highly charged (choice A), nor do they have to involve electronegative atoms (choice B). Furthermore, since radicals have an unpaired electron, they must always have a net magnetic spin equal to that electron, ±1/2 (choice D).

4. **B** As we have alluded to above, radicals remove electrons from other atoms to complete their octets. Therefore, the radicals are acting as oxidants/oxidizing agents (choice B). An electrolyte is a compound that dissociates into ions when it dissolves in water; radicals don't dissociate (choice C). A Lewis base is a molecule that donates a pair of nonbonding electrons to form a covalent bond with another atom; as we have seen, radicals don't give up electrons (choice D).

5. **C** Stability and energy are inverses. So the fact that the hydroxyl radical is reactive and not stable means that it has more energy than the vitamin A radical (choice A). It is certainly true that the hydroxyl radical has much less mass, so choice B is wrong. The hydroxyl radical forms hydrogen bonds with water, hence its high solubility in water (choice D). Highly conjugated (double bonds between every other carbon atom) molecules have a tremendous potential for resonance stability. Therefore, in the vitamin A radical, almost all of the carbon atoms share the burden of having an incomplete octet (it's sort of like playing "hot potato" with the unpaired electron). Therefore, the reactivity of the radical is much less, and poses little danger to sensitive structures in the cell (choice C). Eventually, enzymes use reducing agents to eliminate the radical altogether by pairing it up with another electron.

Passage 17

1. **B** The Lewis structure for the carbonate ion is

Since it has three groups of electrons, all of which are bonding electrons, the geometry and the shape of the molecule is trigonal planar.

2. **D** Just like its family member carbon when bonding to four atoms, silicon has a tetrahedral geometry. So while each Si–F bond is very polar, the overall molecule has no dipole moment; this eliminates choice A and shows that D is correct. Coordination complexes are covalently bonded complexes between nonmetal ligands and a transition metal ion. Silicon is not a transition metal, it is a metalloid (choice B). While the Si–F bond is very polar, it is not ionic in nature (choice C).

3.   C   In order to find the white (no color) compound, we have to find the metal ion with ten d electrons or with no d electrons. Note the electronic configurations for the following metal ions:

Cu(II): [Ar] $3d^9$ (colored blue)

Fe(II): [Ar] $3d^6$ (colored pale green)

Ti(IV): [Ar] (white, no color)

Mn(III): [Ar] $3d^4$ (colored pale pink)

So the correct answer is choice C, TiO_2. (Titanium dioxide is used as a white paint pigment; it is very likely that your walls at home are covered with titanium dioxide.)

4.   D   The passage indicates that sodium and calcium carbonate decompose to form their respective oxides:

$$Na_2CO_3 + Heat \rightarrow Na_2O + CO_2(g)$$

$$CaCO_3 + Heat \rightarrow CaO + CO_2(g)$$

The side product of this reaction must be carbon dioxide, CO_2.

Passage 18

1.   C   The diagram in the passage illustrates that the presence of the ligands increases the energy of two of the d orbitals more than the other three. Therefore, the five d orbitals are no longer degenerate, meaning that they are no longer equal in potential energy (choice C).

2.   C   The terms "stability" and "energy" are applied, loosely speaking, oppositely. That is, having lots of energy means having little stability (and vice versa). Since the crystal field increases the energy of the d_{z2} and d_{x2-y2} orbitals, it decreases their stability.

3.   B   Just as the (mass) density of a substance is its mass per unit volume, the charge density of a molecule is its charge per unit volume. Both ions have a −1 charge (choices A and C are eliminated), yet the fluoride ion is smaller and has less volume than the iodide ion. Therefore, the charge per unit volume of the fluoride ion is greater than that of the iodide ion (choice B). Keep in mind that basicity increases as one moves up and to the left in the periodic table, so fluoride is a stronger base than iodide is (choice D is incorrect).

4.   D   The spectrochemical series indicates that ammonia is a stronger ligand than either water or fluoride (choices A and C are eliminated). The passage also indicates that the crystal field energy increases as the positive charge of the metal ion increases. Since ammonia is a neutral molecule, we conclude that the chromium ions in choices B and D have charges of +2 and +3, respectively. Therefore, choice D is best.

5. **B** If a non-emitting object has the color blue, it must be absorbing blue's opposite color: orange.

6. **B** Light may appear yellow if it's emitting more yellow photons than violet photons while emitting equal amounts (if any) of all the other wavelengths of visible light. The question implies that one color is emitted more than all the others; it has to be yellow (choice B) in the case of a yellow lamp.

Passage 19

1. **C** There is no such thing as the hydrophobic or hydrophilic force. Nonpolar molecules interact via van der Waals forces, and polar molecules interact through dipole and van der Waals forces, although the later is very weak compared to the former and therefore usually ignored.

2. **D** Choices A, B, and C involve functions which only require exposure to the extracellular medium (note that choice C is intercellular anchoring, which means between cells). Structures which actively transport molecules through the cell membrane must, themselves, extend through the membrane; choice D does not.

3. **C** The role of the ion conducting channel is to conduct ions. Ions are extremely hydrophilic due to their strong ion–dipole interactions with water. Therefore the residues which constitute the channel should also be hydrophilic; this eliminates choice A. Moreover, any residues with ionic character should attract cations, not repel them; this eliminates choice B. Choice C is better than choice D because the carboxylate ion has a negative charge.

4. **A** Passive diffusion rate of an ion through a membrane is primarily a function of size. Due to their very small size, protons can easily diffuse through most membranes. All other ions are much larger and therefore have slower diffusion rates.

5. **C** Since the question refers to an organic molecule, the quickest way to determine the oxidation state of any atom is to count the number of bonds that atom has with a more electronegative atom, and then from this number, subtract the number of bonds the atom has with a less electronegative atom. In the case of phosphorous, this would give a $5 - 0 = +5$ oxidation state.

6. **B** Choice A is incorrect because the anionic heads of the phosphates would repel one another if closely grouped together; such an arrangement would therefore be very unstable (high energy). Choice C leaves something to be desired because transmembrane proteins require hydrophobic residues to anchor it in the hydrophobic interior of the membrane. If, as choice C suggests, the protein was composed entirely of hydrophilic residues, it would be quite content to float around in the cytoplasm (as some proteins do). Note: No natural protein is composed entirely of hydrophilic residues. Choice D is wrong because a mixture of H-bonding and ion–dipole attraction is responsible for the hydrous shell in this case. (H-bonding arises from interactions like $HO-H\cdots:O=PO_3-R$.) Choice B is the best answer because the anions have to be electrostatically balanced by an equal number of cations which are abundant in solution.

Passage 20

1. **C** The second diagram in the passage indicated that the energy (space) between vibrational energy levels is much less than that between electronic energy levels. Therefore, if the energy gap between the first two electronic energy levels corresponds to UV photons, then the energy gap between the first two vibrational energy levels must correspond to photons of less energy. Infrared photons have several hundred times less energy than UV photons.

2. **C** When the molecule goes from the first excited ($v = 2$) vibrational energy level to the ground state ($v = 1$) energy level, it decreases in energy (according to the y axis!) by releasing energy to the surroundings (choices A and D are true). In all sciences, the terms energy (or reactivity) and stability are inverses of one another. Therefore, a molecule which decreases in energy increases in stability (choice B is okay). The energy required to break the covalent bond, called the bond dissociation energy, is the energy required to go from the occupied vibrational energy level to $v = \infty$. Less energy is required to go from the $v = 2$ to $v = \infty$ than to go from the $v = 1$ to $v = \infty$. Therefore, the vibrational transition $v = 2$ to $v = 1$ increases the energy required to break the bond.

3. **A** Even without ever seeing a Morse potential diagram, you should know that the stability of any system is inversely proportional to its energy (choice A). Morse potential diagrams indicate that as the energy of a vibrational energy level gets bigger, the change in length of the oscillating bond (the length of the horizontal vibrational line) increases (choice B is wrong). Furthermore, the spacing between these lines gets smaller and smaller as you move up to higher levels (choice C is wrong). Finally, choice D is incorrect because a catalyst decreases the activation energy of a reaction, but it never affects the thermodynamics (energy) of the overall process.

4. **B** This is a deceiving question because it doesn't really require you to consider a specific Morse potential diagram. For example, choices A and C, which are identical, suggest that the C=O bond is weaker than the C–O bond. You should know that a double bond is always stronger than a single bond (choices A and C are eliminated). Furthermore, choice D contradicts the passage—the passage says that all covalent bonds stretch and bend. The answer is choice B, which says that the average bond length of the C=O bond is less than the C–O bond; we don't need a Morse potential diagram to tell us this. The more bonding electrons that are shared between two atoms, the greater the bond strength, and the shorter the bond.

5. **B** Vibrational modes are the oscillatory movement of covalent bonds. In order to have a vibrating covalent bond, you need a covalent bond to vibrate! Neon, a noble gas, is a monatomic gas than never forms any covalent bonds (choice B). (The only noble gases that form any covalent bonds are krypton and xenon [and this occurs only under very exotic conditions].)

6. **B** The Lewis dot structure for nitrous oxide, N_2O is:

$$\overset{\ominus}{\underset{\cdot\cdot}{\overset{\cdot\cdot}{N}}} = \overset{+}{N} = \underset{\cdot\cdot}{\overset{\cdot\cdot}{O}}$$

While choice D is also an acceptable Lewis structure, it cannot be the correct answer because the question tells us that N_2O is not symmetric.

Passage 21

1. **B** None of these molecules are linear. The passage states that the number of normal modes of vibration is $3N - 6$ for non-linear molecules. If there are nine normal modes of vibration, $3N - 6 = 9$, and $N = 5$. Only methane, choice B, has 5 atoms.

2. **A** From the passage, stretching and bending are types of vibration, while translation and rotation are not. All vibrations can potentially produce peaks in IR spectra, so choices B, C, and D are eliminated. Changes in translational and rotational movements alone do not show up in IR.

3. **A** If $v = 0$ and h and u are constant, the equation for vibration energy reduces as follows:

$$E = \left(v + \frac{1}{2}\right)\left(\frac{h}{2\pi}\right)\sqrt{\frac{k}{u}}$$

$$E \propto \sqrt{k}$$

   The energy of the ground state is proportional to the square root of the force constant k. The passage states that k is larger for stronger bonds, and the bond in N_2 is strongest since it has the highest bond energy (see Table 1). N_2 must have the highest vibrational energy in the ground state.

4. **D** The passage states that only those normal modes of vibration that produce a change in the dipole moment of a molecule will absorb IR light. Since O_2 has no dipole, it will not have any peaks in an IR spectrum. Note that while the molecule SO_3 as a whole has no dipole, its individual bonds do have detectable dipoles.

5. **B** Deuterium (D) has one proton, one neutron, and an atomic mass of 2. For D_2, $u = (2 \times 2)/(2 + 2) = 1$. For H_2, $u = 1 \times 1/(1 + 1) = 1/2$. Since v, h, and k are all constant in this comparison, the vibration energy equation in the passage reduces as follows:

$$E = \left(v + \frac{1}{2}\right)\left(\frac{h}{2\pi}\right)\sqrt{\frac{k}{u}}$$

$$E \propto \frac{1}{\sqrt{u}}$$

   The ratio of this energy for D_2 to H_2 is:

$$\frac{E_{D_2}}{E_{H_2}} = \frac{\dfrac{1}{\sqrt{1}}}{\dfrac{1}{\sqrt{1/2}}} = \frac{1}{\sqrt{2}}$$

   The quantity must be greater than 0.5 but less than 1, so only choice B is possible.

6. **D** A molecule essentially exists as an average of its resonance structures. No individual resonance structure exists in isolation. In nitrate there are three bonds of equal strength, containing about 33% N=O double bond character and about 67% N—O single bond character. Therefore, there will be only one stretch peak in the IR spectrum intermediate to the N—O and N=O stretches that accounts for all three of these bonds in nitrate.

Passage 22

1. **C** Given the reaction

    propylamine + cyclohexanone → imine + water,

    one mole of water will be produced for every one mole of imine. The yield of imine in the reaction of 2-to-1 propylamine-to-cyclohexanone is 78%. The percent yield represents the fractional conversion of the limiting reactant to product. In this case, the limiting reactant is 1 mol of cyclohexanone, so 0.78 mol of imine and water are produced in this reaction. Since the mass of water is 18 g/mol, 0.78 mol of water has a mass of about 14 g.

2. **D** As alluded to in the previous solution, the theoretical yield of a reaction only depends upon the number of moles of the limiting reactant.

3. **D** Hydrogen bonding exists between hydrogen covalently bonded to F, N (as in the case of propylamine), or O (as in the case of water) and another F, O, or N atom. Therefore, both propylamine and cyclohexanone hydrogen bond with water (choice B is true). All hydrocarbons are essentially nonpolar and insoluble in polar solvents like water (choice C is true). If the boiling point of toluene is higher than water, then the vapor pressure of toluene near its boiling point must be less than that of water (choice A is true).

4. **D** The nitrogen in the imine has a nonbonding pair of electrons (choice A). All molecules have some degree of van der Waals interactions (choice B). The imine is not a rigidly symmetric molecule, so it will experience some weak dipole forces (choice C). Since there are no hydrogens bonded to F, O, or N, the imine product cannot experience hydrogen bonding with other imine molecules.

Passage 23

1. **C** ΔH_{rxn} is the difference between the total ΔH_f of the products and the total ΔH_f of the reactants. Thus,

    $$\Delta H_{rxn} = \Sigma(\Delta H_{f, products}) - \Sigma(\Delta H_{f, reactants}) = (-110.5 \text{ kJ/mol} + 0 \text{ kJ/mol}) - (0 \text{ kJ/mol} - 241.8 \text{ kJ/mol})$$

    $$= 131.3 \text{ kJ/mol}$$

2. **D** According to the data given with the question, the total energy released by the combustion of one mole of CO and one mole of H_2 is (283 kJ) + (241.8 kJ) = 525 kJ. Thus, if two moles of each are consumed, then the energy released is twice this value: 1050 kJ.

3. **B** According to Le Châtelier's principle, increasing the pressure shifts the reaction to the side with fewer gas molecules. The water gas reaction has one gas molecule on the reactant side but two on the product side. Therefore, the reaction will shift in the reverse direction, eliminating choices A and C. Since decreasing the number of gas molecules leads to a decrease in the entropy of the system, choice B is correct.

4. **D** Since the products have more energy than the reactants, this reaction must be endothermic.

5. **D** No calculation is required if you realize that the water gas reaction must involve an increase in entropy since the products (which are both gases) are more disorganized than the reactants (a solid and a gas). Thus, $\Delta S°$ must be positive.

6. **B** Choices A, C, and D can be eliminated, because these are all kinetic factors with no influence on the thermodynamics of the reaction. Since $\Delta G = \Delta H - T\Delta S$, the value of T (choice B) will affect ΔG.

Passage 24

1. **B** All of these choices sound good; A, C, and D are true statements. However, only the entropy of simple, chemically pure elements is zero at 0.0 K (choice B).

2. **A** The reaction $2\,H_2 + O_2$ produces 2 moles of H_2O. We use $\Delta G°_{rxn} = G°_{f\,(products)} - G°_{f\,(reactants)}$. Since pure elements in their standard state have $G°_f = 0$, $\Delta G°_{rxn} = 2G°_f(water) = -457.2\ kJ\cdot mol^{-1}$.

3. **C** The question tells us that oxidizing agents can be recognized because they have two or more highly electronegative atoms directly bonded together. Choices A and B only have one highly electronegative atom each (Br and N). Neither boron nor hydrogen are highly electronegative, and in fact BH_3 is a known reducing agent. Hydrogen peroxide is a powerful oxidizing agent because its structure is H–O–O–H; the two oxygen atoms are directly bonded together (choice C). This rule is very useful; you might want to keep it in mind!

4. **C** If each H atom has an oxidation state of +1, the total of the oxidation states of the two N atoms must be −4 (so that the molecule has a net oxidation state of zero). Therefore, each N atom has an oxidation state of −2.

5. **D** Since $\Delta H_{rxn} = H_{f\,(products)} - H_{f\,(reactants)}$, we have the following for the reaction of hydrogen and bromine to make hydrogen bromine:

$$\Delta H_{rxn} = 2\cdot H_{f\,(HBr)} - (H_{f\,(H2)} + H_{f\,(Br2)})$$

The question tells us that $H_{f\,(HBr)} = -36\ kJ/mol$. H_f for a pure element in its natural phase is 0.0 kJ/mol at standard conditions. So $H_{f\,(H2)} = 0\ kJ/mol$. However, the natural phase of bromine under standard conditions is liquid, not gas—so in this question $H_{f\,(Br2)} \neq 0.0\ kJ/mol$. Therefore, unless we are told what the $H_{f\,(Br2)}$ for gas phase bromine is, we cannot calculate ΔH_{rxn}.

Passage 25

1. **C** There are a few ways that you can get the right answer. In this case, the best way is to realize that nitrogen has a greater electronegativity than carbon, hence, it will have its oxidation state of choice which is –3. The next step is to recall that the charge of an atom or molecule equals the sum of all the oxidation numbers in that atom or molecule. Since the cyanide molecule has a charge of –1, the oxidation state of the carbon atom must be +2.

2. **A** The passage indicated that the strength of the coordinate covalent bond of a ligand is proportional to the energy of the absorbed photon of the colored solution. Recall that violet is the most energetic photon in the visible region. According to the color wheel, a solution absorbing violet light will appear yellow; both yellow solutions involve complexes formed with the cyanide ion.

3. **D** Choice A disagrees with the chemist's data that indicate chromium halide complexes absorb red light (they are green in color) and chromium hydrate complexes absorb yellow light (they are violet in color). Since the energy of the absorbed light is proportional to the binding strength of the ligand, water is a better ligand that halide anions. Choice B is wrong: All haloacids are very water soluble, and with the exception of HF, are strong acids (which means they completely dissociate in water). Choice C is also incorrect because a Lewis base is a molecule that can donate a nonbonding pair of electrons (which loosely translates into the fact that any molecule with a nonbonding pair of electrons is a Lewis base to some degree). As the data indicated, halide anions are weaker ligands than water, so more of them are required in solution before they can exclude water from the complex.

4. **C** The hexamine copper(II) complex is simply a Cu^{2+} ion surrounded by an octahedron of six ammonia molecules. The charge of the total complex is just the sum of the charge of all of its constituents. Therefore, the charge of the entire complex equals +2 + 6(0) = +2.

5. **B** The term "ligation" describes the process of forming a coordinate covalent bond between an electron pair donor (ligand) and an electron pair acceptor (metal ion). Therefore, ligation is nothing more than a Lewis acid–base reaction (choice B).

6. **C** Based on the passage, we can determine that the colors absorbed by the following compounds are as follows:

Compound	Apparent color	Absorbed
choice A	violet	yellow
choice B	orange	blue
choice C	blue	orange
choice D	yellow	violet

Orange has the longest wavelength among these choices.

Passage 26

1. **D**   The note under Table 1 states that water has a higher heat of vaporization *per gram* than mercury.

2. **A**   Since ethanol is already a gas here, choice B is eliminated. Choice C is wrong since cooling a substance decreases the average kinetic energy of its molecules, and choice D is wrong since vapor pressure increases as the temperature increases. The answer must be choice A. According to Table 1, the boiling point of ethanol is 78.3°C at standard pressure. When the temperature of a sample of ethanol gas is cooled below this temperature, the most likely result is that the gas will condense into a liquid.

3. **B**   Vapor pressure always increases as the temperature increases, so choices C and D are eliminated. According to Table 1, diethyl ether has a lower boiling point than ethanol, which means that diethyl ether must have a higher vapor pressure than ethanol. The graph in choice B is best.

4. **D**   Boiling occurs when the vapor pressure of a liquid equals the atmospheric pressure. All liquids boil at lower temperatures at higher altitudes because the atmospheric pressure decreases with increasing altitude.

5. **C**   Choices A and B can be eliminated because heat capacity is important when calculating a temperature change for a substance upon the addition of heat, but when a liquid vaporizes, it does so at a constant temperature. The energy associated with phase changes is due to the formation or cleavage of intermolecular forces. The energy required to vaporize a liquid is always greater than the energy to melt a solid, because all intermolecular forces must be broken in order to form a gas. Thus, choice C is the correct choice. The statement in choice D is irrelevant to phase change energetics.

6. **B**   Choice A is false, and all molecules experience some intermolecular forces, so choice C is wrong. Ethanol, with its –OH group, is more polar than diethyl ether and experiences hydrogen bonding. Thus, choice B is correct.

Passage 27

1. **A**   Sublimation is the phase change from solid to gas. Segments AB and BC represent solid–gas phase boundaries.

2. **C**   Since ΔH_{fusion} (the energy required to cause the solid-to-liquid phase change) for sulfur is 38.1 J/g, the total amount of energy required to melt 50 g of solid sulfur would be (50 g)(38.1 J/g) = 1905 J.

3. **D**   According to the phase diagram, liquid sulfur cannot be formed at temperatures below 119°C. Therefore, the phase transitions at 100°C cannot include liquid (eliminating choices A and B). Moving up along a vertical line at 100°C, the correct phases are vapor, then monoclinic solid, then rhombic solid.

4. **C** If the combustion of monoclinic sulfur releases 0.1 kJ/mol more energy than the combustion of rhombic sulfur, then S(monoclinic) must have 0.1 kJ/mol more energy locked up inside than S(rhombic) has. So, converting S(rhombic) to S(monoclinic) would require adding an extra 0.1 kJ/mol: choice C.

5. **A** At STP ($T = 0°C$, $P = 1$ atm), the phase diagram shows that the most stable form of sulfur is S(rhombic).

6. **C** If V, n, and R are constants, then the ideal gas law, $PV = nRT$, implies that P is proportional to T. If the temperature is increased, then the pressure must increase, so choice A cannot be correct. Since the absolute temperature increased by a factor of (473 K)/(373 K), which is about 1.25, the answer must be C. (Note: Choice D can be ruled out since 473/373 is less than 2, and choice B can be ruled out since 473/373 is not *too* close to 1.)

Passage 28

1. **D** The gas phase is favored at low pressure and high temperature, which is represented by the lower right portion of a phase diagram. This is Region Z in Figure 1.

2. **B** A liquid will boil when its vapor pressure equals the ambient pressure.

3. **D** The addition of heat energy to a substance can be used either to increase its temperature or to break intermolecular forces (possibly leading to a phase change). Since the researcher measured no temperature change, the answer must be choice D.

4. **C** At constant pressure, increasing the temperature moves us horizontally to the right across the phase diagram. This implies that the phase changes from solid to gas, or, if the pressure is high enough, from solid to liquid to gas. In either case, such phase changes require the input of energy (positive ΔH) and result in greater disorganization (positive ΔS).

5. **A** The solid/gas phase transition occurs along the AB segment, not the AC one, so choice B can be eliminated. Choice D comments on the boiling points of the substances which occur along the AD line segments for each substance. Choice C is a false statement as water is the bent molecule and CO_2 is the linear one. For this reason, and the subsequent three dimensional structures the molecules of each compound make in the solid phase, choice A is the best answer. The open crystal lattice of water due to its structured arrangement of hydrogen bonds leaves large holes between molecules, giving solid water a lower density than its liquid phase. The solid–liquid phase boundary line in the phase diagram for virtually all substances has a positive slope. However, the solid–liquid phase boundary line in the phase diagram for H_2O has a negative slope, because the densest phase of H_2O is the liquid phase.

Passage 29

1. **C** The passage states that the half-life of methane is 7 years. Starting with 100 percent and dividing by 2 for each half-life, six half-lives would leave 1.5 percent of the methane remaining, and seven half-lives would leave 0.8 percent of the methane remaining. Therefore, it would require 42 to 49 years, making answer choice C the correct answer.

2. **C** The pressure at sea level is 1 atm ≈ 100 kPa = 1×10^5 Pa. According to Table 1, nitrogen comprises approximately 80 percent of atmospheric air, thus the partial pressure of nitrogen at sea level is approximately $(0.8)(1 \times 10^5 \text{ Pa}) = 8 \times 10^4$ Pa.

3. **B** The passage states that the density of air is 1.2 kg/m³ and that the density drops by 50 percent every 5.5 km. Therefore, at 8.8 km, the density will be between 25 to 50 percent of the density at sea level, or 0.3–0.6 kg/m³. Choice B is the only answer in this range.

4. **A** Since rate of effusion is inversely proportional to the square root of mass, the gas with the smallest mass will have the highest rate of effusion. Thus, N_2 (28 g/mol) will escape fastest.

5. **B** The passage states that the limit between outer space and the atmosphere is not definite, so choice A is a true statement. The passage also states that the mass of the atmosphere is 5×10^{18} kg, and 75 percent of this (3.75×10^{18} kg) is 11 km from the surface of the earth. Therefore, choice C is also a true statement. Water vapor was listed as a greenhouse gas in the last paragraph, thus choice D is a true statement. Although the majority of ozone is located in the ozone layer, the passage states that concentrations of ozone are 2–8 ppm. To be the primary component, concentrations would have to exceed 500,000 ppm. Choice B is a false statement and therefore the correct answer.

6. **A** STP is 1 atm ≈ 100 kPa and 0°C = 273 K. Solve for the new pressure at the mesosphere temperature given in the passage (–100°C = 173 K) using the combined gas law (since volume is constant, V drops out of the equation):

$$\frac{P_1}{T_1} = \frac{P_2}{T_2}$$

$$P_2 = \frac{T_2 P_1}{T_1} = \frac{(173\text{K})(100\,\text{kPa})}{(273\,\text{K})} = (0.6)(100) = 60\,\text{kPa}$$

Note that pressure must decrease at decreased temperature, eliminating choice D.

Passage 30

1. **B** Intermolecular forces are essentially electrostatic, and the fundamental equation for the electrical interaction between charges is given by Coulomb's law, which is an inverse-square law. The force must decrease as the separation distance increases, so the answer is choice B.

2. **B** Since graphite is softer than diamond, it seems reasonable to conclude that the bonds in graphite are weaker; this eliminates choices C and D. The passage states that graphite is composed of planar sheets of carbon atoms, so choice B is a better answer here than choice A. With the information given to us in the passage, we cannot conclude that *all* the bonds in graphite are weak, only the intermolecular forces between the sheets of graphite.

3. **D** Benzene boils at 80.1°C, so choice A can be eliminated as the temperature range in question is far below the boiling point of the solvent. Choice C is a false statement. Choice B is also wrong since any comparable change in temperature (same magnitude for ΔT) will require the same amount of added heat, as long as the phase does not change. However, unlike the temperature interval from 25 to 35°C, the interval from 75 to 85°C involves a phase change from liquid to gas (see Figure 1), which greatly increases the amount of heat energy required.

4. **B** The cleavage of bonds, and intermolecular forces requires energy (eliminating choice A), while the formation of bonds and intermolecular forces releases energy (eliminating choice D). During condensation, intermolecular forces are being formed to hold the molecules together into a cohesive liquid. Choice B is best.

5. **B** The heat of vaporization is the energy required to convert a liquid at its boiling point temperature to a gas at the same temperature. Therefore, all the chemist needs to measure is the heat consumed between time 2 and the time at which the sample is entirely gaseous.

Passage 31

1. **C** Since *KE* equals $\frac{1}{2}mv^2$ and momentum *p* equals *mv*, the correct relationship between KE and momentum is

$$KE = \frac{1}{2}(mv)(v) = \frac{1}{2}pv \rightarrow 2 \times KE = pv$$

2. **B** If the total pressure within the rocket nozzle is 10 atm, and the contribution of water vapor is one-fourth this (2.5 atm), then the total pressure of the oxygen and hydrogen must be 7.5 atm. Furthermore, we're told that for maximum efficiency, the ratio of H_2 to O_2 should be two to one. Therefore, the partial pressure of 2 H_2 plus that of O_2 equals 7.5 atm. The partial pressure of 2 H_2 must be 5.0 atm.

3. **B** In a mixture of gases, the individual gases are assumed to have identical temperatures. Kinetic energy is proportional to temperature, so the kinetic energies of the gases in this mixture are identical (choice A). Avogadro's law states that gases occupy identical volumes under normal conditions. Therefore, we always assume that equal amounts of two gases occupy the same volume (choice C). Since the molecular mass of O_2 is sixteen times greater than that of H_2, the velocity of H_2 molecules should be four times greater than that of O_2:

$$KE_{O_2} = KE_{H_2} \rightarrow \frac{1}{2}(32\,\text{amu})(v_{O_2}^2) = \frac{1}{2}(2\,\text{amu})(v_{H_2}^2) \rightarrow \frac{v_{H_2}^2}{v_{O_2}^2} = \frac{32}{2} = 16 \rightarrow \frac{v_{H_2}}{v_{O_2}} = 4$$

The momentum of a gas molecule equals its mass times its velocity. So at any given temperature, the momentum of an O_2 molecule will be $16(1/4) = 4$ times greater than that of an H_2 molecule, not equal to it (choice D). The mole fraction of a gas is the number of moles of the gas divided by the total number of moles of the mixture. Since half the gas in the mixture is H_2, the mole fraction of H_2 is 0.5. Now, the mass fraction of a gas is the mass of the gas divided by the total mass of all the gases in the mixture. Since there are equal amounts of H_2 and O_2, the masses of the gases are 2 g/mol + 32 g/mol = 34 g/mol, and the mass fraction of H_2 is

$$\frac{\text{mass of } H_2}{\text{mass of mixture}} = \frac{2 \text{ g/mol}}{34 \text{ g/mol}} = \frac{1}{17} \approx 0.06$$

4. **A** This is a question that could have you do more work than is necessary. First, the explanation for the last question's choice D should have made it clear that two gases with different masses have the same *KE* at the same temperature, but not the same momentum! Eliminate choice D. We are asked to choose whether ten grams of helium or ten grams of neon will provide more rocket lift (momentum). We use the definition: momentum = *mv*. The total masses of both gases are the same (10 g), so we have to choose the gas with the greater velocity. Lighter gases at the same temperature have greater velocities, so the helium would provide more lift.

5. **C** The velocity of H_2 gas will be four times greater than that of O_2 gas at all temperatures, so choice A is okay. Since vaporization is an endothermic process (it absorbs heat), as the liquid vaporizes, it will cool the surroundings (the reason we perspire), so choice B is okay. The reverse process of vaporization, condensation, is an exothermic process (it releases heat), so choice D is fine. While hydrogen gas is extremely explosive when mixed with O_2, the combustion of H_2 requires an initial energy source to get the reaction going. If there is no initial energy source, the reaction between H_2 and O_2 is extremely slow (choice C).

6. **B** The major forces which cause gases to deviate from ideality are most influential when gas molecules are very close together and moving slowly. Therefore, gases are most ideal when their molecules are far apart and zipping around. These conditions correspond to low pressure and high temperature.

Passage 32

1. **A**   Using the phase diagram, water at 100 K and 10^2 torr is in the solid phase.

2. **D**   The last sentence in the passage tells us that high specific heat, heat of fusion, and heat of vaporization are due to strong intermolecular forces. Therefore, we are looking for the molecule with the strongest intermolecular forces. Methane (choice A), hydrogen sulfide (choice B), and oxygen (choice C) are all gases at room temperature because they have weak intermolecular forces. Methanol, CH_3OH, on the other hand, has stronger hydrogen bonding, which is responsible for making it a liquid at room temperature. Methanol has the highest heat of vaporization.

3. **D**   Before water can boil at one atmosphere pressure, it must be heated to 100°C. The amount of energy required to heat 20 g of water from 75°C to 100°C (a temperature change of 25°C or 25 K) is computed as follows:

    $$\text{Heat} = \text{mass} \times \text{specific heat} \times \text{temperature change}$$

    $$= mC_{sp}\Delta T = (20 \text{ g}) \times \frac{4.2 \text{ J}}{\text{g K}} \times 25 \text{ K}$$

    $$= 2100 \text{ J} = 2.1 \text{ kJ}$$

    Energy must then be added to convert the liquid at 100°C to gas at 100°C. This process is vaporization, and the required energy is

    $$\text{Heat} = \text{mass} \times \Delta H_{vap} = 20 \text{ g} \times \frac{40.7 \text{ kJ}}{\text{mol}} \times \frac{1 \text{ mol}}{18 \text{ g}} \approx 45 \text{ kJ}$$

    Therefore, the total energy cost is no less than about 2 + 45 = 47 kJ, so choice D is best.

4. **B**   Normally, the bond angles of a tetrahedral atom, like oxygen in water, are 109.5°. However, lone pairs of electrons repel one another, so the O–H bonds get squeezed a little closer than 109.5°: to 104.5°.

5. **A**   First, the question tells us that the solid phase is carbon's densest phase. So in the phase diagram for carbon, the top of the liquid-solid boundary line should slant to the right because the densest (solid in this case) phase will be favored under high pressures (this eliminates choices B and D). The question also says that the solid phase of carbon is divided into two domains, that of graphite and that of diamond, with the diamond phase being the denser. Therefore, diamond should be favored at high pressures and graphite at low pressures (choice A).

Passage 33

1. **C** Pressure is defined as force per unit area. The force exerted on the rocket pocket cushions is equal to the player's mass, 100 kg, times the acceleration of gravity, 9.8 m/s^2, times 0.98 (because the passage says that only 98% of the wearer's mass rests directly on the cushions). However, the problem wants the pressure for each cushion. Since there is one cushion under each foot, the total weight of the athlete is divided between the sneakers. The force on each cushion is

$$\text{force} = \frac{1}{2} \times 0.98 \times 100 \text{ kg} \times 9.8 \text{ m/s}^2,$$

so the pressure on each cushion is

$$\text{pressure} = \frac{\text{force}}{\text{area}} = \frac{\frac{1}{2} \times 0.98 \times 100 \text{ kg} \times 9.8 \text{ m/s}^2}{25 \text{ cm}^2}.$$

2. **A** We want the gas with the lowest condensation/boiling point (BP). Both water and bromine (choices B and C) are liquids at room temperature, so they are poor choices. Ammonia and carbon dioxide are gases, however, the boiling point of CO_2 is much lower than that of ammonia. If you didn't know this, you should have been able to predict that CO_2—with its dispersion forces—will have a lower BP than ammonia, with its hydrogen bonds.

3. **C** You need to know that the compression of a gas heats it up, and expansion cools the gas. With this in mind, as the subject lifts off the ground, the pressure that his weight is applying to the cushion decreases. As the external pressure of the cushion decreases, the cushion expands and cools (temperature goes down). However, once he lands again, the pressure is reapplied, and the gas is compressed, heating up to its original temperature (choice C).

4. **C** Choices A, B, and D are all legitimate shortcomings of water used in this capacity. The densest phase of water is the liquid phase. So when pressure is applied to water, it is the liquid phase that is favored, not the solid.

5. **C** The balanced equation for the decomposition of sodium azide to sodium nitride is

$$3 \text{ NaN}_3(s) \rightarrow \text{Na}_3\text{N}(s) + 4 \text{ N}_2(g).$$

So for every mole of sodium azide that decomposes, 4/3 = 1.3 moles of nitrogen are liberated. Since one mole of any ideal gas occupies 22.4 L at STP, the decomposition of one mole of sodium azide will produce (22.4 L) × (1.3) ≈ 30 L of nitrogen gas.

6. **B** The Lewis structure for the azide ion is

$$\overset{-}{\ddot{\text{N}}} = \overset{+}{\text{N}} = \overset{-}{\ddot{\text{N}}}$$

Since the central nitrogen has two groups of bonding electrons, its shape is linear.

Passage 34

1. **A** Choices B, C, and D are all correct statements; but the question asks for the false statement. Based upon the data in the passage, the cell shrank the most in Solution 1. This means that the net movement of water was out of the cell. Osmosis tells us that water diffuses into solutions with higher concentrations of solutes, so Solution 1 must be the most concentrated, not the most dilute, solution; the answer is choice A. A solution that causes water to flow out of a cell is hypertonic to the cell, one that causes water to flow into a cell is hypotonic to the cell, and one that causes no net movement of water is an isotonic solution.

2. **B** Cells do not dissolve in ordinary salt solutions (choice A)—if they did, oceanfront property wouldn't be as expensive as it is. The trend in the data suggests that the cells should have increased in size in Solution 4 (choice C). Animal cells, such as lymphocytes, do not have cell walls (choice D). The passage tells us that the solutions were labeled in order of concentration. We have figured out that Solution 1 is the most concentrated, so Solution 4 must be the most dilute. Solution 4 is a hypotonic solution because water is flowing into the cell. Cell membranes can only stretch so much, and when immersed in Solution 4, the cells ruptured.

3. **D** The equation $\Pi = i\Delta MRT$ indicates that osmotic pressure is proportional to temperature, in kelvins. Solution Y has a higher osmotic pressure than Solution X because its temperature, 303 K, is greater than that of Solution X, 288 K. The ratio of the osmotic pressure of Solution Y to that of Solution X is therefore 303 to 288, or about 1.1 to 1, so choice D is best.

4. **B** Since molarity, M, equals moles/volume, the equation $\Pi = iMRT$ may be written

$$\Pi = i(n/V)RT$$

So the osmotic pressure of a solution may be expressed in the form of the ideal gas law,

$$\Pi V = inRT$$

5. **C** In chemistry, all equilibria are dynamic equilibria. What this means here is that while the volumes of the liquids on each side of the membrane are not changing, individual water molecules are still passing through the membrane from both directions, just in equal numbers (choice A). The kinetic energy of a molecule is proportional to its temperature, and the equation in the passage makes it quite clear that osmotic pressure is indeed a function of temperature (choice B). Choice D has it backwards, since osmotic pressure opposes the direction of osmosis. The answer, choice C, correctly and succinctly describes the direction of osmosis (water flow).

Passage 35

1. **B**   If a noble gas like helium or argon is not readily available, chemists often use nitrogen as an inert gas. But how were you supposed to know this? Oxygen and fluorine are strong oxidizing agents and are very reactive gases (choices C and D). Hydrogen is a mild reducing agent, and is used to reduce organic compounds (choice A). Nitrogen, on the other hand, makes up 80% of the Earth's atmosphere because it has accumulated due to its lack of chemical activity. Furthermore, diatomic nitrogen has an internal triple bond that gives N_2 a very high bond dissociation energy, hence N_2 is not very reactive.

2. **D**   According to the data, as the temperature increases linearly, the vapor pressure increases exponentially because the vertical axis of the plot is logarithmic. (Choice B is certainly incorrect; it says that as the temperature goes up, VP should go down). For example, when the temperature is increased from 223 K (= –50°C) to 248 K (= –25°C), the VP goes up ten times. In fact, for every 25 K, the vapor pressure goes up by a factor of ten. The vapor pressure in increasing much, much faster than the temperature, therefore choices A and C are incorrect.

3. **C**   The interaction R–S–H⋯O–R is a dipole interaction (choice C). The electronegativity of sulfur is strong enough to polarize the S–H bond. This is not a hydrogen-bonding interaction; only hydrogen bonded to N, O, or F and interacting with another N, O, or F qualifies as hydrogen bonding (choice B). Ionic interactions only occur between ions; there are no ions here (choice A). While all atoms and molecules with electrons experience dispersion forces, in light of dipole interactions, their contribution is insignificant (choice D).

4. **B**   The molecular mass of pandorium is $(7 \times 12.0) + (2 \times 16.0) + (32.1) + (10 \times 1.0) \approx 158$ g/mol, and the mass of the sample is 5 grams. Therefore, in a 5-gram sample of pandorium, the

$$\text{number of moles} = \frac{5 \text{ g}}{158 \text{ g/mol}} \times \frac{1}{32} \times \frac{3}{100} = 0.03$$

5. **B**   Molecular mass and intermolecular forces determine a compound's physical state at a given temperature. Since all of these compounds have the same molecular mass (approximately), the compound that is most likely to be solid at room temperature is the one with the greatest intermolecular forces. All of the compounds except choice D will experience strong hydrogen bonding. However, the hydroxy groups (OH) in choices A and C lie close to one another, so they will spend a significant amount of the time hydrogen bonding intramolecularly (between OH's of the same molecule). In other words, the intermolecular hydrogen bonding of these compounds are significantly weakened. Choice B has an OH group in a position where it cannot interact intramolecularly, so it would be expected to have the most intermolecular hydrogen bonding and be a solid at room temperature.

Passage 36

1. **C** The activity coefficient is a correction factor that accounts for the anomalous behavior of concentrated solutions. In dilute solutions, the correction factor drops out; the activity coefficients equal 1.0, as the passage states in the last sentence.

2. **C** The plot of the solubility of calcite indicates that $[Ca^{2+}]$ is about 0.001 M at very dilute solutions. Since the K_{sp} for calcite equals $[Ca^{2+}]\cdot[CO_3^{2-}]$, and the concentrations of dissolved calcium and carbonate must be identical, then

$$K_{sp} = [Ca^{2+}]\cdot[CO_3^{2-}] = (0.001)^2 = (10^{-3})^2 = 10^{-6}$$

3. **D** The solubility of an insoluble salt will be lower in solutions if ions present in the salt are already in solution; this is the common ion effect. Therefore, calcium carbonate will be less soluble in solutions that already contain calcium or carbonate ions in solution.

4. **A** Ionic clustering is the principal cause of the departure of concentrated solution from ideality. The amount of ionic interaction in solution is proportional to the charge of the ions. Therefore, the ions that will experience minimal clustering, and thus, behave the most ideally, are ions with the least charge.

Passage 37

1. **A** Since the metal was initially submerged in boiling water, $T_{initial}$ (metal) = 100°C. At equilibrium,

$$T_{final} \text{ (metal)} = T_{final} \text{ (water)}$$

so using the equation given in the passage and the data for Metal #1 from the table, we find

$$C_p = \frac{-100\,g \times 4.2\,J/g°C \times (35.8°C - 25.6°C)}{20\,g \times (35.8°C - 100°C)} \approx \frac{(420)(10)}{(20)(64)}\frac{J}{g°C} \approx 3\frac{J}{g°C} = 3\frac{J}{g\cdot K}$$

2. **B** Since the table indicates that ΔT_{water} is the greatest and ΔT_{metal} is the smallest for Metal #2, the equation given for C_p tells us that this metal will have the greatest specific heat, C_p. In other words, Metal #2 is most resistant to changes in temperature.

3. **D** While coffee cups are useful for their purpose, they cannot handle extreme conditions. For this reason, specialized equipment is needed to operate under the conditions described in choices A, B, and C.

4. **D** The heat capacity of one gram of a substance is called the material's specific heat. Thus,

$$\frac{\text{heat capacity}}{\text{mass}} = \text{specific heat}$$

Passage 38

1. **D** While NAT acts as a reactant in the first reaction, it is regenerated in the last reaction. Therefore, NAT is a catalyst in the formation of chlorine gas (eliminating choices A and B). Since NAT is a solid, and the chlorine radical is a gas, NAT is a heterogeneous catalyst (choice D). Recall that a heterogeneous catalyst is one that has a phase different from the reactants which it is catalyzing.

2. **C** The destruction of O_3 is initiated by the photolysis of Cl_2. The bond energy of a Cl–Cl bond is 243 kJ/mol. If green light has an energy of 225 kJ/mol, then green and yellow light have too little energy to break the bond (choices A and B are eliminated). Furthermore, the questions asks for an answer that is in the visible spectrum—ultraviolet light is not (choice D is eliminated). The energy for blue light is between that of green and violet, i.e., about 240–260 kJ/mol.

3. **B** The third reaction is

    $$Cl\text{–}O(g) + Cl\text{–}O(g) \rightarrow Cl\text{–}O\text{–}O\text{–}Cl(g)$$

    An O–O bond must be formed because halogens only form one covalent bond at a time, while oxygen is happiest with two. The passage tells us that the O–O bond energy is 140 kJ/mol. Recall that the ΔH_{rxn} may be calculated using the bond enthalpies (energies):

    $$\Delta H_{rxn} = (\text{Bond enthalpies})_{reactants} - (\text{Bond enthalpies})_{products}$$

    To save yourself time, realize that to break a bond, we need to put in energy, and when a bond is formed, we get out energy. During this reaction an O–O bond is being formed, so the reaction releases 140 kJ/mol of energy. Therefore, $\Delta H_{rxn} = -140$ kJ/mol.

4. **A** The boiling point temperature of a liquid is that temperature at which the vapor pressure of the liquid is equal to the external pressure. Since the external pressure in the stratosphere is very low, water, and all other liquids, will boil at a much lower temperature than at standard pressure (water has a VP of 8 torr at 5°C): choice A is correct.

    The total pressure equals the sum of all of the partial pressures. If the total pressure of all the gases in the stratosphere is 8 torr, then there is no way that ozone can have a partial pressure greater than this (choice B is impossible). Lowering the pressure over a substance will never substantially increase the melting point of that substance (choice C is impossible). Evidently, gaseous reactions do occur at these low pressures—this passage has been written about them (choice D is eliminated).

5. **C** The rate law only depends upon the reactants in the rate-determining (slow) step of the overall reaction—the third reaction step takes hours, while all of the others take minutes or seconds (choices A, B, and D are all eliminated). The exponent in (the order of) the rate expression reflects the number of those types of molecules that must come together in the rate determining step. Since two ClO are reacting together, this rate law must be second order.

6. **D** This question is just testing if you remember what a catalyst does and does not do. A catalyst works by lowering the activation energy of the rate-determining step (choice A is true). A catalyst does not affect the overall thermodynamics (energy) of the catalyzed reaction (choice B is true). Finally, a catalyst only has a net effect on a reaction that is not at equilibrium, and in this case, the catalyst just increases the rate at which the system reaches equilibrium. Therefore, at equilibrium, the [O_3] has to be much less because the catalyst Cl is just working to get the system to equilibrium by destroying ozone (choice C is true).

Passage 39

1. **D** An open-end manometer measures the pressure within a vessel relative to atmospheric pressure (760 torr). So when the levels of liquid, Z and Z*, are equal (like in the diagram in the passage), the pressure inside the vessel is equal to 760 torr. Choices A and B do not relate the pressure of the gas to atmospheric pressure. Choices C and D only differ in sign. Intuition should lead you to the conclusion that when Z is lower than Z*, the internal pressure of the vessel must be greater than atmospheric pressure. Choice D is the only one that preserves this relationship.

2. **A** In this exercise, the scientist used the partial pressures of the gases as a measure of their concentration. Both the equilibrium and kinetic results were expressed in units of pressure. So the primary assumption here was that the pressure of a gas is directly proportional to the number of moles of that gas. In other words, choice A. Choices C and D are not applicable here because the temperature was constant throughout this experiment. Choice B is never an assumption, it is always a reality.

3. **B** In the case of an inert mixture of gases, the final pressure within the apparatus should be equal to the average of the pressure of each component,

$$\text{final total pressure} = (P_{\text{flask A}} + P_{\text{flask B}})/2,$$

since the volumes of Flasks A and B are equal. Throughout the experiment, the initial pressure of Gas F (in Flask A) was 450 torr. In the individual tests, the initial pressure within Flask B was 240 mm Hg, 620 mm Hg, and 450 mm Hg. So now, all we have to do is plug these numbers into the equation above in order to get the expected final pressure if the component gases did not react. Doing this, one gets 345 mm Hg, 535 mm Hg, and 450 mm Hg for each test. Since the measured final pressure in test 2 equals the expected final pressure of inert gases, Gases F and N must not have reacted.

4. **D** The very first step in determining a rate law is writing

$$\text{Rate} = k[\text{each reactant}]$$

So here, we write

$$\text{Rate} = k[F][P]$$

In order to determine the exponent (called order) for the reaction of gases F and P, we just need a total of three trials, with F at the same pressure in two trials and P at the same pressure in two trials. Based upon the table in the passage, the best trials to use to meet this criterion are trials 4, 5, and 6. Comparing trial 4 to trial 5, we see that the concentration of P is about the same, but the concentration of F twice as great. Looking at the rate of the reaction (Δpressure), we see that the rate of trial 4 twice as great as is trial 5. Therefore, $[F]$ is directly proportional (first order) to the rate of the reaction (eliminate choices B and C).

Now comparing trial 5 to trial 6, as the concentration of P is doubled, the rate increases by a factor of four. Therefore, $[P]^2$ is directly proportional (second order) to the rate of the reaction. So the rate law is

$$\text{Rate} = k[F]^1[P]^2$$

5. **D** The rate constant, k, is only a function of temperature (choice A is eliminated), steric orientation (choice B is eliminated), and activation energy (choice C is eliminated). The free energy of the reaction, ΔG, is a thermodynamic quantity, not a kinetic one.

6. **A** Mercury is one of two elements that are liquids at room temperature (bromine is the other). Therefore, if mercury is a liquid at room temperature (298 K), then its melting point must be lower than 298 K.

Passage 40

1. **C** The equilibrium expression for Reaction 1 is $K_{eq} = [NO][CO_2]/([NO_2][CO])$. Using the given equilibrium concentrations, we find

$$K_{eq} = (0.1)(0.02)/[(0.01)(0.1)] = 2$$

2. **C** The only way to change the value of the equilibrium constant is to change the reaction temperature, so choices A and B are eliminated. According to Le Châtelier's principle, adding more reactant shifts the reaction in the forward direction.

3. **B** Catalysts lower the activation energy, so choice D is immediately eliminated. NO is not consumed in Step 1b, so it is not an intermediate, eliminating choice A. (Note: NO_3 *is* an intermediate in Reaction 1.) The rate-determining step is always the slowest step, so choice B is correct.

4. **C** The passage states that photochemical processes were responsible for maintaining ozone levels in the past. Photochemistry is the study of the effects of light (electromagnetic radiation) on chemical reactions, so choice C is the answer.

5. **D** Reactions 2a and 2b indicate that each NO molecule is regenerated during its reaction with ozone. Therefore, NO is a catalyst since there is no net loss or gain during the reaction. Only choice D is true.

6. **B** Dynamic equilibrium implies that formation and destruction reactions are still occurring (eliminating choice D), but there is no net change in the amount of ozone. In order for this to be true, the rate at which ozone is formed must equal the rate at which it is destroyed.

Passage 41

1. **D** First, note that choice A is wrong since it would imply a constant rate of reaction, independent of [HI], but the data indicate that this is not true. To obtain the rate law, we must compare trials and determine how changes in the initial concentration of the reactant affect the initial rate of the reaction. Comparing Trials 1 and 2, we see that [HI] increased by a factor of 2 and the reaction rate increased by a factor of $4 = 2^2$. Therefore, the reaction is second order, so the rate law is given by Rate = $k[\text{HI}]^2$.

2. **A** The passage states that Reaction 1 is exothermic, so the energy of the products must be less than the energy of the reactants; this eliminates choices C and D. The passage also states that the activation energy for the Pt-catalyzed reaction (59 kJ/mol) is less than the activation energy of the Au-catalyzed reaction (105 kJ/mol). This means that the energy "hump" from the reactants to the activated complex should be smaller for the Pt-catalyzed reaction than for the Au-catalyzed reaction. This is shown in the graph in choice A.

3. **A** Changing the temperature will affect the kinetics and thermodynamics of this reaction. First, an increase in temperature always results in an increase in the initial rate of the forward reaction. Second, since the reaction is exothermic, Le Châtelier's principle predicts that increasing the temperature will then shift the reaction to the left, resulting in an increase in [HI].

4. **D** The passage states that light with a wavelength less than 327 nm (which equals 3.27×10^{-7} m) can photolyze HI. Such wavelengths include ultraviolet light, but not visible or infrared.

5. **B** The dissolution equilibrium for HI is

$$\text{HI}(aq) \rightleftharpoons \text{HI}(g)$$

Since a saturated solution is at equilibrium, the question is asking which perturbation could result in shifting the equilibrium to the right. Choice A is eliminated since catalysts change the rate of a reaction, not the position of equilibrium. Choices C and D are eliminated because decreasing the amount of HI(aq) or increasing the pressure would shift the reaction to the left. This leaves choice B.

6. **C** According to the mechanism given in the passage, HI dissociates into H, and then two H re-associate to form H_2. Therefore, during the course of the reaction, the speciation of hydrogen should evolve from HI to H to H_2. This eliminates choice A. By stoichiometry, the amount of H_2 should end up being half the original amount of HI, so choice C is best.

Passage 42

1. **C** Since an oxygen atom has eight electrons, choices B and D are immediately eliminated, since they account for nine and seven electrons, respectively. The configuration given in choice A is that of an oxygen atom in the ground state, not an excited state. The answer must be choice C.

2. **D** Excitation of electrons in any atom requires the absorption of light (so choice B cannot be correct). The passage states that dark bands are associated with absorption spectra and bright bands with emission spectra. Thus, choice D is the only choice that makes sense.

3. **A** According to the data given with the question, bond strength increases as the radius of the halide atom decreases (choice A). This is primarily due to the fact that the Coulomb force is inversely proportional to the square of the separation distance between the charges; decreasing the distance increases the force of attraction.

4. **D** The equilibrium expression is obtained by placing the product of the concentrations of the products over that of the reactants with the exponents equal to the stoichiometric coefficients. Thus, K_{eq} is given by the expression in choice D.

5. **C** The conjugate bases of the hydrogen halides are the halide ions. Since halide ions have an extra electron, they have noble-gas configurations, which accounts for their remarkable stability.

6. **D** Le Châtelier's principle is a thermodynamic (equilibrium) concept, not a kinetic one, so choice A can be eliminated. Choice B is eliminated since ΔH is the change in potential energy between the reactants and products, while temperature is a measurement of the average molecular kinetic energy; kinetic energy has no effect on potential energy here. Choice C is eliminated because temperature will not affect the molar quantities of gas, so the answer is choice D: Le Châtelier's principle predicts that exothermic reactions will be shifted to the left when the temperature is increased.

Passage 43

1. **D** NH_4^+ is an acidic ion and CO_3^{2-} is a basic ion. Both could potentially affect the equilibrium described in Equation 3, so choice A seems unlikely. Although ammonium carbonate is a basic salt, eliminating choices B and C, this could not be determined without knowing the relative pK_b and pK_a values of NH_3 and HCO_3^- respectively. Given the rise in pH of groundwater and that CO_3^{2-} would likely have a common ion effect on the $CaCO_3$ solubility, less limestone would be expected to dissolve, leading to decreased formations in the cave.

2. **C** This question is best answered by process of elimination, because the answer is unexpected. $CaCO_3$ is an ionic compound with a melting point greater than 800°C, making choice A unlikely. If formation of stalactites and stalagmites were endothermic, increased temperature would favor their formation, eliminating choice B. Increased temperature decreases the concentration of dissolved gases in liquids, eliminating choice D. $CaCO_3$ is one of the exceptions to general solubility rules because its solubility in water actually decreases with increasing temperature. If less $CaCO_3$ gets dissolved, less will be available to precipitate in the cave as a stalactite or stalagmite.

3. C Calcium carbonate dissolves in water as follows:

$$CaCO_3(s) \rightleftharpoons Ca^{2+} + CO_3^{2-}$$

The K_{sp} defines the maximum solubility of a saturated solution. Solve the solubility expression for the maximum theoretical concentration of CO_3^{2-}:

$$K_{sp} = [Ca^{2+}][CO_3^{2-}]$$
$$3.4 \times 10^{-9} = [x][x]$$
$$x^2 = 34 \times 10^{-10}$$
$$x \approx 6 \times 10^{-5} M$$

4. C A buffer must contain a conjugate acid-base pair. CO_3^{2-} is a basic ion so adding the conjugate acid, HCO_3^-, would be required to form a buffer solution. $NaHCO_3^-$ will most readily supply this.

5. B The carbonate ion is trigonal planar and the carbon atom is sp^2 hybridized:

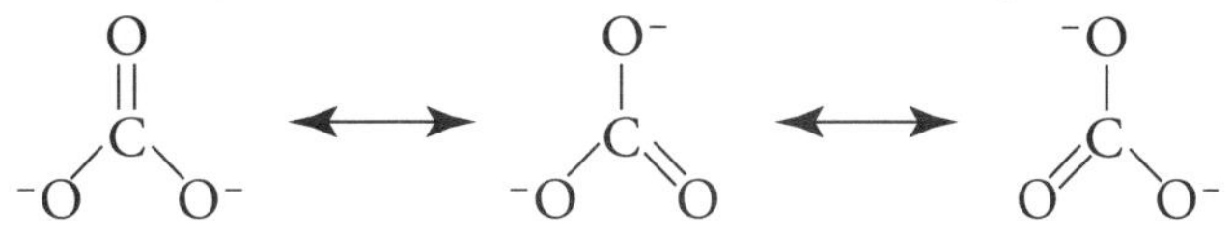

With three total substituents, the carbon atom cannot be sp^3 hybridized, eliminating choices A and D. Tetrahedral shapes require four substituents, eliminating choice C.

6. B According to the passage, increasing the amount of dissolved $CaCO_3$ that makes it to the ground/cave interface or maximizing the difference in ground and cave CO_2 levels will increase stalagmite formation. Choice A would decrease $CaCO_3$ solubility in groundwater by the common ion effect. Choice C would decrease $CaCO_3$ solubility in groundwater because the passage states acidic solutions dissolve $CaCO_3$. Choices B and D are opposite answers, which often means one is correct. The passage states that lower CO_2 levels in the cave compared to the leaking water lead to precipitation of $CaCO_3$. Therefore, choice D is eliminated and choice B is the best answer.

Passage 44

1. B The balanced reaction for the formation of the acetal is

$$CH_3CHO + HOCH_2CH_2OH \rightleftharpoons acetal + H_2O,$$

and the equilibrium expression is simply

$$K_{eq} = [acetal] \cdot [H_2O] / [CH_3CHO] \cdot [HOCH_2CH_2OH].$$

(Note: Water is not the solvent here; this is a toluene solution.)

2. **A**   The passage suggests that the formation of this acetal is an exothermic process (heat is evolved during the reaction). Although increasing the temperature of an exothermic reaction will increase the initial reaction rate, the reaction will shift to the left from a thermodynamic perspective; the product yield will decrease.

3. **C**   Decreasing the concentration of water and the acetal will shift the reaction to the products (choices A and B). Since H^+ is just a catalyst, the removal of H^+ from the equilibrated system will have no effect (choice D). Decreasing the concentration of ethylene glycol will shift the reaction to the reactants.

4. **B**   There is no net consumption or production of H^+ in acetal reactions; H^+ is a catalyst. Therefore, as an acetal is formed, the pH of the solution remains the same.

5. **C**   In general chemistry, we ignore effects of pressure upon equilibria without gas phase constituents. Therefore, the acetal reaction will not be affected by an increase in pressure.

6. **D**   The carbonyl carbon has three groups of electrons (two single bonds and one double bond), so it has a geometry of trigonal planar. In the acetal, this same carbon atom has four groups of electrons (four single bonds), so it has a geometry of tetrahedral. Note that trigonal pyramid is a shape, not a geometry—choices A, B, and C could be eliminated right away.

Passage 45

1. **C**   Lead is highly toxic, and precipitating all halogens from solution would be catastrophic for the human body (choice A). The point of this question is to prevent ^{131}I from entering the body—injecting ^{131}I directly into the patient is doing the opposite (choice B). The radioactive decay rate of a nucleus is not a function of pressure, temperature, or concentration (choice D). The only thing one can do is to have people continuously exposed to ^{131}I consume vast amounts of normal iodine in hopes of shifting the equilibrium given in the passage to the left. The goal is for normal iodine to flood the body's receptors, winning the battle of competitive inhibition against radioactive iodine.

2. **A**   Strontium phosphate dissociates in water according to the reaction

$$Sr_3(PO_4)_2(s) \rightleftharpoons 3\ Sr^{2+}(aq) + 2\ PO_4^{3-}(aq)$$

Therefore, the equilibrium expression is

$$K_{sp} = [Sr^{2+}]^3 \cdot [PO_4^{3-}]^2$$

and given the dissolution of x moles of strontium phosphate, the algebraic expression is

$$10^{-28} = (3x)^3 \cdot (2x)^2 = 27x^3 \cdot 4x^2 \approx 100x^5$$

Thus, $x = 10^{-6}\ M$ and $[Sr^{2+}] = 3 \times 10^{-6}\ M$. This value is certainly closest to choice A.

3. **D**   Remembering solubility rules, all Group I salts are soluble and will not precipitate out of human electrolytic fluids (choice A and B). Furthermore, the chemistry of cesium is much more similar to other Group I ions such as Na^+ and K^+ than to Group II ions like Mg^{2+}. Therefore, the best answer is choice D.

4. **C**   The solubility rules tell us that the salts in choices A, B, and D are very soluble. Therefore, calcium carbonate (choice C), a salt whose solubility is very pH sensitive, is the best answer.

5. **C**   This is a tricky question. Choice D is not true because only fissile elements like ^{235}U and ^{239}Pu can explode in a blaze of nuclear energy. Since there is an equilibrium in solution, the addition of more iodine will have some effect upon the solubility of $Pb^{131}I_2$ (choice B is incorrect). You might have thought that less ^{131}I would be dissolved in solution because of this common-ion effect (choice A), but the right answer is choice C. The common-ion effect tells us that the total $[^{131}I]$ will decrease when NaI is added to the solution. Yet before the NaI is added, the $[^{131}I]$ is only about 0.001 M (K_{sp} of PbI_2 is about 10^{-9})—most of the ^{131}I is sitting as a solid at the bottom of the beaker. When you add a whole bunch more dissolved I^-, eventually, the ^{131}I will be replaced in the $PbI_2(s)$ with the normal I and, in the end, a lot more ^{131}I will be dissolved in the solution.

Passage 46

1. **D**   At any given temperature, the velocity of lighter molecules is greater than that of more massive molecules (choice A is incorrect). Ionization energy increases as one moves upwards and to the right in the periodic table; the ionization of O is greater than N (choice B is incorrect). Each atom in diatomic nitrogen has a single pair of nonbonding electrons (choice C is incorrect). Due to the fact that molecular nitrogen has three covalent bonds to molecular oxygen's two, the total bond dissociation energy of nitrogen is greater than that of oxygen (choice D).

2. **A**   Temperature is proportional to the kinetic energy of a gas, so choices B and C are identical and incorrect. Since the reaction between hydrogen and nitrogen is an exothermic one, decreasing the temperature of the reaction once it is at equilibrium will shift the reaction to the right and favor the production of ammonia.

3. **B**   The passage indicates that the Haber reaction is an exothermic reaction ($\Delta H < 0$). Therefore, the bond energy of the products must be less than that of the reactants. This eliminates choices C and D. Furthermore, a catalyst lowers the activation energy (the hump) of the reaction; it does not affect the initial or final energy of the reaction.

4. **D**   The question says that a three to one mixture of hydrogen and nitrogen had a total pressure of 60 atm. Therefore, the partial pressure of hydrogen and nitrogen must be 45 atm and 15 atm, respectively. Based upon the balanced equation for the Haber process, one nitrogen and three hydrogen molecules must be consumed for every two ammonia molecules formed: $3 H_2 + N_2 \rightarrow 2 NH_3$. The final pressure, 45 atm, equals the sum of the final pressures of hydrogen, nitrogen, and ammonia:

$$45 \text{ atm} = (45 \text{ atm} - 3x) + (15 \text{ atm} - x) + (0 \text{ atm} + 2x)$$

Thus, $x = 7.5$ atm, so the partial pressure of ammonia must be $2x = 15$ atm.

5. **C** At equilibrium, a catalyst has no net effect, so choice D doesn't do anything. From here, you must consider that in the reaction quotient expression for the Haber process, the concentration of hydrogen is cubed and that of ammonia is squared:

$$Q = [NH_3]^2 / [H_2]^3[N_2]$$

Therefore, choices A, B, and C result in the following changes in the reaction quotient:

A: 50% reduction in 1.0 atm of H_2: $(0.5\ atm)^3 = 0.125\ atm^3$ = increase by a factor of $1/(0.125) = 8$;
B: 60% reduction in 1.0 atm of N_2: 0.4 atm = increase by a factor of $1/(0.4) = 2.5$;
C: 70% reduction in 1.0 atm of NH_3: $(0.3\ atm)^2 = 0.09\ atm^2$ = decrease by a factor of $1/(0.09) = 11$.

Considering that we assumed the initial concentrations of all of the gases were 1.0 atm, choice C would result in the greatest perturbation to the equilibrium, since it causes the greatest factor change in the reaction quotient.

6. **D** Carbon monoxide is a ligand (choice D) that forms strong coordinate covalent bonds (choice C is incorrect). A ligand is a Lewis base, not a Lewis acid (choice B is incorrect). While CO is toxic to most organisms (because it is a strong ligand), the toxicity of a molecule to organisms does not mean that the molecule is industrially useless (choice A).

Passage 47

1. **D** Given that the oxidation states for H and O here are +1 and –2, respectively, the oxidation states of S in choices A through D are 0, +4, +5, +6, respectively. Since the oxidation state of S in SO_3 is +6, the answer must be D.

2. **A** The question states that HSO_3 is a radical. Therefore, the correct Lewis dot structure must have an unpaired electron, so choices B and C are eliminated. Finally, the total charge of all atoms must equal zero since HSO_3 is neutral, eliminating D. Choice A is the answer.

3. **A** According to the question, a bond is formed, but no bonds are being broken in the reaction. Since bond formation always releases energy, ΔH_{rxn} must be negative. Choices C and D are eliminated. As for the change in entropy, ΔS_{rxn}, the combination of two molecules into one definitely represents a decrease in entropy, so choice A is correct.

4. **D** By stating that Reaction (1a) is slow, the question is saying that Reaction (1a) is the rate-determining step for the overall Series 1 reaction. Therefore, only changes in reactants in Reaction (1a), specifically COS and hv, will have an impact on the rate. Choice D is correct, because O_2 is not a reactant in the rate-determining step.

5. **A** Choice B is eliminated because the passage states that COS is produced by microorganisms. Furthermore, choice C is wrong because SO_2 actually is a reducing agent in Reaction (3a). Also, both oxidation pathways of COS require UV light, either directly in Series 1, or indirectly through the photolysis of ozone to produce O in Series 2, so choice D is wrong. However, the statement in choice A is supported since the passage states that sulfuric acid droplets rain out of the stratosphere. The process of raining out, also called *sedimentation*, is caused by higher density particles dropping through a lower density fluid.

6. **C** Recall that H_2SO_3 is a weak acid and H_2SO_4 is a strong acid. Therefore, H_2SO_3 does not completely dissociate into H^+ and HSO_3^-, eliminating choices A and B. According to Le Châtelier's principle, the complete dissociation of H_2SO_4 into H^+ and HSO_4^- would, in effect, decrease the concentration of undissociated H_2SO_4. Therefore, decreasing the amount of undissociated H_2SO_4 will shift Equilibrium (2) to the right (choice C).

Passage 48

1. **B** The passage tells us that acids with a pK_a greater than 0 are called weak acids. The pK_a of phosphoric acid, H_3PO_4, is 2.1.

2. **C** Choices A and B are true statements which indicate how fluorine is different from all the other halogens. However, while all of the other halide ions are pH neutral in solution, the fluoride ion is basic.

3. **B** Chemist #1 argues that electronegativity is the principal factor affecting acidity. Compounds that contain more electronegative atoms have weaker H–O bonds and are therefore more acidic. Although choices B, C, and D each have 3 electronegative atoms, the compound with the more electronegative atoms (F) is trifluoroacetic acid, choice B. In fact $HOOCCF_3$ is a stronger acid than sulfuric acid for this reason.

4. **A** Chemist #2 argues that the most acidic compounds have conjugate bases with lots of resonance stability. Unlike all of the other choices, phenol (choice A) has a benzene ring. You should remember that benzene is so special because all of the double bonds resonate (move around) the ring—in organic chemistry, only molecules with double or triple bonds will have multiple resonance structures. Therefore, only the conjugate base of phenol, the phenoxide ion, will experience resonance.

5. **D** The fluoride ion cannot experience resonance with itself (it takes two to tango), so the definition by Chemist #2 is not applicable (choices B and C are eliminated). Considering that fluorine is more electronegative than all the other halogens, the definition by Chemist #1 leads us to believe that HF should be the most acidic halohydride acid—which it is not (choice A is eliminated). Therefore, some other consideration not mentioned here must be made in order to predict the acidity of all compounds.

6. **A** pH equals the negative log of $[H^+]$. Since the first proton of H_2SO_4 is a strong acid, we can assume that all H_2SO_4 is dissociated into H^+ and HSO_4^-. Therefore the pH due to this first proton only is: $pH = -\log [H^+] = -\log (1.0) = 0$. However, unlike all of the other strong acids—HCl, HBr, HI, HNO_3, and $HClO_4$—we must also consider the small contribution of the second acidic proton produced by the dissociation of HSO_4^- to SO_4^{2-}. While this proton is weak, meaning that about 1 out of 1000 of them actually dissociate, they still make the solution slightly more acidic. Therefore, the actual pH of a 1.0 M sulfuric acid solution is less than 0.0. Note that normally we ignore the contribution of the second proton, however choice B uses the word "exact," indicating that we have to be more careful here.

Passage 49

1. **C** One order of magnitude means "one factor of 10." Based upon the pH's given in the passage, the $[H^+]$ of lemon juice is about 10^{-2} M and that for seawater is about 10^{-7} M. Therefore, $[H^+]$ is 10^5 times, i.e., five orders of magnitude greater, in lemon juice than in seawater.

2. **A** Based upon the passage, the concentration of H^+ in gastric juice is 10^{-1} M. If 99.9% of this is neutralized by an antacid, then only 0.1% = 10^{-4} M remains. The pH of a solution with a $[H^+]$ of $[10^{-4}$ $M]$ is 4 (choice A). So a little bit of extra acid makes a big difference in terms of pH!

3. **C** HF is the conjugate acid of F^-, and in turn, F^- is the conjugate base of HF (choices A and B are backwards). The conjugate of a weak acid, such as HF, is a base. Therefore, a solution of NaF will have a higher pH than a solution of HF.

4. **C** The conjugate base of a weak acid is a base, but the conjugate base of a strong acid forms a pH neutral solution; the conjugate acid of a weak base is acidic, but the conjugate acid of a strong base forms a pH neutral solution. Thus, the Na^+ and Cl^- ions form pH neutral solutions, eliminating choice A. The fluoride ion is a weak base, so overall, NaF is a basic salt, eliminating choice B. Now, NH_3 is basic, but not strongly so. Therefore, its conjugate acid will be somewhat acidic.

$$NH_4Cl(aq) \rightleftharpoons NH_3(aq) + H^+(aq) + Cl^-(aq)$$

Thus, there is an excess of H^+ ions, so the solution will be slightly acidic; choice C is the answer. Choice D should be eliminated since potassium hydroxide is a strong base.

5. **A** The $[H^+]$ of gastric juice is 10^{-1} M. Doubling the volume of a 10 mL solution by adding water will cut $[H^+]$ in half, to 0.05 M. The pH of this solution is

$$pH = -\log (0.05) = \log 20 = \log 10 + \log 2 = 1.3$$

Therefore, the only answer that's close is choice A.

6. **C** Calcium carbonate is a basic salt, and sodium oxide is a strong base, so choices A and B are eliminated. Methane is an alkane, and all alkanes form pH neutral solutions (choice D is eliminated). H_2S is a weak acid (acidity increases as you go to the right or down the periodic table). Since sulfur is under oxygen, H_2S must be more acidic than H_2O. Therefore, in aqueous solution, H_2S will behave as an acid.

Passage 50

1. **B** The question indicates that the solution with the greatest [H⁺] will hydrolyze a peptide the fastest. Considering that only about 1 out of 1000 molecules of a weak acid dissociate, and that all of the molecules of a strong acid dissociate, the approximate [H⁺] of the choice solutions are actually:

    choice A: $0.1\ M\ HF \approx 0.0001\ M\ H^+$

    choice B: $0.1\ M\ HNO_3 = 0.1\ M\ H^+$

    choice C: $1.0\ M\ HC_2H_3O_2 \approx 0.001\ M\ H^+$

    choice D: $1.0\ M\ H_3PO_4 \approx 0.001\ M\ H^+$

    Therefore, the solution with the greatest [H⁺] is the one in choice B.

2. **A** If choice B were true, we would expect acidic solutions to be much more damaging than basic solutions—the question says otherwise. The hydrogen ion is the smallest ion possible since it is nothing more than a free proton (choice C is incorrect). Regardless of how fancy choice D may sound, it has one fundamental flaw: Particles with the same charge, such as Na⁺ and the positively-charged carbonyl (C=O) carbon strongly repel one another and will never associate. According to the reaction scheme given in the passage, the acid hydrolysis of a peptide is reversible while the base hydrolysis is not (choice A).

3. **B** Hydrogen bonding exists between the hydrogen in an H–F, H–O, or H–N bond and another F, O, or N atom. Both forms of the carboxylic acid may form hydrogen bonds with the hydrogen in water's H–O bonds (choice A is wrong). Since the deprotonated form of the carboxylic acid is more water soluble, it must be more water-loving; a water-loving molecule is called hydrophilic (choice C is wrong). Therefore, it is the protonated carboxylic acid that is more hydrophobic (water-hating). Choice D has to be incorrect because the oxygen atom in the water molecule has a partial negative charge. The deprotonated form of the carboxylic acid is more soluble than the protonated acid because the ion–dipole interactions between the RCOO⁻ and water are stronger than the dipole–dipole interactions between RCOOH and water (choice B).

4. **D** The compound with the strongest intermolecular forces and greatest molecular mass will have the highest melting point (and boiling point). Since all of these compounds have about the same molecular mass, we conclude that the compound with the greatest intermolecular forces will have the highest MP. Choice A (acetone), choice B (ethanol), and choice C (acetic acid) are all compounds that experience moderately strong dipole interactions—and are liquids at room temperature. However, sodium acetate is a high MP solid at room temperature because it experiences strong ionic interactions (choice D).

5. **C** A pair of resonance structures are two structures that are identical except for the distribution of electrons. All of the answer choices are resonance structures, but we must also consider that hydrogen can never have more than two valence electrons. Since choice C has a hydrogen with four valence electrons, it's an impossible resonance structure.

6. **B** Hydrolysis reactions are reactions in which a bond is broken (lysis) with the addition of water (hydro). Therefore, hydrolysis reactions must occur in water (choice C is eliminated). Obviously, peptides and esters don't hydrolyze in pure water—otherwise bathtub excursions would be very painful (choice D is eliminated). Examining the product, you should notice that all acidic protons have been removed. Therefore, this hydrolysis must have taken place under basic conditions (choice B).

Passage 51

1. **C** The solubility equilibrium constant, K_{sp}, is directly related to solubility. Since K_{sp} for AgCl is greater than for AgI, AgCl must be more soluble.

2. **C** Since the titration curve has two inflection points, the unknown acid must be diprotic. Amphoteric describes a substance that can behave as an acid and a base (choice A). Autoionization is the reaction of molecules of the same substance to produce ions, such as the autoionization of H_2O to produce H_3O^+ and OH^- (choice D).

3. **C** According to Figure 1, the pH of the solution after adding 6.5 mL of NaOH is 4. Therefore, $[H^+] = 10^{-pH} = 10^{-4}\ M$.

4. **B** The question states that the conjugate base of the unknown weak acid is monoprotic. Therefore, the titration curve will have only one inflection point; this eliminates choices C and D. Since strong acid is being added to the solution, the pH must decrease, so the best graph is the one in choice B.

5. **A** The only way to change the value of an equilibrium constant is to change the temperature, so neither choice C nor D can be correct. Given the equilibrium in Reaction 1, increasing the concentration of $Cl^-(aq)$ by adding NaCl will shift the reaction to the left, resulting in the formation of more AgCl(s). This is called the common ion effect.

Passage 52

1. **A** The conjugate base of a chemical species is simply that species after it has lost an H^+. Therefore, the conjugate base of the bicarbonate ion, HCO_3^-, is the carbonate ion, CO_3^{2-}.

2. **C** The most appropriate buffer system is the one in which the pK_a of the conjugate acid most closely matches the desired solution pH. If the desired solution pH is 7.4, then, according to the data in Table 1, the $H_2PO_4^-/HPO_4^{2-}$ buffer system would be the most effective.

3. **B** Carbon atoms may never have more than four bonds; therefore, choices C and D are immediately eliminated. Since the carbonate ion is very stable, it is reasonable to assume that the carbon atom has a complete octet. Generally, stable carbon atoms have a total of four bonds, so choice B is best.

4. C   If the concentrations of a weak acid and its conjugate base are equal, then the pH of the buffer solution equals the pK_a of the acid, and vice versa (this follows immediately from the Henderson–Hasselbalch equation). Given that the pK_a of carbonic acid is 6.37 but the solution pH is 7.4, we conclude that the acid and base concentrations cannot be equal (eliminating choice B). If the pH of a buffer is greater than the pK_a of the acid, then there must be more conjugate base than acid: choice C.

5. C   In order to have complete neutralization, the amount of acid must equal the amount of base. Since the amount of solute (in moles) is equal to the concentration (C, in mol/L) times the volume (V, in L), we have

$$(CV)_{acid} = (CV)_{base}$$

$$(0.1\ M)(0.5\ L) = (0.2\ M)V_{base}$$

$$0.25\ L = V_{base}$$

6. B   Choices C and D cannot be correct since [H$^+$] and pH follow opposite trends (as one increases, the other decreases). Since the passage implies that rapid breathing causes [CO_2] to decrease in the blood, the answer is choice B.

Passage 53

1. D   Adding an acid to any solution, whether it be a buffered or unbuffered solution, will always lower the pH, just by differing amounts (choice A). All carbonate and bicarbonate salts generate $CO_2(g)$ when mixed with acids (choice B). Increasing the [H$^+$] by adding HCl will shift both of the equilibria given in the passage to the right (choice C). Hydrogen gas is only evolved in redox reactions; the reaction between HCl and $NaHCO_3$ constitutes an acid–base reaction, not an oxidation–reduction reaction (choice D).

2. C   The sum of pK_a and pK_b of the conjugate pairs always equals 14 at 25°C. Since the K_b of bicarbonate is 2.7×10^{-8}, the pK_b of HCO_3^- is about 8. Thus, the pK_a of carbonic acid is about 6. Choices A and D can be eliminated because they are unlikely candidates for something that buffers blood which has a pH of 7.4. Remember, a good buffer typically has a pK_a close to the pH you are trying to maintain.

3. A   Consider that carbon dioxide dissolves in water to produce carbonic acid, which can then dissociate to produce H$^+$:

$$CO_2(g) + H_2O(l) \rightleftharpoons H_2CO_3(aq) \rightleftharpoons H^+ + HCO_3^-(aq)$$

Therefore, when tissues release CO_2 into the bloodstream, H$^+$ is ultimately produced causing the pH of the blood to decrease. In the lungs, HCO_3^- and H$^+$ re-associate, leading to the release of $CO_2(g)$ driving the pH of the blood up again (choice A).

4. **B**   In the kidney, reabsorbed substances are taken back into the body from the filtrate, while those that remain in the filtrate are excreted in the urine. For plasma pH to rise, a base must be reabsorbed or an acid must be excreted. Choices A and C do not represent normal physiologic functions of the kidney and can be eliminated. Even if they were possible, they would essentially both represent the reabsorption of an acid because CO_2 or H_2CO_3 would drive the equilibrium in the passage to the left, producing more H^+ in solution and lowering plasma pH. HCO_3^- (choice D) is the conjugate base of H_2CO_3, a weak acid, and therefore it has basic properties. Excretion of HCO_3^-, a base, will therefore lower plasma pH both directly and indirectly by diminishing the buffering capacity of the body to all the CO_2 produced by cellular respiration (choice D can be eliminated). NH_4^+ is the conjugate acid of NH_3, a weak base. Therefore, it has acidic properties and its excretion will act to raise plasma pH.

5. **C**   An ion that can buffer against acids and bases must have the ability to accept and donate a proton. The only ion given that can behave as both an acid and a base is $H_2PO_4^-$ (choice **C**).

$$H_2PO_4^- \rightarrow H^+ + HPO_4^{2-}$$

$$H_2PO_4^- + H^+ \rightarrow H_3PO_4$$

6. **B**   Since the pH of blood is greater than 7, the concentration of OH^- is greater than that of H^+ (choice A is true and thus incorrect). If CO_2 is not allowed to be exhaled from the blood, more and more carbonic acid will be produced, making the blood more acidic, a condition called acidosis (choice C is true). An electrolyte is a compound that dissolves in water to produce a large amount of ions. Since only about 1 out of 1000 molecules of a weak acid or a weak base form ions, weak acids and bases are very poor (weak) electrolytes (choice D is true). Due to the presence of more OH^- in blood (pH 7.4) than in pure water (pH 7.0), the common-ion effect tells us that the solubility of $Mg(OH)_2$ should be less in blood than in pure water (choice B is false and therefore the correct answer here).

Passage 54

1. **D**   The initial pH of solution X is 10.7. Therefore, the dissolved solute must be a base. Acetic acid (choice A) and ammonium nitrate (choice C) are weak acids. Ethanol (choice B) is a normal alkyl alcohol, therefore its chemistry, including its pH, are very similar to that of H_2O. The only base given as a choice is ethylamine, choice D. With only a very few exceptions, a nitrogen atom in any compound that is not positively charged—as in the case of the ammonium ion—will behave as a base.

2. **A**   The titration curve given in the passage indicates that the equivalence point of the titration occurs at pH 7. The titration of a strong acid with a strong base (or vice versa) has an equivalence point which occurs at pH 7. The only strong acid given is choice A.

3. **D**   The conjugate base of a strong acid and the conjugate acid of a strong base form pH neutral solutions. The conjugate base of a weak acid is basic, and the conjugate acid of a weak base is acidic in solution. So Na^+, I^-, HSO_4^- and NO_3^- result in pH neutral solutions. The ferric, and ammonium ions are weak acids, while the chlorite ion, ClO_2^-, is a weak base. Therefore, the only basic salt is $NaClO_2$.

4. **D** The pK_a of the conjugate acid of solute X can be determined from the titration curve in the passage. First, the pK_b for solute X is equal to the pOH of the solution when it is half titrated: half the distance to the equivalence point on the x axis. At 25°C, the pK_b of solute X plus the pK_a of solute X's conjugate acid is equal to 14. While the pH axes are not explicitly marked off in the graphs, we are told that the pH of the initial solution (beginning of the titration curve) is 10.7. Since the pH at the half-equivalence point is between 7 and 10.7, the pOH at this point is between $14 - 10.7 = 3.3$ and $14 - 7 = 7$, so we can conclude that the pK_b of solute X is between 3.3 and 7. Since the pK_b is less than 7, the pK_a of its conjugate acid must be greater than 7.

5. **D** The sum of the pK_a of an acid (H_2X) plus the pK_b of its conjugate base (HX^-) equals 14 at 25°C —not the pK_a + pK_b of the same molecule (eliminating choice A). The K_w for pure water equals 10^{-14} at 25°C or 298 K, not at 273 K (so choice B is eliminated). An electrolyte is a compound that increases the electrical conductivity of water by producing lots of ions. Evidently, Solute Y is the better electrolyte because the electrical conductivity of Solution Y is much greater than that of pure water or Solution X (so choice C is eliminated). The boiling point (BP) of a liquid is the temperature at which the vapor pressure of the liquid equals the atmospheric pressure. Since the BP of Solution Y is greater than that of Solution X, the vapor pressure of Solution Y is less than that of Solution X at every temperature (choice D).

Passage 55

1. **A** Any equilibrium constant, including K's, are only changed by a change in temperature (eliminating choices B and C). Among the remaining choices, choice A sounds the most plausible because an indicator is an acid or base, and in moderate concentrations, can behave as a reactant. Choice D is untrue.

2. **B** The passage indicated that the pK_a of an indicator is about equal to the mid-region of the pH color change range. Therefore, since the pK_a of thymol blue is about 2, the K_a of thymol blue must be about 10^{-2}.

3. **D** The passage tells us that an indicator is a weak acid or base. If the organic group R is not an acid or a base, then the functional group explicitly given in the choices must be the acid or base part. The carboxylic and sulfuric functional groups (choices A and B) are acidic, and the amino group (choice C) is basic. But the methyl group (choice D) is as acid–base inert as any group of atoms can get.

4. **A** In the passage, we are told that the human eye only detects an indicator's color change when one of the species outnumbers the other by an order of magnitude (means 10 times). If methyl green is blue, then there are ten times more unprotonated molecules than protonated ones. Thus the ratio of protonated to unprotonated molecules is $1:10 = 0.1$.

5. **B** We want to use an indicator that changes color right around the pH where we expect the equivalence point. Based upon what we know about titrations, the titration of a weak base with a strong acid has an equivalence point just under pH 7 (about pH 4 to pH 6). Therefore, the best indicator to use would be methyl orange.

6. **B** Since pure alcohol has a pH similar to that of water, we can pretend that the solution is an aqueous solution. Methyl red is a weak acid with a pK_a of 5 (so $K_a = 10^{-5}$):

$$K_a = [H^+][A^-]/[HA] = 10^{-5}$$

Solving for $[H^+]$, we find

$$K_a = \frac{[H^+][A^-]}{[HA]} = 10^{-5} \rightarrow \frac{x \cdot x}{0.01 - x} = 10^{-5}$$

$$\rightarrow \frac{x^2}{0.01} \approx 10^{-5} \rightarrow x^2 = 10^{-7} = 10 \times 10^{-8}$$

$$\rightarrow x = \sqrt{10 \times 10^{-8}} = 3.2 \times 10^{-4}$$

So, $pH \approx -\log(3.2 \times 10^{-4}) \approx -(0.5 - 4) = 3.5$.

Passage 56

1. **C** First of all, if we have 100 times more base in a solution than acid, the solution must be basic (eliminating choices A and B). Because the Henderson–Hasselbalch equation has the unitless term log ([base] / [acid]), as long as you know the ratio of base to acid (100 to 1 in this example) and the pK_a (about 9 for ammonium), you can solve for the pH: pH = 9 + log 100 = 9 + 2 = 11.

2. **B** A buffer must consist of the conjugate pairs of a weak acid and base. Hydrochloric acid is a strong acid, and sodium hydroxide is a strong base (so choices A and D are eliminated). The conjugate base of HF is F^-, not the covalent compound CH_3F (choice **C** is eliminated). Choice B is correct since the weak base bisulfite ion, HSO_3^-, is the conjugate base of the weak acid sulfurous acid.

3. **D** Adding a strong base will reduce the concentration of H^+, shifting the equilibrium to the right (so choice A is OK). The neutralization reaction between any base and acid is an exothermic reaction (so choice B is OK). By shifting the reaction to the right, neutral acetic acid is converted into the acetate ion. The electrical conductivity of a water solution is proportional to the concentration of dissolved ions (so choice C is OK). Finally, whenever a strong base is added to a solution, whether the solution is buffered or not, the pH must increase: choice D.

4. **A** Since $pK_a = -\log K_a$, the pK_a for sulfurous acid = $-\log(1.5 \times 10^{-2})$. Since 1.5×10^{-2} is between 10^{-1} and 10^{-2}, the pK_a of sulfurous acid must be between 1 and 2.

5. **D** The reaction is

$$HCl + H_2O \rightarrow H_3O^+ + Cl^-$$

HCl must be a better H^+ donor (have a smaller pK_a) than water, and water must be a better H^+ acceptor (have a smaller pK_b) than the chloride ion. None of choices A, B, or C correctly states these relationships, so choose D.

6. **A** This type of question is often asked because students regularly get it wrong. One HCl will react with one NH_3 to give one NH_4Cl. So in this reaction the number of ammonium chloride molecules will be the same as the original number of HCl and the original number of NH_3. However, we are mixing two solutions with identical volumes, so in essence, we are doubling the volume of the solution. Thus if the number of NH_4Cl is the same as the initial number of HCl, but the volume is doubled, the solution will be half as concentrated (choice **A**).

Passage 57

1. **B** Since the given titration curve has two equivalence points (points C and E), this is a diprotic acid.

2. **B** As indicated in question 1, this acid is diprotic (choices C and D are eliminated). Both equivalence points occur above pH 7, so both acid protons are weak. Therefore, the correct choice must be sulfurous acid.

3. **A** Point B is the pK_a for the first proton, point D is the pK_a of the second proton, and point E is the equivalence point of the second proton. Recall that the pK_a points are found on the flat domains of a titration curve where the buffering capacity of the solution is maximum, and equivalence points come at the steepest part where the pH of the curve is very sensitive to the addition of more acid or base.

4. **B** The maximum buffering capacity of a solution is at a pH that equals the pK_a of the acidic buffering species. According to the Henderson–Hasselbalch equation, the occurs when [base] equals [acid].

5. **B** A polyprotic base is one that can accept two successive protons. Ammonium hydroxide (choice A) and ammonia (choice C) are both monoprotic bases. *Note that ammonia in water is the same thing as ammonium hydroxide, just like H^+ in water is understood to be the same thing as H_3O^+.* Choice D is not a base at all—in fact, it's an unconventional (but correct) way of expressing the formula for sulfuric acid. The only polyprotic base is sodium oxide (choice B). Sodium oxide reacts with water in the following way:

$$Na_2O + H_2O \rightarrow 2\ NaOH$$

So each mole of Na_2O can consume two moles of acid.

Passage 58

1. **B** The isoelectric point, pI, for an amino acid with only one acid and base group is the average of the pK_a's. The average of 2.2 and 9.2 is 5.7.

2. **D** The pH of a 1.0 M KOH solution is 14. So for valine, both the COOH group and the amino group are deprotonated (COO^- and NH_2) in this solution. Therefore at this pH, the overall charge of the valine is negative, and it will be attracted to the positive plate (choice A is eliminated). Asparagine only has two pK_a's, hence it has only two acid–base groups: the COOH and the NH_2. Therefore, the amide group must not be basic or acidic (moreover, in organic chemistry, you should know that esters and amides are not acidic or basic functional group. The reason being that unlike amines, the lone pair of the nitrogen atom spends a significant amount of time participating in a p bond with the carbonyl (C=O) carbon. Thus, choice B is eliminated. When pH = pI, the amino acid has no net charge and will not migrate in an electric field (choice C is eliminated). At very low pH, all groups are protonated (COOH and NH_3^+), so valine has a net positive charge and will migrate towards the negative plate.

3. **D** At a pH of 9.5, the cysteine and the carboxylic acid groups are mostly deprotonated because their pK_a values are less than the surrounding pH. However, the amino group should still be mostly protonated because its pK_a value is more than the surrounding pH.

4. **B** The pK_a of the carboxylic acid group of asparagine is 2.0 according to the table. By definition, at pH = pK_a the [conjugate acid] = [conjugate base], so choice A is a true statement. Thiols are more acidic than corresponding alcohols, so choice C is a true statement, and amines are Lewis bases, so choice D is a true statement. However, the hydroxy group in serine, just like all other normal alcohol groups, is not a strong acid, so choice B is the false statement here.

5. **D** The pH of a 1.0 M solution of NaOH is 14. If 90% of the NaOH is neutralized and the volume of the solution does not change (dissolving gases in solution does not affect the solution volume), then the [OH^-] of the remaining base must be 10% (one-tenth) that of the original. Therefore, the pOH goes down by log(10 times), or one unit. The pH of the remaining solution is 14 − 1 = 13.

Passage 59

1. **D** Sodium metal is a strong reducing agent. It will only react, and explode, in the presence of an oxidizing agent. The passage tells us that an oxidizing agent is a molecule that has two or more highly electronegative atoms covalently bonded together. Therefore, sodium metal will react if mixed with bromine liquid (choice B) or oxygen gas (choice C), because these compounds are strong oxidizing agents. Although water is a very weak oxidizing agent, sodium metal explodes on contact with water (a fact you should know). The correct answer is choice D because neon, a noble gas, is inert to all chemical reactions.

2. **B** According to this question, the oxidant in household bleach contains an electronegative atom with a +1 or +2 oxidation state. Choice D is eliminated because table salt, NaCl, is not an oxidizing or reducing agent. For all of the remaining compounds, we have to determine the oxidation states. Since sodium has an oxidation state of +1, and each O atom has a −2 oxidation state, the oxidation state of iodine in $NaIO_3$ (choice A) is +5, and the oxidation state of chlorine is +1 in NaClO (choice B) and +7 in $NaClO_4$ (choice C). Therefore, the oxidant in bleach must be sodium hypochlorite, NaClO.

3. **C** Since gunpowder is an explosive, it must consist of an oxidant and a reductant. Both elemental carbon and sulfur are moderate reducing agents, so an oxidizing agent is required to give potency to the mixture. Choice D is neither an oxidizing nor a reducing agent, choice A is a good reducing agent, and choice B is a very, very mild oxidizing agent. Potassium nitrate, on the other hand, is a strong oxidizing agent because the electronegative nitrogen in nitrate is in a very irritated +5 oxidative state. Therefore, choice C is best.

4. **C** Three of these choices are not explosives, i.e., are not mixtures of a reducing agent and an oxidizing agent. Choice A is a mixture of two very strong oxidizing agents, choice B is a mixture of a good reducing agent (methane) and a weak one (ammonia), and choice D is a mixture of a non-reactive salt and a mild reducing agent. The Mn atom in the permanganate ion, MnO_4^-, has an oxidation state of +7, making it one of the strongest known oxidizing agents. Manganese metal (like all metals) is a reducing agent. Heat the mixture in choice C and BANG!

5. **A** Since HCNO is not an oxidizing agent, the electronegative atoms N and O must not be directly bonded to one another. In addition to this, choices B, C, and D violate the valence requirements of hydrogen, oxygen, nitrogen, and carbon, which lead these elements to form one, two, three, and four covalent bonds, respectively.

6. **D** This is a classic redox tug-of-war question. The first problem is to decide who's pulling on whose electrons. You should realize that HCl(*aq*) and $ZnCl_2$(*aq*) are really H^+, Cl^-, and Zn^{2+} in solution. With this in mind, it is easier to figure out that chloride is a spectator ion; it doesn't affect anything (eliminating choice A). Next, it is apparent that the H^+ ion is pulling away (oxidizing) the zinc's electrons, but it cannot take away the copper's electrons. This means that H^+ is a better oxidizing agent than Zn^+ or Zn^{2+} but is not as strong as the Cu^+ ion. Therefore, choices B and C are incorrect and choice D is the best answer.

Passage 60

1. **A** The trick here is to realize that in any oxidation, the oxidation state must become more positive, so choice A is the only possible correct answer.

2. **D** Don't do things the hard way before thinking about what the question asks. If you tried to calculate oxidation states, you'd have a difficult task for this type of molecule. Here's a simpler approach: During the oxidation of NADH (the opposite reaction from the one given in the passage), the nitrogen is going from being neutral to being a cation. Therefore, in the reaction, the aromatic nitrogen atom is losing some electron density and becomes a cation.

3. **A** The question tells us that the metabolism of proteins goes to completion. What this implies is that the carbon atoms which make up most of the mass of a protein will be in their highest oxidation state, just like carbon in CO_2. The highest possible oxidation state of carbon is +4, so the trick is to find the carbon compound with a carbon in the oxidation state +4. To determine the oxidation state of a carbon atom, use the method we used in the solution to the first question in this passage. When you've done this, you will find that the correct answer is choice A, urea. The oxidation state of the carbon in choices B and D are +3 and 0, respectively, and for nitrogen in choice C, it is −3.

4. **C** Any protein that is going to interact with a chemical species must be chemically compatible with that species. The protein must have a hydrophilic (water-attracting) channel, because H^+, like all ions, is strongly hydrophilic. Secondly, in order for the proton to pass through the channel, the proton must not be repelled by it. Therefore, the channel must not be positively charged. The best answer is choice C.

Passage 61

1. **A** Cell voltage (E) and the Gibbs free energy change (ΔG) are related by the equation $\Delta G = -nFE$. Therefore, when E is positive, ΔG is negative, which indicates that the reaction is spontaneous.

2. **A** Electrolytic cells employ electricity generated somewhere else to drive a nonspontaneous chemical reaction. The only nonspontaneous reaction listed in the passage is Reaction 1, since it is the only one with a negative cell voltage.

3. **D** Since $[H^+]$ and pH follow opposite trends, choices B and C can be eliminated. As Reaction 3 proceeds, $[H^+]$ should decrease, which results in a higher pH.

4. **D** The number of electrons flowing in the cell has nothing to do with the cell potential. This eliminates choices A, B, and C. Since both zinc and magnesium lose two electrons per atom to form Zn^{2+} and Mg^{2+}, respectively, equal numbers of electrons will be produced if equal amounts of the metals are reacted.

5. **D** Any equilibrium with gases present will be affected by changes in pressure resulting in change of concentration if the numbers of gas molecules on the reactant and product sides are different. Since this is the case in all the reactions listed in the passage, the answer is choice D.

Passage 62

1. **B** Since Q takes the form of K (that is, it is the ratio of the concentration of the products over those of the reactants), Q will get larger as reactants are converted into products. As Q gets larger, $\log Q$ gets larger, so the term subtracted from $E°$ in the Nernst equation will increase, causing a decrease in E.

2. **C** The number of electrons exchanged in Reaction 2 is two.

3. C   The concentration terms for solids do not appear in the reaction quotient. Therefore, changing the amount of solid will not change Q. If Q does not change, then the Nernst equation implies that E will not change either.

4. C   If the concentrations of all the aqueous species is 1 M, then Q equals 1. Since log 1 = 0, the term subtracted from $E°$ in the Nernst equation is 0, so $E = E° = 1.56$ V.

5. D   Since log Q can be positive, negative, or zero (depending on whether Q is greater than, less than, or equal to 1, respectively), the Nernst equation implies that E can be less than, greater than, or equal to $E°$.

Passage 63

1. C   According to Table 2, the cell always had a positive potential, which indicates that the reactions were spontaneous. This eliminates choices A, B, and D, and supports choice C.

2. D   The anode is always the site of oxidation, and the cathode is always the site of reduction, so choices B and C are eliminated. In a voltaic cell, the anode is labeled as the negative electrode since free electrons are being formed there due to oxidation (and the cathode is the positive electrode since free electrons are consumed there by the reduction reaction). (Note: In an *electrolytic* cell, these designations are reversed: that is, the cathode is the negative electrode and the anode is the positive electrode.)

3. A   If electrons flow from the Zn electrode to the M electrode, then Zn is getting oxidized, and M is getting reduced. The unknown metal M cannot be Li, Ca or K since the reductions of $Li^+(aq)$ and $K^+(aq)$ have large negative potentials (see Table 1). This eliminates choices B, C and D. Since the oxidation of $Zn(s)$ has a potential of +0.76 V, we are looking for a reduction that has a potential of +0.52 V, to give a total cell potential of +1.28 V, as stated in the passage. The reduction of $Cu^+(aq)$ to $Cu(s)$ has such a potential.

4. D   Since the reactions in Experiment 2 actually happened, they must have been favoring the products. Since the K ratio is of products to reactants, this indicates that K should be greater than 1 (eliminate choices A and C). A large value of K corresponds to a negative value of $\Delta G°$, so choice D is correct.

5. B   Table 2 indicates that the battery voltage decreased as the initial $[Zn^{2+}]$ increased. Therefore, choices A and C are false, and choice B is true. There is no evidence that choice D is true.

Passage 64

1. A   The strongest oxidizing agent is the one with the greatest tendency to be reduced. Comparing Reactions 1, 2, and 3, it is clear that VO_2^+ has the highest reduction potential because V has a +5 oxidation state in this molecule.

2. **D** The passage states that it takes a stronger reducing agent to "bring about the reduction to V(II) . . . than to V(IV)." Therefore, it seems likely that an extremely strong reducing agent would indeed produce V(II), which is the lowest oxidation state.

3. **A** Each vanadium atom must lose three electrons to go from vanadium(II) to vanadium(V), but only one electron to go from vanadium(IV) to vanadium(V). Therefore, the number of electrons that must be removed from vanadium(IV) is one-third the number that must be removed from vanadium(II) to achieve the fully-oxidized vanadium(V) state. So, if 6 moles of permanganate ion are required for the complete oxidation of vanadium(II), only 2 moles will be required for the complete oxidation of vanadium(IV).

4. **A** In a redox reaction between MnO_4^- and VO^{2+}, the permanganate ion gets reduced and the vanadyl ion gets oxidized. This is because the reduction potential for MnO_4^- (1.51 V) is greater than the reduction potential for VO^{2+} (0.36 V). The oxidation of $VO^{2+}(aq)$ is the reverse of Reaction 1, so the oxidation reaction has a potential of $E° = -1.00$ V. The reduction potential for MnO_4^- is given in Reaction 4 as $E° = +1.51$ V. Therefore, the total cell potential is +0.51 V. (Remember: When calculating the total cell voltage, the $E°$ values for the half-reactions are *not* multiplied by any stoichiometric factors that are used to balance the numbers of electrons gained and lost in the overall redox reaction. Therefore, there is no need here to balance the half-reactions.)

5. **C** The oxidation number of each oxygen atom in MnO_4^- is –2, and the overall oxidation number for the ion must be –1. Therefore, the oxidation number of Mn is x, where $x + 4(-2) = -1$. This gives $x = +7$.

Passage 65

1. **C** The voltage of identical cells that are wired in *series* is equal to the sum of the individual cell voltages. The voltage of a single standard zinc fluorine cell, $E°_{cell}$, is +2.87 V – (–0.76 V) = 3.63 V. Therefore, the V_{total} of three cells must be 3.63 V + 3.63 V + 3.63 V = 10.89 V.

2. **D** The current of a number of identical cells wired in series is always equal to the current of one of the separate cells. However, this choice does not appear here. The numbers given in choices A and B are grabbed out of thin air, and choice C is an incorrect statement; a cell's voltage cannot be used to predict the current. In order to determine the I_{total}, you must be provided with the current of a single cell, or at the very least, more information that can be used to determine I_{cell}.

3. **D** The passage indicates that in a single cell, the current is a function of the surface area of both electrodes. Therefore, in constructing a high current battery, you would wish to use high surface area electrodes. The surface area of piece of foil would be greater than that of the other choices.

4. **C** This is a tricky question. Choice A is a true statement: The total current output of a battery is dependent upon the number of moles of the reactants, nothing else. Choice B is correct: Lithium–fluorine batteries are the highest voltage, single-cell battery possible, 5.90 volts. Choice D is an excerpt from the passage: last sentence, second paragraph. Choice C is an incorrect statement. While it is true that a cell with a positive voltage will produce a positive current, a cell with a negative voltage (non spontaneous reaction) is considered "dead" and will produce *no* current ($I_{cell} = 0.0$).

5. **A** The passage clearly indicates that in order for the rules of series and parallel wiring as presented here to hold, the cells must be identical.

Passage 66

1. **B** In Reaction #1, iron metal is oxidized to Fe^{2+}, and the hydrogen in the water molecules is reduced to $H_2(g)$. Based upon the schematic and Reaction #1, iron is first oxidized at the iron/droplet interface. Since the anode is *always* the site of oxidation, we conclude that the iron/water interface is the anode (based on this alone you could get the right answer). Oxygen is finally reduced in Reaction #2, and the rust which is produced in the reaction serves as a tracer for this reaction. Therefore, the cathode is the iron/atmosphere/droplet interface.

2. **C** The best way to answer this question is to eliminate the choices that contain scientifically incorrect statements. Choice A is wrong: The chloride ion has no desire to accept more electrons—thus it is not an oxidizing agent. Choice B is wrong because calcium and sodium are among the weakest oxidizing agents around, and further, if calcium and sodium metal *were* being formed on the bottom of your car during wet, sloshy weather, you'd know about it (BOOM!). As for choice D, it is true that the calcium ion is a weak acid, but sodium and chloride ions are neither acids nor bases. In fact, the dilemma in using street salts is that the ions in these salts serve as electrolytes, thereby increasing the conductivity of the thin water film that adheres to metal surfaces of automobiles during wet weather. The salt water film acts like a salt bridge between the metal and the atmosphere, greatly enhancing the corrosion rate of the metal surface.

3. **B** Although Reaction #1 produces two molecules of hydroxide for every molecule of iron, reaction #2 produces four protons for every two iron atoms. Therefore, the same amount of acid and base are produced in the reaction, and over time, the average pH of the whole droplet should remain constant.

4. **A** The first paragraph after the diagrams indirectly states that Reaction #1 and Reaction #2 are redox reactions. Choices B, C, and D are incorrect because a redox reaction supersedes all other types of reactions, that is, if an oxidation or a reduction is occurring in a reaction, *regardless of whether a precipitate or acid or base is being produced*, the reaction is still classified as a redox reaction.

5. **D** In the absence of any other substances, a junction between two different metals poses *no* problems because metals can never act as oxidizing agents becoming anions (there go choices A and B). However, in the presence of oxidizing agents, such as oxygen, both metals will be attacked by O_2. Yet interestingly enough, if the metals are in contact, the metal with the higher reduction potential (more corrosive resistant), in this case copper, will replace electrons lost to oxygen by taking them from the metal with the lower reduction potential, in this case iron. So for the Statue of Liberty, over time, the corrosion of copper was inadvertently minimized at the expense of the iron which was being oxidized by both O_2 and Cu^{2+}. The iron framework served as a *sacrificial anode*.

6. **A** All metal oxides are alkaline. Therefore, immersion in an acid bath will strip off these protective coats and allow the acid to begin to oxidize the metal below. For many metals, such as Al, Zn, and Mg, this reaction is rather fast, and copious amounts of $H_2(g)$ can be generated.

Passage 67

1. **B** According to basic stoichiometry, for every two Al produced, one and one-half molecules of O_2 will be produced. Therefore (dividing by two), for every mole of Al produced, three-quarters of a mole of O_2 is produced.

2. **D** Choice A is cannot be correct because oxygen is being *oxidized* (its oxidation state goes from –2 in water to 0 in oxygen gas!) during the electrolysis of water. Water is a *polar* molecule (*polar* is the adjective implying a *dipole moment*); it has a region of net positive charge and a region of net negative charge, yet the overall charge of the molecule is zero. Therefore, in an applied electric field, the water molecules will point their positive region at the negative terminal, and point their negative region at the positive terminal, but they will not move in either direction (choice B). Hydrogen is produced twice as fast as oxygen because there are two hydrogen for every oxygen in a water molecule. Na_2SO_4 is a soluble salt, and is therefore a good electrolyte.

3. **D** The anode is the site of oxidation. In an aqueous solution of NaCl, the only two possible oxidation products are $O_2(g)$ from H_2O or $Cl_2(g)$ from $Cl^-(aq)$.

4. **B** In the face of an electron configuration problem, one should always try to eliminate choices with the incorrect number of electrons. The configuration [Kr] $5s^1 4d^5$ accounts for 36 + 1 + 5 = 42 electrons. Therefore, the correct choice must have forty-two electrons (choice B). Recall that the electron configurations $ns^1(n-1)d^5$ and $ns^1(n-1)d^{10}$ are stable due to closed-shell stability.

5. **D** By definition, an electrolyte is a compound which, when dissolved in water, will produce lots of ions. Therefore, all ionic compounds, whether soluble or not, are technically electrolytes (this eliminates choices A and B). Moreover, all strong acids and bases are electrolytes because they completely dissociate (choice C is eliminated). The addition of water to water will not increase the concentration of dissolved ions (choice D).

Passage 68

1. **B** It is the convention that the arrow showing the direction of the current represents the direction a positive particle would travel in the applied potential field. Since electrons are negatively charged, the actual electron flow is always *opposite* this current arrow. But without this information, you could still determine which way the electrons were flowing based upon the fact that free electrons are being produce at the zinc electrode ($Zn \rightarrow Zn^{2+} + 2e^-$) and then are consumed at the copper electrode ($Cu^{2+} + 2e^- \rightarrow Cu$). So the electrons must be flowing from the zinc electrode to the copper electrode. Choices A and C are just off by 180°. Note that the atoms in a solid metal *do not* migrate (choice D).

2. **B** Since $G° = -nFE°$, when a cell has a positive voltage, the reaction must be spontaneous. Most often (especially when not dealing with gaseous species where ΔS is appreciable), spontaneous reactions are exothermic, not endothermic (choice C is eliminated). As for choice A, a reaction that is at equilibrium has a 0.00 voltage.

3. C   Choices A, B, and D are true statements. If a student allowed the reductant and the oxidant to come in direct contact, thereby causing a *short circuit*, the current through the wire would stop because the electrons will take the short way to the oxidant—right through the solution (choice A). Copper ions that come in contact with the surface of the zinc electrode would be reduced to copper metal and deposited onto the zinc electrode (choice B). Since the reaction is no longer producing an organized electrical flow, all of the energy of the reaction would be expelled as heat (choice D). Zinc ions cannot spontaneously oxidize copper metal because this process has an $E°_{cell}$ of −1.1 V (it's the reverse of the reaction in a galvanic cell), so choice C will not occur.

4. A   If the solution were allowed to solidify or precipitate out the copper ions, the reaction would completely stop (choices B and D). Copper ions require the ability to float to the cathode in order to be reduced. It is difficult to float without any water. Removal of the salt bridge, choice C, would prevent migratory ions to compensate the charge flow of the electrons. This means that after a second or so, the arriving electrons at the copper cathode would give it an *excess* negative charge. The anode would develop an *excess* positive charge because while it is exporting electrons to the cathode, the cations which are being formed are *not* allowed to migrate to the cathode. Therefore, very quickly, electrons would be unable to flow from the attacking positive anode towards the repulsive negative cathode because of electrostatic force.

5. B   The passage alludes to the fact that the function of the salt bridge is to facilitate ion migration while minimizing electron conduction. The function of the electrodes and wire is to conduct the electrical current, not ions. The passage indicated that choices A and C are good electrical conductors, and in this cell, choice D is actually serving as the anode so zinc must conduct electricity (as all metals do). Thus agar, which makes up the salt bridge, must be the least conducting material.

Passage 69

1. C   The voltage of a cell equals the sum of the voltage of the reduction and the oxidation reaction. Therefore, if the reductive reaction (MnO_2 to Mn^{2+}), has a potential of +1.23 volts and the oxidation reaction (Zn to Zn^{2+} under basic conditions) has a potential of +0.44 volts, then total cell potential is about 1.7 volts.

2. A   Choices B and C are wrong because air (especially moist air) is a poor electrical conductor, and the outermost casing of the battery is insulated from the positive terminal. But the most important reason why these statements are wrong is this: electrons do not flow from the cathode (positive terminal in a voltaic cell) to the anode (negative terminal in a voltaic cell). It's the other way around. Electrons flow from the negative terminal to the positive terminal. Choice D is also wrong for the analogous reason: cations do not spontaneously flow in the air from the negative terminal to the positive terminal. The correct answer, choice A, is an inherent problem of all electrochemical cells. Electrons can slowly pass through the salt bridge in the absence of a better conductor (like a wire), a process which eventually drains the battery over a period of years.

3.   D   (The MCAT sparingly asks questions that require calculations. More often, they ask qualitative questions about the sensitivity of one of the variables in an equation to another variable in that equation.) Careful examination of the graph indicates that for most of its life (measured as T_{use}), the battery output (V_{out}) is constant. Apparently, V_{out} only drops off when T_{use} gets very large. Choice A is incorrect because it states that as T_{use} gets bigger, V_{out} should get bigger. Choice B is incorrect because it suggests that from day one, the voltage should drop steadily to zero—this is the equation of a straight line, contrary to the given plot. Choice C is incorrect because at the instant the battery is first used, when T_{use} is very small, the value of $-K_e/T_{use}$ would be so large that the battery would have a huge, negative voltage for awhile. If this wasn't bad enough, at some later time, as the value of $-K_e/T_{use}$ became small, the voltage would approach a constant voltage that would be maintained forever. In short, choice C is just not realistic. The answer is D. If we assume K_e to be very small, for some stretch of time, T_{use}, the value of $-K_e(T_{use})^3$ would be small and thus V_{out} basically equals $E°_{cell}$ for most of the cell's life. But eventually, the cubic function of T_{use} grows so large that the "drainage" term, $-K_e(T_{use})^3$, becomes significant. At this point, V_{out} rapidly decreases to zero—just like a real cell (choice D).

4.   B   Choice A is not true. Most batteries would explode if you tried to recharge them due to the internal production of hydrogen gas. Choice C is backwards: Oxidation occurs at the anode (remember your vowels). Choice D is also backwards: The anode is often consumed in an electrochemical cell (and the cathode usually grows due to metal deposition).

Passage 70

1.   D   The setup shown is an example of a concentration cell. The difference in concentration will produce an electrical current, until the concentrations in both half-cells become equal. The standard cell voltage for this cell (and all concentration cells) is 0, because reciprocal redox reactions are occurring.

2.   D   No matter the type of cell, electrons always flow from anode to cathode. Also, oxidation always occurs at the anode and reduction always occurs at the cathode. In the concentration cell in the passage, $[Cu^{2+}]$ will increase in Beaker X and decrease in Beaker Y until they equalize. Therefore, oxidation occurs in Beaker X and reduction occurs in Beaker Y. Electrons flow from X to Y, and K^+ ions follow the electrons to minimize the charge build-up in Beaker Y.

3.   D   Assigning oxidation states yields:

$$CH_2F_2: F = -1, H = 0, C = +2;$$

$$K_2O: K = +1, O = -2;$$

$$S_4O_6^{2-}: O = -2, S = \text{average of } +2.5;$$

$$Fe_2O_3: O = -2, Fe = +3;$$

Since +3 is the greatest number, choice D is the best answer.

4.   C   Electrons always travel from anode to cathode. Loss of electrons, or oxidation, always occurs at the anode and gain of electrons, or reduction, always occurs at the cathode. A concentration cell is spontaneous, so electrons will spontaneously flow to a positive charge. Therefore, the cathode must be positively charged, eliminating choices A and B. Since $[Cu^{2+}]$ will increase in X and decrease in Y, X is the site of oxidation, or anode.

5.   B   A concentration cell is spontaneous, eliminating the negative values of potential in choices C and D. The net "reaction" of the concentration cell in the passage is:

$$Cu^{2+}_{1\,M} \rightarrow Cu^{2+}_{0.01\,M}$$

Therefore, the reaction quotient is:

$$Q = \frac{[0.01]}{[1]} = \frac{1}{100}$$

Copper is reacting between the Cu and Cu(II) state, so $n = 2$. Substitute these quantities into the Nernst equation to solve for potential:

$$E = E^{\circ} - \frac{0.0592}{n} \log Q = 0 - \frac{0.0592}{2} \log \frac{1}{100} = 0.059\,V$$

Passage 71

1.   B   Choice A correctly defines the function of n, not of 2.303. The conversion factor between units of energy of calories and joules is 4.184 J cal^{-1} (choice C), and choice D is not true. The value 2.303 is a conversion factor between natural (base e) and common (base 10) logs.

2.   C   The second experiment took the control cell (where the concentration of zinc and copper ions were 1.0 M) and simply heated it to 100°C. According to the Nernst equation, whenever the concentration of zinc and copper ions are equal, $E_{cell} = E^{\circ}_{cell}$, regardless of temperature. This is because log 1 = 0, thereby making the right hand term drop out of the equation. Therefore choices B and D are incorrect, and choice A is not consistent with the data in the passage (which indicates that over time, the voltage of the cell *dropped* to zero).

3.   C   By definition, standard state conditions—represented by the superscript °—means temperature = 25°C = 298 K, pressure = 1 atm = 760 torr, and the concentration of all solutes is one molar.

4.   A   Choice B is inconsistent with everything said about galvanic cells. Why would zinc ions appear in the Nernst equation if they precipitated out of solution? Choice C has it backwards—colorimetry can only be used on colored solutions because transparent solutions do not absorb light. Ions will be colored if they have a partially filled d or f orbitals. The electronic configuration of Cu^{2+} is [Ar] $3d^9$ and that of Zn^{2+} is [Ar] $3d^{10}$—copper solutions are blue or green, and zinc solutions are colorless.

5. **D** The reagents of a galvanic cell are $Cu^{2+}(aq)$ and $Zn(s)$. Therefore, only one of these substances can be the limiting reagent—eliminating choices B and C. The colorimetry data indicates that even after the cell in Trial 2 ceased to produce a voltage, the solution still was absorbing light. This directly suggests that copper ions remained in solution after the cell had died. The zinc anode must have been all used up first, and therefore it is the limiting reagent.

6. **A** The procedure in choice B would increase the current of the cell; the cell voltage would not be affected. Choice C would kill the battery because of an opposing charge separation that would develop on the electrodes. Since the copper cathode is just serving as an electrochemical junction between the solution and the wire and not participating in any chemistry, its chemical identity is irrelevant. Replacing copper with another inert, conducting metal like platinum (choice D) would have no effect. According to the Nernst equation, if the concentration of Zn^{2+} dropped to very low levels via a precipitation reaction, the voltage of the cell would increase because as $[Zn^{2+}]$ becomes small, $[Zn^{2+}]/[Cu^{2+}]$ becomes a small fraction. The log of a small fraction (i.e., a fraction < 1) is a negative number, and because the term on the right is negative, a negative log makes the whole term positive. If the whole right hand term is positive, then $E_{cell} = E^{\circ}_{cell}$ + some more.

Passage 72

1. **C** Choice D is eliminated since decay causes a decrease in the amount of the substance. Radioactive decay is characterized by a rapid initial decrease, but the rate of decrease gets smaller and smaller as time goes on. This is illustrated by choice C.

2. **B** Alpha decay results in the loss of two protons (and two neutrons) per decay. Since atomic number counts the number of protons only, three alpha decays would result in a decrease by $3 \times 2 = 6$ in the atomic number.

3. **D** The identity of an element depends on the number of protons in the nucleus. If there is a change in the charge of the nucleus, there must have been a change in the number of protons (since neutrons have no charge), and thus, a change in the atom's identity.

4. **C** The result of beta decay is the transformation of a neutron into a proton (and an expelled electron). Therefore, the atomic number increases by one. So, if the original atom was magnesium (atomic number 12), the daughter atom will be aluminum (atomic number 13).

5. **B** After one half-life has elapsed, 50% of the radioisotope has decayed, leaving 50% remaining. After a second half-life, one-half of the remaining 50% is lost, leaving just 25% of the original amount. After a third half-life, one-half of the remaining 25% is lost, leaving just 12.5% of the original amount. At this point (3 half-lives), since 12.5% remains, the difference, 87.5%, has decomposed.

6. **A** Choices B and C are wrong since mass number is the total number of protons and neutrons in a nucleus, and atomic weight is the relative mass of an atom based on a scale where ^{12}C is assigned a mass of 12. Choice D is wrong since critical mass is the minimum mass of a fissionable material necessary to sustain a nuclear chain reaction. The answer is choice A.

Passage 73

1. **A** Since ^{42}K has a longer half-life, it will decay more slowly. Therefore, its rate constant will be less than the rate constant for ^{99m}Tc; this eliminates choices C and D. If $t_{1/2}$ denotes the half-life, then Equation 2 implies that the product $kt_{1/2}$ must be a constant (namely, ln 2). By definition then, k is inversely proportional to $t_{1/2}$, so if $t_{1/2}$ is larger by a factor of 2, then the corresponding k is smaller by a factor of 2.

2. **C** A nuclear reaction that releases energy is called exoergic (just as a chemical reaction that releases heat is called exothermic). (Note that you could eliminate both choice A and choice D since they both imply taking in energy [endo- means "taking in"], and the process in Equation 1 certainly does not imply an equilibrium, so choice B is eliminated. This leaves choice C as the correct answer.)

3. **C** After 5 half-lives have elapsed, the amount of any radioisotope that remains is $(1/2)^5 = 1/32$ of the original amount. Thus, 31/32 of the sample decayed.

4. **A** The result of beta decay is the transformation of a neutron to a proton and an expelled electron. The mass number does not change (eliminating choices C and D), but the atomic number increases by one. So, if the original atom was technetium ($^{99}_{43}Tc$), the daughter atom will be ruthenium ($^{99}_{44}Ru$).

5. **B** In this molecule, the oxidation number of the Na atom is +1, and the oxidation number of each O atom is –2. Since the sum of all the oxidation numbers in any neutral molecule must be zero, if we let x denote the oxidation number of Tc in $NaTcO_4$, then we must have $(+1) + x + 4(-2) = 0$, which implies $x = +7$.

6. **D** Sodium pertechnetate is an ionic compound, and all ionic compounds are strong electrolytes; this eliminates A. This compound is not a Group I oxide or hydroxide, so it is not a strong base; this eliminates choice B. Due to the high oxidation state of the central atom, pertechnetate ions are strong oxidizing agents.

Passage 74

1. **D** Magnetic fields can only affect charged particles in motion. Gamma rays are high-energy photons; they are not charged particles.

2. **C** Since Po has atomic number 84, and Pb has atomic number 82, the transmutation of ^{84}Po to ^{82}Pb results in an overall loss of two protons. Two alpha decays would result in a loss of four protons, so other nuclear reactions must have resulted in a gain of two protons. If these are β^- decays, each of which increases the number of protons in the nucleus by one, then there must have been two beta decays.

3. **C** After one half-life, 1/2 of the sample remains. After two half-lives, 1/4 remains. After three half-lives, 1/8 remains, and after four half-lives, 1/16 remains. Since 1/10 is between 1/16 and 1/8, the time that has elapsed when 1/10 of the original amount is left must be between three and four half-lives. So, if each half-life is 4 sec, then the elapsed time must be between 12 and 16 sec. Only choice C falls in this range.

4. **A** Since the identity of a nucleus is determined exclusively by the number of protons it contains, we only need to keep track of the number of protons that results from the series of decays. Radium has atomic number 88, and each alpha decay results in the loss of two 2 protons, and each beta decay results in the gain of 1 proton. Therefore, after four alpha decays and two beta decays, the number of protons left should be $88 - 4(2) + 2(1) = 82$. This is the atomic number of lead (Pb).

5. **C** Mass has been converted into energy, as described by the equation $E = mc^2$. Since $c = 3 \times 10^8$ m/s, we find

$$E = (2.2 \times 10^{-31} \text{ kg})(3 \times 10^8 \text{ m/s})^2 = 2.0 \times 10^{-14} \text{ J}$$

Passage 75

1. **C** The table tells us that gamma rays penetrate into lead a little less than 3 log mm units. But 3 $\log_{10}$ mm units means 10^3 mm = 1 meter.

2. **D** Cesium-137 decays via β^- emission. During this decay process, a neutron is converted into a proton and an electron (which is violently ejected). Therefore, the atomic number increases by one, but the mass number remains constant. This gives barium-137. (Remember that the mass number does not change after any type of beta decay.)

3. **B** Gamma-ray photons (like all photons) are massless, and these have the greatest depth of penetration. Beta particles are electrons, which have less mass and greater penetrability than alpha particles. Thus, there is an inverse relationship between mass and depth of penetrability. Note that choices C and D are identical.

4. **D** Hemoglobin is synthesized in the bone marrow, but there is no strontium in hemoglobin [only four iron(II) ions]; this eliminates choice A. Choice B is wrong since Be is extremely toxic to organisms. (There is no Be in living organisms.) The statement in choice C is only partially true: heavy metals are incorporated into the bone matrix, but heavy-metal induced cancers require chronic exposure to a metal source and take decades to develop. Choice D is the best option: Sr and Ca are chemically compatible.

5. **C** A patient has received radiation burns localized to epithelial surfaces exposed to the environment. Therefore, the radiation in question must not penetrate tissue very well. Based on this, a gamma emitter is ruled out (gamma rays would cause equivalent damage to all tissues, especially dense tissues like bone). The burns to the respiratory track indicate the agent was airborne, which makes radon the primary suspect since radon is a gas.

6. **D** The difference according to the illustration is approximately two $\log_{10}$ units, that is, $10^2 = 100$ times.

Passage 76

1. **C** Nuclear reactions must conserve nucleon number and charge. After a single neutron capture, plutonium-239 becomes plutonium-240, which then undergoes fission. The products must have a total of 240 protons and neutrons; more specifically, the products must account for 94 protons and 146 neutrons. This eliminates choice B which has only 239 nucleons. A second consideration is that fission will generate two nuclei of about the same mass and some free neutrons; this eliminates choices A and D.

2. **B** Progressing through the periodic table, small stable nuclei have the same number of protons and neutrons. But because the intranuclear electrostatic repulsion within a more crowded nucleus is much greater, more neutrons are required to keep bigger nuclei together. Therefore, the number of neutrons, N, should increase faster than the number of protons, Z, and the graph should begin to curve upwards as Z increases.

3. **D** Based on the passage, choice A is wrong. As for choices B and C, there is no evidence supporting these statements and moreover, they are counterintuitive—should a safe reactor have more concentrated fuel than a bomb? The last sentence of the passage gives the correct answer, choice D.

4. **A** The concentration of neutrons is not required for this problem. After one half-life, 50% of any radioactive substance remains. After two half-lives, 25% remains, and after three half-lives, 12.5% remains. Therefore, to achieve a concentration equal to 15% of the original takes almost three half-lives. Since each half-life is 11 minutes, the total time required is a little less than $3 \times 11 = 33$ minutes. Choice A, 30 minutes, is a little less than 33 and is the correct answer choice.

5. **A** By definition, a fissile is a nucleus which will become a fissioning nucleus after the addition of one neutron. If one neutron is absorbed by ^{232}Th, it will become the fissioning isotope ^{233}Th. Thus, ^{232}Th is the fissile.

6. **C** If the neutron to proton ratio in the nucleus is about 1.5, then when the nucleus undergoes fission (splits), the daughter nuclei must have approximately this same ratio. It is true that two neutrons are being lost, so the ratio changes slightly, but 2 neutrons compared to the remaining 144 are negligible. Choice C is best.

Passage 77

1. **C** The phrase "order of magnitude" means "a power of ten." So the last sentence tells us that the fusion reaction releases ten times more energy than the fission reaction.

2. **C** Since some mass is converted into energy in this reaction, nucleus C must be slightly less massive than the total mass of the nuclei A and B.

3. **C** Nuclear reactions conserve charge and (almost) mass. Four hydrogens have a total charge of +4, while helium has a charge of +2; so we're missing +2 charge. The only choice with a charge of +1 is choice C (the coefficient 2 in the equation gives the needed additional +2 on the product side). [Note: If one of the choices had been "Proton," this would balance the charge, but there would be too great an imbalance in mass. The mass on the reactant side is approximately 4 amu, as is the mass on the product right (^{4}He). The additional X particles must be positively charged and have very little mass.]

4. **B** If F is proportional to both Q^2 and to T, then T is proportional to Q^2. The graph of T vs. Q must therefore be a parabola; choice B is best. (Also remember that the trick to fusion is to achieve very high temperatures which force the nuclei together. Therefore, as the charges of the nuclei go up, the temperature required to squeeze them together must also go up [and much faster because if the nuclei charges double, then the force of repulsion increases by a factor of $2^2 = 4$].)

5. **A** Choice B is incorrect because free neutrons are always incorporated into surrounding nuclei. Choice C can be eliminated since neutrons are not contained by a magnetic field (only charged particles can be contained this way, since magnetic fields only affect moving charged particles). Choice D can also be eliminated since pure neutron nuclei don't exist this side of a neutron star.

Passage 78

1. **A** The passage says that PET ultimately involves injecting the patient with ^{11}C or ^{13}N or ^{15}O. Since all of these radionuclides are positron emitters, the product of the decay of these isotopes would be (respectively) ^{11}B or ^{13}C or ^{15}N. Of these, only boron-11 appears among the four choices.

2. **C** X-rays are only at their best when imaging dense material, such as bone, so choices A and B are not the best choices. Typically, however, tumors are rapidly growing clusters of cells that have high demands for nutrient intake. ^{131}I is not a nutrient requirement of cells (thyroid being an exception) and would not be absorbed into the tissues, eliminating D.

3. **D** As indicated by the periodic table, ^{127}I is the naturally occurring, stable form of iodine essential to the diet for normal thyroid function. After administration, ^{131}I overwhelms ^{127}I for uptake in thyroid tissue. The maximum ^{131}I signal achieved after administration will immediately begin to exponentially decrease due to decay, eliminating choices B and C. On Day 3 the large amount of ingested ^{127}I will compete with ^{131}I resulting in a significant decrease in ^{131}I signal intensity in thyroid tissue. Since choice A illustrates an increase in ^{131}I signal intensity follwing Day 3, it is eliminated and D is the best answer.

4. **B** If the half-life of ^{131}I is 8 days and on day 20 the sample radiates 20 counts/sec, then on day 12, one half-life before, the activity rate must have been twice as much: 40 counts/sec. On day 4, another half-life before, there must have been twice as much as day 12, that is, 80 counts/sec. The one answer you should have dismissed right away was choice A; the concentration of the given radionuclide sample cannot increase with time.

5.   **B**   This question requires a little biological background. The passage states that ^{99m}Tc is retained by cells that pass large quantities of fluid or plasma through their membranes, but the best answer is the kidney-liver, two highly vascular organs whose primary function is to purify blood by filtering fluids through cellular membranes. Choice C is wrong since the stomach and intestine allow diffusion through their membranes, from the digestive cavity to the blood; but there's no technetium in the digestive cavity. Tc is administered directly into the circulatory system. It is true that a tremendous amount of blood travels through the heart, but none of it diffuses into any cells.

Passage 79

1.   **B**   The passage states that a control rod is used to capture neutrons. Therefore the atoms of the control rod will become heavier isotopes with time, and these heavier isotopes are often highly radioactive. Graphite (pure ^{12}C) is best suited for this role because each carbon atom can capture one neutron without becoming radioactive. Even with a second neutron capture, carbon forms the very slowly decaying ^{14}C. All of the other choices involve atoms that would become highly radioactive after a single neutron capture.

2.   **B**   One half-life is the time required for half of a radioisotope to decay into another atom. A 110 g sample of ^{28}Al would therefore require two half-lives to decrease to one-fourth its mass ($\approx$ 25 g). Since each half-life is 150 sec = 2.5 minutes, we must wait a little longer than 2×2.5 = 5 minutes.

3.   **B**   We must balance the nuclear reaction

$$^{235}_{92}\text{U} \rightarrow \ ^{142}_{56}\text{Ba} + \ ^{A}_{Z}\text{X} + 3\left(^{1}_{0}\text{n}\right).$$

Since it is the number of protons, Z, that determines the identity of an element, we need only find Z: $92 = 56 + Z + 3(0)$ implies $Z = 36$, so X = Kr (krypton).

4.   **C**   (This question involves a ratio, something commonly tested on the MCAT.) If the size of the nucleus of an atom is 10^{-14} m and that of the entire atom is 10^{-10} m, then the atom is 10^4 = 10,000 times bigger than the nucleus. If the nucleus were the size of a marble (1 cm), then the atom must be 10,000 cm = 100 m, roughly the size of a sports stadium. (Note: An atom is more than 99.99% empty space!)

5.   **A**   Alpha radiation is the emission of a cluster of two protons and two neutrons (a helium nucleus). Shortly after its release, the energetic alpha particle rips off two electrons from another atom to become inert helium.

6.   **A**   The decay of any radioactive sample clearly implies that its concentration must decrease with time. This decrease is always the most rapid when the radioisotope is most abundant, so the slope of the graph should be the steepest at first, then gradually flatten out as $t \rightarrow \infty$. (The curve is an exponential decay graph.)

Passage 80

1. **D** Any molecule or atom that has at least one electron can undergo electronic transitions, regardless of whether the molecule is conjugated or not, eliminating choice A. Energy may not be created, so an atom may not emit photons of greater energy than those absorbed, so choices B and C are wrong. Fluorescent molecules always emit photons of equal or lesser energy (and frequency) than those absorbed: choice D.

2. **B** An sp^3 hybridized carbon atom is bonded to four other atoms. Examining the structure of fluorecein in the passage, there is only 1 carbon atom that satisfies this criterion.

3. **A** This question involves simple dimensional analysis. In all equations, the units on both sides of the equal sign must be identical. Since λ (wavelength) can be measured in centimeters (cm) and absolute temperature is measured in kelvins (K), the units on the right hand side of the equation can be cm·K, choice A (but none of the others). This question is an example of how simple things can be made to look much more complicated!

4. **D** Choice A is the ground state configuration—not an excited configuration—of an oxygen atom. Choice B is the ground state configuration of an atom with nine electrons, so this cannot be correct since an oxygen atom has only eight. Finally, choice C is disqualified because there is no such thing as a $2d$ orbital. Choice D is the answer (one of the $2p$ electrons got excited to the $3s$ subshell).

Passage 81

1. **C** Apparently, alpha particles are emitted from the thorium-228 nucleus at discrete energies. This result supports the idea that nuclear energies are quantized (Theorist #1). However, beta particles emitted from the copper-64 nucleus cover a continuous band of energies. So this experiment supports the idea that the nucleus is not quantized (Theorist #2). Therefore, the experimentalist's results support parts of both models.

2. **A** An alpha particle is a cluster of two protons and two neutrons. It is impossible for ^3H to emit an alpha particle because the tritium nucleus (called a triton) only has one proton and two neutrons.

3. **D** Positrons are antielectrons: same mass as electrons (eliminating choices A and B) but positively charged. Since like charges repel one another, once a positron is formed in the nucleus, it is accelerated out of there by the electrostatic repulsion of the resident protons (choice D). Neutrons have no charge, so they will neither electrostatically attract nor repel charged particles like protons and electrons do (this eliminates choice C).

4. **B** The second graph shows us that β⁻ particles are emitted over a range of energies from 50 keV to 600 keV. However, many more particles are emitted having low energy than high energy. Therefore, the weighted average energy of β⁻ particles emitted from copper-64 nuclei will be a bit less than 325 keV (the ordinary average of 50 and 600 keV). Choice B, 250 keV, is best.

5. **C** Since the β⁺ decay of ^{64}Cu is

$$^{64}Cu \rightarrow {^{64}Ni} + e^+$$

(daughter is ^{64}Ni), we are asked to identify the nuclear reaction whose daughter is also ^{64}Ni. The products of each of the processes presented as choices are given below (verify):

α decay of ^{64}Cu:	$^{64}Cu \rightarrow {^{60}Co} + \alpha$
β⁻ decay of ^{64}Cu:	$^{64}Cu \rightarrow {^{64}Zn} + e^-$
EC by ^{64}Cu:	$^{64}Cu + e^- \rightarrow {^{64}Ni}$ (*)
γ decay of ^{64}Cu:	$^{64}Cu \rightarrow {^{64}Cu} + \gamma$

Positron emission and electron capture always yield the same daughter nucleus.

6. **D** The first graph shows that as the energy of the alpha particles increases, so does their number (choice B is eliminated). Note that the vertical axis is logarithmic. Using the dashed line, we see that a small increase in KE gives a large increase in C. Choices A and C are inconsistent with this observation. The best expression of this relationship is the exponential in choice D.

Passage 82

1. **B** If the conversion of heat to electrical energy was complete (100% efficient), then the temperature of the intake and outflow tertiary water should be the same. It is not (choice A is eliminated). The reaction inside all nuclear reactions is fission, not fusion (choice C is eliminated). Choice D is backwards. Electric turbines are used to convert mechanical energy (the spinning propeller driven by the pressure of the steam) to electrical energy.

    Atmospheric pressure at sea-level is 760 torr. At high enough temperatures, the vapor pressure of water is much greater than this (choice B). Recall that water does not boil until the vapor pressure equals the external pressure. As long as the pressure over the water inside the pipes is greater than the water's vapor pressure, it will remain a liquid.

2. **B** If F ($Z = 9$) were to alpha decay, the daughter nucleus would be N ($Z = 9 - 2 = 7$), and the mass number would decrease from $A = 19$ to $A = 19 - 4 = 15$ (this eliminates choice A). If ^{15}O decayed by positron emission, the daughter nucleus would have $Z = 8 - 1 = 7$, and the mass number, $A = 15$, would remain unchanged (this eliminates choice C). Finally, if ^{15}O experienced electron capture, the net effect is the same as positron emission: The atomic number would decrease by 1 (to $8 - 1 = 7$, which is N), and the mass number (= 15) would remain the same (this eliminates choice D). The correct answer must be choice B. If ^{14}C beta decays, its atomic number will increase by 1 to $6 + 1 = 7$, which is nitrogen, but the mass number would stay at 14. That is, ^{14}C beta decays to ^{14}N, not to ^{15}N.

3. **D** As the temperature of a substance increases, the number of intermolecular forces decreases (choice A is just not true). Furthermore, as the temperature of a substance increases, it expands, so the spacing between molecules increases (choice B is not true). The spacing cannot increase in this particular situation, but it certainly will not decrease. The passage indicates that the primary coolant water is pressurized so it won't boil (choice C is eliminated). As one increases the temperature of a substance, the molecular motion (average kinetic energy) of the molecules increases overcoming ordering intermolecular forces resulting in higher entropy (choice D is the best answer).

4. **A** Based upon the information in the question, we can write:

$$H^+ + OH^- \rightarrow H_2O + heat, \Delta H_{rxn} < 0 \text{ (exothermic)}$$

Increasing the temperature will shift the reaction to the left, increasing $[H^+]$ and $[OH^-]$. Since the pH is nothing more than $-\log[H^+]$, at high temperatures, the pH of water is less than seven. (All K's are a function of temperature [choice B is eliminated]. Pressure does not affect reactions that do not have gaseous products or reactants [choice D is incorrect].)

5. **A** This reaction is a oxidation–reduction (redox) reaction because the oxidation state of the sodium and hydrogen atoms go from 0 to +1 and +1 to 0, respectively. Hint: The production of hydrogen gas is almost always a dead give-away that a chemical reaction is a redox reaction (choice A). Choices B and C are eliminated because these reactions do not involve the change in oxidation states of any of the participating atoms. A combustion reaction is a subclass of redox reactions in which oxygen gas is converted to carbon dioxide and/or water (choice D is not applicable here).

6. **D** The heat content of a substance is $q = m \cdot C_{sp} \cdot \Delta T$. The mass of 1.0 L of water is 1.0 kg or 1000 grams (recall that each mL of water has a mass of one gram). The C_{sp} of water equals 1.0 cal/(g·°C), and ΔT equals 8°C (= 31°C – 23°C). Therefore, the heat content of 1.0 L = 1000 grams of tertiary coolant water is 8000 cal.

MCAT Organic Chemistry

Passages

Passage 1 (Questions 1-5)

Recent research has demonstrated that there is a class of DNA-cleaving molecules that are referred to as *enediynes*. These compounds are known as enediynes because they contain a continuous six-carbon unit in which there is one double bond and two triple bonds. These DNA-cleaving molecules appear to be quite potent and, most importantly, selective in regards to anticancer activity. The following molecule has proven to be one of the more potent of these enediyne molecules:

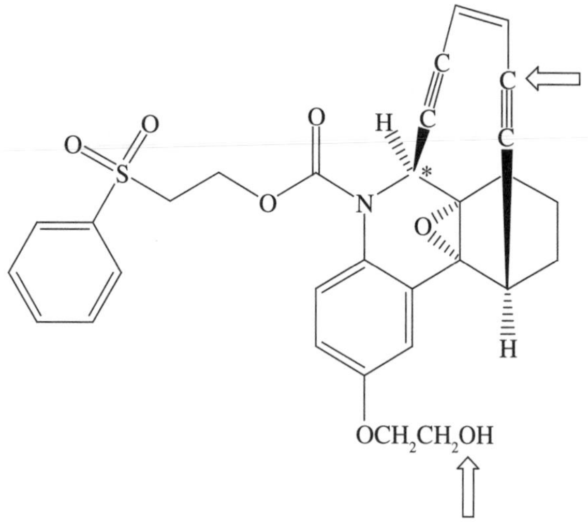

1. Identify the hybridization of the carbon atom and the oxygen atom indicated by the arrows.

    A. C: *sp*, O: *sp*²
    B. C: *sp*, O: *sp*³
    C. C: *sp*², O: *sp*³
    D. C: *sp*³, O: *sp*³

2. How many π bonds does this molecule have?

    A. 12
    B. 13
    C. 14
    D. 15

3. Which of the following functional groups is NOT present in this molecule?

    A. An alcohol
    B. A thiol
    C. An epoxide
    D. An ether

4. Which of the following statements is true about the absolute configuration of the indicated (*) carbon atom?

    A. The carbon is not chiral.
    B. The carbon has an *R* absolute configuration.
    C. The carbon has an *S* absolute configuration.
    D. The absolute configuration at this carbon cannot be determined.

5. How many possible stereoisomers does the molecule have?

    A. 4
    B. 8
    C. 16
    D. 32

Passage 2 (Questions 1-6)

Disparlure, *cis*-7,8-epoxy-2-methyloctadecane (see Figure 1 below), is a pheromone of the gypsy moth *Porthetria dispar*. Synthetic disparlure has proven to be a potent agent for attracting and trapping this harmful pest. It is important to note that the presence of the enantiomer in a sample of natural pheromone dramatically reduces the compound's activity. For this reason, the synthetic preparation of enantiomerically pure disparlure is essential.

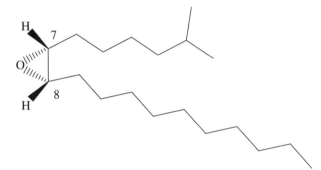

Figure 1 Disparlure

1. In disparlure, what are the absolute configurations of carbons 7 and 8?

    A. 7*R*, 8*R*
    B. 7*R*, 8*S*
    C. 7*S*, 8*R*
    D. 7*S*, 8*S*

2. What is the sign of the optical rotation of disparlure?

    A. (+)
    B. (−)
    C. 0
    D. Cannot be determined from the information given

3. The most reactive functional group in this molecule is the:

    A. isopropyl group.
    B. straight C_{10} alkyl chain.
    C. ketone.
    D. epoxide.

4. Disparlure and the molecule shown below can best be described as:

    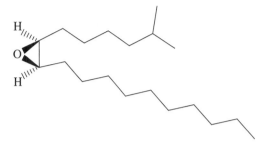

    A. enantiomers.
    B. tautomers.
    C. diastereomers.
    D. identical molecules.

5. If disparlure is treated with H⁺ and H_2O to open the epoxide ring, what product(s) will be formed?

6. In which of the following solvents should disparlure be most soluble?

   A. Water
   B. Methanol
   C. Ethyl acetate
   D. 50:50 Ethanol/water

Passage 3 (Questions 1-6)

When an organic compound is burned completely in oxygen, the energy released is known as the heat of combustion. For simple hydrocarbons, the general formula is given by the following equation:

$$C_xH_y + zO_2 \rightarrow xCO_2 + \frac{y}{2}H_2O.$$

The heat of combustion of a particular compound depends on several factors, including molecular weight, angle strain, and degree of branching. In most cases, the compound with the higher molecular weight will have the larger heat of combustion. For simple alkanes and cycloalkanes, each additional –CH$_2$– adds approximately –156 kcal/mol to the heat of combustion. For cycloalkanes, this value increases with increasing angle strain.

More meaningful information can be obtained by comparing the ΔH_{comb} of several isomeric compounds. This allows chemists to determine which structural features are the most thermodynamically stable. Research has shown that straight-chain hydrocarbons have heats of combustion of greater magnitude than those of more branched isomers. In addition, molecules that have little or no angle strain tend to have lower heats of combustion than compounds with bond angles that substantially deviate from the normal value for that bond type, for example approximately 109° for an sp^3 hybridized carbon atom.

1. The heat of combustion of propane is reported to be –530 kcal/mol. A reasonable approximation for the heat of combustion for n-heptane would be:

   A. –685 kcal/mol.
   B. –840 kcal/mol.
   C. –995 kcal/mol.
   D. –1150 kcal/mol.

2. The complete combustion of one mole of neopentane in oxygen would produce how many moles of CO_2 and H_2O?

   A. 4 moles of CO_2, 5 moles of H_2O
   B. 5 moles of CO_2, 5 moles of H_2O
   C. 5 moles of CO_2, 6 moles of H_2O
   D. 6 moles of CO_2, 5 moles of H_2O

3. Which one of the following molecules would have the heat of combustion of highest magnitude (i.e., most negative)?

   A.

   B.

   C.

   D.

4. The heat of combustion of *n*-hexane is –995 kcal/mol, while the heat of combustion of 2-methylpentane is –994 kcal/mol. One can therefore conclude that:

   A. *n*-hexane has greater angle strain than 2-methyl-pentane.
   B. 2-methylpentane is more branched than *n*-hexane.
   C. 2-methylpentane is thermodynamically less stable than *n*-hexane.
   D. *n*-hexane has a lower molecular weight.

5. A planar ten-membered ring would have bond angles of 144°. Cyclodecane has a heat of combustion of –1574 kcal/mol, suggesting very little angle strain. One might conclude from this information that:

   A. cyclodecane is not a planar molecule.
   B. bond angles larger than 109° do not increase angle strain.
   C. the carbon atoms in cyclodecane are *sp²* hybridized.
   D. 1,3,5,7,9-cyclodecapentaene would have the same heat of combustion.

6. The difference in the heats of combustion of cyclohexane and cycloheptane is due mainly to the difference in:

   A. angle strain.
   B. molecular weight.
   C. branching.
   D. ring conformations.

Passage 4 (Questions 1-4)

Figure 1 presents several possible syntheses of amines from an alcohol. Table 1 classifies these reactions according to type of reaction and the change in the number of carbons.

Figure 1 Possible syntheses of amines from an alcohol

Rxn	Reaction type	Change in the number of carbons
A	Reduction of nitriles	+1
B	Reductive amination of aldehydes	0
C	Ammonolysis of alkyl halides	0
D	Hofmann rearrangement	–1

Table 1 Classification of Reactions in Figure 1

1. Ethanol is aminated through a series of reactions which includes halogenation and hydrogenation. Which reaction type is most likely involved?

   A. Reductive amination of an aldehyde
   B. Reduction of a nitrile
   C. Alkyl halide ammonolysis
   D. Hofmann rearrangement

2. Hydrolysis of a benzylic halide will yield the corresponding:

   A. aromatic hydrocarbon and carboxyl group.
   B. halogenated ring structure.
   C. oxidized nitrile.
   D. alcohol and protonated halide.

3. *p*-Toluidine is somewhat soluble in water due to the polarity of:

   A. benzene.
   B. *p*-toluidinoic acid.
   C. *p*-toluidine's amine group.
   D. *p*-toluidine's aromatic ring structure.

4. Methyl bromide can generate the corresponding methylamine through alkyl halide ammonolysis. The nitrile reduction pathway would generate the corresponding:

   A. reduced methylene group.
   B. dehalogenated methyl group.
   C. ethylmethylamide.
   D. ethylamine.

Passage 5 (Questions 1-4)

Camphor is a naturally-occurring, chiral, bicyclic ketone. It has a distinctive pine odor and is used in many medicines and health aids.

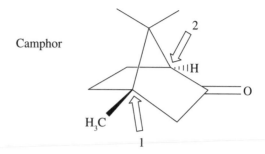

When camphor is treated with MeMgBr, two isomeric compounds are formed: *E* and *F*. Compounds *E* and *F* were individually reacted with concentrated HBr and both produced isomeric bromides *S* and *T*.

1. What is the maximum possible number of stereoisomers of camphor?

   A. 2
   B. 4
   C. 8
   D. 16

2. What is the stereochemical relationship between Compounds *E* and *F*?

   A. They are diastereomers.
   B. They are enantiomers.
   C. They are identical stereoisomers.
   D. They are meso isomers.

3. What are the absolute configurations of carbons 1 and 2 (see figure), respectively, in the camphor molecule?

A. R, R
B. R, S
C. S, R
D. S, S

4. The specific optical rotation of Bromide S was measured to be +52°. What would be the specific optical rotation of Bromide T?

A. −52°
B. 0°
C. +52°
D. Cannot be determined from the information given

Passage 6 (Questions 1-5)

The hydrogenation of alkenes in the presence of a suitable catalyst produces alkanes. The heat of hydrogenation is the amount of heat released when molecular hydrogen is added to the double bond. These exothermic processes are represented by the reaction of ethylene with hydrogen in Reaction 1:

Reaction 1

The table below lists the heats of hydrogenation for a number of unsaturated hydrocarbons.

Alkene	ΔH_{hydrog} (kcal/mol)
Ethylene	32.8
Propylene	30.1
1-Butene	30.3
1-Pentene	30.1
cis-2-Butene	28.6
trans-2-Butene	27.6
2-Methyl-2-butene	26.9
2,3-Dimethyl-2-butene	26.6

Table 1

Alkenes can also undergo oxidation. Ozone, a powerful oxidizing agent, reacts quickly with alkenes by cleaving the double bond to produce two molecules (Figure 1). The oxidation reaction occurs via Intermediates 1 and 2.

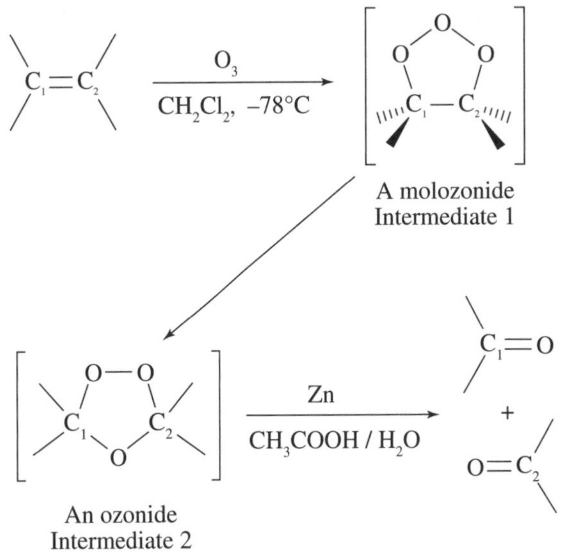

A molozonide
Intermediate 1

An ozonide
Intermediate 2

Figure 1

1. Heptylamine is deaminated via the diazonium salt, and the product is dehydrogenated to yield 1-heptene:

    $$CH_3CH_2CH_2CH_2CH_2CH=CH_2$$

    The heat of hydrogenation of 1-heptene should be closest to the heat of hydrogenation of which one of the following compounds?

    A. Ethylene
    B. Propylene
    C. 1-Butene
    D. 1-Pentene

2. *cis*-2-Butene is less stable than *trans*-2-butene because *cis*-2-butene:

    A. is highly exothermic.
    B. is more highly unsaturated.
    C. has steric strain between the 2 bulky substituents.
    D. shows no stereospecificity.

3. Can *cis*-2-butene be converted easily to *trans*-2-butene?

    A. No, because bond rotations cannot occur under mild conditions.
    B. Yes, because of the hybridized orbitals.
    C. No, because the double bonds differ in spatial arrangement.
    D. Yes, because the two alkenes differ in heats of hydrogenation.

4. To show that ethylene has a higher heat of hydrogenation than *cis*-2-butene, a scientist notes that the catalytic hydrogenation of ethylene:

    A. is stereospecific.
    B. has a positive heat of formation.
    C. requires a much greater energy of activation.
    D. releases more energy than does hydrogenation of *cis*-2-butene.

5. According to the mechanism shown in Figure 1, what is the hybridization of C–1 in the alkene, molozonide, ozonide, and carbonyl product, respectively?

    A. sp^3; sp^2; sp; sp^2
    B. sp^2; sp^3; sp^3; sp^2
    C. sp^2; sp^3; sp^3; sp^3
    D. sp^3; sp^3; sp^2; sp^3

Passage 7 (Questions 1-4)

The addition of hydrogen iodide to 1-pentene produces 2-iodopentane:

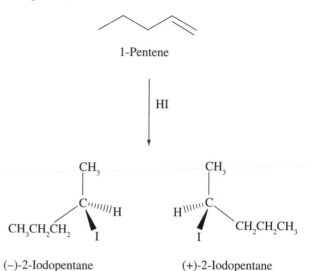

1. The products can be correctly described as:

    A. diastereomers.
    B. meso compounds.
    C. polypeptides.
    D. enantiomers.

2. (–)-2-Iodopentane's absolute configuration is _____, and (+)-2-iodopentane's absolute configuration is _____.

    A. *R, R*
    B. *R, S*
    C. *S, R*
    D. *S, S*

The mechanism of this reaction is such that equal amounts of each product are formed. The reaction mechanism proceeds via a planar intermediate which can be attacked by an iodide ion on either side of the plane to yield equal amounts of (+) and (–) products.

3. What should be the net specific optical rotation for the reaction products?

   A. −30°
   B. 0°
   C. +30°
   D. Cannot be determined from the information given

4. The hybridization of the carbon of the carbocation intermediate can be best described as:

   A. *sp*.
   B. *sp²*.
   C. *sp³*.
   D. *sp³d²*.

Passage 8 (Questions 1-5)

Limonene is the compound that is responsible for the characteristic smell of lemons. Limonene undergoes catalytic hydrogenation to yield both *cis*- and *trans*-1-isopropyl-4-methylcyclohexane.

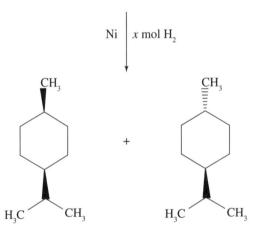

Limonene

Ni | *x* mol H₂

+

cis- and *trans*-1-Isopropyl-4-methylcyclohexane

1. What is the absolute configuration of the chiral carbon in limonene?

   A. *R*
   B. *S*
   C. (+)
   D. (−)

2. How many moles of hydrogen (H₂) will add to limonene upon catalytic hydrogenation?

   A. 1
   B. 2
   C. 3
   D. 4

3. Which of the following represents the most stable chair conformation of *cis*-1-isopropyl-4-methylcyclohexane?

A.

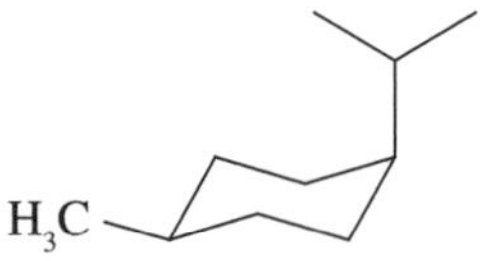

H₃C

B.

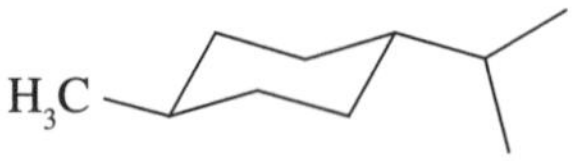

H₃C

C.

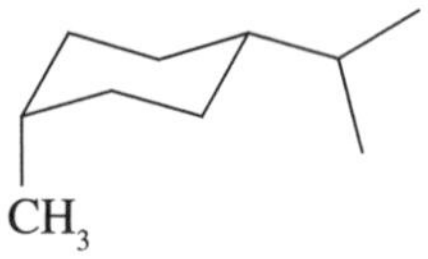

CH₃

D.

CH₃

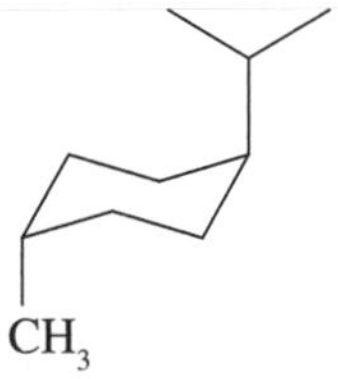

4. Which one of the following represents the most stable chair conformation of *trans*-1-isopropyl-4-methyl-cyclohexane?

A.

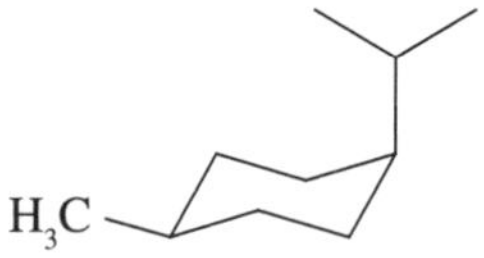

H₃C

B.

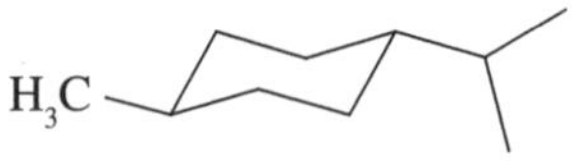

H₃C

C.

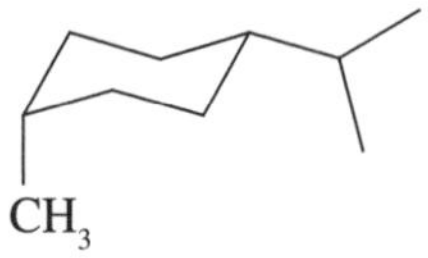

CH₃

D.

CH₃

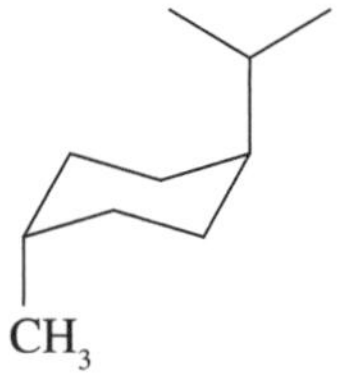

5. Which is the more stable isomer, *cis*- or *trans*-1-isopropyl-4-methylcyclohexane?

A. *Cis*
B. *Trans*
C. Both are equally stable.
D. Cannot be determined from the information given

_____

Passage 9 (Questions 1-5)

The heat of hydrogenation, ΔH_{hydr}, of an alkene is the energy given off when the alkene is reduced (using H_2 gas and a metal catalyst) to the corresponding alkane. Heats of hydrogenation depend mainly on the degree of substitution at the double bond, steric crowding, and angle strain. Changes in the heats of hydrogenation will have a similar effect on the heat of combustion, ΔH_{comb}. The more substituted the double bond, the lower the magnitude of the heat of hydrogenation. Steric crowding of groups directly attached to the double bond will increase the magnitude of the heat of hydrogenation, as will large deviations from 120° bond angles associated with sp^2 carbon atoms.

1. Consider these four compounds:

I: 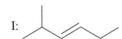   II:

III: IV:

The order of increasing magnitude of the heat of hydrogenation would be:

A. I < II < IV < III.
B. III < II < IV < I.
C. II < III < IV < I.
D. IV < III < I < II.

2. Consider these two compounds:

I: II:

Comparisons of ΔH_{comb} and ΔH_{hydr} of these compounds would reveal that:

A. $|\Delta H_{comb}|$ of II is greater, and $|\Delta H_{hydr}|$ of I is greater.
B. $|\Delta H_{comb}|$ of II is greater, and $|\Delta H_{hydr}|$ of II is greater.
C. $|\Delta H_{comb}|$ of I is greater, and $|\Delta H_{hydr}|$ of I is greater.
D. $|\Delta H_{comb}|$ of I is greater, and $|\Delta H_{hydr}|$ of II is greater.

3. How many isomeric monoalkenes would yield 3-ethylhexane upon hydrogenation?

A. 5
B. 6
C. 7
D. 9

4. A compound with the formula C_8H_8 was exhaustively hydrogenated. The product was found to have absorbed three moles of hydrogen gas. How many rings were present in the starting material?

A. 1
B. 2
C. 3
D. 4

5. One would expect the magnitude of the heat of hydrogenation of 1,3-hexadiene to be:

A. half that of 1-hexene.
B. the same as 1-hexene.
C. slightly less than twice that of 1-hexene.
D. twice that of 1-hexene.

Passage 10 (Questions 1-6)
ADVANCED PASSAGE

A research chemist synthesized Compound A, which was shown to be a powerful analgesic upon clinical testing. Further evidence indicated only one stereoisomer of A was the active agent. The researcher was instructed to separate Compound A into its different stereoisomers to help determine which one was the analgesic.

Compound A, which showed an optical rotation of 0°, was treated with the R stereoisomer of Compound B (melting point 55°C). Two easily separated solids, C and D, whose melting points were 101°C and 90°C, respectively, were isolated from the reaction mixture. Compounds C and D were then independently treated with warm aqueous acid. After workup, Compound C gave Compounds E and B, while Compound D yielded F and B. Testing of Compounds E and F determined that E was the active analgesic, while F was biologically inactive.

1. Compound A could be described as:

   A. a meso compound.
   B. a racemic mixture.
   C. an equal mixture of two diastereomers.
   D. an optically pure compound.

2. If the melting point of Compound E is 80°C, what should be the melting point of Compound F?

   A. 55°C
   B. 80°C
   C. 90°C
   D. 101°C

3. The process by which enantiomers are separated is known as:

   A. differentiation.
   B. resolution.
   C. fractionation.
   D. integration.

4. The absolute configuration of E was determined to be R. Compound E also showed a positive optical rotation. The configuration and optical rotation of Compound F should be:

   A. R, negative.
   B. R, positive.
   C. S, negative.
   D. S, positive.

5. Reaction of Compound A with Racemic B would give how many stereoisomers?

   A. 2
   B. 4
   C. 6
   D. 8

6. Compounds C and D are best described as:

   A. enantiomers.
   B. tautomers.
   C. diastereomers.
   D. rotamers.

_____

Passage 11 (Questions 1-5)
ADVANCED PASSAGE

Dienes, a special group of alkenes, can be classified as conjugated or isolated. *Conjugated dienes* are alkenes with alternating double and single bonds. *Isolated dienes* have double bonds separated by more than one single bond.

conjugated diene   isolated diene

Although conjugated dienes are similar in reactivity to isolated dienes, conjugated dienes are somewhat more stable. The heats of hydrogenation were measured for several alkenes and dienes to determine their stability (Table 1). The data show that alkenes become more stable with increasing substitution and increasing number of double bonds.

For example, in Table 1 the ΔH_{hydrog} of 1,4-pentadiene, an isolated diene, is 60.8 kcal/mol, approximately double the ΔH_{hydrog} of 1-butene. However, 1,3-butadiene has a ΔH_{hydrog} of 57.1 kcal/mol. Based on these results, conjugated dienes are considered more stable because they release less heat on hydrogenation.

Alkene	ΔH_{hydrog} (kcal/mol)
$CH_3CH_2CH=CH_2 + H_2$ Butene-1	30.3
$CH_3CH_2C(CH_3)=CH_2 + H_2$ 2-Methyl-1-butene	26.9
$H_2C=CHCH=CH_2 + H_2$ 1,3-Butadiene	26.7
$H_2C=CHCH=CH_2 + 2 H_2$ 1,3-Butadiene	57.1
$H_2C=CHCH_2CH=CH_2 + 2 H_2$ 1,4-Pentadiene	60.8

Table 1 Heats of Hydrogenation of Alkenes

One explanation for this observation is the hybridization theory. According to the hybridization theory, the stability of conjugated dienes comes from the hybridization of the orbitals forming the carbon–carbon single bonds.

For example, in 1,4-pentadiene, the C–C single bonds result from the overlap of an sp^2 orbital from one carbon with an sp^3 orbital from the adjacent carbon. In conjugated dienes, on the other hand, the C–C single bonds result from σ overlap of sp^2 orbitals on both carbons.

1. Which of the following most accurately represents the carbocation formed when 1,3-butadiene reacts with HCl?

A. $H_2C\overset{\delta+}{\cdots}CH\cdots CH\overset{\delta+}{\cdots}CH_3$

B. $H_3C-CH\overset{\delta+}{\cdots}CH\cdots\overset{\delta+}{CH_2}$

C. $H_3C\overset{\delta+}{\cdots}CH=CH\overset{\delta+}{\cdots}CH_2$

D. $H_3C-CH=CH-CH_3$

2. The carbon–carbon single bond in 1,3-butadiene has a bond length that is shorter than a carbon–carbon single bond in an alkane. This is a result of the:

A. overlap of two sp^2 orbitals.
B. partial double-bond character due to the σ electrons.
C. overlap of one sp^2 and one sp^3 orbital.
D. overlap of two sp^3 orbitals.

3. In comparison to a normal alkane bond, the C(2)–C(3) orbitals in 1,3-butadiene have:

A. more s character.
B. less s character.
C. more p character.
D. less energy.

4. If one mole of 1,3-butadiene is completely hydrogenated, what is the expected amount of heat released?

A. 53.3 kcal
B. 57.1 kcal
C. 60.5 kcal
D. 60.6 kcal

5. Monoalkenes have carbon–carbon double bonds consisting of a σ bond and a π bond. The carbon atoms are sp^2 hybridized and have:

A. two equivalent orbitals and one unhybridized p orbital.
B. two equivalent orbitals and two unhybridized p orbitals.
C. three equivalent orbitals and a fourth unhybridized p orbital.
D. four equivalent orbitals in a hybridized state.

Passage 12 (Questions 1-4)

Figure 1 below illustrates a procedure for classifying compounds according to their solubilities. The solubility of a substance in a given solvent determines the next solvent to be used. Table 1 lists organic compounds representative of each group.

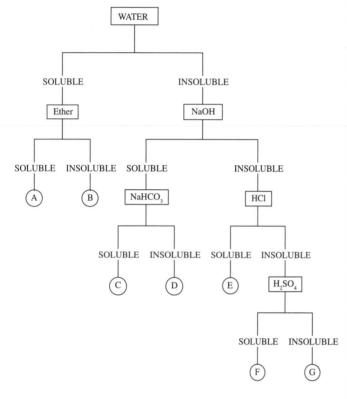

Figure 1 Solubility classification procedure

Group	Compounds
A	acetic acid, propanol, butanal
B	glucose, alanine, glycine
C	fatty acids, dinitrophenol
D	phenol, 1-nitropropane
E	aniline, *p*-toluidine
F	heptanol, diisopropyl ether
G	methane, methyl chloride

Table 1 Representative Organic Compounds Belonging to Groups A–G in Figure 1

1. A hydrazine is determined to be a member of Group E in part because of which of the following solubility characteristics?

   A. It is insoluble in NaOH.
   B. It is soluble in H_2SO_4.
   C. It is soluble in ether but insoluble in NaOH.
   D. It is insoluble in HCl.

2. Hydrolysis of diisopropyl ether in HBr yields an alkyl bromide and an alcohol. The alcohol is classified under Group A because it is:

   A. polar.
   B. hydrophobic.
   C. basic.
   D. acidic.

3. When an amide is hydrolyzed in the presence of a strong acid, it results in the formation of:

   A. a protonated amide and water.
   B. an ether and an ammonium salt.
   C. a ketone and ammonia.
   D. a carboxylic acid and an amine.

4. Aldehyde and alcohol members of Group A will demonstrate decreasing water solubility with:

   A. decreasing chain length.
   B. decreasing number of hydrophilic moieties.
   C. increasing chain length.
   D. increasing hydrogen bonding.

Passage 13 (Questions 1-5)

A flavor chemist attempted to isolate and identify the major flavor component of a recently discovered wild berry. A sample of berries was pureed in a blender, and the resulting slurry was dissolved in ethyl acetate. The solution was first extracted with 0.1 M HCl, followed by extraction with aqueous sodium bicarbonate.

The ethyl acetate portion was concentrated and thin layer chromatography of the resulting oil showed the presence of two compounds, Compound 1 with an R_f of 0.2, and Compound 2 with an R_f of 0.6. The two compounds were separated using column chromatography. Compound 2 was identified as the essential oil with the following physical characteristics:

Formula: $C_{11}H_{14}O_3$

IR: 3100, 2950, 1735, 800 cm^{-1}

^{1}H NMR: 7.5 ppm, multiplet, 4H
            4.5 ppm, septet, 1H
            2.1 ppm, singlet, 3H
            1.4 ppm, doublet, 6H

1. The extraction with 0.1 M HCl would remove what type of compound from the ethyl acetate solution?

    A. Esters
    B. Amines
    C. Amides
    D. Alkenes

2. Compound 1 had a smaller R_f value than Compound 2. This would suggest that Compound:

    A. 1 is more polar than 2.
    B. 2 is more polar than 1.
    C. 1 has a greater molecular weight than 2.
    D. 2 has a greater molecular weight than 1.

3. According to the IR data given, which of the following functional groups is NOT present in Compound 2?

    A. Ester
    B. Alcohol
    C. Carbonyl
    D. Alkene

4. The ^{1}H NMR signal at 1.4 ppm is a doublet and integrates to six hydrogens. These six hydrogens are adjacent to how many other hydrogens?

    A. 1
    B. 2
    C. 3
    D. 6

5. Treatment of Compound 2 with NaOH followed by acid work-up causes the disappearance of the IR absorption at 1735 cm^{-1} and the appearance of a new absorption at 1700 cm^{-1}. What functional group is responsible for the 1735 cm^{-1} absorption?

    A. Aldehyde
    B. Ester
    C. Ether
    D. Ketone

_____

Passage 14 (Questions 1-4)

An organic chemist attempted to determine the structure of an unknown compound (X) with the molecular formula $C_{10}H_{12}O$.

Compound X had the following spectral characteristics:

^{1}H NMR (four signals):

δ 7.25	1 multiplet, 5H
δ 2.4	1 triplet, 2H
δ 2.3	1 triplet, 2H
δ 2.1	1 singlet, 3H

IR: 3100 cm^{-1}, 1705 cm^{-1}

1. Just by looking at the molecular formula, determine which of the following functional groups could NOT be present in Compound X.

   A. An ester
   B. An alcohol
   C. An ether
   D. A double bond

2. The absorption at 1705 cm^{-1} most likely indicates the presence of which of the following functional groups?

   A. An alcohol
   B. An ester
   C. A carbon–carbon double bond
   D. A ketone

3. Which NMR signal represents the proton with the greatest number of neighboring hydrogens?

   A. δ 7.25
   B. δ 2.4
   C. δ 2.3
   D. δ 2.1

4. If Compound X were treated with NaBH$_4$ in ethanol followed by acid work-up, how many new ^{1}H NMR signals would appear in the spectrum?

   A. 1
   B. 2
   C. 3
   D. 4

_____

Passage 15 (Questions 1-5)

In an effort to develop safer and more effective insecticides, a researcher isolated a small quantity of a sex pheromone (Compound I) from a beetle. From the combustion analysis the researcher determined the formula of Compound I to be $C_7H_{12}O_2$, which indicated a degree of unsaturation of 2. The spectral data for Compound I are given below:

^{1}H NMR (3 signals):

δ 2.1, singlet, 6H

δ 2.4, triplet, 4H

δ 1.6, quintet, 2H

IR

2950 cm^{-1}, 1705 cm^{-1}

Treatment of Compound I with NaBH$_4$ yielded Compound II (formula: $C_7H_{16}O_2$) and an IR absorption at 3350 cm^{-1}. Reaction of Compound I with I$_2$ and NaOH in water followed by acidic workup gave Compound III, with formula $C_5H_8O_4$.

1. How many rings are there in Compound I?

A. 0
B. 1
C. 2
D. 3

2. For Compound II, the IR absorption at 3350 cm^{-1} indicates the presence of:

A. a double bond.
B. an aldehyde.
C. a carboxylic acid.
D. an alcohol.

3. What is the degree of unsaturation of Compound III?

A. 1
B. 2
C. 3
D. 4

4. Treatment of the pheromone with excess CH$_3$MgBr followed by aqueous workup would give a compound with a strong IR absorption at:

A. 1700 cm^{-1}.
B. 1735 cm^{-1}.
C. 3100 cm^{-1}.
D. 3350 cm^{-1}.

5. How many signals would be present in the proton NMR spectrum of Compound II?

A. 3
B. 4
C. 5
D. 6

Passage 16 (Questions 1-4)

Table 1 lists many of the substitution reactions that alkyl halides undergo in the presence of nucleophilic reagents.

Reaction Type	
I	$RX + R'M \rightarrow RR' + XM$
II	$RX + I^- \rightarrow RI + X^-$
III	$RX + OH^- \rightarrow ROH + X^-$
IV	$RX + H_2O \rightarrow ROH + HX$
V	$RX + OR'^- \rightarrow ROR' + X^-$
VI	$RX + R'COO^- \rightarrow R'COOR + X^-$
VII	$RX + CN^- \rightarrow RCN + X^-$
VIII	$RX + NH_3 \rightarrow RNH_2 + HX$
IX	$RX + NH_2R' \rightarrow RNHR' + HX$
X	$RX + NHR'R'' \rightarrow RNR'R'' + HX$
XI	$RX + SH^- \rightarrow RSH + X^-$

Table 1

1. Ethers can be formed from methyl chloride in Reaction Type *V*. In this reaction, the incoming OR'^- group represents:

   A. a leaving group.
   B. a nucleophile.
   C. an electrophile.
   D. a solvent.

2. A substitution reaction involving methyl iodide would most likely demonstrate which of the following?

   A. Carbocation formation and optical activity
   B. A unimolecular rate-determining step
   C. Racemization and first-order kinetics
   D. Second-order kinetics

3. A quaternary ammonium salt does NOT carry out substitution reactions with alkyl halides because the nitrogen atom is:

   A. negatively charged.
   B. saturated.
   C. electrophilic.
   D. nucleophilic.

4. An acetate ion can react with a tertiary alkyl halide to form an ester. The reaction occurs more rapidly in water than in dimethylsulfoxide because water stabilizes the:

   A. acetate ion.
   B. carbocation intermediate.
   C. configuration inversion.
   D. intermediate racemates.

Passage 17 (Questions 1-5)

Alkyl halides are of great importance in laboratory synthesis. They undergo displacement reactions with nucleophilic reagents to yield products such as ethers, alcohols, and amines. In reactions, alkyl halides may follow second-order kinetics. The general reaction involving nucleophilic substitution is shown below:

$$R\text{---}X \ + \ :Y^- \ \xrightarrow{\text{solvent}} \ R\text{---}Y \ + \ :X^-$$

substrate   nucleophile   leaving group

S_N2 reactions are influenced by the structure of the alkyl substrate, the type of solvent and the nature of the nucleophilic reagent. The rate of nucleophilic substitution reactions is dependent upon the concentration of the substrate and of the nucleophile as expressed below:

$$\text{Rate} = k[\text{R--X}][\text{Y}]$$

where k is the reaction rate constant. Thus, both reactants are involved in the rate-determining step of the reaction.

R in R—X	Relative Rate
CH_3	1
CH_3CH_2	3.3×10^{-2}
$CH_3CH_2CH_2$	1.3×10^{-2}
$(CH_3)_2CH$	8.3×10^{-4}
$(CH_3)_3CCH_2$	3.3×10^{-7}
$H_2C=CHCH_2$	1.3
$C_6H_5CH_2$	4.0

Table 1 Average Relative S_N2 Rates of Alkyl Groups

1. The *n*-pentyl group has the structure shown below:

$$CH_3CH_2CH_2CH_2CH_2$$

It will have a reaction rate that is closest to which of the following alkyl groups from Table 1?

A. $CH_3CH_2CH_2$
B. $(CH_3)_2CH$
C. $H_2C=CHCH_2$
D. $C_6H_5CH_2$

2. All of the following are characteristics of S_N2 reactions EXCEPT:

A. first-order rate of reaction.
B. complete inversion of stereochemistry.
C. reactivity sequence of $1° > 2° > 3°$.
D. absence of rearrangement.

3. If the concentrations of both CH_3Br and OH^- are doubled in a S_N2 reaction resulting in the formation of CH_3OH and Br^-, then the rate of the reaction will:

A. be halved.
B. remain the same.
C. double.
D. quadruple.

4. The rate equation of S_N2 reactions differs from the rate equation of S_N1 reactions because:

A. only the S_N1 rate depends upon the solvent.
B. only the S_N1 rate depends upon the temperature.
C. the S_N1 rate depends only upon the concentration of the substrate.
D. the S_N1 rate depends only upon the concentration of the nucleophile.

5. The fact that $CH_3CH_2CH_2$ has a slower reaction rate than CH_3 is best explained by the fact that:

A. solvents play a large role in reaction rates.
B. the rate decreases with increasing steric hindrance.
C. bulky groups allow reactions to proceed at a faster pace.
D. propane has a higher boiling point.

Passage 18 (Questions 1-6)

As part of a general study of analgesics, a student attempted to synthesize aspirin from methyl salicylate, a natural analgesic isolated from tree bark. The reaction sequence was as follows:

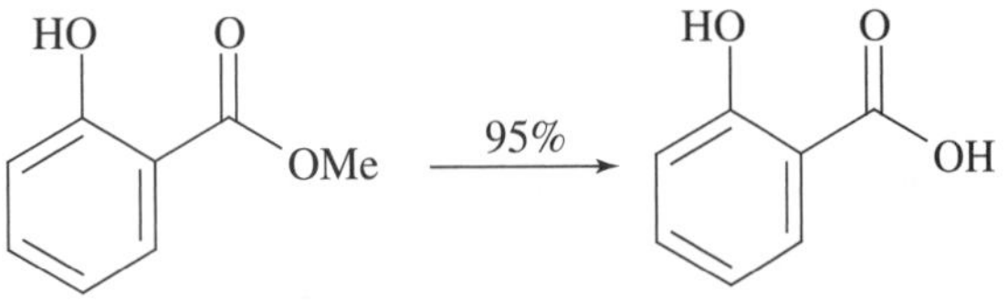

Methyl salicylate   Salicylic acid

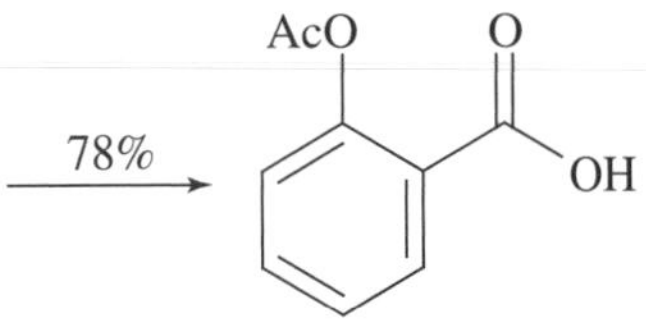

Aspirin

Both the salicylic acid and aspirin were white crystalline solids.

1. What is the overall yield of this reaction sequence?

   A. 74%
   B. 78%
   C. 86%
   D. 95%

2. The best conditions for converting methyl salicylate to salicylic acid would most likely be:

   A. H_2O, reflux.
   B. aqueous NaOH, then aqueous HCl.
   C. $LiAlH_4$, then aqueous HCl.
   D. CrO_3, then aqueous acid.

3. The best conditions for converting salicylic acid to aspirin would be:

   A. CH_3COOH, H^+.
   B. CH_3CO_2Na, heat.
   C. $(CH_3CO)_2O$, H^+.
   D. CH_3COCH_3, H^+.

4. Which of the three compounds would be soluble in aqueous sodium bicarbonate?

   A. Methyl salicylate
   B. Aspirin and salicylic acid
   C. Aspirin and methyl salicylate
   D. All three compounds

5. Treatment of salicylic acid with methanol and dry acid would yield an:

   A. ester.
   B. acid.
   C. acetal.
   D. ether.

6. Both methyl salicylate and aspirin showed a strong absorption in the IR at 1735 cm^{-1}. This absorption indicates the presence of:

   A. a phenol.
   B. an acid.
   C. an aromatic ring.
   D. an ester.

Passage 19 (Questions 1-5)

Carboxylic acids are a class of organic compounds commonly found in nature. Formic acid (HCOOH), from the Latin *formica* meaning "ant," is used by ants as a signal substance or pheromone. More complex acids, exemplified by the prostaglandin family, are potent human bioregulators which are currently receiving much research attention.

The acidity of carboxylic acids ($pK_a \approx 5$) is partially the result of resonance stabilization of the resulting carboxylate anion. Electron withdrawing groups near the acid functional group tend to increase acidity. Carboxylic acids are usually obtained from the oxidation of alcohols or the hydrolysis of esters. Carboxylic acids themselves can be reduced with $LiAlH_4$ to give the corresponding 1° alcohol.

1. Which one of the following carboxylic acids would be the most acidic?

    A.

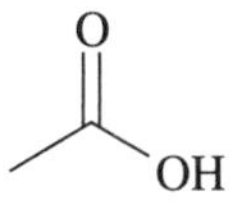

    B.

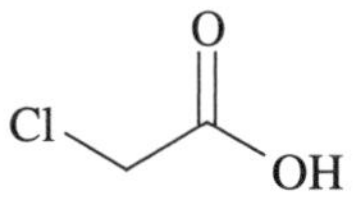

    C.

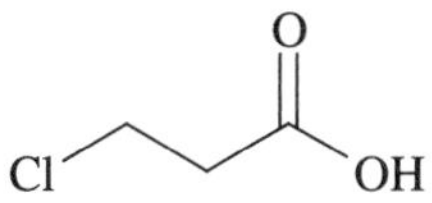

    D.

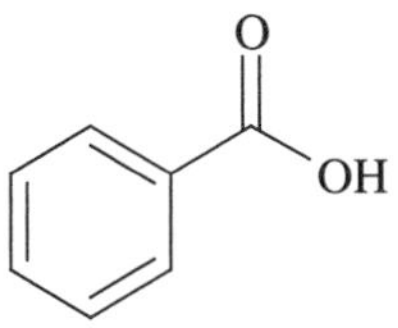

2. Hydrolysis of which of the following esters would yield 2-methylbutanoic acid?

    A.

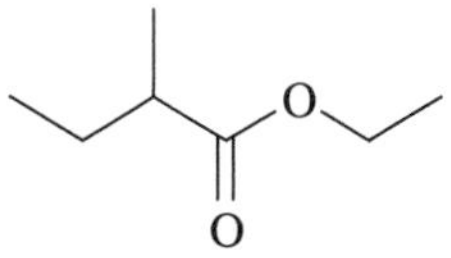

    B.

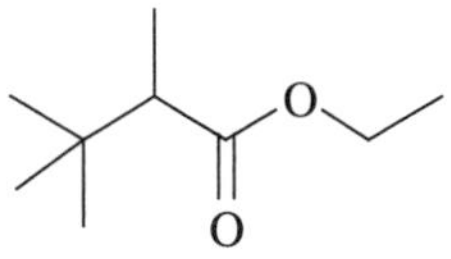

    C.

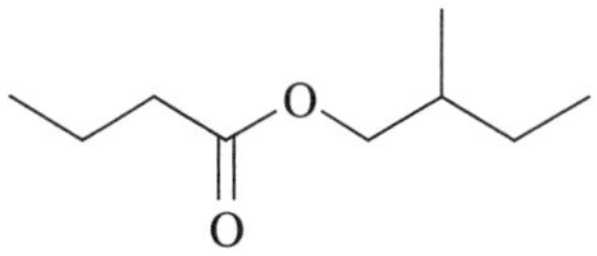

    D.

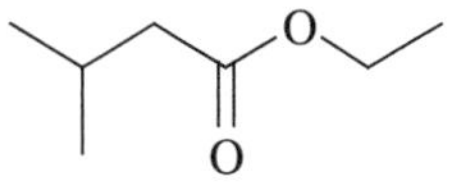

3. The boiling point of acetic acid is 118°C and that of methyl acetate is 57°C. Acetic acid boils at a much higher temperature due to:

    A. its intramolecular hydrogen bonding.
    B. its lower molecular weight.
    C. its intermolecular hydrogen bonding.
    D. the greater polarity of methyl acetate.

4. Reduction of benzoic acid with LiAlH$_4$ gave Compound X. Reaction of X with benzoic acid and a catalytic amount of sulfuric acid would yield which one of the following compounds?

A.

B.

C.

D.

5. Which of the following alcohols CANNOT be oxidized to a carboxylic acid with Na$_2$CrO$_4$?

A.

B.

C.

D.

Passage 20 (Questions 1-5)

Protons at carbons α to a carbonyl functional group are substantially more acidic than are protons on ordinary carbon atoms. This is due to the powerful electron withdrawing effect of the neighboring carbon–oxygen double bond. In addition, the resulting anion is stabilized by resonance as shown below:

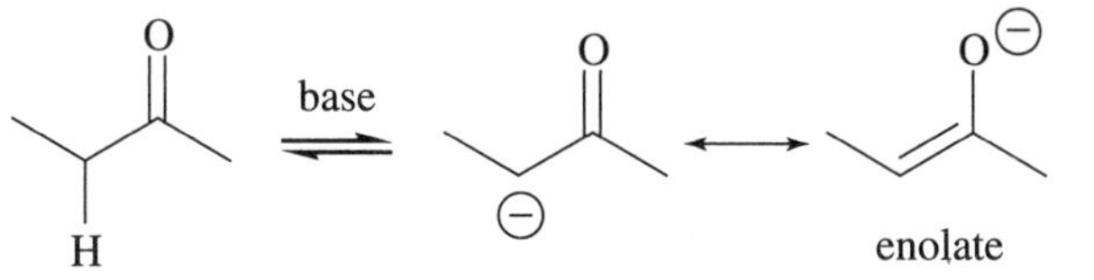

Treatment of the enolate anion with an appropriate alkyl halide or carbonyl compound forms a new carbon–carbon bond at the α position. Condensation of an enolate with an aldehyde or ketone forms an intermediate alcohol which is typically not isolated, but allowed to dehydrate to the corresponding α,β-unsaturated compound.

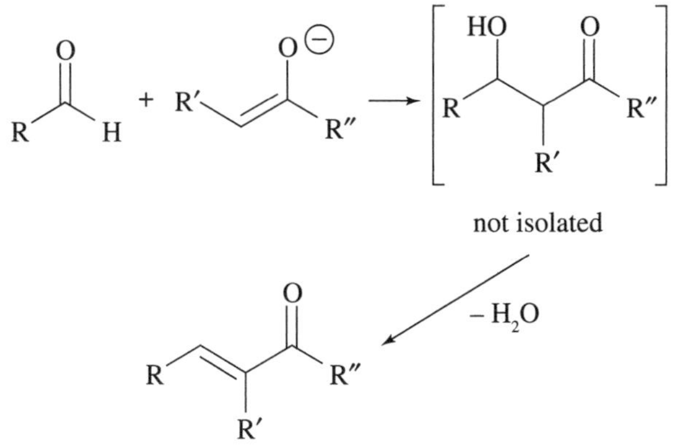

1. Which one of the following carbonyl compounds would be expected to have the most acidic proton?

   A.

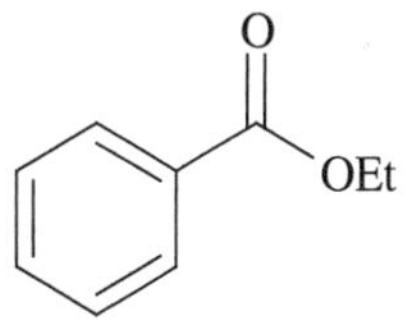

   B.

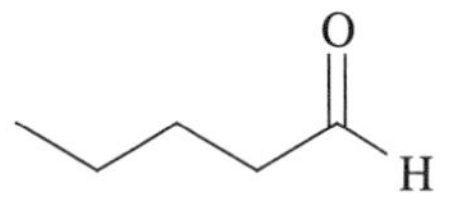

   C.

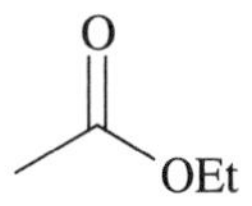

   D.

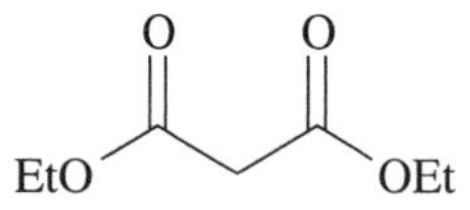

2. Ethyl-2-hexenoate was the product of which of the following sets of reactants?

   A. Butanal, ethyl acetate, LDA; H⁺
   B. Pentanal, ethyl acetate, LDA; H⁺
   C. Propanal, ethyl acetate, LDA; H⁺
   D. Hexanal, ethyl acetate, LDA; H⁺

3.

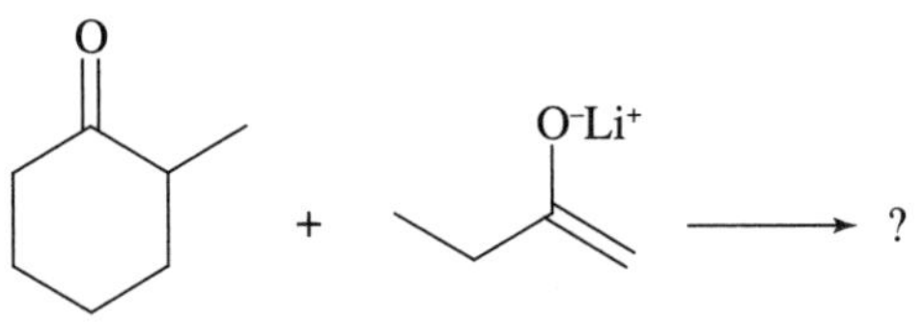

+

⟶ ?

Which one of the following compounds would be the intermediate alcohol from the condensation reaction shown above?

A.

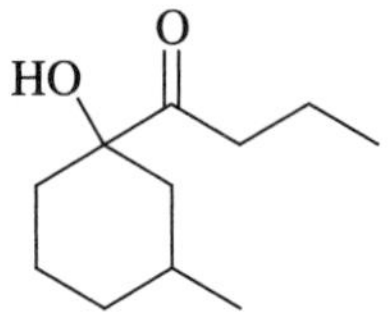

B.

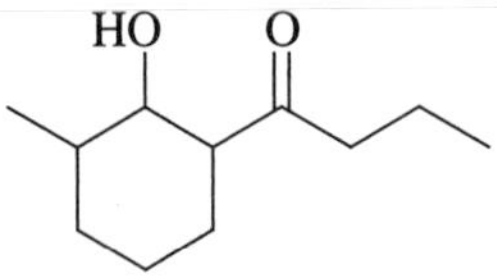

C.

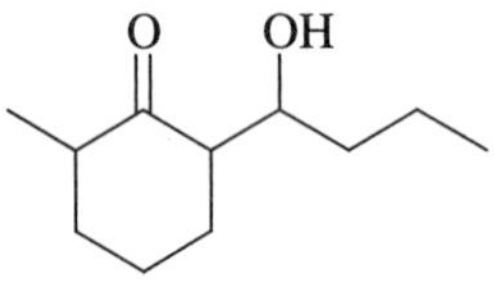

D.

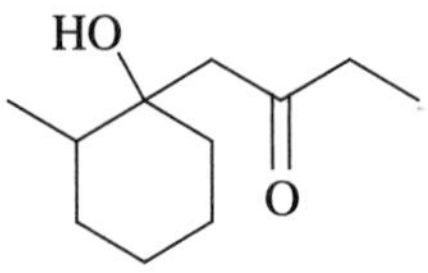

4. What is the order of increasing basicity for the following reagents?

$CH_3O^-Na^+$

I

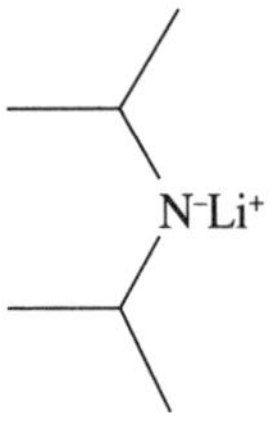

N^-Li^+

III

$NaHCO_3$

II

$H_3C - C \equiv C^-Na^+$

IV

A. I < II < III < IV
B. II < I < IV < III
C. IV < II < III < I
D. III < IV < I < II

5. Which of the following ketones would NOT react with the strong base LDA?

A.

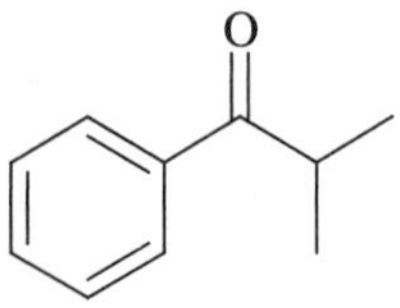

B.

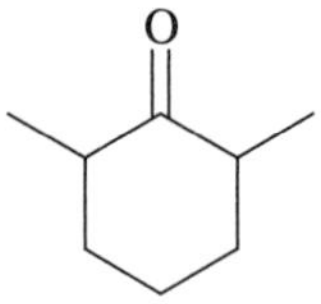

C.

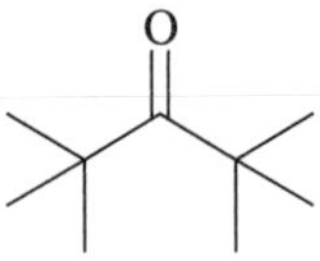

D.

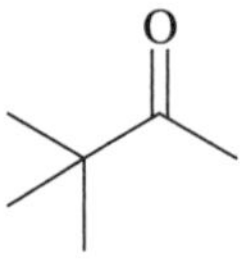

Passage 21 (Questions 1-5)

Amides, esters, anhydrides, and acid chlorides are four important carboxylic acid derivatives that organic chemists frequently use. All can be directly or indirectly synthesized from the corresponding acid. Amides and anhydrides are more conveniently prepared from the acid chloride, which can be made by treating the carboxylic acid with $SOCl_2$.

Each of these derivatives reacts by a similar nucleophilic addition, elimination mechanism:

The rate of reaction depends on a few factors: the leaving group, the steric environment at the carbonyl, and the electrophilic nature of the carbonyl carbon. The better the leaving group, the faster the reaction. In general, the more acidic the conjugate acid, the better the leaving group. In addition, a more electrophilic carbonyl center will add nucleophiles more rapidly. Finally, more steric bulk at the reaction center leads to slower reaction rates.

1. The most reactive of the four derivatives would be the:

   A. amide.
   B. ester.
   C. anhydride.
   D. acid chloride.

2. Each derivative is stabilized to a certain extent by the following resonance structure:

   Which one of the four derivatives discussed would have the greatest amount of stabilization from this resonance structure?

   A. Amide
   B. Ester
   C. Anhydride
   D. Acid chloride

3. Acid bromides are the bromine analogs of acid chlorides. One would expect the reactivity of acid bromides to be:

   A. less than the reactivity of esters.
   B. less than the reactivity of acid chlorides.
   C. equal to the reactivity of acid chlorides.
   D. greater than the reactivity of acid chlorides.

4. Which one of the following esters would react most rapidly with ammonia in methanol by the nucleophilic addition, elimination mechanism?

   A.
   B.
   C.
   D.

5. What organic product is expected from the following reaction sequence?

   A.

   B.
   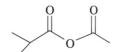
   C.
   D.

Passage 22 (Questions 1-4)

N-Alkyl phthalamides have received a great deal of attention for their medicinal activity. They are conveniently synthesized from a very inexpensive bulk chemical, phthalic anhydride, according to the following scheme:

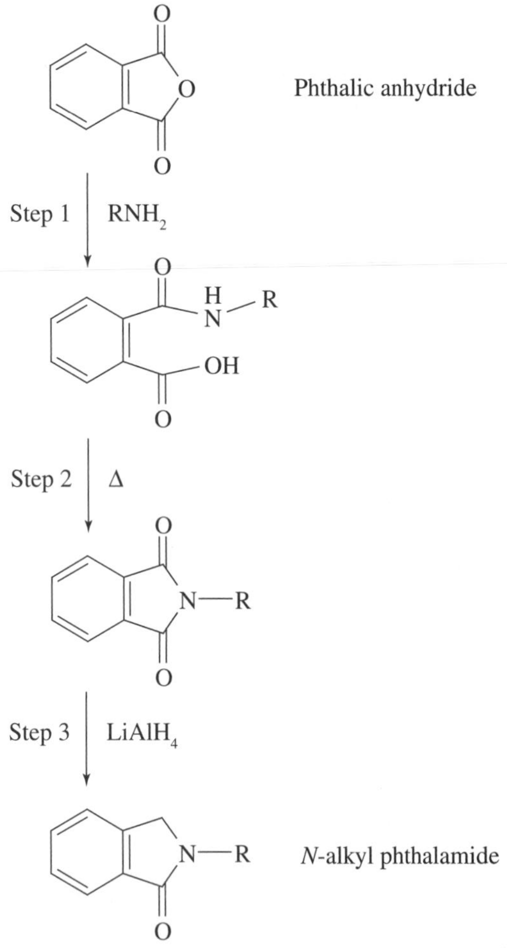

Phthalic anhydride

Step 1 RNH_2

Step 2 Δ

Step 3 $LiAlH_4$

N-alkyl phthalamide

A series of syntheses were carried out to produce phthalamides with various R groups, and the results are tabulated below:

Product	R	Overall Yield (%)
A	CH_3	63
B	C_4H_9	62
C	C_8H_{17}	65
D	$C_{10}H_{21}$	64

Table 1

1. What is the by-product produced in Step 2?

   A. CO_2
   B. RNH_2
   C. O_2
   D. H_2O

2. Step 3 is an example of a(n):

   A. oxidation reaction.
   B. reduction reaction.
   C. cyclization reaction.
   D. dehydration reaction.

3. Of the four compounds shown in the synthetic scheme, which one contains the nitrogen that would be LEAST effective at accepting a hydrogen bond?

   A.

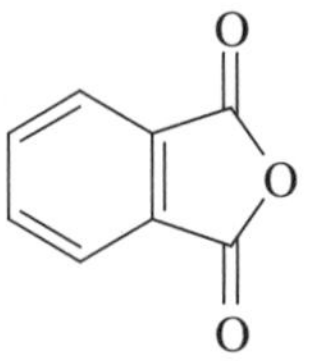

   B.

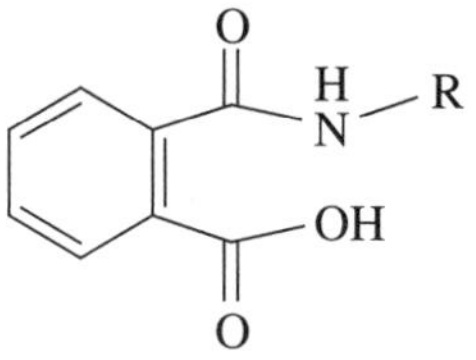

   C.

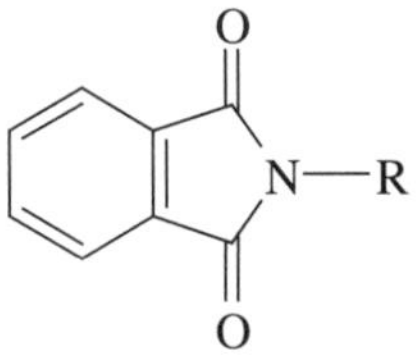

   D.

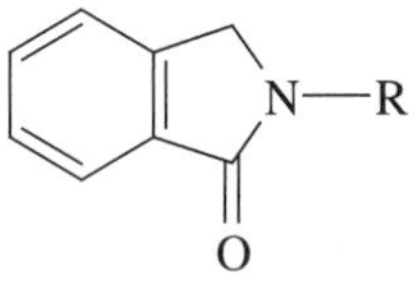

4. What type of compound is produced in Step 2?

   A. An imide
   B. An amide
   C. Formamide
   D. A tertiary amine

Passage 23 (Questions 1-6)

In the early twentieth century, the French chemist Victor Grignard pioneered the development of a new class of organometallic compounds. Grignard reagents, as they are still known today, are produced by adding magnesium metal to alkyl halides:

$$CH_3Br \xrightarrow{\ \ Mg\ \ } CH_3MgBr$$

Reaction 1

Grignard reagents, essentially carbanion salts, are both strong bases and nucleophiles, reacting with acids and electrophiles. For example, the reaction of Grignard reagents with aldehydes and ketones produces alkoxide anions, which may be protonated to yield alcohols.

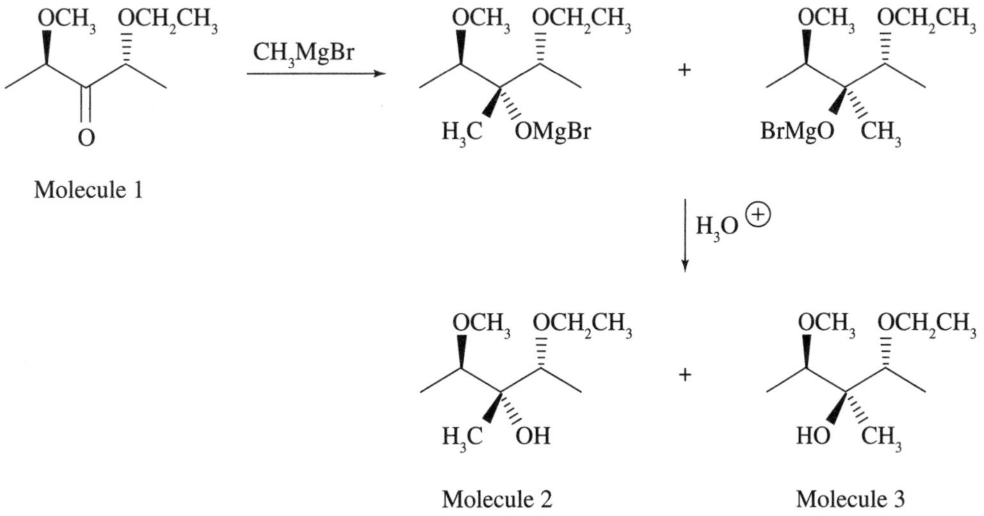

Molecule 1

Molecule 2   Molecule 3

Reaction 2

1. What is the product of this reaction?

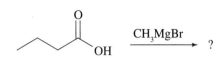

A.

B.   OMgBr

C.

       OMgBr

D.   HO   OMgBr

2. What are the absolute configurations of the three stereocenters in Molecule 2 in Reaction 2?

   A.   R, R, R
   B.   R, R, S
   C.   R, S, S
   D.   S, S, S

3. How many products would result from the following reaction?

   OCH₃ OCH₃

   CH₃MgBr   H₂O⊕

   A.   1
   B.   2
   C.   3
   D.   4

4. Molecules 2 and 3 in Reaction 2 are best described as:

   A.   enantiomers.
   B.   diastereomers.
   C.   conformational isomers.
   D.   a racemic mixture.

5. Which of the following compounds will produce a primary alcohol when treated with CH₃CH₂MgBr?

   A.   B.

        H   H   H   OH

   C.   D.

        H₃C   H   H₃C   CH₃

6. What would be the major product of this reaction?

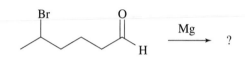

   A.   MgBr   O   B.   OMgBr

   C.   O   D.   OMgBr

Passage 24 (Questions 1-4)

Polymers are large molecules that are formed when simple molecules called *monomers* add in a stepwise fashion to form long chains. For example, polystyrene can be synthesized from styrene in the presence of an initiator, such as benzoyl peroxide (Figure 1).

This reaction proceeds by a radical mechanism, which is initiated by homolysis of the O–O bond of the benzoyl peroxide to form the benzoyl radical. It adds to the C=C bond of styrene to produce a benzylic radical. This benzylic radical adds to another styrene molecule to produce another benzylic radical. This process repeats itself many times to produce a long chain of linked styrene molecules: the polymer.

Polyester, as its name implies, is a polymer that contains many ester functional groups. Many different polyesters have been synthesized by the synthetic fibers industry, and polyester fibers have been used to manufacture clothing. Because of the high strength and low weight of polyesters, they have also been used in sails for racing yachts and in the wings of human-powered planes. A typical polyester-forming reaction is shown in Figure 2. Note that the monomers involved in polyester formation react at both ends to form a polymer.

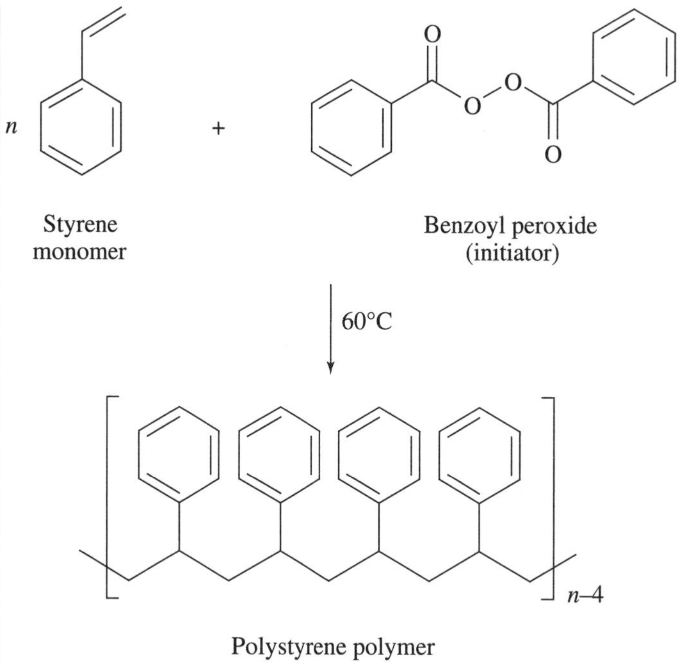

Styrene monomer   +   Benzoyl peroxide (initiator)

60°C

Polystyrene polymer

Figure 1

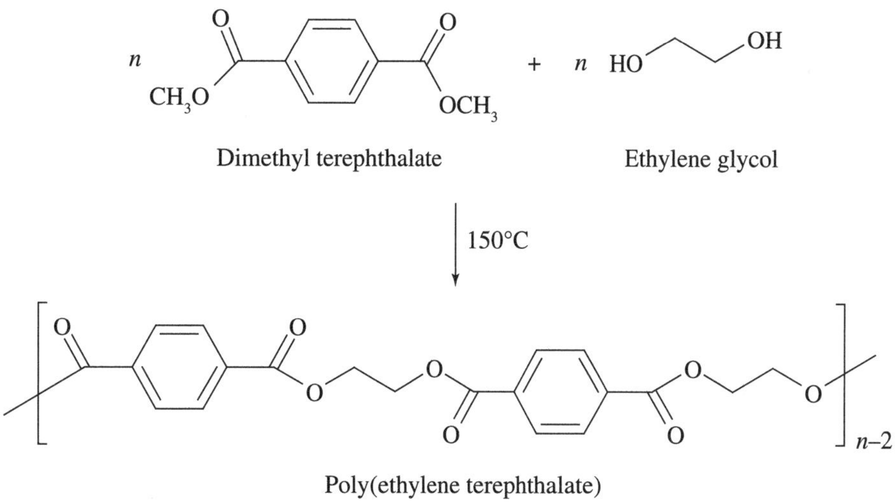

Dimethyl terephthalate   Ethylene glycol

150°C

Poly(ethylene terephthalate)

Figure 2

1. The following polymer is known as *Kevlar*:

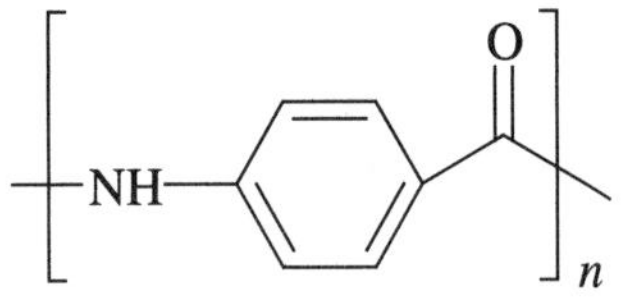

Which of the following is a monomer unit of Kevlar?

A.

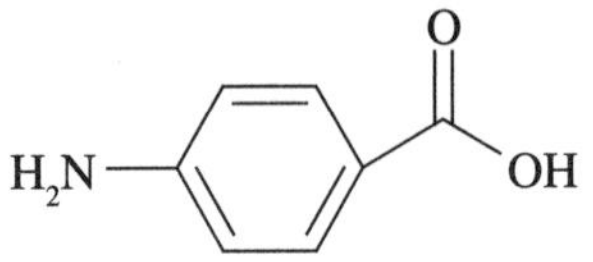

B.

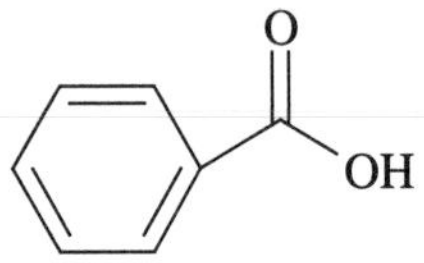

C.

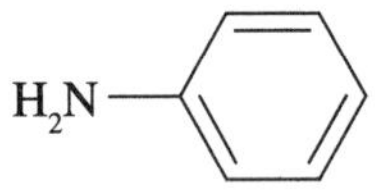

D.

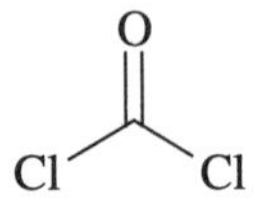

2. Which of the following best describes the most likely mechanism of poly(ethylene terephthalate) formation?

A. Substitution
B. Elimination
C. Addition
D. Addition–elimination

3. If a diamine were used instead of ethylene glycol in the poly(ethylene terephthalate) synthesis shown in Figure 2, a nylon polymer would be produced. This polymer would be a:

A. polyamine.
B. polyamide.
C. polyester.
D. polylactam.

4. Of the following molecules, which is the LEAST likely to be an effective monomer?

A. CH_2CHCl
B. CH_3CH_2CHO
C. $ClCOCH_2CH_2CH_2COCl$
D. $H_2NCH_2CH_2CO_2H$

Passage 25 (Questions 1-6)

Aldol addition reactions of ketone enolates to aldehydes provide a powerful strategy for carbon–carbon bond formation.

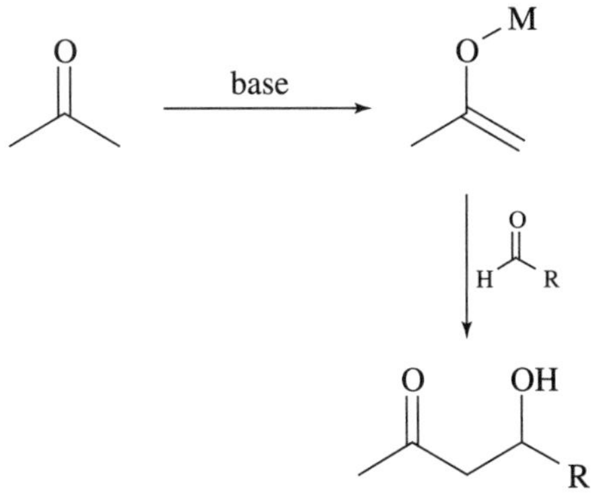

Equation 1

In these reactions, a new stereocenter is often formed. Because of this, chemists have long sought methods for controlling the stereochemistry of the aldol addition reaction.

For example, addition of enolate (Molecule 2 below) to benzaldehyde has been shown to give two products, Molecules 3 and 4:

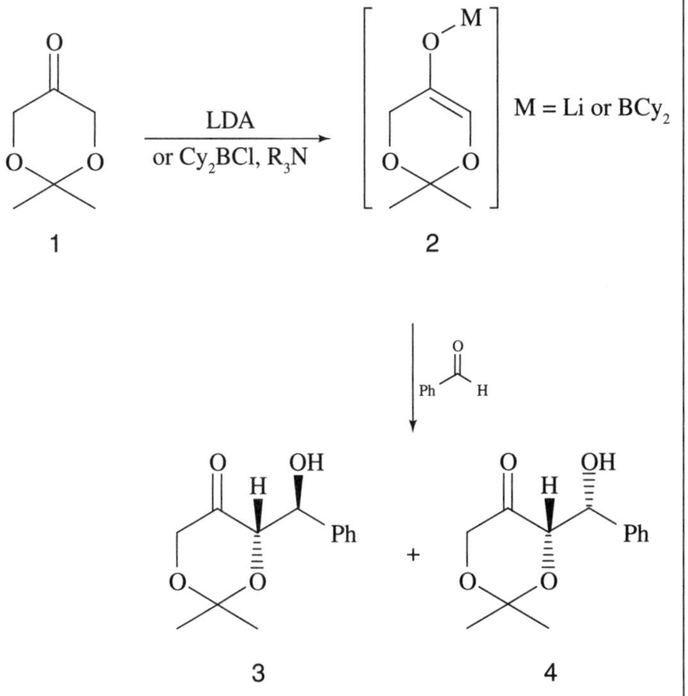

Equation 2

When lithium base enolates are formed using LDA, diastereoselectivity of the reaction is low (the ratio of Molecule 3 to Molecule 4 is 2:1). Such low diastereoselectivities are common for lithium enolates. However, higher diastereoselectivities are often observed using boron enolates. When Molecule 1 is treated with olicyclohexyl chloroborane and a tertiary amine, the ratio increases to 24:1.

1. Aldol product 3 in Equation 2 is often referred to as an *anti aldol*, while product 4 is often referred to as a *syn aldol*. Most likely, this is because:

    A. in Molecule 3, the α-hydrogen and the β-hydroxyl group are on the same side; while in Molecule 4, the α-hydrogen and the β-hydroxyl group are on opposite sides of the new C–C bond.
    B. in Molecule 3, the α-hydrogen and the adjacent alkoxy group are on opposite sides of the molecule as drawn; while in Molecule 4, the α-hydrogen and the adjacent alkoxy group are on the same side of the molecule as drawn.
    C. in Molecule 3, the β-hydroxyl group and the α-alkoxy group are on opposite sides of the molecule as drawn; while in Molecule 4, the β-hydroxyl group and the α-alkoxy group are on the same side of the molecule as drawn.
    D. the α-hydrogen atoms are on opposite sides of the molecule in Molecules 3 and 4.

2. If Product 3 in Equation 2 is treated with acid, Molecule 5 is the major product:

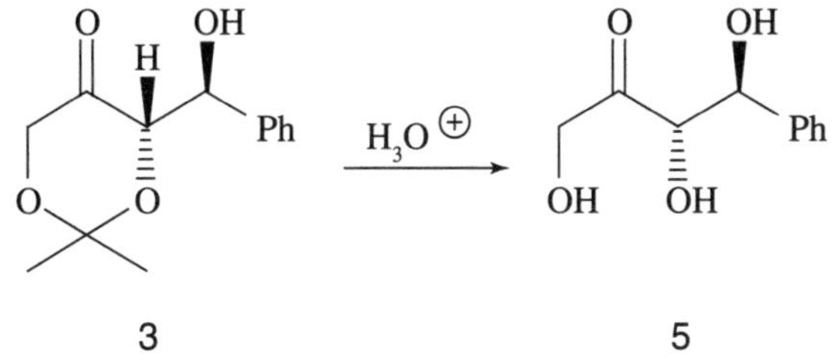

    What is the IUPAC name for Molecule 5?

    A. (3*S*, 4*S*)-1,3,4-Trihydroxy-4-phenylbutan-2-one
    B. (3*R*, 4*S*)-1,3,4-Trihydroxy-4-phenylbutan-2-one
    C. (3*S*, 4*S*)-4-Phenyl-1,3,4-trihydroxybutan-2-one
    D. (3*R*, 4*S*)-4-Phenyl-1,3,4-trihydroxybutan-2-one

3.

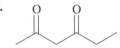

The molecule shown above is the product of an aldol addition of which of the following?

A.

B.

C.

D.

4. Which of the following is an enantiomer of Molecule 3 in Equation 2?

I II III

A. I only
B. II only
C. III only
D. None of these is an enantiomer of Molecule 3.

5. Which of the following is a diastereomer of Molecule 4 in Equation 2?

I II III

A. I only
B. II only
C. I and II only
D. I, II, and III

6. How many resonances would be observed in the ^1H NMR spectrum of Molecule 1?

A. 2
B. 3
C. 4
D. 6

Passage 26 (Questions 1-4)

Penicillins are members of the general class of β-lactams (cyclic amides) that play important antibiotic roles against Gram-positive bacteria. Penicillins are based on the core structure of 6-aminopenicillanic acid (6-APA), and all penicillins share the common action of interfering with bacterial cell wall synthesis.

Bacteria can avoid penicillin's antibiotic effects by producing β-lactamases, which destroy the amide bond of the lactam. Some penicillins have been developed that resist β-lactamase activity, including dicloxacillin and nafcillin.

Penicillins can also be distinguished by their ability to resist acid-catalyzed hydrolysis of the amide bond between the R group and 6-APA. Dicloxacillin and nafcillin are acid stable, while benzylpenicillin is not.

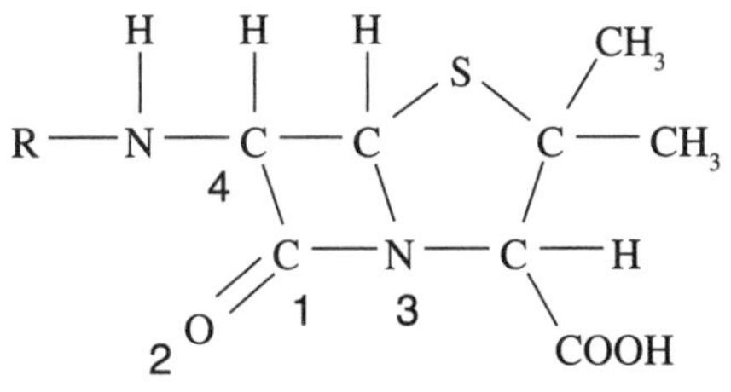

6-APA

R Groups:

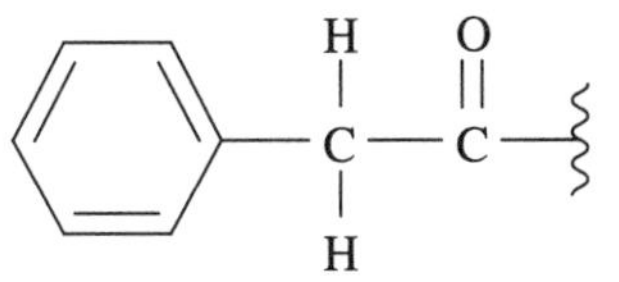

Penicillin G

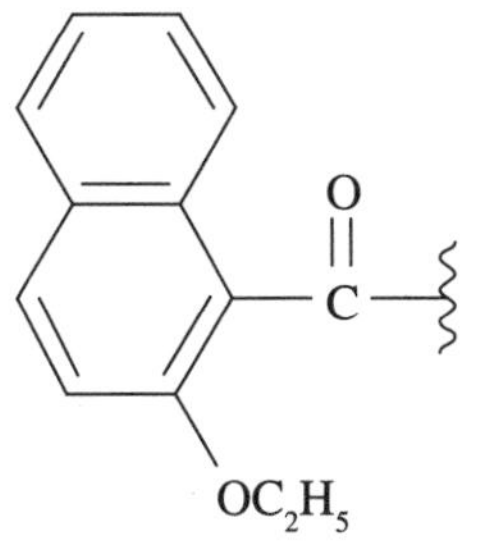

Nafcillin

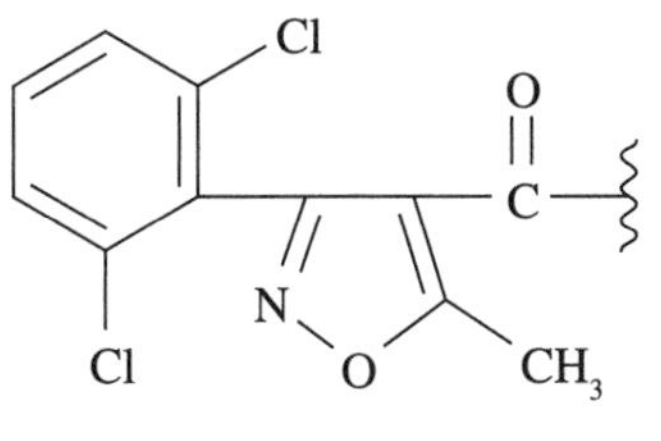

Dicloxacillin

Figure 1

1. β-Lactamases most likely inactivate penicillins by attacking:

   A. C–4 nucleophilically.
   B. C–1 nucleophilically.
   C. O–2 electrophilically.
   D. N–3 nucleophilically.

2. Penicillin G is susceptible to β-lactamases while dicloxacillin is not. Which of the following is the most likely explanation for this?

   A. The chlorines of dicloxacillin are electron-withdrawing, making the lactam more stable.
   B. Benzylpenicillin has a higher melting point than dicloxacillin.
   C. Resonance destabilization in benzylpenicillin makes the lactam bond more reactive.
   D. Steric hindrance blocks β-lactamase attack on the lactam in dicloxacillin.

3. Penicillins can be taken orally if they can survive the low pH of the stomach. The amide bond between the R group and 6-APA of dicloxacillin and nafcillin is stable at low pH because:

   A. aromatic compounds are unaffected by changes in pH.
   B. of stabilization effects by hydrogen bonding.
   C. amide bonds do not easily undergo hydrolysis.
   D. high hydroxide concentration promotes amide stability.

4. How many chiral centers are present in dicloxacillin?

   A. 1
   B. 2
   C. 3
   D. 4

Passage 27 (Questions 1-5)
ADVANCED PASSAGE

Natural fats are complex mixtures of triesters of glycerol. They undergo the typical reactions of esters. The following experiments were performed to study the reaction mechanisms of ester hydrolysis.

Experiment 1

Methyl propanoate was reacted with heavy hydroxide (in the form of Na^+ $^{18}OH^-$). The reaction was allowed to go to completion and then treated with enough $1\ M\ H_2SO_4$ so that the solution turned blue litmus paper pink. The reaction products were then extracted and purified. Spectral analysis provided the following information about the resulting products:

	Product 1	Product 2
IR:	$3000\ cm^{-1}$ and $1720\ cm^{-1}$	$3600\ cm^{-1}$

Experiment 2

Acid-catalyzed hydrolysis of an ester is also possible. Two different esters were labeled with ^{18}O at the ester oxygen (not the carbonyl oxygen) in order to test the mechanism of hydrolysis. The experiments gave the following results:

  I. *n*-Butyl acetate in acid produced normal acetic acid and heavy butanol.
  II. *tert*-Butyl acetate in acid resulted in heavy acetic acid and normal *tert*-butyl alcohol.

The products from both reactions (I and II) were then treated with NaOH until the solution turned pink litmus paper blue; they were then extracted and purified. Analysis of the final products of these reactions showed that significant amounts of the starting materials, *n*-butyl acetate and *tert*-butyl acetate, were present.

Adapted from Streitwieser and Heathcock, *Introduction to Organic Chemistry, 3rd ed.* ©1985 by Macmillan Pub. Co.

1. Based on the spectral analysis given in the passage and the reaction mechanism for alkaline hydrolysis of an ester, the labeled products of Experiment 1 are:

    A. heavy propanoic acid and normal methanol.
    B. normal propanoic acid and heavy methyl alcohol.
    C. normal propanoic acid and normal methanol.
    D. heavy propanoic acid and heavy methyl alcohol.

2. Experiment 2 showed that *tert*-butyl acetate reacts by a different mechanism than does *n*-butyl acetate. This is best explained by the fact that:

    I.   acyl–oxygen bonds are weaker than alkyl–oxygen bonds.
    II. *tert*-butyl acetate forms a stable carbocation that is a reactive intermediate.
    III. steric hindrance due to the *tert*-butyl group slows nucleophilic attack on the carbonyl carbon.

    A. I only
    B. II only
    C. II and III only
    D. I, II, and III

3. The spectral data for Product 1 in Experiment 1 indicate that it is:

    A. an alcohol.
    B. an ester.
    C. a carboxylic acid.
    D. impure.

4. The acid-catalyzed hydrolysis products were identified by spectral analysis and qualitative analysis. It was observed that *tert*-butyl alcohol was more soluble in water than *n*-butyl alcohol. Which of the following statements does NOT support this conclusion?

    A. The *tert*-butyl group is smaller and requires less room than the *n*-butyl group.
    B. The *tert*-butyl group breaks fewer water hydrogen bonds.
    C. A more complex orderly solvation shell is formed around *n*-butyl alcohol.
    D. Solubility of an alcohol increases as the hydrocarbon chain length increases.

5. The experiments showed that acid and base hydrolysis of esters are different in which of the following ways?

    I.   Acid-catalyzed hydrolysis is more readily reversible.
    II. Acid-catalyzed hydrolysis has a larger equilibrium constant.
    III. Base-catalyzed hydrolysis has a larger equilibrium constant.

    A. I only
    B. II only
    C. I and II only
    D. I and III only

Passage 28 (Questions 1-5)

A change in chirality can dramatically change the biological properties of a molecule. The amino acid *dopa* is a prime example of this. The dextrorotatory enantiomer, (+)-dopa, has little physiological effect on humans, whereas the levorotatory enantiomer, (–)-dopa, is used for its activity against Parkinson's disease, a chronic disorder of the central nervous system.

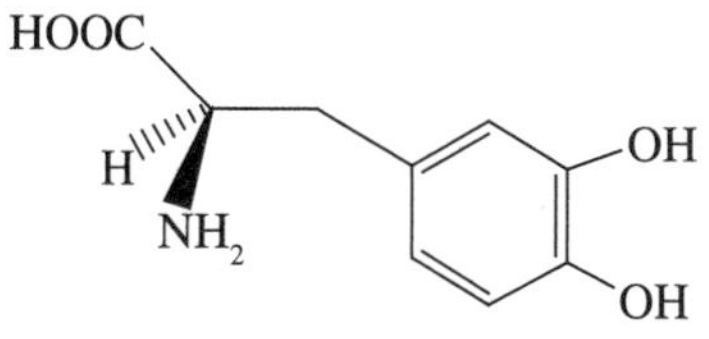

(+)-Dopa (no biological activity)

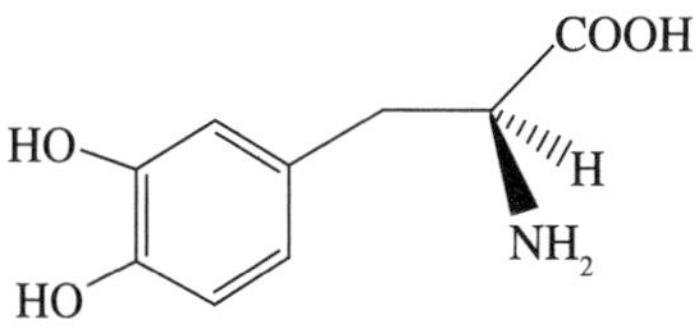

(–)-Dopa (anti-Parkinson agent)

1. The absolute configuration of (+)-dopa is _____ , and the absolute configuration of its enantiomer is _____.

    A. R, R
    B. R, S
    C. S, R
    D. S, S

2. Give the hybridization of the nitrogen of dopa.

    A. sp
    B. sp^2
    C. sp^3
    D. p

3. What would be the relationship between the pI values of (+)-dopa and (–)-dopa?

    A. Equal magnitude but opposite in sign
    B. Similar but not equal
    C. Exactly the same
    D. Cannot be determined without knowing the pK_a values

4. A 50/50 mixture of (+)-dopa and (−)-dopa would be best described as:

    A. optically active.
    B. diastereomers.
    C. a meso compound.
    D. a racemic mixture.

5. The amino acid dopa most closely resembles which one of the following amino acids?

    A. Proline
    B. Cysteine
    C. Aspartic acid
    D. Tyrosine

Passage 29 (Questions 1-6)

A meso compound has chiral centers but is not itself chiral. Tartaric acid is a four-carbon polyol with two carboxylic acids and two chiral centers. There are three stereoisomers: the (+) form, the (−) form, and the meso form. The first two rotate plane-polarized light (as indicated by their names), but *meso*-tartaric acid is achiral. Figure 1 shows the three forms.

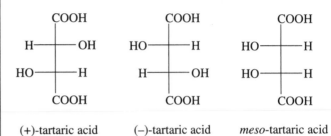

    (+)-tartaric acid   (−)-tartaric acid   *meso*-tartaric acid

Figure 1 Tartaric acid stereoisomers

1. How many stereoisomers do carbohydrates have?

    A. $2n$, where n is the number of chiral centers
    B. 2^n, where n is the number of chiral centers
    C. $2n + m$, where n is the number of chiral centers and m is the number of meso forms
    D. $2^n + m$, where n is the number of chiral centers and m is the number of meso forms

2. Benedict's reagent is used to test for reducing sugars. Tartaric acid would yield:

    A. a positive result.
    B. a negative result.
    C. an ambiguous result.
    D. a positive result only in the open-chain configuration.

3.

```
        COOH
        |
   H————OH
        |
   H————OH
        |
       COOH
```

The compound above is:

I. *meso*-tartaric acid.
II. the mirror image of meso-tartaric acid.
III. chiral.

A. I only
B. II only
C. I and II only
D. II and III only

4. If one of the carboxylic acids of tartaric acid is replaced with a CH$_2$OH group, and the other is reduced to an aldehyde, which of the following will result?

A. A ketotriose
B. An aldotriose
C. An aldotetrose
D. None of the above

5. How many chiral centers must a meso compound have?

A. 0
B. 1
C. 2
D. Any even number greater than or equal to 2

6. Which of the following is/are (+)-tartaric acid?

I.
```
        COOH
        |
    H————OH
        |
   HO————H
        |
       COOH
```

II.
```
        COOH
        |
    H————OH
        |
    H————COOH
        |
        OH
```

III.
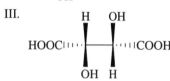

A. I only
B. III only
C. I and II only
D. I and III only

Passage 30 (Questions 1-5)

In 1905, William Young and Arthur Harden added a cell-free yeast extract to a glucose solution and observed the consumption of glucose and the production of alcohol. They also observed that the rate of fermentation declined rapidly unless inorganic phosphate was added to the broth. After more study, they concluded that this phosphate coupled with a glucose molecule as part of the reaction pathway. They realized that the crucial components of this reaction were the two substrates (glucose and phosphate) and some catalytic elements of the yeast extract.

When these reactions were later demonstrated in animal muscle tissue, it led to a flurry of research. The mysterious yeast catalysts were labeled enzymes, and it was discovered that they were not only capable of linking phosphates as anhydrides or esters, but could also isomerize sugars. By 1940, the pathway for glucose metabolism to pyruvate, known as glycolysis, had been elucidated by a number of scientists working independently. Figure 1 shows the first three steps of glycolysis.

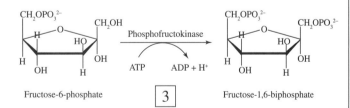

Figure 1 Steps 1, 2, and 3 of glycolysis

1. The bond resulting from the first reaction in Figure 1 is:

    A. an ether.
    B. an anhydride.
    C. an ester.
    D. a phosgene.

2. The cell-free extract that Young and Harden isolated must have contained each of the following chemicals EXCEPT:

    A. ATP.
    B. magnesium.
    C. sugars.
    D. proteins.

3. Glucose undergoes an isomerization to yield fructose 1,6-bisphosphate. Which of the following is an isomerization reaction?

    A. $CH_2OH–CO–CH_2CH_3 \rightarrow CHO–CHOH–CH_2CH_3$
    B. $CH_3CH_2CHOH–CH_3 \rightarrow CH_3CH=CHCH_3$
    C. $CH_3COCl + H_2O \rightarrow CH_3COOH + HCl$
    D. $CH_2OH–CO–OCH_2CH_3 + CH_3OH \rightarrow CH_2OH–CO–OCH_3 + CH_3CH_2OH$

4. Which of the sugars in the first three steps of glycolysis have the D configuration?

    I.   Glucose-6-phosphate
    II. Fructose-6-phosphate
    III. Fructose-1,6-bisphosphate

    A. I and II only
    B. I and III only
    C. II and III only
    D. I, II, and III

5. Which of the following is correct regarding the classification of carbohydrate isomers?

    A. Glucose has the same number of stereoisomers as fructose.
    B. There are 8 aldohexose stereoisomers.
    C. There are 16 D-aldohexose stereoisomers.
    D. Each D-aldohexose has exactly two anomers.

Passage 31 (Questions 1-4)

AZT and ddI were, as of this writing, the only drugs approved for clinical treatment of AIDS in the United States.

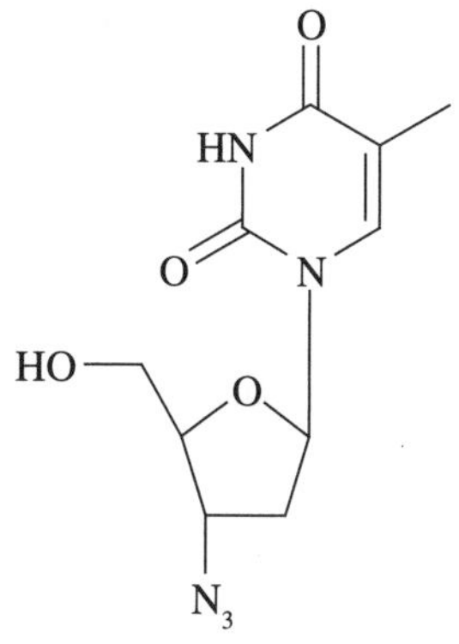

AZT 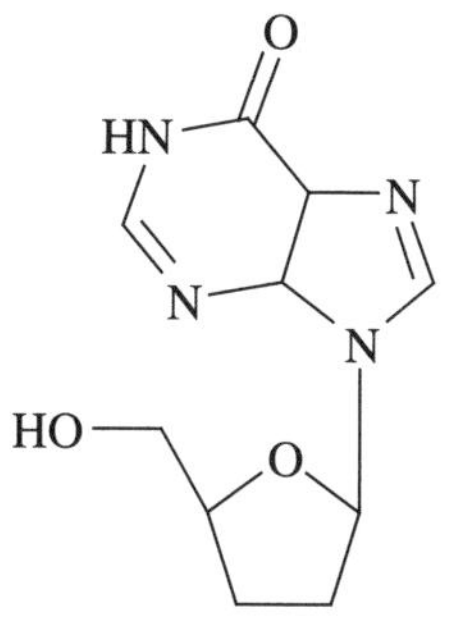   ddI

Unfortunately, they both lead to severe side effects, such as bone marrow suppression (AZT) and peripheral neuropathy and pancreatitis (ddI). Recent work has been directed towards development of new anti-viral drugs that are similar in structure to AZT and ddI, but are more effective and less toxic. Several structurally similar nucleosides have already been shown to be potentially excellent anti-HIV agents, including D4T and D4C, shown below.

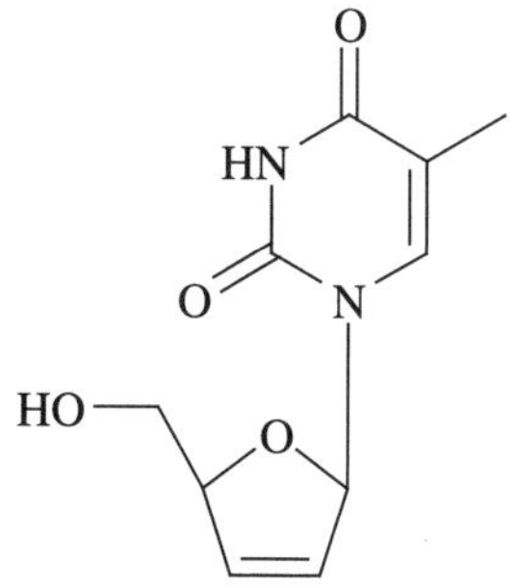

D4T 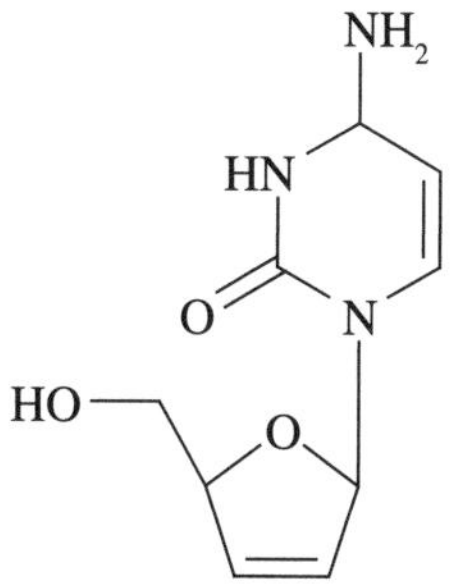   D4C

Both agents have proven to be less toxic than AZT in preliminary *in vitro* trials.

1. How many chiral centers are there in AZT?

   A. 1
   B. 2
   C. 3
   D. 4

2. Which of these four antiviral drugs is basic?

   I. D4C
   II. ddI
   III. D4T

   A. I only
   B. I and II only
   C. II and III only
   D. I, II, and III

3. Given that azide is a good nucleophile, what is the most likely method for the incorporation of the azido portion of the AZT molecule?

   A. S_N1
   B. S_N2
   C. Reduction
   D. Nucleophilic addition

4. Phosphoric acid esters of nucleosides are known as:

   A. RNA.
   B. purines.
   C. glycosides.
   D. nucleotides.

Passage 32 (Questions 1-5)

Aspartame, a simple dipeptide, is better known by its commercial name, *Nutrasweet®*. Aspartame is 200 times sweeter than sucrose and has effectively displaced saccharin as the most popular sugar substitute.

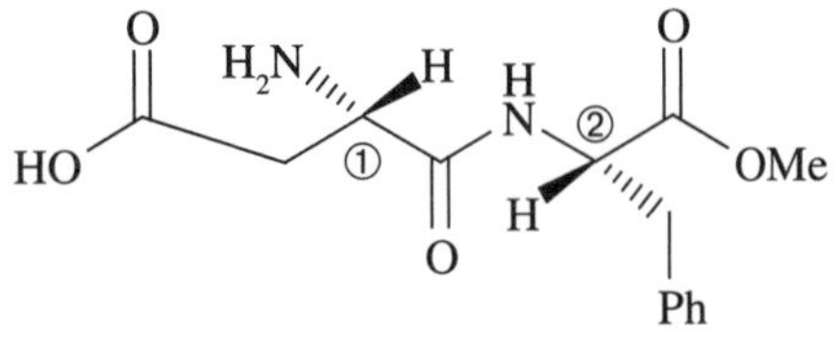

Aspartame (Asp-Phe)

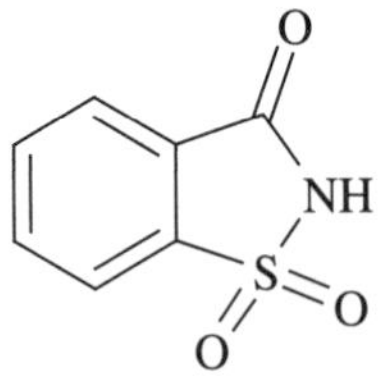

Saccharin

1. The absolute configurations of the carbons labeled 1 and 2 on aspartame are, respectively:

    A. *R* and *R*.
    B. *R* and *S*.
    C. *S* and *R*.
    D. *S* and *S*.

2. The most basic functional group of aspartame would be the:

    A. aromatic ring.
    B. ester carbonyl oxygen.
    C. amino group.
    D. amide nitrogen.

3. At pH 8, which of the following would be true for aspartame?

    A. The acid group would be deprotonated.
    B. The amino group would be deprotonated.
    C. Both the amino group and the acid group would be protonated.
    D. Both the amino group and the ester group would be deprotonated.

4. The protons of the methyl ester group of aspartame would show which of the following splitting patterns in the proton NMR spectrum of aspartame?

    A. Singlet
    B. Doublet
    C. Triplet
    D. Quartet

5. The proton on the nitrogen of saccharin is much more acidic than the proton on the amide nitrogen of aspartame. This is best explained by which one of the following statements?

    A. Cyclic amides are more acidic than acyclic amides.
    B. The adjacent sulfone group stabilizes the anion because it is an electron-donating group.
    C. The saccharin nitrogen is *sp* hybridized.
    D. Extra resonance stabilization of the resulting anion is provided by the sulfone group.

Passage 33 (Questions 1-5)

Before polysaccharides can be absorbed through the small intestine, they must be broken down into their component monosaccharides. This breakdown is accomplished primarily by enzymes known as *α-glucosidases*, which catalyze the hydrolysis of α-glycosidic linkages between the individual sugars of complex carbohydrates. Therefore, inhibitors of α-glucosidases slow the degradation of polysaccharides and the absorption of monosaccharides.

The first α-glycosidase inhibitor discovered was *acarbose*, a pseudo-tetrasaccharide. See Figure 1. Acarbose has been used to slow carbohydrate absorption and thereby improve glycemic control in patients with both insulin- and noninsulin-dependent diabetes mellitus.

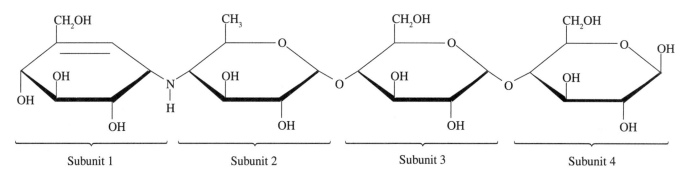

Figure 1 Acarbose

1. Which subunit(s) in Figure 1 will act as reducing sugars
    when Benedict's test is performed on acarbose?

    A. Subunit 1 only
    B. Subunits 1 and 4 only
    C. Subunit 3 only
    D. Subunit 4 only

2. The anomeric carbons of Subunits 2 and 4 are in the
    forms:

    A. acetal and acetal.
    B. acetal and hemiacetal, respectively.
    C. hemiacetal and hemiacetal.
    D. hemiacetal and acetal, respectively.

3. How many units of unsaturation are there in acarbose?

    A. 1
    B. 3
    C. 4
    D. 5

4. The linkage between Subunits 2 and 3 in acarbose is best
    described as which of the following?

    A. α-1,4
    B. α-1,6
    C. β-1,2
    D. β-1,4

5. Mutarotation of acarbose could result in a change in the
    stereochemistry of which subunit?

    A. Subunit 1
    B. Subunit 2
    C. Subunit 3
    D. Subunit 4

Passage 34 (Questions 1-6)

The extended amino acid γ-aminobutyric acid (GABA, Figure 1) is not found in proteins but is a ubiquitous, inhibitory neurotransmitter in the mammalian brain. Since the GABA pathway is implicated in a wide range of neurological phenomena (including anxiety, analgesia, convulsions, coma, dementia, epilepsy, hypertension, and schizophrenia), these conditions may be treated with compounds, such as barbiturates and benzodiazepines, that modulate the activation of GABA receptors.

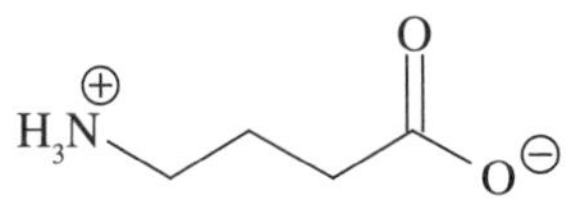

Figure 1 GABA

Like all amino acids, GABA is polyprotic; it contains two or more dissociable protons. Titration of GABA yields two distinct pK_a values, corresponding to the carboxyl terminus (about pH 2.3) and the amino terminus (about pH 9.7). The Henderson–Hasselbalch equation relates pK_a to the pH of a solution containing a certain concentration of an acid (HA) and its conjugate base (A$^-$):

$$pH = pK_a + \log\frac{[A^-]}{[HA]}$$

Equation 1 Henderson–Hasselbalch

The isoelectric point (pI), the pH at which the zwitterionic form of GABA predominates, is 6.0, the average of its two pK_a values.

The Gabriel synthesis (Figure 2) may be used to synthesize GABA from potassium phthalimidate.

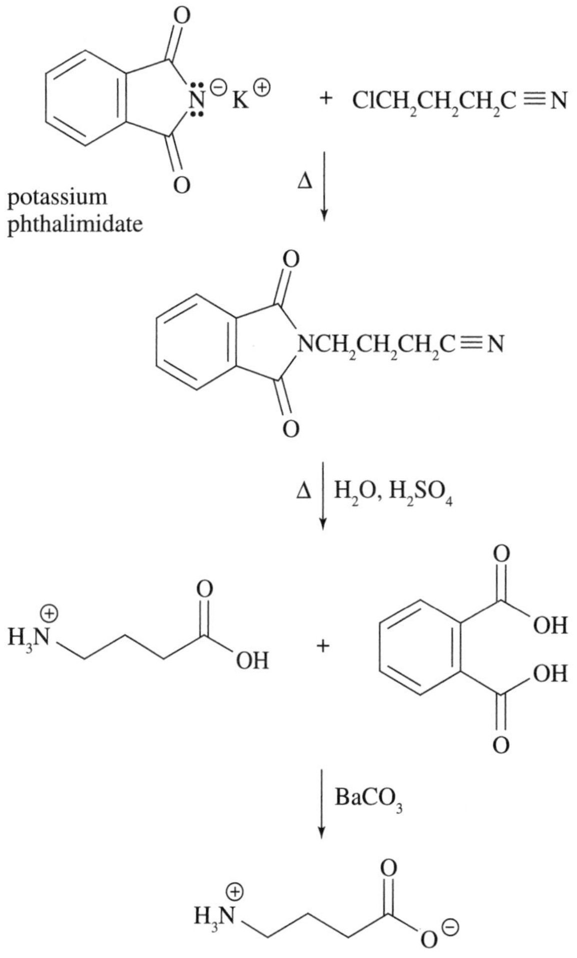

Figure 2 Gabriel synthesis of GABA

1. The isoelectric point of lysine is:

   A. less than the pI of GABA.
   B. equal to the pI of GABA.
   C. greater than the pI of GABA.
   D. Cannot be determined

2. What role does potassium phthalimidate play in the Gabriel synthesis of GABA?

   A. Leaving group
   B. Acid
   C. Nucleophile
   D. Electrophile

3. Which one of the following best represents the zwitterionic form of GABA?

A.

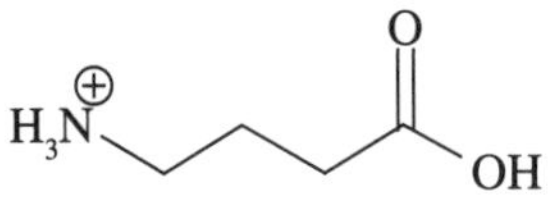

B.

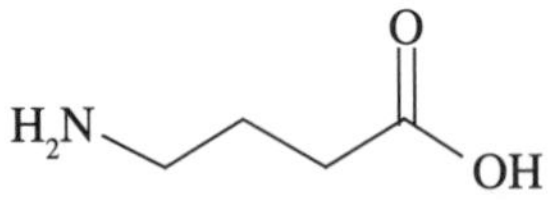

C.

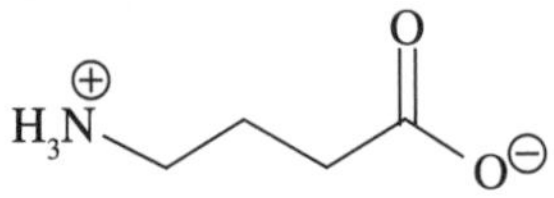

D.

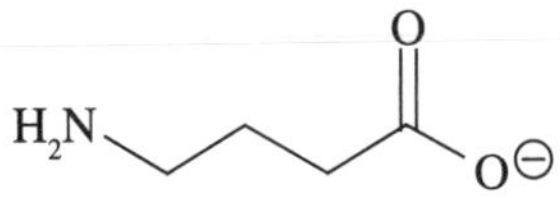

4. Which of the following statements is true when GABA is in a solution buffered at pH 9.7?

A. The concentration of the zwitterion is equal to the concentration of GABA with a net charge of –1.
B. The concentration of the zwitterion is less than the concentration of GABA with a net charge of –1.
C. GABA is completely deprotonated.
D. None of the above

5.

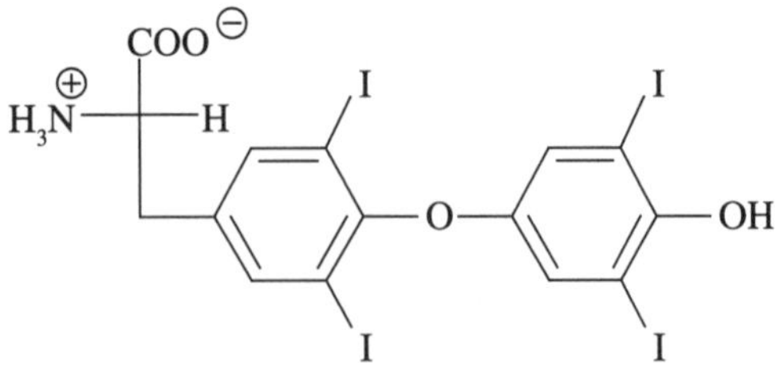

L-Thyroxine (shown above) is a biologically important amino acid that is *not* found in proteins. The pK_a of the hydroxyl group on the L-thyroxine side chain is 9.8. Which of the following statements is/are true?

 I. The pI of L-thyroxine is less than the pI of GABA.
 II. L-Thyroxine has three pK_a values, whereas GABA has two.
III. L-Thyroxine is not polyprotic.

A. I only
B. II only
C. I and II only
D. II and III only

6. Which of the following best depicts the structure of GABA in a solution buffered at pH 10?

A.

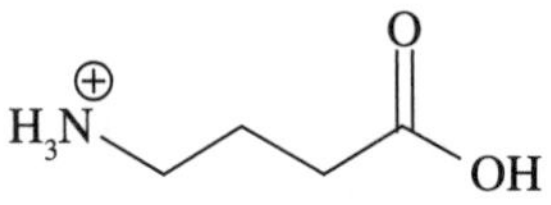

B.

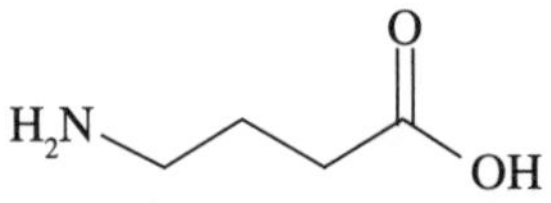

C.

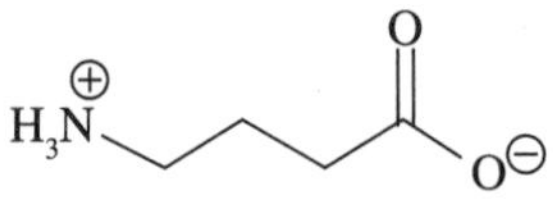

D.

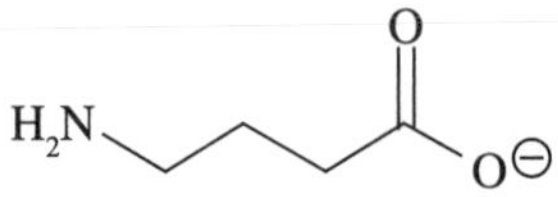

Passage 35 (Questions 1-4)

Triglycerides, or fats, are comprised of a molecule of glycerol bonded through ester linkages to three fatty acids. Plant and animal fats contain a varying number of carbon–carbon double bonds in those side chains. In general, plant oils have a higher degree of unsaturation compared to animal fats. Compound 1 shows the structure of an unsaturated fatty acid.

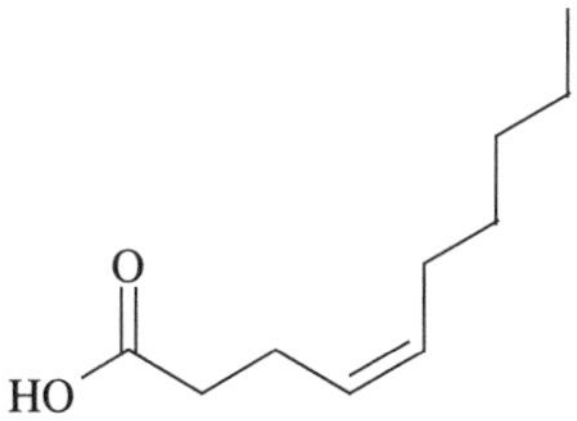

Compound 1

Unsaturated vegetable oils are often hydrogenated to increase their shelf life and flavor stability. This process also increases their melting points, and can convert them into a semisolid state. Most natural, unsaturated fatty acids exist in the *cis* isomeric form. However, during partial hydrogenation the double bonds of the natural oils are sometimes isomerized, converting *cis* molecules into their *trans* isomers.

Fats are an important part of a healthy diet; they are the body's main form of energy storage and are necessary for hormone production. Unsaturated fats aid in the absorption of many vitamins that are essential for the human body. Saturated fats, however, increase the risk of coronary heart disease by raising LDL cholesterol blood levels. The biochemistry of *trans* fatty acids is poorly understood, but studies suggest that *trans* fats behave similarly to saturated fats.

1. Of the following, the best explanation of why the melting points of triglycerides increase upon hydrogenation is that hydrogenation:

   A. adds hydroxyl groups to the molecules, allowing them to hydrogen bond.
   B. isomerizes double bonds, decreasing London dispersion forces between molecules.
   C. cleaves double bonds, lowering the molecular weight of the molecules.
   D. eliminates double bonds, increasing London dispersion forces between molecules.

2. The common name for Compound 1 is obtusilic acid. The IUPAC name for this compound is:

   A. (*E*)-4-decenoic acid.
   B. (*Z*)-4-decenoic acid.
   C. (*E*)-6-decenoic acid.
   D. (*Z*)-6-decenoic acid.

3. Which of the following best represents the products of an ester saponification?

   A. + HOR′
   B. + $^{\ominus}$OR′
   C. + HOR′
   D. + $^{\ominus}$OR′

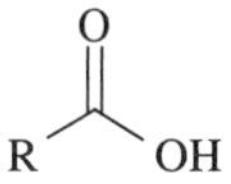

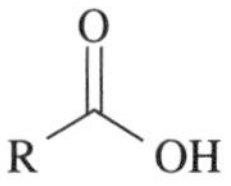

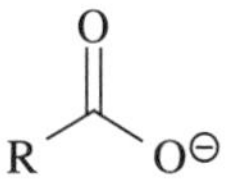

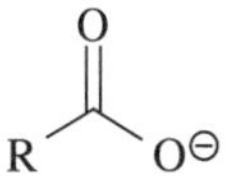

4. *Cis/trans* isomers can best be described as:

   A. enantiomers.
   B. geometric isomers.
   C. structural isomers.
   D. stereoisomers.

Passage 36 (Questions 1-4)
ADVANCED PASSAGE

A biochemist isolated an unknown peptide from a recently discovered bacterium. To determine the peptide's structure, the following experiments were performed.

Experiment 1

A sample of the protein was completely hydrolyzed, yielding the six amino acid residues listed below:

2 Ala residues,

1 Phe,

1 Gly,

1 Ser,

1 Pro.

Experiment 2

Another sample of the protein was partially hydrolyzed, yielding the following fragments:

Ala-Phe,

Ala-Pro,

Ser-Ala,

Phe-Gly.

Experiment 3

A third sample of protein was treated with 2,4-dinitrofluorobenzene, followed by complete hydrolysis. Analysis of the resulting residues indicated the dinitrophenyl group was attached to an alanine residue.

1. Amino acids are linked to one another in a protein by which of the following bonds?

   A. Ester bonds
   B. Amine bonds
   C. Amide bonds
   D. Carboxylate bonds

2. 2,4-Dinitrofluorobenzene is used in protein analysis to determine:

   A. the most frequent amino acid found in the protein.
   B. the amino acid at the *N*-terminus.
   C. the amino acid at the *C*-terminus.
   D. the most reactive amino acid in the protein.

3. The reaction conditions typically used to hydrolyze a protein are:

   A. concentrated acid, heat.
   B. concentrated base, heat.
   C. dilute acid, room temperature.
   D. dilute base, room temperature.

4. The most likely amino acid sequence for this protein is:

   A. FGSAPA
   B. APAFSG
   C. AFGSAP
   D. SAFGAP

Passage 37 (Questions 1-6)
ADVANCED PASSAGE

In 1958 Dr. Frederick Sanger was awarded the first of his two Nobel prizes in Chemistry for being the first scientist to establish the sequence of amino acids within a protein. In his determination of the primary sequence of human insulin, Sanger developed 2,4-dinitrofluorobenzene (DNFB).

DNFB reacts with free amino groups in a nucleophilic aromatic substitution reaction. Thus, DNFB can be used to selectively label the N-terminal residue of a protein. Following complete hydrolysis of the protein, the free amino acids can be separated and the modified residue identified spectroscopically. In the course of his ten-year study, Sanger used DNFB on a series of partial hydrolysis fragments of insulin to reconstruct the sequence of the entire protein.

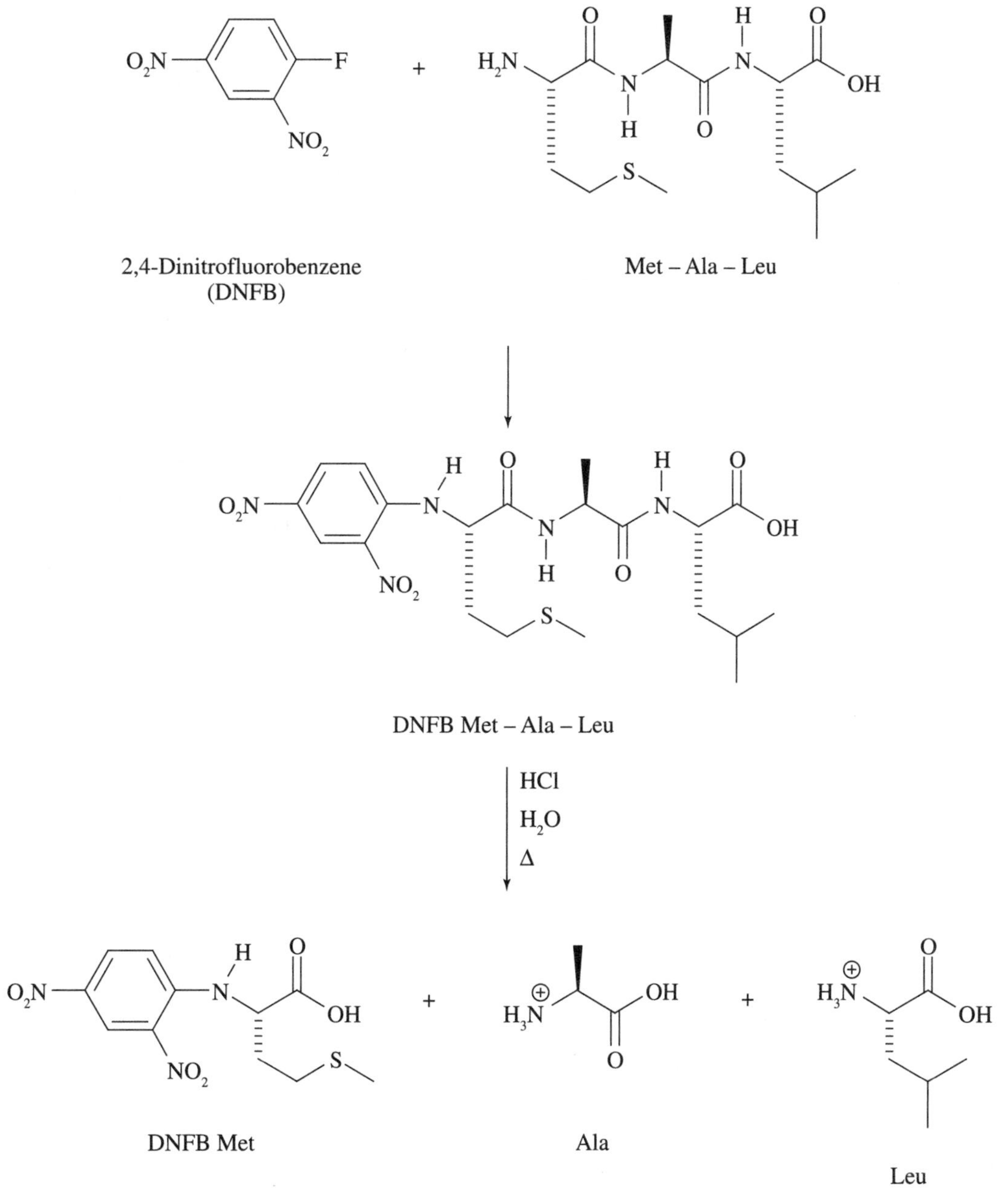

2,4-Dinitrofluorobenzene
(DNFB)

Met – Ala – Leu

DNFB Met – Ala – Leu

HCl
H_2O
Δ

DNFB Met

Ala

Leu

Figure 1

1. Which of the following would NOT be an intermediate in the acid hydrolysis of the DNFB-labeled tripeptide shown in Figure 1?

A.

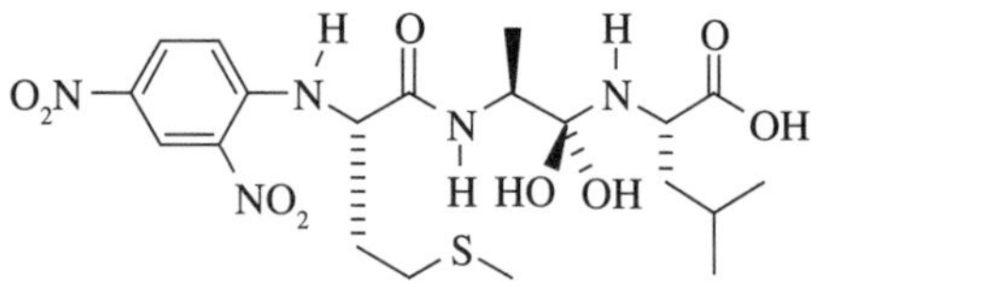

B.

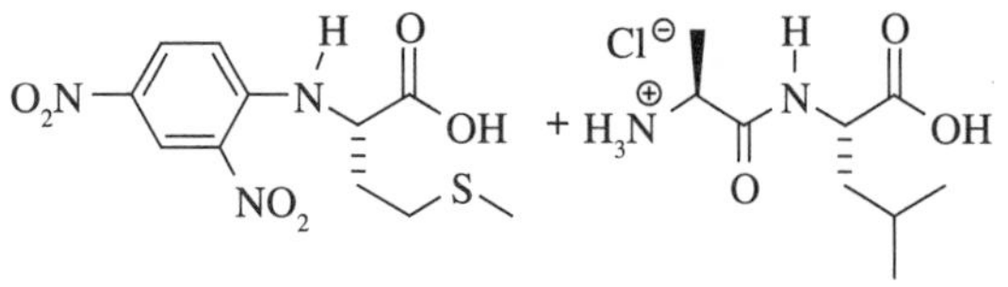

C.

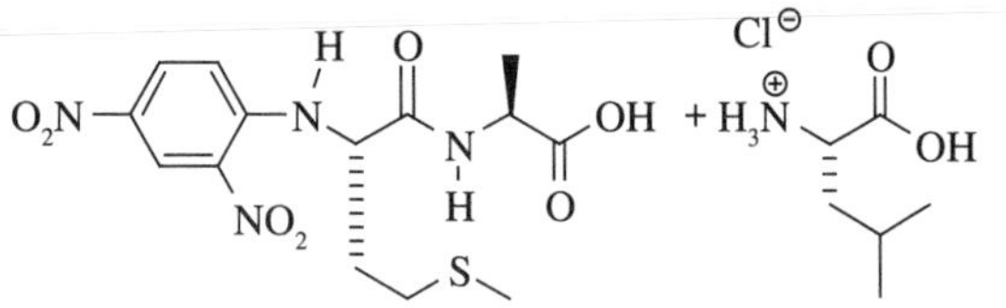

D.

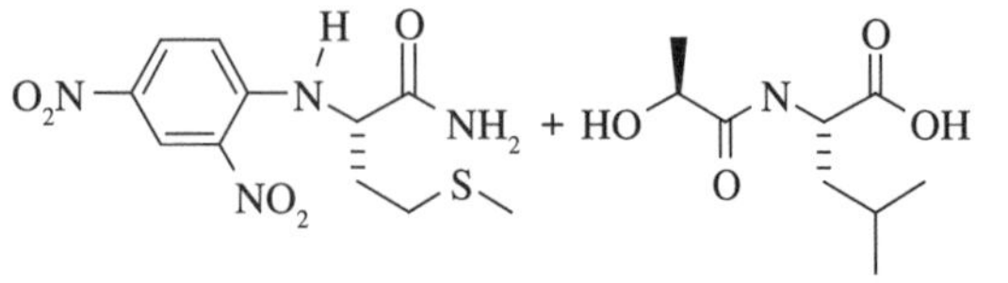

2. Which one of the following would NOT be used to synthesize the Met–Ala–Leu tripeptide in Figure 1?

A.

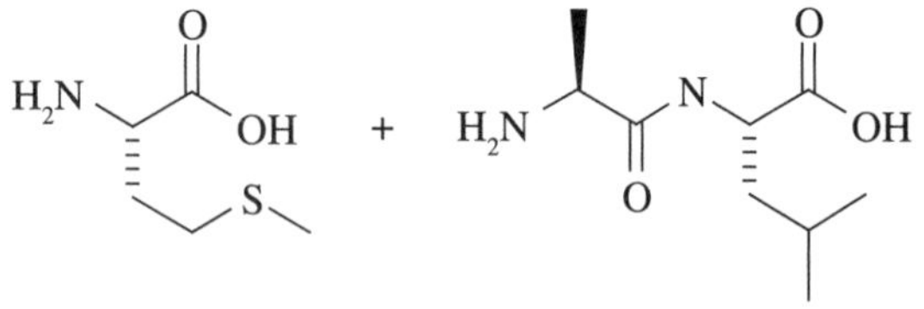

B.

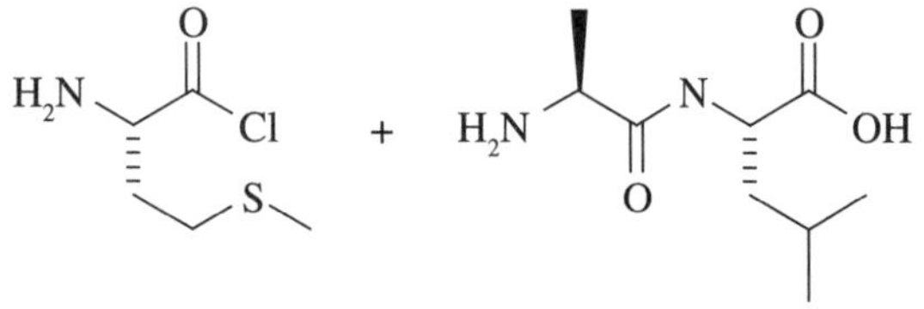

C.

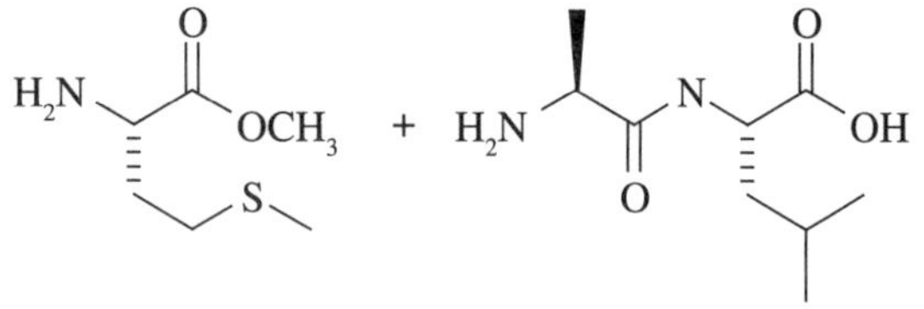

D.

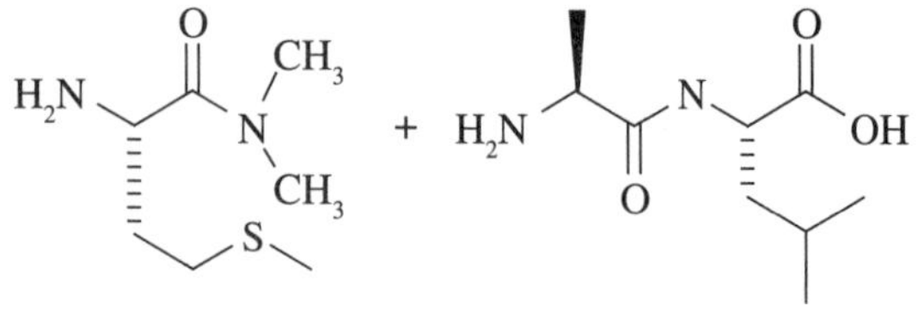

3. One of Sanger's initial experiments demonstrated that reducing agents broke the 51-residue insulin molecule into 20-residue and 31-residue peptides. This experiment indicates the presence of what in insulin?

   A. α helices
   B. β sheets
   C.   Disulfide bonds
   D.   Tertiary structure

4. Which amino acid will DNFB label, even when it does not occur at the N-terminus of a peptide?

   A.   Aspartic acid
   B.   Cysteine
   C.   Lysine
   D.   Proline

5. Following separation of the hydrolysis products, which technique would be most useful for determining the identity of the DNFB-labeled amino acid?

   A.   Fractional distillation
   B. ^{1}H NMR spectroscopy
   C.   IR spectroscopy
   D.   Liquid–liquid extraction

6. All amino acids—except glycine—are naturally optically active. However, during acid hydrolysis, amino acids may lose their optical activity. Formation of which of the following species may account for this phenomenon?

   A.   Anomers
   B.   Disulfide bonds
   C.   Enols
   D.   Zwitterions

MCAT Organic Chemistry
Solutions

Passage 1

1. **B** The carbon atom has two σ bonds and two π bonds. It is therefore *sp* hybridized. The oxygen atom has two σ bonds and two lone electron pairs and is therefore *sp³* hybridized.

2. **C** In this molecule, every double bond contains one π bond and every triple bond contains two π bonds.

3. **B** The functional group that is not present on the molecule is a thiol (–SH). An alcohol (–OH) group is present. An epoxide (a three-membered ring that has oxygen bridging the two carbons) is present. An ether (C–O–C) connects the ethylene/alcohol groups to the aromatic ring.

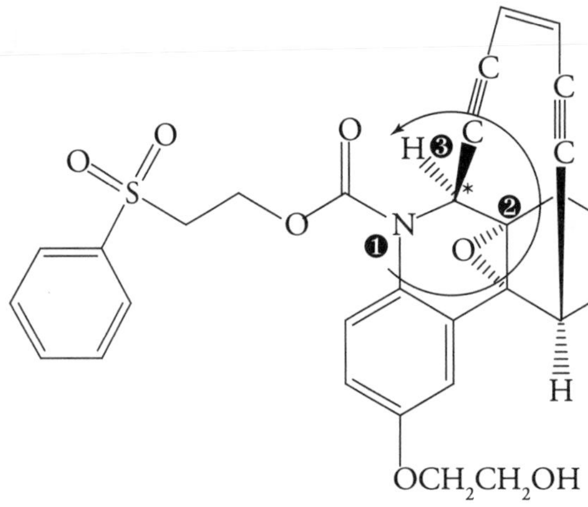

4. **C** Since the trace of the prioritized groups is counterclockwise, the absolute configuration is *S*.

5. **C** Since the molecule has 4 chiral centers (as indicated by the asterisks in the diagram below), it has $2^4 = 16$ possible stereoisomers.

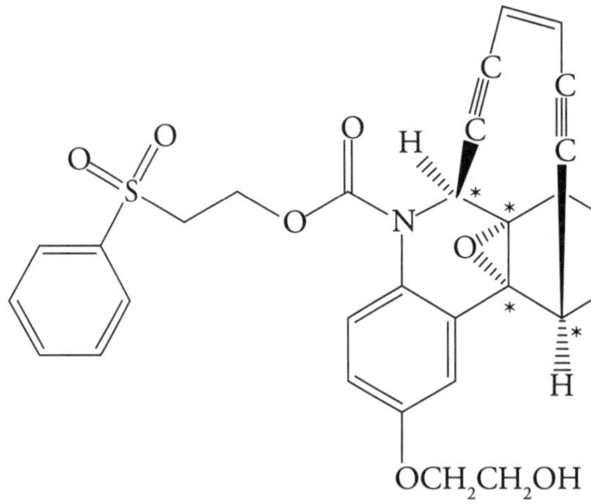

Passage 2

1. **B**

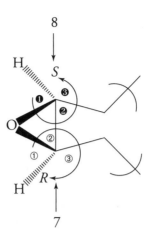

2. **D**   There is no relationship between optical rotation and a molecule's absolute stereochemistry. The passage does not provide enough information to answer this question.

3. **D**   In general, alkyl groups are much less reactive than are epoxides. There is no ketone functional group in this molecule.

4. **A**   The molecule shown differs from disparlure at both stereocenters, and, thus, the two molecules are enantiomers.

5. **C**   Water can attack the epoxide at either C-7 or C-8. Since disparlure is a *cis*-epoxide, the resulting diols must have *trans* configuration.

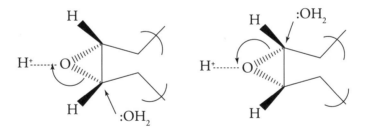

6. **C**   Disparlure has two long alkyl chains. For this reason, it has hydrophobic properties. Water, methanol, and ethanol are all hydrophilic solvents because of their small size and ability to hydrogen bond. In fact, methanol and ethanol are miscible with water. Ethyl acetate, on the other hand, cannot extensively hydrogen bond and is immiscible with water. This indicates hydrophobic properties, so disparlure should be most soluble in ethyl acetate.

Passage 3

1. **D** *n*-Heptane has 4 more CH_2 groups, so -156×4 kcal per mol $= -624$ kcal/mol. This gives

$$-530 + -624 \approx -1150 \text{ kcal/mol}$$

2. **C** Since neopentane has the formula C_5H_{12}, the combustion of one mole of neopentane would produce 5 moles of CO_2 and 6 moles of H_2O.

3. **D** The compound in D has one more carbon than any of the others, and thus it should have the heat of combustion of highest magnitude (most negative).

4. **B** Both compounds have the same molecular weight (choice D can be eliminated), straight chains don't have angle strain (choice A can be eliminated), and choice C can be eliminated because the Heats of Combustion are essentially the same value.

5. **A** Since cyclodecane has very little ring strain we know it isn't planar. Instead, it is puckered to allow all bond angles to be close to 109°. Bond angles greater than 109° *do* increase angle strain (choice B is wrong), and cyclodecane, like all alkanes, is comprised of only sp^3 centers (choice C is wrong). Lastly, 1,3,5,7,9-cyclodecapentaene contains five π bonds, and hence will have a very different heat of combustion (choice D is wrong).

6. **B** Cycloheptane has only 6.5 kcal/mol of strain energy more than cyclohexane (choice A can be eliminated). Neither compound has branching (choice C can be eliminated), and both rings interconvert rapidly between conformations (choice D can be eliminated).

Passage 4

1. **B** If ethanol is halogenated, this can occur only by Synthesis A or Synthesis C. If it is hydrogenated, this occurs only in Syntheses A and B. So, for both to occur, it must be by Synthesis A. The last step of Synthesis A is the hydrogenation (or reduction) of a nitrile ($R–C\equiv N$).

2. **D** Hydrolysis of a benzylic halide looks like this:

$$\text{(benzyl alcohol)}$$

3. **C** The polar amino group of *p*-toluidine makes it soluble in water:

4. **D** Ethylamine is the product since nitrile reduction adds a carbon to the alkyl chain.

Passage 5

1. **A** For any chiral molecule, there are 2^n possible stereoisomers, where n = the number of chiral centers in the molecule. Camphor has $n = 2$ chiral centers, so it has a maximum of $2^2 = 4$ stereoisomers. However because camphor is a bicyclic molecule, the bridge carbon stereocenters cannot be inverted. Therefore, camphor only has one enantiomer and no diastereomers.

2. **A** Addition of MeMgBr to camphor yields two alcohols with opposite stereochemistry because the methyl can add either to the top face or the bottom face of the carbonyl plane. Since the other two chiral centers on camphor were not affected during the reaction, the resulting alcohols differ in stereochemistry only at the alcohol stereocenter. When the configuration between two compounds differs only at one of several chiral positions, the compounds are diastereomers. To be enantiomers, all the centers would have to have opposite configurations.

3. **D** To determine the absolute configuration of a particular carbon, you must place the lowest priority group away from you. Assign priority to the remaining three groups, and starting with the highest-priority group, count either clockwise (*R*) or counterclockwise (*S*) to the lowest priority group. Both centers are *S*. For C-1, the bridging quaternary C gets first priority (it's connected to three other Cs) while the CH$_2$ group to the right gets second priority because of the carbonyl. For C-2, the ketone gets first priority because it is closer to the chiral center.

4. **D** Since *S* and *T* are diastereomers of each other, no conclusions can be made about Compound *T*'s optical rotation.

Passage 6

1. **D** The heat of hydrogenation of 1-heptene should be closest to that of 1-pentene since they are most similar in size.

2. **C** *cis*-Alkenes are always less stable than their *trans* isomers because of steric strain.

3. **A** C–C double bond rotation does not occur until very high temperatures are reached because the π bond must first be broken.

4. **D** This is true by definition. The heat of hydrogenation is defined as the amount of heat released upon addition of H$_2$ across a double bond.

5. **B** The alkene carbon is *sp²* hybridized (choices A and D are wrong). The carbonyl carbon is *sp²* hybridized (choice C is wrong).

Passage 7

1. **D** (+)-2-Iodopentane and (–)-2-iodopentane are nonsuperimposable mirror images and therefore enantiomers. Diastereomers are stereoisomers that are not mirror images. A meso compound is one that has chiral centers but is not optically active (i.e., does not rotate plane-polarized light) because of an internal plane of symmetry. Polypeptides are polymers of amino acids.

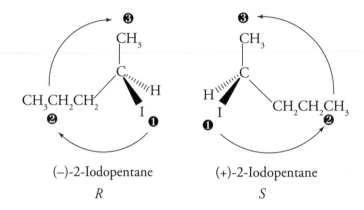

(–)-2-Iodopentane (+)-2-Iodopentane
R *S*

2. **B** Enantiomers have opposite stereochemistry. Once it is determined that the configuration for (–)-2-iodopentane is *R*, choices A and D can be eliminated because the stereocenters are not opposite. Choice C can be eliminated because it defines (–)-2-iodopentane as *S*.

3. **B** Whenever there is an equal mixture of enantiomers (a racemic mixture), there is no net optical rotation. While one enantiomer will rotate plane polarized light with a given magnitude in one direction, the other enantiomer will rotate plane polarized light with the same magnitude in the opposite direction. Thus, there is a net cancellation.

4. **B** The positive carbon of the carbocation intermediate is flat and planar with three σ bonds and no lone electron pairs. Thus, its hybridization is *sp²*.

Passage 8

1. **B** Counterclockwise rotation, therefore *S*:

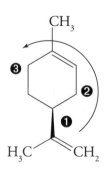

Note: (+) and (–) refer to the sign of optical rotation and say nothing about absolute stereochemistry.

2. **B** Limonene has two π bonds. It will therefore take up 2 moles of H_2.

3. **C** We can immediately eliminate choices B and D since they are *trans* isomers. The isomer in choice C is more stable than the one in choice A because the more bulky isopropyl group is in the roomier equatorial position.

4. **B** We can immediately eliminate choices A and C because they are *cis* isomers. Choice B is the answer, since in this isomer both groups are equatorial rather than axial as in choice D.

5. **B** In this kind of question, you must compare the most stable chair conformation of each isomer. The most stable *trans* isomer is choice B.

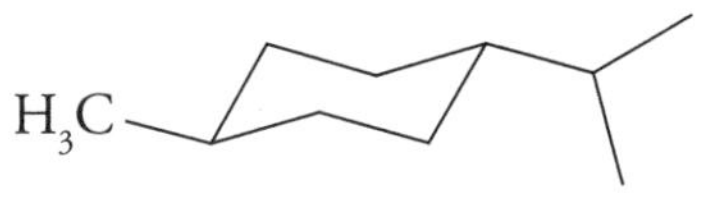

and the most stable *cis* isomer is choice C:

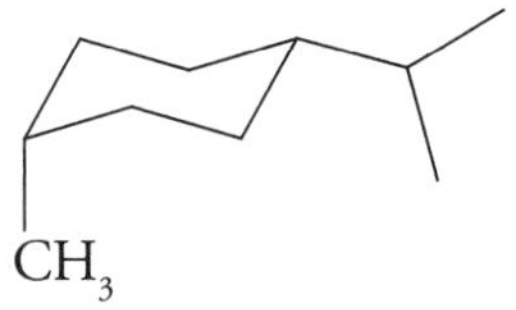

The isomer in choice B is more stable than the one in choice C since both groups are equatorial. Therefore, the *trans* isomer is the more stable.

Passage 9

1. **B** The magnitude of the heat of hydrogenation increases with decreasing substitution. Compared to equally substituted *trans* double bonds, *cis* double bonds have a higher magnitude of ΔH_{hydr} because of unfavorable steric interactions.

2. **B** Because *cis*-double bonds have higher heats of hydrogenation than *trans*-double bonds, choices A and C can be eliminated. Choice D can be eliminated because changes in the heats of hydrogenation have a similar effect on the heat of combustion.

3.   **C**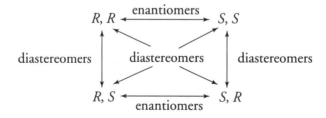

4.   **B**   First determine the degrees of unsaturation which is 5. Then determine that the molecule has three π bonds because it absorbs three moles of hydrogen. Therefore, the remaining two degrees of unsaturation would be attributed to rings.

5.   **C**   Because the two double bonds are conjugated, they are slightly stabilized. The heat of hydrogenation will be slightly less than the value for two isolated double bonds.

Passage 10

1.   **B**   From the information given, Compound A is a mixture of two stereoisomers. Compound A shows an optical rotation of zero degrees, which means it must be an equal mixture of the two enantiomers, which by definition makes A a racemic mixture.

2.   **B**   The two stereoisomers of A are E and F. These two isomers are enantiomers of each other and will show identical physical properties (except that they will show equal, but opposite, optical rotations). Therefore, F must have the same melting point as E, which is 80°C.

3.   **B**   Resolution is the process of separating two enantiomers from each other.

4.   **C**   Enantiomers will differ only in their configuration and in the sign of rotation of plane polarized light. Since Isomer E had a configuration of R and a positive sign of rotation, Isomer F must have a configuration of S and a negative sign of rotation.

5.   **B**   Since Compound A is a mixture of two stereoisomers, and Racemic B would also contain two stereoisomers, reaction between the two racemic compounds would give a mixture of four stereoisomers as a result of all possible combinations between A and B.

6.   **C**   Compound C has configuration R, R while compound D has configuration S, R. These are different at only one center and are therefore diastereomers.

$$
\begin{array}{ccc}
R, R & \xrightarrow{\text{enantiomers}} & S, S \\
\Big\updownarrow \text{ diastereomers} & \text{diastereomers} & \Big\updownarrow \text{ diastereomers} \\
R, S & \xrightarrow[\text{enantiomers}]{} & S, R
\end{array}
$$

Passage 11

1. **B** Protonation of 1,3-butadiene by HCl makes

which is resonance stabilized:

The hybrid of these two resonance forms is choice B.

2. **A** There can be no partial double bond character due to σ electrons; double bonds result from π electrons (choice B is wrong). If you draw the structure of 1,3-butadiene, you see that all carbons are sp^2 hybridized, so there can be no overlap with an sp^3 carbon (choices C and D are wrong).

3. **A** An sp^2 orbital is $33\frac{1}{3}\%$ s, while an sp^3 orbital is 25% s. This causes an sp^2–sp^2 bond to have higher s character than an sp^3–sp^3 bond.

4. **B** This value is obtained directly from Table 1.

5. **C** This is precisely what it means to say that an atom is sp^2 hybridized.

Passage 12

1. **A** Choice B can be eliminated because the table does not illustrate the solubility of Group E in sulfuric acid. Choice C can be eliminated because E is not soluble in ether. Choice D can be eliminated because E is soluble in HCl.

2. **A** Isopropanol is hydrophilic (eliminating choice B), because it can hydrogen bond with water. It is neither a good acid or base (eliminate choices C and D). Of the four choices, isopropanol is best characterized as polar because of its OH group and water solubility.

3. **D**

4. **C** In general, organic compounds are less soluble in water when they have long chains.

Passage 13

The structure of Compound 2 is:

1. **B** Functional groups that are basic will react with dilute acid. Of the choices, amines are the only basic functional group.

2. **A** The more polar the compound, the more it will interact with the silica gel on the TLC plate. This means it will move up the plate more slowly and therefore have a smaller R_f value.

3. **D** Alkenes generally absorb around 1650 cm^{-1}, so the absence of a peak in this region rules out a C=C. The remaining peaks could indicate a carbonyl (1735 cm^{-1}), and therefore an ester, as well as an alcohol (3100 cm^{-1}).

4. **A** A signal will be split into a number of peaks equal to the number of adjacent hydrogens plus one. A doublet indicates one adjacent hydrogen.

5. **B** IR absorptions around 1700 cm^{-1} are indicative of carbonyls. Since treatment of Compound 2 with NaOH results in a change in carbonyl peak, Compound 2 must contain a carboxylic acid derivative that is hydrolyzed by NaOH. Based on the molecular formula, only an ester (choice B) can be present in Compound 2.

Passage 14

1. **A** If you only consider the molecular formula, an ester is the only functional group that could not be present, because it requires two oxygen atoms.

2. **D** The absorbance at 1705 cm^{-1} in the IR spectrum indicates the presence of either a ketone or possibly an aldehyde. Since there is no aldehyde proton resonance in the proton NMR (δ 9–10), it must be a ketone. It is not possible for the compound to contain an ester functional group because there is only one oxygen in the given formula.

3. **A** The signal that is split into the largest number of lines (multiplet) is the one with the greatest number of neighboring hydrogens. In this case, it's the signal at δ 7.25.

4. **B** Treatment of Compound X with NaBH$_4$ followed by acidic workup would yield the corresponding Alcohol Y. Compound Y would have two new proton resonances, one for the hydroxyl proton and one for the C–H that the hydroxyl group is attached to.

Passage 15

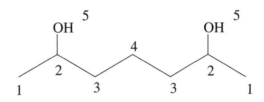

I   II   III

1. **A** Compound 1 has two degrees of unsaturation. The IR data indicates there is at least one car-
    bonyl group. A structure that accounts for the carbonyl group and a ring will not fit the ^{1}H
    NMR data. There are no double bonds according the ^{1}H NMR data, so it must be assumed that
    the other degree of unsaturation comes from another carbonyl group. In addition, both degrees
    of saturation disappeared upon treatment with NaBH$_4$, indicating that both were carbonyls.

2. **D** 3350 cm^{-1} is the typical absorption for an alcohol.

3. **B** Compound III has two degrees of unsaturation. They represent the C=O of the two carboxylic
    acid functional groups.

4. **D** Addition of Grignard to a ketone will give an alcohol, which will absorb around 3350 cm^{-1}.

5. **C** There will be five different signals due to the four different hydrogens (don't forget—this is a
    symmetrical compound), *plus* one signal for the hydrogens on the OH groups, for a total of 5
    different signals.

Passage 16

1. **B** Nucleophiles are "nucleus-seeking" species that have either a full negative formal charge or a partial negative charge.

2. **D** Carbocation formation is not stabilized by a methyl group (choice A can be eliminated). Choices B and C can be eliminated because they represent first-order mechanisms.

3. **C** Electrophiles are species that usually have either a full formally positive charge or a partial positive charge.

4. **B** Since the alkyl halide is tertiary, a unimolecular reaction will occur. Water stabilizes the carbocation intermediate, speeding the reaction.

Passage 17

1. **A** The n-pentyl group will most closely resemble the n-propyl group, because, of the choices given, they are the closest in structure and size.

2. **A** Answer choices B, C, and D are all characteristics of S_N2 reactions. The only false statement is A. S_N2 reactions operate by second-order kinetics.

3. **D** Doubling $[CH_3Br]$ doubles the rate, and doubling $[OH^-]$ also doubles the rate. Therefore, both of these concentration increases will quadruple the rate.

4. **C** S_N1 rates depend only on the rate of leaving group loss (so only on substrate concentration). Eliminate both choices A and B because both S_N1 and S_N2 depend on solvent and temperature. Choice D can be eliminated because S_N1 does not depend on the nucleophile.

5. **B** The slower rate of $CH_3CH_2CH_2$ relative to CH_3 is best explained by sterics. S_N2 reactions proceed more slowly with increased substituent size.

Passage 18

1. **A** The overall yield is the product of the yields of the steps: $0.95 \times 0.78 = 0.74$.

2. **B** Saponification of the ester occurs with NaOH, and isolation of the free acids are achieved using a mineral acid such as HCl.

3. **C** Conversion of an alcohol to an ester can be done with acetic anhydride.

4. **B** Compounds that have carboxylic acids would be soluble in aqueous sodium bicarbonate (a weak base). The phenolic proton is not acidic enough to impart solubility.

5. A   Treatment of salicylic acid with methanol and dry acid are standard conditions for making an ester in a process known as *Fischer esterification*.

6. D   Absorption at 1735 cm^{-1} is characteristic of an ester group.

Passage 19

1. B   The most acidic compound will be the one with the strongest electron withdrawing group attached to it. Both choices B and C have a chlorine, but the chlorine on Compound B is closer to the carboxylic acid so it would have the greatest influence on acidity.

2. A   Hydrolysis of Ester A gives a four-carbon acid, with a methyl branch at the 2 position. Remember, the carbonyl carbon of the acid is the 1 position.

3. C   Even though methyl acetate is slightly heavier, it boils at a substantially lower temperature than acetic acid. Acetic acid has strong intermolecular hydrogen bonding which is responsible for the high boiling point.

4. D   LiAlH$_4$ reduces acids to alcohols. Alcohols react with carboxylic acids to form esters (Fischer esterification). Although A is an ester, the alcohol portion is missing a CH$_2$ group.

5. D   Only primary alcohols can be oxidized to carboxylic acids. Choice D is a secondary alcohol.

Passage 20

1. D   The protons between two carbonyl groups would be most acidic. Choice A doesn't even have any alpha protons. Choices B and C show roughly the same acidity, but far less than choice D.

2. A   The product requires a total of eight carbons. Everything is the same in each answer choice except the length of the aldehyde. Ethyl acetate contains four carbons, so butanal must be the correct aldehyde.

3. D   Attack of the enolate of 2-butanone will occur at the ketone carbon of 2-methylcyclohexanone. This will produce a tertiary alcohol adjacent to the ring methyl group.

4. B   The more stable the anion, the less basic it is. Resonance stabilization or powerful electron withdrawing groups will decrease basicity. The only anion fitting such criteria is HCO$_3^-$, which has resonance structures. Since NaHCO$_3$ is the weakest base here answer choices A, C and D can be eliminated. Thus, choice B is best.

5. C   Ketone C has no alpha protons to react with LDA.

Passage 21

1. **D** Cl⁻ is the best leaving group of the list, thus acid chlorides are predicted to be the most reactive.

2. **A** The resonance structure depicted puts positive charge on the X group and forms a carbon=X double bond. N and Cl have lower electronegativity values than oxygen, so choices B and C can be ruled out. Chlorine has a larger atomic radius than nitrogen, so p orbital overlap is much worse in the chlorine case. Therefore, the amide most easily forms the pictured resonance structure. The contribution of this resonance structure is one of the reasons that amides are often quite unreactive.

3. **D** Br⁻ is a better leaving group than Cl⁻ (HBr is more acidic) so acid bromides are predicted to be more reactive than acid chlorides.

4. **B** Choices B and D are the most sterically unhindered of the four molecules. Structure B has an electron-withdrawing group (F) close to the carbonyl group, making the carbonyl carbon more electrophilic. For these reasons, choice B is expected to be the most reactive.

5. **A** This is a classic acetylation reaction.

Passage 22

1. **D** One molecule of H_2O is lost:

2. **B** The reaction taking place is the conversion of an imide to an amide (C=O to CH_2). This is a classic reduction reaction where oxygen is replaced by hydrogen.

3. **C** Compound A does not contain a nitrogen, so it can be eliminated. Compounds B and D are amides, so the N lone pairs are partially tied up in resonance interactions with one oxygen. (B also has a proton on the N that would allow it to function as a hydrogen-bond donor.) The lone pair on N in Compound C is tied up by *two* resonance interactions, making it the least basic of all, and the poorest hydrogen-bond acceptor.

4. **A**

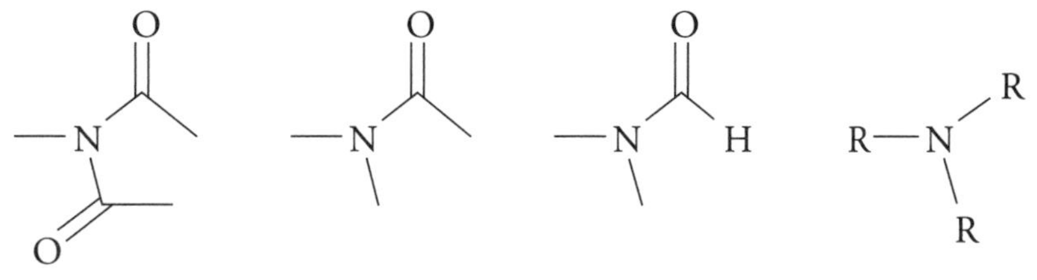

| imide | amide | formamide | tertiary amine |

Passage 23

1. **C** A Grignard reagent (here, CH_3MgBr) is a strong base and will deprotonate any available acid before acting as a nucleophile. Therefore, the reaction of butanoic acid with CH_3MgBr produces the butanoate (choice C) and methane.

2. **A** Assigning priorities to the substituents about C-2, C-3, and C-4, and looking down the bond to the lowest-priority substituent, we see that the priorities of the substituents all proceed in a clockwise fashion, which means Molecule 2 has (*R, R, R*) stereochemistry.

3. **A** As in Reaction 2 in the passage, the Grignard reagent shown (CH_3MgBr) can attack either face of the carbonyl. Note, however, that the two products this reaction *appears* to produce are two representations of the same meso molecule:

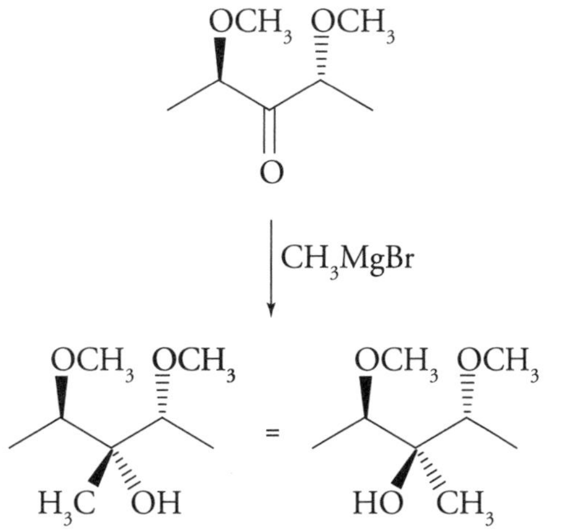

4. **B** Molecules 2 and 3 differ only in their stereochemistry at C-3, making them stereoisomers. Since they are not mirror images of each other (the stereochemistries are inverted at C-3 but not at C-2 or C-4), they are diastereomers.

5. **A** The reaction of CH_3CH_2MgBr with formaldehyde (choice A) produces 1-propanol, a primary alcohol. Reaction choices C and D produce secondary and tertiary alcohols, respectively, while formic acid (choice B) will only be deprotonated by the Grignard reagent.

6. **B** Since the starting material given in the question has a carbon–halogen bond, addition of magnesium metal will convert it into a Grignard reagent (choice A). However, since the molecule also contains an aldehyde, it will undergo a spontaneous intramolecular addition reaction, producing a five-membered ring (choice B).

Passage 24

1. **A** Kevlar is the product of condensing the terminal amino group with the carboxylic acid group in 4-aminobenzoic acid.

2. **D** In the formation of poly(ethylene terephthalate), many condensation reactions occur between the hydroxyl groups of ethylene glycol and the ester groups of dimethyl terephthalate. These transesterification reactions occur by addition of the alcohol to the ester, and elimination of methanol.

3. **B** Addition of an amine to an ester forms an amide. Therefore, a polyamide would form between a diamine and dimethyl terephthalate.

4. **B** Most monomers are either alkenes or di-functional molecules (having two polymerizable groups). Choice A is an alkene and can therefore be polymerized. Choice C and D have two polymerizable groups. Only choice B has a single functional group that is not an alkene.

Passage 25

1. **C** The terms "*syn*" and "*anti*" refer to groups on the "same side" and "opposite sides," respectively, of the growing alkyl chain in the aldol product. In Molecule 3, the α-alkoxy and the β-hydroxyl groups are the only substituents that are *anti*. In Molecule 4, the α-alkoxy and the β-hydroxyl groups are the only substituents that are *syn*. Therefore, the correct answer is choice C.

2. **A** Since the longest carbon chain in Molecule 5 is a 4-carbon chain, the root of the name is "butan". There is a ketone at C-2, so the molecule is called a "butan-2-one". The three hydroxyl groups—at C-1, C-3, and C-4—make it a "1,3,4-trihydroxybutan-2-one". And the phenyl group at C-4 must be added to the name *after* the "1,3,4-trihydroxy," since the "p" in "phenyl" comes after the "h" in "hydroxy," alphabetically so eliminate answer choices C and D. Finally, the molecule is named 3S, not 3R (to distinguish between choices A and B) because looking down the Cα–H^4 bond, the groups proceed **1-2-3** in a counterclockwise fashion:

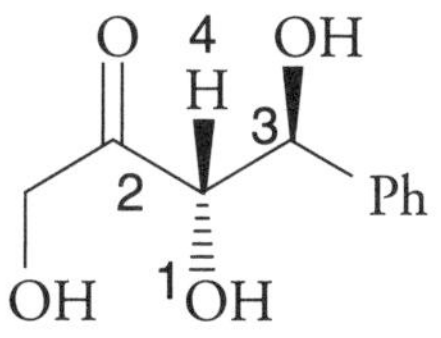

3. **D** To determine the starting material for an aldol addition product, one must imagine which C–C bond was formed in the reaction. For an aldol, this is always the C–C bond between the α-C and the C bonded to the –OH group:

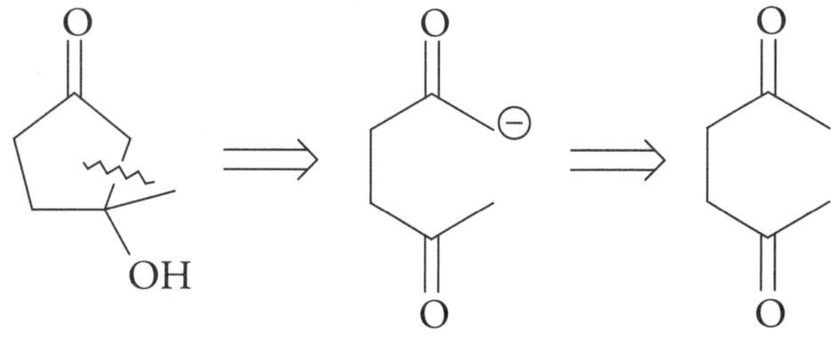

Therefore, choice D is correct.

4. **B** The enantiomer of a molecule is the stereoisomer in which all stereocenters are of opposite configuration (Roman numeral II). Therefore, the following molecules are enantiomers:

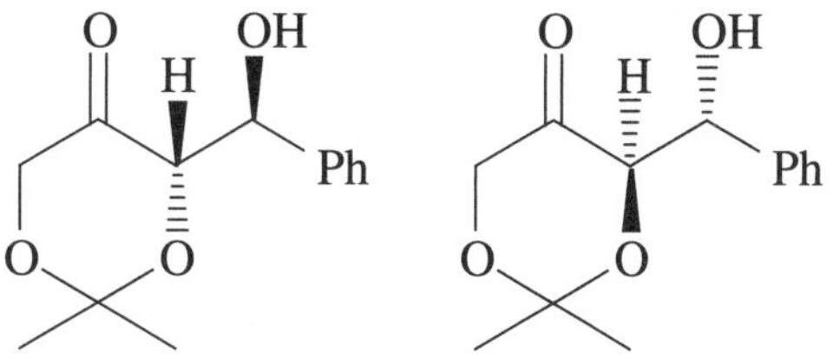

5. **C** Diastereomers are stereoisomers in which all the stereocenters are not opposite. Therefore, both I and II are diastereomers of Molecule 4:

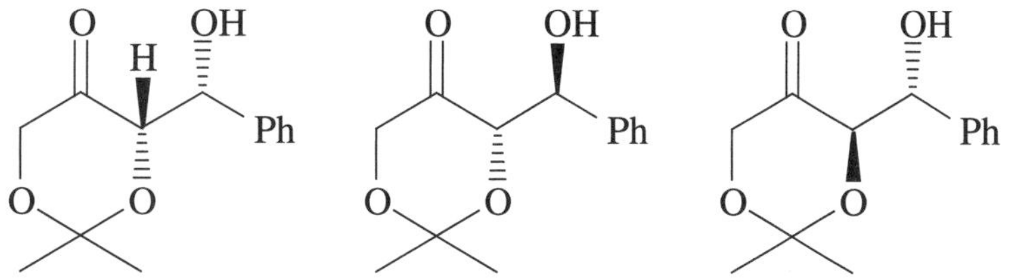

Molecule III is not a diastereomer of Molecule 4; it is the enantiomer of Molecule 4.

6. **A** For Molecule 1, the distinguishable hydrogen atoms are illustrated below:

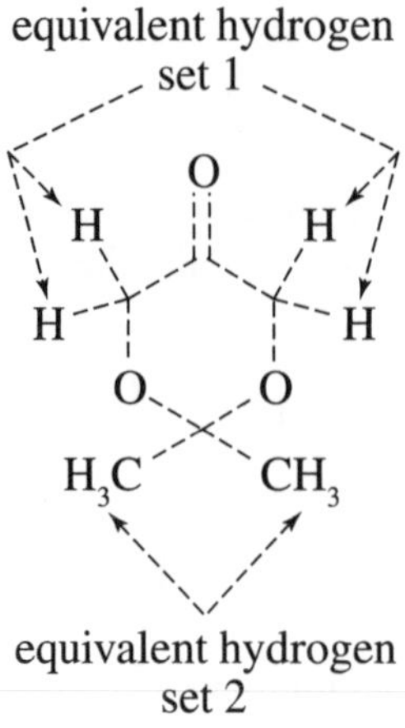

equivalent hydrogen
set 1

equivalent hydrogen
set 2

Therefore, only 2 resonances would appear in the ^{1}H NMR spectrum.

Passage 26

1. **B** To destroy an amide, a nucleophile must attack the carbon on an adjacent carbonyl by an addition–elimination mechanism so choices C and D can be eliminated. Based on Figure 1 this would be the C-1 carbon so choice B is correct.

2. **D** The greatest difference between the two penicillin derivatives is their size; therefore, sterics is the most likely explanation.

3. **C** Because amides are stabilized by the ability of the nitrogen lone pair to donate electron density to the eletrophilic carbonyl carbon, amides do not easily undergo hydrolysis.

4. **C** There are three chiral centers in dicloxacillin:

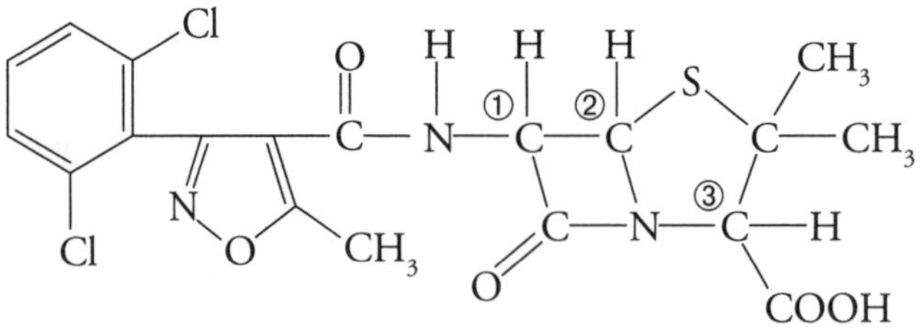

Passage 27

1. **A** The IR data indicate that a carboxylic acid and an alcohol are present. Based on the mechanism of basic hydrolysis, the labeled hydroxide acts as a nucleophile, and CH_3O^- acts as the leaving group. Normal methanol and propanoic acid result.

2. **C** Experiment 2 is more complicated than Experiment 1, so we sketch the reaction.

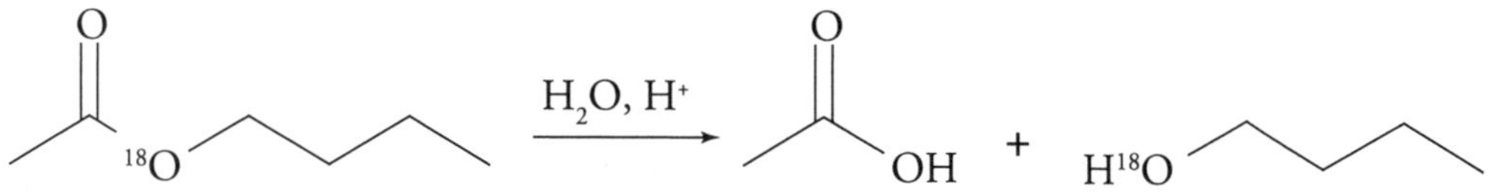

n-butyl acetate   acetic acid   heavy butanol

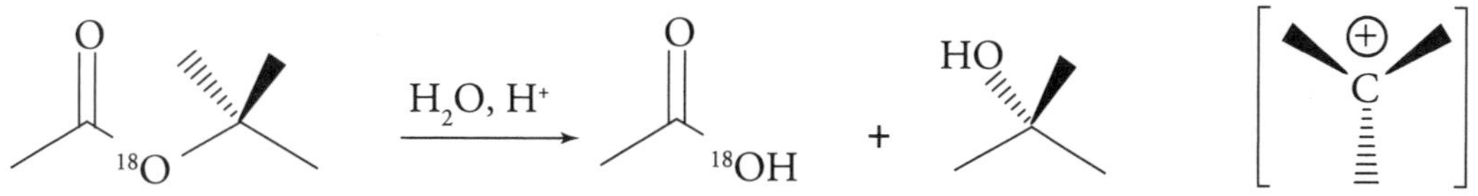

tert-butyl acetate   heavy acetic acid   *tert*-butanol   stable carbocation intermediate

Item I is false. In one case the alkyl–O bond breaks and in the other case the acyl–O bond breaks. Item II is true. The carbocation shown above is such a stable intermediate that the bond between it and the labeled oxygen is more easily replaced than the bond between the labeled oxygen and the carbonyl carbon. And Item III is also true. The steric bulk of the t-butyl group slows the nucleophilic attack on the carbonyl, thereby allowing the carbocation more time to dissociate and yield normal alcohol rather than heavy alcohol.

3. **C** The C=O bond of carboxylic acids exhibits a peak at 1700 cm^{-1}, and the C–OH bond exhibits a peak at 3000 cm^{-1}.

4. **D** Choices A, B, and C can be eliminated since they are all true. Branched hydrocarbons do take up less space in aqueous solution than their unbranched equivalents. This means they disrupt fewer water hydrogen bonds and require a less complex solvation shell (orderly solvation shells are unfavorable entropically). As for choice D, just the opposite is true.

5. **D** Item I is true. The passage states that at the end of Experiment 2, "significant amounts of the starting materials, *n*-butyl acetate and *tert*-butyl acetate, were present." This indicates that the acid-catalyzed reaction was reversible. We know that the base-catalyzed reaction was not readily reversible, because no reactants were identified by spectroscopy at the end of the experiment. Item II is false since a larger K means the reaction is *less* reversible, but the acid-catalyzed reaction was more readily reversible (see Item I). Item III is true: Less readily reversible reactions have larger Ks.

Passage 28

1. **B** The absolute configuration of (+)-dopa is R, and that of (–)-dopa is S:

(+)-Dopa   (–)-Dopa

2. **C** Since the nitrogen has three σ bonds and one unshared electron pair that is not delocalized, its hybridization is sp^3.

3. **C** (+)-Dopa and (–)-dopa are enantiomers and therefore have identical physical properties, except for the direction in which they rotate plane-polarized light. Therefore, their pI's will be exactly the same.

4. **D** (+)-Dopa and (–)-dopa are nonsuperimposable mirror images and therefore enantiomers (eliminate choice B). A 50/50 mixture of enantiomers forms a racemic mixture thus answer choice D is correct. This mixture would be optically inactive (eliminate choice A) and meso compounds are one molecule with a plane of symmetry that are optically inactive (eliminate choice C).

5. **D** The amino acid dopa most closely resembles the amino acid tyrosine. (In fact, the hydroxylation of tyrosine to form dopa is the first step in the synthesis of the catecholamine neurotransmitters dopamine and epinephrine.) Choice A can be eliminated because proline has a unique structure compared to the other amino acids in that its side chain forms a ring with the amino group. Choice B is incorrect since cysteine contains an SH group in its sidechain. Choice C can be eliminated because the side chain of dopa does not contain an acid.

Tyrosine

Passage 29

1. **B**   For any chiral molecule with n chiral centers, there are 2^n possible stereoisomers. (Note on choices C and D: If there were any meso carbohydrates, which there are not, one would subtract them from the total number of stereoisomers.)

2. **B**   Benedict's test for reducing sugars works this way: An oxidized copper reagent is reduced by a sugar's aldehyde or ketone, and the aldehyde or ketone is oxidized in the process. Tartaric acid has no aldehyde or ketone to react, since its first and last carbons have carboxylic functional groups. It cannot reduce the reagent, so it would yield a negative result.

3. **C**   Item I is true (eliminate choices B and D): Rotate the page 180° and look at the drawing; it's the same as the meso compound in Figure 1. Item II is also true (thus choice C is correct): Meso compounds are identical to their mirror images. Item III is false: As stated in the passage, meso compounds are achiral, even though they have chiral centers; this is because of their internal symmetry.

4. **C**   An aldotetrose (tetra) has four carbons and an aldehyde.

5. **D**   If a compound has one and only one chiral center, it must be chiral. It is the internal symmetry allowed by an even number (at least 2) of chiral centers that yields a compound which is achiral even though it contains chiral centers. Think of it this way: The rotation of light caused by one part of a meso compound is undone by the other part.

6. **C**   Item I is certainly true (eliminate answer choice B); this is (+)-tartaric acid as drawn in Figure 1. Item II is also true (eliminate answer choices A and D, thus choice C is correct). Making two switches on a chiral carbon in a Fischer projection results in no change. It is a rule worth remembering. Item III is false. Rotate the page 90° and you have the Fischer projection as oriented in Figure 1. The compound shown is the mirror image of (+)-tartaric acid, and since this is a chiral molecule, it's not the same as its mirror image. The drawing in Item III shows the conventional implications of a Fischer drawing, with the horizontal bonds coming out of the page and the vertical backbone chain bending into the page.

Passage 30

1. **C**   An ester is formed by the nucleophilic attack of an alcohol upon a carbonyl or, in the case of a phosphate ester, upon a P=O group; therefore, the correct answer is choice C. Choice A is wrong because an ether is the linkage of two carbon atoms by an oxygen, as in diethyl ether: $(CH_3CH_2)_2O$. Choice B is incorrect since an anhydride is formed when two carbonyls (or P=O groups) are linked together by an oxygen, as in acyl phosphate (see figure below). And choice D is wrong since phosgenation is the addition of a phosgene group to a parent molecule (phosgene = ClCOCl).

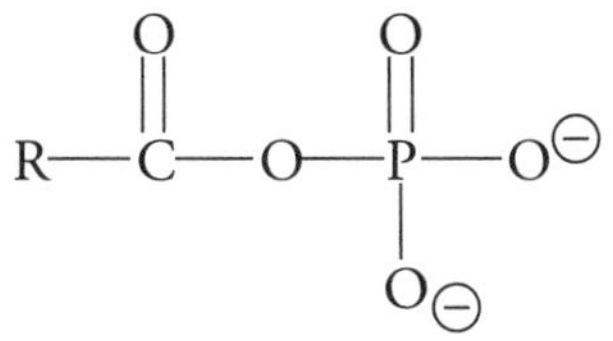

Acyl phosphate

2. **C** The passage states that the cell-free extract was added to a glucose solution. Hence, glucose (or any other sugar) need not be present in the cell-free extract; thus, choice C is the answer. Choice A is eliminated since ATP must be present in the broth, as one molecule is utilized in the formation of G-6-P and one for fructose-1,6-bisphosphate. Choice B is incorrect since magnesium is a cofactor for nearly all reactions involving ATP. And choice D is wrong since enzymes are composed of proteins, and the yeast broth must provide these for the reaction to occur.

3. **A** Isomers have identical atoms in different arrangements. Notice that the double bond and hydroxyl groups shift positions, indicating that one carbon was oxidized and another reduced. It is thought that phosphoglucose isomerase assists in the removal of a hydrogen anion, called a *hydride ion*, which will attack a carbonyl group, resulting in the formation of a hydroxyl group. The carbon that had the hydride ion pulled from it is left open to attack by water molecules, as it is now a cation. Choices B, C, and D are incorrect since choice B is a dehydration, choice C is an addition–elimination reaction (resulting in the formation of a carboxylic acid with chloride as the leaving group), and choice D is a transesterification reaction.

4. **D** All sugars involved in glycolysis have the Δ configuration. They are so named by a convention which states that all sugars whose last chiral carbon has the same configuration as Δ-glyceraldehyde are Δ sugars. When a phosphate is added to C-6 of glucose or fructose, this carbon remains achiral, since it still bears two hydrogen substituents. The configuration of the last chiral carbon, C-5, remains unchanged.

5. **D** The formula to calculate the number of carbohydrate stereoisomers is 2^n, with n representing the number of chiral centers. Glucose has 4 chiral centers, while fructose has 3 chiral centers (eliminating choices A and B). Since one of the chiral centers in an aldohexose is on the penultimate carbon (the carbon whose –OH group orientation determines Δ or Λ), all 16 of the stereoisomers for an aldohexose would not retain the Δ conformation, thus making choice C false. It is correct that each Δ-aldohexose has two anomers, since each one can only form either an α- or a β-anomer.

Passage 31

1. **C** There are three chiral centers in AZT:

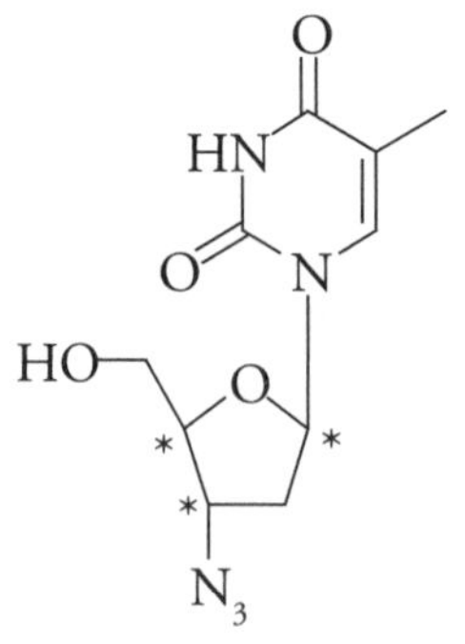

The nitrogens on the six-membered ring participate in extensive delocalization (π bonding) such that they are both sp^2 hybridized (i.e., planar), so they are not chiral centers.

2. **B**   Only ddI and D4C have an unshared pair of electrons on nitrogen that are not delocalized into a π system.

3. **B**   Since azide is a good nucleophile, it was delivered in an S_N2 reaction. This is important for setting the proper stereochemistry at the carbon bearing the azide. Weak nucleophiles favor S_N1 so choice A can be eliminated. Reduction adds H to the molecule, not N (eliminate choice C), and an addition-elimination reaction would mean a <pi symbol> bond should be present (eliminate choice D).

4. **D**   A nucleotide is a phosphoric acid ester of a nucleoside. RNA is comprised of a series of nucleotides so choice A can be eliminated. Purines are a type of nucleotide (guanine and adenine) so choice B is eliminated. Glycosides pertain to sugars and not to nucleic acids so choice C can be eliminated.

Passage 32

1. **D**

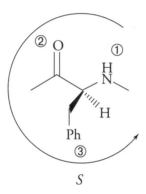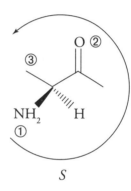

2. **C**   π clouds of aromatic rings are not very basic at all; eliminate choice A. Lone pairs on carbonyl oxygens (sp^2) are more basic than π clouds, but not as basic as sp^3 hybridized lone pairs on nitrogen; eliminate choice B. Lastly, amine nitrogens are more basic than amide nitrogens because the electrons on the latter are partially tied up in resonance; eliminate choice D. The best answer is choice C.

3. **A**   A pH of 8 indicates a basic solution. The carboxylic acid will be deprotonated.

4. **A**   The protons of the methyl group are all equivalent by rotation. There are no protons on adjacent atoms, thus no splitting of the signal is expected; therefore, a singlet should result.

5. **D**   Choice A can be eliminated because you are not comparing a cyclic amide to an acyclic amide. The adjacent sulfone group is electron withdrawing so this statement is incorrect and choice B can be eliminated. The saccharin nitrogen is sp^3 hybridized so choice C is a false statement and can be eliminated. Extra resonance stabilization as stated in choice D would make the proton on the nitrogen in saccharin more basic.

Passage 33

1. **D** Benedict's test oxidizes hemiacetals/aldehydes to carboxylates. Since only Subunit 4 contains a hemiacetal (at C-1), only this subunit will test positive.

2. **B** The anomeric carbon of Subunit 2, which is bound to two –OR groups, is an acetal. However, the anomeric carbon of Subunit 4, which is bound to one –OR group and one –OH group, is a hemiacetal.

3. **D** Both multiple bonds and rings introduce units of unsaturation. Acarbose has one double bond and four rings, giving it a total of five units of unsaturation.

4. **A** Numbering of carbohydrates begins at the terminal carbon closest to the most oxidized carbon (here the anomeric carbon). Therefore, C-1 of Subunit 2 is joined to C-4 of Subunit 3 (eliminate choices B and C). Since the linking oxygen is down (axial) in the Haworth representation, it is an α-linkage.

5. **D** Mutarotation is the interconversion between two anomers. The anomeric carbons of Subunits 1, 2, and 3 are stable as acetals and will not mutarotate. However, Subunit 4, having a free hemiacetal, will mutarotate between the α- and β-anomers.

Passage 34

1. **C** The basic side chain of lysine ($pK_a \approx 10$) would give it a higher pI than that of GABA (pI = 6.0).

2. **C** The negatively charged phthalimidate acts as a nucleophile to displace chloride (the leaving group) in a substitution reaction.

3. **C** A zwitterion has both positive and negative charges, but a net total charge of zero.

4. **A** Note that pH 9.7 corresponds exactly to the pK_a at the amino terminus of GABA. Using the Henderson–Hasselbalch equation, we find that

$$pH = pK_a + \log \frac{[A^-]}{[HA]}$$

$$9.7 = 9.7 + \log \frac{[RNH_2]}{[RNH_3^+]}$$

$$1 = \frac{[RNH_2]}{[RNH_3^+]}$$

$$[RNH_2] = [RNH_3^+]$$

At pH 9.7, the carboxyl terminus (pK_a = 2.3) will be completely deprotonated, so

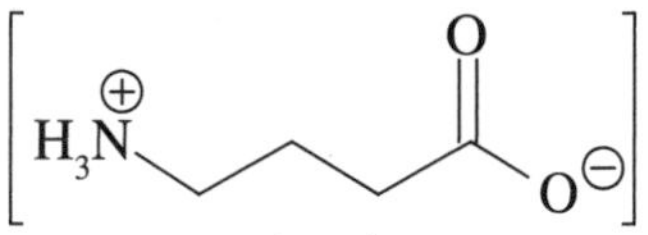

zwitterion

equals

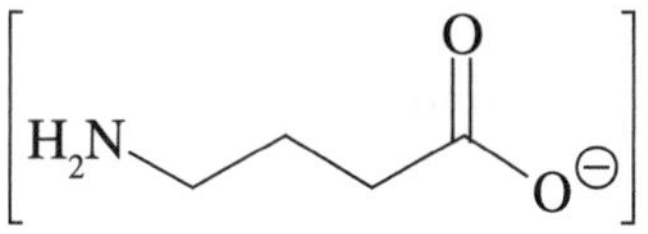

5. **B** As the passage states, all amino acids are polyprotic, making Statement III false (eliminate choice D). Dissociation of the Λ-thyroxine hydroxyl proton introduces a third pK_a value (in addition to those of the amino and carboxyl termini), making Statement II true (eliminate choice A). Finally, since the pK_a of the Λ-thyroxine side chain (9.8) is greater than the pI of GABA (6.0), the pI of Λ-thyroxine will be greater than that of GABA, making Statement I false.

6. **D** Since the pK_a values of the amino and carboxyl termini (9.7 and 2.3, respectively) are both less than 10, they will both be mostly deprotonated at pH 10.

Passage 35

1. **D** The melting point of a compound is dependent upon the strength of its intermolecular interactions. The stronger the forces, the higher the melting point. Based on this information alone, choice B can be eliminated. Molecules with lower molecular weights will typically have weaker dispersion forces, eliminating choice C. Choice A can be eliminated since the addition of water describes a hydration, not a hydrogenation. Hydrogenation adds H_2 across the carbon–carbon double bonds of unsaturated fatty acids, thereby removing the "kinks" in the side chains. This allows for a greater degree of overlap between adjacent molecules, increasing London dispersion forces. Choice D is the best answer.

2. **B**   Choices A and C can be eliminated since the *cis* isomer of a double bond may also be described using the *Z* designation. Furthermore, fatty acids are numbered from the carboxylic acid end, thereby putting the double bond at the 4 position. (Choice D would be correct if the molecule were numbered from the other end.)

3. **C**   Saponification is a term used to describe base-mediated ester hydrolysis. The ester bond is initially cleaved to yield the carboxylic acid and alkoxide anion (choice B). However, since the reaction is carried out under basic conditions and the COOH group is acidic, the alkoxide will deprotonate the carboxylic acid. The final products are the carboxylate anion and the neutral alcohol. Choice A may only be achieved after an acidic workup, and choice D will never occur in the presence of the hydroxide base required for the reaction.

4. **B**   Structural isomers (choice C) can be eliminated since all the atoms in *cis/trans* isomers have the same connectivity, but different orientations of the atoms in space (the definition of a stereoisomer). However, choice D is not specific enough. Both choices A and B are types of stereoisomers. Enantiomers require a mirror image relationship between molecules, and therefore a chiral center. Since carbon–carbon double bonds in *cis/trans* isomers cannot contain a chiral center, they must be geometric isomers.

Passage 36

1. **C**   Amino acids are linked together in peptides by way of amide bonds, which are formed between the carboxylate carbonyl of one amino acid and the amino group of another.

2. **B**   2,4-Dinitrofluorobenzene is used to identify the *N*-terminus of a peptide. It reacts with the *N*-terminal amino acid, and remains attached even after complete acid hydrolysis. This allows isolation of the *N*-terminal amino acid from the rest of the residues. The passage states in Experiment 3 that the dinitrophenyl group was attached to an alanine residue. If choice A was correct, one would expect it to be attached to both alanines so that answer choice can be eliminated. Choice D can also be eliminated because if it attached to the most reactive amino acid it should have attached to both alanines. Based on the data from Experiment 2, alanine cannot be located at the *C*-terminus.

3. **A**   The standard conditions for peptide hydrolysis are concentrated HCl and several hours worth of reflux. The reaction time depends on whether partial or complete hydrolysis is desired.

4. **C**   By careful analysis of the peptide fragments and other bits of data, it is clear that Ala is the *N*-terminal amino acid (eliminate choices A and D). One three-residue fragment must be AFG. The other must be SAP. This leaves only one combination (choice C), starting with the AFG as the first piece, followed by the SAP. The peptide is AFGSAP.

Passage 37

1. **D** Hydrolysis of peptide bonds occurs by an addition–elimination reaction. Water acts as a nucleophile, reacting with the peptide (amide) bond to form a tetrahedral intermediate, such as choice A. Elimination of the amino group reforms the carbonyl (now a carboxylic acid) and cleaves the peptide bond. Hydrolysis of peptide chains does not occur in a particular order, making choices B and C equally likely intermediates. Cleavage does not occur along the N–C α bond, however, making choice D an incorrect intermediate.

2. **A** Recall the relative reactivity of carboxylic acid derivatives: acid chlorides > acid anhydrides > esters > amides. The peptide (amide) bond may be synthesized by addition–elimination reactions with acid chlorides (choice B), esters (choice C), and other amides (choice D). However, the fast acid–base reaction prevents addition–elimination reactions from occurring between amines and carboxylic acids (choice A).

3. **C** Two cysteine residues may form disulfide bonds within proteins to stabilize its tertiary or quaternary structure. Since disulfide bonds are an oxidized form of cysteine, they are broken by reducing agents. While disulfide bonds commonly stabilize the tertiary structure of proteins, it is apparent that the disulfide bond(s) of insulin bridge two distinct polypeptides. Therefore, they support the quaternary structure of insulin.

4. **C** The passage states that DNFB reacts with amino groups. Therefore, it could be used to label the side chains of lysine residues (which have an amino group), even when they are not the N-terminal residue.

5. **B** Distillation and extraction are separation/purification procedures and are not useful for compound identification (eliminating choices A and D). While IR spectroscopy is useful for determining the presence or absence of major functional groups, it is not convenient for discriminating between closely related compounds (such as DNFB–Leucine and DNFB–Isoleucine), eliminating choice C. ^{1}H NMR spectroscopy alone would allow easy identification of the amino acid that had been labeled with DNFB.

6. **C** Amino acids contain carbonyls, and under certain conditions may reversibly tautomerize to an enol-containing compound. Upon reversal of tautomerism, the Cα may be protonated in such a way as to form the Δ-amino acid or the Λ-amino acid.

Thus, a racemic mixture is formed, and the amino acid loses its optical activity.

MCAT Physics
Passages

Passage 1 (Questions 1-7)

A vector is a quantity that incorporates both magnitude and direction. A vector can be pictured as an arrow whose orientation indicates direction and whose length indicates magnitude. A scalar quantity possesses magnitude only.

Vectors can be added (or subtracted) using the "tip-to-tail" method and resolved into components using trigonometry.

Figure 1 shows three vectors plotted on a pair of x-y coordinate axes. Vectors **P** and **R** each have a magnitude of 20 m, and **Q** has a magnitude of 40 m.

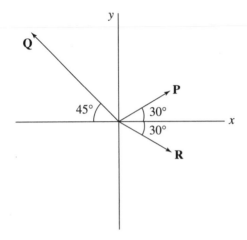

Figure 1

1. What are the horizontal and vertical components, respectively, of Vector **P**?

    A. 20 sin 30° and 20 cos 30°
    B. 20 sin 30° and 20 tan 30°
    C. 20 cos 30° and 20 tan 30°
    D. 20 cos 30° and 20 sin 30°

2. Which one of the following is NOT a vector quantity?

    A. Velocity
    B. Displacement
    C. Speed
    D. Acceleration

3. What is the magnitude of the x-component of Vector **P**?

    A. 6 m
    B. 10 m
    C. 17 m
    D. 20 m

4. What is the magnitude of the y-component of Vector **P**?

    A. 6 m
    B. 10 m
    C. 17 m
    D. 20 m

5. Which of the following vectors best illustrates the direction of the vector –**R**?

    A.   B.

    C.   D.

6. Which of the following vectors best illustrates the direction of the vector **P** + **R**?

    A.    B.

    C.   D.

7. Which of the following vectors best illustrates the direction of the vector **Q** – **P**?

    A.   B.

    C.   D.

_____

Passage 2 (Questions 1-7)

A car travels in a straight line for 30 seconds. The graph below represents the car's velocity as a function of time.

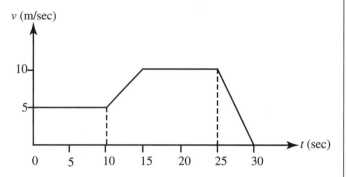

Figure 1

Since acceleration is defined as change in velocity per interval of time, acceleration at any time equals the slope of the velocity graph at that time. Similarly, since distance traveled is directly proportional to time and speed, the distance the car has traveled at any time equals the area under the velocity graph up to that time. For the first 10 seconds the car traveled at a fixed speed. The slope of the graph in that section is, as expected, zero. Also, the area under the graph between $t = 0$ and $t = 10$ sec is 50 m, the expected value.

1. How far does the car travel between times $t = 0$ and $t = 10$ sec?

   A. 2 m
   B. 5 m
   C. 25 m
   D. 50 m

2. What is the car's acceleration between times $t = 10$ sec and $t = 15$ sec?

   A. 0.67 m/sec²
   B. 1.0 m/sec²
   C. 1.5 m/sec²
   D. 25.0 m/sec²

3. How far does the car travel between times $t = 10$ sec and $t = 15$ sec?

   A. 12.5 m
   B. 25.0 m
   C. 37.5 m
   D. 50.0 m

4. What is the car's average speed between times $t = 10$ sec and $t = 15$ sec?

   A. 5.0 m/sec
   B. 7.5 m/sec
   C. 10.0 m/sec
   D. 12.5 m/sec

5. At time $t = 25$ sec, the car:

   A. slowed down and changed direction.
   B. slowed down but did not change direction.
   C. sped up and changed direction.
   D. sped up but did not change direction.

6. Which of the graphs best represents the car's acceleration, a, between times $t = 0$ and $t = 30$ sec?

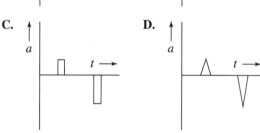

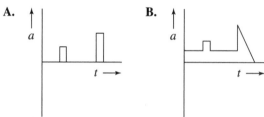

7. Which one of the following graphs best represents the distance traveled by the car as a function of time?

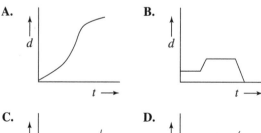

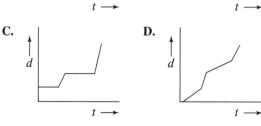

Passage 3 (Questions 1-12)

A car of mass 1000 kg is tested on a straight, flat track. The graph below illustrates the results of the test. The speed (v) of the car in miles per hour (mph) is plotted against the time (t) in seconds. The graph has been divided into three time periods: I (from $t = 0$ to $t = 6$ sec), II (from $t = 6$ to $t = 10$ sec), and III (from $t = 10$ to $t = 12$ sec). The graph supplies enough information so that the average and instantaneous velocities and accelerations can be calculated for any time period or instant in time. In addition, the distance traveled by the car can be calculated for any time period (Δt) in which the acceleration is constant by using the equation

$$x - x_0 = v_0\Delta t + \tfrac{1}{2}a(\Delta t)^2,$$

where x_0 and x are the initial and final positions, respectively, v_0 is the initial velocity, and a is the acceleration.

Some of the important forces on the car are the propulsive force provided by the engine (through the force of static friction), the retarding force provided by the brakes (when engaged), and the retarding force due to air resistance. The drag force, resulting from the fact that the car is immersed in a fluid (the air), depends on the density, temperature, and composition of the fluid as well as the shape and velocity of the moving object. The magnitude of the force due to air resistance is approximately proportional to the velocity of the object: $F_r \approx bv$ where the proportionality constant $b > 0$ is determined by a combination of the factors discussed above. As fuel economy becomes more important, cars are being designed with shapes that minimize the air resistance proportionality constant b. Finally, it is worthwhile to note that driving with windows closed lowers the value of the constant b, thereby improving gas mileage.

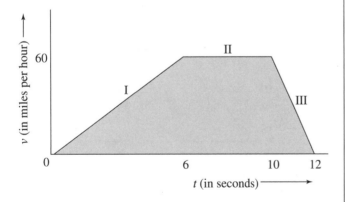

1. What is the average acceleration during time period I?

   A. 0 mph/sec
   B. 10 mph/sec
   C. 20 mph/sec
   D. 30 mph/sec

2. During which of the three time periods is the value of the acceleration constant?

   A. I and III only
   B. II only
   C. I, II, and III
   D. The acceleration is not constant during any of the three time periods.

3. During which time period does the car travel the farthest?

   A. I
   B. II
   C. III
   D. Cannot be determined from the information given

4. The magnitude of the net force exerted on the car is:

   A. greatest during time period I.
   B. greatest during time period II.
   C. greatest during time period III.
   D. the same during all three time periods.

5. The area of the shaded region in the graph represents:

   A. the total distance traveled by the car.
   B. the total change in momentum of the car.
   C. the average velocity of the car between times $t = 0$ and $t = 12$ sec.
   D. the average acceleration of the car between times $t = 0$ and $t = 12$ sec.

6. What is the net force on the car during period II?

   A. 0 N
   B. 4.4×10^3 N
   C. 8.9×10^3 N
   D. 1.3×10^4 N

7. The average speed of the car during time period III is:

    A. 0 mph.
    B. 10 mph.
    C. 20 mph.
    D. 30 mph.

8. If the frictional force on the car due to air resistance, F_r, is directly proportional to the speed of the car, then which one of the following statements must be true during period I?

    A. The force provided by the engine was increasing with time.
    B. The force provided by the engine was kept equal to F_r.
    C. The force provided by the engine remained constant.
    D. The same acceleration would have been achieved regardless of the force provided by the engine.

9. Suppose that at $t = 8$ sec, the previously closed windows suddenly shatter, thereby causing the proportionality constant b to increase. Which of the following best describes the subsequent behavior of the car?

    A. Its speed begins to increase due to the change in F_r.
    B. Its speed begins to decrease due to the change in F_r.
    C. The momentum of the car compensates for the change in F_r so the speed remains constant.
    D. The speed remains temporarily constant but then begins to decrease as the air resistance dissipates.

Questions 10 through 12 refer to the following position vs. time (x vs. t) graphs:

A.
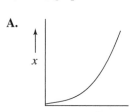

B.
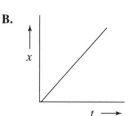

C.
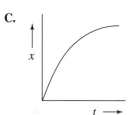

D.
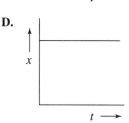

10. Which one of the graphs above best illustrates the shape of that portion of the car's position vs. time graph for the interval between $t_1 = 0$ sec and $t_2 = 6$ sec (that is, during period I)?

    A. Graph A
    B. Graph B
    C. Graph C
    D. Graph D

11. Which one of the graphs above best illustrates the shape of that portion of the car's position vs. time graph for the interval between $t_1 = 6$ sec and $t_2 = 10$ sec (that is, during period II)?

    A. Graph A
    B. Graph B
    C. Graph C
    D. Graph D

12. Which one of the graphs above best illustrates the shape of that portion of the car's position vs. time graph for the interval between $t_1 = 10$ sec and $t_2 = 12$ sec (that is, during period III)?

    A. Graph A
    B. Graph B
    C. Graph C
    D. Graph D

Passage 4 (Questions 1-7)

A woman of mass $m = 100$ kg is standing on the edge of a rotating platform of radius $r = 10$ m and mass $M = 1000$ kg. The period of rotation of the platform is set so that the woman moves with a constant speed of $v = 5$ m/s. The coefficient of static friction, μ, between the soles of the woman's shoes and the platform is equal to 0.1. A rope of negligible mass connects the woman to the center of the platform. This situation can be discussed in terms of (i) centripetal forces, (ii) pseudo-forces (sometimes called centrifugal forces), or (iii) angular momentum.

(i) In order to cause the woman standing 10 m from the center of the platform to move in a circle, a centripetal force is needed, of magnitude $F_c = mv^2/r$ directed toward the center. In the above example, F_c is provided by the tension in the rope and the frictional force. In terms of the rotation period T, the centripetal force on the woman is

$$F_c = 4\pi^2 mr/T^2$$

(ii) A *pseudo-force* is a nonexistent force that is experienced by observers in accelerated reference frames. The accelerated observer accounts for her lack of motion relative to her reference frame by inventing a force that cancels out the real forces. The woman on the rotating platform feels real forces of tension and friction directed toward the center. However, she is at rest relative to the platform despite these forces. She therefore experiences a pseudo-force opposite to the real forces. From her point of view, the pseudo-force and the real force cancel, and this allows her to be "at rest" in her frame of reference.

(iii) The magnitude of the angular momentum of the woman is $L_w = mr^2\omega$, where ω is the angular velocity of the platform (and the woman) and r is the distance of the woman from the center. For the platform, $L_p = I\omega$, where $I = Mr^2/2$ is the rotational inertia of the platform. In the absence of external torques, total angular momentum is a conserved quantity. This means that the sum $L_w + L_p$ is a constant as long as the platform rotates freely without friction. Under these conditions, the sum will not change even if the woman changes her distance from the center.

1. What is the minimum tension in the rope?

    A. 50 N
    B. 100 N
    C. 150 N
    D. 250 N

2. Approximate T, the period of rotation of the platform.

    A. 6 sec
    B. 12 sec
    C. 24 sec
    D. 36 sec

3. Suppose the platform is covered with grease, thereby reducing μ to zero. Then the rope is cut. What is the direction of the woman's subsequent motion?

    A. Radially inward
    B. Radially outward
    C. Inward but not along a radius
    D. Tangent to the platform

4. Suppose the platform rotates freely without friction so that angular momentum is conserved. If the woman moves in toward the center, what happens to the period of rotation of the platform?

    A. It increases.
    B. It decreases.
    C. It remains the same.
    D. It first decreases then increases.

5. When the woman is standing on the edge of the rotating platform, her (real) acceleration is:

    A. directed radially inward.
    B. directed radially outward.
    C. tangent to the platform.
    D. zero.

6. What is the direction of the net pseudo-force felt by the woman?

   A. Radially inward
   B. Radially outward
   C. Tangent to the platform
   D. Perpendicular to the surface of the platform

7. Suppose the platform is driven by a motor so that it always rotates with constant period T. The rope is shortened to 5 meters in length, the woman moves to a point 5 meters from the center and grasps the rope. Compared to the original tension, the new tension is:

   A. greater.
   B. smaller.
   C. the same.
   D. equal in magnitude but opposite in direction.

_____

Passage 5 (Questions 1–5)
ADVANCED PASSAGE

After studying purely translational motion, a student begins to study rotational motion and is assigned a physics lab exercise to help with this study.

The rotational analog of Newton's Second law is

$$\tau_{net} = I\alpha$$

Equation 1

where τ_{net} is the net torque, I is rotational inertia, and α is rotational (or angular) acceleration. The rotational inertia depends not only on an object's total mass but also on how the mass is distributed relative to the axis of rotation: the greater the mass or the farther it is (on average) from the axis of rotation, the greater the value of I. Figure 1 lists formulas for the rotational inertias of several different objects.

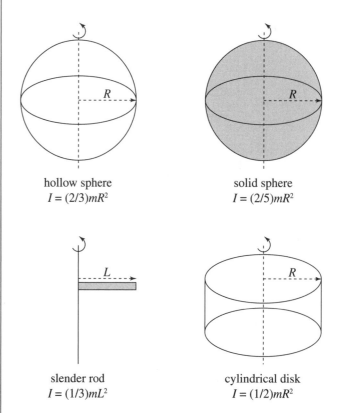

hollow sphere
$I = (2/3)mR^2$

solid sphere
$I = (2/5)mR^2$

slender rod
$I = (1/3)mL^2$

cylindrical disk
$I = (1/2)mR^2$

Figure 1 Rotational inertias of objects of mass m

In Figure 1, the spheres and disk have radius R, and each is rotating around an axis that passes through its center. The rod has length L and is rotating around an axis that passes through one of its endpoints. Except for the hollow sphere, each of the objects in Figure 1 has uniform density.

If the center of mass of an object of mass m translates with speed v, then the kinetic energy of the object is given by the equation $KE = (1/2)mv^2$. Similarly, if an object rotates about an axis that passes through it, the object has rotational kinetic energy given by

$$KE = (1/2)I\omega^2$$

Equation 2

where ω is the object's rotational (or angular) speed.

For an object that is both translating and rotating, its total kinetic energy is just the sum of its translational and rotational kinetic energies.

In the physics lab experiment, an inclined plane is set up with an angle of inclination θ. Three objects—a hollow sphere, a solid sphere, and a cylindrical disk, all of the same mass m and radius R—are placed at the top of the plane, all at the same distance from the bottom. At time $t = 0$, the objects are released from rest simultaneously, and they roll without slipping down the length of the plane. The student correctly determines that the net force on each object as it rolls down the plane is given by the equation

$$F_{net} = mg \sin \theta - Ia/R^2$$

Equation 3

In this equation, g is the magnitude of the acceleration due to gravity, and a is the (translational) acceleration of the center of mass. Furthermore, as each object rolls down the plane, its rotational speed and acceleration are related to the translational speed and acceleration of its center of mass by these equations:

$$\omega = v/R$$

Equation 4a

$$\alpha = a/R$$

Equation 4b

1. What force provides the torque that causes the rotation of each of the objects down the inclined plane?

   A. The force of gravity parallel to the plane
   B. The normal force
   C. The force of static friction
   D. The force of kinetic friction

2. What is the acceleration of the center of mass of the solid sphere as the sphere rolls down the plane?

   A. $(2/5)g \sin \theta$
   B. $(3/5)g \sin \theta$
   C. $(2/3)g \sin \theta$
   D. $(5/7)g \sin \theta$

3. In the experiment described in the passage, which of the three objects will reach the bottom of the inclined plane first?

   A. Hollow sphere
   B. Solid sphere
   C. Cylindrical disk
   D. Because they have the same mass, they will all reach the bottom of the inclined plane at the same time.

4. As the cylindrical disk rolls down the plane, its rotational kinetic energy at any point is always a constant times its translational kinetic energy at that point. What is the value of this constant?

   A. 1/4
   B. 1/2
   C. 1
   D. 2

5. The student measures the translational speed of each object as it reaches the bottom of the inclined plane. Which object will have the *lowest* such speed?

   A. Hollow sphere
   B. Solid sphere
   C. Cylindrical disk
   D. They will all have the same translational speed when they reach the bottom of the inclined plane.

perfectly elastic = conserved KE

Passage 6 (Questions 1-6)

For an ideal elastic collision between two objects, the sum of their linear momenta, $\mathbf{p}_1 + \mathbf{p}_2$, has the same value after the collision as before. The total kinetic energy of the system is also unchanged, that is, none of the system's kinetic energy is converted into other energy forms.

The principal condition necessary for a collision to be perfectly elastic is the absence of friction. At atomic and subatomic levels this condition usually exists, and atoms and nuclear particles often undergo ideal elastic collisions. The condition necessary for a perfectly elastic collision is not achievable for macroscopic bodies situated on the earth. All such bodies produce collisions that are, to some extent, inelastic, in which the kinetic energy of each body is therefore converted into other forms of energy.

In order to simulate motion and contact that is free of friction, researchers conduct experiments with miniature carriages that slide along a track and which are supported by air streams projecting from the track's surface. The air streams allow the carriages to slide almost free of friction.

Researchers conduct an experiment involving the collision of two miniature carriages situated on an air track. Attached to each carriage at the front and back ends are light springs that undergo compression and extension and obey Hooke's law. One carriage has a mass of 1 kg and the other a mass of 2 kg. With the air streams turned off, the coefficient of kinetic friction between each carriage and the surface of the track is 0.4. When the air streams are activated, the coefficient of kinetic friction drops to less than 0.01, so frictional effects can be ignored. The carriages are made to slide toward each other, and immediately prior to the collision, the lighter carriage has a speed of 4 m/s, and the heavier carriage has a speed of 2 m/s.

1. Just before the collision, what is the total kinetic energy of the system?

   A. 0 J
   B. 8 J
   C. 12 J
   D. 24 J

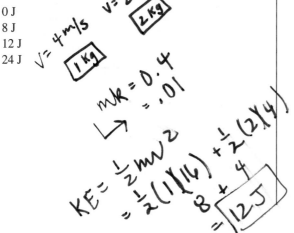

2. Which of the following statements applies to a system in which two objects undergo an ideal elastic collision?

   I. Kinetic energy is conserved.
   II. Momentum is conserved.
   III. The velocity of each object remains unchanged.

   A. I only
   B. II only
   C. I and II only
   D. I, II, and III

3. If the carriages were redesigned so that collisions between them were perfectly inelastic, each collision would cause energy dissipation of:

   A. 0 J.
   B. 4 J.
   C. 8 J.
   D. 12 J.

4. When the two carriages approach each other, collide, and then separate, their movements are associated with corresponding energy transfers of:

   A. kinetic to elastic potential to kinetic.
   B. elastic potential to kinetic to elastic potential.
   C. gravitational potential to heat to kinetic.
   D. heat to kinetic to gravitational potential.

5. If the air streams are deactivated and the carriages are in motion, what is the ratio of the frictional force acting on the heavier carriage to the frictional force acting on the lighter carriage?

   A. 1:2
   B. 2:1
   C. 1:4
   D. 4:1

6. If the plane on which the carriages are sliding is inclined to an angle of 55° with the horizontal, what is the magnitude of the component of a carriage's weight, mg, normal to the plane?

   A. $mg \sin 35°$
   B. $mg \cos 35°$
   C. $mg \sin 55°$
   D. None of the above

Passage 7 (Questions 1-5)

Figure 1 depicts a dam preventing the flow of water. Using the base of the dam as the pivot line (Line X in Figure 1), we can determine the torque exerted by the water on the dam by using the equation

$$\tau = \rho g L d^3/6$$

Equation 1

where ρ is the density of the water (1000 kg/m³), g is the acceleration due to gravity, L is the length of the dam, and d is the total depth of the water behind the dam.

Knowing the sheer strength of the dam's structure, it can be determined whether the dam can withstand the fluid pressure exerted by the water behind it. The pressure due to the water at depth y below the surface is given by the equation

$$P = \rho g y$$

Equation 2

The total pressure at depth y is equal to the pressure exerted by the water plus the atmospheric pressure, which is approximately 10^5 N/m².

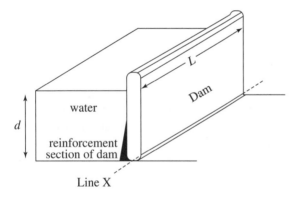

Figure 1

1. What is the pressure exerted on the dam by the water at a point 5 m below the surface?

   A. 4.9×10^4 N/m²
   B. 9.8×10^4 N/m²
   C. 4.9×10^5 N/m²
   D. 9.8×10^5 N/m²

2. If the area of the dam exposed to water is quadrupled by doubling the length of the dam and doubling the depth of the water retained, then this will cause the torque due to the water to increase by what factor?

   A. 2
   B. 4
   C. 8
   D. 16

3. If the dam is 5 m high, approximately how fast (neglecting friction) would water flowing over the top be moving when it struck the river at the base of the dam?

   A. 7 m/s
   B. 10 m/s
   C. 14 m/s
   D. 20 m/s

4. Which one of the following graphs best depicts the relationship between the magnitude of the torque, τ, caused by the water and the depth, d, of the water behind the dam?

   A.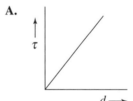

   B.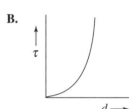

   C.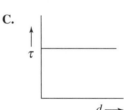

   D.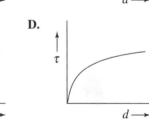

5. Assume that water has risen to a height d and exerts a torque τ on the dam. Assume also that a single force $\mathbf{F}$ is to be applied at a height d perpendicular to the opposite face of the dam so that the its torque will exactly cancel the torque due to the water. Which one of the following expressions gives the magnitude of $\mathbf{F}$?

   A. $\rho g L d^2/6$
   B. $\rho g L d^3/6$
   C. $\rho g L d^4/6$
   D. $\rho g L d^5/6$

Passage 8 (Questions 1-9)

A projectile launched near the surface of the Earth is, to a good approximation, influenced only by the gravitational field of the Earth. The acceleration due to gravity near the Earth's surface is given by $g \approx 10$ m/s^2. If the y coordinate of the projectile is plotted as a function of time, a parabola is obtained. The graph of the x coordinate vs. time yields a straight line with a positive slope since the horizontal velocity is constant. The trajectory of the projectile (y coordinate plotted as a function of x) is a symmetric parabola in which the maximum y coordinate coincides with the midpoint in the x coordinate.

The horizontal distance traveled by the projectile when the y coordinate has returned to its initial value is called the range. If θ_0 is the angle above the horizontal at which the projectile is launched, then the range depends on θ_0, varying from its maximum at $\theta_0 = 45°$ to zero at $\theta_0 = 90°$.

If the projectile is launched in the Earth's atmosphere, air resistance will slightly alter the above results. Energy will be carried away from the system, and the range attained by the projectile—as well as its time of flight—will be reduced. The trajectory of the projectile (y vs. x) will no longer be parabolic, or even symmetric. The horizontal velocity decreases with time, and the horizontal distance traveled after the high point in the trajectory is less than the horizontal distance traveled before the high point is reached.

Unless otherwise indicated, neglect any aerodynamic forces on the projectile. The projectile has a mass of 2 kg and is launched from ground level; the ground is perfectly flat. The kinetic energy at launch time is $E_0 = 1000$ J. At the top of the trajectory, the kinetic energy is $E_{top} = 600$ J.

1. What is the maximum height above the ground attained by the projectile?

   A. 20 m
   B. 40 m
   C. 60 m
   D. 80 m

2. What is the magnitude of its initial horizontal velocity?

   A. 15.5 m/s
   B. 20.0 m/s
   C. 24.5 m/s
   D. 32.0 m/s

3. If T denotes the total time of flight of the projectile, which of the following expressions correctly gives the initial vertical velocity, v_{0y}?

   A. $v_{0y} = gT/2$
   B. $v_{0y} = gT \sin 45°$
   C. $v_{0y} = gT$
   D. $v_{0y} = 2gT$

4. Which of the following best approximates the magnitude of the projectile's initial total velocity?

   A. 10 m/s
   B. 20 m/s
   C. 24 m/s
   D. 32 m/s

5. What is the kinetic energy of the projectile when it strikes the ground?

   A. 400 J
   B. 600 J
   C. 1000 J
   D. 1600 J

6. Let v_x be the projectile's horizontal speed when it is at its maximum height, and let V_x be the horizontal speed just before the projectile strikes the ground. Then the ratio v_x/V_x:

   A. is less than 1.
   B. is equal to 1.
   C. is greater than 1.
   D. depends on the angle at which the projectile is launched.

7. If T denotes the total flight time of the projectile, and v_{0x} and v_{0y} denote its initial horizontal and initial vertical velocity, respectively, then the range R is given by which one of the following equations?

   A. $R = v_{0x}T^2/2$
   B. $R = v_{0x}T - \frac{1}{2}gT^2$
   C. $R = (v_{0x}^2 - v_{0y}^2)/2g$
   D. $R = v_{0x}T$

8. If air resistance is considered, the ratio H_{vac}/H_{atm} of the maximum height attained by a projectile in vacuum to the maximum height that it attains in the atmosphere given the same initial kinetic energy at launch is:

   A. less than 1.
   B. equal to 1.
   C. greater than 1.
   D. less than 1 for a spherical object but greater than 1 for an irregularly-shaped object.

9. Let X denote the horizontal distance traveled when a projectile (launched at an angle θ_0 with $30° < \theta_0 < 60°$) has attained its maximum height. If the effect of air resistance is taken into account, then which one of the following relations is correct concerning the projectile's range R?

   A. $R/2 < X$
   B. $(R \cos \theta_0)/2 > X$
   C. $(R \sin \theta_0)/2 > X$
   D. $R/2 > X$

Passage 9 (Questions 1-10)

The gravitational attraction between the Earth (mass M) and an object of mass m on its surface is given approximately by the formula $F_{grav} = GMm/R^2$, where G is the universal gravitational constant and R is the radius of the Earth. The formula is exact for a uniform perfect sphere. The gravitational acceleration of an object near the surface of a planet is given by $g = GM/R^2$, which is very nearly 10 m/s^2 for the Earth.

The above equation for F_{grav} may be generalized so that it is valid both near and far from the surface: $F_{grav} = GMm/r^2$ where r is now the distance between the object of mass m and the center of the Earth. On the surface, of course, $r = R$, so the two formulations are consistent.

The potential energy of an object near the surface of the Earth at a height h above the ground is $E_p = mgh$. The change in potential energy when an object is moved from height h_1 to h_2 is $\Delta E_p = mg(h_2 - h_1)$. If an object is falling in a vacuum, energy is conserved so $\Delta E_p + \Delta E_k = 0$, where ΔE_k is the change in kinetic energy of the object.

If h is larger than about $0.01R$, then $E_p = mgh$ is no longer a good approximation since the gravitational acceleration g decreases as one moves away from the Earth's surface. To handle problems involving objects far from the surface of the Earth, we use, in analogy with electrostatics, the gravitational potential $V = -GM/r$ where r is the distance of the object from the center of the planet. If an object of mass m is moved from a point at r_1 to a point at r_2, the change in potential energy will be $\Delta E_p = m(GM/r_1 - GM/r_2)$.

If $r_1 = \infty$ and $r_2 = R$, then ΔE_p applies to an object dropped to the ground from far away (outer space). If the situation is reversed, and $r_1 = R$ and $r_2 = \infty$, then ΔE_p applies to an object launched into outer space from the surface of the Earth. In either case, conservation of energy can be used to determine the velocity of the object. The computed velocities will have the same magnitude; one will be an impact velocity and the other will be an escape velocity.

All of the above can be applied to any celestial body as long as one can ignore air resistance. Some convenient approximations for the relevant constants are $G = 6.7 \times 10^{-11}$ N·m^2/kg^2, $M = 6 \times 10^{24}$ kg, and $R = 6 \times 10^6$ m. The Earth is roughly 100 times more massive than the Moon, and the Earth's radius is about 4 times greater. The Earth–Moon distance is about 60R, and the Earth–Sun distance is about 25,000R. The Sun's mass is about 300,000M.

1. What would be the acceleration of an object dropped near the surface of the Moon?

   A. 0.1 m/s^2
   B. 0.4 m/s^2
   C. 1.6 m/s^2
   D. 2.5 m/s^2

2. An object that weighs 15 N near the surface of the Earth is transported to an altitude of 1.2×10^7 m. Compute its weight at this altitude.

   A. 1.67 N
   B. 3.75 N
   C. 5.00 N
   D. 7.50 N

3. Assuming the Moon's orbit is a perfect circle, at what speed does it orbit the Earth?

   A. 10^1 m/s
   B. 10^3 m/s
   C. 10^5 m/s
   D. 10^7 m/s

4. Which one of the following expressions correctly gives the minimum speed with which one must launch a rock of mass m in order to ensure that it escapes the Earth's gravitational field (air resistance neglected)?

   A. $\sqrt{2GM/R}$
   B. $\sqrt{2GMm/R}$
   C. $\sqrt{GM/2R}$
   D. $\sqrt{GMm/2R}$

5. If the gravitational force exerted by the Earth on the Moon is denoted F_1, and the gravitational force exerted by the Moon on the Earth is F_2, then:

   A. $F_1 = 1600F_2$
   B. $F_1 = 100F_2$
   C. $F_1 = 6.25F_2$
   D. $F_1 = F_2$

6. If α is the ratio of the value of the gravitational constant G on the Earth to its value on the Moon, then which of the following is correct?

   A. $\alpha \approx 0.16$
   B. $\alpha \approx 1$
   C. $\alpha \approx 6$
   D. $\alpha \approx 25$

7. If two objects of masses m_1 and m_2 (with $m_1 > m_2$) are dropped from a great height above the surface of the Moon, what is the ratio v_1/v_2 of their impact velocities?

   A. 1
   B. m_1/m_2
   C. $(m_1/m_2)^2$
   D. $\sqrt{m_1/m_2}$

8. If an object is moved from a point 10 m above the surface of the Earth to a point 5 m above the surface, what is the magnitude of the change in potential energy?

   A. 0 J
   B. 50 J
   C. 150 J
   D. Cannot be determined from the information given

9. Suppose the Moon suddenly stopped in its orbit and began to fall toward the Earth. Approximate its initial acceleration in terms of g, where $g \approx 10 \text{ m/s}^2$.

   A. $g/4$
   B. $g/60$
   C. $g/100$
   D. $g/3600$

10. The Moon is 400 times closer to the Earth than to the Sun, and the Sun is 30 million times more massive than the Moon. Which one of the following best approximates the ratio F_{Sun}/F_{Moon} of the gravitational force exerted by the Sun on the Earth to the gravitational force exerted by the Moon on the Earth?

    A. 7.5×10^4
    B. 2.0×10^2
    C. 5.0×10^{-3}
    D. 1.3×10^{-5}

Passage 10 (Questions 1-8)

Earth's atmosphere currently consists of 78% N_2, 21% O_2, 1% Ar, and minute quantities of carbon dioxide, hydrogen, neon, helium, krypton, and xenon. This does not include water vapor. Molecules of atmospheric gas move in random directions with a broad distribution of speeds.

For each gas in the atmosphere, a curve known as the *Maxwell–Boltzmann speed distribution* may be determined. A typical example of such a curve is shown below. The probability that a molecule has a speed between v_1 and v_2 is equal to the area below the curve between v_1 and v_2, as illustrated in Figure 1. Each gas has an associated curve whose details depend on the mass of the molecules and the temperature of the gas. For example, the most probable speed for a gas with molecular mass m at temperature T (in kelvins, K) is

$$v_0 = \sqrt{\frac{2kT}{m}}$$

where $k = 1.38 \times 10^{-23}$ J/K is Boltzmann's constant. The distribution of speeds is slightly asymmetrical, favoring higher speeds. Some molecules have speeds much higher than the most probable speed.

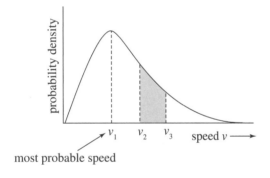

Figure 1 Maxwell–Boltzmann speed distribution

The probability of finding a molecule of a gas at temperature T with a speed v within some given range $v_1 < v < v_2$ is equal to the area under the curve between v_1 and v_2.

If a molecule of gas in the atmosphere has a velocity greater than escape velocity, then it will leave the Earth forever as long as it does not collide with any other molecules on its way into outer space. The escape velocity v_e for an object close to the surface of the Earth is given by

$$v_e = \sqrt{2gR_E}$$

where R_E is the radius of the Earth, and g is the gravitational acceleration.

1. The most probable speed of a helium atom at 300 K is 1.12 km/sec. What is its most probable speed at 600 K?

   A. 0.56 km/sec
   B. 1.58 km/sec
   C. 2.24 km/sec
   D. 3.36 km/sec

2. Let the most probable speeds of H_2, N_2, and O_2 at 300 K be denoted v_H, v_N, and v_O, respectively. Which of the following is correctly lists these speeds in order from lowest to highest?

   A. v_H, v_N, v_O
   B. v_O, v_N, v_H
   C. v_H, v_O, v_N
   D. v_N, v_O, v_H

3. Precise measurements taken over a period of many years show that the concentration of a Gas X in the atmosphere is constant. Which one of the following best explains this finding?

   A. Gas X has a very small molecular weight.
   B. Gas X is extremely reactive.
   C. No molecules of Gas X can achieve escape velocity.
   D. Some molecules of Gas X escape, but an equal number are produced.

4. The most probable kinetic energy of a gas molecule is:

   A. directly proportional to the temperature in K.
   B. directly proportional to the square root of the temperature in K.
   C. inversely proportional to the temperature in K.
   D. inversely proportional to the square root of the temperature in K.

5. For molecules near the surface of the Earth, the escape velocity for hydrogen molecules is:

   A. less than that for oxygen molecules.
   B. greater than that for oxygen molecules.
   C. equal to that for oxygen molecules.
   D. greater than that for oxygen molecules only at sufficiently high temperatures.

6. The area under the entire Maxwell–Boltzmann velocity distribution curve is:

   A. equal to 1.
   B. greater than 1.
   C. equal to Boltzmann's constant.
   D. dependent on the temperature of the gas.

7. The most probable velocity of a hydrogen gas molecule at 300 K is 1.9 km/sec. The escape velocity at the surface of the Earth is 11.2 km/sec. This means that:

   A. no hydrogen molecule can escape at temperatures under 1000 K.
   B. some hydrogen molecules will have escape velocity.
   C. hydrogen gas will escape only if it is produced in the upper atmosphere.
   D. hydrogen gas will not escape until it exists in the atmosphere at higher concentrations.

8. The gravitational acceleration on the surface of Jupiter is 26.2 m/s^2. The radius of Jupiter is 7×10^7 m (ten times greater than that of the Earth). Jupiter is also much colder than Earth. This means that compared to Earth:

   A. the escape velocity on Jupiter is smaller.
   B. on average, molecular velocities are higher in Jupiter's atmosphere.
   C. it is less likely that a given molecule of gas will escape from Jupiter.
   D. the Maxwell–Boltzmann speed distribution does not work as well on Jupiter.

Passage 11 (Questions 1-7)

Before the invention of smart bombs, which have built-in navigation computers to guide them to their targets, human bombardiers had to rely on targeting systems which would calculate when to drop a bomb based on simple equations of projectile motion. The figure below depicts a plane dropping a bomb which has no power or guidance of its own.

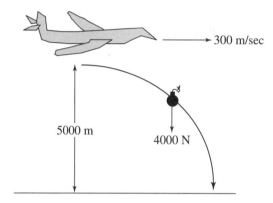

(Note: Ignore forces of air friction and air turbulence. Use 10 m/sec^2 for the value of acceleration due to gravity.)

1. What is the kinetic energy of the bomb as it exits the plane?

   A. 6.0×10^4 J
   B. 6.0×10^5 J
   C. 1.8×10^7 J
   D. 1.8×10^8 J

2. What is the potential energy of the bomb (relative to the ground) as it exits the plane?

   A. 4×10^3 J
   B. 2×10^6 J
   C. 2×10^7 J
   D. 2×10^8 J

3. What is the horizontal component of the bomb's velocity when it strikes the ground?

A. 300 m/sec
B. 375 m/sec
C. 410 m/sec
D. 436 m/sec

4. What is the vertical component of the bomb's velocity when it strikes the ground?

A. 300 m/sec
B. 316 m/sec
C. 410 m/sec
D. 436 m/sec

5. Approximately how much time will elapse between the time when the bomb is dropped and the time when it strikes the ground?

A. 22 sec
B. 32 sec
C. 71 sec
D. 100 sec

6. If the horizontal velocity of the plane is doubled, how will the time spent in the air by the bomb be affected?

A. It will be quadrupled.
B. It will be doubled.
C. It will be halved.
D. It will be the same.

7. If the airplane were to release the bomb from a height of 5000 m while flying vertically upward at 300 m/sec instead of horizontally, how would the kinetic energy of the bomb at the moment it hits the ground be changed?

A. It would be increased.
B. It would be decreased.
C. It would not be changed.
D. It cannot be determined.

Passage 12 (Questions 1-10)

The total momentum vector $\mathbf{p}_{total}$ is conserved in all types of collisions (assuming no external forces act). This is expressed by the equation $\mathbf{p}'_{total} = \mathbf{p}_{total}$, where the prime denotes *after* the collision and no prime denotes *before* the collision. Each component of momentum (p_x and p_y) is separately conserved. For an object of nonzero mass m, such as an atom, $\mathbf{p} = m\mathbf{v}$. In situations where an external force $\mathbf{F}$ does exist (and acts for a time interval Δt), the resulting change in momentum is found from the equation $\Delta \mathbf{p} = \mathbf{F}\Delta t$.

For a photon, which is massless, the magnitude of the momentum is given by $p = E/c$, where E is the energy of the photon and c is the speed of light. In terms of Planck's constant, h, and the frequency of the light, f, the photon's energy is given by $E = hf$. The photon's frequency and wavelength λ are connected by the equation $\lambda f = c$. The constant $h = 4.1 \times 10^{-15}$ eV·sec $= 6.6 \times 10^{-34}$ J·sec, and the speed of light $c = 3 \times 10^8$ m/sec $= 3 \times 10^{17}$ nm/sec.

When a photon is absorbed by an atom, an electron can be excited to a higher energy level. The difference in energy between the higher level and the original level is equal to the energy of the photon (E). If no higher level exists such that the difference in energy is equal to E, then the photon will not be absorbed; that is, the atom will be transparent to photons of energy E. Similarly, a photon is emitted when an electron falls from a higher to a lower energy level.

When a photon is absorbed or emitted by an atom, momentum is conserved. For photon absorption we have

$$\mathbf{p}'_{atom} = \mathbf{p}_{atom} + \mathbf{p}_{photon}$$

For photon emission, the equation expressing conservation of momentum is

$$\mathbf{p}_{atom} = \mathbf{p}'_{atom} + \mathbf{p}_{photon}$$

Absorption causes the photon's momentum to be added to the atom's, and emission gives the atom a "kick" or "recoil" much like the recoil of a gun after it is fired.

1. What is the frequency of a photon whose wavelength is 400 nm?

A. 7.5×10^5 sec^{-1}
B. 1.2×10^{11} sec^{-1}
C. 7.5×10^{14} sec^{-1}
D. 1.2×10^{20} sec^{-1}

2. An initially stationary atom of mass 1.7×10^{-27} kg emits a photon of energy 3.3×10^{-19} J. What is the magnitude of the momentum of the atom after the emission?

   A. 5.6×10^{-46} kg·m/s
   B. 1.1×10^{-27} kg·m/s
   C. 9.9×10^{-11} kg·m/s
   D. 5.2×10^{-9} kg·m/s

3. An atom is moving to the right along the x axis with velocity $\mathbf{v}_{atom} = v_x\mathbf{i}$. A photon, moving upward along the y axis with velocity $\mathbf{v}_{photon} = c\mathbf{j}$, is absorbed by the atom at the origin. If $\mathbf{i}$ and $\mathbf{j}$ are the unit vectors along the x and y axes, respectively, which of the following applies to the atom after the absorption?

   A. $v'_x = 0$
   B. $v'_y < 0$
   C. $v'_y = 0$
   D. $v'_y > 0$

4. An atom with momentum $\mathbf{p}$ (magnitude p) moving to the right along the x axis emits a photon that then travels at an angle of $+45°$ (counterclockwise) with respect to the positive x axis. The magnitude of the photon's momentum is $p/100$. Which of the following is true about the components of the velocity of the atom after it emits the photon?

   A. $v_x < 0$ and $v_y < 0$
   B. $v_x < 0$ and $v_y > 0$
   C. $v_x > 0$ and $v_y < 0$
   D. $v_x > 0$ and $v_y > 0$

5. Which of the following vectors could represent the velocity of a photon ?

   I. $(c/2)\mathbf{i} + (c/2)\mathbf{j}$
   II. $c\mathbf{i} + c\mathbf{j}$
   III. $(2c)\mathbf{i} - c\mathbf{j}$

   A. I only
   B. II only
   C. III only
   D. None of these

6. Which of the following is/are units of momentum?

   I. J·sec/m
   II. N·sec
   III. kg·m/sec

   A. I only
   B. II only
   C. III only
   D. I, II, and III

7. A stationary atom of mass 5×10^{-27} kg absorbs a photon of energy 3.0×10^{-19} J. What is the magnitude of the velocity of the atom after the absorption?

   A. 0.2 m/s
   B. 0.5 m/s
   C. 2.0 m/s
   D. 5.0 m/s

8. A photon collides head-on with an atom traveling in the opposite direction and is absorbed by the atom. The magnitude of the momentum of the incident photon is twice the magnitude of the initial momentum of the atom. As a result of the absorption, the atom:

   A. continues in its original direction of motion but with increased speed.
   B. continues in its original direction of motion but with decreased speed.
   C. reverses direction.
   D. stops.

9. Suppose that an atom is in its ground state and the next energy level is 10.2 eV above the ground state. If a 5.1-eV photon is in the vicinity of this atom, then:

   A. the atom's momentum will be changed slightly.
   B. the photon will pass the atom and have no effect.
   C. the atom will absorb the photon, but no electron will move to a different energy level.
   D. the photon will cause one of the electrons to be ejected from the atom.

10. An atom, whose momentum has magnitude p and whose velocity vector is perpendicular to an infinitely heavy wall, strikes the wall and recoils elastically. What is the magnitude of the change in the atom's momentum?

   A. 0
   B. $p/2$
   C. p
   D. $2p$

Passage 13 (Questions 1-10)

Momentum is conserved in both elastic and inelastic collisions, as long as there is no net external force. According to Newton's Third Law, the internal forces in any system occur in equal and opposite pairs, thus precluding any change in momentum due to these forces.

Two collision experiments are conducted. They are observed in two reference frames, A and B. Frame B is moving to the right with speed v relative to Frame A. The diagrams below show the experiments as seen in the two frames. In both experiments, the velocities are small compared to the speed of light, so relativistic effects are negligible. There is no fundamental difference between the two frames, so the laws of physics apply equally to both.

Experiment I:

An elastic collision between two clean steel balls each of mass m is observed. In Frame A, the balls are moving toward each other along a line with velocities **v** and –**v** as shown in the diagram. They collide, and each ball's velocity reverses direction. The situation from the point of view of Frame B looks somewhat different. This is indicated in the diagram.

Experiment II:

The balls are covered with a thin coat of glue that does not impede their rolling but does cause them to stick together. In Frame A, the balls are initially moving with velocities **v** and –**v**, just as in Experiment I. They collide, stick together, and stop. The situation in Frame B looks somewhat different.

EXPERIMENT I

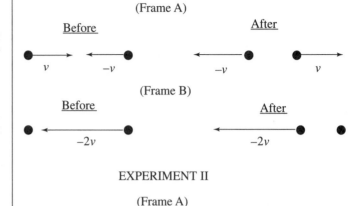

EXPERIMENT II

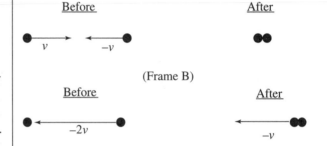

1. If an object is moving to the right with speed $v/2$ in Frame A, what is the magnitude and direction of its velocity in Frame B?

    A. $3v/2$ to the right
    B. $3v/2$ to the left
    C. $v/2$ to the right
    D. $v/2$ to the left

2. An object is moving upward with speed v in Frame B. What is the direction of the velocity of the object in Frame A?

    A. Up and to the right
    B. Up and to the left
    C. To the right
    D. To the left

3. For an observer in Frame A watching Experiment I, what is the magnitude of the change in momentum of the left-hand mass due to the collision?

    A. 0
    B. $mv/2$
    C. mv
    D. $2mv$

4. In Frame B, momentum is conserved in:

    A. Experiment I but not in Experiment II.
    B. Experiment II but not in Experiment I.
    C. neither Experiment I nor Experiment II.
    D. both Experiment I and Experiment II.

5. When particles of neon gas at room temperature collide, the collisions are usually perfectly elastic. This is because:

    A. the electron cloud of a neon atom cannot be deformed.
    B. most of the collisions do not cause electron transitions between energy levels.
    C. neon atoms are usually left in an excited state by the collisions.
    D. neon atoms have unusually small radii, so collisions are very unlikely.

6. In an elastic collision between two steel balls, the average magnitude of the internal forces exerted by each ball on the other is:

    A. directly proportional to the contact time.
    B. directly proportional to the square of the contact time.
    C. inversely proportional to the contact time.
    D. inversely proportional to the square of the contact time.

7. In Experiment II, the kinetic energy of the steel balls:

    A. is conserved in both Frame A and B.
    B. is conserved in Frame A only.
    C. is conserved in Frame B only.
    D. is not conserved in either Frame A or Frame B.

8. Which of the following is/are true?

    I.   The collision in Experiment I is elastic in both frames.
    II. The collision in Experiment II is elastic in Frame A but inelastic in Frame B.
    III. The collision in Experiment II is inelastic in Frame A but elastic in Frame B.

    A. I only
    B. I and II only
    C. I, II, and III
    D. None of the above

9. An observer in Frame B notes in Experiment I that the change in momentum of the ball on the left caused by the collision is equal to δ. What is the change in momentum of the other ball?

    A. δ
    B. 2δ
    C. $-\delta$
    D. -2δ

10. An observer in Frame B notes that in Experiment II, the right-hand ball exerts an average force of magnitude F on the left-hand ball when they collide. What is the magnitude of the average force exerted by the left-hand ball on the right-hand ball?

    A. 0
    B. $F/2$
    C. F
    D. $2F$

_____

Passage 14 (Questions 1-6)

Refrigerators exploit the thermodynamics of expanding and compressing gases. By controlling when and where the refrigerant gas expands and compresses, heat can be transported from the refrigerated chamber out to the environment. A compressor is a pump that pressurizes the refrigerant. Just as with all other types of heat engines, the conversion of heat to work in a refrigerator is not 100% efficient. So energy, in the form of electrical current, must be periodically added to the system in order to maintain the refrigeration cycle.

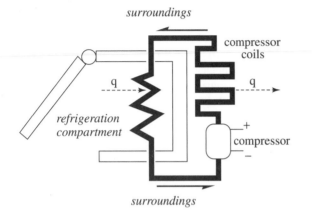

The refrigerant is compressed while it is outside the refrigeration compartment. Compression heats the gas. Once this heat is lost to the surroundings, the refrigerant is pumped back into the refrigeration chamber where it is allowed to expand back to its original pressure. Expanding gases cool, and if the gas is cooler than its surroundings, it will absorb heat.

In this way, heat energy from objects in the refrigeration chamber is removed. The refrigerant is then pumped back out of the chamber and is recompressed, beginning the cycle again.

The best refrigerants are gases that are nonreactive and which liquefy at temperatures below –20°C. Ammonia and freons are the most commonly used refrigerants.

1. The key step in refrigeration is allowing the refrigerant to release its heat to the surroundings immediately after it is compressed. Based upon this, which one of the following statements is true?

    A. An outdoor refrigerator works better on a hot day than on a cold day.
    B. Highly insulating material should cover all of the refrigerator's tubing.
    C. The compressed gas should be rapidly pumped back into the refrigerator before it cools.
    D. The temperature of the compressed gas should be allowed to equilibrate with the temperature of the surroundings.

2. If an opened refrigerator were placed in a closed insulated closet at 25°C and were allowed to run for three days, the final air temperature in the closet would be:

    A. less than 25°C.
    B. the same.
    C. greater than 25°C.
    D. indeterminable.

3. Based upon the thermodynamics of gases, which one of the following phenomena should NOT be real?

    A. The chilling of a cylinder of compressed air when gas is allowed to escape
    B. The heating of the air in a commercial airliner when the passenger's cabin is first pressurized
    C. The cooling of an air bubble as it rises from the ocean bottom to the surface
    D. The heating of liquid water by placing it under a vacuum and allowing it to boil

4. Which one of the following processes will absorb heat from the surroundings?

    A. Sublimation
    B. Freezing
    C. Condensation
    D. Deposition

5. The compressor increases the internal energy of the refrigerant because it:

    A. does work on the gas.
    B. is worked upon by the gas.
    C. allows the gas molecules to occupy more volume.
    D. converts pressure energy into electrical energy.

6. If the heat lost by the refrigerant to the surrounding environment as it passes through the compressor coils is 50% of its internal energy, the absolute temperature of the refrigerant

   A. decreases by a factor of $\sqrt{2}$
   B. decreases by a factor of 2
   C. decreases by a factor of 4
   D. decreases by a factor of 16

Passage 15 (Questions 1-4)

The compressibility of a gas may be measured by incrementally increasing the pressure exerted upon a gas and recording the change in volume. Devices that measure compressibility in this way typically consist of a high-pressure cylinder and piston.

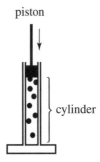

In one particular experiment, a scientist increased the force applied by a piston onto a sample of oxygen gas in 100-N increments. She recorded the distance the piston moved and converted this to a corresponding change in volume of the cylinder compartment. Two versions of the experiment were performed: one in which the cylinder walls were adiabatic, and one in which they were heat conducting.

The pressure (P) at the base of the cylinder is equal to the force (F) divided by the area of the base. If the base is circular, with radius r, then

$$P = \frac{\text{force}}{\text{area}} = \frac{F}{\pi r^2}$$

1. In the case where the walls are isothermal, as pressure is steadily increased which of the following must be true?

   A. The temperature of the system will increase.
   B. The volume of the system will decrease.
   C. The volume of the system will increase.
   D. The average kinetic energy of the gas will increase.

2. If the diameter of the cylinder were doubled, and the force were also doubled, then the pressure would:

   A. decrease by a factor of 4.
   B. decrease by a factor of 2.
   C. remain the same.
   D. increase by a factor of 2.

3. If the cylinder has adiabatic walls, then the walls:

   A. allow heat to flow through.
   B. do not prevent heat from flowing through.
   C. resist corrosion.
   D. insulate against heat entering or leaving the system.

4. What happens to the absolute temperature of an ideal gas if its pressure is doubled at constant volume?

   A. Decreases by a factor of 4
   B. Remains the same
   C. Increases by a factor of 2
   D. Increases by a factor of 4

Passage 16 (Questions 1-5)
ADVANCED PASSAGE

The surface and atmosphere of the Earth are in *radiative equilibrium*. This means that the Earth absorbs as much energy from the Sun (primarily in the form of visible light) as it emits (as infrared and microwaves) back into space. Measurements taken over the last two decades have led physicists to construct the following illustrations for the visible light (Figure 1) and infrared/microwave (Figure 2) energy budget of the Earth.

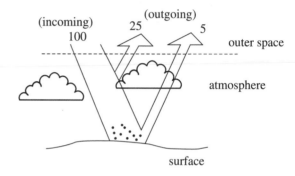

Figure 1

Not all incoming sunlight is absorbed by the Earth. Bright clouds, snow, and ice-covered surfaces reflect about 30% of all the sunlight reaching the Earth.

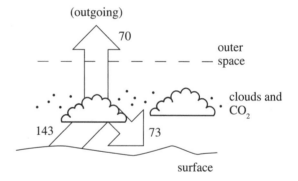

Figure 2

Clouds and carbon dioxide prevent most of the outgoing energy radiated from the surface from directly reaching outer space. Instead, they absorb this energy, and then emit more than half of it back down to the surface. In this way, a large amount of energy is trapped between the surface and the middle atmosphere, energy which warms the surface and the lower atmosphere. This phenomenon is called *the greenhouse effect*. Without any greenhouse effect, like on the Moon, the sunlit surface of the Earth would have an average temperature of $-20°C$!

1. The passage does NOT suggest that:

    A. some degree of the greenhouse effect is necessary for life as we know it.
    B. clear winter nights should be much warmer than cloudy winter nights.
    C. clear summer days should be hotter than cloudy summer days.
    D. CO_2 has the ability to interact with infrared and/or microwave photons.

2. If a sample of air ("the system") absorbs more energy than it emits, then its Q is:

    A. negative.
    B. positive.
    C. equal to ΔE – work done by the system.
    D. both B and C.

3. Considering that the Earth is in radiative equilibrium, then the number of emitted IR/microwave photons should be:

    A. less than the number of absorbed visible photons.
    B. the same as the number of absorbed visible photons.
    C. greater than the number of absorbed visible photons.
    D. zero during the day.

4. The Sun and the Earth convert thermal energy at their surfaces to light, a process called *blackbody emission*. The total energy emitted by a blackbody is proportional to the fourth power of the temperature of the surface. Identify the plot that best illustrates the dependence of the emitted energy E on the surface temperature T.

    A.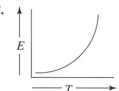
    B.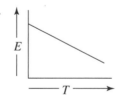
    C.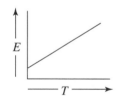
    D.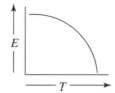

5. *Sensitive heat flux* is a term describing the conduction of heat from the warm surface to cooler air in contact with that surface. If $T_s - T_{air}$ is the difference between the surface and air temperatures, and Q is the *net* heat conducted out of the surface, then which plot illustrates the dependence of Q on $T_s - T_{air}$?

    A.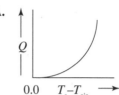
    B.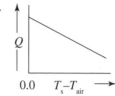
    C.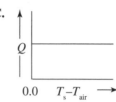
    D.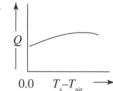

Passage 17 (Questions 1-6)

Before their trip up to the mountain retreat in Pure Springs, Dave, Sally, and their son Jesse stop at a convenience store to buy a six-pack of Pure Springs water. The water, initially chilled to 10°C, is packaged in 1-liter clear plastic bottles that are tightly sealed by a screw-on cap. The diameter of the base of each bottle is 8 cm, and the diameter of the neck is 2 cm (Figure 1).

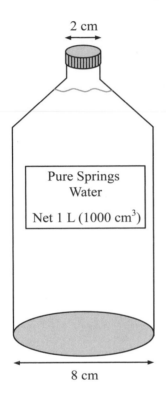

Figure 1 One liter water bottle

To keep himself occupied during the long trip, Jesse decides to monitor the temperature of the bottled water and report exactly when it reaches 30°C, the temperature inside the car. He hangs an unopened bottle in the bright sunlight by a string connected to the car's garment hook. After poking a small hole near the bottle's neck, he inserts a thermometer from their first-aid kit and begins his observations.

About halfway up a steep mountain grade, the car begins to overheat. As they approach a turn-out in the mountain road, Sally explains to Dave the details of how a car's cooling system works. On a typical rear-wheel-drive vehicle, a pump is driven by a belt connected to the car's crankshaft which forces water through channels within the engine. The heated water is then forced through the thermostat and into the thin multiple tubes of the radiator. Heat is then lost to the air that streams through the radiator due to the car's forward motion and/or by a fan that is

also driven via a belt by the crankshaft. The cooled water then returns to the pump, and the cycle is repeated.

After finding a small leak in the radiator and pouring in the contents of two bottles of spring water and a radiator-sealing material, the trio start out once again for Pure Springs.

To keep Jesse occupied during the last leg of the trip, Sally constructs a toy using a small, empty cosmetic bottle. After adding a little sand and sealing it, she forces the small flexible bottle into the neck of a spring-water bottle and tightly seals the cap. She notices that the cosmetic bottle floats with one-fourth of its volume above the surface of the spring water (Figure 2). Then, after additional water is added to fill the spring-water bottle, Jesse squeezes and then releases the spring-water bottle and observes that the small bottle inside sinks to the bottom (and then rises again to the top when he stops squeezing).

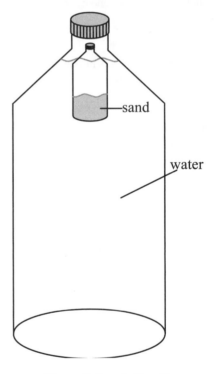

Figure 2 Jesse's New Toy

1. By what primary mechanism does Jesse's hanging water bottle gain energy?

   A. Conduction
   B. Convection
   C. Radiation
   D. Work done as the hanging bottle jiggles because of the car's motion

2. At the convenience store, Dave guzzles half of the contents of a bottle of spring water in 20 sec. At what average speed does the water flow into his mouth?

   A. 2 cm/sec
   B. 4 cm/sec
   C. 6 cm/sec
   D. 8 cm/sec

3. Based on information given in the passage, the primary mechanism(s) of energy transfer in cooling a car engine is/are best described as:

   A. conduction and radiation.
   B. forced convection.
   C. free convection.
   D. radiation and work done by the water pump.

4. What is the average density of the partially-filled small cosmetic bottle in Jesse's new toy?

   A. 250 kg/m³
   B. 333 kg/m³
   C. 500 kg/m³
   D. 750 kg/m³

5. Which one of the following best explains what happens to the small bottle partially filled with sand in Jesse's new toy when he squeezes the large bottle?

   A. The buoyant force acting on it increases.
   B. Its volume decreases.
   C. Its weight decreases.
   D. Its weight increases.

6. After waking from a nap of unknown duration, Jesse discovers that the spring water in his hanging bottle is at 30°C. What minimum amount of heat did it absorb? (Note: the specific heat of water is 4.2 J/g·°C.)

   A. 84 J
   B. 126 J
   C. 84 kJ
   D. 126 kJ

_____

Passage 18 (Questions 1-6)

Bernoulli's law concerns the phenomenon of ideal fluid flow. Torricelli's theorem is derived from Bernoulli's law with respect to a system in which a fluid of uniform density escapes through a hole situated at the bottom of a chamber or tank. The theorem establishes the following relationship between the speed of the escaping fluid and the depth of the hole beneath the fluid surface:

$$v = \sqrt{2gh}$$

v = escape speed
g = acceleration due to gravity
h = depth of the hole beneath the fluid surface

A vat is filled with equal amounts of three different liquids which quickly separate into three distinct layers. A spigot is located at the foot of the vat. The layers labeled ρ_1, ρ_2 and ρ_3, have densities of 736 kg/m³, 1000 kg/m³, and 1490 kg/m³, respectively. Each layer has a thickness of 0.3 m. A solid ball of density ρ_o is dropped into the vat. The ball settles at the interface of Layers 2 and 3. An object floating or submerged in a fluid experiences a net force F, which is the difference between the weight of the object and the buoyant force B acting on the object by the fluid. An expression for this force is based upon Archimedes' principle:

$$F = w - B = \rho_o gV - \rho_f gV'$$

where w is the weight of the object, ρ_f is the density of the fluid, ρ_o is the density of the object, V is the volume of the object, and V' is the submerged volume of the object. When the object is stationary, the net force F on the object must be zero. (Note: Assume that the gravitational acceleration, g, equals 10 m/s², and that the ball and fluids are stationary.)

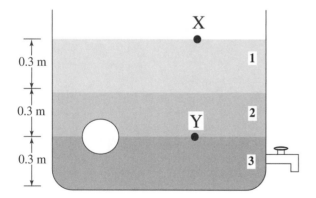

Figure 1

1. Which of the following statements is true for the density of the ball in comparison to the densities of the fluids?

   A. $\rho_1 < \rho_o < \rho_2$
   B. $\rho_2 > \rho_o > \rho_1$
   C. $\rho_3 < \rho_o < \rho_2$
   D. $\rho_3 > \rho_o > \rho_2$

2. What is the approximate gauge pressure at a point 0.1 m below the surface of Fluid 1?

   A. 27 Pa
   B. 74 Pa
   C. 368 Pa
   D. 736 Pa

3. Which of the following expressions is equal to a unit of pressure?

   A. N/m
   B. N·m
   C. N/m²
   D. N·m²

4. A second ball, with density 490 kg/m³, is tossed into the vat. Approximately what fraction of the ball's volume will remain above the surface?

   A. 1/4
   B. 1/3
   C. 2/3
   D. 3/4

5. What is the approximate difference in pressure between Points X and Y?

   A. 3.0 kPa
   B. 4.5 kPa
   C. 5.2 kPa
   D. 10.0 kPa

6. A tank is filled to a height of 4 meters with a fluid of density 900 kg/m³. A spigot at the bottom of the tank is opened. What is the approximate velocity of the fluid flowing through the spigot at the moment that it is opened?

   A. 4 m/s
   B. 6 m/s
   C. 7 m/s
   D. 9 m/s

Passage 19 (Questions 1-5)

A section of glass tubing has three different cross-sectional areas, A_1, A_2, and A_3, which are in decreasing order. Fluid is continually pushed through the tube at a constant rate. Narrow vertical columns of identical diameters are inserted into the tube at each of the three different sections to measure the hydrostatic pressure. Fluids in motion at the same elevation follow Bernoulli's equation:

$$P + \frac{1}{2}\rho v^2 = constant$$

For a given cross-sectional area, P is the pressure, v is the flow speed, and ρ is the density of the fluid.

(Note: Assume that the fluid is incompressible and that it flows in a nonturbulent fashion.)

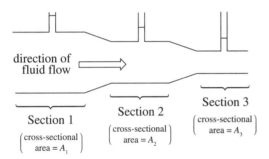

direction of fluid flow

Section 1
(cross-sectional area = A_1)

Section 2
(cross-sectional area = A_2)

Section 3
(cross-sectional area = A_3)

Figure 1

1. Which of the following correctly relates the pressure readings obtained from each pressure gauge in terms of the locations at which the gauges are situated?

   A. $P_1 < P_2 < P_3$
   B. $P_1 < P_2 = P_3$
   C. $P_1 = P_2 < P_3$
   D. $P_1 > P_2 > P_3$

2. If in Section 2 the cross-sectional area is 8 cm² and fluid is flowing through there at a velocity of 10 cm/s, and if in Section 1 the cross-sectional area is 20 cm², what is the fluid velocity in Section 1?

   A. 4 cm/s
   B. 8 cm/s
   C. 10 cm/s
   D. 16 cm/s

3. If the ratio of A_2 to A_3 is tripled, then the ratio of the flow speeds, v_2 to v_3, will:

   A. decrease by a factor of 9.
   B. decrease by a factor of 3.
   C. increase by a factor of 3.
   D. increase by a factor of 9.

4. If the fluid velocity in Section 1 is 0.4 m/s and in Section 3 it is 0.6 m/sec, what is the pressure difference between Sections 1 and 3? (Assume that the density of the fluid is 1000 kg/m³.)

   A. 50 Pa
   B. 100 Pa
   C. 200 Pa
   D. 260 Pa

5. Two entirely separate Pipes 1 and 2 conduct Fluids A and B, respectively, at equal rates of flow. The cross-sectional area of Pipe 1 is greater than that of Pipe 2. Which of the following would best explain the equality of flow?

   A. The density of Fluid A is less than that of Fluid B.
   B. The viscosity of Fluid A is greater than that of Fluid B.
   C. The vapor pressure of Fluid A is greater than that of Fluid B.
   D. The velocity of Fluid A is less than that of Fluid B.

Passage 20 (Questions 1-5)

A cylindrical pole made of a homogeneous material whose density is 7100 kg/m³ stands upright with one end attached securely to the ground. The pole's length and cross-sectional area are 15 m and 0.03 m², respectively. The figure below shows such a pole and three hypothetical cross sections at 5-meter intervals.

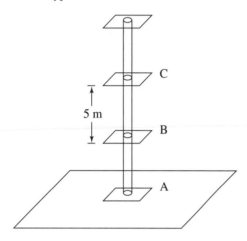

Figure 1

The pole can be thought of as a very rigid spring that follows Hooke's law. If an object were placed on top of the pole, the pole would be compressed by an amount proportional to the object's weight. However, if the object were so heavy as to make the pole buckle, Hooke's law would no longer apply. Assume the pole behaves as a Hooke's law spring until the instant of collapse. Young's modulus, E, is similar to the spring constant in Hooke's law. Equation 1 below relates E to the pressure—or *stress*—applied to a body, σ, and the fractional change in length the body undergoes, ε (as defined by Equation 2):

$$E = \frac{\sigma}{\varepsilon} \qquad\qquad \varepsilon = \frac{\Delta l}{l}$$

Equation 1   **Equation 2**

It is important to consider that a real pole must support its own weight. If the diameter of a pole is held fixed, there will be an upper limit on the height. The pressure on the pole due to the pole's own weight is $\sigma = \rho g h$ at any given point where ρ is the density of the pole and h is the height of the pole above the given point.

For the pole above, $E = 10^{10}$ N/m². Assume that the acceleration due to gravity, g, equals 9.8 m/s².

1. Which of the following best relates the pressures at each of the cross sections A, B, and C?

   A. $\sigma_A > \sigma_B > \sigma_C$
   B. $\sigma_A < \sigma_B < \sigma_C$
   C. $\sigma_A = \sigma_B = \sigma_C$
   D. $\sigma_A < \sigma_B > \sigma_C$

2. Consider two cylindrical poles, I and II. Pole I has a greater cross-sectional area than does Pole II. At its base, each pole experiences a pressure exerted by its own weight. If the poles themselves are of equal weight, then pressure at the base due to the pole's own weight will be:

   A. greater for Pole I than for Pole II.
   B. greater for Pole II than for Pole I.
   C. equal for Poles I and II.
   D. dependent on the relative heights of the two poles.

3. What is the pressure due to the pole's own weight at cross section B?

   A. 5.4×10^5 Pa
   B. 7.0×10^5 Pa
   C. 8.7×10^5 Pa
   D. 9.9×10^5 Pa

4. If a metal pole can be subjected to great stress while undergoing relatively little fractional change in length, then Young's modulus for the pole has a:

   A. large negative value.
   B. small negative value.
   C. small positive value.
   D. large positive value.

5. How tall could the pole become before buckling under its own weight if it collapses when compressed by more than a factor of ε_C?

   A. $\dfrac{\varepsilon_C}{E}$

   B. $\dfrac{g\varepsilon_C}{E}$

   C. $\dfrac{gE}{\rho\varepsilon_C}$

   D. $\dfrac{\varepsilon_C E}{\rho g}$

Passage 21 (Questions 1-5)

To observe the effects of the buoyant force, the following simple apparatus is constructed: Two 3-meter-tall cylindrical containers of fluid rest on a flat table, and mounted directly beneath the containers is a strong electromagnet. An insulated cork will be used as the buoy.

The cork (whose specific gravity is much less than that of the fluids in the containers) has a very thin iron plate glued to its base, which will allow it to be held submerged at the bottom of each container by the magnet mounted underneath.

The first container is filled with Fluid #1 (whose density will be denoted by ρ_1), and the second container contains Fluid #2 (with density ρ_2).

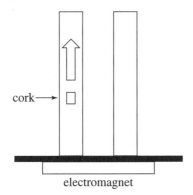

cork

electromagnet

1. If ρ is the density of water, what is the specific gravity of Fluid #1?

    A. ρ_1/ρ
    B. ρ/ρ_1
    C. $\rho_1 - \rho$
    D. $(\rho_1 - \rho)/\rho$

2. When the cork is placed in Fluid #1, it floats at the surface with only 10% of its volume submerged. When the cork is placed in Fluid #2, the percentage submerged is 15%. Which one of the correctly compares the densities of the two fluids?

    A. $\rho_1 = \dfrac{2}{3}\rho_2$

    B. $\rho_1 = \dfrac{17}{18}\rho_2$

    C. $\rho_1 = \dfrac{18}{17}\rho_2$

    D. $\rho_1 = \dfrac{3}{2}\rho_2$

3. How many times more dense is Fluid #2 than the cork?

    A. $\dfrac{14}{3}$

    B. $\dfrac{17}{3}$

    C. $\dfrac{20}{3}$

    D. $\dfrac{23}{3}$

4. The cork is placed in Fluid #1, pushed to the bottom of the container and held there by the magnet. When the magnetic force is suddenly removed, the cork begins to rise to the surface. Compute the magnitude of its initial upward acceleration (in terms of the gravitational acceleration, g) given that Fluid #1 is 10 times more dense than the cork.

    A. $8g$
    B. $9g$
    C. $10g$
    D. $11g$

5. As the cork as it rises to the surface, its acceleration:

    A. remains constant.
    B. decreases from its initial value due to viscosity.
    C. increases from its initial value due to the increasing kinetic energy.
    D. decreases from its initial value due to the decreasing potential energy.

Passage 22 (Questions 1-3)

Consider three identical vessels, two of which (X and Y) contain fluid. The third container is empty. The first vessel contains Fluid X whose specific gravity is 0.75, and the second one contains Fluid Y whose specific gravity is 1.5.

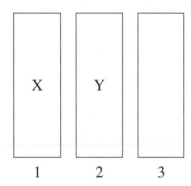

1. If an object with density 500 kg/m³ is placed in the container filled with Fluid X, what fraction of the object will be exposed above the surface?

    A. 1/3
    B. 1/2
    C. 2/3
    D. 3/4

2. Which one of the following statements is true?

    A. If an object floats in Fluid Y, then it floats in Fluid X.
    B. If an object sinks in Fluid X, then it sinks in Fluid Y.
    C. If an object floats in both Fluids X and Y, then the buoyant force on the floating object exerted by Fluid Y is greater than the buoyant force on the floating object exerted by Fluid X.
    D. If an object floats in both Fluids X and Y, then the volume submerged in Fluid X is twice the volume submerged in Fluid Y.

3. If we wish to form (in the third container) a mixture of Fluids X and Y that has the same weight as an equal volume of water, what should be ratio of the amount of Fluid X to the amount of Fluid Y?

    A. 1:2
    B. 1:1
    C. 3:2
    D. 2:1

Passage 23 (Questions 1-4)

A simple hydraulic jack consists of two vertical cylindrical vessels (each with constant diameter and connected near their bases by a horizontal tube) filled with fluid. The piston in one of the vessels (#1) has a cross-sectional area of 5 cm², and the other piston (#2) has a cross-sectional area of 500 cm².

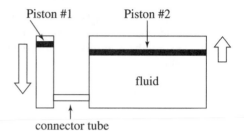

1. Which physical principle best describes the relationship between the motion of the two pistons?

    A. Poiseuille's law
    B. Archimedes' principle
    C. Pascal's law
    D. Bernoulli's principle

2. What weight on the small piston will support a weight of 5000 N on the larger one?

    A. 50 N
    B. 100 N
    C. 250 N
    D. 500 N

3. How far must the small piston be pushed down to raise the larger piston a distance of 1 millimeter?

    A. 5 cm
    B. 10 cm
    C. 25 cm
    D. 50 cm

4. Let W_1 be the work done by the force pushing down on Piston #1, and let W_2 be the work done by Piston #2 as it raises the load it supports. Calculate the ratio W_1/W_2.

    A. 1/100
    B. 1
    C. 5
    D. 100

Passage 24 (Questions 1-6)

An open cylindrical tank (completely filled with water) of height 6 meters and radius 3 meters sits atop an 8-meter high platform of width 6 meters. There are three plugs in a vertical line up the side of the tank, which can be removed (thereby creating a hole). Plug #1 is above Plug #2, which in turn is above Plug #3. The cross-sectional area of each of the holes filled by the plugs is 5 cm². If a plug is removed, a stream of water emerges from the hole with an initial velocity that is directed horizontally. The flow of the water may be described by Bernoulli's equation,

$$P_1 + \rho g h_1 + \tfrac{1}{2}\rho v_1^2 = P_2 + \rho g h_2 + \tfrac{1}{2}\rho v_2^2$$

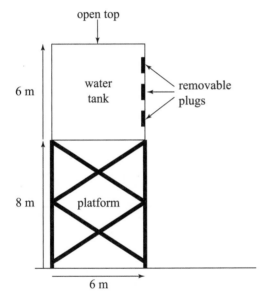

1. What is the gauge pressure at the base of the water tank?

    A. 20 kPa
    B. 60 kPa
    C. 80 kPa
    D. 140 kPa

2. Which plug should be removed for the emerging stream of water to have the greatest exit speed?

    A. Plug #1
    B. Plug #2
    C. Plug #3
    D. All three plugs would give the same speed.

3. If Plug #2 is 4 meters below the surface of the tank, with what speed would the water emerge from the hole that is created if this plug were removed?

    A. 4.5 m/s
    B. 6.3 m/s
    C. 8.9 m/s
    D. 10.7 m/s

4. In a certain time interval, 1.4 m³ of water is lost through one of the holes. Estimate the resulting drop in the water level in the tank.

    A. 0.05 m
    B. 0.10 m
    C. 0.20 m
    D. 0.50 m

5. If Plug #3 were removed, what can we say about the speed of the water emerging from the hole as the water level in the tank drops to the level of the hole?

    A. The speed decreases.
    B. The speed increases.
    C. The speed remains constant.
    D. The speed increases, then decreases.

6. When Plug #1 is opened, let the speed of the water emerging from the hole be denoted by v. What would this speed be if the tank were instead filled with a fluid of specific gravity 0.5 (and negligible viscosity)?

    A. v/2
    B. v
    C. 2v
    D. 4v

Passage 25 (Questions 1-5)

If the flow of blood through a vessel is laminar, then certain aspects of this flow can be analyzed using Poiseuille's law:

$$\Delta P = \frac{8\eta L f}{\pi R^4}$$

Here, R is the radius of the blood vessel, L is its length, f is the volume flow rate, η is the viscosity, and ΔP is the drop in pressure between the ends of the vessel.

However, if the flow is turbulent, then Poiseuille's law is not applicable. (Turbulent flow actually has a practical application: When blood pressure is measured with a sphygmomanometer, a stethoscope is used to hear the resulting noisy, turbulent blood flow.) The state of the flow can be predicted by computing the *Reynolds number, N,* which is given by the equation

$$N = \frac{2v\rho R}{\eta}$$

where v is the speed of the flow, and ρ is the density of the blood. If $N < 2000$, then the flow is laminar; if $N > 3000$, then the flow is turbulent; and if $2000 < N < 3000$, no prediction can be made.

Consider a small section of an arteriole with diameter 50 μm, length 1 cm, and a 120-Pa pressure drop across its length. The viscosity of blood is 0.002 Pa-s, and its specific gravity is 1.06.

1. Approximate the volume flow rate through this artery.

    A. 9×10^{-13} m³/s
    B. 1×10^{-11} m³/s
    C. 1×10^{-8} m³/s
    D. 9×10^{-5} m³/s

2. Which one of the following can be used as an alternate expression for calculating the Reynolds number through a tube with circular cross section in terms of the volume flow rate, f?

    A. $\dfrac{2fR}{\pi\eta\rho}$

    B. $\dfrac{2R\rho}{\pi\eta f}$

    C. $\dfrac{2f\rho}{\pi R\eta}$

    D. $\dfrac{2R\rho f}{\pi\eta}$

3. If the artery were occluded (that is, blocked) so that its effective radius were halved, but the volume of blood flow per second through the artery remained unchanged, then the pressure change would:

    A. decrease by a factor of 4.
    B. decrease by a factor of 16.
    C. increase by a factor of 4.
    D. increase by a factor of 16.

4. Which one of the following best illustrates the graph of pressure drop magnitude versus tube length for laminar flow (with steady volume flow rate) in a tube of constant diameter?

    A. 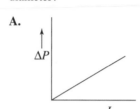   B.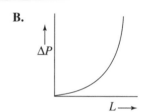

    C. 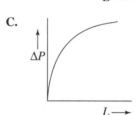   D.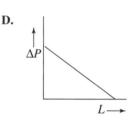

5. Which one of the following changes could cause a laminar flow to become turbulent?

    A. Increasing the viscosity of the fluid
    B. Decreasing the density of the fluid
    C. Increasing the length of the flow tube
    D. Increasing the speed of the fluid

Passage 26 (Question 1-5)
ADVANCED PASSAGE

Blood flow through the vascular system of the human body is controlled by several factors. The rate of flow, Q, is directly proportional to the pressure differential, ΔP, between any two points in the system and inversely proportional to the resistance, R, of the system:

$$Q = \Delta P / R$$

Equation 1

The resistance, R, is dependent on the length of the vessel, L, the viscosity of blood, η, and the vessel's radius, r according to the equation

$$R = \frac{8\eta L}{\pi r^4}$$

Equation 2

Under normal conditions, vessel length and blood viscosity do not vary significantly. However, certain conditions can cause changes in blood content, thereby altering viscosity. Veins are generally more compliant than arteries due to their less muscular nature. The flow of blood through the major arteries can be approximated by the equations of ideal flow.

The dynamics of fluid movement from capillaries to body tissue and back to capillaries is also driven by pressure differentials. The net filtration pressure is the difference between the hydrostatic pressure of the blood in the capillaries, P_c, and the hydrostatic pressure of tissue fluid outside the capillaries, P_i. The oncotic pressure is the difference between the osmotic pressure of the capillaries, Π_c (approximately 25 torr), and the osmotic pressure of the tissue fluids, Π_i (negligible). Whether fluid moves into or out of the capillary network depends on the magnitudes of the net filtration and oncotic pressures. The direction of fluid movement can be determined by calculating the following pressure differential:

$$\Delta P = (P_c + \Pi_i) - (P_i + \Pi_c)$$

Equation 3

The sum in the first set of parentheses gives the pressure acting to move fluid out of the capillaries, while the sum in the second set of parentheses gives the pressure acting to move fluid into the capillaries.

Capillaries are porous, and the blood pressure on the arterial end of a capillary bed is enough to push fluid out of the capillaries and into the surrounding tissues. However, blood proteins and cells are too big to fit through the pores. Consequently, as the blood travels across the capillary bed, it becomes relatively more concentrated in proteins and cells; this leads to an osmotic influx of fluid on the venous side of the capillary bed. Note, however, that the volume of fluid lost to the tissues due to pressure is greater than the volume of fluid returned to the blood due to osmosis, so there is a net outward flow of fluid to the tissues. This excess fluid is recaptured and returned to the cardiovascular system via the lymphatic vessels.

1. The cross-sectional area of the aorta is approximately 4 cm² and the total cross-sectional area of the major arteries is 20 cm². If the speed of the blood in the aorta is 30 cm/sec, what is the average blood speed in the major arteries?

   A. 5 cm/sec
   B. 6 cm/sec
   C. 120 cm/sec
   D. 150 cm/sec

2. Blood flow to the various systems in the body is regulated by the dilation and constriction of the blood vessels. After a person has eaten a large meal, the blood vessels supplying the digestive system dilate, increasing their radii by 50%. As a result of this blood vessel dilation, the flow of blood to the digestive system will:

   A. increase to 500% of the original flow.
   B. increase to 225% of the original flow.
   C. increase to 150% of the original flow.
   D. decrease to 50% of the original flow.

3. Adaptation to life at high altitudes is characterized by polycythemia (high red blood cell count). Excluding other physiological compensations, what is the effect of this change on the flow of blood?

   A. Flow is decreased because viscosity is decreased.
   B. Flow is increased because viscosity is decreased.
   C. Flow is decreased because viscosity is increased.
   D. Flow is increased because viscosity is increased.

4. At the venular end of skeletal muscle capillaries, the hydrostatic pressure of the capillary is 17 torr and the hydrostatic pressure of the surrounding tissue is 1 torr. Fluid movement is from:

   A. the capillary to the tissue, at a rate proportional to 7 torr.
   B. the tissue to the capillary, at a rate proportional to 7 torr.
   C. the capillary to the tissue, at a rate proportional to 9 torr.
   D. the tissue to the capillary, at a rate proportional to 9 torr.

5. According to the following schematic diagram of systemic circulation, which of the following is true?

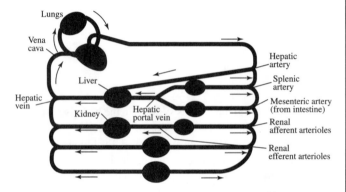

   A. Vascular architecture of organs is in series so total peripheral resistance is greater than the resistance of individual organs.
   B. Vascular architecture of organs is in parallel so total peripheral resistance is greater than the resistance of individual organs.
   C. Vascular architecture of organs is in series so total peripheral resistance is less than the resistance of individual organs.
   D. Vascular architecture of organs is in parallel so total peripheral resistance is less than the resistance of individual organs.

Passage 27 (Questions 1-7)
ADVANCED PASSAGE

If an incompressible fluid is flowing steadily through a pipe, the amount of fluid passing any given point must be the same everywhere in the pipe—otherwise, there would be a pileup at some point—an impossibility if the fluid is incompressible. This notion is expressed mathematically by the continuity equation: $A_1v_1 = A_2v_2$ for any two points (1 and 2) in the pipe. The A's denote the cross-sectional areas of the pipe at the indicated points, and the v's are flow speeds.

If, in addition to being incompressible and flowing steadily, the fluid is nonviscous, then we can use conservation of energy to derive a useful equation. We have $W = \Delta K + \Delta U$ where W is the work done on some given small volume of fluid by the forces exerted by the surrounding fluid, and the right-hand side represents the total change in energy (kinetic, K, and potential, U) of the given volume of fluid when it moves from Point 1 to Point 2. By dividing this equation by the volume of fluid under consideration, we obtain Bernoulli's equation:

$$P_1 + \tfrac{1}{2}\rho v_1^2 + \rho g h_1 = P_2 + \tfrac{1}{2}\rho v_2^2 + \rho g h_2$$

where P represents fluid pressure, ρ is fluid density, g is the gravitational acceleration, h is the height of the fluid above some reference point, and v is the flow speed.

Two typical situations in which Bernoulli's equation is useful are shown below:

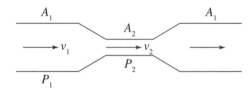

Figure 1

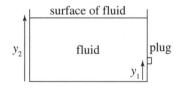

Figure 2 The surface of the fluid is exposed to the atmosphere

1. Which of the following is true regarding the flow speeds and pressures in Figure 1?

   A. $v_1 > v_2$ and $P_1 > P_2$
   B. $v_1 < v_2$ and $P_1 < P_2$
   C. $v_1 > v_2$ and $P_1 < P_2$
   D. $v_1 < v_2$ and $P_1 > P_2$

2. Which of the following is one reason that Bernoulli's equation does NOT apply to a viscous fluid?

   A. The density, ρ, depends on the viscosity.
   B. Energy is not conserved in viscous fluid flow.
   C. Turbulence is more likely if the fluid is viscous.
   D. There is no term in the equation corresponding to the production of heat.

3. In Figure 2, if the plug is pulled out, what is the speed of the water as it exits the hole? (Ignore viscosity and assume that the hole is small so that the speed at which the level of water in the tank is falling is negligible.)

   A. $\sqrt{2gy_1}$
   B. $\sqrt{2gy_2}$
   C. $\sqrt{g(y_2 - y_1)}$
   D. $\sqrt{2g(y_2 - y_1)}$

4. In Figure 2, the pressure on the plug which tries to push it outward:

   A. is higher than the atmospheric pressure.
   B. is lower than the atmospheric pressure.
   C. is equal to the atmospheric pressure.
   D. may be higher or lower than atmospheric pressure, depending on the value of y_2.

5. In Figure 1, if the fluid flows in such a way that $A_1 v_1 > A_2 v_2$, then we may conclude that:

   A. the fluid is not incompressible.
   B. energy is not conserved.
   C. the fluid has high viscosity.
   D. the cross-sectional area of the pipe is actually larger at Point 2 than at Point 1.

6. If Fluid #1 has density ρ_1 and viscosity η_1, while Fluid #2 has density ρ_2 and viscosity η_2, where $\rho_1 > \rho_2$, which of the fluids would be described more accurately by Bernoulli's equation?

   A. Fluid #1
   B. Fluid #2
   C. The equation would work equally well for either fluid.
   D. Cannot be determined from the information given

7. In a straight pipe of uniform cross-sectional area filled with a nonviscous, incompressible fluid, the pressure at one end is equal to the pressure at the other end. Which of the following statements is/are true?

   I. The volume flow rate is zero because there is no net force on the fluid.
   II. The volume flow rate is constant throughout the pipe.
   III. The pipe is not inclined relative to the horizontal since the pressure is constant.

   A. I and III only
   B. II and III only
   C. II only
   D. I, II, and III

Passage 28 (Questions 1-6)

A positive charge $Q = 10^{-9}$ coulomb is fixed at the origin of an x-y coordinate system. Three positions X, Y, and Z are to be considered: Point X is 3 cm from the origin on the x axis, Point Y is 3 cm from the origin on the y axis, and Point Z is 4 cm from the origin on the x axis, as shown in the diagram below.

Another positive charge $q = 10^{-14}$ coulomb will be used to observe various electrostatic effects produced by the electric field created by the charge Q. (Note: The value of Coulomb's constant is $9 \times 10^9 \, \text{N·m}^2 / \text{C}^2$.)

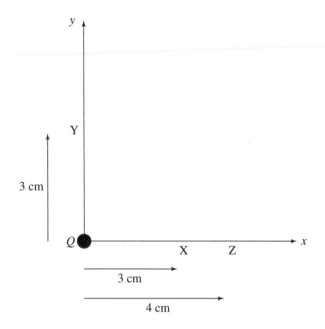

1. Let F_X be the magnitude of the electrostatic force felt by q (due to Q) when q is placed at Point X, and let F_Y be the magnitude of the electrostatic force felt by q (due to Q) when q is placed at Point Y. Which of the following is true?

   A. $F_X = F_Y$
   B. $F_X = 2F_Y$
   C. $F_X = 3F_Y$
   D. $F_X = 9F_Y$

2. Let F_X be the magnitude of the electrostatic force felt by q (due to Q) when q is placed at point X, and let F_Z be the magnitude of the electrostatic force felt by q (due to Q) when q is placed at Point Z. Which of the following is then true?

   A. $F_X = \dfrac{3}{4} F_Z$

   B. $F_X = \dfrac{4}{3} F_Z$

   C. $F_X = \dfrac{9}{16} F_Z$

   D. $F_X = \dfrac{16}{9} F_Z$

3. By how much will the electrostatic potential energy of q change when q is moved from Position Z to Position X?

   A. It will decrease by 7.5×10^{-15} joule.
   B. It will decrease by 7.5×10^{-13} joule.
   C. It will increase by 7.5×10^{-15} joule.
   D. It will increase by 7.5×10^{-13} joule.

4. What is the electric field at Point X due to the Charge Q (i represents the positive x direction)?

   A. $(10^{-4} \, \text{N} / \text{C}) \mathbf{i}$
   B. $(10^{-4} \, \text{N} / \text{C})(-\mathbf{i})$
   C. $(10^4 \, \text{N} / \text{C}) \mathbf{i}$
   D. $(10^4 \, \text{N} / \text{C})(-\mathbf{i})$

5. Let W_1 be the work required (against the electrostatic field) to move q from Position Z to Position Y, and let W_2 be the work required to move q from Position Z to position X. Which one of the following is true?

   A. $W_1 = W_2$
   B. $W_1 = 3W_2$
   C. $W_1 = 4W_2$
   D. $W_1 = 5W_2$

6. If q is placed at Position X and released, then:

   A. q will move toward Q with increasing acceleration.
   B. q will move toward Q with decreasing acceleration.
   C. q will move away from Q with increasing acceleration.
   D. q will move away from Q with decreasing acceleration.

Passage 29 (Questions 1-7)

Consider the two equal positive charges $Q = 1.1 \times 10^{-10}$ coulomb placed on the x and y axes a distance $d = 1$ mm from the origin as shown in the diagram below. These charges are fixed in place and create a steady electric field. Furthermore, every position in the plane also possesses a value for the electrostatic potential. The potential at each position is uniquely determined by the standard assumption that at points infinitely far from the charges, the potential is zero.

Two small test charges (a proton and an electron) will be used to observe the effects of this electric field. The magnitude of the charge on both the proton and the electron is the elementary charge, $e = 1.6 \times 10^{-19}$ C. The mass of a proton is 1.67×10^{-27} kg, and the mass of an electron is 9.11×10^{-31} kg. (Note: The value of Coulomb's constant is $k = 9 \times 10^{9}$ N·m²/ C².)

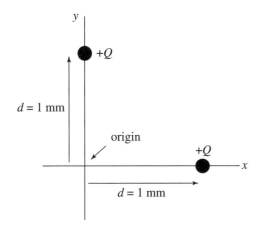

1. At how many positions in the x-y PLANE diagram above is the electric field strength equal to 0?

    A. 0
    B. 1
    C. 2
    D. 4

2. How many times greater would the magnitude of electrostatic force between the two charges Q be if one of the charges were instead fixed at the origin and the position of other Q were unchanged?

    A. $\sqrt{2}$
    B. 2
    C. $2\sqrt{2}$
    D. 4

3. If a proton were placed at the origin and released, it would move:

    A. along the x axis, away from the charges.
    B. along the y axis, away from the charges.
    C. at a 45° angle to the x axis, away from the charges
    D. at a 45° angle to the x axis, toward the charges.

4. What is the magnitude of the electric field at the origin?

    A. 1.4×10^{3} N/C
    B. 2.0×10^{3} N/C
    C. 1.4×10^{6} N/C
    D. 2.04×10^{6} N/C

5. At how many positions (not including the position at "infinity") in the x-y PLANE diagram above is the electrostatic potential equal to 0?

    A. 0
    B. 1
    C. 2
    D. 4

6. What is the electrostatic potential at the origin?

    A. 1000 volts
    B. 1400 volts
    C. 2000 volts
    D. 2800 volts

7. Let a_p be the magnitude of the initial acceleration of a proton placed and released at the origin, and let a_e be the magnitude of the initial acceleration of an electron placed and released at the origin. Compute the ratio a_e/a_p.

    A. 5.5×10^{-4}
    B. 1
    C. 1.8×10^{3}
    D. 1.6×10^{19}

Passage 30 (Questions 1-7)

Figure 1 shows a circuit consisting of a resistor network, a capacitor network, and a battery. Points 1, 2, 3, and 4 can be connected in various ways so that the circuit can perform different functions. When Points 1 and 2 are connected, for example, the capacitor network is discharged. In order to supply an external component with power, it could be connected between Points 1 and 4.

In the circuit below, each resistor has a resistance of 2 Ω, and each capacitor has a capacitance of 2 μF (unless otherwise stated).

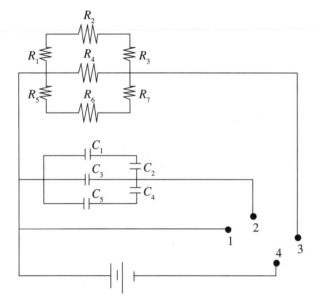

Figure 1

1. Points 3 and 4 are connected. Charge is flowing out of the battery at a rate of 2 A and through Resistors R_1 and R_5 at a rate of 0.4 A. How much current is flowing through R_4?

   A. 0.4 A
   B. 0.8 A
   C. 1.2 A
   D. 2.0 A

2. What is the total resistance across Resistors 1, 2 and 3?

   A. 2/3 Ω
   B. 2 Ω
   C. 6 Ω
   D. 8 Ω

3. Points 3 and 4 are connected. Assume the resistor network has a total resistance of 10 Ω. If the battery produces a potential difference of 15 V, how much charge will flow through the network in 1 second?

   A. 2/3 C
   B. 3/2 C
   C. 10/3 C
   D. 36/5 C

4. Assume that Points 3 and 4 are connected and that the battery produces a potential difference of 30 V. If the resistor network consumes energy at a rate of 3 W, what is the resistance of the network?

   A. 0.3 Ω
   B. 3 Ω
   C. 30 Ω
   D. 300 Ω

5. What is the total capacitance across C_1 and C_2?

   A. 1/2 μF
   B. 1 μF
   C. 2 μF
   D. 4 μF

6. The capacitor network is charged so a potential difference of 10 V exists across the network. Points 2 and 3 are then connected. If the resistor network has a total resistance of 10 Ω and the capacitor network has a capacitance of 1 μF, how much energy will be consumed by the resistors?

   A. 1×10^{-6} J
   B. 1×10^{-5} J
   C. 5×10^{-5} J
   D. 1×10^{-4} J

7. A component that does NOT obey Ohm's law is connected between Points 1 and 4. The unknown component behaves as shown in the graph below.

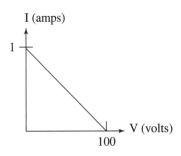

   If a battery that produces a potential difference of 50 V is used, at what rate will energy be consumed by the component?

   A. 5 W
   B. 25 W
   C. 50 W
   D. 100 W

Passage 31 (Questions 1-7)

The capacitance of a parallel-plate capacitor is given by the equation $C = K\varepsilon_0 A/d$, where K is the dielectric constant for the insulating material between the plates ($K = 1$ for vacuum), ε_0 is a constant known as the permittivity of free space ($\varepsilon_0 = 8.85 \times 10^{-12}$ C²/N-m²), A is the area of each plate, and d is the distance between the plates.

A circuit containing a voltage source, a capacitor, and a resistor is shown in Figure 1. When the switch S is moved to Position 1, the capacitor is charged by the battery. When the switch is moved to Position 2, the capacitor discharges through the resistor, R.

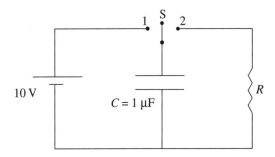

Figure 1

1. In order for charged parallel plates to act as a capacitor, which of the following must be true?

   A. The material between the plates must not conduct electricity.
   B. The plates must be connected to ground.
   C. There must be zero potential difference between the plates.
   D. The plates must be connected to a voltage source.

2. If the plates of the capacitor in Figure 1 are separated by a distance of 1 cm, what is the magnitude of the electric field generated between the plates when the capacitor is fully charged?

   A. 1 V/m
   B. 10 V/m
   C. 100 V/m
   D. 1000 V/m

3.   When the capacitor in Figure 1 is fully charged, how much energy is stored in it?

   A. 1×10^{-5} J
   B. 5×10^{-5} J
   C. 1×10^{-4} J
   D. 5×10^{-4} J

4.   When the capacitor in Figure 1 is fully charged, what is the magnitude of charge on each plate?

   A. 1×10^{-5} C
   B. 5×10^{-5} C
   C. 1×10^{-4} C
   D. 5×10^{-4} C

5.   How much work must be done to move a –2 coulomb charge from the positive plate to the negative plate of a capacitor charged to 10 V?

   A.   0.2 J
   B.   5 J
   C.   20 J
   D.   200 J

6.   If two capacitors of unequal capacitance are connected in series, the capacitance of the combination will be:

   A.   greater than that of the capacitor with higher capacitance.
   B.   equal to that of the capacitor with higher capacitance.
   C.   between the capacitances of the two capacitors.
   D.   less than that of the capacitor with lower capacitance.

7.   If two capacitors of unequal capacitance are connected in parallel, the capacitance of the combination will be:

   A.   greater than that of the capacitor with higher capacitance.
   B.   equal to that of the capacitor with higher capacitance.
   C.   between the capacitances of the two capacitors.
   D.   less than that of the capacitor with lower capacitance.

Passage 32 (Questions 1-6)

The movement of electric charge through a wire is known to produce a magnetic field whose direction at a given point is in accordance with the "Right Hand Rule." If the wire is straight and relatively long, then the strength of the field produced by such a wire carrying a current I is given by the equation:

$$B = \frac{\mu_0 I}{2\pi r}$$

Equation 1

where μ_0 is a constant (= 1.26×10^{-6} T m/A, the permeability of free space) and r is the distance from the wire.

It is also known that if a wire carrying a current I is itself in an externally-produced magnetic field **B**, then the wire will experience a force, $\mathbf{F} = I\mathbf{L} \times \mathbf{B}$, where **L** is the vector whose magnitude is the length L of the wire and whose direction is the same as the direction of the current in the wire. The magnitude of this magnetic force is given by

$$F = ILB \sin \theta$$

Equation 2

where θ is the angle between **L** and **B** and the direction of the force is given by a separate Right Hand Rule.

A researcher works with the apparatus shown below in Figure 1. The circuit contains a voltage source and a resistor, and a portion (denoted XY, with a length of 4 meters) of one of the wires is situated in an externally-produced magnetic field, B_{ext}. The wires lie in the plane of the page, and $\mathbf{B}_{ext}$ is directed perpendicularly into the plane of the page.

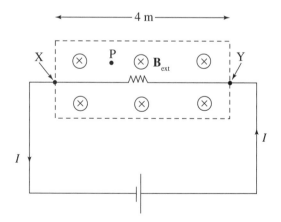

Figure 1

1. The direction of the force exerted on the wire by the field is:

   A. parallel to the wire and perpendicular to the field lines.
   B. parallel to the wire and parallel to the field lines.
   C. perpendicular to the wire and parallel to the field lines.
   D. perpendicular to the wire and perpendicular to the field lines.

2. The magnetic field at Point P created by the current in the wire is:

   A. parallel to $\mathbf{B}_{ext}$.
   B. antiparallel to $\mathbf{B}_{ext}$.
   C. perpendicular to $\mathbf{B}_{ext}$ and parallel to the wire.
   D. perpendicular to both $\mathbf{B}_{ext}$ and the wire.

3. If the current within a wire is 6.28 A, what is the magnitude (in teslas) of the magnetic field created by the current at a point 50 cm from the wire?

   A. $\frac{1}{2}\mu_0$
   B. μ_0
   C. $2\mu_0$
   D. $4\mu_0$

4. Assume that the potential difference between Points X and Y is 9 V, that the combined resistance of the Wire XY and resistor is 3 Ω, and that the magnitude of the external field $\mathbf{B}_{ext}$ is 0.5 T. What is the strength of the magnetic force exerted on wire XY?

   A. 6 N
   B. 9 N
   C. 12 N
   D. 24 N

5. Assume that the current in Wire XY is 12 A and that the magnitude of the external magnetic field is 2 T. If the wire were moved so that is was parallel to the external field, then it would experience a magnetic force of:

   A. 0 N.
   B. 48 N.
   C. 96 N.
   D. 192 N.

6. If the combined resistance of Wire XY and the resistor were 15 Ω, and the power dissipated from one end of the wire to the other is 60 W, what would be the current within the wire?

   A. 0.5 A
   B. 1 A
   C. 2 A
   D. 4 A

Passage 33 (Questions 1-8)

The apparatus depicted in Figure 1 consists of two long parallel wires suspended from light insulating threads.

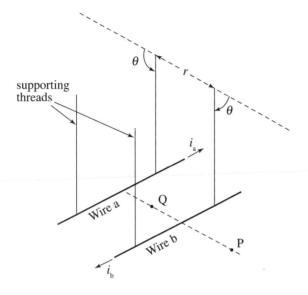

Figure 1

The current in each wire creates a magnetic field whose strength at a point a distance r from the wire is given by

$$B = \frac{\mu_0 i}{2\pi r}$$

Equation 1

where i is the current in the wire and μ_0 is a constant known as the permeability of free space.

A charged particle traveling through a magnetic field experiences a magnetic force. In particular, the electrons moving through one current-carrying wire are exposed to the magnetic field produced by another current-carrying wire. If the wires are separated by a distance r, then each wire will experience a force per unit length proportional to i_a and i_b:

$$\frac{F}{L} = \frac{\mu_0 i_a i_b}{2\pi r}$$

Equation 2

If the currents in the wires flow in the same direction, then the force **F** will tend to draw the wires together; this would cause each of the angles marked θ in Figure 1 to be greater than 90°. On the other hand, if the currents in the wires flow in opposite directions, the force **F** will tend to push the wires apart, thereby causing each of the angles marked θ in Figure 1 to be smaller than 90°.

1. Among the following graphs, which one best depicts the possible values of i_a and i_b for which both the distance between the two wires and the force between them will remain constant?

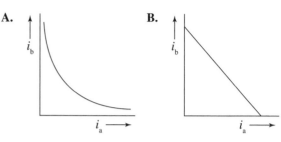

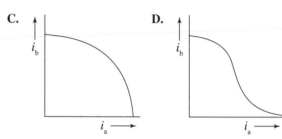

2. Assume for purposes of this question that the two wires depicted in Figure 1 each carry the same current, i. An error in measuring which one of the following quantities would have the greatest effect on the accuracy of prediction for the attractive or repulsive force, F, on each wire?

   A. μ_0
   B. i
   C. π
   D. r

3. If all other experimental factors are held constant, doubling the magnitude of current in either of the wires would:

   A. halve the attractive or repulsive force on each wire.
   B. double the attractive or repulsive force on each wire.
   C. quadruple the attractive or repulsive force on each wire.
   D. have no effect on the attractive or repulsive force on each wire.

4. Suppose that Wires a and b carry current of equal magnitude in opposite directions. If B is the magnitude of the magnetic field created by Wire a at Point Q (which lies within the plane defined by the wires and is equidistant from each wire), what is the magnitude of the net magnetic field at Point Q due to both wires?

   A. 0
   B. $B/2$
   C. B
   D. $2B$

5. If Point P is 1 m from Wire b and i_b is 3.1 A, then the magnitude and direction of the magnetic field due to Wire b at Point P would be approximately:

   A. $\frac{1}{2}\mu_0$ T, downward.
   B. $\frac{1}{2}\mu_0$ T, upward.
   C. $2\mu_0$ T, downward.
   D. $2\mu_0$ T, upward.

6. If one of the two wires depicted in Figure 1 carries a current of 10 A and the potential difference between the ends of the wire is 5 V, what is the effective resistance between the ends of the wire?

   A. $0.5\ \Omega$
   B. $2.5\ \Omega$
   C. $20\ \Omega$
   D. $50\ \Omega$

7. If the two wires depicted in Figure 1 dissipate energy at the rate of 100 W, how long will it take for the apparatus to release 1.5 kJ of energy?

   A. 0.067 sec
   B. 1.5 sec
   C. 15 sec
   D. 67 sec

8. The definition of the ampere reads as follows: "One ampere is that current which, if present in each of two parallel wires of infinite length and one meter apart in empty space, causes each wire to experience a force of exactly 2×10^{-7} newtons per meter of length." What then is the numerical value of μ_0?

   A. $\frac{1}{2}\pi \times 10^{-7}$ N/A²
   B. $\pi \times 10^{-7}$ N/A²
   C. $2\pi \times 10^{-7}$ N/A²
   D. $4\pi \times 10^{-7}$ N/A²

Passage 34 (Questions 1-7)

The circuit below contains a battery, a capacitor, and two resistor networks. Each component is wired in series with a switch that when closed connects that component to the rest of the circuit. Consider the schematic diagram below.

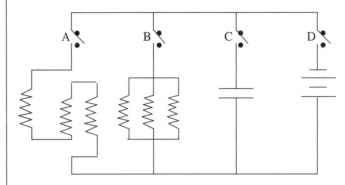

Figure 1

Each of the resistors shown has a resistance of 2 ohms. The capacitor has a capacitance of 0.5 F. The battery generates a potential difference of 10 V across its terminals. Unless otherwise specified, assume that the resistance of all other components, including the wire used, is negligible.

An experiment was performed to investigate how a capacitor discharges. Switches C and D were closed. Later, after the capacitor had sufficient time to fully charge, Switch D was then opened and Switch A was closed. The potential difference between the plates of the capacitor and the current flowing through the resistors were periodically measured. The results are listed in Table 1.

Time (s)	Potential Difference (V)	Current (A)
0	10.0	1.67
1	7.2	1.20
2	5.2	0.87
3	3.7	0.62

Table 1

Notes: Since the charge of an electron is -1.6×10^{-19} C, it takes 6.25×10^{18} electrons to give a total charge magnitude of one coulomb. Unless otherwise specified, assume that a switch in Figure 1 is open.

1. The electric field is measured at a distance r from a charged particle with charge q and found to be E. How strong will the field be at a distance $4r$ from the charge?

    A. $\frac{1}{16}E$
    B. $\frac{1}{8}E$
    C. $8E$
    D. $16E$

2. Which one of the following graphs best represents the dependence of stored charge on time as a capacitor discharges?

    A. 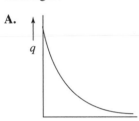   B.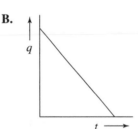

    C. 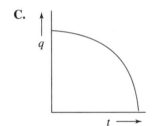   D.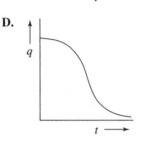

3. If Switches A and D are closed, what is the current in the circuit?

    A. 1.0 A
    B. 1.7 A
    C. 5.0 A
    D. 15.0 A

4. A large reduction in the temperature of the resistors would increase current in the circuit because:

    A. heat causes the components to expand.
    B. the resistance of most substances increases with temperature.
    C. the components give off energy in the form of heat.
    D. the conductance of most substances increases with temperature.

5. Switches B and D are closed. If the number of resistors connected in parallel were doubled, the rate at which energy was consumed by the resistors would:

    A. decrease by a factor of 2.
    B. remain the same.
    C. increase by a factor of 2.
    D. increase by a factor of 4.

6. A potential difference of 10 V is present between the plates of a capacitor. How much work must be done to move 6.25×10^{18} electrons from the positive plate to the negative plate?

    A. 5 J
    B. 10 J
    C. 20 J
    D. 40 J

7. Which of the following diagrams best represents the electric field present between the plates of a capacitor when the top and the bottom plates are positively and negatively charged, respectively?

    A. 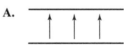   B.

    C.    D.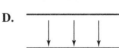

Passage 35 (Questions 1-6)

The most basic electric circuit consists of a source of emf (a battery) and a resistor. A more complicated circuit—such as that used in a cardiac pacemaker, for example—also contains a capacitor. Figure 1 shows an example of such an "RC circuit," with resistors of resistances R_1 and R_2, an air capacitor of capacitance C, an ideal battery of voltage V, and three switches (S_1, S_2, S_3). The resistance of the connecting wires is negligible.

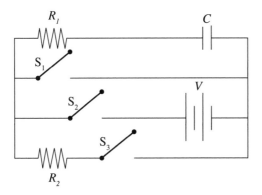

Figure 1 An RC circuit

A student performs the following sequence of steps with the circuit shown above in a physics lab experiment. Initially all three switches are open, and there is no charge on the capacitor.

Step 1

Switch S_2 is closed, and the current is measured to be $i_0 = V/R_1$. However, the current immediately begins to decrease, because as this current deposits charge on the capacitor, it becomes increasingly more difficult to deposit more. The value of the time-varying current is given by a decaying exponential:

$$i = i_0 e^{-t/(R_1 C)}$$

Equation 1

where i_0 is the initial current. The expression $R_1 C$ is called the *time constant*, and it determines how rapidly the exponential term decays. While the current decreases, the charge on the capacitor builds up according to the following equation, whose graph is shown in Figure 2:

$$q = CV[1 - e^{-t/(R_1 C)}]$$

Equation 2

After a duration much longer than the time constant has elapsed, the charging current is essentially zero, and the capacitor is fully charged.

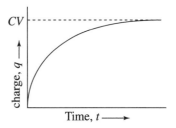

Figure 2 The graph of Equation 2

Step 2

Then switch S_2 is opened and switch S_1 is closed. This allows the capacitor to discharge. The equation for the amount of current during discharge also obeys Equation 1, but the charge on the capacitor decreases according to the following equation:

$$q = q_0 e^{-t/(R_1 C)}$$

Equation 3

1. What are the units of the product of capacitance and resistance?

    A. Amps
    B. Volts
    C. Seconds
    D. Watts

2. Which one of the following equations best describes the voltage across the plates of the capacitor during the charging process described in Step 1?

    A. $v = Ve^{-t/(R_1 C)}$
    B. $v = V[1 - e^{t/(R_1 C)}]$
    C. $v = Ve^{t/(R_1 C)}$
    D. $v = V[1 - e^{-t/(R_1 C)}]$

3. At any time t, the slope of the graph shown in Figure 2 is equal to the instantaneous

    A. voltage across the capacitor.
    B. electrical potential energy stored in the capacitor.
    C. power supplied by the battery.
    D. current through resistor R_1.

4. For which of the following combinations of R_1 and C would the capacitor in Step 2 have discharged most rapidly?

    A. $R_1 = 10\ \Omega,\ C = 2\ \mu F$
    B. $R_1 = 20\ \Omega,\ C = 3\ \mu F$
    C. $R_1 = 30\ \Omega,\ C = 2\ \mu F$
    D. $R_1 = 40\ \Omega,\ C = 2\ \mu F$

5. Suppose that the experiment was repeated but with the capacitor in the circuit fitted with a solid dielectric prior to Step 1. Compared to the experiment described in the passage, the student would have observed

    A. less potential energy stored in the capacitor at the end of Step 1.
    B. a slower build up of charge during Step 1.
    C. a more rapid decrease in current during Step 1.
    D. a lower voltage across the capacitor at the end of Step 1.

6. If switch S_3 were closed instead of S_1 at the beginning of Step 2, what would have been the initial current?

    A. $\dfrac{q_0}{(R_1 + R_2)C}$

    B. $\dfrac{q_0}{R_1 C} - \dfrac{q_0}{R_2 C}$

    C. $\dfrac{q_0}{C}\left(\dfrac{1}{R_1} + \dfrac{1}{R_2}\right)$

    D. $\dfrac{q_0}{\left(\dfrac{1}{R_1} + \dfrac{1}{R_2}\right)C}$

Passage 36 (Questions 1-4)

A 9 V battery (with negligible internal resistance) drives a simple circuit containing three identical 1 Ω resistors, two of which are placed in parallel as shown.

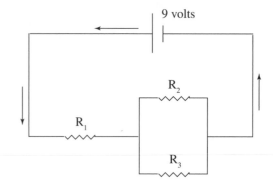

1. Find the current through R_1.

    A. 1.5 amps
    B. 3.0 amps
    C. 4.5 amps
    D. 6.0 amps

2. If V_2 is the voltage drop across R_2, and V_3 is voltage drop across R_3, then which of the following is true?

    A. $V_2 = 2V_3$
    B. $V_3 = 2V_2$
    C. $V_2 = V_3$
    D. $V_2 + V_3 = 9$

3. Find the current through R_2.

    A. 1.5 amps
    B. 3.0 amps
    C. 4.5 amps
    D. 6.0 amps

4. Find the heat energy dissipated in 4 seconds by R_3.

    A. 12 joules
    B. 24 joules
    C. 36 joules
    D. 144 joules

Passage 37 (Questions 1-5)

Consider the following circuit, containing two seats of electromotive force: a 9 V battery and a 12 V battery (each with negligible internal resistance). Two resistors, $R_1 = 1\ \Omega$ and $R_2 = 2\ \Omega$, are placed within the circuit as shown.

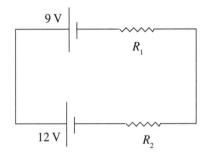

1. Find the current flowing through R_1.

    A. 0 amps
    B. 1 amp
    C. 3 amps
    D. 4 amps

2. If I_1 is the current through R_1, and I_2 is the current through R_2, then which of the following is true?

    A. $I_1 = I_2$
    B. $I_1 = 2I_2$
    C. $I_2 = 2I_1$
    D. $I_1 + I_2 = 3$

3. How much power is dissipated as heat by R_2?

    A. 1 watt
    B. 2 watts
    C. 4 watts
    D. 12 watts

4. How much energy is provided by the 12-volt battery in 3 seconds?

    A. 9 joules
    B. 12 joules
    C. 27 joules
    D. 36 joules

5. If the 9 V battery has an internal resistance of 10 mΩ Ω and has a terminal resistance of 9 V in this circuit, what is the emf of the battery?

    A. 8.99 V
    B. 9.00 V
    C. 9.01 V
    D. 9.10 V

Passage 38 (Questions 1-4)

The source of electromotive force in the following circuit is provided by a direct-current generator (denoted G), The effectively providing an 18 V potential difference between its terminals. The resistor R_1 is rated at 3 Ω, and R_2 is 6 Ω.

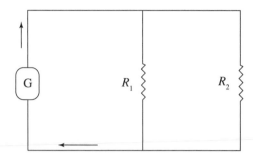

1. Find the current through R_1, the 3 Ω resistor.

   A. 2 amps
   B. 3 amps
   C. 6 amps
   D. 9 amps

2. Find the current through R_2, the 6 Ω resistor.

   A. 2 amps
   B. 3 amps
   C. 6 amps
   D. 9 amps

3. Let V_1 be the voltage drop across R_1 and let V_2 be the voltage drop across R_2. Which of the following statements is true?

   A. $V_1 = 2V_2$
   B. $V_1 = V_2$
   C. $V_2 = 2V_1$
   D. $V_2 = 4V_1$

4. If P_1 is the power dissipated by R_1, and P_2 is the power dissipated by R_2, then which of the following is true?

   A. $P_1 = 2P_2$
   B. $P_1 = P_2$
   C. $P_2 = 2P_1$
   D. $P_2 = 4P_1$

Passage 39 (Questions 1-8)

Figure 1 below shows a 20 cm × 20 cm square loop of wire, carrying a current $I = 10$ amps (A), in a uniform magnetic field **B** pointing to the right with magnitude $B = 0.5$ tesla (T). The magnetic forces on the left side (PQ) and right side (RS) of the loop each have magnitude

$$F = ILB$$

Equation 1

The force F will be in newtons when the current is expressed in amperes, the length of the side, L, is in meters, and the field strength, B, is in teslas. The torque on the loop has magnitude

$$\tau = IAB \sin \theta$$

Equation 2

where A is the area of the loop and θ is the angle between the magnetic field and a vector normal to the plane of the loop.

No matter how the loop is oriented in the field, the net force on the loop is zero because the forces on the left and right sides of the loop point in opposite directions and are of the same magnitude. This result, as well as the formula given above for the torque τ, apply for a loop of wire of any shape.

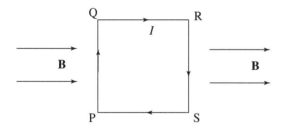

Figure 1

1. Which one of the following correctly describes the SI unit of magnetic field, the tesla?

    A. 1 tesla = 1 N·A/m
    B. 1 tesla = 1 N·m/A
    C. 1 tesla = 1 N/(A·m)
    D. 1 tesla = 1 N·m²/A

2. What is the magnitude of the torque on the loop PQRS in Figure 1?

    A. 0 N·m
    B. 0.1 N·m
    C. 0.2 N·m
    D. 2×10^3 N·m

3. What is the magnitude of the magnetic force on wire QR?

    A. 0 N
    B. 1 N
    C. 10 N
    D. 100 N

4. What is the direction of the force on wire PQ?

    A. Into the plane of the loop
    B. Out of the plane of the loop
    C. To the left, perpendicular to PQ
    D. To the right, perpendicular to PQ

5. If the loop were rotated so that the magnetic field were perpendicular to the plane of the wire, what would then be the torque on the loop?

    A. 0 N·m
    B. 0.1 N·m
    C. 0.2 N·m
    D. 2×10^3 N·m

6. If a circular loop of wire with a 10 A current were suspended from a thread and a uniform 1.0 T magnetic field pointing to the right were turned on, the center of mass of the loop would:

    A. move to the right.
    B. move to the left.
    C. execute periodic motion.
    D. remain fixed.

7. Suppose the loop in the figure were rotated 180° to the following configuration:

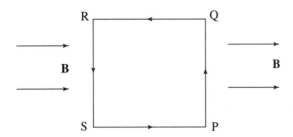

Compared to the torque in the original orientation in Figure 1, the torque on the loop would now be:

A. zero.
B. unchanged in magnitude and direction.
C. unchanged in magnitude but pointing in the opposite direction.
D. changed in both magnitude and direction.

8. If the magnetic field in Figure 1 were pointing upward rather than to the right, then:

A. there would be no magnetic forces on the loop.
B. the torque would have the same magnitude as before.
C. the flow of current would be impeded by the magnetic forces.
D. there would be no torque on the loop.

Passage 40 (Questions 1-6)

One of the fundamental roles of a capacitor in a circuit is to store electrical potential energy. If C is the capacitance [equal to Q/V, where Q is the magnitude of charge on each plate, and V is the resulting potential difference (voltage)], then the quantity of energy stored is given by the equation

$$PE = \tfrac{1}{2}CV^2$$

Capacitance is measured in farads, where 1 farad (F) = 1 C/V. Standard capacitors can be combined in an electrical circuit in order to provide whatever particular capacitance is desired. One method of combining capacitors is placing them in series (that is, one after the other), and another is placing them in parallel (that is, side by side). Whenever a group of capacitors is placed either in series or in parallel, we can calculate the equivalent capacitance, C_{eq}, of the combination.

Figure 1 below illustrates three capacitors, C_1, C_2, and C_3, in series:

Figure 1   Capacitors in series

Capacitors in series are characterized by the fact that the charge magnitudes on them are identical. The capacitance equivalent to a group in series is calculated by adding the reciprocals of the individual capacitances, then taking the reciprocal of that sum. That is, for the series combination in Figure 1, the equivalent capacitance would be computed from the following equation:

$$\frac{1}{C_{eq}} = \frac{1}{C_1} + \frac{1}{C_2} + \frac{1}{C_3}$$

Equation 1

Figure 2 illustrates three capacitors in parallel:

Figure 2   Capacitors in parallel

Capacitors in parallel are characterized by the fact that the voltages across them are identical. The capacitance equivalent to a group in parallel is calculated by simply forming the sum of the individual capacitances. That is, for the parallel combination in Figure 2, the equivalent capacitance would be:

$$C_{eq} = C_1 + C_2 + C_3$$

Equation 2

1. Assume that in Figure 1, $C_1 = 8$ nF, $C_2 = 4$ nF, and $C_3 = 8$ nF. Find C_{eq} for this combination.

   A. 0.2 nF
   B. 0.5 nF
   C. 2 nF
   D. 20 nF

2. Assume that in Figure 2, $C_1 = 2$ μF, $C_2 = 4$ μF, and $C_3 = 4$ μF. If the charge on capacitor C_1 is $Q_1 = 10$ μC, what is the charge on capacitor C_2?

   A. 5 μC
   B. 10 μC
   C. 20 μC
   D. Cannot be determined from the information given

3. During charging, four microcoulombs of negative charge are transferred from one plate of an 8 μF capacitor to the other plate. How much work was done by the electric field during this charging process?

   A. −4 μJ
   B. −1 μJ
   C. 1 μJ
   D. 4 μJ

4. Given two capacitors C_1 and C_2 in series, their equivalent capacitance is:

   A. always less than either C_1 or C_2.
   B. always in between C_1 and C_2.
   C. always greater than either C_1 or C_2.
   D. None of the above is necessarily true.

5. Using three 2 μF capacitors, which one of the following combinations yields an equivalent capacitance of 3 μF?

   A.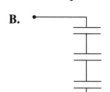

   B.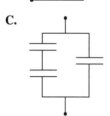

   C.

   D.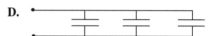

6. With Switch S open, an external voltage source (not shown) is connected between points a and b and charges capacitor C_1 so that $V_{ab} = 12$ V. The voltage source is then disconnected. The capacitances of the capacitors shown are $C_1 = 2$ mF and $C_2 = 4$ mF.

   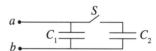

   After the switch S is closed, what will then be the common voltage across each of these parallel capacitors (when electrostatic conditions are re-established)?

   A. 2 V
   B. 3 V
   C. 4 V
   D. 6 V

Passage 41 (Questions 1-7)
ADVANCED PASSAGE

Two experiments are performed with a 2 µF parallel-plate capacitor, a 12 V battery, and an insulator with dielectric constant equal to 4 whose dimensions will allow it to just fit between the plates of the capacitor.

Initial set-up procedure:

With empty space between the plates, the battery is used to charge the capacitor so that the potential difference between the two plates is the same as the rating of the battery (12 V). The charge on the plates is then calculated, and the uniform electric field between the plates is measured.

Experiment #1:

When the set-up procedure is completed and with the battery *still connected,* the insulator is inserted between the plates of the capacitor. Various measurements are taken and recorded, the insulator is removed, and the capacitor is discharged.

Experiment #2:

When the initial set-up procedure is repeated and completed, the battery is *disconnected* from the plates, and the insulator is then inserted between the plates. Measurements are taken and recorded, the insulator is removed, and the capacitor is discharged.

1. Find the magnitude of the charge on each plate at the end of the set-up procedure.

    A. 1.6×10^{-7} coulomb
    B. 2.4×10^{-5} coulomb
    C. 1.4×10^{-4} coulomb
    D. 6.0×10^{6} coulomb

2. If Q is the magnitude of the charge on each plate at the end of the set-up procedure, what is the magnitude of the charge after the insertion of the dielectric in Experiment #1?

    A. $Q/4$
    B. Q
    C. $4Q$
    D. $8Q$

3. Let E be the strength of the electric field between the plates at the end of the set-up procedure, and let E_1 be the strength of the field after the insertion of the dielectric in Experiment #1. How does E_1 compare to E?

    A. $E_1 = E$
    B. $E_1 = 2E$
    C. $E_1 = 4E$
    D. $E_1 = 16E$

4. How much work is required to insert the dielectric in Experiment #1?

    A. 6.0×10^{-6} joule
    B. 1.2×10^{-5} joule
    C. 9.6×10^{-5} joule
    D. 4.3×10^{-4} joule

5. If Q is the magnitude of the charge on each plate at the end of the set-up procedure, what is the magnitude of the charge after the insertion of the dielectric in Experiment #2?

    A. $Q/4$
    B. Q
    C. $4Q$
    D. $8Q$

6. Let E be the strength of the electric field between the plates at the end of the set-up procedure, and let E_2 be the strength of the field after the insertion of the dielectric in Experiment #2. How does E_2 compare to E?

    A. $E_2 = E/16$
    B. $E_2 = E/4$
    C. $E_2 = E/2$
    D. $E_2 = E$

7. How has the stored electrical potential energy of the capacitor changed as a result of inserting the dielectric in Experiment #2?

    A. It decreases to 1/4 of the previous value.
    B. It decreases to 3/4 of the previous value.
    C. It increases to 4/3 of the previous value.
    D. It increases to 4 of the previous value.

Passage 42 (Questions 1-8)
ADVANCED PASSAGE

The free electrons in a copper wire at room temperature are in constant thermal motion. They move in random directions and frequently "collide" with flaws in the crystalline lattice structure of copper atoms that makes up the metal. Such flaws are always present in crystalline solids. The flaws are responsible for the phenomenon of resistance to electric current because they impede the progress of electrons moving through a wire. After a collision, an electron could be moving in any direction regardless of its initial momentum. Thus, the collisions randomize the electron motion.

If the ends of a wire are attached to a source of potential difference, an electric field is created in the wire along its length. The resulting force causes electrons to accelerate in a direction opposite to that of the field until they collide with a flaw in the lattice. After the collision, the electron moves off in a random direction and is again influenced by the electric field until the next collision.

The extra speed of the electrons due to the field is, in ordinary circuits, much smaller than their thermal speed. So an ordinary potential difference causes only a slight systematic drift in a direction opposite to the field direction, superimposed on the random thermal motion. Under these conditions, the magnitude of the drift velocity is directly proportional to the field strength, E, and Ohm's law holds.

1. If the drift velocity of the electrons doubles, then the value of the current, I, in coulombs per second:

   A. is reduced by a factor of 2.
   B. is increased by a factor of 2.
   C. is unchanged.
   D. may increase or decrease depending on the resistance.

2. If the temperature of a piece of copper is lowered, the average random velocity of the free electrons will:

   A. increase.
   B. decrease.
   C. remain the same.
   D. be reduced to zero.

3. Which diagram best represents the velocities of electrons in a copper wire in which the electric field points to the right?

   A.   B.

   C.   D.

4. Ohm's law might NOT be obeyed if:

   A. the temperature of the wire were kept constant.
   B. there were a large number of flaws in the crystalline lattice of the wire.
   C. the temperature of the wire were very high.
   D. the electric field in the wire were very large.

5. An electron and a proton are very far apart, initially held in place in a uniform electric field. A few seconds after the particles are released, their velocities will be:

   A. equal in magnitude and direction.
   B. equal in magnitude but opposite in direction.
   C. unequal in magnitude but in the same direction.
   D. unequal in magnitude and opposite in direction.

6. It is observed that high temperatures cause the resistance of metals to increase. A possible explanation for this phenomenon is that:

   A. higher temperatures produce more flaws in the metal's lattice structure.
   B. higher temperature electrons move more slowly.
   C. high temperatures cause Ohm's law to fail.
   D. high temperatures reduce the number of free electrons.

7. The terminals of a battery are connected to two points on a circular loop of copper wire and a current flows. The battery is then removed. The current will:

A. continue to flow steadily because the loop is a complete circuit.
B. decrease and then remain constant.
C. decrease to zero because of the flaws in the copper lattice.
D. drop immediately to zero because electrons cannot move without an applied electric field.

8. The statement of Ohm's law described in the passage allow one to conclude that:

A. resistance is directly proportional to current.
B. drift velocity is directly proportional to resistance.
C. electric field is inversely proportional to the square of the distance between two point charges.
D. electric field is directly proportional to potential difference.

Passage 43 (Questions 1-7)

A galvanometer is a sensitive electromechanical device at the core of many instruments such as ammeters, which measure current, and voltmeters, which measure voltage. As shown in Figure 1, a galvanometer consists of two magnetic poles shaped to produce a radial magnetic field, a coil consisting of multiple rectangular loops of fine wire, a spring that produces a restoring force that is proportional to angular deflection, and a needle to indicate the angular deflection against a scale.

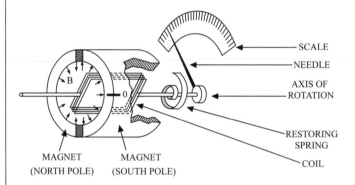

Within a deflection of ±60 degrees from the *zero position*, the plane of the galvanometer coil is always parallel to the external magnetic field as shown in Figure 1. Current flowing through the loops of the coil creates a magnetic torque that rotates the coil around an axis perpendicular to the magnetic field. The total magnetic torque increases proportionally with the number of loops. The magnitude of this magnetic torque acting at the center of the coil is given by the following expression:

$$\tau_B = NIAB$$

Equation 1

in which N is the number of loops of wire, I is the current, A is the area of the coil, and B is the external magnetic field strength at the sides of the coil parallel to the axis of rotation. The spring of the galvanometer produces a restoring torque that opposes the rotation of the coil and increases with the amount of deflection until the system reaches equilibrium.

A voltmeter measures the voltage between its input terminals, as shown in Figure 2, and can be considered to be an ideal voltage measurement device with infinite resistance that is in parallel with a very large resistance, R_{in}. An ammeter measures the current that passes through it, as shown in Figure 3, and can be considered to be an ideal current measurement device with zero resistance that is in series with a very small resistance, R_{in}. For both voltmeters and ammeters, this resistance R_{in} is called the *input* resistance.

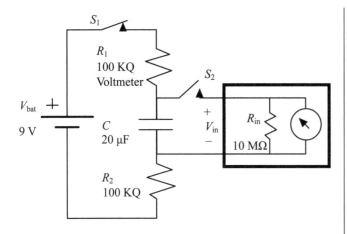

Figure 2

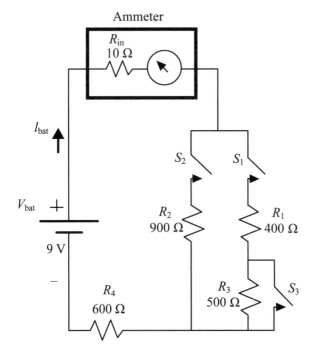

Figure 3

1. The needle of a well designed galvanometer has an angular deflection that is proportional to the current through the coil. The angular deflection of the needle (θ) divided by the coil current (I) that produces that deflection is the sensitivity, given by the expression: *Sensitivity* $= \theta/I$. Which of the following changes does NOT increase the sensitivity of the galvanometer?

   I. Increasing the number of loops in the coil
   II. Increasing the spring constant of the restoring spring
   III. Increasing the length of the indicator needle

   A. I only
   B. II only
   C. I and II only
   D. II and III only

2. The coil shown in Figure 1 has four sides each 2.0 cm long, and consists of 100 loops. A 0.1 mA current flows through the loops of the coil. The magnitude of the magnetic field is 0.1 T at a radius of 1.0 cm from the axis of rotation. What is the magnetic torque exerted on the loop?

   A. 4×10^{-9} N·m
   B. 2×10^{-7} N·m
   C. 4×10^{-7} N·m
   D. 8×10^{-7} N·m

3. When only switch S_2 is closed in the circuit of Figure 3, the power dissipated by resistor R_4 is:

   A. 1/3 the power dissipated by resistor R_2
   B. 1/2 the power dissipated by resistor R_2
   C. 2/3 the power dissipated by resistor R_2
   D. 3/2 the power dissipated by resistor R_2

4. In the circuit of Figure 3, what current does the ammeter measure after switch S_1 is closed, with S_2 and S_3 left open?

   A. 0.0 mA
   B. 6.0 mA
   C. 8.6 mA
   D. 15.0 mA

5. Why should an ammeter have a small resistance and a voltmeter have a large resistance?

   A. Small resistance in an ammeter causes negligible change in current when the ammeter is inserted in a circuit, and large resistance in a voltmeter causes negligible change in voltage when the voltmeter is connected across a circuit.

   B. Small resistance in an ammeter causes a large change in current when the ammeter is inserted in a circuit, and a large resistance in a voltmeter causes negligible change in voltage when the voltmeter is connected across a circuit.

   C. Small resistance in an ammeter causes negligible change in current when the ammeter is inserted in a circuit, and large resistance in a voltmeter causes large change in voltage when the voltmeter is connected across a circuit.

   D. Small resistance in an ammeter causes large change in current when the ammeter is inserted in a circuit, and a large resistance in a voltmeter causes large change in voltage when the voltmeter is connected across a circuit.

6. The magnitude of the torque exerted by the spring of the galvanometer is given by the expression $\tau = \kappa\theta$, in which κ is a constant with units of N-m/degree and θ is the angular deflection in degrees of the coil from the *zero position*. Which of the following statements is true when sufficient current flows through the coil to deflect it until it comes to rest at an angle of 30 degrees from the *zero position*?

   A. Magnetic torque rotates the coil and friction in the galvanometer mechanism stops the movement at the deflection of 30 degrees.

   B. Torque caused by electric force rotates the coil and torque exerted by the spring at the deflection of 30 degrees is equal and opposite to the torque due to the electric force.

   C. Magnetic torque rotates the coil and torque exerted by the spring at the deflection of 30 degrees is equal and opposite to the magnetic torque.

   D. Magnetic torque on the coil varies with θ and is less at the deflection of 30 degrees than at the *zero position*.

7. In a test using the circuit of Figure 2, switch S_2 is open while S_1 has been closed for a long time to allow capacitor C to charge fully. Then S_2 closes to connect the voltmeter across capacitor C, while S_1 remains closed. Which of the following graphs best illustrates the voltmeter measurement, V_{in}, in the time after S_2 has closed?

   A.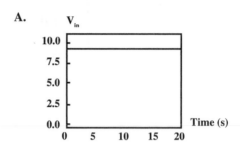

   B.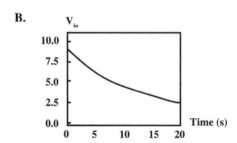

   C.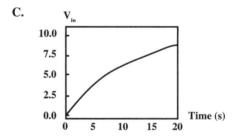

   D.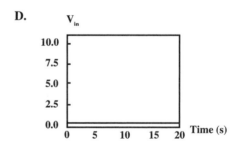

Passage 44 (Questions 1-6)

A particular spring is oriented horizontally. At one end, it is fixed to a wall; at the other, it is attached to a roller that slides on a frictionless surface. The spring is 4 m in length when no force is exerted on it, and its spring constant is 10 N/m.

Figure 1 below shows the kinetic energy possessed by this system when a roller with a mass of 20 kg is pulled to an initial displacement of 28 cm from the zero-force position and released from rest.

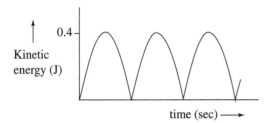

Figure 1

1. If the roller had first been pulled a distance of 2 m from the equilibrium point and then released, what would have been the approximate speed of the roller as it passed through the equilibrium position?

    A. 1 m/s
    B. 1.4 m/s
    C. 2 m/s
    D. 2.8 m/s

2. According to the graph, what is the speed of the roller when its kinetic energy is at a maximum?

    A. 0.1 m/s
    B. 0.2 m/s
    C. 0.4 m/s
    D. 0.8 m/s

3. According to the graph, what is the total mechanical energy possessed by the roller at any instant in time?

    A. 0.2 J
    B. 0.4 J
    C. 0.8 J
    D. 1.6 J

4. Which of the following best describes how the potential energy curve would differ from the kinetic energy curve shown in Figure 1?

    A. It would be identical.
    B. It would be inverted.
    C. Its maximum energy value would be doubled.
    D. Its maximum energy value would be halved.

5. How much force must be exerted on the spring in order to stretch it to a distance of 50 cm from its rest position?

    A. 5 N
    B. 10 N
    C. 50 N
    D. 100 N

6. How much potential energy is contained in the spring when it is compressed to a distance of 2 m from its rest position?

    A. 5 J
    B. 10 J
    C. 20 J
    D. 40 J

_____

Passage 45 (Questions 1-5)

Simple harmonic motion involves the oscillation of an object about an equilibrium point with a restoring force directed toward that point such that at each moment, the magnitude of the restoring force is proportional to the object's displacement from equilibrium. Therefore, the force responsible for maintaining simple harmonic motion obeys Hooke's law: $F = -kx$, where F = the restoring force, k = the force constant, and x = the displacement from equilibrium.

The apparatus shown in Figure 1 consists of two pendulums, 1 and 2, each consisting of a massless rod and identical bobs. The pendulums are connected by a light spring which can transfer energy between them. The length of each pendulum is L, and the spring is attached at a point a distance R below the suspension point on each of the pendulum rods. The distance between the fixed suspension points is d.

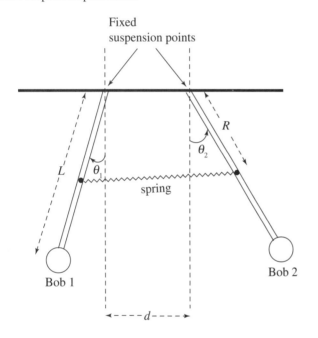

Figure 1

A researcher performs the following experiment. Pendulum 1 is raised to form an angle θ_1 with the vertical while Pendulum 2 is held at its vertical, equilibrium position. Then, both pendulums are released, and the resulting oscillations are depicted in Figure 2. To simplify the analysis, all forces of friction are to be ignored.

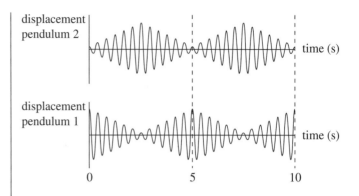

Figure 2

1. Once the apparatus has been set into motion, energy will be repeatedly converted among which of the following forms?

   A. Kinetic, gravitational potential, and elastic potential
   B. Kinetic, gravitational potential, and heat
   C. Kinetic, elastic potential, and heat
   D. Elastic potential, gravitational potential, and heat

2. How much time elapses between the moment when Pendulum 1 has maximum kinetic energy and the moment when Pendulum 2 next has maximum kinetic energy?

   A. 2.5 sec
   B. 5 sec
   C. 7.5 sec
   D. 10 sec

3. Referring to the apparatus depicted in Figure 1, if the pendulums are pulled apart so that each makes an angle of θ_0 with the vertical, what will be the distance between the two pendulum bobs?

   A. $2L \sin \theta_0$
   B. $d + 2L \cos \theta_0$
   C. $d + 2L \sin \theta_0$
   D. $d + L \sin \theta_0 + L \cos \theta_0$

4. Assume that a spring with spring constant k is fixed at one end. If the spring is compressed to the point that it has potential energy of U, which one of the following expressions gives the distance by which the spring has been compressed?

A. $\dfrac{U}{2k}$

B. $\dfrac{2U}{k}$

C. $\sqrt{\dfrac{U}{2k}}$

D. $\sqrt{\dfrac{2U}{k}}$

5. With the *spring removed*, one of the pendulum bobs is pulled to a height of 0.2 m above its equilibrium position and released. What maximum speed will it attain?

A. 2 m/s
B. 4 m/s
C. 12 m/s
D. 20 m/s

Passage 46 (Questions 1-6)

It is known that the velocity at which a longitudinal wave will propagate through a given medium depends on the medium's density and its resistance to compression. An increase in density brings about a decrease in velocity, while an increase in resistance to compression produces an increase in velocity.

Two longitudinal waves, like two transverse waves, may propagate simultaneously through the same medium. At points at which the waves meet so that one is superimposed on the other, the waves are said to *interfere* with one another. At the point of interference, the waves "merge" into one, with the displacement equal to the sum of the individual displacements of the two original waves.

Two waves of equal frequency are said to be *in phase* if crests of one are synchronized with crests of the other. They are said to be 180° *out of phase* if crests of one are synchronized with troughs of the other. If two waves are in phase and of equal amplitude, interference between them produces an amplitude that is twice the amplitude of each individual wave, a phenomenon known as *completely constructive interference*. If two waves of equal amplitude and frequency are 180° out of phase, interference will produce an amplitude of zero; this is known as *total destructive interference*.

A thick wire 25 m in length is connected between two blocks constructed of very dense and rigid material. Thus, the two ends of the wire can be considered essentially fixed. The left-hand block can generate a wave in the wire at any desired frequency by causing movement in the part that connects it to the wire. Horizontal oscillations of the mechanism in the left-hand block create longitudinal waves, while tiny vertical oscillations create transverse waves. The density of the wire is 2000 kg/m³, longitudinal waves propagate through the wire at a speed of 2000 m/s, and transverse waves travel down the wire at a speed of 20 m/s.

1. What would be the length of a longitudinal wave if its frequency were 100 Hz?

A. 0.02 m
B. 0.2 m
C. 2 m
D. 20 m

2. If the wire has a cross-sectional area of 4×10^{-4} m², what is its mass?

    A. 10 kg
    B. 20 kg
    C. 40 kg
    D. 100 kg

3. The apparatus is set up to create longitudinal waves of a fixed frequency and amplitude. If the wire in the apparatus is replaced with one of lower density and identical resistance to compression, how would the waves produced by the new arrangement differ from those produced by the original apparatus?

    A. The new wavelength would be longer than the old wavelength.
    B. The new wavelength would be shorter than the old wavelength.
    C. The new frequency would be greater than the old frequency.
    D. The new velocity would be less than the old velocity.

4. What is the LOWEST frequency that can set up a standing wave on the given apparatus?

    A. 0.2 Hz
    B. 0.4 Hz
    C. 20 Hz
    D. 40 Hz

5. Two wave trains that are out of phase by only a small amount propagate through the same medium as shown below. Which of the following figures best represents the combined waveform?

    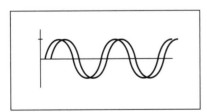

    A.

    B.

    C.

    D.

6. Suppose two longitudinal waves of identical frequencies propagate through the same medium and interfere. If Wave 1 has an amplitude of X, and Wave 2 has an amplitude of Y, where X is greater than Y, then which of the following gives the minimum and maximum values of the amplitude of the resulting waveform?

    A. Minimum = $X - Y$; maximum = $X + Y$
    B. Minimum = $X + Y$; maximum = $X - Y$
    C. Minimum = X/Y; maximum = XY
    D. Minimum = XY; maximum = X/Y

Passage 47 (Questions 1-9)

A simple pendulum consists of a ball of mass $m = 0.5$ kg attached to the end of a rod with length $L = 40$ cm and negligible mass. Its natural equilibrium position is vertical. The pendulum is pulled to the right so that the ball is at Position X, where the angle the rod makes with the vertical is 10°. Simple harmonic oscillations are then initiated by releasing the pendulum from rest. Position Y to the left of vertical is the mirror image of Position X to the right; that is, the angle the pendulum makes with the vertical when the ball is at Y also has magnitude 10°. The point where the pendulum is attached to the ceiling (the pivot point) is considered to be fixed, and air resistance is to be ignored.

The period of the pendulum is given by $T = 2\pi\sqrt{L/g}$. The following table of trigonometric function values is provided for the questions in this passage, although not all the listed values will necessarily be needed.

θ	$\sin \theta$	$\cos \theta$	$\tan \theta$
10°	0.174	0.985	0.176
20°	0.342	0.940	0.364

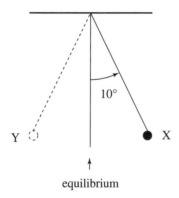

equilibrium

1. Compute the torque on the rod at Position X.

   A. 0.35 N·m
   B. 0.70 N·m
   C. 0.97 N·m
   D. 1.93 N·m

2. In terms of the amplitude angle θ, how much work is done by gravity as the ball moves from Position X to the equilibrium position?

   A. $mgL \sin \theta$
   B. $mgL \cos \theta$
   C. $mgL(1 - \sin \theta)$
   D. $mgL(1 - \cos \theta)$

3. If W is the amount of work done by gravity as the ball moves from Position X to equilibrium, find the speed v of the ball as it passes through the equilibrium position.

   A. $\dfrac{1}{2}\sqrt{\dfrac{W}{m}}$

   B. $\sqrt{\dfrac{W}{2m}}$

   C. $\sqrt{\dfrac{2W}{m}}$

   D. $2\sqrt{\dfrac{W}{m}}$

4. Let v be the speed of the ball (in m/s) as it passes through equilibrium, and let w be the weight of the ball (in N). When the ball is at the equilibrium position, calculate the tension in the rod.

   A. $w - [(5/2) \text{ kg/m}]v^2$
   B. $w - [(5/4) \text{ kg/m}]v^2$
   C. $w + [(5/4) \text{ kg/m}]v^2$
   D. $w + [(5/2) \text{ kg/m}]v^2$

5. How long does it take for the ball to travel from Position X to Position Y?

   A. 0.63 sec
   B. 1.27 sec
   C. 7.78 sec
   D. 15.5 sec

6. When the angle the pendulum makes with the vertical is θ, find the magnitude of the restoring force (that is, the force that brings the pendulum back to equilibrium and maintains the simple harmonic motion).

   A. mg
   B. $mg \sin \theta$
   C. $mg \cos \theta$
   D. $mg \tan \theta$

7. Let v be the speed of the ball as it passes through equilibrium. Let v' be the speed of the ball as it passes through equilibrium if the original maximum angle that the pendulum made with the vertical had been 20° instead of 10°. Which one of the following statements best compares v' and v?

   A. $v' = v\sqrt{2}$
   B. $v' = 2v$
   C. $v' = 2v\sqrt{2}$
   D. $v' = 4v$

8. Let f denote the frequency of the pendulum when released from Position X as described in the passage. If the original angle that the pendulum made with the vertical had instead been 20°, let the frequency of the oscillations be denoted f'. Which one of the following statements best compares f' and f?

   A. $f' = f$
   B. $f' = f\sqrt{2}$
   C. $f' = 2f$
   D. $f' = 4f$

9. If the length of the rod were increased by 21%, by how much would the period increase?

   A. 4.6%
   B. 10%
   C. 21%
   D. 44%

_____

Passage 48 (Questions 1-6)

Muscles consists of long, slender cylindrical cells called fibers which have a cross-sectional radius of about 20 μm. These are composed of finer long filaments called myofibrils which have a cross-sectional radius of about 1 μm. Myofibrils are composed of thick filaments of myosin and thin filaments of actin and other proteins that slide past each other. A single myofibril is capable of producing a tension T_m between its ends. This tension is translated into the contraction of the muscle.

Long before these facts were known about muscles, Galileo deduced some essential properties of the forces that muscles produce. In particular he noted that the strength of a muscle was proportional to its cross-sectional area. His reasoning depended on the idea that every filament of a muscle (he did not know of cells) must produce a given tension.

A human bicep can produce a maximum tension of approximately 3000 N for short periods of time. The bicep's cross-sectional radius is about 2 cm. A flea (mass = 1 mg) can jump to a height of about $h = 0.2$ m. The length of its leg is about 0.5 mm (assume that a flea jumps by fully contracting and then extending its leg).

1. A muscle can be modeled as a number of springs (the myofibrils) in parallel and in series. If n springs are in parallel, each with tension T, what is the total tension T_{total}?

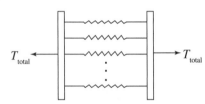

   A. nT
   B. $\sqrt{n} \cdot T$
   C. T
   D. T/n

2. If n springs are in series, each with tension T, what is the total tension T_{total}?

   A. nT
   B. $\sqrt{n} \cdot T$
   C. T
   D. T/n

3. What is the approximate tension (T_m) that a single myofibril can sustain?

   A. 3×10^{-12} N
   B. 4×10^{-10} N
   C. 7.5×10^{-6} N
   D. 1.5×10^{-1} N

4. What is the approximate energy expended in the jump of a flea?

   A. 5×10^{-9} J
   B. 2×10^{-6} J
   C. 2×10^{-3} J
   D. 5×10^{-1} J

5. What is the approximate force F_{leg} a flea exerts on the ground during a jump?

   A. 2×10^{-7} N
   B. 1×10^{-5} N
   C. 4×10^{-3} N
   D. It cannot be determined from the information given.

6. If a flea were enlarged by a linear factor of 100 (to about the size of a rat) but proportioned the same, approximately how high could it jump (lift its center of mass)?

   A. $100h$
   B. $10h$
   C. h
   D. $h/10$

Passage 49 (Questions 1-5)
ADVANCED PASSAGE

A pendulum clock is designed to keep accurate time at a normal room temperature of 20°C. The length of the pendulum (at this temperature) is $L = 25$ cm. The center of the rod (which is made of brass) is encircled by a 4-ohm resistor which is connected by light, flexible wire (of negligible resistance) to a 80-V source of emf. (See the diagram on the next page.) When the switch S is closed, current flows in the circuit, and heat is dissipated by the resistor. Two small insulators on the top horizontal support keep the current confined to the indicated circuit. Assume that the rod absorbs 75% of this heat energy.

The change in temperature ΔT of the rod due to the absorption of q joules of heat energy is given by the equation

$$q = mc\Delta T$$

where m is the mass of the rod (equal to 0.2 kg) and c is the specific heat capacity of the brass, 380 J/(kg-°C). When heated, the rod expands: the change in length is

$$\Delta L = \alpha L \Delta T$$

where L is the original length, and α is the coefficient of linear expansion for brass, which is (2×10^{-5})/°C.

An experiment consists of closing the switch S and observing the change in the period of the pendulum due to its increased length. The pendulum is carefully insulated, so we may assume that its temperature (after heating by the resistor) stays constant for the duration of the experiment.

The period of a pendulum is given by

$$T = 2\pi\sqrt{L/g}$$

where g is the acceleration due to gravity.

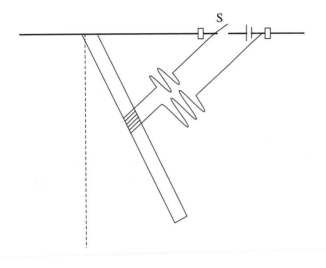

1. What is the period of the pendulum at 20°C?

   A. 0.25 second
   B. 0.5 second
   C. 1 second
   D. 2 seconds

2. At what rate is heat absorbed by the rod during the time that Switch S is closed?

   A. 1.2×10^2 joules/sec
   B. 1.6×10^2 joules/sec
   C. 1.2×10^3 joules/sec
   D. 1.6×10^3 joules/sec

3. If the switch were closed long enough to allow the rod to absorb q joules of heat, then which of the following expressions gives the increase in its length?

   A. $q/(\alpha Lmc)$
   B. $\alpha Lq/(mc)$
   C. $mc/(\alpha Lq)$
   D. $\alpha Lmc/q$

4. If the rod of equal dimensions were instead composed of a different material with twice the density of brass but the same specific heat, then for the same amount of absorbed heat energy, the change in length would have been:

   A. 1/4 as much.
   B. 1/2 as much.
   C. the same.
   D. twice as much.

5. If this clock with the new, heated brass pendulum is allowed to run and record time for 1 hour (as measured by an independent, accurate timepiece), it will run:

   A. too fast, because the pendulum is too long.
   B. too slow, because the pendulum is too long.
   C. too fast, because the pendulum is too short.
   D. too slow, because the pendulum is too short.

_____

Passage 50 (Questions 1-8)
ADVANCED PASSAGE

A *simple pendulum* is one in which all the mass is concentrated at the very end; the string or rod connecting the bob to the pivot point is assumed to be of negligible mass. However, if the mass of the pendulum is not concentrated only at the end but is instead distributed along the entire length, then the pendulum is termed a *physical pendulum.* An example of a physical pendulum is a uniform bar. Figure 1 shows a simple pendulum (with bob of mass M) and a uniform-bar physical pendulum of total mass M, each with length L.

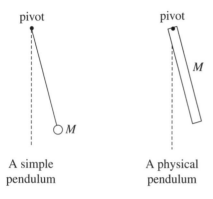

A simple pendulum   A physical pendulum

Figure 1

For the simple pendulum, the period of oscillation, T, is given by the formula

$$T = 2\pi \sqrt{\frac{L}{g}} \times \left[1 + \frac{1}{4}\sin^2\left(\frac{\theta_{max}}{2}\right) + \frac{9}{64}\sin^4\left(\frac{\theta_{max}}{2}\right) + ... \right]$$

Equation 1

where g is the acceleration due to gravity and θ_{max} denotes the amplitude of the angular motion, measured from the vertical equilibrium position where $\theta = 0$.

If θ_{max} is small, then the restoring force at any position is approximately proportional to the angle of displacement, and the motion is nearly simple harmonic. Furthermore, in such a case, the terms in Equation 1 that involve $\sin(\theta_{max}/2)$ are very small, and the period is essentially independent of the amplitude. For example, if $\theta_{max} = 20°$, then the period as given by Equation 1 differs from that calculated from the simpler formula $T = 2\pi\sqrt{L/g}$ by less than 1%, and the difference becomes even smaller if θ_{max} is smaller. This independence of period on amplitude is described by saying that the oscillations of the pendulum are *isochronous* (from the Greek meaning "equal time"). However, if θ_{max} is large, then deviations from simple harmonicity and isochronism can be significant.

Students performed an experiment to measure the periods of the two pendulums shown in Figure 1 with various lengths and masses. They conducted three trials with each pendulum type. In all six trials, the amplitude angle (θ_{max}) was 10°. The data collected are given in Table 1. Dissipative effects such as friction at the pivot and air resistance were negligible.

Pendulum	Trial	L	M	T
Simple	Trial 1	0.5 m	0.5 kg	1.4 sec
	Trial 2	1.0 m	1.0 kg	2.0 sec
	Trial 3	2.0 m	2.0 kg	2.8 sec
Physical	Trial 1	0.5 m	1.0 kg	1.2 sec
	Trial 2	1.0 m	2.0 kg	1.6 sec
	Trial 3	2.0 m	2.0 kg	2.3 sec

Table 1

1. If the mass of the bob of the simple pendulum in Trial 1 had instead been 1.0 kg, what would have been the period of oscillation?

   A. 0.7 sec
   B. 1.2 sec
   C. 1.4 sec
   D. 2.8 sec

2. Which of the following best characterizes v, the speed, and a, the magnitude of the tangential acceleration, of the simple pendulum when its angular position, θ, is θ_{max}?

   A. Minimum v, minimum a
   B. Minimum v, maximum a
   C. Maximum v, minimum a
   D. Maximum v, maximum a

3. Which one of the following statements best explains the difference between the period of the simple pendulum in Trial 3 and the period of the physical pendulum in Trial 3?

   A. The restoring force on the physical pendulum is smaller.
   B. The restoring force on the physical pendulum is greater.
   C. The physical pendulum offers less resistance to angular acceleration than does the simple pendulum.
   D. The physical pendulum offers greater resistance to angular acceleration than does the simple pendulum.

4. What is the change in the gravitational potential energy of the bob on the simple pendulum between the two extremes of its position ($\theta = \theta_{max}$ and $\theta = -\theta_{max}$) during oscillation?

   A. 0
   B. $MgL(\sin \theta_{max})$
   C. $MgL(1 - \cos \theta_{max})$
   D. $MgL(2 \sin \theta_{max})$

5. If θ_{max} during the experimental trials had been 5°, each of the measured periods given in Table 1 would have:

   A. decreased by a factor of 2.
   B. decreased by a factor of $\sqrt{2}$.
   C. remained the same.
   D. increased by a factor of 2.

6. The students' results best support which of the following conclusions?

   A. The frequency of oscillation of the physical pendulum increases as the length increases.
   B. The frequency of oscillation of a simple pendulum increases as the length increases.
   C. The frequency of oscillation of the physical pendulum is lower than the frequency of oscillation of a simple pendulum of the same length.
   D. The frequency of oscillation of the physical pendulum is higher than the frequency of oscillation of a simple pendulum of the same length.

7. If Trial 3 with the simple pendulum had been conducted with $\theta_{max} = 85°$, the period would have been most nearly:

   A. 2.2 sec.
   B. 2.4 sec.
   C. 2.6 sec.
   D. 3.0 sec.

8. Which one of the following best depicts the force diagram for the gravitational force on the physical pendulum (of length L and mass M) and also gives the correct expression for the torque it produces about the pivot?

   A.

   torque = $(L)(Mg \sin \theta)$

   B.

   torque = $(L)(Mg \sin \theta)$

   C.

   torque = $(L/2)(Mg \sin \theta)$

   D.

   torque = $(L)(Mg \cos \theta)$

Passage 51 (Questions 1-5)

When a light wave passes obliquely from one medium to another, the angle at which it emerges from the boundary between the two media will differ from the angle at which it strikes it. The change in medium causes the light to refract. In any such situation, the angle of refraction (θ_2) is related to the angle of incidence (θ_1) according to Snell's Law:

$$n_1 \sin \theta_1 = n_2 \sin \theta_2$$

where n_1 = the refractive index of Medium 1, and n_2 = the refractive index of Medium 2. For any medium, the refractive index is equal to c/v, where c is the speed of light in vacuum and v is the speed of light in the medium. For air, $n \approx 1$.

If a light wave traveling in a medium of greater refractive index encounters a medium of smaller refractive index, it may exhibit the phenomenon of *total internal reflection*. This occurs whenever the angle of incidence is greater than or equal to the critical angle θ_c for the two media. For any two media for which $n_1 > n_2$, $\sin \theta_c$ is equal to n_2/n_1.

It has been discovered that for any material medium, n will vary slightly depending on the frequency of light propagating through it. The value of n increases with increasing frequency. For example, for any given change in medium, blue light experiences greater refraction than does red light. It is this variability in n that causes a prism to disperse a beam of white light into its component color wavelengths. The various wavelengths emerge from the prism at diverse angles and hence are visible as a spectrum.

A change in medium will alter a light wave's speed but not its frequency. The change in speed is compensated by a change in wavelength since wave speed is the product of wavelength and frequency.

1. Blue light has a wavelength of 4.5×10^{-7} m in air. What is its frequency?

   A. 6.7×10^{14} Hz
   B. 7.5×10^{15} Hz
   C. 3.6×10^{16} Hz
   D. 1.5×10^{17} Hz

2. A beam of light moving through the air strikes the surface of a transparent medium at an angle of 54° to the normal. If the beam continues into the medium at an angle of 37° to the normal, what is the approximate refractive index of this medium? (Note: sin 37° = 0.6, sin 54° = 0.8)

   A. 0.75
   B. 1.3
   C. 1.6
   D. 2.1

3. If an investigator working with red and blue light sources wishes to determine the relative magnitude of the wavelengths emitted from each, he would be justified in concluding that the shorter of the two wavelengths is emitted from:

   A. the red light source, since red light experiences greater refraction than does blue light.
   B. the blue light source, since blue light experiences greater refraction than does red light.
   C. the red light source, since red light experiences less refraction than does blue light.
   D. the blue light source, since blue light experiences less refraction than does red light.

4. On passing from a medium of lower refractive index to a medium of greater refractive index, a light wave would experience:

   I. decreased frequency.
   II. decreased wavelength.
   III. decreased velocity.

   A. II only
   B. III only
   C. II and III only
   D. I, II, and III

5. After repeated trials, an investigator determines that when violet light travels through a diamond and encounters an interface with air, the smallest angle of incidence that will allow for total internal reflection is approximately 25°. The investigator would be justified in calculating which of the following as the refractive index of diamond? (Note: sin 25° = 0.4)

   A. 1.25
   B. 1.4
   C. 2.5
   D. 4.0

Passage 52 (Questions 1-5)

The speed of a longitudinal wave (such as a sound wave) through a fluid medium is given by

$$v = \sqrt{\frac{B}{\rho}}$$

Equation 1

where B is the bulk modulus and ρ is the density of the medium. The formula for the speed of longitudinal waves through a solid is the same as the one above except the bulk modulus B is replaced by the Young's modulus, Y. When a fluid medium experiences an increase in pressure, its volume decreases (assuming no temperature change). The bulk modulus is the ratio that describes this effect:

$$B = -\frac{F/A}{\Delta V/V_0}$$

Equation 2

where F/A is the external pressure, ΔV is the change in volume of the medium, and V_0 is the initial volume. Because an increase in pressure always causes a decrease in volume, a minus sign is required for B to be a positive quantity. Fluids with higher bulk moduli are affected less by changes in external pressure than those with lower bulk moduli.

The ratio that defines the Young's modulus, Y, of a solid is the same as the ratio given above that defines the bulk modulus, B, of a fluid except that the denominator is replaced by $\Delta L/L_0$, where L represents the length of the solid.

Material	Modulus (N/m²)	Density (kg/m³)
Copper	$Y = 1.2 \times 10^{11}$	8900
Aluminum	$Y = 7.0 \times 10^{10}$	2700
Water	$B = 2.2 \times 10^{9}$	1000
Air*	$B = 1.4 \times 10^{5}$	1.2

*at 20 °C and 1 atm

Table 1 Moduli and Densities for Various Media

1. What is the ratio of the speed of sound through aluminum to the speed of sound through water?

    A. 0.3
    B. 3.4
    C. 9.3
    D. 11.8

2. Suppose that a block of aluminum with volume V_0 is taken to a depth $d > 1000$ m underwater. If ρ denotes the density of the water and B is the bulk modulus of aluminum, which one of the following expressions gives the change in the block's volume?

    A. $-\dfrac{V_0}{B\rho g d}$

    B. $-\dfrac{B}{V_0 \rho g d}$

    C. $-\dfrac{B\rho g d}{V_0}$

    D. $-\dfrac{V_0 \rho g d}{B}$

3. Using Equation 1 and the data in Table 1, it can be shown that the speed of sound through water is approximately 1500 m/s. What is the wavelength of a 100-kHz sound wave emitted by a dolphin underwater?

    A. 0.015 cm
    B. 0.15 cm
    C. 1.5 cm
    D. 15 cm

4. The speed of sound in vulcanized rubber is 54 m/s. How long would it take a 440-Hz sound wave to travel through a 0.50-m cube of rubber?

    A. 1.1 ms
    B. 9.3 ms
    C. 108 ms
    D. 123 ms

5. The speed of sound in hydrogen gas at 0°C and 1 atm is 1260 m/s, nearly four times the speed in air under the same conditions. Which of the following statements best accounts for this tremendous difference in the speed of sound?

   A. Hydrogen gas is significantly more compressible than air.
   B. Hydrogen molecules have a lower mass and therefore move more rapidly when exposed to a sound wave.
   C. Hydrogen molecules experience lower London dispersion forces than nitrogen and oxygen.
   D. Hydrogen gas is denser than air at STP.

Passage 53 (Questions 1-5)

The phenomenon of beats results when two sound waves of equal amplitudes and nearly equal frequencies interfere. The waves move from being in phase to out of phase then back to in phase, and so forth. The resulting alternating constructive and destructive interference produces a composite sound wave of varying intensity. If each sound wave has amplitude A_0, then the resultant wave form has an amplitude which varies sinusoidally between 0 and $2 A_0$. The beat is heard each time the amplitude of the composite waveform reaches its maximum.

The frequency of the beats is the difference between the frequencies, f_1 and f_2, of the two parent waveforms:

$$f_{beat} = |f_1 - f_2|$$

Equation 1

and the frequency of the composite waveform is given by the average of the two:

$$f_{composite} = \tfrac{1}{2}(f_1 + f_2)$$

Equation 2

The amplitude of the resulting waveform varies according to the equation

$$A(t) = 2A_0 \cos[\pi(f_1 - f_2)t]$$

Equation 3

The human ear can detect beats when they occur with a frequency of less than 15 Hz. Beats are often used to tune stringed musical instruments, by first sounding a tuning fork then playing the instrument. The string is tightened or loosened until beats are no longer heard.

1. A tuning fork for an A note (440 Hz) is struck. A string with too high a frequency is sounded and adjusted until the beats can no longer be heard. What is the frequency of the tuned string?

   A. 420 Hz
   B. 430 Hz
   C. 440 Hz
   D. 460 Hz

2. Two tuning forks, with frequencies of 260 and 265 Hz, are struck, and beats are heard. What is the frequency of the resultant sound wave and the frequency of the beats, respectively?

   A. 262.5 Hz; 2.5 Hz
   B. 262.5 Hz; 5 Hz
   C. 525 Hz; 2.5 Hz
   D. 525 Hz; 5 Hz

3. A sound wave ($f_1 = 400$ Hz, $A_1 = 5$ units) interferes with another sound wave ($f_2 = 410$ Hz, $A_2 = 5$ units). What is the maximum amplitude of the resultant sound wave?

   A. 2.5 units
   B. 5 units
   C. 10 units
   D. 25 units

4. The speed of sound through air at 20°C is 343 m/s. What is the wavelength of a sound wave of frequency 686 Hz?

   A. 0.5 m
   B. 1.0 m
   C. 2.0 m
   D. 5.0 m

5. Which of the following is a longitudinal wave?

   A. A wave traveling down a stretched string
   B. Waves from a pebble dropped in a pool of water
   C. Sound waves
   D. Light waves

Passage 54 (Questions 1-7)

Figure 1 depicts an experimental apparatus designed to measure the speed of light. The apparatus consists of a light source, a partially-silvered glass (Mirror P), a toothed wheel, a second Mirror (Mirror M), and an eyepiece. The portion of Mirror P that is silvered acts as a mirror. That portion of a light beam which strikes the silvered area of Mirror P is reflected toward the toothed wheel and Mirror M. The remainder of the beam is transmitted through the non-silvered glass. Figure 2 depicts the toothed wheel from a different perspective. Adjacent teeth are separated by a fixed angle, θ.

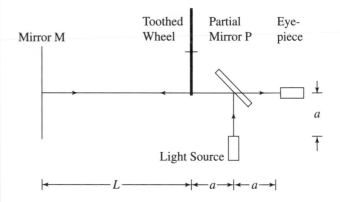

Figure 1

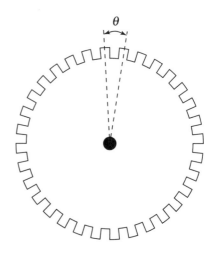

Figure 2

If the light source were activated in the *absence* of the toothed wheel, a beam of photons would be emitted, and a portion would be reflected by the silvered area of Mirror P to Mirror M. That portion would then be reflected back by Mirror M to Mirror P, and a portion of *that* beam would pass through the non-silvered portion of Mirror P to the eyepiece where an observer would perceive it.

The experiment, however, is conducted with the toothed wheel in place and rotating. Light passes from Mirror P to Mirror M and from Mirror M back to Mirror P (and the eyepiece) *only* if an open notch is aligned with the beam each time it reaches the wheel. Adjusting the rate at which the wheel rotates allows the experimenter to calculate the total time necessary for a light beam to (1) pass through an open notch, (2) reach Mirror M, and (3) return to the wheel at the moment the adjacent open notch is aligned with the beam. From that determination, the speed of light can be ascertained by mathematical calculation.

1. A light beam traveling through vacuum has a wavelength of 5.0×10^{-7} m. What is its frequency?

   A. 1.7×10^{14} Hz
   B. 6.0×10^{14} Hz
   C. 1.7×10^{15} Hz
   D. 6.0×10^{15} Hz

2. Given that c represents the speed of light, how long will it take for a photon to travel from the wheel to Mirror M and back to the wheel?

   A. L/c
   B. $2L/c$
   C. $c/(2L)$
   D. c/L

3. If the wheel is spinning at 500 rev/sec and θ is 0.36°, how much time will elapse between the moments at which adjacent notches are aligned with the light beam?

   A. 2.0×10^{-6} sec
   B. 1.8×10^{-5} sec
   C. 7.2×10^{-4} sec
   D. 5.6×10^{-3} sec

4. Seen through the eyepiece, the light source will appear to be located at a distance of:

   A. $L - 2a$ in front of Mirror M.
   B. $L - a$ behind Mirror M.
   C. $L + a$ behind Mirror M.
   D. $L + 2a$ behind Mirror M.

5. Assume that the light source is replaced by one which emits light at a frequency 10 times greater than that emitted by the original. How will this alteration affect the speed of light as perceived by the experimenter?

   A. It will be 1/10 as great.
   B. It will be 10 times greater.
   C. It will be 100 times greater.
   D. It will remain the same.

6. Which of the following best represents the path taken by the light beam as it is transmitted through Mirror P after returning from Mirror M and the toothed wheel?

   A.
   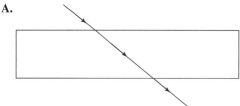

   B.
   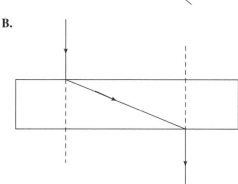

   C.
   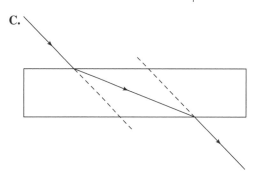

   D.
   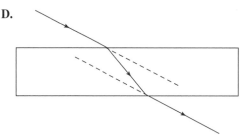

7. Suppose Mirror P is to be replaced by a converging lens. If the lens has a power of 20 diopters, what is its radius of curvature?

   A. 5 cm
   B. 10 cm
   C. 20 cm
   D. 40 cm

Passage 55 (Questions 1-6)

The human eye can be approximated by the lens system shown below:

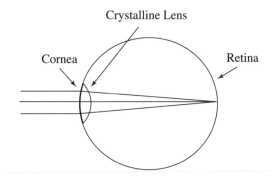

Figure 1

The combination of the cornea and the crystalline lens can be thought of as a converging lens that projects an image on the retina. The muscles around the eye act to adjust the power of the eye's lens, depending on whether the eye is focused on a nearby or on a distant object.

The lens power P of the eye is equal to $1/f$, where f is the focal length of the eye's lens. The reciprocal of the focal length also satisfies the equation $1/f = 1/(o) + 1/(i)$, where o and i denote, respectively, the object distance and image distance from the lens. The image distance is fixed and equal to the distance between the retina and the lens, which is about 2 cm for a normal-sized eye. When the eye is relaxed, as when it is focused on a distant object, the focal point should lie on the retina, as shown in Figure 1.

The common vision problem of hyperopia, or farsightedness, occurs when the lens is too weak or when the retina is too close to the lens. Both of these conditions make it impossible for the eye to bring nearby objects into focus on the retina. Hyperopia can be corrected by using an additional lens in conjunction with the eye; see Figure 2. The power of the resulting lens combination can be found by adding the individual lens powers:

$$P_{Combination} = P_{Eye} + P_{Corrective\ lens}$$

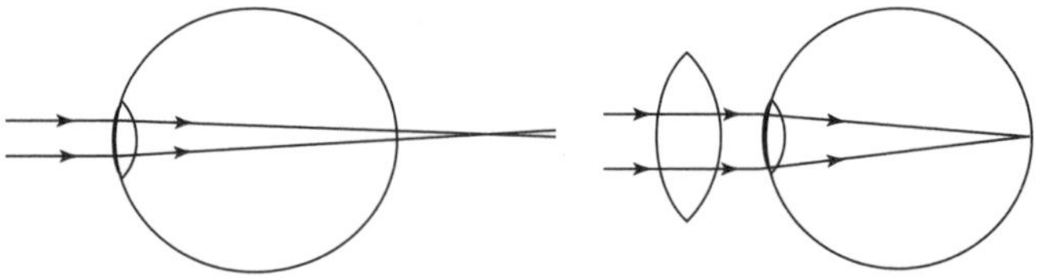

Relaxed hyperopic eye   Relaxed hyperopic eye with corrective lens

Figure 2

1. As the muscles of the eye contract, increasing the power of the eye's lens, the focal length of the lens will:

   A. increase.
   B. decrease.
   C. remain the same.
   D. depend upon the size of the object in focus.

2. When the eye is focused on a distant object, such as a star, the image will appear:

   A. on the surface of the lens.
   B. between the lens and the focal point.
   C. at the focal point.
   D. beyond the focal point.

3. What is the lens power of the eye when it is focused on an object at a distance of 20 cm?

   A. 7 diopters
   B. 50 diopters
   C. 55 diopters
   D. 70 diopters

4. The lens used to correct hyperopia will be a:

   A. converging lens, resulting in a decreased focal length.
   B. converging lens, resulting in an increased focal length.
   C. diverging lens, resulting in a decreased focal length.
   D. diverging lens, resulting in an increased focal length.

5. If a normal sized hyperopic eye has a 48-diopter crystalline lens, what strength corrective lens must be used if the relaxed eye is to be focused on a distant object?

   A. –2 diopters
   B. –1 diopters
   C. 1 diopter
   D. 2 diopters

6. What is the magnification of an object viewed at a distance of 1 m from a normal eye?

   A. 1/50
   B. 1/2
   C. 2
   D. 50

Passage 56 (Questions 1-3)

A police car, equipped with a sonar device for measuring the speeds of passing motorists, is at rest by the side of the road. The frequency of the (inaudible) sound waves emitted by the device is 1 megahertz (MHz). These waves are reflected off a passenger vehicle, and the frequency of the waves received back at the police car can be measured. By comparing this value with the original 1 MHz, the speed of the vehicle is easily computed.

The Doppler effect causes a change in the detected frequency when there is relative motion between source and detector. If v_s is the speed of the source, v_D is the speed of the detector, and v is the speed of sound, then the ratio of the detected frequency to the source frequency is

$$\frac{f_{detected}}{f_{source}} = \frac{v \pm v_D}{v \mp v_s}$$

1. A truck is approaching the police car at a speed equal to 1/10 the speed of sound. With what frequency do the sound waves emitted by the police car strike the truck?

   A. 0.9 MHz
   B. 1.0 MHz
   C. 1.1 MHz
   D. 1.2 MHz

2. As the truck continues to approach the police car, it reflects the incident sound waves back to the car. Calculate the frequency of these waves when detected at the police car.

   A. 1.1 MHz
   B. 1.2 MHz
   C. 1.3 MHz
   D. 1.4 MHz

3. If the officer remains at her hiding place, what frequency will her device detect from a truck moving away at a speed equal to 1/10 the speed of sound?

   A. 0.72 MHz
   B. 0.82 MHz
   C. 0.98 MHz
   D. 1.20 MHz

Passage 57 (Questions 1-6)

Before loudspeakers came into wide use, people used megaphones to address crowds. Megaphones perform two functions: They help transfer energy from the vocal cords to sound waves, and they reduce the *diffraction*, or spreading, of sound waves so that most of the energy is directed toward the crowd.

In order to see how the megaphone helps transform energy, consider a light rope connected, or *coupled*, to a heavy rope. The resistance to motion, or *impedance*, of the heavy rope is different from that of the light rope, and a wave on the heavy rope will be mostly reflected at the transition, illustrated as follows:

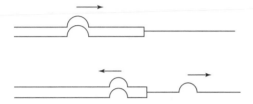

However, if the transition is gradual, that is, if the transition length is much greater than the wavelength, then the reflection is minimized:

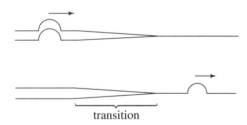

transition

The transition region is said to match the impedances of the heavy and light ropes. In the case of the megaphone, the impedance of the vibration of the vocal cords is coupled to the vibration of air inside the megaphone, which is coupled to the vibration of the open air.

The megaphone also prevents the sound energy from spreading in all directions, so that most of the sound energy reaches the crowd. When any kind of wave emerges from a hole (e.g., a mouth or a megaphone horn), it tends to spread. The spreading angle is given by

$$\Delta\theta = \frac{\lambda}{d},$$

where λ is the wavelength of the wave, d is the diameter of the hole, and $\Delta\theta$ is measured in radians. (Note: 1 radian $\approx 57°$.)

1. Sound waves are similar to waves on a string in all of the following ways EXCEPT:

   A. both transfer energy.
   B. both are transverse waves.
   C. both can be modeled as a collection of masses interacting via spring-like forces.
   D. in both, the frequency is equal to the ratio of wave speed to wavelength.

2. If a beam of red light (wavelength = 0.65 μm) passes through a pinhole with diameter 4 μm, what is the diameter of the spot on a wall 3 m beyond the pinhole?

   A. 2×10^{-6} m
   B. 1×10^{-2} m
   C. 0.5 m
   D. 18 m

3. Which of the following best explains why sound waves do not pass easily through a solid wood door?

   A. Diffraction disperses out the energy.
   B. The wavelength of sound is approximately equal to size of the door.
   C. There is a poor impedance match between the air and the door.
   D. The door absorbs the sound energy.

4. Why does a voice projected through a megaphone have a better-defined direction than an unaided voice?

   A. The megaphone reduces diffraction by decreasing the wavelength of the sound.
   B. The megaphone reduces diffraction by having a larger projection hole.
   C. The megaphone reduces the reflections of sound from nearby buildings.
   D. The megaphone helps convey more energy from the vocal cords toward the crowd.

5. Which of the following can be inferred from the passage about the efficiency of the megaphone in converting vocal-cord energy into sound energy?

   A. The megaphone is more efficient for a louder voice.
   B. The megaphone is more efficient for a voice of lower frequency.
   C. The megaphone is more efficient for a voice of higher frequency.
   D. The megaphone is equally efficient for all volumes and frequencies.

6. Historically, the diffraction of sound waves was noticed long before the diffraction of light waves. Which of the following best explains this?

    A. The wavelength of visible light is very much smaller than that of sound.
    B. Only laser light diffracts, and lasers were only recently invented.
    C. Apparatus for measuring light was developed later than that for sound.
    D. Light diffracts only if it is not in the form of photons.

Passage 58 (Questions 1-6)

The interaction of light with the human eye illustrates several properties of waves. The human eye can be modeled by a hole (the pupil) with a lens (cornea and lens) which focuses light on a screen (the retina).

When waves pass through a hole (water waves encountering the entrance to a bay, for example) a certain amount of directional information is lost, and the waves spread. This is called *diffraction*. The minimum spreading is given approximately by

$$\Delta\theta = \frac{\lambda}{d},$$

where λ is the wavelength of the wave, d is the size (diameter) of the hole, and $\Delta\theta$ is in radians.

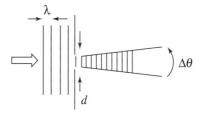

As a wave passes from one medium (such as air) to another (such as cornea material), it bends according to the refractive indices of the materials. This phenomenon, called refraction, is responsible for focusing light passing through a lens. If θ_i and θ_r are the angles (taken from the normal) of the incident and refracted ray, respectively, and n_i and n_r are the indices of refraction for the two media, then $n_i \sin \theta_i = n_r \sin \theta_r$. This is Snell's Law. The index of refraction for air is very nearly $n = 1$. The index of refraction for the cornea is $n_r = 1.3358$ for red light ($\lambda = 656$ nm) and 1.3416 for blue light ($\lambda = 486$ nm). For the following questions, you may use these values:

pupil diameter $= d = l_{pupil} = 2$ mm

front-to-back length of the eye $= l_{eye} = 2.4$ cm

radius of curvature of the cornea $= r_{cornea} = 8$ mm

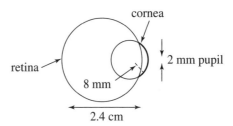

1. In the bay shown in the first figure, if size of the entrance were increased by a factor of 2 and the frequency of the wave were increased by a factor of 2, then how would the spreading angle change?

   A. It would decrease by a factor of 4.
   B. It would decrease by a factor of 2.
   C. It would remain stay the same.
   D. It would increase by a factor of 4.

2. The resolution of an eye is its ability to distinguish light coming from different directions. If the resolution of the human eye is set by its geometry and optics, what is the resolution angle for red light?

   A. 3×10^{-6} radian
   B. 3×10^{-4} radian
   C. 3×10^{-2} radian
   D. 3×10^{-1} radian

3. A certain animal has visual resolution $\theta_{res} = 10^{-2}$ radian. How far apart are two objects which the animal can just distinguish at 10 m?

   A. 0.01 m
   B. 0.05 m
   C. 0.1 m
   D. 0.5 m

4. The difference in refractive index of the cornea with respect to wavelength has which of the following consequences?

   A. More directional information is preserved for blue light.
   B. The eye is more sensitive to red light.
   C. The eye is more sensitive to blue light.
   D. The eye cannot focus on red and blue light simultaneously.

5. All of the following will change the focal length of the eye EXCEPT changing the:

   A. wavelength of the light.
   B. polarization of the light.
   C. cornea's radius of curvature.
   D. cornea's index of refraction.

6. An ideal lens would focus waves from a distant object to a point, so that the resolution would be infinitely good. The lens of the eye in the passage focuses such waves to a small splotch. This is due to diffraction, which causes the waves to spread even as they are focusing. If diffraction sets the size of the splotch at the retina, how large is the splotch?

   A. $l_{eye}\, \Delta\theta$
   B. $l_{pupil}\, \Delta\theta$
   C. $l_{eye}\, l_{pupil}\, \Delta\theta\, /\, r_{cornea}$
   D. $l_{pupil}\, (\Delta\theta)^2$

Passage 59 (Questions 1-6)
ADVANCED PASSAGE

Positron-emission tomography (PET) is an imaging technology used by cognitive scientists to gain real-time images of the physiology associated with thought processes. Glucose metabolism, oxygen consumption, and blood flow can be measured with this technique. The most reliable indicator of moment-to-moment brain function has proven to be blood flow.

PET is based on two physical processes: beta decay and pair annihilation. Radioactive water—two hydrogen atoms combined with ^{15}O, a radioactive isotope of oxygen—is injected into the subject. As the radioactive water begins to accumulate in the brain, the ^{15}O decays by *positron emission*, a form of beta decay. During this process (Reaction 1), a proton (p) decays into a neutron (n), a positron (e^+), and a neutrino (v). The positron has the same mass and charge magnitude as the electron (e^-), but is positively charged. It is the electron's antiparticle. The neutrino (and its anti-particle, the antineutrino, $\bar{v}$) are massless, chargeless particles that travel at the speed of light and rarely interact with other forms of matter.

$$p \rightarrow n + e^+ + v$$

Reaction 1

After the decay, the emitted positron is ejected from the nucleus into an environment full of electrons where it has a very high probability of colliding with one. When a particle meets its antiparticle (such as the positron and electron in Reaction 2), the pair annihilate one another and give off two equally energetic gamma rays, a process called *pair annihilation*. A gamma ray photon (γ) is electromagnetic radiation that possesses both high energy and momentum. The energy (in electron volts, eV) of a photon of electromagnetic radiation is given by $E = hf$ where f is the wave's frequency and $h = 4.1 \times 10^{-15}$ eV-s is Planck's constant. In free space, wavelength λ and frequency f are related by the equation $\lambda f = c$, where c is the speed of light.

$$e^+ + e^- \rightarrow \gamma + \gamma$$

Reaction 2

The PET image is formed by detecting the gamma rays given off during the pair annihilation and sending the information through a computer designed for image processing. The computer calculates the spatial and temporal origin of the gamma rays by using the fact that both energy and momentum are conserved in both processes, and then infers a real-time image of the mental process.

1. For the PET process, what would be wrong with using water composed of ordinary oxygen and radioactive hydrogen atoms that decayed according to the reaction

$$n \rightarrow p + e^- + \bar{v}$$

   instead of using $H_2{}^{15}O$, which decays by Reaction 1?

   A. This radioactivity would be toxic.
   B. The lifetime of the isotope would be too short.
   C. The gamma rays produced would be too energetic.
   D. No gamma rays would be produced.

2. If the "before" state of a pair annihilation is given by

$$e^+ \rightarrow \qquad \leftarrow e^-$$

   where each arrow represents the particle's momentum, which of the following is a possible "after" state (expressed in the same reference frame)?

   A. $\leftarrow \gamma \qquad e^- \rightarrow$
   B. $\leftarrow e^+ \qquad \gamma \rightarrow$
   C. $\leftarrow \gamma \qquad \gamma \rightarrow$
   D. $\gamma \rightarrow \qquad \gamma \rightarrow$

3. If the total energy released in an e^-/e^+ annihilation is 4 MeV, what is the frequency of each emitted gamma ray?

   A. 2.4×10^{20} Hz
   B. 4.8×10^{20} Hz
   C. 9.6×10^{20} Hz
   D. 9.6×10^{21} Hz

4. Actually, there are three types of beta decay reactions: electron emission, positron emission, and electron capture. Each of these conserves charge, energy, and momentum. Which of the following reactions could NOT be a beta decay?

   A. $p \rightarrow n + e^+ + v$
   B. $n \rightarrow p + e^- + \bar{v}$
   C. $n \rightarrow p + e^+ + v$
   D. $p + e^- \rightarrow n + \bar{v}$

5. A gamma ray traveling through the air has a frequency of 2×10^{22} Hz. Approximate its wavelength.

A. 1.5×10^{-15} m
B. 6.7×10^{-15} m
C. 1.5×10^{-14} m
D. 6.0×10^{-14} m

6. When an oxygen-15 (^{15}O) nucleus decays by positron emission, into which of the following is it transformed?

A. ^{14}N
B. ^{15}F
C. ^{15}N
D. ^{16}O

Passage 60 (Questions 1-7)
ADVANCED PASSAGE

Fiber optics has revolutionized the telecommunications industry. The former network of bulky copper cables has been replaced by thin glass fibers that transmit information more efficiently. Glass fibers also have a far greater information-carrying capacity, called *bandwidth*, than copper cables. Theoretically, the bandwidth of a fiber-optic cable is 50 THz = 50×10^{12} Hz, though current technology can only achieve a bandwidth of a few GHz (equal to 10^9 Hz).

Fiber optics works by the principle of total internal reflection. At the center of the fiber is the glass *core*, which carries the light signal. Around the core is a concentric layer of glass, called *cladding*. The cladding has a lower index of refraction than the core, which prevents the light from escaping. Typically, infrared light of wavelength 1310 nm is used. A transmitter converts an electrical signal to light, the fiber then transmits the light, and a receiver captures the light at the other end and converts it back to an electrical signal.

Because of the absorption within the fiber or scattering at imprecise fiber connections, a weakening, or *attenuation*, of the signal occurs. Currently, attenuation is about 1 dB/km. Because of attenuation, the light signal must periodically be regenerated by devices called *repeaters*. The repeater decodes the incoming signal and transmits an identical one, but with greater strength and purity.

1. If a telephone conversation requires 3 kHz of bandwidth, what is the theoretical maximum number of conversations that could simultaneously be carried on a fiber optic cable?

A. 1.7×10^{10}
B. 1.7×10^{13}
C. 1.5×10^{14}
D. 1.5×10^{17}

2. It is more difficult to illegally tap into fiber optics systems than into copper cable systems because:

A. glass has a lower index of refraction than does copper.
B. glass does not bend as easily as does copper.
C. splicing optical fibers requires more precision than does splicing copper cable.
D. light travels faster than do electrons.

3. In fiber optics systems, infrared light is used instead of visible light because:

   A. total internal reflection would not be possible with visible light.
   B. infrared light contains more energy and therefore experiences less attenuation.
   C. infrared light has a higher index of refraction in glass than does visible light and so travels faster than visible light.
   D. visible light has a shorter wavelength and is more readily absorbed by the fiber.

4. After a light ray has traveled 20 km along the fiber, its intensity has decreased by what factor?

   A. 20
   B. 100
   C. 200
   D. 1000

5. If the index of refraction of the core is 2.0 and the index of refraction of the cladding is 1.73, what is the minimum angle of incidence necessary for total internal reflection?

   A. 30°
   B. 45°
   C. 53°
   D. 60°

6. Narrowing the core would reduce distortion because:

   A. the number of different paths the light can take would decrease.
   B. the speed of light in the fiber would increase.
   C. the available bandwidth would decrease.
   D. more light would enter the core at an end point of the fiber.

7. If a ray of light were to travel through the air and then enter a glass fiber, its wavelength would:

   A. increase.
   B. decrease.
   C. remain the same.
   D. It cannot be determined without knowing the initial wavelength.

Passage 61 (Questions 1-6)
ADVANCED PASSAGE

A student performed a series of experiments to study the photoelectric effect, using the apparatus shown in Figure 1.

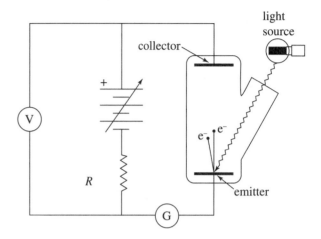

Figure 1 Experimental apparatus for studying the photoelectric effect

A light source emits radiant energy—whose frequency and intensity can be varied—onto a metal plate (labeled the emitter plate in Figure 1). This radiant energy can cause the ejection of electrons—called *photoelectrons*—from the surface of this plate, and, under certain conditions, these electrons can impact the collector plate. The emitter plate and the collector plate are enclosed in an evacuated glass tube and connected across a source of variable voltage and a resistor. The voltage is measured with a voltmeter, V, and any current in the circuit—which is due to photoelectrons moving from the emitter to the collector—can be measured by a sensitive galvanometer, G.

Experiment 1:

The student performs six trials, using a different metal for the emitter plate in each trial; the six metals used are listed in Table 1. The student observes that each metal only ejects photoelectrons when the frequency of the incident light is above a certain threshold frequency, f_0, which varies from metal to metal. If the frequency of the incident light is lower than f_0, no photoelectrons are produced, regardless of the intensity of the incident light. However, if the frequency is higher than f_0, then the number of photoelectrons produced is proportional to the intensity of the incident light.

The student learns the explanation for the results of Experiment 1. Each metal has its own *work function*, ϕ, which is the minimum energy an electron on its surface must absorb in order to be liberated. Furthermore, the incident energy is absorbed in individual packets of energy, called *photons*, where the energy of a photon is proportional to the frequency of the light. The constant of proportionality is called Planck's constant, denoted by h, and its value is 4.14×10^{-15} eV·s. Therefore, the energy of a photon with frequency f is given by the equation $E = hf$. Photoelectrons will be ejected from the surface of the emitter plate only if the energy of each incoming photon is at least as great as the metal's work function. If E_{photon} is greater than ϕ, then the maximum kinetic energy a photoelectron can have as it leaves the surface is

$$KE_{max} = hf - \phi$$

Equation 1

Table 1 below gives the work functions for the various metals used in the experiment.

Metal	Work function, ϕ
Na	2.28 eV
Al	4.08 eV
Pb	4.14 eV
Fe	4.50 eV
Cu	4.70 eV
Pt	6.35 eV

Table 1 Work Functions of Selected Metals

Experiment 2:

The student now varies the voltage to see its effects on the current in the circuit. She finds that if the collector plate is positive (as illustrated in Figure 1), nearly all of the photoelectrons make it to the collector. However, if the voltage's polarity is reversed, so that the collector plate is made negative with respect to the emitter, there's a certain voltage at which all the photoelectrons are repelled, and none make it to the collector. At this point, the current stops, and this voltage is called the *stopping potential*, V_{stop}. The equation that relates the maximum kinetic energy of the photoelectrons to the magnitude of their electric charge, e, and the magnitude of the stopping potential is

$$KE_{max} = eV_{stop}$$

Equation 2

The student used the following values in the lab write-up: $e = 1.6 \times 10^{-19}$ C, 1 eV = 1.6×10^{-19} J, and $hc = 1240$ eV·nm, where h is Planck's constant and c is the speed of light.

1. When the emitter plate is made of lead, what is the threshold frequency for ejection of photoelectrons?

   A. 1.7×10^{-14} Hz
   B. 1.0×10^{15} Hz
   C. 1.5×10^{15} Hz
   D. 2.0×10^{15} Hz

2. When incident light of intensity $I = 1000$ W/m² with a photon energy of 2.25 eV is incident on an emitter plate made of iron, the reading on the galvanometer in Figure 1 is recorded. If the intensity of this light is increased to $4I$, how will the reading on the galvanometer change?

   A. It will go up.
   B. It will decrease.
   C. It will stay the same.
   D. Any of the above choices is possible, depending on the value of the resistance, R.

3. The work function depends on:

   A. the frequency of the incident light only.
   B. the frequency and intensity of the incident light.
   C. the current measured by the galvanometer.
   D. None of the above

4. Which of the following best describes the relationship between i, the current in the circuit, and I, the intensity of the incident light on the emitter plate?

   A. i is proportional to I.
   B. i is proportional to I^2.
   C. i is inversely proportional to I.
   D. i is independent of I.

5. Ultraviolet light of wavelength 310 nm is incident on a sodium emitter plate. What is the maximum kinetic energy of the photoelectrons?

   A. 0.8 eV
   B. 1.7 eV
   C. 4.6 eV
   D. 6.3 eV

6. For a fixed emitter plate, which of the following graphs best illustrates the relationship between the stopping potential and the frequency of the incident light?

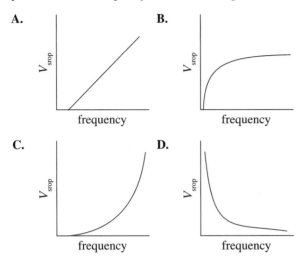

A.

B.

C.

D.

Passage 62 (Questions 1–5)

Heated objects, electrical devices, gas discharge tubes, and lasers all generate electromagnetic (EM) radiation. It is observed at various intensities and frequencies, extending from radio waves through visible light to high-energy gamma rays. But what *is* light? Early theories stated that light was a stream of particles called *corpuscles* that were emitted by light sources. Newton himself was a proponent of the *particle theory* of light. However, experiments by such physicists as Snell, Hooke, Huygens, Young, and Fresnel in the seventeenth through early nineteenth centuries demonstrated that light behaved as a wave and thus seemed to establish firmly the *wave theory* of light. Phenomena such as interference, polarization, and diffraction were best explained in terms of light as a wave.

But around the beginning of the twentieth century, work by such physicists as Planck, Einstein, and Compton showed that the wave theory of light alone could not explain certain experimental results, and the particle theory resurfaced. This led to the *dual wave–particle theory* of light, which says that light propagates as a wave but in its interactions with matter (emission or absorption) behaves as a stream of particles, discrete bundles of energy called *photons*. A photon of frequency f has an energy equal to hf and a momentum of hf/c, where h is a universal constant called Planck's constant and c is the speed of light.

Figure 1 shows Young's famous double-slit diffraction experiment, which he was able to use to deduce the average wavelength of sunlight. Incident light passes through a single narrow slit, S, in a barrier. The wave spreads out (diffracts) after emerging from the slit. The wave then falls on a second barrier containing two closely-spaced slits, S_1 and S_2. Coherent waves emerge from these slits and travel to the screen.

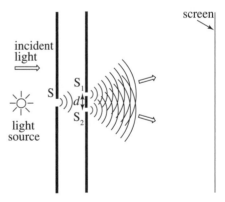

Figure 1

When light from the two slits reaches the screen, superposition takes place. Constructive interference—which creates a bright fringe—occurs at a point P on the screen where the distances traveled by the two waves differ by an integer multiple of the light's wavelength, λ; that is, when

$$d \sin \theta = m\lambda$$

Equation 1

where d is the distance between slits S_1 and S_2, θ is the angle measured from the center of the slits to P (Figure 2), and m is an integer (the order of the fringe). Destructive interference—which creates a dark fringe—occurs at a point on the screen where

$$d \sin \theta = (m + 1/2)\lambda$$

Equation 2

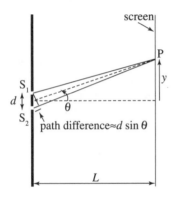

Figure 2

Because $L \gg d$, the value of $\sin \theta$ is approximately equal to $\tan \theta$, so the distance y in Figure 2—which is measured from the point on the screen directly opposite the center of the slits—can be approximated by $L \sin \theta$. Because $\sin \theta$ is equal to $m\lambda/d$ for a bright fringe and $(m + 1/2)\lambda/d$ for a dark fringe, the positions of the bright and dark fringes on the screen are found from the equations

bright fringe: $y_m = m\lambda L/d$

dark fringe: $y_{m+1/2} = (m + 1/2)\lambda L/d$

Equation 3

1. When illuminated by sunlight, a thin film of oil floating on water produces a spectrum of colors that depends on the depth of the oil film. Which theory of light mentioned in the passage best explains this phenomenon?

   A. The particle nature of light
   B. The wave nature of light
   C. The dual wave–particle nature of light is needed.
   D. Neither the particle nor the wave nature of light is correct because the wavelength of the light is altered.

2. Two waves are exactly in phase and have the same frequency. One wave has amplitude $2A$ and the other has amplitude $3A$. If these waves interfere, what will be the amplitude of the combined wave?

   A. A
   B. $4A$
   C. $5A$
   D. $6A$

3. In a Young's double-slit diffraction experiment, mono-chromatic light of wavelength 500 nm is used. Let S_1P and S_2P be the distances from the slits to any point P on the screen. If P is the center of a dark fringe on the screen, then $S_2P - S_1P$ could be equal to which of the following?

   A. 125 nm
   B. 500 nm
   C. 625 nm
   D. 750 nm

4. Which of the following best describes what would happen to the pattern of bright and dark fringes on the screen in Young's double-slit diffraction experiment if the distance between the slits were reduced?

   A. The fringes would widen and move farther apart.
   B. The fringes would become more narrow and move closer together.
   C. The bright fringes would widen, but the dark fringes would become more narrow.
   D. The dark fringes would widen, but the bright fringes would become more narrow.

5. The double-slit diffraction experiment described in the passage is conducted first with violet light of wavelength 400 nm, and then with orange–yellow light of wavelength 600 nm. In both cases, $d = 0.4$ mm and $L = 4.0$ m. The researcher notices that some of the locations of the bright fringes on the screen for the orange–yellow light coincided with locations of the bright fringes on the screen for the violet light. Find the smallest value of the distance y shown in Figure 2 where this occurs.

   A. 6 mm
   B. 8 mm
   C. 9 mm
   D. 12 mm

Passage 63 (Questions 1–6)

In the early decades of the twentieth century, Einstein's *General Theory of Relativity* marked the first major revision in the explanation of the interactions of massive bodies in space since Newton's Theory of Universal Gravitation. For most phenomena the two theories predicted almost identical behavior, but for situations involving extremely large masses in close interaction the theories differed. For instance, Einstein's theory successfully explained a small deviation in the orbit of Mercury (the closest planet to the Sun) that Newton's could not. General Relativity also predicted that a sufficiently massive object like the Sun would bend the path of light that passed in its proximity (Newton predicted that light would always move in straight lines). In 1919 this prediction was confirmed during a solar eclipse, and Einstein became internationally famous. Later that same year, Sir Oliver Lodge showed how this bending of light could be used to focus distant star light by acting as a *gravitational lens*, an effect that was finally observed in 1979.

Much like a normal optical lens, a gravitational lens focuses light by deflecting its path as it passes through the lensing region. The degree to which an optical lens bends the path of light depends upon its shape and the *index of refraction*, $n = c/v$, of the material composing it. Similarly, the action of a gravitational lens depends upon the dimensions of the deflecting mass and its effective "index of refraction," which can be estimated by

$$n \approx 1 + \frac{2GM}{rc^2}$$

Equation 1

where G is the universal gravitational constant ($G = 6.7 \times 10^{-11}$ m³/kg·s²), M is the deflecting mass, r is the radial distance from the center of mass to the deflected ray, and c is the speed of light in vacuum. For a mass the size of the entire Milky Way galaxy deflecting rays just beyond its galactic halo, this yields a value $n = 1 + (1 \times 10^{-6})$: the deflection angle is therefore very small, given by

$$\phi = \frac{4GM}{rc^2} \text{ (radians)}$$

Equation 2

Figure 1 shows a simplified version of the gravitational lens phenomenon. The central star is the light source, with the large, deflecting mass M lying between it and the observer located where the rays converge; d_L is the distance from the observer to the deflecting mass, and d_S is the distance from the observer to the source.

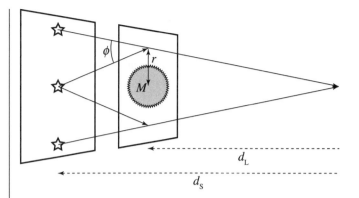

Figure 1

Note in the figure that multiple images of the same object can be observed (two are shown). In fact three different general observational phenomena occur: multiple images; *arc lensing*, in which the optical image of a source is warped over part or all of a circle; and *radio rings*, in which galaxies observed at radio frequencies appear warped into a doughnut shape, presumably by intervening galactic masses.

1. Taking $M_{Sun} = 2 \times 10^{30}$ kg and $r_{Sun} = 7 \times 10^8$ m, find the maximum deflection angle for light originating behind the sun observed during a solar eclipse.

    A. 8.5×10^{-6} rad
    B. 8.5×10^{-5} rad
    C. 8.5×10^{-6} degrees
    D. 8.5×10^{-5} degrees

2. Usually a source object will not lie on the axis determined by the observer and the deflecting mass. Which of the following are probable consequences of that asymmetric arrangement?

    I.   In a dual-image lens effect, one image will show a time delay from the other.
    II. The effective index of refraction for the gravitational lens will differ significantly from its value for on-axis sources.
    III. An observed radio ring will appear thicker and brighter on one side than the other.

    A. I only
    B. I and III only
    C. II and III only
    D. I, II, and III

3. Determine the effective focal length of a gravitational lens created by a celestial object of mass M_0 and radius r_0 by assuming both that $d_s \gg d_L$, so that rays coming from the source are parallel at the lens, and that $\tan\theta \approx \theta$ (in radians) for small angles.

   A. $f = \dfrac{rc^2}{4GM_0}$ meters

   B. $f = \dfrac{r^2c^2}{4GM_0}$ meters

   C. $f = \dfrac{4GM_0}{r^2c^2}$ meters

   D. The focal length is essentially infinite because the index of refraction is essentially one.

4. For which of the following data would the predictions of Newton's Theory of Universal Gravitation most likely agree with those of General Relativity?

   A. The rate at which a red giant star loses matter into a super massive black hole.
   B. The angular size of a radio ring.
   C. The degree to which light slows as it passes by a globular cluster.
   D. The orbital period of Earth around the Sun.

5. In 2004, the Chandra orbiting X-ray telescope imaged a rare quadruple quasar through a hugely powerful gravitational lens. Which of the following best explains why these X-ray images could only be resolved from space whereas radio rings are observed from earth?

   A. X-ray photons are readily absorbed by the atmosphere; radio waves are not.
   B. Radio photons are more energetic than X-ray photons and so do not attenuate as much in the atmosphere.
   C. There is far more interference from terrestrial X-ray sources than from radio sources.
   D. X rays are lower frequency than radio waves, so there are fewer X-ray photons to observe.

6. Gravitational lensing has become an important tool in astrophysics. All of the following are likely applications of gravitational lensing EXCEPT:

   A. observational data of multiple image sources can be used to determine the mass of the lensing object.
   B. the light-collecting effect of gravitational lenses can be used to see far greater distances and dimmer objects than would otherwise be possible.
   C. the time delay between multiple images of different optical path lengths could be used to study suddenly occurring, short-lived phenomena.
   D. moving a gravitational lens across the sky can allow astronomers to select which objects to focus on.

MCAT Physics
Solutions

Passage 1

1. **D** If θ is the angle that **P** makes with the horizontal, then the horizontal component of **P** is $P_x = P \cos \theta$, and the vertical component of **P** is $P_y = P \sin \theta$. Thus, if $P = 20$ and $\theta = 30°$, then the horizontal and vertical components of **P** are $20 \cos 30°$ and $20 \sin 30°$, respectively.

2. **C** By definition, displacement, velocity, and acceleration are all vector quantities. Speed, however, is a scalar (it is the magnitude of the velocity).

3. **C** The horizontal component of **P** is $P_x = P \cos 30°$, which equals $(20 \text{ m})\cos 30° = (20 \text{ m})(0.87) = 17$ m.

4. **B** The vertical component of **P** is $P_y = P \sin 30°$, which equals $(20 \text{ m})\sin 30° = (20 \text{ m})(0.5) = 10$ m.

5. **C** Since **R** points down to the right, $-\mathbf{R}$ points up to the left.

6. **A** The vertical component of **P** is $P_y = P \sin 30°$, and the vertical component of **R** is $R_y = R \sin (-30°) = -R \sin 30°$. Therefore, the vertical component of $\mathbf{P} + \mathbf{R}$ is $P_y + R_y = 20 \sin 30° + (-20 \sin 30°) = 0$. Thus, the vector $\mathbf{P} + \mathbf{R}$ is purely horizontal, eliminating choices B and C. Furthermore, since both **P** and **R** have positive horizontal components, so will their sum, $\mathbf{P} + \mathbf{R}$. The answer must be choice A.

7. **C** Moving $-\mathbf{P}$ to the tip of **Q** and adding them shows that (1) their sum, $\mathbf{Q} + (-\mathbf{P}) = \mathbf{Q} - \mathbf{P}$, points into the second quadrant from the origin, and (2) the angle that $\mathbf{Q} - \mathbf{P}$ makes with the negative x axis is *less than* 45°. Thus, the answer must be choice C.

Passage 2

1. **D** Displacement is equal to the area under the velocity vs. time graph. Therefore, the distance traveled between times $t = 0$ and $t = 10$ is equal to the area of the rectangle bounded above by the horizontal line $v = 5$ and on the left and right by the vertical lines $t = 0$ and $t = 10$, respectively. This gives $d = vt = (5 \text{ m/s})(10 \text{ s}) = 50$ m.

2. **B** Acceleration is the slope of the velocity vs. time graph. Therefore, the acceleration between times $t = 10$ and $t = 15$ is equal to the slope of the line segment joining the points $(t_1, v_1) = (10, 5)$ and $(t_2, v_2) = (15, 10)$. Applying the slope formula, we find $a = (10 - 5)/(15 - 10) = 1 \text{ m/s}^2$.

3. **C** Displacement is equal to the area under the velocity vs. time graph. Therefore, the distance traveled between times $t = 10$ and $t = 15$ is equal to the area of the region bounded above by the slanted line segment joining the points $(t_1, v_1) = (10, 5)$ and $(t_2, v_2) = (15, 10)$ and bounded on the left and right by the vertical lines $t = 10$ and $t = 15$, respectively. By drawing the horizontal line segment joining the points $(t_1, v_1) = (10, 5)$ and $(t_3, v_3) = (15, 5)$, we see that this trapezoidal region is composed of a right triangle sitting atop a rectangle. The total area is equal to the area of the triangle plus the area of the rectangle: $d = \frac{1}{2}(15 - 10)(10 - 5) + (15 - 10)(5) = 37.5$ m.

4. **B**   Average speed is defined as total distance traveled divided by time. In this case, the total distance is equal to the displacement (because the motion is in one direction only); thus, average speed equals the magnitude of the average velocity in this situation. The average of 5 m/s and 10 m/s—the velocities at times $t = 10$ and $t = 15$, respectively—is 7.5 m/s.

5. **B**   Since the car's velocity never changes from positive to negative, its direction never changes; this eliminates choices A and C. Now, since the car's speed was 10 m/sec just before $t = 25$ but less than 10 m/sec just after, the car slowed down.

6. **C**   Acceleration is the slope of the velocity vs. time graph. During the time interval from $t = 0$ to $t = 10$ and during the time interval from $t = 15$ to $t = 25$, the v vs. t graph is flat, so the slope is zero. This observation eliminates choice B. Since the v vs. t graph is descending during the last time interval ($t = 25$ to $t = 30$), the acceleration here is negative. This eliminates choice A. Finally, the slope of the v vs. t graph jumps (not gradually increases) from 0 to 1 m/s^2 at time $t = 10$. Thus, the answer must be choice C, not choice D.

7. **A**   During the car's first ten seconds of travel, its velocity is a constant 5 m/s. Thus, at any time t during this time interval, the distance traveled is $d = vt = 5t$. The graph of this equation is a straight line of slope 5 through the origin. This observation eliminates choices B and C. Now, during the time interval from $t = 10$ to $t = 15$, the v vs. t graph is a line with slope 1 (which is the acceleration, a), so the distance traveled during this time interval is given by the equation $d = v_0 t + \frac{1}{2} at^2 = 5t + \frac{1}{2} at^2$. This is a (portion of a) parabola. Since the graph in choice D is composed only of straight line segments, it is eliminated, leaving choice A as the answer.

Passage 3

1. **B**   The car goes from 0 to 60 mph in 6 seconds. That means it gains—on average—10 mph every second. Or, by definition, the acceleration is

$$a = \Delta v / \Delta t = (60 \text{ mph} - 0)/6 \text{ sec} = 10 \text{ mph/sec}$$

2. **C**   The acceleration is the slope of the velocity vs. time graph. If the velocity vs. time graph is a straight line during a particular time interval, then the acceleration is constant during that interval. (The only way to have a nonconstant acceleration would be to have a curvy [that is, nonlinear] velocity vs. time graph.) Since the graph given in the passage is composed of three straight lines, the acceleration is constant over each of the three time intervals I, II, and III. (In fact, we have $a = 10$ mph/sec over period I, $a = 0$ during period II, and $a = -30$ mph/sec over period III; all constants.)

3. **B**   The easiest way is to look at the average speed. During period I, the average speed is 30 mph. During period II, the speed is a constant 60 mph. During period III, the average speed is 30 mph. Multiplying the average rate times the time interval will give us the distance traveled during each such interval:

Period I: $\Delta x_1 = (30 \text{ mph})(6 \text{ sec})$

Period II: $\Delta x_2 = (60 \text{ mph})(4 \text{ sec}) = (30 \text{ mph})(8 \text{ sec})$

Period III: $\Delta x_3 = (30 \text{ mph})(2 \text{ sec})$

Note that we have made the following observation: traveling 60 mph for 4 seconds covers the same distance as traveling 30 mph for 8 seconds (go half as fast for twice as long). Clearly, we get the greatest value (that is, the most distance) in period II. There's no need to do a unit conversion (seconds to hrs or hrs to seconds) and compute the actual values since all we are asked to do is make a comparison.

4.   **C**   Since $F = ma$, we will find the greatest F when we find the greatest a. From our solution to question 2 above, the acceleration has the greatest *magnitude* during period III: the car goes from 60 mph to 0 in 2 seconds, giving a magnitude of 30 mph/sec. Therefore the magnitude of the net force must have been the greatest during period III. (Note: $a = -30$ mph/sec is a very large acceleration [the driver must have slammed on the brakes really hard], so F_{net} is very large. For a 1000 kg car [typical], this would equal about 180,000 pounds of force. That's why you can break bones if you stop too suddenly [e.g., if you crash into a brick wall].)

5.   **A**   Each block of area under the speed vs. time graph is calculated by multiplying the base (a *time* interval) times height ("a *speed* interval"). But *distance* equals speed × time. So the area of the entire region gives us the total distance traveled by the car.

6.   **A**   The MCAT *loves* this question. If the velocity is constant, then there is no acceleration, so there is no *net* force (since $F_{net} = ma$).

7.   **D**   In period III, the car started off going 60 mph and then steadily decreased in speed until it was going 0 mph. The average speed is right smack in the middle of the initial and final speeds as long as the speed changes at a steady rate (that is, as long as the acceleration is constant). That is, the correct answer is simply the average of 60 mph and 0 mph: 30 mph. Remember: If the acceleration is constant, then $\bar{v} = \frac{1}{2}(v_0 + v)$.

8.   **A**   To maintain the constant acceleration during time period I (or any time period for that matter), you need a constant net force (since $F_{net} = ma$). So if the drag increases as speed increases, the engine has to work harder and harder to compensate. Choice B is false because the engine force must be larger than the drag force if there is going to be a net force forward. Choice C is false because a constant engine force and a changing drag force would mean a changing net force. Choice D is wrong because acceleration always depends on the net force.

9.   **B**   At $t = 8$ sec, the net force on the car is zero. (See the graph. Since v is constant during the time period $t = 6$ to $t = 10$ sec, we know $a = 0$ and therefore $F_{net} = 0$ during period II.) When the windows shatter, the air resistance suddenly increases causing a net force on the car opposing its motion. The car slows down.

10. **A** There are at least three ways to look at Question 10. During period I,

(1) Since the speed is increasing, the distance traveled increases at an increasing rate as in A.

(2) Look at the equation given in the passage. The correct answer is a parabola with a positive number in front of the quadratic term since the acceleration, a, is positive. Again, choice A.

(3) Remember that the velocity graph is the slope of the position graph. Choice A has a steadily increasing slope corresponding to the steadily increasing velocity during period I.

11. **B** During period II,

(1) The speed is constant, so the distance traveled increases at a steady rate: a straight line.

(2) The equation in the passage gives a straight line since the coefficient of the quadratic term is zero, and the coefficient of the linear term is a constant.

(3) The velocity is constant and positive so the slope of the position graph is constant and positive.

12. **C** During period III, the acceleration is constant (but negative), so the curve is very similar to the period I curve. Since v is still positive, the car's position is still increasing, but the fact that the acceleration is negative means that the car is slowing down. The only graph that shows x increasing—but increasing more and more slowly as time goes on—is C.

Passage 4

1. **C** The tension and the friction together provide the necessary centripetal force $\mathbf{F}_c$. We find that

$$F_c = \frac{mv^2}{r} = \frac{(100 \text{ kg})(5 \text{ m/s})^2}{10 \text{ m}} = 250 \text{ N}$$

This means that the woman needs a total force of 250 N (directed toward the center) to continue in her circular path. Friction provides a maximum force of

$$\mu N = \mu mg = (0.1)(100)(10) = 100 \text{ N}$$

so tension must provide the remaining 250 − 100 = 150 N.

2. **B** We simply need distance equals rate × time. The distance traveled by the woman in one rotation is the circumference of the platform (since she's standing at the edge), so

$$T = \frac{d}{v} \quad \Rightarrow \quad T = \frac{2\pi r}{v} = \frac{(2\pi)(10 \text{ m})}{5 \text{ m/sec}} = 4\pi \sec \approx 12 \sec$$

3. **D** If the (centripetal) force holding the object in its circular path is suddenly taken away, the object will fly off in whatever direction it was headed at the instant the centripetal force was removed. Velocity is always tangent to an object's path.

4. **B** This is the famous "twirling ice skater effect." When the ice skater pulls in her arms, she suddenly begins to spin faster (because her rotational inertia decreases). In the same way, if the woman walks closer to the center, the platform will start to rotate faster. This is because when she walks toward the center, L_W decreases since r decreases. The sum, $L_W + L_p$, has to stay constant (total angular momentum, L_{total}, is conserved when no net external torque acts, just as total linear momentum, p_{total}, is conserved when no net external force acts), so ω has to increase. Since the platform now rotates faster, its period of rotation decreases.

5. **A** In circular motion, the net force is directed toward the center in order to ensure that the velocity bends around in a circle, and the acceleration and net force always point in the same direction. (The word "centripetal" means "toward the center." The centripetal acceleration and centripetal force vectors always point toward the center of the circular path.)

6. **B** As discussed in the passage, the pseudo-force always points in the direction opposite to that of the real force. Since the real force is directed radially inward (centripetal), the pseudo-force is directed radially outward.

7. **B** The second equation given for F_c, namely $F_c = 4\pi^2 mr/T^2$, shows the dependence of the force on r. When the woman moves closer to the center of the platform (that is, when r gets smaller), less centripetal force is needed, and therefore (since the frictional force doesn't change) less tension is required. (Be careful that you *don't* say "Since $F_c = mv^2/r$, F_c must become larger if r gets smaller." The problem here is that v is changing too. Use the other equation for F_c here; it has only one variable.)

Passage 5

1. **C** Neither the force of gravity parallel to the plane nor the normal force provides any torque about the center of mass (because the lever arm for both of these forces is zero, as can be seen from the figure on the left below); this eliminates choices A and B. Because the objects roll without slipping (that is, without sliding), it is not kinetic friction (choice D is wrong) but static friction that is responsible for the rotation.

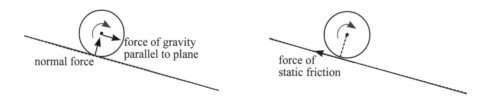

2. **D** Substitute the solid sphere's expression for I (given in Table 1) into Equation 3. Because F_{net} is always equal to ma, we have $mg \sin\theta - (2/5)ma = ma$, so $g \sin\theta = (7/5)a$, which gives $a = (5/7)g \sin\theta$.

3. **B**   One way to answer this question is to repeat the calculation in Question 2 for the other two objects (the hollow sphere and the disk); one would find that $a = (3/5)g \sin \theta$ for the hollow sphere and $a = (2/3)g \sin \theta$ for the disk. Of the three, the solid sphere has the greatest translational acceleration, so it would reach the bottom of the plane before the other two. For a more conceptual solution, notice that Table 1 tells us that of the three objects, the solid sphere has the smallest rotational inertia (i.e., least resistance to rotational acceleration). As a result, it will roll more easily than the others and thus reach the bottom of the plane first.

4. **B**   Begin with Equation 2. Then substitute the cylindrical disk's expression for I (as given in Table 1) and use Equation 4a to substitute for ω: $KE_{rot} = \frac{1}{2}I\omega^2 = \frac{1}{2}(\frac{1}{2}mR^2)(v/R)^2 = \frac{1}{2}(\frac{1}{2}mv^2) = \frac{1}{2}KE_{trans}$.

5. **A**   Think of $PE \rightarrow KE_{total}$, that is, $mgh = \frac{1}{2}mv^2 + \frac{1}{2}I\omega^2$. The available gravitational potential energy at the top of the plane—identical for each of the three rolling objects—provides both their translational and rotational kinetic energy. Whichever object has the greatest rotational KE will therefore have the lowest translational KE. Because the hollow sphere has the greatest I, it will have the greatest rotational KE, and thus the lowest translational KE. So, when the hollow sphere reaches the bottom (last in the race among the three objects, by the way), it will have the lowest speed

Passage 6

1. **C**   The total kinetic energy of the two carriages is the sum of their individual kinetic energies: $KE_{total} = \frac{1}{2}m_1v_1^2 + \frac{1}{2}m_2v_2^2 = \frac{1}{2}(1)(4^2) + \frac{1}{2}(2)(2^2) = 8 + 4 = 12$ J.

2. **C**   Momentum is always conserved in an isolated collision (elastic or not), and kinetic energy is conserved, by definition, in an elastic collision. Thus, both Statements I and II are true. However, if the two objects actually collide, then Statement III cannot be true.

3. **D**   In a perfectly inelastic collision, these carriages would come to rest after they collide, because they approach the collision with equal but opposite momenta: $m_1v_1 = (1 \text{ kg})(+4 \text{ m/s}) = +4$ kg·m/s, while $m_2v_2 = (2 \text{ kg})(-2 \text{ m/s}) = -4$ kg·m/s. Thus, they must have a total momentum of zero after the collision also, meaning that their final (common) velocity is zero. Thus, their final total kinetic energy is also zero. Since we calculated for the first question in this passage that their total kinetic energy before the collision was 12 J, the energy dissipated by this perfectly inelastic collision would be the entire 12 J.

4. **A**   Assuming negligible friction, there will be effectively no heat transfer, so choices C and D can be eliminated. First, the carriages possess kinetic energy as they approach each other. Then, when they collide and momentarily come to rest, the springs between the carriages experience maximum compression and are thus given maximum elastic potential energy. The springs then expand back to their original lengths, converting their stored elastic potential energy back into the kinetic energy of the (now separating) carriages.

5. **B**   Since the heavier carriage has twice the weight of the lighter carriage, the normal force on the heavier carriage is twice as great as the normal force on the lighter one. Since the force of sliding friction is proportional to the strength of the normal force, we conclude that the friction force exerted on the heavier carriage must also be twice as great as that exerted on the lighter one. That is, the desired ratio is 2:1.

6. **A**   If $w = mg$ denotes the magnitude of the carriage's weight, then the component of this force which is normal to the inclined plane is $mg \cos \theta$ where θ is the incline angle. Since $\cos 55° = \sin 35°$ (because the angles 55° and 35° are complementary), the correct answer is choice A.

Passage 7

1. **A**   The pressure exerted by the water—the gauge pressure, P_{gauge}—at depth y is given by Equation 2. We find that

$$P_{gauge} = \rho g y \\ = (1000 \text{ kg/m}^3)(10 \text{ N/kg})(5 \text{ m}) \\ = 5 \times 10^4 \text{ N/m}^2$$

2. **D**   Equation 1 indicates that τ is proportional to Ld^3. Therefore, if both L and d are doubled, then τ will increase by a factor of $(2)(2^3) = 16$.

3. **B**   The potential energy of the water at the top of the dam will be transformed into kinetic energy at the bottom. Setting mgh equal to $\frac{1}{2} mv^2$, we find that $v = \sqrt{2gh}$. With $g = 10 \text{ m/s}^2$ and $h = 5$ m, this gives $v = 10$ m/s.

4. **B**   Equation 1 for the torque τ implies that τ is proportional to d^3. The graph of τ vs. d must therefore be a curve that rises (without leveling off) as d increases. Only the graph in choice B fits this description.

5. **A**   The torque τ of the single force **F** at a distance d from the pivot line is given by $\tau = dF$. Since Equation 1 states that $\tau = \rho g L d^3/6$, we have $dF = \rho g L d^3/6$, which gives, after canceling one factor of d from both sides, $F = \rho g L d^2/6$.

Passage 8

1. **A**   Examine how much kinetic energy was lost on the way up: 400 J. So the potential energy, mgh, is 400 J at the top of the trajectory. Since $m = 2$ kg and $g = 10 \text{ m/s}^2$, h is 20 meters.

2. **C**   The horizontal velocity is constant and is responsible for all of the kinetic energy at the top of the trajectory (that is, the vertical velocity is zero at the top). Therefore, set $KE = 600$ J to get the horizontal velocity for the entire flight:

$$KE = \tfrac{1}{2}mv^2 \quad \Rightarrow \quad v = \sqrt{\frac{2KE}{m}} = \sqrt{\frac{2(600)}{2}} = 24.5 \text{ m/s}$$

3. **A** The key to this one is to consider the top of the trajectory: the vertical velocity, v_y, is zero, and the travel time to this point is $t = T/2$ (half the total flight time). Calling "up" positive, we find

$$v_y = v_{0y} - gt = 0 \implies v_{0y} = gt = gT/2$$

4. **D** Get the initial total velocity from the initial kinetic energy of 1000 J. Plugging in $\frac{1}{2}mv^2$ leaves you with $v = \sqrt{1000}$, which is a bit more than 30 m/s.

5. **C** Since we are assuming the projectile travels in a vacuum, no energy is lost. Therefore, the final kinetic energy is the same as the initial kinetic energy: 1000 J.

6. **B** Since the horizontal velocity is constant, the ratio equals 1.

7. **D** Since the horizontal velocity is constant ($v_x = v_{0x}$), the horizontal distance (the range, R) is calculated using rate × time: $R = v_{0x}T$.

8. **C** The increased downward acceleration (drag) from the air resistance while the projectile is on its way up, means that the object won't go as high as it would have in a vacuum. Or, you could think about the energy lost by the object—mgh has to be smaller with air resistance since the air saps some energy (2nd sentence, 3rd paragraph gives a hint about this). Anyway, H_{vac} is greater than H_{atm} and the ratio asked for in the problems is greater than 1.

9. **A** The question can be solved using intuition or by considering the last sentence in the third paragraph. Since the object is slowing down, it goes further in the first part of its flight (going up) than in the second part (coming down). This means that $R < 2X$, or $R/2 < X$.

Passage 9

1. **C** We are asked to find little g for the Moon. The last line of the first paragraph gives the equation for little g for the Earth. The mass of the Moon is smaller by a factor of 100. This by itself would give a g 100 times smaller. But the radius of the Moon is smaller by a factor of 4. This by itself would give a g 16 times *greater* since the radius is squared ($4^2 = 16$) and it's on the bottom. Putting these two effects together, we divide $g_{Earth} = 10$ by 100 then multiply by 16; this gives $g_{Moon} = (10)(16)/100 = 1.6$. Here's a more explicit presentation:

$$g_{Earth} = \frac{GM_{Earth}}{R_{Earth}^2} = \frac{G(100M_{Moon})}{(4R_{Moon})^2} = 6.25\frac{GM_{Moon}}{R_{Moon}^2} = 6.25g_{Moon}$$

$$\implies g_{Moon} = \frac{g_{Earth}}{6.25} = \frac{10 \text{ m/s}^2}{6.25} = 1.6 \text{ m/s}^2$$

2. **A** The object is now at two Earth radii from the surface ($1.2 \times 10^7 = 2R$). That means it's now at distance $3R$ from the center of the Earth, compared to R from the center previously. Since the distance has increased by a factor of 3, the force *decreases* by a factor of $3^2 = 9$. This gives 15/9 = 1.67 N.

3. **B**   The force that holds the Moon in the circular orbit—gravity—must provide the necessary centripetal force ($m_{Moon}v^2/r$). Equate the gravitational force and the centripetal force and solve for v:

$$\frac{GM_{Earth}m_{Moon}}{r^2} = \frac{m_{Moon}v^2}{r} \implies v = \sqrt{\frac{GM_{Earth}}{r}}$$

$$\implies v = \sqrt{\frac{(6.7 \times 10^{-11})(6 \times 10^{24})}{60(6 \times 10^6)}} = 10^3 \text{ m/s}$$

4. **A**   The second to last paragraph tells you about escape velocity. The object must have enough kinetic energy to supply the change in potential energy needed to go from $r_1 = R$ to $r_2 = \infty$. Using the equation at the end of the fourth paragraph and conservation of energy, you get $\frac{1}{2}mv^2 = GMm/R$. A little algebra yields the correct expression for v:

$$\frac{1}{2}mv^2 = \frac{GMm}{R} \implies v = \sqrt{\frac{2GM}{R}}$$

5. **D**   Newton's third law states that if object 1 exerts a force on object 2, then object 2 exerts an equal (but oppositely directed) force back on object 1.

6. **B**   The value of the universal gravitational constant, big G, is the same everywhere in the universe, so the ratio is 1. (It's little g, the acceleration due to gravity, that varies from place to place.)

7. **A**   Without air resistance, two objects dropped from the same height will fall with the same acceleration and hit at the same time with the same velocity, regardless of their masses.

8. **D**   You can't compute $mg\Delta h$ if you don't know the mass m.

9. **D**   Little g corresponds to the acceleration of an object dropped near the surface of the Earth ($r = R$). Since the Moon is $60R$ away, its acceleration would be *decreased* by a factor of $60^2 = 3600$.

10. **B**   The force from the Sun is greater by a factor of 30 million because of its mass (mass appears to the first power on top of the force equation), and smaller by 400^2 because of its distance (distance appears squared on the bottom of the force equation). The ratio 30 million/400^2 is just about 200 (which is 2.0×10^2). (Hint: Make the 30 into a 32 to make the estimate work out more easily; the choices are so far apart that 2 parts in 30 won't mean a thing.)

Passage 10

1. **B**   The equation for most probable speed is $v_0 = \sqrt{2kT/m}$. The question tells you that the temperature doubles. Does the most probable speed double? Not quite. It increases, but only with the square root of the temperature. So if T goes up by a factor of 2, v_0 goes up by a factor of $\sqrt{2} \approx 1.4$. Choice A is too small, and choices C and D are doubling and tripling, respectively. That leaves only choice B.

2. **B** Use the equation $T = 2\pi\sqrt{\frac{m}{k_a}}$. It says that large mass means low speed, and small mass means high speed (because the m is in the denominator). If you've forgotten that oxygen molecules are heavier than nitrogen molecules, you can use the periodic table that is provided during this section. Of the three gases mentioned in the question, oxygen is heaviest and slowest, and hydrogen is lightest and fastest.

3. **D** Gas can be produced by chemical reactions on the surface of the Earth. If production and escape balance, the atmospheric concentration will stay constant.

4. **A** The most probable kinetic energy is $\frac{1}{2}mv_0^2$. Looking at the equation for the most probable velocity, $v_0 = \sqrt{2kT/m}$, you can see that if you square the velocity, you clear the square root and have plain old T for the temperature dependence of kinetic energy. The most probable kinetic energy is therefore $\frac{1}{2}m(2kT/m) = kT$. This means that the most probable kinetic energy is directly proportional to temperature.

5. **C** The escape velocity, $v_e = \sqrt{2gR_E}$, does *not* depend on the mass of the object trying to escape. The escape velocity is the same for any object on the surface of the Earth, whether it's a molecule or a rocket.

6. **A** The passage tells you how to interpret the area under some section of the curve. It is the probability that the speed has some value between two given values. What about the area under the whole curve from $v = 0$ to $v = \infty$? What is the probability that a molecule has *some* speed? A molecule *must* have *some* speed, so the probability is 1.

7. **B** Even though most hydrogen molecules don't have the necessary escape velocity, some do. The hydrogen in our atmosphere has been dribbling away into space ever since the Earth was formed. Look again at the last sentence in the second paragraph.

8. **C** The equation given in the passage for escape velocity can apply to any planet. Since Jupiter has a bigger radius and a bigger gravitational acceleration than Earth, it has a higher escape velocity for objects on its surface. In addition, the colder temperatures mean that the most probable velocity for gas molecules on Jupiter is smaller than it is on Earth. So molecules in the Jovian atmosphere need to go faster to escape, but they actually go slower on average. Thus, Jupiter can hold onto its atmosphere better than Earth can. (But there are still a few molecules on the tail on the right hand side of the Maxwell–Boltzmann curve that are going fast enough to escape.)

Passage 11

1. **C** The speed of the bomb as it exits the plane is the same as the speed of the plane, 300 m/s. Since the mass of the bomb is $m = w/g = (4000\text{ N})/(10\text{ N/kg}) = 400$ kg, its kinetic energy is

$$KE = \tfrac{1}{2}mv^2 = \tfrac{1}{2}(400\text{ kg})(300\text{ m/s})^2 = 1.8 \times 10^7 \text{ J}$$

2.　C　The gravitational potential energy of the bomb relative to the ground is equal to mgh, where h is its altitude. In this case, we compute

$$PE = mgh = (400 \text{ kg})(10 \text{ N/kg})(5000 \text{ m}) = 2 \times 10^7 \text{ J}$$

3.　A　If air resistance is ignored, then a projectile's horizontal velocity remains constant during the entire flight. Since the bomb had an initial horizontal velocity of 300 m/s, it will have this same horizontal velocity at impact.

4.　B　We use the equation $v_y^2 = v_{0_y}^2 + 2a_y\Delta y$. Setting $v_{0_y} = 0$, $a_y = g$, and $\Delta y = h$, we find that $v_y = \sqrt{2gh}$. Substituting $g = 10 \text{ m/s}^2$ and $h = 5000 \text{ m}$ yields

$$v_y = \sqrt{2(10 \text{ m/s}^2)(5000 \text{ m})} = 100\sqrt{10} \text{ m/s} = 316 \text{ m/s}$$

5.　B　We use the equation $\Delta y = v_{0_y}t + \frac{1}{2}at^2$. Since $\Delta y = h$, $v_{0_y} = 0$, and $a_y = g$, we find that $t = \sqrt{2h/g}$, so

$$t = \sqrt{2(5000 \text{ m})/(10 \text{ m/sec}^2)} = \sqrt{1000} \text{ sec} = 31.6 \text{ sec}$$

6.　D　Note that in the calculation of the bomb's descent time (t) in the preceding question, the bomb's horizontal velocity (v_{0x}) was never used. Thus, doubling v_{0x} will have no effect on t.

7.　C　Apply Conservation of Total Mechanical Energy. Since frictional effects are being ignored, $KE_i + PE_i$ will equal $KE_f + PE_f$. Calling the ground our "$PE = 0$" level, we have $PE_f = 0$ and $PE_i = mgh$, so $KE_f = \frac{1}{2}mv_i^2 + mgh$. Comparing the case depicted in the figure (the bomb released with a purely horizontal velocity) with the case described in the question (bomb released with a purely vertical velocity), we find that $h = 5000$ m in both cases and that $v_i = 300$ m/s in both. (Remember: Kinetic energy cares only what the speed is; the direction of the velocity is irrelevant.) Thus, the value of $KE_f = \frac{1}{2}mv_i^2 + mgh$ must be the same in both cases.

Passage 12

This is one of those passages that throws some advanced material at you. Don't let it scare you. In general, the harder the material, the easier the questions. The passage tests your ability to handle momentum conservation and to use the language of vectors. You are given some momentum conservation equations in the passage and they can be used to obtain some of the answers. But we don't bother. The solutions below emphasize conceptual thinking rather than the equations. Conceptual is faster. The equation for the momentum of a photon is not something you could be expected to know without reading the passage. But $E = hf$, $\mathbf{p} = m\mathbf{v}$, and $\lambda f = c$ may not always be given. They will usually give you whatever constants you need, so you *don't* need to memorize Planck's constant. However, you should know the speed of light.

1.   **C**   Using the equation $\lambda f = c$ provided in the second paragraph, we find

$$f = \frac{c}{\lambda} = \frac{3 \times 10^{17} \text{ nm/sec}}{4 \times 10^2 \text{ nm}} = 7.5 \times 10^{14} \text{ sec}^{-1}$$

2.   **B**   Since momentum is conserved, the atom has to take on the photon's momentum. (The atom originally had none; it was stationary.) According to the equation in the passage, you just divide the photon energy E by the speed of light c to get the momentum p:

$$p = \frac{E}{c} = \frac{3.3 \times 10^{-19} \text{ J}}{3 \times 10^8 \text{ m/s}} = 1.1 \times 10^{-27} \text{ kg} \cdot \text{m/s}$$

3.   **D**   The x component of the atom's velocity is not affected by the photon (since the photon has no x velocity). The photon's momentum points in the $+y$ direction, so the absorption adds a $+y$ component to the atom's momentum. So the y component of velocity of the atom is greater then zero after the absorption.

4.   **C**   To conserve momentum, the atom has to lose whatever momentum it gave to the photon. The photon's momentum has a positive x and a positive y component. After emitting the photon, the atom's x velocity is reduced slightly (but is still positive) to make up for the photon's $\mathbf{p}_x$. The atom initially had no y component of momentum, so after the emission, the atom must have a negative p_y to balance the positive p_y carried off by the photon.

5.   **D**   The magnitude of a photon's velocity *must* equal c. Using the Pythagorean theorem, we find that vector I has magnitude

$$\sqrt{(c/2)^2 + (c/2)^2} = (c/2)\sqrt{2}$$

vector II has magnitude

$$\sqrt{c^2 + c^2} = c\sqrt{2}$$

and vector III has magnitude

$$\sqrt{(2c)^2 + (-c)^2} = c\sqrt{5}$$

None of these equals c.

6.   **D**   Choice I comes from the equation $p = E/c$: $[p] = $ J/(m/sec) = J·sec/m. Choice II comes from $\Delta p = F\Delta t$: $[p] = $ N·sec. Choice III comes from $\mathbf{p} = m\mathbf{v}$: $[p] = $ kg·m/sec. The units in I, II, and III are equivalent.

7. **A** The photon's momentum is $p = E/c$, which is how much momentum is given to the atom. We then find the velocity of the atom from $p = mv$:

$$v = \frac{p}{m} = \frac{E/c}{m} = \frac{(3 \times 10^{-19})/(3 \times 10^{8})}{5 \times 10^{-27}} = 0.2 \, \text{m/s}$$

8. **C** The photon has twice the momentum of the atom, and the photon's momentum points in the opposite direction. Adding the photon's momentum to the atom's, $\mathbf{p} + -2\mathbf{p} = -\mathbf{p}$, we see that the atom reverses direction.

9. **B** The passage states that atoms are transparent to "wrong-energy" photons. If a photon doesn't have enough energy to cause a transition, it won't do anything. This may run counter to one's intuition, but that's the way nature operates.

10. **D** The word "elastically" means that no kinetic energy is lost in the collision. Since the wall doesn't move, it can't absorb any kinetic energy (objects have to move to have kinetic energy). All of this means that the atom bounces off the wall with the same speed as it had coming in. Since momentum is a vector, we have $\Delta \mathbf{p} = \mathbf{p}_{\text{final}} - \mathbf{p}_{\text{initial}} = (-\mathbf{p}) - \mathbf{p} = -2\mathbf{p}$.

Passage 13

1. **D** How do you go from Frame A to Frame B? The passage states that Frame B moves to the right with speed v relative to Frame A. So what do we do to get the velocities in B from those in A? *We subtract* **v**. (Note: In A in Experiment I, the masses are initially moving at velocities **v** and $-\mathbf{v}$. In B, the initial velocities are 0 and $-2\mathbf{v}$, respectively.) So for this question, subtract **v** from $+\mathbf{v}/2$ to get $-\mathbf{v}/2$. The negative sign means "to the left." (In general, a person in a moving frame thinks he or she is standing still. In order to have this perspective they must subtract their velocity from everything, including themselves.)

2. **A** To go from Frame A to Frame B, you subtract B's velocity (see solution to question 1 above), so to go from Frame B to Frame A, you add B's velocity. If you add a velocity **v** (to the right) to a velocity **v** (up), you get a velocity up and to the right.

3. **D** First, the left-hand mass had momentum mv to the right. Then the collision took place, and now it has momentum mv to the left. So it lost mv in one direction and gained mv in the other. That's a total change of $2mv$. Or you can write

$$|\Delta \mathbf{p}| = |\mathbf{p}_{\text{after}} - \mathbf{p}_{\text{before}}| = |(-mv) - (mv)| = 2mv$$

4. **D** Momentum is always conserved unless there are external forces. It doesn't matter what frame you're talking about or whether or not the balls stick to each other.

5. **B** The only way to have an inelastic collision is to have a way to absorb some of the energy. That's pretty easy to arrange with macroscopic objects: the objects can deform, fall apart, stick together, etc. The only way to change the energy of a neon atom is to excite one of its electrons into a higher energy level. If this does not happen, then the collision has to be perfectly elastic.

6. **C** The equation $F = \Delta p/\Delta t$ (which is an alternative way of writing Newton's second law and is also known as the impulse-momentum theorem) shows that F is inversely proportional to the contact time.

7. **D** Experiment II is a completely inelastic collision since the balls stick together. When the objects stick, some kinetic energy is always lost. It doesn't matter what frame you're in—conservation or non-conservation of energy is frame-independent. Something that does depends on the reference frame is the velocity. In Frame A, the original kinetic energy was $\frac{1}{2}mv^2 + \frac{1}{2}mv^2 = mv^2$, and the final kinetic energy was zero. In Frame B, the original kinetic energy was $2mv^2$, and the final kinetic energy was $\frac{1}{2}(2m)v^2 = mv^2$. So in both frames the amount of kinetic energy lost was mv^2.

8. **A** Experiment I is elastic (kinetic energy is conserved in both frames) and Experiment II is inelastic (kinetic energy is not conserved in either frame; see the solution to question 7 above). Collisions might look different in different frames, but this is really only an illusion—like the platform "moving" when you are on a slowly-moving train, or the illusion that you are not moving at 600 mph when you are on an airplane having lunch.

9. **C** Since momentum is conserved, the total change in momentum has to be zero. A change of δ must therefore be compensated by a change of $-\delta$.

10. **C** The first paragraph says that the internal forces occur in equal and opposite pairs. In other words, the balls each exert a force of magnitude F on the other. This is true regardless of the velocities of the balls or their masses. This is Newton's third law.

Passage 14

1. **D** The compressed refrigerant will release more energy to the environment when the environment is cooler (so choice A is eliminated). The passage tells us that the compressed gas has to be allowed to release its heat to the surroundings. Therefore, you do not want the gas to be insulated from the environment (choice B). Again, the compressed gas has to be allowed to release its heat to the surroundings. Thus the compressed gas should be allowed to equilibrate with the surroundings (choice C is eliminated, choice D is the best).

2. **C** The passage indicates that the refrigerator, just like all other heat engines (system in which work and heat are converted to one another and then back again), is not completely efficient. Therefore, energy (in the form of electrical current) must be periodically added to keep the cycle going. So while the cooling inside the refrigerator is counteracting the heat released by the compression coils, over three days, the additional energy is getting pumped into the closet from the electrical outlet causes the temperature to go up.

3. **D** This is a NOT question, which means that it is often useful to think of answer choices as true or false, and then selecting the odd one out at the end. Recall that expanding gases cool, and compressing gases warm. When compressed air escapes to the lower, external atmospheric pressure, it must cool, so Choice A is true. When air is pressurized, it's compressed, so it heats up, so Choice B is true. Gauge pressure is proportional to depth, so as the depth of the gas bubble decreases, it is subjected to less pressure and expands. This expansion leads to cooling, which makes Choice C true. Water boils under vacuum because it lowers the external pressure to the vapor pressure of the water. The conversion of a liquid to a gas is an endothermic process, which will chill the water in the process. Thus, Choice D is false. Since Choices A, B, and C are true and Choice D is false, Choice D is the correct answer.

4. **A** This question is asking us to identify an endothermic process. Freezing (liquid to solid), condensation (gas to liquid), and deposition (gas to solid) are all exothermic processes. Sublimation (solid to gas) requires the absorption of energy from the environment.

5. **A** The change of the internal energy of a gas may be written as $\Delta E = Q - W$, in which W is defined as the work done by the gas. If the compressor does work on the gas, this implies a negative value of W. Since W is subtracted from Q, this leads to a positive change in the internal energy of the gas, so Choice A is true. The gas doesn't do work on the compressor, so Choice B is incorrect. Choice C is a fancy way of saying that the gas has been allowed to expand, which is the opposite of what a compressor does, making Choice C incorrect. The compressor converts electrical energy into mechanical energy, which makes Choice D incorrect.

6. **B** If the heat transferred to the environment is half of its internal energy, then half of the internal energy remains. Thus the internal energy decreases by a factor of 2. Since the internal energy of a gas is proportional to absolute temperature, this corresponds to a decrease in the temperature of the gas by a factor of 2, corresponding to Choice B.

Passage 15

1. **B** By the ideal gas law we know that is T is constant, and P is increased, V must decrease. Answer choices A and D say the same thing, since average kinetic energy of a gas is a measure of its temperature; both are wrong as the system is isothermal.

2. **B** Doubling the diameter means that the radius is also doubled. Pressure is proportional to force/area, or force/radius². So, doubling the force and doubling the radius results in changing the pressure by $2/2^2 = 2/4 = 1/2$. The pressure therefore decreases by a factor of 2, Choice B.

3. **D** Adiabatic (from the Greek: *a*, not + *diabatos*, passable) walls are defined as barriers that do not permit the transfer of heat. Thus any heat produced by a system will remain in the system.

4. **C** From the ideal gas law, $PV = nRT$, we see that P is proportional to T if V is held constant. Thus, T will double if P is doubled.

Passage 16

1. **B** This question requires the understanding of the diagrams in the passage. Foremost, the passage says that without the greenhouse effect of clouds and CO_2, the temperature of the surface would be $-20°C$. Life as we know it requires liquid water to metabolize and grow. Therefore choice A is OK. Furthermore, clouds reflect 25% of the sunlight reaching the Earth. Therefore, during the day, clouds end up cooling the surface (choice C). Obviously, CO_2 must interact with IR and/or microwaves because it is a greenhouse gas.

   The passage suggests that the greenhouse effect of clouds ends up warming the surface at night (last paragraph). Choice B is neither correct nor suggested by the passage.

2. **B** By definition, when the net heat (energy) flux is into the system, Q is positive, eliminating Choice A and making Choice B true. Recall that $\Delta E = Q - W$ (in which W is the work done by the gas), so that $Q = \Delta E + W$, eliminating Choices C and D. Therefore, Choice B is the correct answer.

3. **C** According to the passage, radiative equilibrium means that the Earth absorbs as much energy from the Sun as it emits. Recall that the energy of a photon is given by $E = hf$, so that an IR/microwave photon has less energy than a visible photon. Therefore in order for the energy absorbed to equal the energy emitted, the earth must emit more IR/microwave photons than the number of visible photons it absorbs, making Choice C correct. Note that while visible photons are only absorbed during daylight hours, the Earth is constantly emitting IR/microwave photons, which eliminates Choice D.

4. **C** The question tells us that $E = \text{constant} \times T^4$. Therefore, as T gets larger, E gets much, much larger.

5. **A** Recall that the rate of conduction of energy from one material to another, $\Delta Q/\Delta t$ is proportional to the difference in temperature between the two materials, ΔT. Therefore, as ΔT increases, so does Q, eliminating Choices B, C, and D and making Choice A correct. Note that the factor of Δt in the relationship means that the graph of Q vs. ΔT won't necessarily be linear.

Passage 17

1. **C** The water is heated as it absorbs radiation from the sunlight. Other effects are negligible. The correct answer is C.

2. **D** The volume flow rate, f, is $(0.5 \text{ L})/20 \text{ s} = 500/20 \text{ cm}^3/\text{s} = 25 \text{ cm}^3/\text{s}$. Since $f = Av$, where A, the cross-sectional area of the neck of the bottle, is given by $A = \pi r^2 = \pi(1 \text{ cm})^2 = \pi \text{ cm}^2$, the average speed of the water is $v = f/A = (25 \text{ cm}^3/\text{s} / \pi \text{ cm}^2) = 8 \text{ cm/s}$.

3. **B** Heat is transferred away from the engine by the flowing water (forced convection) and then away from the hot water in the radiator by the streaming air (again, forced convection). This eliminates choices A and C. The radiation of heat away from the engine (which does occur) is not enough to cool the engine, and the work done by the pump does not in itself cool the engine; it only transfers the cool fluid that takes up the energy. This eliminates choice D.

4. **D** Since the small bottle is floating while 3/4 submerged, its density must be 3/4 the density of the surrounding fluid (this follows from Archimedes' principle). Hence, its density is $(3/4)$ $(1000 \text{ kg/m}^3) = 750 \text{ kg/m}^3$.

5. **B** Choices C and D can be eliminated since the gravitational force acting on the small bottle does not change. Since the small bottle sinks when the outer bottle is squeezed, the buoyant force it feels cannot *increase*, which eliminates choice A. Squeezing the water bottle increases the pressure on every surface and at every point in the water (Pascal's law), thus shrinking the volume of the small bottle (which is partially filled with air, which is easily compressible). This reduces the buoyant force acting on it.

6. **C** Use the equation $Q = mc\Delta T = \rho Vc\Delta T$ (if you did not remember this formula from general chemistry, you could determine it by unit analysis, given that the question asks for heat and the provided constant for water is in units of heat per mass per temperature). The specific heat of water is $c_{water} = 4.2 \text{ J/(g·°C)} = 4.2 \text{ kJ/(kg·°C)}$. The density of the water is $\rho = 10^3 \text{ kg/m}^3$, its volume is $1 \text{ L} = 10^{-3} \text{ m}^3$, and $\Delta T = 30°C - 10°C = 20°C$. Therefore, $Q = (10^3 \text{ kg/m}^3)(10^{-3} \text{ m}^3) [4.2 \text{ kJ/} (\text{kg·°C})](20°C) = 84 \text{ kJ}$.

Passage 18

1. **D** Note first that choices A and B are identical, so they can both be eliminated. Since ρ_3 is greater than ρ_2—as given in the passage—the answer must be choice D.

2. **D** Gauge pressure at depth d below the surface of a liquid of density ρ is given by the equation $P_{gauge} = \rho gd$. In this case, we find

$$P_{gauge} = (736 \text{ kg/m}^3)(10 \text{ N/kg})(0.1 \text{ m}) = 736 \text{ Pa}$$

3. **C** By definition, pressure is force per unit area: $P = F/A$. Therefore, $[P] = [F]/[A] = \text{N/m}^2$ (which is called a pascal, Pa).

4. **B** Using Archimedes' principle, it can be shown that the ratio of a floating object's density to the density of the surrounding fluid is equal to the fraction of the object's volume that is submerged. Thus, if ρ'_0 denotes the density of the second ball, then the fraction of its volume that is submerged in Fluid 1 is ρ'_0/ρ_1. Since $\rho'_0/\rho_1 = 490/736 = 2/3$, the fraction of the ball's volume that is *above* the surface is 1/3.

5. **C** The difference in pressure between Points X and Y is simply the gauge pressure at Point Y. Gauge pressure at depth d below the surface of a liquid of density ρ is given by the equation $P_{gauge} = \rho gd$. Thus, at Point Y, the gauge pressure is

$$\rho_1 gd_1 + \rho_2 gd_2 = (\rho_1 + \rho_2)gd$$
$$= (1736 \text{ kg/m}^3)(10 \text{ N/kg})(0.3 \text{ m})$$
$$= 5.2 \times 10^3 \text{ Pa}$$

6. **D** Using Torricelli's theorem—$v = \sqrt{2gh}$, an equation given in the passage—we find that

$$v = \sqrt{2(10\,\text{m/s}^2)(4\,\text{m})} = 9\,\text{m/s}$$

Passage 19

1. **D** Since the tube constricts from Section 1 to Section 2 to Section 3, the flow speed increases: $v_1 < v_2 < v_3$ (this follows from the continuity equation). Now, since Bernoulli's equation predicts that faster flow speed implies lower fluid pressure, it must be true that $P_1 > P_2 > P_3$.

2. **A** The continuity equation states that the flow rate through Section 1 equals the flow rate through Section 2: $f_1 = f_2$. Since $f = Av$, we have $A_1v_1 = A_2v_2$. Substituting the given values yields (20 cm²) $v_1 = $ (8 cm²)(10 cm/s), which gives $v_1 = 4$ cm/s.

3. **B** The continuity equation gives $A_2v_2 = A_3v_3$, so $A_2/A_3 = v_3/v_2$. If A_2/A_3 increases by a factor of 3, then v_3/v_2 also increases by a factor of 3. Therefore, the inverse ratio, v_2/v_3 decreases by a factor of 3.

4. **B** Applying Bernoulli's equation, we find

$$P_1 + \tfrac{1}{2}\rho v_1^2 = P_3 + \tfrac{1}{2}\rho v_3^2$$
$$P_1 - P_3 = \tfrac{1}{2}\rho(v_3^2 - v_1^2)$$
$$= \tfrac{1}{2}(100)[(0.6)^2 - (0.4)^2]$$
$$= 100\,\text{Pa}$$

5. **D** Since Pipes 1 and 2 carry equal flows, $f_1 = f_2$, which means $A_1v_1 = A_2v_2$. So, if A_1 is greater than A_2, then v_1 must be less than v_2.

Passage 20

1. **A** Since the pressure at any point in the pole is given by $\sigma = \rho gh$, where h denotes the height of the pole above the given point, the lower the point on the pole, the greater the pressure. Since A is lower than B, which is lower than C, we must have $\sigma_A > \sigma_B > \sigma_C$.

2. **B** The pressure at the base of the pole is equal to the pole's weight divided by the cross-sectional area. Since both poles have the same weight, the one with the smaller cross-sectional area (which is Pole II) will feel the greater pressure at its base.

3. **B** Since the pressure at any point in the pole is given by $\sigma = \rho gh$, where h denotes the height of the pole above the given point, we compute

$$\sigma = (7100\ \text{kg/m}^3)(9.8\ \text{N/kg})(10\ \text{m}) = 7 \times 10^5\ \text{Pa}$$

4. **D** If σ is "great" while ε is "relatively little," then their ratio, σ/ε is large (and positive). But this ratio is precisely Young's modulus, E. Note that a negative Young's modulus would imply that a compressive force would cause the pole to extend, which is illogical.

5. **D** One way to answer this question is to check the units of the answer choices. Use the fact that E has units of N/m², g has units of m/s², ρ has units of kg/m³, and ε has no units to find that only the expression in choice D has units of meters and must therefore be the answer. The mathematical solution proceeds as follows: Let σ_C denote the critical stress (that is, the stress at the buckling point, when ε becomes the critical strain, ε_C). Then $\sigma_C/E = \varepsilon_C$. But $\sigma_C = \rho g h_C$, where h_C denotes the critical height (that is, the maximum height before buckling). Combining these last two equations gives

$$\frac{\rho g h_C}{E} = \varepsilon_C \quad \Rightarrow \quad h_C = \frac{\varepsilon_C E}{\rho g}$$

Passage 21

1. **A** The definition of specific gravity simply says: "Divide the density of the substance by the density of water." Therefore, the specific gravity of Fluid #1 is ρ_1/ρ.

2. **D** When the cork is sitting in Fluid #1, its weight is balanced by the buoyant force due to Fluid #1; similarly, when the cork sits in Fluid #2, its weight is balanced by the buoyant force due to Fluid #2. Since the weight of the cork is a constant, the two buoyant forces (due to Fluid #1 and Fluid #2) are identical. Therefore,

$$F_{buoy1} = F_{buoy2} \quad \Rightarrow \quad \rho_1 V_{sub,1} g = \rho_2 V_{sub,2} g \quad \Rightarrow$$

$$\rho_1 \cdot \frac{10}{100} V = \rho_2 \cdot \frac{15}{100} V \Rightarrow \rho_1 = \frac{15}{10}\rho_2 = \frac{3}{2}\rho_2$$

3. **C** With the cork floating in Fluid #2, we equate the weight of the cork with the buoyant force:

$$w = F_{buoy} \quad \Rightarrow \quad \rho_{cork} V g = \rho_1 (\underbrace{\frac{15}{100} V}_{V_{sub}}) g \quad \Rightarrow$$

$$\rho_1 = \frac{100}{15}\rho_{cork} = \frac{20}{3}\rho_{cork}$$

4. **B** When the cork is sitting at the bottom of the container at the moment the magnetic force is removed, the only forces acting are the weight downward and the buoyant force upward. Thus, $F_{net} = F_{buoy} - mg$, and since F_{net} always equals ma, we find

$$\overbrace{F_{buoy} - mg}^{net\ force} = ma$$

$$\rho_1 V g - (\rho_{cork} V)g = (\rho_{cork} V)a$$

$$\therefore a = \frac{\rho_1 - \rho_{cork}}{\rho_{cork}} g = \frac{10\rho_{cork} - \rho_{cork}}{\rho_{cork}} g = 9g$$

5. **B** As the cork moves through the fluid, it experiences a frictional drag force due to the fluid's viscosity. This additional force opposes the propelling upward buoyant force, thereby decreasing the upward acceleration.

Passage 22

1. **A** When the object floats at the surface of the fluid, its weight downward is balanced by the buoyant force upward. Therefore,

$$w = F_{buoy} \implies \rho_{object} V g = \rho_X V_{sub} g \implies$$

$$\frac{V_{sub}}{V} = \frac{\rho_{object}}{\rho_X} = \frac{500 \text{ kg/m}^3}{0.75(1000 \text{ kg/m}^3)} = \frac{2}{3}$$

Since 2/3 of the object is submerged, we know that 1/3 must be exposed above the surface.

2. **D** Since Fluid Y is denser than Fluid X, neither choice A nor B is necessarily true: An object could float in the denser Fluid Y but sink in the less dense Fluid X; similarly, it could sink in Fluid X but float in the denser Fluid Y. Choice C is also not true because the buoyant forces in both cases are identical, each being equal to the weight of the object. This leaves only choice D: Fluid X is two times less dense, so the volume submerged in X will necessarily have to be twice the volume submerged in Fluid Y.

3. **D** Let x be the fraction of Fluid X in the mixture of X and Y; this means that $1 - x$ is the fraction of Y in the mixture. The volume of Fluid X is therefore xV and the volume of Y is $(1 - x)V$, where V is the total volume of the mixture. Since weight equals mass times g, and mass is density times volume, we write (using ρ for the density of water)

$$\overbrace{\rho_X (xV)g}^{\text{weight of X}} + \overbrace{\rho_Y [(1 - x)V]g}^{\text{weight of Y}} = \overbrace{\rho V g}^{\text{weight of water}}$$

$$\frac{3}{4}\rho x + \frac{3}{2}\rho(1 - x) = \rho$$

$$3x + 6(1 - x) = 4$$

$$x = \frac{2}{3}$$

Since 2/3 of the mixture is X and 1/3 is Y, the ratio of X to Y is 2:1.

Passage 23

1. **C** Since the additional pressure we provide on Piston #1 causes an equal increase in pressure at Piston #2, the movement of the pistons is most directly described by Pascal's law.

2. **A** By Pascal's law, the pressure is the same at both pistons 1 and 2, so

$$P_1 = P_2 \quad \Rightarrow \quad \frac{F_1}{A_1} = \frac{F_2}{A_2} \quad \Rightarrow$$

$$F_1 = \frac{A_1}{A_2} F_2 = \frac{5\,\text{cm}^2}{500\,\text{cm}^2}(5000\,\text{N}) = 50\,\text{N}$$

3. **B** The volume of fluid pushed down in Vessel #1 must appear in Vessel #2: $V_1 = V_2$. Since volume equals cross-sectional area times the distance pushed, this equation becomes $A_1 d_1 = A_2 d_2$, so

$$d_1 = \frac{A_2}{A_1} d_2 = \frac{500\,\text{cm}^2}{5\,\text{cm}^2}(1\,\text{mm}) = 100\,\text{mm} = 10\,\text{cm}$$

4. **B** The work done on Piston #1 and the work done by Piston #2 are identical. (You can verify this directly by actually computing $F_1 d_1$ and $F_2 d_2$; F increases by a factor of 100, but d decreases by a factor of 100.) Therefore the desired ratio is 1.

Passage 24

1. **B** The gauge pressure is $\rho g d = (1000)(10)(6) = 60$ kPa.

2. **C** Since the gauge pressure at the depth of Plug #3 (the lowest one) is the greatest, the water would be pushed out most forcefully here and would therefore have the greatest horizontal exit speed. (This can also be done using Bernoulli's equation.)

3. **C** We apply Bernoulli's equation, with "Point 1" as the surface of the water in the tank, and "Point 2" as Hole #2. Since the tank is very large and the hole is small, the speed with which the water level in the tank drops will be very low. Thus, v_1 is small, so v_1^2 is very small, and the term involving v_1^2 will just drop out. Furthermore, the pressure at both points is atmospheric and will therefore cancel out of the equation. (When the hole is created, the water is open to the atmosphere.) This gives

$$P_1 + \rho g h_1 + \tfrac{1}{2}\rho v_1^2 = P_2 + \rho g h_2 + \tfrac{1}{2}\rho v_2^2$$

$$\rho g h_1 = \rho g h_2 + \tfrac{1}{2}\rho v_2^2$$

$$v_2 = \sqrt{2g(h_1 - h_2)}$$

$$= \sqrt{2(10\,\text{m/s}^2)(4\,\text{m})}$$

$$= 9 \text{ m/s}$$

4. **A** Since volume equals cross-sectional area times distance ($V = Ah$), we have

$$h = \frac{V}{A} = \frac{V}{\pi r^2} = \frac{1.4}{\pi(3^2)} \approx \frac{1.4}{28} = \frac{0.1}{2} = 0.05\,\text{m}$$

5. **A** We can see from the solution to question 3 above that the speed with which the water emerges from the hole is $v = \sqrt{2g(\Delta h)}$, where Δh is the difference in height between the water level in the tank and the hole (you may recall this as Torricelli's result). As the water level drops, this difference in height decreases, so the speed of the emerging water also decreases.

6. **B** In the solution to question 3 above, the density of the fluid cancels out of the equation when finding the speed of the emerging stream. Therefore, we should expect the same speed for a fluid of any specific gravity (and negligible viscosity).

Passage 25

1. **A** Solve Poiseuille's law for the volume flow rate f and plug in the given numbers:

$$f = \frac{\pi R^4 \Delta P}{8\eta L} \approx \frac{3(25 \times 10^{-6})^4 (1.2 \times 10^2)}{8(2 \times 10^{-3})(10^{-2})}$$

$$\approx \frac{4(25)^4}{20} \times 10^{-15} = \frac{100(25^3)}{20} \times 10^{-17} = 5(25^3) \times 10^{-17}$$

which means that **A** is the best choice. The quantity $5(25)^3$ is much less than $100^3 = 10^6$, so f must be much less than $10^6 \times 10^{-17} = 10^{-11}$. Thus, choice B is too large, and choices C and D are really too large.

2. **C** To get f into the formula for the Reynolds number, we note that $f = Av$, so

$$N = \frac{2v\rho R}{\eta} = \frac{2(f/A)\rho R}{A\eta} = \frac{2f\rho R}{A\eta} = \frac{2f\rho R}{\pi R^2 \eta} = \frac{2f\rho}{\pi R\eta}$$

3. **D** From Poiseuille's law, we see that ΔP is inversely proportional to R^4. Therefore, if R is cut in half (that is, decreased by a factor of 2), then ΔP must increase by a factor of $2^4 = 16$.

4. **A** Poiseuille's law states that ΔP is directly proportional to L if all the other quantities are constant. The graph of a proportion is always a straight line through the origin.

5. **D** We want to find the option that would increase the Reynolds number (because when the Reynolds number is too high, the flow becomes turbulent). Looking at the formula given for the Reynolds number N, we see that the changes mentioned in choices A and B would decrease N, and choice C has no effect (since N does not depend on the length L of the tube). The change mentioned in choice D does increase N, so this is the only possibility.

Passage 26

1. **B** Use the equation of continuity in the form $A_1v_1 = A_2v_2$. Substituting the given values, this equation becomes (4 cm²)(30 cm/sec) = (20 cm²)v_2, which gives v_2 = 6 cm/sec.

2. **A** Combining the first two equations given in the passage yields $Q = \dfrac{\pi r^4 \Delta P}{8\eta L}$ (Note: This is Poiseuille's law.) Thus, the flow rate Q is proportional to r^4. So, if r increases by 50%—to $1.5r$— then Q increases by a factor of $(1.5)^4 = (3/2)^4 = 81/16 = 5 = 500\%$.

3. **C** Adding more RBCs to the blood will increase its viscosity. Since Q is inversely proportional to η (recall the statement of Poiseuille's law given in the preceding solution), increasing the viscosity will decrease the flow rate.

4. **D** Since the osmotic pressure of the tissue fluids is negligible (Π_i = 0), the total pressure acting to move fluid out of the capillaries is just $P_c + \Pi_i$ = 17 + 0 = 17 torr. On the other hand, the total pressure acting to move fluid *into* the capillaries is *more*: $P_i + \Pi_c$ = 1 + 25 = 26 torr. Thus, the fluid movement should be into the capillaries at a rate proportional to 26 – 17 = 9 torr.

5. **D** The presence of the various parallel branches (arteries and arterioles) makes it clear that the architecture is in parallel (eliminating choices A and B). Furthermore, from the analogy with electrical circuits, the total resistance of a collection of parallel resistors is *less* than that of any of the individual resistances. The best answer is choice D.

Passage 27

1. **D** The continuity equation in the first paragraph shows that the fluid's speed must increase when it enters the narrow part. This eliminates choices A and C. Bernoulli's equation (with the h's canceling out) then tells us that P_2 must actually be lower than P_1 (since v_2 is greater than v_1). This is the Bernoulli effect.

2. **D** Choice A is a false statement (think of mercury and molasses; molasses is much more viscous but much less dense). Choice B is also false; if energy lost to heat is taken into account, energy is always conserved. And choice C is also false: In fact, fluids with high viscosity can hold off turbulence better than less viscous fluids. The answer must be choice D.

3. **D** Once the plug is removed, the fluid at both levels is exposed to the atmosphere, so both P_1 and P_2 equal P_{atm}, and they cancel out of Bernoulli's equation. Now set v_2 = 0 (because the water level in the tank drops very slowly), cancel out the ρ's on both sides, and solve for v_1. (This is Torricelli's result.)

4. **A** The (total) pressure comes from the fluid plus the atmosphere on top of it. (Although the plug also feels atmospheric pressure from the outside trying to push it inward, the question asks for the pressure trying to push it outward.)

5. **A** The first paragraph of the passage explains that the continuity equation is valid as long as the fluid is incompressible. Since we are told that the continuity equation does not hold here, it must be the case that the fluid is not incompressible (maybe it's a gas).

6. **D** To determine how well the equation works, you need to know the viscosities. The passage states that Bernoulli's equation works when the viscosity is negligible. Since we are not given any information about the values of the viscosities, no determination can be made.

7. **B** Even with no (static) pressure differential between the two ends, there can be fluid flow; it just means the fluid can't accelerate along a horizontal pipe ($F_{net} = 0$ means $a = 0$, not necessarily $v = 0$). Thus, Statement I is not necessarily true. The volume flow rate is also constant because the fluid is incompressible. So, Statement II is true. Moreover, since f is constant and the cross-sectional area, A, doesn't change, the flow speed, v, must be constant as well. Finally, Bernoulli's equation says that when fluid rises within a closed pipe, the pressure goes down (that is, if h_2 is large, then P_2 must be low). Thus, Statement III is true.

Passage 28

1. **A** The magnitude of the electrostatic force is given by $F = kqQ/r^2$. Since Positions X and Y are at the same distance away from the charge Q, the force that q would feel would have the same magnitude at either position.

2. **D** First, note that the force F_X is greater than F_Z since Position X is closer to the charge Q; this observation rules out choices A and C. To actually compute the ratio, we write

$$\frac{F_X}{F_Z} = \frac{kqQ/r_X^2}{kqQ/r_Z^2} = \left(\frac{r_Z}{r_X}\right)^2 = \left(\frac{4\text{ cm}}{3\text{ cm}}\right)^2 = \frac{16}{9} \Rightarrow F_X = \frac{16}{9}F_Z$$

3. **D** Since we are pushing a positive charge toward a position of higher potential, the potential energy must increase (eliminating choices A and B). To be precise,

$$\Delta PE = qV = q\left(\frac{kQ}{r_X} - \frac{kQ}{r_Z}\right) = qkQ\left(\frac{1}{r_X} - \frac{1}{r_Z}\right)$$
$$= (10^{-14})(9\times10^9)(10^{-9})\cdot\left(\frac{1}{.03} - \frac{1}{.04}\right)$$
$$= (9\times10^{-14})\cdot(33-25) = 7.2\times10^{-13}\text{ J}$$

(In the above calculation, I simplified the fractions as follows. 0.03 equals 3/100, so 1 over .03 [that is, the reciprocal of .03] is 100/3, which is about 33. Similarly, 1 over .04 is the reciprocal of 4/100, which is 100/4 = 25.)

4.   **C**   First, note that since the Charge Q is positive, the electric field vector at Position X must point in the positive x direction, directly away from Q; this rules out choices B and D. Thus, the direction of E at Position X is $+\mathbf{i}$ (which is the unit vector in the positive x direction), and its magnitude is

$$E = k\frac{Q}{r^2} = (9 \times 10^9)\frac{10^{-9}}{(3 \times 10^{-2})^2} = 10^4 \text{ N/C}$$

5.   **A**   The work done by an external force to move a charge is equal to the change in potential energy which is also equal to the charge moved times the potential difference: $W = \Delta PE = q\Delta\phi$. The potential due to charge Q is given by $\phi = kQ/r$. Since X and Y are at the same distance from Q, the potentials at these positions are identical. Therefore, the change in potential from Z to X is the same as from Z to Y. Since we move the same charge between two places where the changes in potentials are the same, we must get the same value for the work required. (Important note: The distance from Z to Y being greater than the distance from Z to X is irrelevant. The formula "work equals force times distance (along the line of force)" may make you think that if the distance is greater, then the work must be greater. But this simple formula does not apply here, because it works only if the force is *constant*. The force is *not* constant in this problem since F clearly depends upon the distance r from the charge Q. Thus, we must use "work equals charge times change in potential.")

6.   **D**   Since both q and Q are positive charges, q will be repelled from the fixed charge Q. This eliminates choices A and B. Furthermore, as the distance between q and Q increases (due to the motion of q), the electric force decreases, which in turn decreases the acceleration (since $F = ma$).

Passage 29

1.   **B**   The individual electric field vectors (one due to each of the two given charges) will cancel only when their magnitudes are equal and their directions are opposites. This can only happen at the midpoint of the imaginary line joining the charges, so there is only one position in the (finite) x-y plane where the electric field is zero.

2.   **B**   The distance between the charges in their pictured positions is $R = \sqrt{2}$ mm, but if one of the charges is moved to the origin, their separation will then only be $r = 1$ mm. Therefore, the ratio of the electrostatic force when one is at the origin to the force in their pictured positions is

$$\frac{kQ^2/r^2}{kQ^2/R^2} = \frac{R^2}{r^2} = \frac{(\sqrt{2}\,\text{mm})^2}{(1\,\text{mm})^2} = 2$$

3. C   A positive charge placed at the origin would feel a downward repulsive force due to the charge on the y axis and a repulsive force to the left due to the charge on the x axis. The resultant force would therefore be at a 45° angle, pointing into the third quadrant.

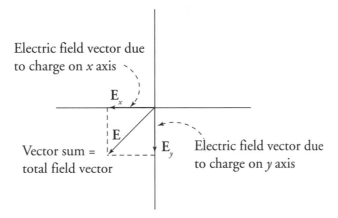

4. C   Refer to the figure in Question 3 above. The magnitude of the vector sum is $\sqrt{2}$ times each of the individual field vector magnitudes since the hypotenuse of an isosceles right triangle is $\sqrt{2}$ times the length of each leg. Therefore, the desired magnitude is

$$E_{\text{total}} = \sqrt{2} \cdot E_{\text{individual}} = \sqrt{2} \cdot \frac{kQ}{r^2}$$

$$= (1.4) \cdot \frac{(9 \times 10^9)(1.1 \times 10^{-10})}{(10^{-3})^2} = 1.4 \times 10^6 \text{ N/C}$$

5. A   The potential due to a point charge is given by $\phi = kQ/r$. Since this is not a vector quantity, the potential due to a positive charge is positive (relative to "infinity" being designated zero potential). The potential at any point in this plane due to both charges would simply be the sum of two positive values, which couldn't possibly equal 0. Therefore (excluding the point "at infinity"), there are no points in the plane where the potential is 0.

6. C   Since ϕ is not a vector quantity, the potential due to two point charges is simply the sum of the individual potentials. The potential at the origin due the charge on the y axis is the same as the potential at the origin due to the charge on the x axis (since the charges are the same and the distance from each charge to the origin is the same), therefore we easily find the total potential:

$$\phi = \frac{kQ}{r} + \frac{kQ}{r} = \frac{2kQ}{r} = \frac{2(9 \times 10^9)(1.1 \times 10^{-10})}{10^{-3}} = 2000 \text{ V}$$

7. C   The (magnitude of the) force that a charge q would feel when placed at the origin is $F = qE$, where E is the magnitude of the total electric field vector at the origin. But both the proton and electron share the same charge magnitude (namely e), so they would feel the same magnitude of force. But, since F equals ma, their accelerations would be different because their masses are different. Choice C is best since a quick estimate gives

$$\frac{a_e}{a_p} = \frac{F/m_e}{F/m_p} = \frac{m_p}{m_e} = \frac{1.67 \times 10^{-27}}{9.11 \times 10^{-31}} \approx \frac{1}{5} \times 10^4 = 2000$$

Passage 30

1. **C** The current flowing into the branch point between R_1 and R_5 must equal the current flowing out of it; this is Kirchhoff's Junction Rule. Since the current flowing through the branch containing Resistors R_1, R_2, and R_3 is equal to 0.4 A, and the current flowing through the branch containing Resistors R_5, R_6, and R_7 is also equal to 0.4 A, this leaves $2 - (0.4 + 0.4) = 1.2$ A to flow through the middle branch, that is, the one containing Resistor R_4.

2. **C** Since resistors R_1, R_2, and R_3 are in series the total or equivalent resistance R_{eq} is given by $R_{eq} = R_1 + R_2 + R_3 = 2\,\Omega + 2\,\Omega + 2\,\Omega = 6\,\Omega$

3. **B** By definition, charge equals current times time: $Q = It$. Since $I = V/R$, we have

$$Q = Vt/R = (15\text{ V})(1\text{ s})/(10\,\Omega) = 3/2\text{ C}$$

4. **D** The power dissipated by a circuit can be written as $P = VI$, $P = V^2/R_{eq}$, or $P = I^2R_{eq}$. We have been given V and R_{eq}, therefore we use $P = V^2/R_{eq}$. Solving for R we get

$$R = V^2/P = (30\text{ V})^2/(3\text{ W}) = 300\,\Omega$$

5. **B** The total or equivalent capacitance of a collection of capacitors in series is calculated by the same type of equation used to calculate the total resistance of a collection of resistors in parallel. That is, $1/C_{eq} = 1/C_1 + 1/C_2$. Since $C_1 = C_2 = 2\,\mu F$ we find that $1/C_{eq} = 1/2 + 1/2 = 1$, which implies that $C_{eq} = 1\,\mu F$ A quicker way would be to remember that the equivalent capacitance of a collection of n identical capacitors of value C in series is given by $C_{eq} = C/n$. In this case, $C_{eq} = (2\,\mu F)/2 = 1\,\mu F$.

6. **C** The energy consumed by the resistor network is equal to the energy supplied by the capacitor network. Since the amount of energy stored in the charged capacitor network is given $PE = \frac{1}{2}QV$, which equals

$$PE = \tfrac{1}{2}CV^2 = \tfrac{1}{2}(10^{-6}\text{ F})(10^2\text{ V}) = 5 \times 10^{-5}\text{ J}$$

this will be the total amount of energy consumed by the resistors.

7. **B** According to the graph, $I = 0.5$ A when $V = 50$ V. Thus, energy is consumed by this component at a rate of $P = IV = (0.5\text{ A})(50\text{ V}) = 25$ W.

Passage 31

1. **A** While choice D is often true, just having a voltage source does not guarantee that the plates will act as a capacitor. If the material between the plates conducted electricity, then the plates could not hold charge, rendering them useless as a capacitor. Choices B and C both say that the potential difference between the plates would be zero. If there is no potential difference, then $Q = CV$ implies that there would be no charge stored, which is the primary function of a capacitor.

2. **D** The equation $V = Ed$ implies that $E = V/d = (10\text{ V})/(0.01\text{ m}) = 1000$ V/m.

3. **B** $PE = \frac{1}{2}QV = \frac{1}{2}CV^2 = \frac{1}{2}(10^{-6}\text{ F})(10^2\text{ V}) = 5 \times 10^{-5}\text{ J}$

4. **A**   By definition, $C = Q/V$. Therefore,

$$Q = CV = (10^{-6}\text{ F})(10\text{ V}) = 10^{-5}\text{ C}$$

5. **C**   The work W required to move a charge q across a potential difference $\Delta\phi$ is given by $W = q\Delta\phi$. We are moving a negative charge to the negative plate (i.e. the lower potential plate). Therefore, both q and $\Delta\phi$ are negative.

$$W = q\Delta\phi = (-2\text{ C})(-10\text{ V}) = 20\text{ J}$$

Note that $W = q\Delta\phi = qV$ can be used when moving a charge across an already existing potential difference, while $W = \frac{1}{2}QV$ is used to represent the work the battery does in moving *the total charge* from one plate to another. The difference in equations occurs because the potential difference across the plates changes during the charging process.

6. **D**   The total or equivalent capacitance of a collection of capacitors in series is calculated by the same type of equation used to calculate the total resistance of a collection of resistors in parallel. That is, $1/C_{eq} = 1/C_1 + 1/C_2$. This implies that C_{eq} will be less than both C_1 and C_2.

7. **A**   The total or equivalent capacitance of a collection of capacitors in parallel is calculated by the same type of equation used to calculate the total resistance of a collection of resistors in series. That is, $C_{eq} = C_1 + C_2$. This implies that C_{eq} will be greater than both C_1 and C_2.

Passage 32

1. **D**   Since $\mathbf{F} = I\mathbf{L} \times \mathbf{B}$, the force $\mathbf{F}$ is, by definition, perpendicular to both $\mathbf{L}$ and $\mathbf{B}$, that is, perpendicular to both the wire and to the magnetic field lines.

2. **A**   The magnetic field lines produced by a straight current encircles the wire. This eliminates choices C and D since the field must point either into or out of the page at a point above the wire. By the Right Hand Rule, with the thumb pointing in the direction of the current, the fingers curl in the direction of the circular magnetic field lines. Grabbing Wire XY in your right hand with your thumb pointing to the left (which is the direction of the current), your fingers point *into* the page above XY (which is where the Point P is located), parallel to $\mathbf{B}_{ext}$.

3. **C**   Substituting the values given in the question into Equation 1, we find

$$B = \frac{\mu_0 I}{2\pi r} = \frac{\mu_0(6.28\text{ A})}{2(3.14)(0.5\text{ m})} = 2\mu_0 \text{ (in teslas)}$$

4. **A**   Equation 2 becomes $F = ILB$, since $\theta = 90°$ implies $\sin\theta = 1$. We substitute V/R for I to derive the equation $F = (V/R)LB$. Using the values given in the question, we find that

$$F = [(9\text{ V})/(3\text{ W})](4\text{ m})(0.5\text{ T}) = 6\text{ N}$$

5.   **A**   If the wire is parallel to the magnetic field lines, then $\theta = 0°$, so $\sin\theta = 0$. Thus, $F = ILB \sin\theta = 0$.

6.   **C**   Since the power dissipated by a resistor can be expressed as $P = I^2R$, the current is given by the equation $I = \sqrt{P/R}$. Thus,

$$I = \sqrt{(60\,\text{W})(15\,\Omega)} = 2\,\text{A}$$

Passage 33

1.   **A**   If $F = \dfrac{\mu_0 i_a i_b}{2\pi r}$ is constant and r is constant, then the product $i_a i_b$ is constant. Thus, i_b is inversely proportional to i_a, so the graph of i_b vs. i_a will be (one branch of) a hyperbola: choice A. Note that choice B is often mistaken for an inverse relation. Rather, it is a linear relationship with a negative slope.

2.   **B**   If $i_a = i_b = i$, then $F = \dfrac{\mu_0 i_a i_b}{2\pi r}$ becomes $F = \dfrac{\mu_0 i^2}{2\pi r}$. The value of F is more sensitive to variations in i than in r, since the quantity i is squared, while r appears to the first power only. (Note: Choices A and C, μ_0 and π, are constants.)

3.   **B**   Since $B = \dfrac{\mu_0 i}{2\pi r}$ doubling i will double the strength of the magnetic field. The other wire, feeling twice the magnetic field strength, will experience twice the magnetic force. You can also use the equation for F/l to get the same answer.

4.   **D**   The magnetic field created by a straight current is given by the Right Hand Rule: point the thumb of your right hand in the direction of the current, and the direction of **B** is the direction your fingers curl. Therefore, the magnetic field at Point Q due to the current i_a points downward, and the magnetic field at Q due to the current i_b also points downward. Since Point Q is equidistant from both wires, the field due to i_a is the same as that due to i_b. Since they are of equal magnitude B and in the same direction, the magnitude of the resultant magnetic field is $2B$.

5.   **B**   By the Right Hand Rule as explained in the previous solution, the magnetic field at Point P due to the current i_b points upward. This eliminates choices A and B. Using the equation $B = \dfrac{\mu_0 i}{2\pi r}$ we find that

$$B = \frac{\mu_0(3.1)}{2(3.1)(1)} = \tfrac{1}{2}\mu_0\,\text{T}$$

6. **A** By definition, $R = V/I = (5 \text{ V})/(10 \text{ A}) = 0.5 \ \Omega$

7. **C** By definition, power is equal to energy dissipated per unit time: $P = E/t$. Thus,

$$t = E/P = (1500 \text{ J})/(100 \text{ W}) = 15 \text{ sec}$$

8. **D** Using Equation 2 with $i_a = i_b = 1$ A, $r = 1$ m, and $F/L = 2 \times 10^{-7}$ N/m, we find

$$2 \times 10^{-7} \text{ N/m} = \frac{\mu_0 (1 \text{ A})(1 \text{ A})}{2\pi (1 \text{ m})}$$
$$4\pi \times 10^{-7} \text{ N/A}^2 = \mu_0$$

Passage 34

1. **A** The magnitude of the electric field due to a single source charge q is given by $E = kq/r^2$. E is inversely proportional to the square of the distance from the charge. Therefore, if r is increased by a factor of 4, then E decreases by a factor of $4^2 = 16$.

2. **A** From the data in the table, the potential difference between the plates drops by 2.8 V in the first second, by 2 V in the second, and by 1.5 V in the third. Thus, the loss of voltage is greatest at the beginning and steadily decreases as time goes on. Since the charge of a capacitor is proportional to the voltage (since $q = CV$), this same behavior also applies to q. That is, q drops rapidly at first and gradually decreases more and more slowly with time. This is best depicted by the graph in choice A.

3. **B** With Switches A and D closed (and B and C open), the circuit is composed of a battery and three resistors in series. Since each resistor is 2 Ω, the equivalent resistance R_{eq} is found by adding the individual resistors, or $R_{eq} = 2 \ \Omega + 2 \ \Omega + 2 \ \Omega = 6 \ \Omega$, so $I = V/R_{eq} = (10 \text{ V})/(6 \ \Omega) = 1.7$ A.

4. **B** Current is defined as the amount of charge that flows past a certain point per unit time. If something inhibits charge from making this migration, then current is lowered. Heating causes increased agitation of the atoms that compose the substance, which will, in the vast majority of substances, make it more difficult for free electrons to make their way through. (It is more difficult to cross a room in which people are dancing wildly than to cross the same room when the people are slow dancing.) Choice A can be eliminated because expanding a resistor wouldn't necessarily change its resistance, as both length and area would change (to say nothing of thermal dependence of resistivity). Choice C can be eliminated because it confuses heat with temperature (a cold or hot resistor could transfer heat to a cooler environment). Choice D is the opposite of choice B.

5. **C** The resistors in the parallel network along Branch 2 are identical. The equivalent resistance R_{eq} of n identical resistors (each equal to R) is given by $R_{eq} = R/n$. Doubling the number of such resistors will therefore halve the total resistance. Since V is fixed, the power consumed by the network is best expressed by the equation $P = V^2/R$, which is inversely proportional to R. Since we have seen that doubling the number of resistors would decrease the total resistance by a factor of 2, the power consumed by the network would increase by a factor of 2.

6. **B** First, note that 6.25×10^{18} electrons carry a charge of $q = -1$ C. (This is stated at the end of the passage.) If W is the work done *against* the electric field, then, by definition, $W = q\Delta\phi$. Since we are moving from the positive plate to the negative plate, the potential decreases, so $\Delta\phi. = -10$ V. Therefore, $W = q\Delta\phi. = (-1 \text{ C})(-10 \text{ V}) = 10$ J.

7. **D** By convention, electric field vectors always point away from positive source charges and toward negative ones. Since the top plate is positive and the bottom plate is negative, the electric field between the plates must point downward.

Passage 35

1. **C** The passage says that "the expression R_1C is called the *time constant*," so the product of resistance and capacitance is equal to a time interval. Another solution is to notice that the formulas involve e^{-t/R_1C}, and the exponent $-t/R_1C$ must be dimensionless (the argument of a transcendental function cannot have units). So, because t has units of time, R_1C must also have units of time. Alternatively, one can work out the units directly; because $R = V/I$ and $C = Q/V$ by definition, we can write $[R][C] = \text{V/A} \times \text{C/V} = \text{C/A} = \text{C/(C/s)} = \text{s}$.

2. **D** Because voltage = charge/capacitance, we can use Equation 2 to find that: $v = q/C = CV(1 - e^{-t/R_1C})/C = V(1 - e^{-t/R_1C})$

3. **D** The slope of any graph is "rise over run," so for Figure 2, which is a graph of charge vs. time, the slope will be "charge divided by time." This is current.

4. **A** As the passage states, the expression R_1C "determines how rapidly the exponential term decays." Because both choices B and C give the same value for the product R_1C (namely, 60 $\Omega\cdot\mu$F, or 60 μs), they would both give the same rate of decay; therefore, they must both be wrong. To select between choices A and D, it is useful to compare this scenario to radioactive decay, described by the equation describing radioactive decay with $t_{1/2}$ is the half-life. This equation has exactly the same form as Equation 3, with the half-life (divided by a constant) playing the role of the time constant. We know that the shorter the half-life, the more rapid the decay; so, the shorter the time constant, the more rapid the decay.

5. **B** First, note that V, the voltage across the capacitor, is the same at the end of Step 1 in both experiments. One way to interpret Step 1 is that the current eventually dies out because the voltage across the capacitor matches the voltage of the battery. Because the "polarities" of these voltages are the same (the left side of the battery *and* the left plate of the capacitor are at the higher potential, so they behave like competing voltage sources—the battery would want to send current clockwise, while the capacitor would want to send current counterclockwise), the *net* voltage in that part of the circuit is *zero*, which is why no current flows at the end of Step 1. This eliminates choice D. Next, the potential energy stored in a capacitor is given by $\frac{1}{2}CV^2$; because V is the same at the end of Step 1 in both experiments, and because C is greater in the second experiment (the presence of a dielectric always increases the capacitance), there will be *more* potential energy stored in the capacitor at the end of Step 1; this eliminates choice A. The fact that C has increased means that the time constant R_1C has increased. The longer the time constant, the slower the decay of the exponential term, so the slower the decay in current (Equation 1) and the slower the build up of charge (Equation 2). Therefore, choice B is correct and choice C is wrong.

6. **A** If switch S_3 were closed (and S_1 and S_2 were open), then the capacitor would discharge through both R_1 and R_2, which are in series. Therefore, the total resistance would be $R_1 + R_2$, and the current would have the form $I = V/R_{\text{equivalent}} = V/(R_1 + R_2)$. Only choice A contains this form, so that's the answer.

Passage 36

1. **D** First, we find the equivalent resistance for the circuit. Since R_2 and R_3 are in parallel, their equivalent resistance is computed as follows:

$$\frac{1}{R} = \frac{1}{R_1} + \frac{1}{R_2} \quad \Rightarrow \quad R = \frac{R_1 R_2}{R_1 + R_2} = \frac{(1)(1)}{1+1} = 0.5 \text{ ohm}$$

Or, it is useful to remember that the equivalent resistance of n identical resistors in parallel, each with resistance R, is equal to R/n. Next, R_1 and this equivalent resistor are in series, so the overall resistance is given by $R_{eq} = R_1 + R = 1 + 0.5 = 1.5 \ \Omega$. Now that we have reduced the circuit to an equivalent one with just one resistor, we can use $V = IR_{eq}$ to find the total current I in the circuit: $I = V/R_{eq} = (9 \text{ V})/(1.5 \ \Omega) = 6$ amps. This amount of current flows through R_1.

2. **C** Since R_2 and R_3 are in parallel, they must share the same voltage drop: $V_2 = V_3$.

3. **B** The result of Problem 1 states that 6A of current flows through R_1 and reaches the junction of R_2 and R_3. Some of the 6-amp current will flow through R_2, and the rest will flow through R_3. Since R_2 and R_3 have the same resistance, there is no reason for the current to favor one resistor over the other; therefore, half (3 A) will flow through each one.

Here's an alternate solution: The voltage drop across R_1 is $V_1 = IR_1 = (6 \text{ A})(1 \ \Omega) = 6$ V, so the voltage drop across the parallel combination must be the remainder, $9 - 6 = 3$ V. Since R_2 and R_3 are in parallel, they *each* have a voltage drop of 3 volts. Since we know the individual voltage drops and the individual resistances, we can compute the individual currents. In both cases, we have $I = V/R = (3 \text{ V})/(1 \ \Omega) = 3$ A.

4. **C** From our solution to the preceding question, we know that the current through R_3 is 3 amps. Therefore, the power dissipated by R_3 is $P = I_3^2 R_3 = (3 \text{ A})^2 (1 \ \Omega) = 9$ J/s. Therefore, in 4 seconds, R_3 dissipates a total of $(9 \text{ J/s})(4 \text{ s}) = 36$ J of heat energy.

Passage 37

1. **B** First, notice that the batteries are opposing each other: that is, the 9 V battery wants to send current counterclockwise around the circuit, but the 12 V battery wants to send current clockwise. When batteries oppose each other, the net result is a battery with a voltage equal to the difference of the two individual voltages. In this case, we can replace these two batteries by a single $12 \text{ V} - 9 \text{ V} = 3$ V battery that sends current clockwise (since the 12 V battery wins out). The resistors are in series, so $R_{eq} = R_1 + R_2 = 1 \ \Omega + 2 \ \Omega = 3 \ \Omega$. Therefore, the circuit is equivalent to a simple circuit containing just a 3 V battery and a 3 Ω resistor, so the current is $I = V/R_{eq} = (3 \text{ V})/(3 \ \Omega) = 1$ A.

2. **A** Since R_1 and R_2 are in series, they must share the same current: $I_1 = I_2$.

3. **B** The current through R_2 is 1 A (see the solutions to the preceding questions), so the power dissipated by R_2 is $P = I^2 R_2 = (1 \text{ A})^2 (2 \text{ }\Omega) = 2$ W.

4. **D** Since the current in the circuit is 1 A, the power supplied by the 12-volt battery is $P = IV = (1 \text{ A})(12 \text{ V}) = 12$ J/s. So in 3 seconds, the total energy supplied is $(12 \text{ J/s})(3 \text{ s}) = 36$ J. Note that using the formula $P = I^2 R_{eq}$ or $P = V^2/R_{eq}$ would not give the correct answer. These expressions give the total power consumed by the resistors, which is not equal to the power supplied by the 12V battery. The 9 V battery, experiencing current moving the "wrong" way across its terminals (in other words, from high potential to low potential), eats up some the voltage and therefore, some of the power.

5. **C** Recall that the relationship between terminal voltage and emf is given by $V = \varepsilon - Ir$. If the terminal voltage is 9 V, then the current is still $I = V_{eq}/R_{eq} = (12 \text{ V} - 9 \text{ V})/(1 \text{ }\Omega + 2 \text{ }\Omega) = 1$ A. So, the emf of the 9 V battery is $\varepsilon = V + Ir = 9 \text{ V} + (1 \text{ A})(0.01 \text{ }\Omega) = 9.01$ V.

Passage 38

1. **C** The voltage drops across R_1 and R_2 are each equal to 18 V since they are in parallel. Therefore, we can use $I = V/R$ to calculate the current: through the 3 Ω resistor, we have $I = V/R = (18 \text{ V})/(3 \text{ }\Omega) = 6$ A.

2. **B** By the same reasoning as Problem 1, through the 6 Ω resistor, we have $I = V/R = (18 \text{ V})/(6 \text{ }\Omega) = 3$ A.

3. **B** Since R_1 and R_2 are in parallel, they must share the same voltage drop: $V_1 = V_2$.

4. **A** The power dissipated by a resistor can be written as $P = I^2 R$ or $P = V^2/R$. At first glance, these appear to contradict each other—the first equation seems to imply that bigger resistors dissipate more power, while the second equation seems to imply the opposite. The key is to make sure you know what is the same for each resistor. Since R_1 and R_2 are in parallel, they have the same voltage. Therefore, $P = V^2/R$ is the more useful equation. V being constant means that power is inversely proportional to R. Since $R_2 = 2R_1$, then $P_2 = (1/2)P_1$. Note: you can also use $P = IV$, noting that larger resistors in parallel receive less current.

Passage 39

1. **C** According to Equation 1, $F = ILB$. Or, in units: N = A·m·T. Therefore, T = N/(A·m). It is also possible to use Equation 2, remembering that the unit for torque is N·m and the unit for area is m^2.

2. **C** According to Equation 2, $\tau = IAB \sin \theta$. The first thing to realize is that the angle θ between the field and the normal is 90° since the normal is (by definition) perpendicular to the plane of the loop. This gives 1 for the sine term. Since the area A of the loop is 0.2 m × 0.2 m = 0.04 m^2, we find $\tau = IAB \sin \theta = (10 \text{ A})(0.04 \text{ m}^2)(0.5 \text{ T})(1) = 0.2$ N·m.

3. **A** The magnetic force on a current or on a single charge moving parallel (in the same direction) or antiparallel (in the direction precisely opposite) to a magnetic field is zero. ($F_B = ILB \sin \theta$ for currents and $F_B = |q|vB \sin \theta$ for point charges, where θ is the angle between the current (or velocity) and the magnetic field.)

4. **A** The magnetic force acting on a current in the presence of an external magnetic field is perpendicular to the direction of the current and to the magnetic field. This eliminates choices C and D. The Right-Hand Rule states that if you point the thumb of your right hand in the direction of the current (upward) and your fingers in the direction of the magnetic field (right), the force is directed out of your palm (into the page).

5. **A** If the field is perpendicular to the plane of the wire, then it is parallel to the vector normal to the plane of the wire. When visualizing normal vectors it is helpful to imagine a stubby little arrow pointing out of the plane. When the loop rotates, the little arrow rotates with it. If the field and the normal are parallel, the angle θ is either $0°$ or $180°$. Either way, $\sin \theta = 0$, so the torque is zero.

6. **D** As stated at the end of the passage, the *net* force on any current loop in a uniform magnetic field is zero. Since $F_{net} = ma_{CM}$, the fact that $F_{net} = 0$ means that the center of mass can't move (since it was initially at rest and its $a = 0$, its velocity remains zero).

7. **C** The reason you have a torque is that, in the original orientation, there is a force into the page on PQ and a force out of the page on RS. Use the Right Hand Rule to convince yourself of this (see question 4). With PQ on the right and RS on the left, the inward force will be on the right and the outward force will be on the left so the loop rotates in the opposite direction. This is the same thing as saying the torque points in the opposite direction. The magnitude would still be as calculated in question 2.

8. **B** If the magnetic field pointed up, everything would be the same as before except the wire would rotate top over bottom instead of right over left. But nothing in the torque equation would be any different, that is, the magnitude of the torque would be unchanged.

Passage 40

1. **C** Since the capacitors are in series, their equivalent capacitance is calculated as follows:

$$\frac{1}{C_{eq}} = \frac{1}{8} + \frac{1}{4} + \frac{1}{8} = \frac{1}{2} \implies C_{eq} = 2 \text{ nF}$$

A trickier method involves remembering the fact that the equivalent capacitance of n identical capacitors (with magnitude C) in series is given by $C_{eq} = C/n$. The capacitors in this problem are not all identical, but you can combine them in steps. The two 8 nF capacitors combine to form a 4 nF capacitor, which then combines with the other 4 nF capacitor to create an equivalent capacitance of 2 nF.

2. **C** The voltage across C_1 is $V_1 = Q_1/C_1 = (10 \text{ μC})/(2 \text{ μF}) = 5$ V. Since the capacitors are in parallel, the voltage across C_2 is the same as across C_1; thus, $V_2 = 5$ V also. From this we find $Q_2 = C_2 V_2 = (4 \text{ μF})(5 \text{ V}) = 20 \text{ μC}$. A proportion can also be used. In parallel, because V is the same for all capacitors, Q is proportional to C. Since $C_2 = 2C_1$, then $Q_2 = 2Q_1 = 20 \text{ μC}$.

3. **B** After the first negative charge is transferred, the plate becomes negative. To continue to transfer negative charges to a negative plate requires work done *against* the electric field. Therefore, the work done *by* the electric field must be negative. This eliminates choices C and D. To find the magnitude of the work, remember that $W = \Delta PE$. Since the initial potential energy is zero, the magnitude of the work done is equal to the potential energy of the fully charged capacitor:

$$PE = \frac{1}{2}CV^2 = \frac{1}{2}C\left(\frac{Q}{C}\right)^2 = \frac{Q^2}{2C} = \frac{(4 \times 10^{-6}\ C)^2}{2(8 \times 10^{-6}\ F)} = 1\mu J$$

Therefore, the work done by the electric field must have been $-1\ \mu J$.

4. **A** The equivalent capacitance of C_1 and C_2 in series is

$$\frac{1}{C_{eq}} = \frac{1}{C_1} + \frac{1}{C_2} \quad \Rightarrow \quad C_{eq} = \frac{C_1 C_2}{C_1 + C_2}$$

But notice that

$$\frac{C_1 C_2}{C_1 + C_2} < \frac{C_1 C_2}{C_2} = C_1 \quad \text{and} \quad \frac{C_1 C_2}{C_1 + C_2} < \frac{C_1 C_2}{C_1} = C_2$$

so C_{eq} is always less than either C_1 or C_2.

5. **C** It is easiest to look at the pure series and the pure parallel choices first. We can eliminate choice B since three 2-μF capacitors all in series would yield an equivalent capacitance of

$$\frac{1}{C_{eq}} = \frac{1}{2} + \frac{1}{2} + \frac{1}{2} = \frac{3}{2} \quad \Rightarrow \quad C_{eq} = \frac{2}{3}\ \mu F$$

Choice D is also wrong since three 2-μF capacitors in parallel are equivalent to a single $2 + 2 + 2 = 6\ \mu F$ capacitor. The configuration in choice A has a parallel combination in series with one of the individual capacitors. The pair in parallel is equivalent to a single $2 + 2 = 4\ \mu F$ capacitor, and this in series with a 2 μF capacitor yields an overall equivalent capacitance of 4/3 μF (verify). Thus, the answer must be choice C. Here we have a series combination (equivalent to a single 1 μF) in parallel with a 2 μF capacitor, giving an overall equivalent capacitance of $1 + 2 = 3\ \mu F$, as desired.

6. **C** Before the switch is closed, the charge on C_1 is $Q_1 = C_1 V_1 = (2\ mF)(12\ V) = 24\ mC$. After the switch is closed, this charge will re-distribute itself over the two capacitors in such a way that the resulting voltages across the capacitors are identical (because they're in parallel). Therefore, if Q'_1 denotes the new charge magnitude on C_1 and Q'_2 denotes the new charge magnitude on C_2, then

$$Q'_1 + Q'_2 = Q_1$$
$$C_1 V' + C_2 V' = Q_1$$
$$(C_1 + C_2)V' = Q_1$$
$$V' = \frac{Q_1}{C_1 + C_2} = \frac{24\ mC}{2\ mF + 4\ mF} = 4\ V.$$

A quicker way of thinking about it is that, since V is the same for all resistors in parallel, Q is proportional to C. Since $C_2 = 2C_1$, then $Q_2 = 2Q_1$. 24 mC are being shared by two capacitors such that C_2 gets twice as much as C_1. This means that Q_1 must equal 8 mC and Q_2 must equal 16 mC. To find the resulting voltage, use $Q = CV$ for either C_1 or C_2: V = (8 mC)/(2 mF) or V = (16 mC)/(4 mF).

Passage 41

1. **B** By definition of capacitance, $Q = CV = (2 \times 10^{-6} \text{ F})(12 \text{ V}) = 2.4 \times 10^{-5}$ C.

2. **C** The capacitance is increased by a factor of 4 because of the dielectric, and, because the battery is still connected to the plates, the potential difference between the plates will still be V = 12 V. With V a constant, Q is directly proportional to C and therefore also increases by factor of 4.

3. **A** The electric field between the plates is given by "Ed's formula": $V = Ed$. Since the potential difference V will be the same (because the 12 V battery is still connected to the plates), and the distance d between the plates does not change, then E will not change: $E_1 = E$.

4. **D** We cannot use "work equals force times distance," because we have no way of knowing either the force or the distance (the distance is not the plate separation); we need a completely different method. Remembering that work against the electric field equals the change in electrical potential energy, we can write

$$W_{\text{against field}} = \Delta PE = \tfrac{1}{2}C'V^2 - \tfrac{1}{2}CV^2$$
$$= \tfrac{1}{2}V^2(4C - C)$$
$$= \tfrac{1}{2}(12^2)[3(2 \times 10^{-6})] = 4.3 \times 10^{-4} \text{ J}$$

Note that you can also use $W = \tfrac{1}{2}QV$, noting that $Q' = 4Q$ (see Problem #2).

5. **B** Unlike in question 2, the battery is now disconnected from the plates, so the transferred charge Q that resides on each plate is trapped. The way charge *could* transfer from one plate to the other was through the wires connecting them through the battery. But those wires have been removed, so the charge magnitude on the plates cannot change. (We tacitly assume that the field is weak enough that "electrical breakdown" does not occur, that is, we assume that the excess charge does not jump through the dielectric.)

6. **B** First, we know that Q does not change with the insertion of the dielectric in Experiment #2, as explained in the preceding solution: Q stays constant. But Q always equals CV, so C increasing by a factor of 4 means that V must decrease by a factor of 4 (to keep Q constant). But $V = Ed$, so, if V decreases by a factor of 4, then so does E (because d is constant). Thus, $E_2 = E/4$.

7. **A** Since C increases by a factor of 4, and V decreases by a factor of 4 (from the preceding solution), the new potential energy is 1/4 the old:

$$PE' = \tfrac{1}{2}C'V'^2 = \tfrac{1}{2}(4C)(\tfrac{1}{4}V)^2 = \tfrac{1}{4}(\tfrac{1}{2}CV^2) = \tfrac{1}{4}PE$$

Note that you can also use $PE = \tfrac{1}{2}QV$, where Q is a constant and V decreases by factor of 4.

Passage 42

1. **B** Drift velocity is a direct measure of current. If the electrons go by faster, you get more coulombs per second, i.e., more current. If the drift velocity doubles, then we get twice as many coulombs per second: twice the current.

2. **B** Random thermal motion is an indication of temperature. The hotter something is, the faster the random motion of its constituent particles. If it's colder, thermal motion velocities decrease.

3. **B** The passage emphasized that in an ordinary circuit the random velocities are much larger than the drift velocity. The key sentence is the one in the third paragraph about the drift being superimposed on the random motion. Choice B shows random motion with a bias toward the left (remember, since the field points right, the electrons [being *negatively* charged] feel a force toward the *left*). All of the other choices show motion which clearly is not random.

4. **D** In the middle of the last paragraph in the passage, we read, "Under these conditions..." What conditions? Look at the two preceding sentences: (1) The electron speed due to the field is *much smaller* than the thermal speed, and (2) the systematic drift is *slight*. Which of the choices would render these conditions invalid? Constant temperature (choice A) is pretty harmless. A lot of flaws (choice B) would mean a large resistance. Ohm's law is valid for a huge range of resistances. High temperature (choice C) would mean high thermal speeds. That's fine. But high field (choice D) would mean a *lot* of extra electron speed and a *high* drift velocity, thereby invalidating the conditions for Ohm's law discussed in the passage.

5. **D** Both particles feel a force of magnitude $F = eE$, but since they attract each other, they will accelerate toward each other from rest in opposite directions. This eliminates choices A and C. Since $F = ma$, the lighter particle (the electron) will accelerate more than the heavier particle (the proton). A greater acceleration means a greater final velocity after a fixed amount of time.

6. **A** The first paragraph gives you the connection between flaws and resistance. Choice B is never true; in fact, the opposite is true. As for choice C, look at the solution to Problem #4—higher temperature creates higher thermal speed compared to the drift velocity, which supports the conditions for Ohm's law. More importantly, the question concerns an increase in resistance, not a failure of Ohm's law, so this choice doesn't apply. The number of free electrons in a metal would tend to increase with temperature or stay roughly the same—it certainly wouldn't decrease (choice D), although it is true that fewer free electrons would mean higher resistance. So the only possible answer is A even though the passage doesn't say that higher temperatures produce flaws. Note that the question asks for a *possible* explanation rather than *the* explanation. Actually, it makes sense. Higher temperatures cause the atoms in the lattice to vibrate faster. This shake-up produces flaws in the structure.

7. **C** Flaws slow down the current. That's the point made in the first paragraph. Without a battery to drive it, the collisions with these flaws will cause the current to decrease and stop. It doesn't stop *immediately* because the electrons have some inertia. Choice D is definitely not true since an electron, once moving will continue moving forever unless something stops it. Choice A could happen if the wire were superconducting (i.e., no resistance) but you must assume the wire is ordinary unless they say otherwise.

8.   **D**   The standard $V = IR$ way of stating Ohm's law says that more voltage gives more current. The "drift velocity is proportional to field" way says more field gives more current. Thus, since current is directly proportional to both electric field and voltage, they must be proportional to each other. Choice A is wrong because resistance depends on the material and on how thick the wire is—it doesn't depend on the current. Choice B is wrong because, given constant potential difference, the drift velocity (which is proportional to the current) will be *inversely* proportional to resistance. Choice C is true but has nothing to do with the question. You are familiar with choice D in another context. When you set up a potential difference V between two capacitor plates, you can calculate the strength of the electric field if you know the distance d between them: $E = V/d$. The equation relating electric field and potential difference is more complicated inside a wire but the basic relationship is the same: a large potential difference means a large field.

Passage 43

1.   **D**   This is a NOT question, so keep in mind that "true" means "does not increase the sensitivity of the galvanometer." Item I is false: increasing the number of loops in the coil increases the magnetic torque as given in Equation 1, which causes more deflection for a given current and increases sensitivity, eliminating Choices A and C. Item II is in both remaining answer choices, so III should be analyzed next. Item III is true: increasing the length of the needle only increases the resolution of the scale to allow the human eye to see smaller changes but does not impact either θ or I, eliminating Choice B. Item II is true, increasing the spring constant, increases the restoring torque opposing the magnetic torque that rotates the coil, and decreases sensitivity.

2.   **C**   From equation 1, the magnetic torque is $\tau B = NIAB = (100)(0.1 \times 10^{-3}\ \text{A})(4 \times 10^{-4}\ \text{m}^2)(0.1\ \text{T}) = 4 \times 10^{-7}\ \text{N·m}$.

3.   **C**   When only switch S_2 is closed, resistors R_2 and R_4 are in series and the same current flows through both. The power dissipated by a resistor is given by $P = I^2R$. Since the current flowing through both is the same, the power dissipated by one of these resistors is proportional to its resistance. So the power dissipated by R_4 compared to R_2 is $R_4/R_2 = 600\ \Omega/900\ \Omega = 2/3$.

4.   **B**   Because the ammeter's input resistance is very small compared to the resistances in the circuit, one can make the approximation that the ammeter has no influence on the circuit. Since R_1, R_3, and R_4 are connected in series, $I_{bat} = V_{bat}/(R_1 + R_3 + R_4) = 9\ \text{V}/1500\ \Omega = (3/500)\ \text{A} = 6.0\ \text{mA}$.

5.   **A**   This is a 2 × 2 question in which two concepts are being tested in the answer choices, so one should consider one concept at a time. A measurement device should affect the quantity being measured as little as possible. An ammeter is inserted in series with a circuit, measures current passing through it, and should not add resistance that would decrease this current; therefore an ammeter should have a small resistance, which eliminates Choices B and D. A voltmeter is inserted in parallel with a circuit, measures the voltage between its terminals, and should not draw current that would decrease the voltage across the part of the circuit that it is measuring; therefore a voltmeter should have a large resistance, eliminating Choice C.

6. **C**   When the needle comes to rest at a deflection of 30 degrees from the zero position, it is in equilibrium, so the applied torques sum to zero. The passage tells us that the torques in equilibrium are the magnetic torque on the coil and the torque from restoring spring, eliminating Choices A and B because they misidentify the torques involved. The passage also states that the magnetic field within the range of ±60 degrees is always perpendicular to the plane of the coil and the magnetic torque given by Equation 1 is constant at all deflections within this range, eliminating Choice D.

7. **A**   At the instant just before switch S_2 closes, capacitor C is fully charged to the battery voltage, which is 9.0 V, and no current flows through resistors R_1 and R_2. The input resistance of the voltmeter is very large compared to the resistances in the circuit, and the voltmeter has negligible effect on the voltage across the capacitor. Therefore the measured voltage is initially 9.0 V, and this value remains almost constant, so Choice A is the best answer.

Passage 44

1. **B**   The elastic potential energy stored in the stretched spring would be entirely converted to kinetic energy as the roller passed through the equilibrium position. Setting $\frac{1}{2}kx^2 = \frac{1}{2}mv^2$, we find that

    $$v = x\sqrt{k/m} = 2\sqrt{10/20} = \sqrt{2} = 1.4\,\text{m/s}$$

2. **B**   According to Figure 1, the maximum kinetic energy is 0.4 J. Since $KE = \frac{1}{2}mv^2$, the maximum speed of the roller is therefore

    $$v_{max} = \sqrt{2KE_{max}/m}$$
    $$= \sqrt{2(0.4)/20} = \sqrt{0.04} = 0.2\,\text{m/s}$$

3. **B**   Since the surface upon which the roller moves is frictionless, we conclude that total mechanical energy, E, is conserved. That is, the sum $KE + PE$ is the same at all points. When KE is at its maximum, PE is at its minimum (namely, zero). Thus, $E = KE + PE = 0.4$ J $+ 0$ J $= 0.4$ J.

4. **B**   Since the surface upon which the roller moves is frictionless, we conclude that total mechanical energy is conserved. That is, the sum $KE + PE$ is the same at all points. When KE is increasing, PE is decreasing, and vice versa. Therefore, the PE curve would be inverted relative to the KE curve.

5. **A**   Hooke's law states that $F = -kx$. Therefore, the strength of the force required to stretch the spring must be $kx = (10\text{ N/m})(0.5\text{ m}) = 5$ N.

6. **C**   Relative to its natural-length position, the elastic potential energy of a stretched or compressed spring is given by the equation $PE = \frac{1}{2}kx^2$. In this case, then, we find that $PE = \frac{1}{2}(10\text{ N/m})(2\text{ m})^2 = 20$ J.

Passage 45

1. **A** Since the passage states that "all forces of friction are to be ignored," we ignore any heat generated by the motions under study. Thus, the correct answer must be choice A.

2. **A** A pendulum has maximum kinetic energy when its displacement is zero. From Figure 2, we see that Pendulum 1 has zero amplitude at time $t = 2.5$ sec, and Pendulum 2 next has amplitude zero at time $t = 5$ sec. Thus, the elapsed time between these two events is $5 - 2.5 = 2.5$ sec.

3. **C** When one of the pendulums makes an angle of θ_0 with the vertical, the pendulum bob is at a horizontal distance of $L\sin\theta_0$ from the vertical.

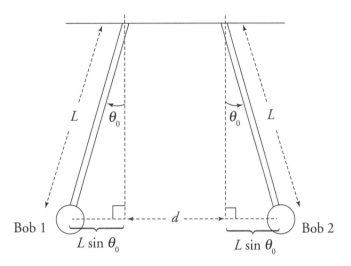

Therefore, the total horizontal distance between the two bobs is

$$L\sin\theta_0 + d + L\sin\theta_0 = d + 2L\sin\theta_0$$

4. **D** Relative to its natural-length position, the elastic potential energy of a spring stretched or compressed a distance x from equilibrium is given by the equation $U = \frac{1}{2}kx^2$. Solving this for x yields $x = \sqrt{2U/k}$.

5. **A** The maximum speed of the pendulum bob occurs when it is swinging through its lowest point. This is when the gravitational potential energy is converted to the maximum kinetic energy at the bottom of the arc. Thus, setting mgh equal to $\frac{1}{2}mv^2$, we find that $v = \sqrt{2gh} = \sqrt{2(10\,\text{m/s}^2)(0.2\,\text{m})} = 2$ m/s.

Passage 46

1. **D** According to the fundamental equation $\lambda f = v$, we have $\lambda = v/f = (2000 \text{ m/s})/(100 \text{ Hz}) = 20$ m.

2. **B** Mass equals density times volume: $m = \rho V$. The volume of the wire is equal to its cross-sectional area times its length: $V = AL$. Therefore,

$$m = \rho AL$$
$$= (2 \times 10^3 \text{ kg/m}^3)(4 \times 10^{-4} \text{ m}^2)(25 \text{ m})$$
$$= 20 \text{ kg}$$

3. **A** The first paragraph explains that "an increase in density brings about a decrease in velocity", so we can assume that a decrease in density will increase velocity. More technically, the speed of a longitudinal wave through a solid medium depends on its Young's modulus, Y (which measures its resistance to compression) and on its density, ρ, according to the equation $v = \sqrt{Y/\rho}$. Therefore, if ρ is lower but Y remains the same, then v increases. Since $\lambda f = v$ and f is fixed, an increase in v will result in an increase in λ.

4. **B** Assuming that both ends are essentially fixed, the longest harmonic wavelength—the fundamental wavelength, λ_1—is equal to twice the length of the wire: $\lambda_1 = 2L = 2(25 \text{ m}) = 50$ m. Therefore, the lowest harmonic frequency—the fundamental frequency, f_1—is calculated as follows: $f_1 = v/\lambda_1 = v/(50 \text{ m})$. Now, since we can generate two kinds of traveling waves (longitudinal and transverse), we can set up two kinds of standing waves. Since transverse waves travel more slowly than longitudinal waves in this wire, if we are looking for the lowest wave frequency that will generate a standing wave, then we choose to create transverse waves ($v = 20$ m/s), with a frequency of $f_1 = (20 \text{ m/s})/(50 \text{ m}) = 0.4$ Hz.

5. **D** Since the two waves will combine constructively (since they are nearly in phase), the resultant maximum amplitude should be nearly twice as great as the amplitude of the two individual waves. We can therefore eliminate choices A and C because their amplitudes are too low. (Note the little notches on the vertical axes. Since the two given waves have an amplitude equal to the height of the little notch, the combined wave should have an amplitude nearly twice as high.) Furthermore, the frequency of the resultant wave should be the same as the frequency of each individual wave, so we can eliminate choice B because its frequency is too high.

6. **A** Completely constructive interference occurs when the two waves are exactly in phase; in this case, the amplitude of the resultant wave is equal to the sum of the individual amplitudes, giving the maximum possible amplitude. Thus, $A_{max} = X + Y$. On the other hand, total destructive interference occurs when the two combining waves are exactly out of phase; in this case, the amplitude of the resultant wave is equal to the difference between the individual amplitudes, giving the minimum possible amplitude. Thus, $A_{min} = X - Y$ (since $X > Y$).

Passage 47

1. **A**   The force of gravity—that is, the weight of the ball—provides the torque:

    $$\tau = L(mg) \sin \theta = (0.4)(0.5)(10) \sin 10° = 0.35 \text{ N-m}$$

2. **D**   The work done by gravity is equal to the force of gravity times the distance that the ball drops: $W = mgh = mgL(1 - \cos \theta)$. The following diagram demonstrates that $h = L - L \cos \theta = L(1 - \cos \theta)$:

    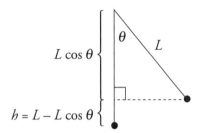

3. **C**   We use the work-energy theorem: the work done by gravity is equal to the change in kinetic energy, which is the same as the final kinetic energy, since the initial kinetic energy is 0. Thus,

    $$W = KE \implies \tfrac{1}{2}mv^2 = W \implies v = \sqrt{\frac{2W}{m}}$$

4. **C**   The ball follows a circular arc, so the force responsible for its motion is centripetal, and it is the net force (which equals the tension T minus the weight w) that provides the necessary centripetal force:

    $$T - w = \frac{mv^2}{L} \implies T = w + \frac{mv^2}{L}$$
    $$= w + \frac{(0.5 \text{ kg})v^2}{0.4 \text{ m}}$$
    $$= w + (\tfrac{5}{4} \text{ kg/m})v^2$$

5. **A**   The journey from X to Y is half a cycle, so the time required is half the period. Using the given formula for the period of the pendulum, we find

    $$t = \tfrac{1}{2}T = \pi\sqrt{\frac{L}{g}} = \pi\sqrt{\frac{0.4 \text{ m}}{10 \text{ m/s}^2}} = \pi(0.2 \text{ s}) = 0.63 \text{ sec}$$

6. **B** The restoring force on the ball is equal to the component of its weight in the direction that the ball is moving, $mg \sin \theta$:

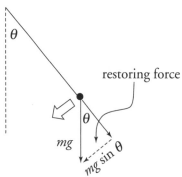

7. **B** From our solution to question 2, we know how to compute the speed of the ball as it passes through the vertical position. The speed is $v = \sqrt{2W/m}$ where $W = mgh$ is the work done by gravity. We therefore compute the following ratio:

$$\frac{v'}{v} = \frac{\sqrt{2W'/m}}{\sqrt{2W/m}} = \sqrt{\frac{W'}{W}} = \sqrt{\frac{mgh'}{mgh}} = \sqrt{\frac{h'}{h}}$$

$$= \sqrt{\frac{L(1-\cos\theta')}{L(1-\cos\theta)}} \approx \sqrt{\frac{1-0.940}{1-0.985}} = \sqrt{\frac{0.060}{0.015}} = \sqrt{4} = 2$$

8. **A** The frequency is *independent* of the amplitude, an important characteristic of simple harmonic motion. Therefore, $f' = f$.

9. **B** Using the given formula for the period, we compute the effect of increasing L by 21%:

$$T' = 2\pi\sqrt{\frac{1.21L}{g}} = \sqrt{1.21} \times 2\pi\sqrt{\frac{L}{g}} = 1.1 \times 2\pi\sqrt{\frac{L}{g}}$$

$$= 1.1 \times T = 110\% \text{ of } T \implies T \text{ increases by } 10\%.$$

Passage 48

1. **A** Each spring maintains a tension T between its two ends. Let us look at the force diagram for the left slab:

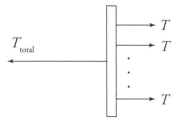

Since there are n springs in our model, the total tension pulling the left slab to the right is $T + T + \cdots + T = nT$, which must balance T_{total} to the left. Thus, $T_{total} = nT$.

2. **C**   Again, each spring maintains a tension T between its ends, so the force diagram on the left slab looks like:

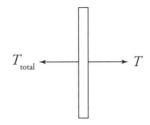

In this case, there is only one spring pulling on the left slab, so the force to the right is T. Since the force to the left is T_{total}, we must have $T_{total} = T$. Note that the tension along the length of the springs is everywhere equal to T, and that this is why the strength of a muscle does not increase with length.

3. **C**   If the strength of a muscle is proportional to the cross-sectional area, then we can write $T = k\pi r^2$. We can evaluate k using the information that the human bicep supports 3000 N with a radius of 2 cm:

$$k = \frac{T}{\pi r^2} = \frac{3000\,\text{N}}{\pi(2 \times 10^{-2})^2}$$

Then we obtain T_m using the radius 1 μm = 10^{-6} m:

$$T_m = k\pi r^2 = \frac{3000\,\text{N}}{\pi(2 \times 10^{-2})^2} \cdot \pi(10^{-6})^2$$
$$= \frac{3 \times 10^{-9}}{4 \times 10^{-4}} = 0.75 \times 10^{-5} = 7.5 \times 10^{-6}\,\text{N}$$

4. **B**   Since the passage gives the height of the flea's jump, we can calculate the potential energy at this height:

$$PE = mgh = (10^{-6}\,\text{kg})(10\,\text{N/kg})(0.2\,\text{m})$$
$$= 2 \times 10^{-6}\,\text{J}.$$

But this must be the same as the kinetic energy at the beginning of the jump.

5. **C**   The length of the flea's leg gives the distance over which the force acts. Since we have the energy of the jump, we can write $mgh = F_{leg}d_{leg}$. The result is

$$F_{leg} = \frac{mgh}{d_{leg}} = \frac{2 \times 10^{-6}\,\text{J}}{0.5 \times 10^{-3}\,\text{m}} = 4 \times 10^{-3}\,\text{N}.$$

6. **C**   For the small flea, we can write $m_1gh_1 = F_1d_1$, and for the large flea we can write $m_2gh_2 = F_2d_2$. The length of the large leg is $d_2 = 100d_1$. According to Galileo, the strength of the flea's leg muscle is $F_2 = (100)^2F_1$. Since the flea's size increases in three dimensions, we have $m_2 = (100)^3m_1$. Putting this together yields

$$h_2 = \frac{F_2d_2}{m_2g} = \frac{(100)^2F_1(100d_1)}{(100)^3 m_1 g} = \frac{F_1d_1}{m_1g} = h_1$$

Passage 49

1. **C**   We use the given formula for the period (with $L = 0.25$ meter at 20°C):

$$T = 2\pi\sqrt{\frac{L}{g}} = 2\pi\sqrt{\frac{0.25}{10}} = 2\pi\frac{0.5}{\sqrt{10}} \approx 2(0.5) = 1 \text{ sec}$$

(Note: The final fraction above was simplified by using $\pi \approx \sqrt{10}$, both of which are slightly more than 3.)

2. **C**   The resistor wrapped around the rod loses energy at a rate of $P = I^2R$, and the rod absorbs 75%, or 3/4, of this heat energy. Therefore, the power absorbed by the rod is

$$P_{absorbed} = \frac{3}{4} \times I^2R = \frac{3}{4} \times \left(\frac{V}{R}\right)^2 R = \frac{3}{4} \times \left(\frac{80}{4}\right)^2 \cdot 4$$
$$= 3 \times (20^2) = 1.2 \times 10^3 \text{ J/s.}$$

3. **B**   Combining the two given equations, we express the change in length of the pendulum as follows:

$$q = mc\Delta T \implies \Delta T = \frac{q}{mc} \implies \Delta L = \alpha L \Delta T = \frac{\alpha Lq}{mc}$$

4. **B**   From our solution to the preceding question, we know that the change in length is inversely proportional to the mass:

$$\Delta L = \frac{\alpha Lq}{mc} \implies \Delta L \propto \frac{1}{m}$$

Therefore, if the material had twice the density, the rod would have twice the mass, so the change in length would be half as much.

5. **B** Since the rod lengthens when heated, the formula given for the period tells us that the period will be longer, too. The clock ticks 1 second at some specific point in the pendulum's cycle. Now that the period is longer, the clock will tick 1 second when actually more than 1 second has passed. The clock will run slow because the pendulum is too long.

Passage 50

1. **C** Neither equation for the period T given in the passage depends on the mass of the pendulum, only on its length. Therefore, a change in M without a change in L will have no effect on the period.

2. **B** When a simple harmonic oscillator is at its greatest displacement from equilibrium—a "turning point"—the restoring force is strongest, and thus the acceleration is maximized. Also, the speed at this point is zero (since the velocity is changing direction here), which is certainly the minimum speed.

3. **C** Neither choice A nor B can be correct, since the restoring force on both pendulums is the same, namely $Mg \sin \theta$ (and they both have the same M). However, since the physical pendulum has a shorter period than the simple pendulum of the same mass, it must have, on average, a greater angular velocity than the simple pendulum. Therefore, we conclude that it offers less resistance to angular acceleration.

4. **A** Since the passage states that dissipative effects are negligible, the bob will rise to the same height from which it was released. Therefore, the gravitational potential energy does not change.

5. **C** For small angles of oscillation, the pendulum's motion is isochronous. Amplitude angles of 10° or 5° are certainly small enough for isochronism to be observed. (Note: Although Equation 1 does say that, strictly speaking, a smaller θ_{max} implies a smaller T, the difference is *very* slight for these small amplitude angles, much less than 1%. Choices A and B represent far greater decreases than what would be observed, so choice C is definitely the best choice here.)

6. **D** Both choices A and B are wrong: Table 1 shows that for both pendulums, the *period* increases as L increases; therefore, the frequency *decreases* as L increases. Since Table 1 shows that the period of the physical pendulum is shorter than the period of a simple pendulum of the same length, the frequency of the physical pendulum is higher than the frequency of a simple pendulum of the same length.

7. **D** $\theta_{max} = 85°$ is a very large amplitude angle, so Equation 1 would predict a measurable deviation—in particular, a measurable increase—in the period. The only choice greater than 2.8 sec is choice D.

8. **C** The gravitational force acts at the center of mass, eliminating choices B and D. The distance r from the pivot to the point of application of the force is $L/2$, so by definition of torque, $\tau = rF \sin \theta = (L/2)(Mg \sin \theta)$.

Passage 51

1. **A**   Wavelength and frequency are related by the fundamental equation $\lambda f = v$, where v is the wave's speed. In the case of light through air, v is nearly equal to c, the speed of light through vacuum. Thus

$$f = c / \lambda = (3 \times 10^8 \text{ m/s}) / (4.5 \times 10^{-7} \text{ m})$$
$$= \frac{2}{3} \times 10^{15} \text{ Hz} = 6.7 \times 10^{14} \text{ Hz}$$

2. **B**   Substituting the given values into Snell's law, $n_1 \sin \theta_1 = n_2 \sin \theta_2$, gives $(1)(0.8) = n_2(0.6)$, which implies $n_2 = 8/6 = 4/3 = 1.3$.

3. **B**   The passage explicitly states that "blue light experiences greater refraction than does red light," so choices A and D are eliminated immediately. Furthermore, since the passage also states that "the value of n increases with increasing frequency," blue light must have the higher frequency—and therefore the shorter wavelength—since it experiences greater refraction (a direct result of its greater n). (Note: You should know the relative order of the colors in the visible spectrum: ROYGBV gives the order by increasing frequency.)

4. **C**   As the refractive index increases, the speed of light decreases; thus Statement III is true (eliminating choice A). Furthermore, frequency does not change when a wave passes from one medium into another, so Statement I is false (eliminating choice D). Since $\lambda f = v$ is always satisfied, a decrease in v results in a decrease in λ (since f is constant here). Thus, Statement II is true, and the correct answer is choice C.

5. **C**   The critical angle for TIR, θ_c, is given by the equation $\sin \theta_c = n_2/n_1$, as stated in the passage. Thus,

$$n_1 = n_2/\sin \theta_c = 1/(0.4) = 2.5.$$

Passage 52

1. **B**   We use Equation 1 and set up a ratio:

$$\frac{v_{\text{Al}}}{v_{\text{H}_2\text{O}}} = \sqrt{\frac{Y_{\text{Al}}}{B_{\text{H}_2\text{O}}} \cdot \frac{\rho_{\text{H}_2\text{O}}}{\rho_{\text{Al}}}} = \sqrt{\frac{7 \times 10^{10}}{2.2 \times 10^9} \cdot \frac{1000}{2700}} = 3.4$$

2. **D**   Use Equation 2, with $F/A = P = \rho g d$ (which is the formula for hydrostatic gauge pressure; we ignore atmospheric pressure here because at depths below 1000 m, atmospheric pressure is less than 1% of the total pressure). This gives

$$\frac{\Delta V}{V_0} = -\frac{P}{B} \quad \Rightarrow \quad \Delta V = -\frac{V_0 P}{B} = -\frac{V_0 \rho g d}{B}$$

3. **C** Using the equation $\lambda f = v$, we find that

$$\lambda = v/f = (1500 \text{ m/s})/(10^5 \text{ Hz}) = 1.5 \times 10^{-2} \text{ m}$$

4. **B** Using distance equals rate times time, $d = vt$, we find that $t = d/v = (0.5 \text{ m})/(54 \text{ m/s}) = 5/540 \text{ s} = 1/108 \text{ s} \approx 9.3 \text{ ms}$.

5. **B** Choice D is eliminated immediately: air is composed mostly of nitrogen and oxygen, each of which has a greater molecular mass than hydrogen. Choice A is false; hydrogen gas and air have comparable compressibilities (bulk moduli). In any case, even if it were true, choice A would not explain why sound travels at a higher speed through hydrogen than through air. The correct answer must be choice B. In fact, it can be shown that the speed of sound through an ideal diatomic gas is given by the equation $v = \sqrt{1.4RT/M}$, where R is the gas constant, T the absolute temperature, and M the molecular mass. Approximating the diatomic gases hydrogen (H_2) and air (N_2 and O_2) as ideal, we see that the difference in speed is due to the difference in mass: v is inversely proportional to $\sqrt{M}$. Therefore, since H_2 has roughly 16 times *less* molecular mass than air, sound travels roughly $\sqrt{16} = 4$ times *faster* through H_2 than through air.

Passage 53

1. **C** Beats are heard only if the frequencies of the two individual waves are different. If no beats are heard, the "parent" frequencies must be identical.

2. **B** The frequency of the resultant wave is equal to the average of the frequencies of the two parent waves: $f_{composite} = (f_1 + f_2)/2 = (265 + 260)/2 = 262.5$ Hz. The beat frequency is equal to the difference between the frequencies of the parent waves: $f_{beat} = f_1 - f_2 = 265 - 260 = 5$ Hz.

3. **C** When two waves interfere, the maximum possible amplitude of the resultant wave is equal to the sum of the two individual amplitudes (this is completely constructive interference). In this case, then, $A_{max} = A_1 + A_2 = 5 + 5 = 10$ units.

4. **A** Using the fundamental equation $\lambda f = v$, we find that $\lambda = v/f = (343 \text{ m/s})/(686 \text{ Hz}) = 0.5$ m.

5. **C** Sound waves are longitudinal.

Passage 54

1. **B** From the fundamental equation $\lambda f = v$, we find:

$$f = c/\lambda = (3 \times 10^8 \text{ m/s})/(5 \times 10^{-7} \text{ m}) = 6 \times 10^{14} \text{ Hz}.$$

2. **B** The round-trip distance from the wheel to Mirror M and back to the wheel is $L + L = 2L$. Therefore, using distance equals rate times time, we find that the round-trip time is $t = 2L/c$.

3. **A** The time between adjacent notches aligning with the light beam is equal to the fraction of the circle between adjacent notches times the time required for a complete revolution. The fraction of the circle between adjacent notches is $0.36°/360° = 1/1000$, and the time required for a full revolution is 1/500 sec. Thus, the desired time is $(1/1000)(1/500 \text{ sec}) = 2 \times 10^{-6}$ sec.

4. **C** The object (the light source) is at a distance of $L + a$ in front of Mirror M (or, more accurately, the optical path length from the light source to the Mirror M is $L + a$). Since the mirror is flat, the image will appear to be at this same distance, $L + a$, behind Mirror M.

5. **D** Because n_{air} is so close to 1 (the index of refraction for empty space), we can treat air as if it were vacuum for purposes of this experiment. Light travels through vacuum at a constant speed, regardless of frequency. Though the speed of light does vary by frequency for some media, the effect in air is negligible. Moreover, we have no way of knowing the magnitude of that effect, so we can only assume that Big Rule #1 for waves holds and v is independent of f.

6. **D** Upon entering the glass from the air, a light beam will refract toward the normal; as it leaves the glass and re-enters the air, it will refract away from the normal. Only the diagram in choice D depicts this behavior.

7. **B** The power of a lens (in diopters) is the reciprocal of the focal length (in meters). Thus, $f = 1/P = 1/20 = 0.05$ m = 5 cm. The radius of curvature is always twice the focal length; therefore, $r = 2f = 2(5 \text{ cm}) = 10$ cm.

Passage 55

1. **B** Since the focal length of a lens is the reciprocal of its power, an increase in the power implies a decrease in the focal length.

2. **C** If o is very distant, then we can set "$o = \infty$", and conclude that "$1/o = 0$". The lens equation, $1/o + 1/i = 1/f$, then implies that $1/i = 1/f$, that is, $i = f$.

3. **C** Since $P = 1/f$, the lens equation, $1/o + 1/i = 1/f$, implies that $1/o + 1/i = P$ (if o and i are expressed in meters). Because the eye is focused, the image falls on the retina, which, as we are told in the passage, is 2 cm from the lens, $i = 2$ cm = 0.02 m. If $o = 20$ cm = 0.2 m, then $P = 1/(0.2) + 1/(0.02) = 5 + 50 = 55$ diopters.

4. **A** Figure 2 shows a "hyperopic eye with corrective lens," and the corrective lens is clearly a converging one. Adding a corrective converging lens to the converging crystalline lens of the eye results in an increase in lens power, which is necessary to correct hyperopia (the passage states that "hyperopia...occurs when the lens is too weak..."). An increase in lens power implies a decrease in focal length, since power is the reciprocal of focal length.

5. **D** If the image is to fall on the retina, then we must have $i = 2$ cm = 0.02 m. If the object is "distant," then, as we did earlier, we set "$o = \infty$", and conclude that "$1/o = 0$." The lens equation, $1/o + 1/i = 1/f$, then gives $1/f = 1/i = 1/(0.02 \text{ m}) = 50$ diopters. Thus, if the power of the eye is only 48 diopters, a corrective lens of power 2 diopters is needed to bring the total power of the lens combination to the required 50 diopters.

6. **A** Using $i = 0.02$ m (since the image falls on the retina, which is 2 cm $= 0.02$ m from the lens of the eye) and $o = 1$ m, we calculate that m $= -i/o = -(0.02$ m$)/(1$ m$) = -0.02$. Thus, the magnitude of the magnification is $0.02 = 1/50$.

Passage 56

1. **C** The truck is considered the detector in this question (since we are asked at what frequency the waves strike the truck). Since the source (the police car) is not moving, but the truck is moving toward the source, the Doppler effect predicts that the frequency received will be

$$f' = \frac{v + v_{\text{truck}}}{v} f = \frac{v + \frac{1}{10} v}{v} f = \frac{\frac{11}{10} v}{v} f$$
$$= \frac{11}{10} (1 \text{ MHz}) = 1.1 \text{ MHz}$$

2. **B** Now we consider the truck the source and the car to be the detector (since the waves are bounced off the truck and head back to the police car). Since the source is moving toward the stationary detector,

$$f'' = \frac{v}{v - v_{\text{truck}}} f' = \frac{v}{v - \frac{1}{10} v} f' = \frac{v}{\frac{9}{10} v} f'$$
$$= \frac{10}{9} (1.1 \text{ MHz})$$
$$\approx 1.2 \text{ MHz}$$

3. **B** We now combine the two different situations. In the first part, the police car is the source and the truck is the detector. Then the waves bounce off the truck and head back to the police car, so for the second part of the sound wave's journey, the truck is the source and the car is the detector. Let f be the frequency emitted by the car, let f' be the frequency at the truck, and let f'' be the frequency received back at the police car. Then

$$\left. \begin{array}{l} \underset{(\text{source} = f)}{\text{police car}} \rightarrow \underset{(\text{detector} = f')}{\text{truck}} : \quad f' = \dfrac{v - \frac{1}{10} v}{v} \times f \\[3em] \underset{(\text{source} = f')}{\text{truck}} \rightarrow \underset{(\text{detector} = f'')}{\text{police car}} : \quad f'' = \dfrac{v}{v + \frac{1}{10} v} \times f' \end{array} \right\}$$

$$\Rightarrow \quad f'' = \frac{v}{\frac{11}{10} v} \times \overbrace{\frac{\frac{9}{10} v}{v} f}^{f'} = \frac{9}{11} f$$

Since $f = 1$ MHz, we have $f'' = 9/11 \approx 0.82$ MHz.

Passage 57

1. **B** Choices A and D are properties of all waves. Choice C is true of both sound and string waves, since both involve the displacement of matter (as opposed to light waves). You should know that sound is a longitudinal pressure wave.

2. **C** Light passing through a pinhole spreads due to diffraction. The spreading angle is given by

$$\Delta\theta \approx \lambda/d = 0.65\ \mu m/4\ \mu m \approx 1/6\ \text{radian}$$

The size of the spot can now be obtained from the following diagram:

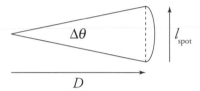

Applying the definition of radian measure, we find $l_{spot} \approx D\Delta\theta \approx$ (3 m)(1/6 rad) = 0.5 m.

3. **C** First, eliminate choice A: the sound is not passing through a hole, so diffraction does not apply. Choice B is a true statement but does not explain the observation. Concerning choice C, a poor impedance match would result in good reflection and poor transmission of the wave, in analogy with the ropes in the passage. Nothing in the passage supports choice D, and, in fact, the statement is false.

4. **B** In order to have a better defined direction (i.e., to minimize the spreading angle $\Delta\theta$), we need to reduce diffraction by decreasing λ or increasing d. The megaphone does not change the wavelength of the sound, which depends only on sound speed and frequency, but it does increase the effective size of the hole.

5. **C** The third paragraph of the passage implies that the energy coupling in a megaphone is most efficient when the wavelength of the sound is smaller than the transition length (which is the length of the megaphone). Since a higher frequency has a shorter wavelength, the megaphone is most efficient for a high voice.

6. **A** The small wavelength of light implies the diffraction angle is quite small. Concerning choice B, all waves diffract. As for choice C, the only apparatus needed are the ear and eye. Choice D is not true.

Passage 58

1. **A** If we replace λ by v/f, the equation for the spreading angle becomes $\Delta\theta = v/fd$. Thus, if both d and f increase by a factor of 2, $\Delta\theta$ will decrease by a factor of $2 \times 2 = 4$.

2. **B** Again we use the equation given for $\Delta\theta$. The lower limit for the uncertainty in direction in the human eye is given by $\Delta\theta \approx \lambda_{red}/l_{pupil} = (0.65 \times 10^{-6}\ m)/(2 \times 10^{-3}\ m) \approx 3 \times 10^{-4}$ radian.

3. **C** We draw the following diagram:

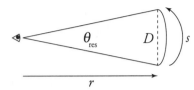

and then calculate (by definition of radian measure)

$$D \approx s = r\theta_{res} = (10 \text{ m})(10^{-2} \text{ rad}) = 0.1 \text{ m}.$$

4. **D** Since the index of refraction is greater for blue light, it bends more easily as it goes through a lens. The following diagram shows, consequently, that blue light has a different focus than red light:

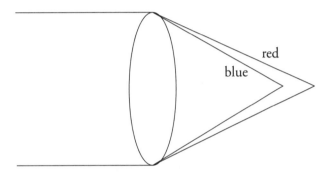

Although choice A is true, it is not a consequence of the refractive index of the cornea but of the diffraction of the eye.

5. **B** Changing the characteristics of the cornea changes its index of refraction, so choices C and D can be eliminated. Changing the wavelength of the light (choice A) changes the index of refraction for reasons given in #4 above.

6. **A** If we look only at the spreading of the wave, then our diagram looks like the following:

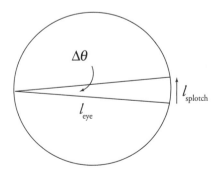

Once again applying the definition of radian measure, we find $l_{splotch} \approx l_{eye} \Delta\theta$.

Passage 59

1. **D** The decay scheme mentioned for the radioactive hydrogen isotope does not produce a positron, and without a positron there will be no pair annihilation and therefore no gamma rays to detect. This would be a problem since the passage states (last paragraph) that the PET image is formed by the detection of gamma rays. Nothing in the passage supports choices A, B, or C, and, in fact, they are false (and/or irrelevant).

2. **C** Choices A and B can be eliminated because (1) pair annihilation gives off two gamma rays, and neither answer has two or because (2) the total charge of the reaction is not conserved. The total momentum of the "before" state is zero since the momentum vectors are equal in magnitude and opposite in direction. Since total momentum is conserved, we must exclude choice D, because both momentum vectors are pointing in the same direction and therefore would not cancel. Only in choice C are the momentum vectors of the two gamma ray photons equal and opposite.

3. **B** The total energy released in the pair annihilation is shared equally by the two emitted gamma rays, so *each* gamma ray has an energy $E = 2$ MeV $= 2 \times 10^6$ eV. Solving $E = hf$ for f we find

    $$f = \frac{E}{h} = \frac{2 \times 10^6 \text{ eV}}{4.1 \times 10^{-15} \text{ eV} \cdot \text{s}} \approx \frac{1}{2} \times 10^{21} \text{ Hz} = 5 \times 10^{20} \text{ Hz.}$$

4. **C** Although we are told that each reaction conserves charge, energy, and momentum, the only one of these three properties that is evident from the available choices is the charge before and after the reaction. Choices A, B, and D all have the same net charge before and after the reaction: reaction A conserves charge $+e$, while reactions B and D conserve net charge 0. Reaction C, however, has charge zero before but charge $+e + e = +2e$ after, so it does not conserve charge and therefore cannot be a beta decay reaction.

5. **C** The speed of electromagnetic radiation through air is virtually the same as through free space: c. Therefore,

    $$\lambda = \frac{c}{f} = \frac{3 \times 10^8 \text{ m/s}}{2 \times 10^{22} \text{ Hz}} = 1.5 \times 10^{-14} \text{ m.}$$

6. **C** As a result of the reaction $p \rightarrow n + e^+ + \nu$, a proton is lost (so the atomic number drops by 1) and a neutron is gained (so the mass number—the total number of protons and neutrons—stays the same). That is, the reaction is $^{15}_{8}\text{O} \rightarrow {}^{15}_{7}\text{N} + {}^{0}_{+1}e^+ + \nu$.

    The positron is ejected, and the nucleus that remains (the daughter nucleus) is ^{15}N.

Passage 60

1. **A**   The theoretical bandwidth of a fiber-optic cable is given to be 50×10^{12} Hz. A telephone conversation needs only 3 kHz = 3×10^3 Hz. Therefore, there could be a maximum of $(50 \times 10^{12})/(3 \times 10^3) = 17 \times 10^9 = 1.7 \times 10^{10}$ conversations.

2. **C**   Choice A is wrong because the index of refraction of copper is irrelevant: Light does not travel through a copper cable. While choices B and D may be true statements, there is no evidence to support them as reasons for the difficulty of tapping into optical fibers. The passage mentions, however, that light will be lost at imprecise connections. This implies that choice C is the best answer.

3. **D**   Choice A is untrue. Choice B is also untrue: Infrared light contains less energy than visible does. Choice C contradicts itself: a higher index of refraction implies a slower speed. Choice C is also untrue: Infrared light has a lower index of refraction than visible light. (In general, the longer the wavelength, the lower the index of refraction; see the discussion of dispersion in the text.) The correct answer is choice D. In general, electromagnetic radiation with a short wavelength is more easily absorbed, bent, scattered, etc.

4. **B**   After traveling 20 km, the attenuation of the ray is (20 km) × (1 dB/km) = 20 dB. Because the decibel level is logarithmic, $\beta = 10 \log (I/I_0)$, a decrease of 20 dB = (10 + 10) dB translates into a decrease in intensity by a factor of 10 × 10 = 100.

5. **D**   If the light originates in the core (the medium with the higher index of refraction), then the critical angle for total internal reflection from the cladding is

    $$\theta_{\text{crit}} = \sin^{-1} \frac{n_2}{n_1} = \sin^{-1} \frac{n_{\text{cladding}}}{n_{\text{core}}}$$
    $$= \sin^{-1} \frac{1.73}{2.0} \approx \sin^{-1} \frac{\sqrt{3}}{2} = 60°.$$

6. **A**   Choice B is untrue, and there is nothing in the passage to support choice C. Choice D is wrong because less light, not more, would enter a smaller core. Since light bounces back and forth between the boundaries of the core, there could be a number of different possible light paths within the core, all striking at different angles. These different paths have different path lengths, and therefore will take different amounts of time to reach the end. As a result, the light rays will interfere with each other. The narrower the core, the fewer different possible paths the light can travel, and hence, the smaller the distortion.

7. **B**   As the light ray enters a more optically dense medium, its speed decreases (by definition of the index of refraction). Since the frequency of the wave does not change, the wavelength must decrease (since $\lambda f = v$).

Passage 61

1. **B** The threshold frequency is the frequency at which photoelectrons can barely make it off the surface of the emitter plate. We therefore set KE_{max} equal to zero in Equation 1 and get $f_0 = \phi/h$. Since Table 1 tells us that $\phi = 4.14$ eV for lead, we find that f_0 for lead is (4.14 eV)/(4.14 × 10^{-15} eV·s) = 1×10^{15} Hz.

2. **C** The work function for iron is 4.50 eV, so incident photons with an energy of only 2.25 eV will not be able to produce any photoelectrons, regardless of intensity. Therefore, the galvonometer will read a current of 0 when the intensity is I and when the intensity is $4I$.

3. **D** The passage states that the work function "is the minimum energy an electron on [a metal's] surface must absorb in order to be liberated." That is, the work function gives the energy that binds a valence electron to the metal lattice. It is independent of the apparatus used in the experiment (eliminating choices A and B), and along with the frequency and intensity of the incident light, as well as the resistance R, the work function of the emitter plate determines the value of the photocurrent in the circuit (not the other way around, eliminating choice C).

4. **A** The last sentence in the first paragraph describing Experiment 1 reads, "...if the frequency [of the incident light] is higher than f_0, then the number of photoelectrons produced is proportional to the intensity of the incident light." If the number of electrons is proportional to the intensity, and the current is a measure of how many photoelectrons jump from the emitter to the collector, we can conclude that the current is proportional to the intensity.

5. **B** The energy of each photon of this incident light is $E = hf = hc/\lambda$, where $hc = 1240$ eV·nm (this value is given in the passage). Therefore, if $\lambda = 310$ nm, it's easy to calculate that $E = 4$ eV. Now, since Table 1 tells us that $\phi = 2.28$ eV for sodium, Equation 1 says that $KE_{max} = E - \phi = (4 \text{ eV}) - (2.28 \text{ eV}) = 1.72$ eV, so choice B is the best answer.

6. **A** Combining Equations 1 and 2 gives $eV_{stop} = hf - \phi$, so dividing both sides by e gives $V_{stop} = (h/e) f - (\phi/e)$. If V_{stop} is graphed versus f, this equation tells us that the graph is a straight line (with slope h/e).

Passage 62

1. **B** The wave nature of light explains this phenomenon. Colors in the oil film result from interference between the light waves of different wavelengths reflected off the layers of water and oil. (There are different colors in layers because *dispersion* means that different frequencies refract at different angles, and so interfere in different locations along the surface of the oil slick.)

2. **C** Because the waves are exactly in phase, they interfere completely constructively, and their amplitudes add. Because the interfering waves have amplitudes of 2A and 3A, the amplitude of the resultant combined wave will be $2A + 3A = 5A$.

3. **D** A dark fringe is caused by destructive interference, so the difference in the distances traveled by the waves from the slits to point P must be an odd multiple of $\lambda/2$ (this follows from Equation 2). Because $\lambda = 500$ nm, the difference $S_1P - S_2P$ must be an odd multiple of 250 nm. Of the choices given, only choice D, 750 nm, is an odd multiple of 250 nm.

4. **A** Look at the relationships in Equations 3. Because the distance between the slits, d, is in the denominator in both expressions for the positions of the fringes, a smaller d would cause the fringes to move farther apart and widen.

5. **D** Use the first relationship given in Equation 3. Using the values given in the question, we have $L/d = 10,000$, so $y_m = (10,000)m\lambda$. For violet light, we're told that $\lambda = 400$ nm, so $y_{m,\text{violet}} = (4\text{ mm})m$; and for orange-yellow light, we have $\lambda = 600$ nm, so $y_{n,\text{orange}} = (6\text{ mm})n$. We want $y_{m,\text{violet}}$ to be equal to $y_{n,\text{orange}}$ for some values of m and n; that is, we want $4m$ to be equal to $6n$. The smallest whole numbers that make this equation true are $m = 3$ and $n = 2$, which gives $y = 12$ mm. This is the position of the third-order bright fringe for violet light and the second-order bright fringe for orangeyellow light.

Passage 63

1. **A** Use the given Equation 2 to calculate the deflection angle ϕ for the given values.

$$\phi_{\text{Sun}} \frac{4GM_{\text{Sun}}}{r_{\text{Sun}}c^2} = \frac{4(6.7\cdot10^{-11})(2\cdot10^{30})}{(7\cdot10^8)(3\cdot10^8)} \cong \frac{4\cdot7\cdot2}{7\cdot9}\cdot10^{-5} = \frac{8}{9}\cdot10^{-5} = 8.9\cdot10^{-6}\text{rad}$$

Note that our estimate is slightly larger than the correct answer because we rounded up from 6.7 to 7.

2. **B** If the light source is off-axis, it is closer to one side of the gravitational lens (say, the top) than the other (say, the bottom). For this reason the optical path length—the distance a ray of light travels—from the source to the observer will be less for the top path than for the bottom path, so Item I is true. Similarly, the images on either side of the asymmetry will be larger and brighter or smaller and dimmer depending upon that difference in object distance from the lens, so Item III is also true. However, there is no relation between the source-to-lens distance and the radial distance r—and obviously the other terms in Equation 1 remain constant—so the index of refraction is unaffected and Item II is false.

3.   B   First, we eliminate choice D by recognizing that if the gravitational lens had an infinite focal length, it could not possibly function as a lens (because it would not deflect light, as it clearly does). The easiest way to proceed from here is by unit analysis: only choice B works out to be in meters. Choice A must be unitless because it is the inverse of Equation 2; therefore, choice B with the additional r term is in meters and choice C is in m^{-1}. To solve the problem, redraw Figure 1 with parallel incident rays (the top suffices):

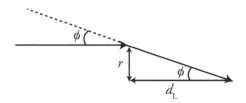

Notice that the angle of deflection ϕ is congruent to the angle between the ray reaching the observer and d_L and also that the drawing is not to scale (the angle is much smaller than depicted). Now we solve for the focal length d_L:

$$\frac{r}{d_L} = \tan\phi \approx \phi = \frac{4GM}{rc^2} \Rightarrow d_L = \frac{r^2 c^2}{4GM}$$

4.   D   Three of the answers can be eliminated because they contradict the passage, which states that Newton's theory does not agree with General Relativity either in cases of very large masses closely interacting (eliminating choice A) or in cases when light is deflected by a large mass (eliminating choices B and C). Note particularly that because "light" is a just form of electromagnetic radiation, Newton's predictions for light implicitly hold for other forms of EM radiation like radio waves. Moreover, it makes little sense that Newton's theory would incorrectly predict the length of a year, which is easily observable and has been well known for thousands of years (Newton's theory would hardly have held up for so long if it were so obviously contradicted by evidence).

5.   A   You may recall that X-rays are absorbed by air within a few meters whereas radio waves move through the atmosphere easily (or else our car radios wouldn't work). Otherwise, by process of elimination we can put aside the other choices. Choice B is false because $E = hf$, so high-frequency X-ray photons are more energetic than low-frequency radio photons. Choice C should be recognized as false by common sense: there are many powerful radio sources in everyday use—radio and TV stations, cell phones, and others—whereas X-ray sources (like medical X-ray machines) are relatively rare. Choice D is false because the frequency of a photon or wave bears no relation to the number of photons occurring.

6.   D   Gravitational lenses are generated by huge masses in the vastness of space: they cannot practically be moved. All the other choices are potential applications of gravitational lenses.

MCAT
Biochemistry and Biology
Passages

Passage 1 (Questions 1-5)

The carnitine/acylcarnitine transporter (CACT) is essential in the transport of acyl groups, carried as acylcarnitines, into mitochondria for beta-oxidation. The carnitine that is released into the mitochondrial matrix is transported back into the cytosol by the same transporter via an antiport process. The CACT contains six Cys residues that play an important role in carnitine transport. It is known that C136 and C155 form a disulfide bond during carnitine transport and that these residues react with disulfide-forming agents. Omeprazole, a drug commonly used in the treatment of gastroesophageal reflux disease, is known to react with compounds containing thiol groups. This pharmacological agent is known to inhibit the gastric H^+/K^+ ATPase by forming a mixed disulfide.

A recent study examined the effects of omeprazole on the carnitine/acylcarnitine transporter inserted into liposomes. The uptake of 100 μM carnitine into a liposome, containing 15 mM carnitine to mimic carnitine antiport, was followed over time in the presence of omeprazole. To determine if the CACT's cysteine residues played an essential role in interacting with omeprazole, a variant of the CACT that lacked these residues, called "C-less", was also tested. To further determine if the interaction of omeprazole with the CACT resulted from the formation of disulfide bonds, dithioerythritol (DTE), a reagent known to break disulfide bonds, was added. The results of these experiments are shown in Figure 1 below.

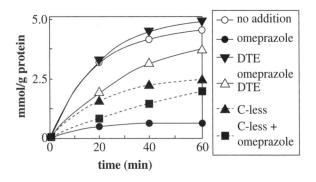

Figure 1 Uptake of carnitine by the CACT over time in the presence and absence of omeprazole

To determine the effect of omeprazole interacting covalently and non-covalently with the CACT, a series of kinetic experiments were performed with the wild-type (WT) CACT and C-less CACT. Using the same liposome under similar conditions, increasing concentrations of omeprazole were added to the transporter system. The antiport rate was measured as a function of carnitine concentration with various levels of omeprazole, shown in Figures 2.

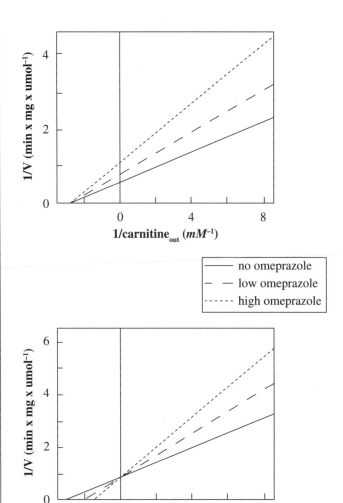

Figure 2 Lineweaver-Burk plots for carnitine transport by WT CACT (top) and C-less CACT (bottom) in the presence of omeprazole

Adapted from Tonazzi A, Eberini I, Indiveri C (2013) *Molecular Mechanism of Inhibition of the Carnitine/Acylcarnitine Transporter by Omeprazole Revealed by Proteoliposome Assay, Mutagenesis, and Bioinformatics.* PLoS 8

1. When a 14-carbon saturated fatty acid undergoes beta-oxidation, how many total NADH and $FADH_2$ are produced, assuming all of the acetyl CoA generated enters the TCA cycle?

   A. 21 NADH and 7 $FADH_2$
   B. 28 NADH and 14 $FADH_2$
   C. 27 NADH and 13 $FADH_2$
   D. 6 NADH and 6 $FADH_2$

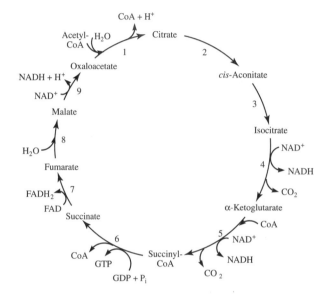

2. What is the most likely role of DTE in the experiment described in the passage?

   A. Oxidizing agent
   B. Reducing agent
   C. Lewis acid
   D. Brønsted-Lowry acid

3. Based on the results shown in Figure 1, does omeprazole inhibit the CACT exclusively through covalent interactions?

   A. Yes, the presence of omeprazole causes a substantial decrease in the rate of carnitine uptake.
   B. Yes, DTE decreases omeprazole's inhibition of carnitine uptake.
   C. No, the C-less CACT shows a decrease in carnitine uptake compared to the WT.
   D. No, addition of omeprazole to the C-less CACT results in decreased carnitine uptake.

4. Based on the results of Figure 2, through what type of inhibition does omeprazole inhibit the WT and C-less CACT, respectively?

   A. Uncompetitive inhibition; mixed inhibition
   B. Uncompetitive inhibition; competitive inhibition
   C. Noncompetitive inhibition; competitive inhibition
   D. Noncompetitive inhibition; mixed inhibition

5. Which of the following is likely true regarding omeprazole?

   I. It is most active at a low ph.
   II. It exhibits quaternary structure.
   III. It acts an acyl group carrier.

   A. I only
   B. III only
   C. I and II only
   D. II and III only

Passage 2 (Questions 1-6)

In oxidative metabolism, mitochondria produce energy by using acetyl-CoA to ultimately fuel the conversion of ADP to ATP. The processes employed in cellular respiration are called the citric acid cycle and oxidative phosphorylation. The citric acid cycle, also known as the Krebs cycle, generates high-energy electrons using acetyl-CoA which is derived from the end product of glycolysis. The citric acid cycle is presented in Figure 1.

Reaction step	Enzyme
1	Citrate synthetase
2	Aconitase
3	Aconitase
4	Isocitrate dehydrogenase
5	α-Ketoglutarate dehydrogenase complex
6	Succinyl-CoA synthetase
7	Succinate dehydrogenase
8	Fumarase
9	Malate dehydrogenase

Figure 1

A study was conducted to determine the nature of the enzyme attack on a symmetrical molecule in the citric acid cycle:

- Radioactive labeling was applied to the carboxyl carbon more distant from the keto group of oxaloacetate. The labeled oxaloacetate was added to cell extract including the necessary enzymes and cofactors of the citric acid cycle.

- The intermediates of the citric acid cycle were then isolated and examined for the presence of radioactive labeling.

Radioactive labeling persisted in citrate, isocitrate, and α-ketoglutarate but disappeared entirely in the formation of succinate, as shown in Reaction 1.

$$
\begin{array}{c}
COO^- \\
| \\
CH_2 \\
| \\
C=O \\
| \\
{}^*COO^-
\end{array}
+ \text{acetyl-CoA} \rightarrow
\begin{array}{c}
COO^- \\
| \\
CH_2 \\
| \\
HO-C-COO^- \\
| \\
CH_2 \\
| \\
{}^*COO^-
\end{array}
\rightarrow
\begin{array}{c}
COO^- \\
| \\
CH_2 \\
| \\
HC-COO^- \\
| \\
HO-CH \\
| \\
{}^*COO^-
\end{array}
\rightarrow
\begin{array}{c}
COO^- \\
| \\
CH_2 \\
| \\
CH_2 \\
| \\
C=O \\
| \\
{}^*COO^-
\end{array}
\rightarrow
\begin{array}{c}
COO^- \\
| \\
CH_2 \\
| \\
CH_2 \\
| \\
COO^-
\end{array}
+ {}^*CO
$$

Oxalo-acetate   Citrate   Isocitrate   α-Keto-glutarate   Succinate

Reaction 1

The CO_2 molecule was discovered to be labeled with 100% of the ^{14}C. [Note: (*) represents radioactive carbon.]

1. Based on Reaction 1, an important interpretation of the experimental results is that the:

    A. two symmetrical halves of the citrate molecule were acted upon equally by aconitase.
    B. two symmetrical halves of the citrate molecule were not acted upon equally by aconitase.
    C. α-ketoglutarate decarboxylation was the rate-limiting step in the reaction α-ketoglutarate → succinate.
    D. α-ketoglutarate was acted upon by the asymmetrical enzyme succinate dehydrogenase.

2. If, in an aerobic organism, the Krebs cycle were suddenly arrested while glycolysis proceeded, the cell would most likely experience an increase in:

    A. glucose consumption.
    B. number of cytochromes.
    C. quantity of lactic acid.
    D. quantity of ATP.

3. With reference to Figure 1, what types of reactions occurred to yield α-ketoglutarate from isocitrate?

    A. Substrate-level phosphorylation and hydration
    B. Decarboxylation and hydration of NADH
    C. Decarboxylation and oxidation of NADH
    D. Decarboxylation and reduction of NAD^+

4. The fact that all of the radioactive carbon was found in the released CO_2 and none had remained in succinate was an important experimental finding. Given the symmetrical nature of the citrate metabolite, what alternative outcome might a scientist assume to find?

    A. 75% of the labeling in the CO_2 and 25% of the labeling in the succinate
    B. 25% of the labeling in the CO_2 and 75% of the labeling in the succinate
    C. 100% of the labeling in the succinate
    D. 50% of the labeling in the CO_2 and 50% of the labeling in the succinate

5. In order to study the mechanism by which pyruvate is converted to acetyl CoA, the enzyme responsible for the conversion had to be located. It would most likely be found in the:

    A. cytosol of the cell. PDC
    B. plasma membrane.
    C. endoplasmic reticulum.
    D. matrix of the mitochondria.

6. Aconitase is able to approach citrate in a specific orientation which differentiates between citrate's CH_2COO^- groups. Which of the following is true concerning the citrate molecule?

    I. It is symmetrical.
    II. It lacks a chiral center.
    III. It is optically inactive.

    A. I only
    B. I and II only
    C. I and III only
    D. I, II, and III

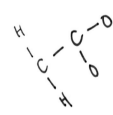

Passage 3 (Questions 1-6)

Lysozyme is a small enzyme that cleaves the cell walls of bacterial organisms. A major component of the bacterial cell wall is made of alternating polymers of N-acetylglucosamine (NAG) and N-acetylmuramate (NAM) polysaccharides. NAG and NAM are joined together by β glycosidic bonds between C–1 of one sugar and C–4 of the other (see Figure 1). Hydrolytic reactions have shown that lysozyme cleaves the bond between one of the sugar residues and the oxygen of the adjacent residue.

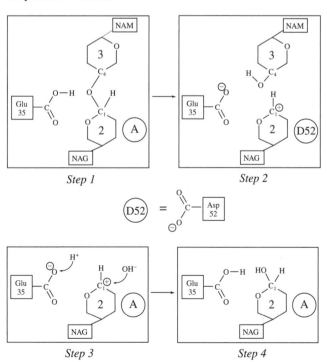

Figure 1

X-ray studies were conducted to determine the steps in the catalytic mechanism of the enzyme. Initial studies conducted to isolate the active site of the enzyme were difficult because the enzyme lacks a prosthetic group. Current studies have found that several amino acids, in particular glutamic acid and aspartic acid, participate in the hydrolysis of the reaction. The result of the study is shown below:

1. All of the following are examples of enzymes which participate in hydrolytic reactions EXCEPT:

    A. pepsin.
    B. insulin.
    C. chymotrypsin.
    D. amylase.

2. If the cell wall of a bacterium in hypotonic medium is destroyed by lysozyme, this will lead to an:

    A. increase in the osmotic pressure in the cell.
    B. increased rate of ATP consumption.
    C. influx of water through the plasma membrane.
    D. increase in protein production in the cell.

3. The cleavage of the bond between the NAM and NAG residues is due to the hydrolysis of a(n):

    A. α-1,4-glycosidic bond.
    B. β-1,4-glycosidic bond.
    C. α peptide bond.
    D. α hydrogen bond.

4. A prosthetic group plays a major role in the identification of an enzyme. Which of the following statements about prosthetic groups are true?

    I. They are non-protein organic molecules associated with the enzyme.
    II. They are added to proteins after translation.
    III. They are needed in order for some enzymes to catalyze reactions.

    A. I and II only
    B. I and III only
    C. II and III only
    D. I, II, and III

5. In Steps 1 and 2 depicted in the diagram, it can be concluded that E35 acts as:

    A. a hydrogen acceptor.
    B. a hydrogen donor.
    C. an inorganic catalyst.
    D. a weak base.

6. Which of the following procedures would be the best method to identify the specific site of cleavage by the enzyme?

   A. Using radioactive water as a solvent
   B. Using radioactive Asp 52 in the reaction
   C. Using excess Glu 35 in the reaction
   D. Lowering the pH

Passage 4 (Questions 1-6)

Photosynthesis is the process plants use to derive energy from sunlight and is associated with a cell's chloroplasts. The energy is used to produce carbohydrates from carbon dioxide and water. Photosynthesis involves light and dark phases. Figure 1 represents two initial steps associated with the light phase.

The light phase supplies the dark phase with NADPH and a high-energy substrate.

A researcher attempted to produce a photosynthetic system outside the living organism according to the following protocols:

• Chloroplasts were extracted from green leaves and ruptured, and their membranes were thereby exposed, then a solution of hexachloroplatinate ions carrying a charge of –2 was added.

• The structure of the composite was analyzed, and the amount of oxygen produced by the system was measured.\

The researcher concluded that the ions were bound to the membrane's Photosystem 1 site by the attraction of opposite charges. The resulting composite is shown in Figure 2. It was found that the hexachloroplatinate-membrane composite was photosynthetically active.

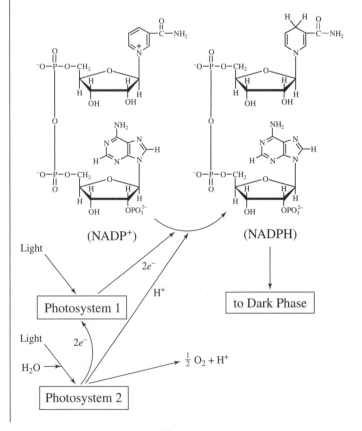

Figure 1

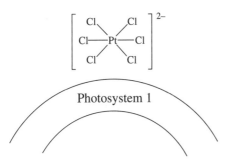

Photosystem 1

Figure 2

1. In concluding that the hexachloroplatinate ions were bound to Photosystem 1 due to the attraction of opposite charges, the researchers apparently assumed that the structure of the membrane was:

   A. determined solely by hydrophobic bonding.
   B. positively charged.
   C. covalently bound to the platinate.
   D. negatively charged.

2. Figure 1 indicates that:

   A. photoactivation of the chloroplast membrane results in the reduction of the anhydride-containing molecule NADP$^+$.
   B. electrons are lost from Photosystem 1 through the conversion of NADPH to NADP$^+$, and are replaced by electrons from Photosystem 2.
   C. there is a net gain of electrons by the system.
   D. electrons are lost from Photosystem 1 through the conversion of NADP$^+$ to NADPH, but are not replaced by electrons from Photosystem 2.

3. In addition to NADPH, the photosynthetic light phase must supply the dark phase with another molecule which stores energy for biosynthesis. Among the following, the molecule would most likely be:

   A. ADP.
   B. CO_2.
   C. inorganic phosphate.
   D. ATP.

4. If in a given cell the photosynthetic dark phase were artificially arrested while the light phase proceeded, the cell would most likely experience:

   A. decreased levels of NADPH.
   B. increased levels of NADPH.
   C. increased levels of carbohydrate.
   D. increased photoactivation of the chloroplast.

5. To determine the primary structure of the protein portion of Photosystem 1, a series of cleavage reactions was undertaken. To break apart the protein, the most logical action to take would be to:

   A. decarboxylate free carboxyl groups.
   B. hydrolyze peptide bonds.
   C. repolymerize peptide bonds.
   D. hydrolyze amide branch points.

6. A researcher examined a sample of the principal substance produced by the photosynthetic dark phase and concluded that he was working with a racemic mixture of glucose isomers. Which of the following experimental findings would be inconsistent with such a conclusion?

   A. The sample is composed of carbon, hydrogen, and oxygen only.
   B. The sample consists of an aldohexose.
   C. The sample rotates the plane of polarized light to the left.
   D. The sample is optically inactive.

Passage 5 (Questions 1-6)

Fermentation is an anaerobic process that results in the conversion of high-energy substrates to various waste products. Fermentation harvests only a small amount of the energy stored in glucose. There are two common types: alcoholic fermentation and lactic acid fermentation. In alcoholic fermentation the conversion of pyruvic acid to ethanol is a two-step process. In lactic acid fermentation the conversion of pyruvic acid to lactic acid is a one-step process (Figure 1).

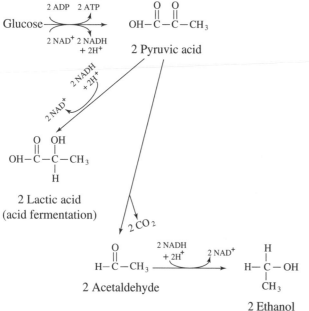

Figure 1

1. In all fermentation processes the final acceptor of electrons from NADH is:

    A. O_2.
    B. NAD^+.
    C. an alcohol.
    D. an organic compound.

2. During alcoholic fermentation, the molecules pyruvic acid and acetaldehyde are, respectively:

    A. decarboxylated and phosphorylated.
    B. reduced and decarboxylated.
    C. decarboxylated and reduced.
    D. decarboxylated and oxidized.

3. In lactic acid fermentation, pyruvic acid (the end product of glycolysis) serves as an:

    A. electron acceptor for the oxidation of NADH.
    B. electron acceptor for the reduction of NAD^+.
    C. electron donor for the oxidation of NADH.
    D. electron donor for the reduction of NAD^+.

4. When lactic acid accumulates in muscles it is gradually carried away by the blood to the liver. What effect does lactic acid have on respiratory rate?

    A. It increases respiratory rate.
    B. It decreases respiratory rate.
    C. It has no effect on respiratory rate.
    D. Respiratory rate will initially decrease and then rapidly level off.

5. One of the ways in which fermentation differs from glycolysis is that, in fermentation:

    A. glucose is oxidized.
    B. NAD^+ is regenerated.
    C. high-energy electrons are passed to NAD^+.
    D. ATP is produced.

6. Human muscle cells behave in a manner similar to:

    A. strict aerobes.
    B. facultative anaerobes.
    C. anaerobes.
    D. obligate aerobes.

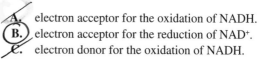

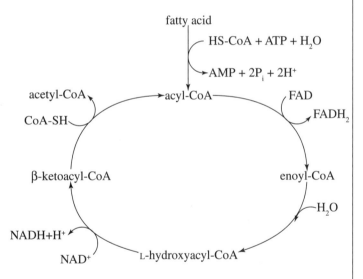

Passage 6 (Questions 1-8)
ADVANCED PASSAGE

Fatty acid oxidation proceeds by the sequential removal of two-carbon units. Before fatty acids are oxidized they are covalently bound to coenzyme A (CoA) on the outer mitochondrial membrane. CoA has a sulfur atom which attacks the carbonyl carbon of the fatty acid; water is the leaving group. This reaction is driven forward by the hydrolysis of two high-energy phosphate bonds. The rest of the oxidation occurs in the mitochondrial matrix; the acyl-CoA is transported across the inner mitochondrial membrane by a special transport molecule. In each cycle of fatty acid degradation (Figure 1), an acyl-CoA is shortened by two carbons, until only a two- or three-carbon chain remains. This occurs by a process known as β-oxidation, in which the β-carbon of the fatty acyl-CoA is oxidized to a carbonyl and then attacked by another CoA's sulfur atom. In this case the original CoA molecule plus its bound acetyl group is the leaving group. The acetyl-CoA produced from fatty acid oxidation can enter the citric acid cycle for further oxidation to carbon dioxide. The citric acid cycle yields 3 NADH + 1 FADH$_2$ + 1 GTP per acetate which can all be converted to ATP and has an overall $\Delta G^{\circ\prime}$ of -9.8 kcal/mol.

Phenylpropionate

Phenylbutyrate

fatty acid

HS-CoA + ATP + H$_2$O

AMP + 2P$_i$ + 2H$^+$

acetyl-CoA

CoA-SH

acyl-CoA

FAD

FADH$_2$

β-ketoacyl-CoA

enoyl-CoA

H$_2$O

NADH+H$^+$

NAD$^+$

L-hydroxyacyl-CoA

Figure 1 The cycle of β-oxidation

A key experiment in elucidating this mechanism of fatty acid oxidation was carried out by Francis Knoop. When he fed dogs the fatty acid phenylpropionate, their urine contained benzoate. Similarly, phenylbutyrate in the dogs' food resulted in phenylacetate in their urine. In both instances, the starting fatty acid was shortened by two carbons.

1. The equation for one turn of the fatty acid degradation cycle is:

    A. C$_n$-acyl-CoA + FAD + NAD$^+$ + H$_2$O + CoA → C$_{n-2}$-acyl-CoA + FADH$_2$ + NADH + acetyl-CoA + H$^+$
    B. C$_n$-acyl-CoA → C$_{n-2}$-acyl-CoA + acetyl-CoA
    C. C$_n$-acyl-CoA + H$_2$O → acetyl-CoA
    D. C$_n$-acyl-CoA + FAD + NAD$^+$ + H$_2$O → C$_{n-2}$ acyl-CoA + FADH$_2$ + NADH + acetyl-CoA

2. The conversion of acyl-CoA to enoyl-CoA is best classified as a(n):

    A. isomerization.
    B. hydration.
    C. reduction.
    D. oxidation.

3. How many ATP would be produced if a 16-carbon fatty acid, were completely oxidized to CO$_2$ and H$_2$O?

    A. 28 ATP
    B. 35 ATP
    C. 106 ATP
    D. 108 ATP

4. Fatty acid oxidation and fatty acid biosynthesis share which of the following traits?

    A. Both occur in the mitochondrial matrix.
    B. Both pathways use or produce NADH.
    C. Both pathways use the same enzymes.
    D. Both pathways use or produce acetyl-CoA.

5. Which of the following would be present in the urine of dogs that were fed phenylpalmitate? (Note: Palmitate is a 16-carbon fatty acid.)

A. 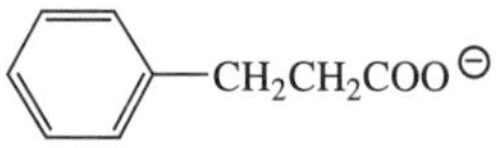
$CH_2CH_2COO^{\ominus}$

B. 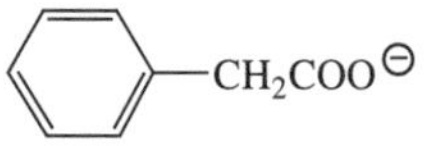
$CH_2COO^{\ominus}$

C. 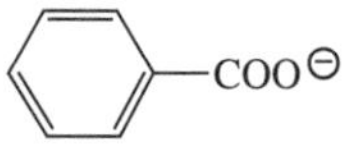
$COO^{\ominus}$

D. 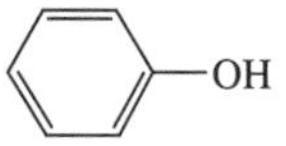
OH

6. If the concentration of acetyl-CoA produced from fatty acid oxidation is very high, the citric acid cycle is overwhelmed and acetoacetate and other ketone bodies form. The reason this occurs is that:

   A. insufficient citrate is present to combine with acetyl CoA.
   B. insufficient oxaloacetate is present to combine with acetyl-CoA.
   C. acetyl-CoA can be converted to glucose.
   D. acetoacetate spontaneously decarboxylates to give acetone.

7. The enzyme responsible for the conversion of L-hydroxyacyl-CoA to ketoacyl-CoA is a:

   A. hydratase.
   B. reductase.
   C. dehydrogenase.
   D. transacylase.

8. Depriving a cell of oxygen would have what effect on the cycle of β-oxidation?

   A. The cycle would accelerate as energy needs increased.
   B. The availability of CoA would decrease.
   C. $FADH_2$ and NADH would accumulate and the cycle would slow.
   D. Fermentation would occur instead of acetyl-CoA synthesis.

Passage 7 (Questions 1-6)

In times of fasting, the body relies more heavily on catabolism of amino acids to produce either ketone bodies (in the case of ketogenic amino acids) or precursors of glucose (in the case of glucogenic amino acids) through a series of interactions involving an α-ketoacid intermediate. A representative reaction is shown in Figure 1.

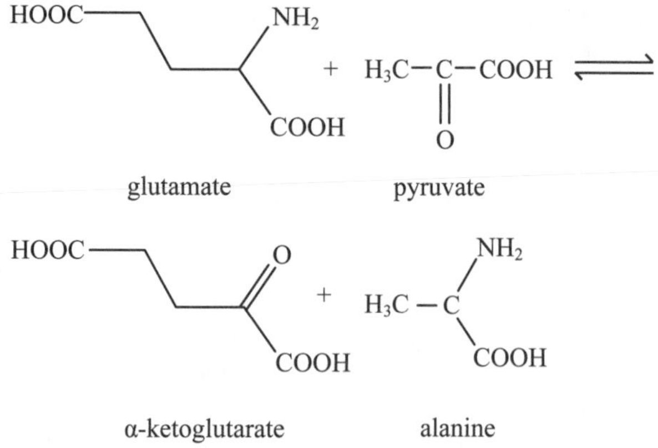

glutamate   pyruvate

α-ketoglutarate   alanine

Figure 1 Interconversion of pyruvate and alanine

"Low carb" diets capitalize on this feature of metabolism to achieve a ketogenic state in which the body is chronically deprived of carbohydrate sources of energy and thus forced to produce ketone bodies from either fat or amino acids to obtain energy. Interested in changes in the makeup of energy molecules in blood during this ketogenic state, researchers measure the levels of ketone bodies, glucose, insulin, glucagon, and fatty acids at various time points after a participant begins a ketogenic diet. Their findings are shown below.

	After normal meal	Overnight fasting	2 days after starting diet	5 days after starting diet
Insulin	↑	↓	↓	↓
Glucagon	↓	↑	↑	↑
Glucose	Normal	Normal	Normal	Normal
Fatty Acids	↑	↓	↑	↑↑↑
Ketones	↓	↓	↑	↑↑↑

Figure 2 Results of experiment

Adapted from Harvey, R. A., & Ferrier, D. R. (2011). *Lippincott's illustrated reviews, biochemistry* (5th ed.). Philadelphia: Wolters Kluwer Health.

1. The reaction shown in Figure 1 is catalyzed by what type of enzyme?

   A. Oxidoreductase
   B. Transferase
   C. Isomerase
   D. Ligase

2. As shown in Figure 2, glucose is maintained at an approximately equal serum concentration throughout the fasting period, in spite of decreased dietary intake. Which of the following accounts for most of the glucose in circulation during the overnight fast?

   A. Production of glucose from glycerol
   B. Dietary intake from the last meal
   C. Breakdown of stored glycogen
   D. Ketogenesis

3. All of the following are true of ketone bodies EXCEPT:

   A. Ketone bodies are soluble in blood and thus do not require a carrier molecule (e.g. albumin) for transport to peripheral tissues
   B. Ketone bodies may take the place of glucose in the brain, conserving glucose in times of fasting
   C. Ketone bodies may be produced directly from glycerol, a breakdown product of triglycerides
   D. Ketone bodies are produced by the liver

4. The interconversion of acetoacetate to 3-hydroxybutyrate and vice-versa is important in ketone body production and use. Which of the following is true of the reaction shown below?

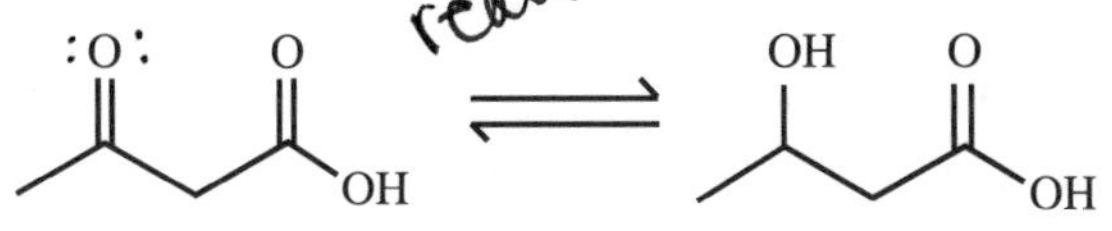

   Acetoacetate   3-Hydroxybutyrate

   A. Conversion of acetoacetate to 3-hydroxybutyrate is a reduction reaction and requires one molecule of NADH
   B. Conversion of acetoacetate to 3-hydroxybutyrate is an oxidation reaction and requires one molecule of NADH
   C. Conversion of acetoacetate to 3-hydroxybutyrate is a reduction reaction and releases one molecule of NADH
   D. Conversion of acetoacetate to 3-hydroxybutyrate is an oxidation reaction and releases one molecule of NADH

5. The neurotransmitter serotonin is derived from tryptophan (structures shown below). Conversion from tryptophan to serotonin involves which of the following reactions?

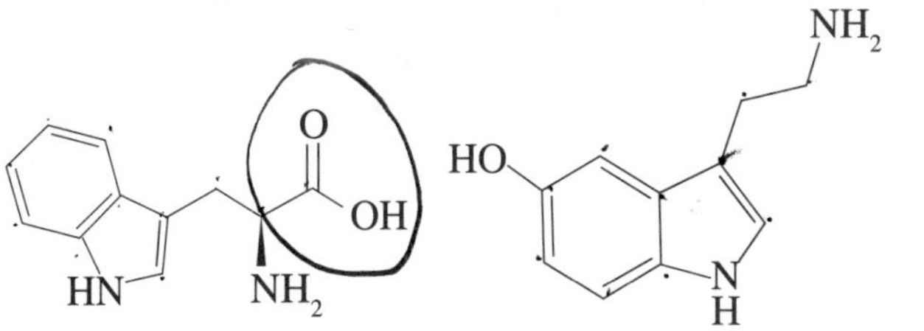

   Tryptophan   Serotonin

   I. Deamination
   II. Decarboxylation
   III. Hydroxylation

   A. III only
   B. II and III
   C. I, II, and III
   D. I and II

6. Which of the following enzymes in the liver is most active five days after starting a ketogenic diet?

   A. Hexokinase
   B. Phosphofructokinase I
   C. HMG-CoA synthase
   D. Glycogen phosphorylase

Passage 8 (Questions 1-6)

A multicellular, eukaryotic organism under investigation is known to have highly active mechanisms for DNA replication, transcription, and translation. The organism has both a haploid and a diploid state. In the haploid state, there is only one copy of each chromosome in the DNA complement. The diploid form has two copies of each chromosome that are usually homozygous for most traits. To further study this organism, two mutations were induced (mutants No. 127 and No. 136). These mutants demonstrated unique phenotypes when observed under ultraviolet light.

Experiment 1:

To elucidate the chain of events in transcription and translation, a wild-type variant of the organism was exposed to standard mutagens, including nitrous acid, which resulted in the creation of the two mutants. The researchers then analyzed the exact sequence of events leading from DNA to RNA to protein products. Figure 1 illustrates this sequence for the wild-type organism and the two mutants created.

Normal Type				
TCA	CGA	ATG	GTA	← Sense DNA
AGT	GCT	TAC	CAT	← Template DNA strand
1 2 3	4 5 6	7 8 9	10 11 12	
	↓ transcription			
UCA	CGA	AUG	GUA	← RNA strand
S —	R —	M —	V	← Amino acids
Mutant No. 127				
TCA	CGA	GTG	GTA	
AGT	GCT	CAC	CAT	← Template DNA strand
UCA	CGA	GUG	GUA	← RNA strand
S —	R —	V —	V	← Amino acids
Mutant No. 136				
TCA	TGA	ATG	GTA	
AGT	ACT	TAC	CAT	← Template DNA strand
UCA	UGA	AUG	GUA	← RNA strand
S	Termination codon			

Figure 1

Mutant No. 127 was plated onto a petri dish and grown with D-glucose as its carbon source. The organism showed growth and reproduction patterns similar to the wild type, including the generation of a haploid stage. Mutant No. 136 was similarly treated and also showed stable growth patterns.

Experiment 2:

Mutants No. 127 and No. 136 were exposed to a virus to which the wild type is immune. Mutant No. 127 was also found to be resistant, while mutant No. 136 was destroyed by the virus. The haploid form of mutant No. 136 was then fused with the haploid form of the normal type. This produced a diploid organism which was protected against the action of the virus. The diploid form of mutant No. 136 was not protected.

Figure adapted from Alice Smith, *Principles of Microbiology*, 8th edition © 1977.

1. In labeling the RNA but not DNA in mutants No. 127 and No. 136, which of the following radioactive molecules would be most useful?

    A. Labeled phosphate
    B. Labeled thymine
    C. Labeled uracil
    D. Labeled D-ribose

2. In Experiment 2, how many copies of the No. 136 mutation occurred in the surviving diploid?

    A. 1
    B. 2
    C. 3
    D. 4

3. The No. 136 mutation seen in Figure 1 is caused by a defect in:

    A. DNA replication.
    B. transcription.
    C. translation.
    D. post-translational modification.

4. One can reason that mutant No. 136 represents a less "fit" organism in the Darwinian sense than mutant No. 127 by noting which of the following results?

    A. Mutant No. 127 replicates at a different rate than does mutant No. 136.
    B. Mutation No. 127 protects against a naturally occurring virus while mutation No. 136 does not.
    C. The No. 127 mutant is found in man; the No. 136 mutant is found in birds.
    D. Both mutations (No. 127 and No. 136) produce protein products of variable length.

5. A student, upon studying Figure 1, concluded that single point mutations in DNA can alter the size of the translated product. What finding allowed her to reach this conclusion?

   A. Mutant No. 136 produces a larger-sized protein than mutant No. 127.
   B. Valine is represented by two different codons in the growing polypeptide.
   C. Point mutations lead to an increased size of the RNA segment.
   D. An DNA point mutation can create a termination codon which abruptly ends the growing polypeptide.

6. If mutants No. 127 and No. 136 are kept in separate dishes and other mutations arise such that the two mutants can no longer reproduce sexually with each other, the process that has taken place can be described as:

   A. genetic variability in a population.
   B. phenotypic variation due to niche variability.
   C. geographic isolation leading to speciation.
   D. random mutation leading to population control.

Passage 9 (Questions 1-6)

Prokaryotic protein synthesis takes place in three phases: initiation, elongation, and termination. The machinery of translation is the 70S ribosome, which consists of 30S and 50S subunits. First, an initiation complex forms that is made up of the 30S subunit, mRNA, and a special initiator tRNA that binds formyl methionine, which is used only in prokaryotic translation initiation. Certain "initiation factors" are also essential. The 50S subunit then binds the initiation complex. Once the entire 70S ribosome has formed, two binding sites become available. One is the P (peptidyl transferase) site; the other is the A (amino acyl) site. The initiator tRNA occupies the P site.

Elongation begins with the binding of tRNA #2, with its amino acid, in the A site. The appropriate amino acid is selected due to the ability of its tRNA to hydrogen bond with the next codon of mRNA to be translated. Peptide-bond formation is catalyzed by the P-site peptidyl transferase, which transfers the carboxyl of amino acid #1 in the P site to the N-terminus of amino acid #2 in the A site. The tRNA in the P site, now lacking an amino acid, dissociates from the complex, and the nascent chain with the remaining tRNA (in this case the second one) translocates from the A site to the P site, leaving the A site free to bind tRNA #3. This cycle of binding, peptide bond formation, and translocation creates a polypeptide chain.

Termination occurs when a stop codon in the mRNA appears in the A site. Termination factors catalyze the hydrolysis of the polypeptide chain from the tRNA to which it is attached.

Protein synthesis requires energy in the form of ATP and GTP. Two high-energy phosphate bonds (from ATP) fuel the formation of one aminoacyl tRNA (i.e., the attachment of each amino acid to its tRNA). Formation of the initiation complex requires the energy from one GTP. Delivery of each new tRNA to the A site also requires one GTP. Translocation of the peptidyl tRNA requires one GTP. Termination requires the hydrolysis of one GTP.

Figure 1 shows the traditional genetic code table. The coded amino acid or start/stop signal is found at the intersection of the correct three "letters" of the codon.

First position (5′)	Second position				Third position (3′)
	U	**C**	**A**	**G**	
U	phe	ser	tyr	cys	U
	phe	ser	typ	cys	C
	leu	ser	STOP	STOP	A
	leu	ser	STOP	trp	G
C	leu	pro	his	arg	U
	leu	pro	his	arg	C
	leu	pro	gln	arg	A
	leu	pro	gln	arg	G
A	ile	thr	asn	ser	U
	ile	thr	asn	ser	C
	ile	thr	lys	arg	A
	met	thr	lys	arg	G
G	val	ala	asp	gly	U
	val	ala	asp	gly	C
	val	ala	glu	gly	A
	val	ala	glu	gly	G

Figure 1 The genetic code

Adapted from *Biochemistry, Third Edition*, by Stryer, © 1988 by Lubert Stryer.

1. How many high-energy phosphate bonds are required for the translation of a 100 amino acid polypeptide, starting with mRNA, tRNA, amino acids, and all the necessary enzymes?

    A. 200
    B. 300
    C. 400
    D. 402

2. A portion of prokaryotic mRNA has the following base sequence: 5′-ACAUCUAUGCCACGA-3′. Which of the following could result from a mutation that changes the underlined base to A?

    I. Inhibition of initiation of translation
    II. Truncation of the polypeptide
    III. No effect on protein synthesis

    A. I only
    B. II only
    C. I and II only
    D. I, II, and III

    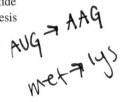

3. Puromycin is a drug that is an analog of aminoacyl tRNA. It has an amino group that is capable of forming a peptide bond, but no carboxyl group with which to form another peptide linkage. Which of the following is a possible effect of adding puromycin to cultures of bacteria engaged in protein synthesis?

    A. Termination of protein synthesis with puromycin covalently attached
    B. Inhibition of entry of aminoacyl tRNA into the P site during elongation
    C. Substitution of puromycin for another amino acid in the protein, yielding a protein of normal length
    D. Inhibition of initiation of protein synthesis

4. Ribosomes isolated from bacteria grown in heavy medium (^{14}C, ^{15}N) and from bacteria grown in light medium (^{12}C, ^{14}N) were added to a cell-free *in vitro* protein synthesis system. At a later time, a sample was removed and 70S ribosomes were analyzed for differing densities. How many 70S ribosome densities were found?

    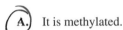

    A. 1
    B. 2
    C. 4
    D. 8

5. How is the methionine residue used for prokaryotic initiation of translation unique?

    A. It is methylated.
    B. It is acetylated.
    C. It is formylated.
    D. It is hydrophilic.

6. Which of the following is NOT true of prokaryotic translation?

    A. The N-terminal amino acid of every nascent polypeptide is formylated.
    B. The mRNA chain being translated may not be fully transcribed at the time of translation.
    C. Hydrogen bonds between amino acids and mRNA codons are essential for translation of the genetic code.
    D. The mRNA is not spliced before initiation.

Passage 10 (Questions 1-7)

Viruses which infect bacteria of the genus *Escherichia* are known as coliphages. One such phage is called T4. Its optimal host is *E. coli* strain B. The first laboratory procedures required to study their relationship are to produce a good working volume of a high titer (concentration) coliphage suspension and to determine that titer.

A culture of *E. coli* is grown by inoculating 150 mL of sterile tryptone broth with 0.5 mL of a culture of bacteria grown overnight to reach stationary phase. The broth is then incubated at 37°C with air bubbling through, until the medium appears *faintly* cloudy or turbid, but not yet milky. This usually requires 2 hours. Next, 1 mL of stock high titer coliphage is added to the bacterial culture. After 3 hours, the culture appears nearly clear and may have some foaming.

In order to determine the titer of coliphage in this suspension, a serial dilution is performed. In the serial dilution, 0.1 mL of the starting solution (or suspension) is diluted by a factor of 10. Then 0.1 mL of the resulting dilute suspension is diluted by a factor of 10. This is repeated until a series of solutions are obtained, each 10 times as dilute as the previous one. Next, 0.1 mL of each dilution is mixed with soft agar which has been inoculated with 2 drops of a pure *E. coli* suspension. This mixture is then spread evenly on a hard agar base. The plates are allowed to solidify and are turned upside-down in a 37°C incubator overnight. The next day, the plates are observed for evidence of lysis, and this allows determination of the titer.

Adapted from *Bacteriophage Culture and Titer Determination*, © 1979 by Carolina Biological Supply Company.

1. Lysis is marked in the *E. coli* suspension by:

   A. slight cloudiness.
   B. a large increase in turbidity.
   C. clearing.
   D. no visible change.

2. Replication of virus is marked on the overnight agar plates by:

   A. bacterial colonies on the agar surface.
   B. growth of a smooth layer of bacteria across the plate.
   C. no visible change.
   D. growth of bacteria across the entire plate except for small clear patches.

3. Why do the researchers put 0.5 mL of bacteria from an overnight culture into sterile tryptone broth and inoculate the resulting culture with phage, rather than just inoculating the overnight culture with phage directly?

   A. Because the bacteria in the overnight culture are already infected
   B. So that the inoculated bacterial culture will be in growth phase
   C. Because the bacteria in the overnight culture are probably dead
   D. Because the overnight culture is probably contaminated

4. Plaque counts are used to calculate the density, or titer, of infective particles in the phage suspension. One hundred fifty plaques on the plate from the 10^{-2} dilution indicates a phage suspension titer of:

   A. 1.5 per mL.
   B. 1.5×10^2 per mL.
   C. 1.5×10^4 per mL.
   D. 1.5×10^5 per mL.

5. Three hours after the addition of 1 mL of stock high titer coliphage to the turbid *E. coli* culture, the culture contains:

   I. dead *E. coli*.
   II. live infected *E. coli*.
   III. free coliphage.

   A. I only
   B. III only
   C. I and II only
   D. I, II, and III

6. The optimal host of phage T4 contains all of the following EXCEPT:

   A. lysosomes.
   B. a cell wall.
   C. ribosomes.
   D. both RNA and DNA.

7. Which of the following is true regarding T4 infection of *E. coli*?

   A. T4 buds through the plasma membrane to leave the cell.
   B. The final stages of viral assembly occur once the virus leaves the cell.
   C. One of the first T4 genes expressed during viral infection is a lysozyme enzyme that facilitates cell lysis.
   D. T4 has mRNA which is translated by bacterial ribosomes while it is still being transcribed from DNA.

Passage 11 (Questions 1-4)

Acute viral hepatitis, a diffuse inflammatory disease of the liver, is caused by at least three different microbial agents, including the hepatitis B virus (HBV). Active HBV infection is indicated by the presence in the patient's serum of hepatitis B surface antigen, a viral marker found on the outer protein coat.

HBV is a DNA virus which contains DNA polymerase. After initial infection of a liver cell, the polymerase directs the lengthening of the short strand of the double-stranded viral genome. The DNA then migrates to the nucleus, where it undergoes transcription to form the pre-genome, which is made of RNA.

After being packaged into a new capsid, the pre-genome serves as a template for the production of a new single strand of DNA, which is a duplicate of the original long strand. A complementary short strand is then polymerized. Before the virus exits the cell, it becomes enclosed in an envelope derived from the host cell membrane. The enveloped virus is then capable of infecting other liver cells.

The main route of transmission of HBV is via contaminated blood or blood products. Since there is no specific treatment for HBV infection, the following prophylactic measures remain the focus of disease control:

1. Careful screening of blood and blood products and careful handling of medical supplies that come in contact with blood

2. Passive immunization with immune serum globulin or hepatitis B immune globulin

3. HBV vaccination of members of high-risk groups, such as health care personnel

In test studies, HBV vaccine provokes an immune response to the HBV surface antigen. Part of this response involves the production of the immunoglobulin IgG, an antibody which has the general structure shown below.

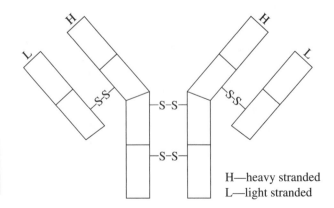

H—heavy stranded
L—light stranded

review transcription + translation

Topic = viruses

1. Which of the following would NOT be produced during transcription and translation of the hepatitis B genome?

   A. Hepatitis B surface antigen
   B. Hepatitis B core antigen
   C. DNA polymerase
   D. Double-stranded DNA

   ↳ not produced during viral trans. + transl.

2. Incubating HBV-infected liver cells with radiolabeled thymine will NOT allow an investigator to locate the viral pre-genome because:

   RNA contains U not T

   A. the amount of radioactivity will decrease considerably during semiconservative replication.
   B. the nuclear pores will not accommodate radioactive substances.
   C. the pregenome contains no thymine.
   D. viral DNA polymerase is only involved in viral transcription.

3. Which of the following processes must occur after a newly developing HBV particle forms its capsid but before it leaves the cell?

   A. Virally derived RNA must undergo reverse transcription.
   B. The viral pre-genome must become single-stranded.
   C. Host cell membrane components must be exocytosed.
   D. Double-stranded viral DNA must unwind.

4. Based on the information in the passage, escape of the HBV particle from the host cell causes:

   A. the host cell to lose lipid components of its plasma membrane.
   B. the host cell to undergo a process identical to that of endocytosis.
   C. the production of immunoglobulin by the host cell.
   D. the fusion of the viral pre-genome with the host cell membrane.

Passage 12 (Questions 1-6)
ADVANCED PASSAGE

Dementia is one of the most feared human conditions, both by those observing it and those experiencing it. It is defined as a persistent and progressive impairment of intellectual function, and can affect memory, emotions, personality, language, judgment, and cognition. It is frequently associated with other medical conditions, including Alzheimer's disease, stroke, and spongiform encephalopathies.

Encephalopathies are diseases of the brain. The spongiform encephalopathies are named for their characteristic deterioration of central nervous system tissue, resulting in a sponge-like appearance of the brain. They include kuru, Creutzfeldt–Jakob disease (CJD), Gerstmann–Straussler–Scheinker (GSS) disease, and familial fatal insomnia (FFI). Unlike Alzheimer's disease and strokes, the spongiform encephalopathies can be transmissible. Transmission of the disease was originally thought to be due to a virus; however, subsequent information suggests that the agent of transmission is simply a protein, with no associated nucleic acid. These proteins were termed *prions*, and are normal proteins found primarily in CNS tissue. Disease is associated with abnormal versions of the prion proteins.

The normal function of prion proteins is unclear, but they are thought to protect critical brain cells from dying. Mice that lack normal prions develop *ataxia* (coordination problems) that resembles the ataxia of kuru and CJD patients. Prion-free mice develop symptoms at approximately 70 weeks (late middle age for a mouse).

Since proteins are unable to self-replicate, it seemed unlikely that a transmissible disease could be caused by protein alone. However, upon further investigation, it was found that the prion proteins exist in two conformations, normal (PrP^c) and pathogenic (PrP^{Sc}). Pathogenic protein is relatively resistant to digestion by proteases and is insoluble in denaturing detergents. The initial appearance of PrP^{Sc} can be due to ingestion of diseased brain tissue (kuru), a missense mutation of the PrP^c gene (CJD and FFI), or simply a spontaneous conversion of PrP^c to PrP^{Sc}. Regardless of the specific initial event, additional copies of PrP^{Sc} are generated by using the initial copy as a "folding template." Contact between the two forms of the protein can cause a conformational change from the normal to the pathogenic form, if the abnormal and normal proteins are sufficiently similar. Disease is due to the slow accumulation of PrP^{Sc} and a resulting decrease in the amount of PrP^c.

Encephalitis (inflammation of the brain) can present with similar initial symptoms as the spongiform encephalopathies, most notably ataxia and mental disorientation. Encephalitis can have several causes, some of which are viral infections. Subacute sclerosing panencephalitis (SSPE) is caused by a defective measles virus. Powassan (POW) virus and the West Nile virus can also cause encephalitis; these are members of the flavivirus family. Flaviviruses are enveloped, (+)-RNA viruses that are transmitted through the bites of insects such as ticks and mosquitoes.

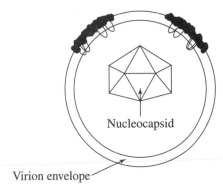

Figure 1   Flavivirus virion

An experiment was performed in which researchers tested 40-week-old normal and prion-free mice (genetic lack of normal prion proteins) for ataxia. Prior to evaluation, the mice were trained to walk across a round stick, 50 cm long and 1 cm in diameter. During the evaluation, the number of successful walks (walks in which the mouse did not fall from the stick) were recorded. The mice were then injected intracerebrally with abnormal prion protein and observed for several months. During the observation period, the test for ataxia was repeated every four weeks. Groups of mice were tested and the results averaged. Results are presented in Figure 2.

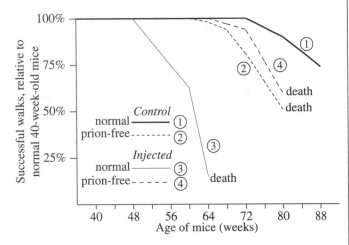

Figure 2   Results of tests for ataxia in normal and prion-free mice

1. Which region of the brain is most likely affected in patients experiencing ataxia?

   A. Medulla oblongata
   B. Hypothalamus
   C. Cerebrum
   D. Cerebellum

2. Based on Figure 2, which of the following is the most likely explanation for the development of ataxia in prion-free injected mice?

   A. Conformational changes in PrP^c caused by injection of PrP^{Sc}
   B. Normal loss of coordination due to aging
   C. Absence of PrP^c which led to premature death of critical brain cells
   D. Infection of the mice with West Nile virus

3. All of the following diseases could be inherited *except*:

   A. Creutzfeldt–Jakob disease.
   B. kuru.
   C. fatal insomnia.
   D. hemophilia.

4. In a separate experiment, researchers injected 40-week-old normal mice with an unknown solution. Within one week the mice developed high fevers, ataxia, mental disorientation, and encephalitis. Within four weeks most mice were dead. If treating the unknown solution with a detergent and a protease prior to injection prevented symptoms, the solution most likely contained:

   A. abnormal prion proteins, since the mice developed ataxia.
   B. normal prion proteins, and the symptoms were the result of an immune reaction.
   C. viral particles, since the symptoms developed rapidly.
   D. abnormal prion proteins, since symptoms were prevented by protease treatment.

5. According to information provided in the passage, which of the following could cause prion disease?

   I.   A spontaneous conversion of PrP^c to PrP^{Sc}
   II. Ingestion of diseased tissue
   III. Mutation of an amino acid codon into a STOP codon

   A. I only
   B. I and II only
   C. II and III only
   D. I, II, and III

6. Which of the following would *not* be acceptable cells in which to culture West Nile virus?

   A. Yeast
   B. Neurons
   C. Osteoblasts
   D. Muscle

Passage 13 (Questions 1-5)
ADVANCED PASSAGE

There have been recent studies that indicate an association between viruses and cancer induction. Many DNA viruses, such as adenovirus, induce cellular proliferation as part of their life cycle. These viruses are dependent on the host cell DNA replication apparatus to replicate their genome, and in quiescent cells the enzymes required for DNA synthesis are absent or inactive. The entry into S phase is rigidly controlled, preventing progression through the cell cycle where it is not appropriate. To successfully replicate in human cells, adenovirus must overcome these inherent blocks to S-phase entry, and in so doing increases the probability of transformation and possibly carcinogenesis.

Two factors encoded by the adenovirus genome, the E1A and E1B proteins, are essential for viral replication. In human cell lines, expression of either adenovirus E1A or E1B protein can cause transformation and immortalization of cells, leading to the classification of these virus-encoded factors as oncogenes. Transformation is much more efficient with the combination of both genes together than with either gene alone. E1A stimulates cellular proliferation and overcomes the block against cell-cycle progression. Viruses with the E1A gene deleted are able to enter the cell but do not stimulate progression through the cell cycle. They can replicate only in cells which enter S phase naturally and continue to progress normally through the cell cycle. Viruses with the E1B gene deleted have a different phenotype. Infected cells begin to proliferate in response to the E1A-produced response, but before these cells pass through S phase, they are induced to die in the process known as *apoptosis* (programmed cell death) which prevents replication of the virus.

Cells usually introduce apoptosis in circumstances where cell division is inappropriate but occurs anyway, such as viral infection, cancer, or cells with DNA damage. A protein known as p53 is responsible for the induction of apoptosis in these circumstances (see Figure 1). p53 was originally identified as a tumor-suppressor gene, a gene which prevents the development of cancer. Mutations in p53 are one of the most common genetic defects in tumors. Cancer treatments such as radiation therapy or chemotherapy appear to rely on p53-induced apoptosis in response to DNA damage, and cancer cells which lack p53 are resistant to these therapies.

In cells infected by the wild-type adenovirus, E1B protein interacts with p53, preventing it from inducing apoptosis. The cell can then proceed through S phase, replicating both the cellular and viral genomes in response to E1A-induced DNA replication. In cells lacking p53, E1B protein is not required for viral replication. The interaction between p53 and E1B is currently an area of intense interest in both the virology and cancer fields.

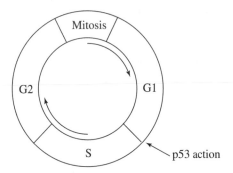

Figure 1 The cell cycle

In one set of experiments, the ability of different mutant forms of adenovirus to replicate in an immortalized human osteosarcoma cell line was examined. The cell line was found to lack p53 expression, unless the p53 gene was reintroduced back into the cells, as indicated in Figure 2. All forms of the virus were able to bind to the cells equally, and all forms of the virus were internalized equivalently. The production of new virus was measured over time in each experiment.

Mutant A adenovirus had the E1A gene deleted.

Mutant B adenovirus had the gene for E1B truncated due to the introduction of a premature stop codon.

Mutant C adenovirus had a point mutation in the gene encoding a viral capsid protein.

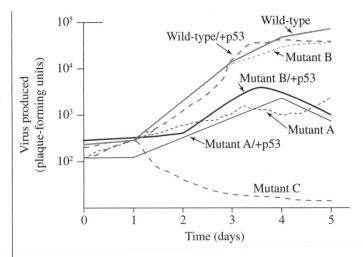

Figure 2

1. Which of the following is the most likely effect of infection by an adenovirus in which the E1B gene had been deleted?

   A. Viral replication in normal cells will proceed unhindered.
   B. New cancers will be induced frequently by the recombinant virus.
   C. The virus will prevent response of malignant tumors to chemotherapy.
   D. The virus will replicate in some cells but leave others unaffected.

2. An adenovirus named Virus Y is prepared which has the E1B gene deleted. This virus is unable to replicate in a cell line in which the p53 gene is intact. If this same cell line has the gene for the E1B protein inserted into its genome and expressed at high levels, which of the following is most likely to be observed when the E1B-expressing cell line is infected with Virus Y?

   A. Virus Y will enter the cells but induce apoptosis.
   B. Virus Y will produce progeny from the infection that are able to replicate in either E1B-expressing or E1B-lacking cells, regardless of p53 expression.
   C. Virus Y will produce progeny from the infection that are able to replicate only in E1B-expressing cells in which p53 is present.
   D. Virus Y will produce progeny from the infection that are able to replicate only in E1B-lacking cells in which p53 is present.

3. Which of the following statements best describes the function(s) of p53 in normal cells?

   A. It blocks aberrant cellular proliferation signals that lead to cancer.
   B. It induces cell death in the event of aberrant cell division.
   C. It prevents cancer and adenovirus infection.
   D. It prevents cancer but increases the risk of viral infection.

4. The E1A protein interacts with Rb protein, the product of the (tumor-suppressor) Retinoblastoma gene. Based on this as well as the information in the passage, it can be inferred that:

   A. Rb has the same activity in the cell as p53.
   B. E1A will also interact with p53.
   C. Rb and p53 are likely to interact with each other.
   D. inactivation of both Rb and p53 increases the risk of cellular transformation.

5. Which of the following statements is best supported by Figure 2?

   A. Mutant B produced approximately twice as much virus in the absence of p53 than in the presence of p53.
   B. E1A protein is not required for replication in the absence of E1B.
   C. p53 cannot induce apoptosis in this cell line.
   D. p53 does not affect replication by wild-type adenovirus in this cell line.

Passage 14 (Questions 1-6)

Alzheimer's disease is a neurodegenerative disorder which results partly from the deposition of pathological Aβ-amyloid (Aβ) plaques in the extracellular space between neurons. Aβ is formed from cleavage of a precursor protein of unknown function, amyloid precursor protein (APP). Amyloid precursor protein is a large (~135 kDa) transmembrane protein with a substantial extracellular component which may be cleaved to Aβ40, a lower molecular weight (40 kDa), non-aggregating cleavage product, or to Aβ42, a higher molecular weight (42 kDa) product with the potential to form amyloid plaques. It is believed that Aβ deposition proceeds in a prion-like fashion when pathologically misfolded Aβ protein induces misfolding of normal Aβ, thus creating insoluble plaques that result in neuron death.

Experiment 1

To determine whether Aβ plaques are prions, researchers carried out an experiment in which they introduced Aβ plaques purified from the brain of a diseased mouse into a disease-free mouse (via either peripheral IV or via direct injection into the brain) and waited for the animal to mature. They then sacrificed the mouse, prepared a brain homogenate, and measured the level of Aβ plaque in the homogenate. They observed the following:

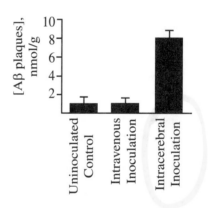

Figure 1 Levels of Aβ plaque in each test group.

Experiment 2

Interested in the localization of Aβ plaques within the brains of the animals, the researchers sectioned the brains of the affected animals and visualized them under microscopy, then quantified the number of plaques observed in each area. The results are shown below in Figure 2.

Brain region	Plaques observed
Hippocampus	+++
Association cortices	++
Precentral gyrus	None
Thalamus	++
Occipital cortex	None

Figure 2 Relative amount of Aβ plaque observed
in each brain region

Eisele et al. *Induction of cerebral β-amyloidosis: Intracerebral versus systemic Aβ inoculation.* PNAS 2009; Published online Jul 21, 2009, doi:10.1073/pnas.0903200106

Henry W. Querfurth and Frank M. LaFerla. *Alzheimer's Disease.* N Engl J Med 2010; DOI: 10.1056/NEJMra0909142

Jan Stöhr, Joel C. Watts, Zachary L. Mensinger, Abby Oehler, Sunny K. Grillo, Stephen J. DeArmond, Stanley B. Prusiner, and Kurt Giles. *Purified and synthetic Alzheimer's amyloid beta (Aβ) prions.* PNAS 2012; published ahead of print June 18, 2012, doi:10.1073/pnas.1206555109

1. The plaque formation process may result in changes in all of the following structural elements of Aβ EXCEPT:

   A. hydrophobic interactions.
   B. hydrogen bonding.
   C. amino acid sequence.
   D. salt bridges.

2. Based on Figure 2, which of the following are changes that might be observed in Alzheimer's disease patients?

   I. Problems encoding new memories
   II. Problems seeing color (while sparing other aspects of vision)
   III. Paralysis

   A. I and II only
   B. I only
   C. II and III only
   D. I and III only

3. Which of the following conclusions is supported by the data in Figure 1?

   A. Amyloid plaques cannot cross the blood-brain barrier, likely because of their large molecular weight.
   B. Amyloid plaques cannot cross the blood-brain barrier, likely because of their approximately neutral charge.
   C. Amyloid plaques can cross the blood-brain barrier, likely because of their large molecular weight.
   D. Amyloid plaques can cross the blood-brain barrier, likely because of their approximately neutral charge.

4. It is believed that the identity of the APP cleavage product, normal Aβ40 or pathological Aβ42, is determined by the type of protease (1 or 2) which acts on APP. Researchers purify APP and digest it with each of two candidate proteases in two separate reactions. Each of these reaction mixtures is run out on polyacrylamide gel electrophoresis, and the following results are obtained:

   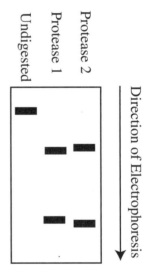

   Which of the following accurately describes the meaning of this result?

   A. A patient with a transcription-enhancing mutation in the promoter of Protease 1 is more likely to develop Alzheimer's disease.
   B. A patient with a transcription-enhancing mutation in the promoter of Protease 2 is more likely to develop Alzheimer's disease.
   C. A patient with a deleterious mutation in the Shine-Dalgarno sequence of the gene for Protease 1 is more likely to develop Alzheimer's disease.
   D. A patient with a deleterious mutation in the Shine-Dalgarno sequence of the gene for Protease 2 is more likely to develop Alzheimer's disease.

5. Creutzfeldt-Jakob disease (CJD) is a prion disease transmissible by blood, among other routes. A surgeon used instruments that had previously been used to perform intracranial surgery on an individual with CJD, for the same procedure on a disease-free patient. Although normal heat sterilization protocols (at >100°C) were followed with the instruments between procedures, the previously disease-free patient nonetheless developed CJD. Which of the following explanations for this occurrence is most likely?

   A. The prion plaques' tertiary and quaternary structure renders them extremely stable; thus, they were not denatured during heating.
   B. The prion plaques are highly resistant to proteolysis and thus were not affected by the heat.
   C. The prion plaques were likely denatured during heating, but spontaneously refolded after cooling to form a plaque structure again.
   D. The strong covalent bonds between prion subunits prevented the plaques from coming apart during heating.

6. Researchers intracerebrally inject a rabbit with the purified Aβ plaques described in Experiment 1. Besides an inflammatory reaction, none of the rabbits show any response to the injection. Brain homogenates taken from the rabbits in the months following injection show no evidence of Alzheimer's disease. Which of the following procedures might increase the chances that these rabbits would develop Alzheimer's?

   A. Intracerebrally injecting an antibody against the rabbits' native Aβ42.
   B. Giving the rabbits a drug which increases the permeability of the blood-brain barrier.
   C. Injecting the rabbits with a protease inhibitor.
   D. Giving the rabbits corticosteroids.

Passage 15 (Questions 1-6)
ADVANCED PASSAGE

Plasmids are small circular double-stranded DNAs that carry extrachromosomal genetic information in bacteria. Plasmids with an origin of replication can be replicated by bacterial proteins and stably transmitted from one generation to another. The proteins encoded by genes on plasmids often provide resistance to antibiotics by degrading the antibiotic. Through recombinant DNA technology, plasmids can also be engineered to carry other genes not normally found in bacteria. Plasmids can be introduced into cells by transformation techniques which allow DNA to cross through the cell wall and plasma membrane without killing bacterial cells. After transformation, exposure to the correct antibiotic allows selection of bacteria that received plasmid. Bacteriophages such as bacteriophage λ are viruses that infect bacterial cells. Bacteriophage λ can also be engineered to carry novel genes not normally present in bacteria or bacteriophages.

Among the tools that has made recombinant DNA technology possible are *restriction enzymes*. Restriction enzymes are endonucleases which cut DNA at specific sequences, usually inverted repeat sequences that read the same if rotated 180°. After cutting, the ends of the double-stranded DNA fragments are left by some restriction enzymes with short regions of single-stranded DNA called "sticky ends." Since a restriction enzyme always cuts in the same manner, the sticky end from one fragment can be annealed with the sticky end from another fragment cut by the same enzyme. After annealing, DNA fragments can be covalently bound together by the enzyme DNA ligase. If ligation closes a plasmid into a circular DNA, the plasmid can be re-introduced into bacteria. Maps of the plasmid pBR325 and the phage λ dnrd⁺ are given in Figures 1 and 2.

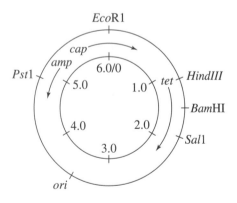

Figure 1

amp: ampicillin resistance gene
tet: tetracycline resistance gene
cap: chloramphenicol resistance gene
ori: origin of replication

Figure 1 is a restriction map of plasmid pBR325. The plasmid has genes encoding resistance factors to three antibiotics and sites of cleavage by the following restriction enzymes (the locations are given in parentheses with the *Eco*RI site as a point of reference). *Eco*RI (0/6), *Hind*III (1.1), *Bam*HI (1.5), *Sal*I (1.8), and *Pst*I (4.8). All sizes are in kilobase pairs (kb). (A kb is a length of double-stranded DNA consisting of 1000 nucleotide pairs.) The arrows show the location and direction of transcription of the antibiotic resistance genes.

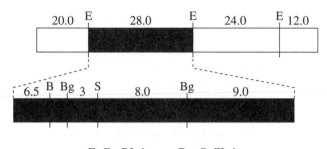

E: *Eco*RI site   Bg: *Bgl*II site
B: *Bam*HI site   S: *Sst*I site

Figure 2

Figure 2 is a map of the *Eco*RI cleavage sites of bacteriophage λ dnrd⁺, with fragment sizes in kb. An expanded map of *nrd*⁺, a gene carried by the phage, is also shown, with the cleavage sites of three other restriction enzymes and the resulting fragment sizes.

The *nrd*⁺ gene encodes resistance to hydroxyurea (Hyu), which kills wild-type bacteria. It can be inserted into pBR325 in two different orientations (A to E or E to A). The orientation can be determined by restriction analysis of the resulting recombinant plasmids, because fragments of different sizes will be produced from restriction enzyme cleavage of plasmids having the gene in each orientation.

Whether both orientations are present is of interest because it provides information about whether the *nrd*⁺ gene carries its own promoter. If not, the gene must rely on a nearby plasmid promoter for expression. In this case, the gene is read in only one direction, and the resistance to hydroxyurea encoded by the gene is only correctly expressed in plasmids that have the gene in the correct orientation. Hence, if plasmids were selected for hydroxyurea resistance, analysis of plasmids would find the *nrd*⁺ genes to be present in only a single orientation. However, if the *nrd*⁺ segment did contain a promoter, plasmids having the *nrd*⁺ genes in both orientations would be found after plasmids were selected for resistance to hydroxyurea.

Adapted from *An Introduction to Recombinant DNA Techniques*, by Perry B. Hackett, et. al., © 1984 by the authors.

1. Inserting the *nrd*+ genes into the *Eco*RI site of pBR325 will produce which of the following phenotypes? (Superscript S means sensitive, R means resistant.)

   A. *amp*R *tet*R *cap*R
   B. *amp*R *tet*R *cap*S
   C. *amp*R *tet*R *cap*R *hyu*R
   D. *amp*R *tet*R *cap*S *hyu*R

2. When pBR325 is digested to completion with *Sal*I and *Hin*dIII, which of the following fragment sizes is/are produced?

   A. One fragment, 6000 base pairs
   B. Two fragments, 700 base pairs, and 5300 base pairs
   C. Two fragments, 1100 base pairs, and 1800 base pairs
   D. Three fragments, 700 base pairs, 1100 base pairs, and 4126 base pairs

3. Which of the following is (are) true of plasmids?

   I. They are small organelles in the bacterial cytoplasm.
   II. They are transcribed and translated simultaneously.
   III. They are replicated by bacterial enzymes.

   A. I only
   B. I and II only
   C. II and III only
   D. I, II, and III

4. In a recombination experiment, the *nrd*+ gene is isolated and recombined with pBR325 plasmids that have been cleaved by *Eco*RI. The resulting plasmids are placed into bacteria, one plasmid per cell, and the bacteria are raised in the presence of hydroxyurea. Then the plasmids are isolated and cleaved with *Bam*H1. DNA fragments of the following sizes (kb) are found: 23, 11, 8, and 26. One can conclude that:

   A. plasmid replication may be initiated from an origin within the *nrd*+ gene.
   B. coupling to a plasmid promoter is necessary for expression of the *nrd*+ gene.
   C. the *nrd*+ gene is not present.
   D. the *nrd*+ gene contains a promoter.

5. How is it possible for a fragment of DNA produced by cutting with a restriction enzyme to be ligated into a plasmid in two different orientations?

   A. DNA ligase enzymes are able to link any two pieces of DNA together.
   B. Plasmid DNA is single-stranded, and so the pieces to be recombined can form double-stranded segments.
   C. Both ends of a fragment produced by a restriction enzyme are identical if rotated 180°.
   D. The existing strands serve as primers for DNA polymerase.

6. What fragments are produced when a recombinant pBR325 plasmid containing the *nrd*+ gene is fully digested by the restriction enzyme *Eco*RI?

   A. One 28-kb fragment
   B. One 34-kb fragment
   C. Two fragments, 6 and 28 kb
   D. Three fragments, 20, 28, and 36 kb

Passage 16 (Questions 1-6)

Conjugation of bacteria is mediated by a small genetic element, called the *fertility* (F) *factor*, that can exist either independent of, or integrated into, the larger bacterial chromosome. The F factor encodes the F pilus, which forms a bridge and allows for the transfer of genetic material between mating cells. The cells carrying the F factor are F⁺, and they transfer it to F⁻ cells. The F factor is replicated during conjugation so that F⁺ cells remain F⁺. The F factor can insert into the bacterial chromosome, creating an Hfr (*high frequency of recombination*) cell. During mating between an Hfr cell and an F⁻ cell, part of the bacterial chromosome can be transferred along with the F factor. The bridge usually breaks before the entire chromosome is transferred, but the point of origin, as well as the order of the genes transferred, is always the same in a given Hfr strain.

The following experiments were designed to characterize the transfer of genetic information between bacteria by conjugation.

Experiment 1

A mixture of *E. coli* strains with differing nutrient requirements is plated onto solid media containing the amino acids arginine, leucine, and threonine, glucose as the carbon source, and certain necessary salts. From this plate, colonies are replicated onto five additional plates (A through E below) supplemented with different combinations of nutrients. Dots indicate numbered colonies that have grown.

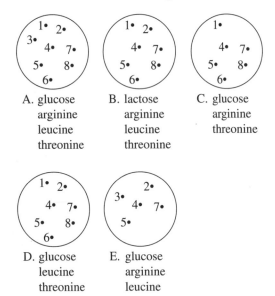

A. glucose
arginine
leucine
threonine

B. lactose
arginine
leucine
threonine

C. glucose
arginine
threonine

D. glucose
leucine
threonine

E. glucose
arginine
leucine

Experiment 2

Bacteria from Colony 3 and Colony 6 on Plate A are grown up separately in liquid cultures. A sample from each liquid culture is taken and mixed; conjugation is allowed to take place for a few hours. The cells from the mixed and unmixed cultures are spun down, washed, and plated onto solid minimal media containing glucose as the carbon source. The results are summarized below:

Colony 3:   No Growth
Colony 6:   No Growth
Mixture: Growth

Experiment 3

A wild-type Hfr strain, sensitive to streptomycin, is mated to a mutant F⁻ strain (Arg⁻ Leu⁻ Thr⁻) that is resistant to streptomycin. Samples are removed at 5, 15, and 30 minutes and plated onto selective media as indicated. It is known that the gene for streptomycin sensitivity is transferred at approximately 70 minutes in this Hfr strain. The plates are checked for the growth of colonies, and the results are summarized in the following table:

Growth Medium	Time allowed for mating		
	5 min	15 min	30 min
min + Arg, Leu	No growth	No growth	Growth
min + Leu, Thr	No growth	Growth	Growth
min + Arg, Thr	Growth	Growth	Growth

1. What is the genotype of Colony 1, Experiment 1?

    A. Lac⁺ Arg⁻ Leu⁻ Thr⁺
    B. Lac⁺ Arg⁺ Leu⁺ Thr⁻
    C. Lac⁻ Arg⁻ Leu⁻ Thr⁺
    D. Lac⁻ Arg⁺ Leu⁺ Thr⁻

2. Which of the following genotypes could grow on Plate D in Experiment 1?

    I.   Lac⁺ Arg⁺ Leu⁺ Thr⁺
    II. Lac⁻ Arg⁻ Leu⁺ Thr⁺
    III. Lac⁻ Arg⁺ Leu⁻ Thr⁻

    A. I only
    B. I and II only
    C. I and III only
    D. II and III only

3. Bacteria that have mutations affecting metabolism, making them unable to grow on minimal media, are called:

   A. auxotrophs.
   B. prototrophs.
   C. heterotrophs.
   D. chemotrophs.

4. To map the order of bacterial genes on the chromosome in a given Hfr strain which of the following assumptions must be true?

   A. Bacterial genes are polycistronic.
   B. The inserted F factor and bacterial genes are replicated by different mechanisms.
   C. The rate of chromosome transfer varies between bacteria of the same strain.
   D. A given Hfr strain will always transfer its genes in the same order.

5. What is the order of the three loci, Arg, Leu, and Thr, following the point of origin in the Hfr?

   A. Arg, Leu, Thr
   B. Leu, Arg, Thr
   C. Thr, Arg, Leu
   D. Leu, Thr, Arg

6. What is the genotype of the colonies formed from the mixed culture in Experiment 2?

   A. Arg⁻ Leu⁻ Thr⁺
   B. Arg⁺ Leu⁺ Thr⁻
   C. Arg⁺ Leu⁺ Thr⁺
   D. Arg⁻ Leu⁻ Thr⁻

Passage 17 (Questions 1-6)

The genus *Chlamydomonas* consists of unicellular green algae that undergo both sexual and asexual reproduction. In sexual reproduction, a haploid cell undergoes a series of morphological changes giving rise to haploid gametes, which can later fuse to form a diploid zygote. In asexual reproduction, a mature haploid cell divides to form two haploid cells. *Chlamydomonas* is sensitive to certain mutagens found in the natural environment.

Experiment 1

Chlamydomonas colonies were treated with a mutagen, and then transferred by velveteen pad to either a rich-medium plate or a plate lacking either histidine or phenylalanine. The number of colonies was counted on all three plates. Figure 1 illustrates the results of using such a replica plating technique for mutagen-exposed *Chlamydomonas*.

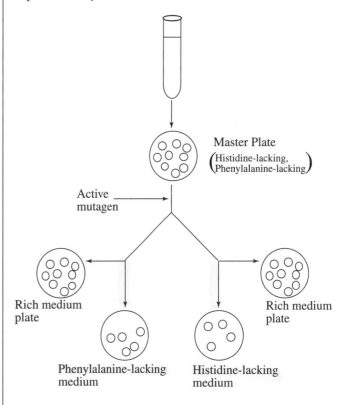

Figure 1

Experiment 2

A zygote form of the original, unmutated organism was induced to undergo meiosis, and the resulting haploid form was fused with a haploid mutant that could not synthesize phenylalanine (Phe⁻). The new zygote survived plating on a phenylalanine-lacking medium.

Experiment 3

A Phe⁻ haploid was mated with the haploid mutant that could not produce histidine (His⁻). The resulting zygote survived plating on both a phenylalanine-lacking medium and a histidine-lacking medium. The zygote was then induced to undergo meiosis and replated back onto the rich-medium plate. The resulting Phe⁻ and His⁻ haploids established colonies in a ratio of 44:56 (Phe⁻ : His⁻).

1. The phenotypic effects of the mutations, illustrated in Figure 1, most likely resulted from the cessation of:

   A. DNA synthesis.
   B. rRNA synthesis.
   C. mRNA synthesis.
   D. protein synthesis.

2. Which reasoning supports the conclusion that colonies surviving the histidine-poor medium incurred different mutations than phenylalanine-deprived survivors?

   A. When haploid survivors from each plate fuse to form a zygote, this diploid thrives on both media.
   B. Phe⁻ haploids grow at a similar rate to His⁻ haploids.
   C. When fused with unmutated haploids, haploid survivors fail to grow.
   D. His⁻ haploids produce more colonies than His⁺ haploids on rich agar.

3. How can one determine whether unmutated *Chlamydomonas* haploids can produce phenylalanine?

   A. By radiolabeling for rRNA
   B. By fusing with other unmutated *Chlamydomonas* haploids
   C. By fusing with Phe⁻ haploids on histidine-lacking medium
   D. By plating on phenylalanine-lacking nutrient agar

   if cells grow on media w/o something = can produce their own

4. From the experiment illustrated in Figure 1, a researcher concluded that normal-type *Chlamydomonas* is able to produce both phenylalanine and histidine. What assumption must be true to establish the validity of this conclusion?

   A. The control plate colonies produced greater quantities of both amino acids.
   B. The *Chlamydomonas* cells incurred no mutations prior to plating on the master plate.
   C. The colonies grown on different minimal media were roughly equal in number.
   D. The mutagen-affected colonies were lacking in either phenylalanine or histidine.

5. In Experiment 2, a new zygote was produced as a result of:

   A. sexual reproduction.
   B. asexual reproduction.
   C. fission.
   D. budding.

6. Which of the following observations would NOT identify sexual reproduction in *Chlamydomonas*?

   A. An alignment of homologous chromosome pairs on the spindle
   B. An intact centromere at anaphase
   C. A separation of homologous pairs of chromosomes
   D. DNA replication in a haploid cell

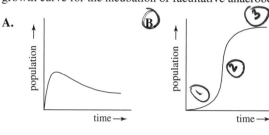

Passage 18 (Questions 1-5)

A clinician wished to determine the etiology of a patient's urinary tract infection. To differentiate between the presence of the Gram-negative, facultative anaerobic bacilli *Escherichia coli* and *Klebsiella pneumoniae*, the following procedures can be used:

1. Add test organism to a 1% tryptophan broth containing sodium chloride and distilled water.

2. Incubate the culture at 35°C for 18 to 24 hours.

3. Apply 15 drops of Ehrlich's reagent containing p-dimethylaminobenzaldehyde to the walls of the test container.

4. The presence of a bright red color at the interface of the reagent and broth indicates the presence of indole, a metabolite of tryptophan. An alternative method uses Kovac's reagent instead of Ehrlich's reagent, but the results are similar since they contain the same active chemical.

For rapid spot tests, filter paper strips impregnated with Kovac's reagent can be used.

1. Both *E. coli* and *K. pneumoniae* are classified as prokaryotic organisms in part because of the lack of which of the following subcellular structures?

    A. Ribosome
    B. Flagellum
    C. Cell wall ✓
    D. Nucleus

2. If *E. coli* is incubated under aerobic conditions, how many molecules of ATP would be produced upon the complete oxidation of one molecule of glucose?

    A. 28
    B. 30
    C. 32
    D. 34

3. Which of the following graphs most accurately depicts a growth curve for the incubation of facultative anaerobes?

    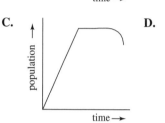
    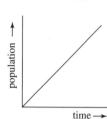

    A.
    B.
    C.
    D.

4. Which of the following processes allow(s) the division of genetic material between bacteria in the production of daughter cells?

    I.   Binary fission
    II. Transformation
    III. Conjugation

    A. I only
    B. I and II only
    C. II and III only
    D. I, II, and III

5. If a staining procedure indicates the presence of tryptophan at the surface of a bacterial cell, it would be most reasonable for a researcher to conclude that among the following, the bacterial cell surface is abundant in:

    A. lipid.
    B. protein.
    C. carbohydrate.
    D. nucleic acid.

Passage 19 (Questions 1-5)

Malaria has been a major cause of death throughout history. Today, it remains endemic in certain regions of Africa and contributes significantly to childhood mortality. The parasite that causes this disease is a small unicellular protozoan belonging to the genus *Plasmodium*.

The parasite assumes several forms during its complex life cycle. *Plasmodium* enters the bloodstream of the host through the bite of an infected *Anopheles* mosquito. At this stage it is called a sporozoite. The parasite then migrates to the liver where it undergoes growth and multiplication. It then assumes another form, called a merozoite. The merozoite reenters the bloodstream and settles in red blood cells at which point it is said to be in the erythrocytic stage. The parasite digests hemoglobin, thereby acquiring amino acids that it uses for its own protein synthesis. The parasite's action eventually lyses red blood cells. Malaria leads to symptoms such as episodes of fever, chills, and other more debilitating conditions including severe organ damage and possible cerebral complications.

Several types of antimalarial drugs have been developed to prevent or curtail the effects of malaria:

1. Prophylactic drugs have been developed that prevent the parasite from replicating in the bloodstream.

2. Another class of drugs is intended to kill sporozoites and to prevent the parasite from invading the liver.

3. Other drugs are directed at merozoites once they invade red blood cells. These drugs inhibit the synthesis of DNA and RNA. One such drug, chloroquine, is an agent that suppresses the effects of the illness and achieves clinical cure of the infection.

The chloroquine molecule (Figure 1) has a quinoline ring. In some experiments it was found that the 7-chloro-quinoline ring interferes with the cellular process in the malarial parasite by inserting into plasmodial DNA and altering its three-dimensional structure. All of the above drugs differ in their implications for morbidity and mortality of the patient population.

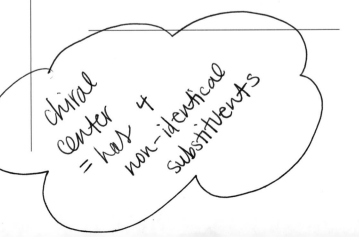

Figure 1 Chloroquine

1. Which of the following is NOT true of members of the phylum *Protozoa*?

   A. They are unicellular.
   B. They are primarily heterotrophic.
   C. They are eukaryotic.
   D. They only reproduce asexually.

2. Chloroquine is inactive during certain stages of the parasite life cycle. This could be due to the fact that:

   A. the ring fails to enter the bloodstream.
   B. the liver detoxifies chloroquine.
   C. no cell division occurs during these stages.
   D. elevated temperatures during a fever destroy chloroquine's effectiveness.

3. Chloroquine is toxic to merozoites because it:

   A. inhibits replication and transcription of the plasmodial genome.
   B. alters the three-dimensional structure of membranes.
   C. inhibits translation of plasmodial RNA.
   D. prevents release of plasmodial progeny from red blood cells.

4. An experimental anti-malarial drug tested *in vitro* was designed to act as a protease inhibitor. Based on the information in the passage, at which stage of the plasmodial life cycle is this drug most likely to act?

   A. Sporozoite stage
   B. Hepatocytic stage
   C. Merozoite stage
   D. Erythrocytic stage

5. How many chiral centers does chloroquine have?

   A. 0
   B. 1
   C. 2
   D. 3

Passage 20 (Questions 1-6)

Tuberculosis is a chronic disease of humans that can take many years to develop. The infecting organism, *Mycobacterium tuberculosis hominis*, is a strictly aerobic bacterium that will not grow in oxygen-poor environments. The tuberculosis bacillus is called an acid-fast bacterium because it retains the Ziehl–Neelsen carbolfuchsin stain even after washing with acid alcohol. Mycobacteria, in general, have waxy coats that protect them against desiccation and allow them to survive for years as latent microbes. *Mycobacterium tuberculosis hominis* is difficult to grow in culture because it can take 4 to 8 weeks to see significant growth on a medium.

After primary infection in the lungs, the bacteria can lie latent in host macrophages for years until reactivation of the infection causes secondary tuberculosis. The infected macrophages live in tubercles, which are walled-off areas of immunologic activity. The bacterial cell wall possesses a sulfated glycolipid that prevents lysosomal fusion with phagosomes, the macrophage structures that contain phagocytosed bacteria. Reactivation of latent mycobacteria in immunocompromised patients, among others, allows microbial spread from the lungs to other organs of the body and the manifestation of disease.

1. The difficulty in observing mycobacterial growth in culture is most likely due to the fact that:

   A. most laboratory growth conditions do not supply sufficient oxygen.
   B. the tubercle bacillus replicates once every 2 days.
   C. most of the mycobacteria dry out before being able to replicate.
   D. tubercle bacilli fail to take up the Ziehl–Neelsen carbolfuchsin stain.

2. If a Ziehl–Neelsen stain were applied to a lung sample from a tuberculosis victim one would expect to find:

   A. stained spherical bacteria after acid alcohol washing.
   B. unstained spherical bacteria after acid alcohol washing.
   C. stained rod-like bacteria after acid alcohol washing.
   D. unstained rod-like bacteria after acid alcohol washing.

3. The lung is a more common site of primary tuberculosis than the small intestine because:

   A. pancreatic acid secretion destroys most of the tuberculosis bacilli that enter it.
   B. the lung has a higher oxygen tension than the stomach.
   C. the small intestine's low pH inactivates tubercle bacilli.
   D. mycobacteria cannot survive in organs other than the lung.

4. Tuberculosis-causing bacilli are able to survive in host macrophages, which normally destroy bacteria, because the bacteria:

   A. avoid digestion by the lysosomes.
   B. survive in the low pH of the lysosomes.
   C. produce a substance toxic to the macrophages.
   D. divide rapidly enough to continually replace killed bacteria.

5. Rifampin, one of the drugs used to treat tuberculosis, inhibits an enzyme that catalyzes RNA polymerization based on a DNA template (transcription). Rifampin's relative lack of toxic effects in human beings is most likely due to the fact that:

   A. human cells are not actively dividing.
   B. the bacterial enzyme is different from the human RNA polymerase.
   C. when taken orally the drug is not absorbed.
   D. human cells do not carry out DNA-directed RNA polymerization.

6. Tuberculosis is a highly infectious disease. Which of the following is the most likely vector of transmission?

   A. Blood contact with skin
   B. Air
   C. Rotting food
   D. Semen

Passage 21 (Questions 1-5)

One of the most successful classes of antibiotics developed by man are the penicillins. Preliminary investigations into the structure of penicillin presented a confusing picture because of discrepancies in the analytical results obtained in different laboratories. These discrepancies were resolved once it was discovered that *Penicillium notatum* produces different kinds of penicillin depending on the nature of the medium in which it is grown. Initially six different penicillins were recognized, and all proved ultimately to be acyl derivatives of 6-aminopenicillanic acid. Today the term penicillin is used as a generic name to include all acyl derivatives of 6-aminopenicillanic acid.

The basic structure of pencillin consists of a five-membered ring containing both nitrogen and sulfur (a thioazolidine ring) fused to a four-membered ring containing a cyclic amide (a β-lactam). The structural integrity of these two rings is essential for the biological activity of penicillin, and cleavage of either ring leads to products devoid of antibacterial activity.

Selective hydrolysis of the β-lactam ring is catalyzed by the enzyme penicillinase and results in penicilloic acid. This product has no antibacterial activity.

An investigator conducted three experiments to determine how pencillin caused the death of bacterial cells.

Experiment 1

Two species of bacterial cells were selected and cultured. One species had a normal cell wall made of peptidoglycan and the other had an incomplete cell wall. Both groups were treated with penicillin and it was noted that the bacteria with incomplete cell walls survived while 95% of those with complete cell walls did not.

Experiment 2

Two populations of bacteria were selected and cultured. Both populations had normal cell walls made of peptidoglycan. One population was treated with penicillin and the other was not. It was noted that 95% of the bacteria in the population that had been treated with penicillin underwent cell wall lysis and death. It was further noted that the bacteria not treated with penicillin were unharmed.

Experiment 3

The 5% who survived the treatment of penicillin in Experiment 2 were cultured and treated repeatedly with penicillin. It was noted that the culture grew continuously and that none of the bacteria were affected by the antibiotic.

1. In these experiments, the bacterial species LEAST susceptible to penicillin are those:

   A. unable to synthesize DNA polymerase.
   B. with the highest internal osmotic pressure.
   C. with normal cell walls.
   D. with incomplete cell walls.

2. In both Experiments 2 and 3, it is reasonable to hypothesize that 5% of the cell-walled bacteria treated with penicillin survived because:

   A. penicillin did not permeate the entire culture.
   B. random mutation provided some bacterial cells with the ability to synthesize more penicillinase.
   C. penicillin cannot cross the bacterial cell wall.
   D. penicillin is rapidly degraded in bacterial culture medium.

3. It would be plausible to hypothesize that penicillin causes bacterial death by:

   A. creating cell walls in abnormal locations.
   B. rendering cell walls excessively rigid.
   C. disrupting the bacterial cell wall.
   D. disrupting the bacterium's access to nutritional substances.

4. Which of the following explains the fact that bacterial cells lyse upon losing their cell wall?

   A. Lipid insoluble substances cross the cell membrane by facilitated diffusion.
   B. Active transport mechanisms force solutes out of the bacterial cell.
   C. Osmotic pressure causes water to enter the cells.
   D. Proteins can no longer exit the cell via vesicles.

5. Penicillin G, one of the common forms of penicillin, is rapidly hydrolyzed under acidic conditions. Which of the following limitations would this likely place on the use of Penicillin G?

   A. It must be administered intravenously.
   B. It must be taken on an empty stomach.
   C. It should not be given to children.
   D. It is not active at physiological pH.

Passage 22 (Questions 1-7)

Bacterial glycolysis involves the oxidation of simple sugars, resulting in a net production of ATP. Aerobic bacteria generate further ATP in a process similar to that which occurs on the electron transport chain along the mitochondrial membrane in animal cells. Anaerobic bacteria use some of the ATP derived from glycolysis to establish a transmembrane proton-motive force that drives a variety of cellular functions. Both systems are illustrated in Figure 1.

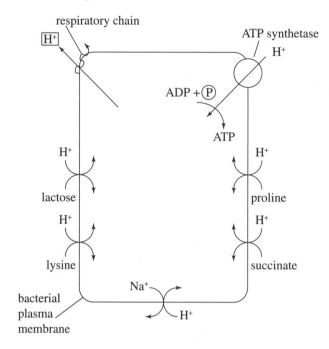

(A) aerobic conditions

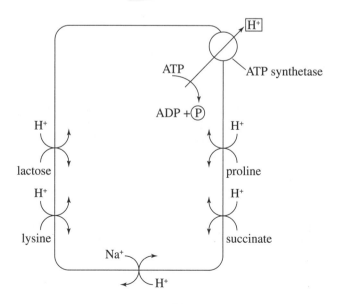

(B) anaerobic conditions

Figure 1

Vibrio alginolyticus is an alkali-tolerant marine bacterium with an internal salt concentration less than that of its normal surrounding medium. In studying the activity of various transport systems in *V. alginolyticus*, researchers devised the following experiment: One batch of *V. alginolyticus* was grown in a sodium-free environment, enriched with radiolabeled lysine, while another batch was exposed to both hypertonic sodium and radiolabeled lysine. The bacteria were removed from the media and then analyzed for radioactivity. The researchers discovered that the uptake of basic amino acids by *V. alginolyticus* is dependent on the activity of the cation-driven transport mechanism shown in Figure 2. Only the bacteria grown in a sodium-enriched environment took up the labeled lysine.

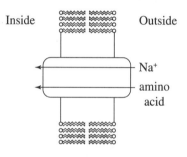

Figure 2

1. Any conclusions derived from the experiment are justified only with the assumption that the radioactive labeling technique:

   A. increases the uptake of neutral amino acids.
   B. does not affect the transport mechanism.
   C. decreases the uptake of aspartate.
   D. increases the rate of acidic amino acid uptake.

2. None of the following is supported by the information in the passage EXCEPT:

   A. aerobes only import hydrogen ions, while strict anaerobes must import and export hydrogen ions.
   B. anaerobes have an ATP synthetase that is only active when bound to a phosphate group, whereas aerobic ATP synthetase is active when it loses a phosphate group.
   C. anaerobic ATP synthetase functions identically to aerobic ATP synthetase, but anaerobes lack a fully functioning respiratory chain.
   D. aerobes establish a proton gradient to generate ATP from ADP and inorganic phosphate, while anaerobes hydrolyze ATP to generate a proton gradient.

3. One of the necessary components of bacterial glycolysis is:

   A. molecular oxygen.
   B. lactic acid.
   C. NAD⁺.
   D. sodium chloride.

4. In the experiment, if the researchers had replaced sodium with magnesium, they most probably would have found:

   A. substantially decreased lysine uptake in the two samples of bacteria.
   B. substantially greater uptake of lysine in the sodium-free portion.
   C. enhanced flagellar movement in the magnesium-enriched sample.
   D. enhanced uptake of aspartate and glutamate.

5. If no radiolabel is found inside cells at the end of the experiment measuring lysine import in *V. alginolyticus*, then which of the following can be concluded?

   A. *V. alginolyticus* are aerobic bacteria.
   B. *V. alginolyticus* produce ATP strictly anaerobically.
   C. ATP is required in the medium for lysine import.
   D. The Na⁺ gradient is insufficient to drive lysine import.

6. For the aerobic bacteria depicted in Figure 1, which of the following will occur if the pH of the medium is lowered slightly by the addition of lactic acid?

   A. ATP synthesis will decrease.
   B. The bacteria will switch to anaerobic ATP production.
   C. The rate of lactose import will increase.
   D. Electron transport and ATP production will be uncoupled.

7. A student transported specimens of *V. alginolyticus* from their original habitat to a basin of fresh water. With reference to their surrounding medium, they:

   A. changed from hypertonic to hypotonic.
   B. changed from hypotonic to hypertonic.
   C. changed from isotonic to hypotonic.
   D. remained isotonic in both environments.

Passage 23 (Questions 1-6)

Amphioxus is a chordate that has an embryological development similar to that of human. Cleavage of the fertilized zygote results in the formation of a morula. The blastula stage follows; the blastula is composed of about 500 cells. Gastrulation then occurs, resulting in three distinct germ layers. The experiments below studied the effect of irradiation on embryological development from zygote to gastrula. Only non-irradiated cells formed normal embryos.

Experiment 1

To determine the effects of radiation on embryological development, *Amphioxus* zygotes were exposed to gamma radiation, while unexposed zygotes served as controls. The timing of morula, blastula, and gastrula formation was closely watched. Figure 1 illustrates the results for controls and two samples of irradiated zygotes with unique developmental patterns.

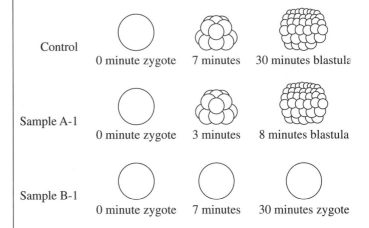

Figure 1

Experiment 2

Irradiated sample A-1 was analyzed for the production of a protein which induces mitosis. It was significantly above normal levels. When non-irradiated controls were exposed to these increased levels of mitosis-inducing protein, blastulas were formed within 8 minutes.

Experiment 3

Irradiated sample B-1 was analyzed for the production of mitosis-inducing protein. It was found that levels of this protein was significantly below normal. When the B-1 sample was exposed to higher levels of the protein at 30 minutes, the endoderm, mesoderm, and ectoderm layers were detected at 40 minutes. Induction protein produced by this sample was analyzed and found to have the same amino acid sequence as that produced by non-irradiated controls.

1. In studying the effects of radiation on *Amphioxus* blastula development, what process would be of greatest interest?

    A. Oogenesis
    B. DNA replication
    C. Transcription
    D. DNA double helix formation

2. The process illustrated in Figure 1 most directly affected by irradiation which alters the rate of embryo development is:

    A. double helix formation.
    B. base-pair specificity.
    C. replication of both DNA templates.
    D. translation.

3. The reduction in cell size from zygote to blastula in the *Amphioxus* controls and Sample A-1 is most likely due to:

    A. loss of DNA.
    B. decreases in amount of cytosol per cell.
    C. feedback inhibition.
    D. rRNA degeneration.

4. On what basis can one assume that the change in the development of Sample B-1 is NOT due to mutation of the genome coding for the mitosis-inducing protein?

    A. The B-1 protein has the same sequence as the control protein.
    B. The gene for the B-1 protein assorts according to the Hardy–Weinberg principle.
    C. Non-irradiated controls underwent morulation when exposed to Sample A-1 levels of inducing protein.
    D. Neither the A-1 nor the B-1 sample developed into normal embryos.

5. What finding demonstrates that A-1 protein levels did not induce B-1 type growth patterns in non-irradiated controls?

    A. The rate of development increased in controls exposed to A-1 protein levels.
    B. The rate of development in sample B-1 was very slow after irradiation.
    C. Radiation-induced mutations were present in both A-1 and B-1.
    D. The absence of meiosis in blastulation

6. On studying the results summarized in Figure 1, a scientist concluded that radiation affected *Amphioxus* development by causing mutations in DNA. What assumption must be true for this conclusion to be valid?

    A. Embryological development is not affected by protein induction.
    B. Translation activity is radiation-insensitive.
    C. Radiation decreased levels of inducing proteins in all samples.
    D. Many genes in both A-1 and B-1 must be defective after irradiation.

Passage 24 (Questions 1-6)

Protein synthesis occurs either on free ribosomes or ribosomes bound to the endoplasmic reticulum (ER). According to the signal hypothesis, it is the growing polypeptide that cues the ribosomes to remain free or attach to the ER. Proteins targeted to the ER, Golgi, lysosomes, plasma membrane, or to be secreted contain a signal peptide of 15 or more continuous amino acids. These N-terminus signal peptides are responsible for the co-translational insertion of the growing polypeptide into the membrane of the ER. After the leading end of the protein is inserted into the ER lumen, the signal peptide is cleaved by an enzyme.

Proteins destined for the secretory pathway are packaged into vesicles that pinch off from the membrane of the ER and fuse with the *cis* face of the Golgi apparatus. Often the packaging of a protein into a transport vesicle requires the presence of a region on the protein that is recognized by a receptor in the Golgi membrane. This receptor–protein complex will localize to a vesicle and target the vesicle to its destination.

One of the best-characterized pathways of vesicular transport involves proteins destined to become lysosomal enzymes. These proteins carry a unique mannose-6-phosphate (M6P) marker that is recognized by the specific M6P receptor in the membrane of the Golgi apparatus. M6P receptors bind proteins and sequester them along one region of the Golgi membrane, facilitating their packaging into vesicles. Once the vesicle has budded from the Golgi apparatus, it travels to the lysosome, where it fuses with the lysosomal membrane. The M6P receptor releases its bound protein when it encounters the acidic pH of the interior of the lysosome. The acidity of the lysosome also activates lysosomal enzymes.

1. Proteins that are to be secreted pass through what series of organelles?

   A. ER → Golgi → lysosomes → plasma membrane
   B. ER → Golgi → secretory vesicles
   C. cytoplasm → Golgi → ER → secretory vesicles
   D. ER → secretory vesicles → lysosomes

2. Where in the cell would the M6P receptor be transcribed?

   A. In the nucleus
   B. In the cytoplasm
   C. In the rough ER
   D. In the Golgi

3. The transport of proteins to the lysosomes requires which of the following?

   A. Acidic pH in the ER
   B. Vesicle movement from the rough ER to the Golgi
   C. Endocytosis
   D. Inhibition of signal peptidase

4. Which of the following enzymes would be expected to function well within an acidic environment?

   A. Signal peptidase
   B. Trypsin
   C. Pepsin
   D. Pancreatic lipase

5. Which of the following processes would be disrupted in a cell that failed to label proteins with the M6P marker?

   A. Intracellular digestion of macromolecules
   B. Protein synthesis
   C. Oxidative phosphorylation
   D. Golgi formation

6. The ER lumen corresponds most closely to which of the following compartments?

   A. The interior of the nucleus
   B. The cytoplasm
   C. The extracellular environment
   D. The intermembrane space in mitochondria

Passage 25 (Questions 1-6)

The cytoskeleton of eukaryotic cells is composed of three elements: microtubules, microfilaments, and intermediate filaments. Microtubules are hollow tubes composed of tubulin $\alpha\beta$ heterodimers and are the largest of the three cytoskeletal structures. They function in cell structure, movement of cilia and flagella, transportation of organelles, and sister chromatid separation during mitosis. They are anchored to the microtubule organizing center, which contains the centrioles. Microfilaments are fibrous polymers of the globular protein actin which are essential for amoeboid motility, cell–cell adhesion, and contractile processes. The function of microtubules and microfilaments in the eukaryotic cell depends on a dynamic equilibrium between monomeric and polymerized forms of the proteins. Microtubules and microfilaments are constantly depolymerizing and repolymerizing, and it is thought that this is the mechanism whereby they mediate motility, for example in the extension of a pseudopod due to formation of long actin polymers.

The following experiment was conducted to study the functions of microtubules and microfilaments in eukaryotic cells:

Three groups of cultured cells were placed in media containing all necessary growth requirements. To Group A, nothing was added. To Groups B and C, the drugs cytochalasin and vinblastine, respectively, were added. Cells were observed over time for changes in morphology and function. The results are summarized below:

Effect	Drug	Group
A	None	5% of cells in mitosis at any one time; normal morphology/function
B	Cytochalasin	Cells arrested in cytokinesis; inhibition of amoeboid motility
C	Vinblastine	Cells arrested in metaphase of mitosis; no effect on amoeboid motility

1. The drug cytochalasin affects:

   A. microtubules.
   B. microfilaments.
   C. both microfilaments and microtubules.
   D. Cannot be determined from the information given

2. Which of the following accurately describes the role of cytoskeletal proteins in mitosis?

   I. Microtubules known as polar fibers radiate from the centrioles to connect with kinetochore fibers, also composed of microtubules, emanating from the centromere.
   II. Contraction of microtubules is responsible for formation of the cleavage furrow during anaphase.
   III. After recombination between homologous chromosomes, homologous chromosomes are pulled to opposite poles by microtubules.

   A. I only
   B. I and II only
   C. I and III only
   D. I, II, and III

3. A researcher stains actin of cells in interphase with a fluorescent anti-actin antibody. As seen under the microscope, the fluorescence would be:

   A. seen as two star-shaped structures near the nucleus.
   B. uniformly dispersed throughout the cell, giving it an even color.
   C. concentrated in the cytoplasm.
   D. concentrated solely inside the nucleus.

4. A researcher studies the effect of phalloidin, a chemical that prevents actin depolymerization. Which of the following is a likely effect of phalloidin?

   A. Inhibition of organelle movement within the cell
   B. Inhibition of mitotic spindle formation
   C. Inhibition of protein synthesis
   D. Cessation of amoeboid movement

5. Which of the following is NOT true of eukaryotic flagella?

   A. They are structurally identical to prokaryotic flagella.
   B. They are cytoplasmic extensions with a 9 + 2 arrangement of microtubules.
   C. ATP hydrolysis is required for their movement.
   D. They are similar in structure to cilia.

6. Which of the following best describes the cells of Group C as viewed under the microscope?

    A. A set of chromosomes can be seen at either end of the cells; no nuclear envelope is visible.
    B. Chromosomes are aligned in the middle of the cell; no nuclear envelope is visible.
    C. The chromosomes are partially thickened, and the nuclear envelope is partially disintegrated.
    D. No chromosomes are visible, and the nuclear envelope is fully intact.

Passage 26 (Questions 1-6)

Dividing eukaryotic cells pass through a regular sequence of growth and division, known as the cell cycle. The cycle consists of four major phases: mitosis, G_1, S, and G_2. G_1 is a period of general growth and replication of cytoplasmic organelles and proteins. In the S phase, chromosomal material is replicated, and in the G_2 phase the structures associated with mitosis are assembled. See Figure 1.

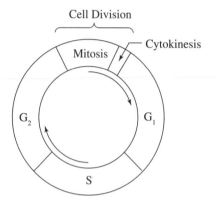

Figure 1

The duration of the cell cycle varies from one species to another, and from one cell type to another. The G_1 phase varies the most. For example, embryonic cells can pass through the G_1 phase so quickly that it hardly exists. On the other hand, differentiated skeletal muscle cells and nerve cells are arrested in the cell cycle and normally do not divide.

Two experiments were conducted to determine the causes of G_1 and G_2 arrest.

Experiment 1

The nucleus of a cell in the S phase is removed, and the nucleus of a cell in G_1 arrest is transplanted into the enucleated cell in S phase. The transplanted nucleus soon becomes activated itself and enters the S phase.

Experiment 2

A cell in G_2 arrest is fused with a mitotic cell. The nucleus originally in G_2 arrest promptly shows signs of entering mitosis.

Adapted from *Biological Science* by William T. Keeton and James L. Gould, © 1986 by W.W. Norton & Company, and *Biology*, by Helena Curtis, © 1983 by Worth Publishers, Inc.

1. In Experiment 1, the substance in control of G_1 arrest must be present:

    A.) in the nucleus.
    B. someplace within the cell, but a more specific location cannot be determined from this experiment.
    C. outside the cell wall.
    D.) in the cytoplasm.

2. In Experiment 2, the first sign of mitosis would be:

    A. the formation of nuclear membranes.
    B. the disappearance of the nuclear membrane.
    C. condensing of the chromosomes.
    D. splitting of the centromeres.

3. Mitosis occurs in which of the following human cell types?

    I.   Primary spermatocyte
    II. Bone marrow cells
    ✓ III. Mature erythrocytes

    A. II only
    B. I and III only
    C.) II and III only
    D. I, II, and III

4. Which of the following meiotic characteristics does mitosis share?

    A. Crossing over occurs between paired homologues before they separate into two different nuclei.
    B. It occurs only in diploid cells.
    C. Each cell divides twice, producing a total of four cells.
    D. Replication of chromosomes occurs prior to prophase.

5. Chloroplasts and mitochondria have their own chromosomes. The genomes of chloroplasts and mitochondria must replicate during:

    A. the S phase.
    B. the G_1 phase.
    C. mitosis.
    D. cytokinesis.

6. Which of the following gives the correct order of the phases of mitosis?

    A.) Prophase, metaphase, anaphase, telophase
    B. Prophase, anaphase, telophase, metaphase
    C. Anaphase, prophase, metaphase, telophase
    D. Telophase, anaphase, metaphase, prophase

_____

Passage 27 (Questions 1-6)

Schizosaccharomyces pombe, or fission yeast, has a cell cycle that resembles that of mammalian cells. During interphase, fission yeast grow to twice their normal size, and at the end of mitosis both daughter offspring are equal in size to the original parent cell. Genes that regulate the division of fission yeast are known as cell-division cycle, or *cdc*, genes.

The following experiments were conducted to determine the effect of cdc gene mutations on yeast cell division.

Experiment 1

In order to determine the effect of *cdc* mutations, wild-type cells and mutants were grown at 37°C in the presence of a radioactive drug that specifically binds to the spindle apparatus. Stages of the cell cycle were elucidated for both cell types incubated at this temperature. At 37°C, temperature-sensitive *cdc* mutants were unable to re-enter interphase after mitosis. The illustration below depicts the results for wild-type cells and *cdc* mutants.

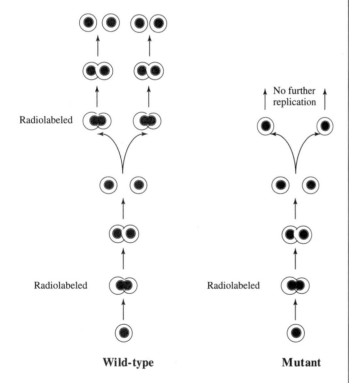

Wild-type   **Mutant**

Figure 1

Experiment 2

Cdc mutants were initially incubated at 25°C for 30 minutes and several rounds of mitosis occurred. Separate colonies were then exposed to temperatures near 37°C at different times during the cell cycle. For each colony, the cell cycle was arrested immediately after the last phase of mitosis.

Experiment 3

Cdc mutant cells were made to express two cell division regulatory proteins, *cdc2* and *cdc25*, during incubation. These cells were able to undergo complete cell cycling, passing through mitosis, interphase, and mitosis again. After each round of mitosis, two haploid cells were produced for each original parent cell. When supplies of the regulatory proteins were depleted, the *cdc* mutants were again unable to progress through the cell cycle beyond the end of mitosis.

1. Yeasts are similar to molds in all of the following characteristics EXCEPT that yeasts:

    A. are eukaryotic.
    B. are unicellular.
    C. remain haploid throughout most of their lives.
    D. are spore-producing organisms.

2. Based on the results in Figure 1, the *cdc* mutants were unable to enter the stage of the cell cycle that is characterized by:

    A. crossing-over.
    B. meiotic division.
    C. DNA replication.
    D. the reduction division.

3. Which of the following results could support the hypothesis that mutations of the *cdc* gene affect a specific stage of the cell cycle?

    A. The wild-type cells were able to pass through the cell cycle several times.
    B. Mutants incubated at 25°C were able to enter mitosis.
    C. Mutants exposed to high temperatures at different times halted at the same point in the cell cycle.
    D. Mutants exposed to cell division regulatory proteins were able to produce daughter cells.

4. What finding would best justify a researcher's conclusion that wild-type fission yeast have a competitive advantage over *cdc* mutants?

  A. The wild-type spindle apparatus forms during late interphase.
  B. The *cdc* mutants replicate in the presence of cell division regulatory proteins.
  C. The *cdc* mutant cell cycle occurs at temperatures below 35°C.
  D. In a culture inoculated with both wild-type and *cdc*-mutant yeast, only wild-type are found after 24 hours.

5. If, because of mutation, a diploid cell should arrest at the end of mitosis and fail to enter interphase, then as a direct result:

  A. there will be a failure of protein synthesis.
  B. there will be a failure of genome replication.
  C. daughter cells will emerge haploid.
  D. the mitotic process will be converted to a meiotic process.

6. If the *cdc* mutation is recessive, then fusion of wild-type and *cdc* mutant haploid cells would produce a diploid cell that has a:

  A. wild-type phenotype and heterozygous genotype.
  B. wild-type phenotype and homozygous genotype.
  C. heterozygous genotype and mutant phenotype.
  D. homozygous genotype and mutant phenotype.

Passage 28 (Questions 1-6)
ADVANCED PASSAGE

Many membrane transport processes are not driven directly by the hydrolysis of ATP. Instead, they are coupled to the flow of an ion down its electrochemical gradient. For example, glucose is transported into some animal cells by the simultaneous entry of Na^+. Sodium ions and glucose bind to a specific transport protein and enter together. A protein responsible for the concerted movement of two such species is called a symport. An antiport carries two species in opposite directions. The rate and extent of glucose transport depends on the Na^+ gradient across the plasma membrane. Sodium ions entering the cell in the company of glucose are pumped out again by the Na^+/K^+ ATPase pump.

A group of researchers wished to gain information about a type of bacteria that was known to take in glucose across its cell membrane by use of a sodium–glucose cotransport mechanism. The researchers conducted two experiments in which bacterial cells were placed in glucose-containing media that differed with respect to relative ion concentration and ATP content. Glycolysis was inhibited in the cells during these experiments.

Experiment 1:

Bacterial cells with relatively low intracellular sodium concentration were placed in a glucose-rich medium that had a relatively high sodium concentration but no ATP. At regular time intervals, the medium was analyzed for glucose concentration and sodium concentration. See Figure 1.

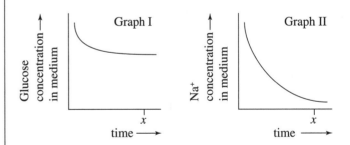

Figure 1 Glucose and Na^+ concentrations in medium (no ATP in medium)

Experiment 2:

Bacterial cells with relatively low intracellular sodium concentration were placed in a glucose-rich medium that had a relatively high sodium concentration and that was also rich in ATP. At regular time intervals, the medium was analyzed for glucose, sodium, and ATP concentration (see Figure 2). If radiolabeled ATP is used in this experiment, the majority of the radiolabel at the end of the experiment is found as ADP inside the cells.

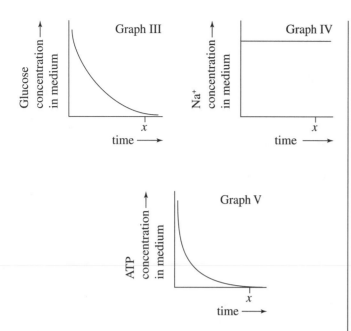

Figure 2 Glucose, Na⁺, and ATP concentrations in medium

1. The results of Experiments 1 and 2 suggest that the cells take up glucose:

   A. in exchange for ATP, as long as extracellular sodium concentration remains constant.
   B. in exchange for sodium, as long as ATP concentration is zero.
   C. together with sodium, as long as a favorable sodium concentration gradient is maintained.
   D. together with sodium, as long as extracellular ATP concentration is increasing.

2. On the basis of Experiments 1 and 2, a researcher hypothesized that all of the cells under study ultimately depend on energy to operate the sodium–glucose cotransport mechanism. Is this hypothesis reasonable?

   A. No; Figure 1 indicates that glucose can cross the cell membrane indefinitely in the absence of exogenous energy.
   B. No; Figure 2 indicates that extracellular glucose and ATP concentrations are independent.
   C. Yes; Figure 1 indicates that a sodium gradient drives glucose transport, and Figure 2 indicates that ATP maintains the sodium gradient.
   D. Yes; Figures 1 and 2 indicate that glucose crosses the cell membrane in exchange for phosphate.

3. If, in Experiment 1, ATP had been added to the medium at time x, which of the following would represent the appearance of Graphs I and II?

A.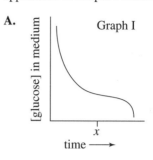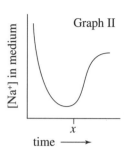

B.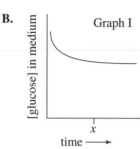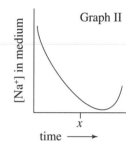

C.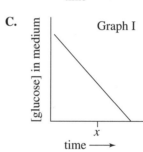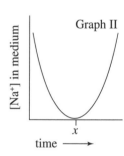

D.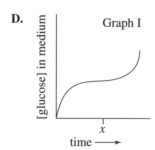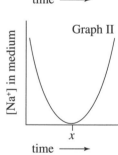

4. According to Figure 1, as sodium concentration in the medium approaches the same concentration found in the cells, glucose concentration in the medium would:

A. remain at its original level, because sodium concentration does not affect glucose concentration.
B. increase, because less glucose is transported into the bacterial cells.
C. level off, because a sodium gradient is not available to drive cotransport.
D. approach zero, because glucose and sodium are transported together.

5. In Figure 1, if the initial Na⁺ concentration in the medium were doubled, which graph below would best depict the glucose concentration in the medium?

A.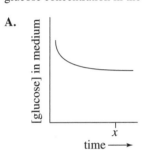

B.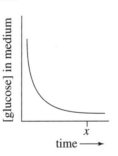

C.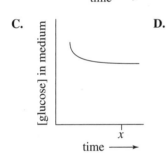

D.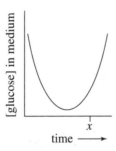

6. Based on the information in the passage, the first step in the transport of sodium and glucose into a cell is:

A. binding of specific secreted proteins to sodium in the surrounding medium.
B. direct hydrolysis of ATP in the cytoplasm by the sodium–glucose cotransporter.
C. direct hydrolysis of ATP on the extracellular surface by the sodium–glucose cotransporter.
D. binding of specific proteins in the membrane to sodium and glucose in the surrounding medium.

[handwritten at top: 1 ATP → 3 Na⁺ out, 2 K⁺ in]

Passage 29 (Questions 1-6)

The Na⁺/K⁺ ATPase found in the plasma membrane of cells throughout the body pumps Na⁺ out of cells and K⁺ into cells, using the energy of ATP hydrolysis to drive the transport of these ions against concentration gradients. Hydrolysis of one ATP to ADP + P_i drives the transport of 3 Na⁺ out of the cell and 2 K⁺ into the cell at the same time. The Na⁺/K⁺ ATPase consists of a catalytic transmembrane subunit with a molecular weight of 100,000 daltons and an associated 45,000-dalton glycoprotein. The ATP hydrolysis which fuels the pump can account for a significant fraction of a cell's energy usage, as great as 70% of the energy needs of cells that transmit action potentials.

The plasma membrane is impermeable to the passive diffusion of sodium and potassium ions. However, animal cells have potassium ion leak channels that allow potassium ions to diffuse down a concentration gradient out of the cell. The more potassium that diffuses out of the cell, the greater the negative charge remaining in the cellular interior. When the negative transmembrane potential becomes large enough to counterbalance the K⁺ concentration gradient and halt the net flow of K⁺ ions, the transmembrane electric potential is the *resting membrane potential*. The resting membrane potential plays a key role in propagating action potentials. During an action potential, the resting membrane potential helps to drive sodium movement into the cell and depolarize the membrane. After depolarization, the Na⁺/K⁺ ATPase and potassium leak channels help to re-establish the resting membrane potential.

The Na⁺/K⁺ ATPase is also important in other processes, such as balancing the osmotic pressure in the cell with the extracellular environment. The cell contains many macromolecular ions such as nucleic acids and proteins. The net movement of ions out of the cell created by the Na⁺/K⁺ ATPase ensures that the osmotic pressure within the cell created by these ions is not greater than the extracellular osmotic pressure. The concentration gradient of sodium created by the Na⁺/K⁺ ATPase is also used to drive

[handwritten: more K⁺ out = (−) inside cell]

several different transmembrane transport processes. In the small intestine, for example, the absorption of glucose into the intestinal epithelium against a gradient is driven by cotransport of sodium down a concentration gradient.

1. Treatment of cells with ouabain, an inhibitor of the Na⁺/K⁺ ATPase, causes cells to swell and burst. Which of the following is the most likely explanation for this?

    A. Ouabain prevents proteins from leaving the cell.
    B. The movement of sodium ions out of the cell is decreased by ouabain.
    C. The movement of potassium ions into the cell is increased by ouabain.
    D. Ouabain also opens potassium leak channels.

2. A drug that blocks the passage of potassium ions through potassium leak channels would be most likely to have what effect on the electric potential across the plasma membrane?

    A. The resting membrane potential would become more negative in the cellular interior relative to the extracellular environment.
    B. The resting membrane potential would become less negative in the cellular interior relative to the extracellular environment.
    C. The resting membrane potential would become positive in the cellular interior relative to the extracellular environment.
    D. The drug would have no effect on membrane potential.

    [handwritten: can't make it (+) b/c you're not even moving (+) ions into the cell!]

3. The membrane-spanning regions of the ATPase would most likely consist of amino acids with side groups that are:

    I. hydrophobic. ✓
    II. basic.
    III. nonpolar.

    A. II only
    B. I and II only
    C. I and III only
    D. I, II, and III

    [handwritten: basic amino acids are (+)-charged = hydrophilic]

Handwritten note in top margin: ↑ΔG & equil. are related txs

4. In the generation of the resting membrane potential, high concentrations of lithium, cesium, rubidium, or thallium can substitute for potassium outside the cell, but they cannot substitute for sodium inside the cell. This suggests which of the following concerning the Na^+/K^+ ATPase?

    A. The internal ion binding site is specific for sodium.
    B. The external ion binding site is specific for potassium.
    C. The Na^+/K^+ ATPase is poisoned by those ions.
    D. The Na^+/K^+ ATPase performs a vital function in transporting a wide variety of positive ions.

5. Linking ATP hydrolysis to Na^+ and K^+ transport affects ion transport in which of the following ways?

    A. The equilibrium and ΔG for Na^+ and K^+ transport are altered.
    B. The equilibrium for Na^+ and K^+ transport are not affected, but ΔG is made negative.
    C. The equilibrium for Na^+ and K^+ transport are altered, but ΔG remains unchanged.
    D. Neither the equilibrium nor ΔG for Na^+ and K^+ transport is affected.

6. If a single Na^+/K^+ ATPase were inserted into an artificial membrane impermeable to all ions, with high concentrations of ATP, Na^+, and K^+ on both sides of the membrane, which of the following would result?

    I.   Substantial ATP hydrolysis on both sides of the membrane
    II. Substantial ATP hydrolysis on only one side of the membrane, with accumulation of potassium on the opposite side
    III. Substantial ATP hydrolysis on only one side of the membrane, with accumulation of sodium on the opposite side

    A. I only
    B. II only
    C. III only
    D. II and III only

Passage 30 (Questions 1-7)

Lipid bilayer membranes are impermeable to passive diffusion by ions such as chloride (Cl^-), sodium (Na^+), and potassium (K^+). To diffuse across the plasma membrane, ions travel through transmembrane proteins that act as ion channels. Each type of ion channel allows specific ions to diffuse through the membrane down a concentration gradient. The frequency and duration of ion-channel opening are regulated by different receptors in several different ways. Voltage-gated ion channels open and close in response to alterations in the electric potential across the plasma membrane. Ligand-gated ion channels open in response to the binding of small molecules on the extracellular surface of the protein. Mechanical stimuli can also trigger the opening of ion channels. For example, stretch-activated channels open in response to stretching of the cell and plasma membrane. Other ion channels, such as potassium leak channels, are always open.

The net flux of ions across a plasma membrane is related to the concentration gradient of ion across the membrane and to the electrical gradient across the membrane. The net flux of ions is also related to a membrane permeability constant. The permeability constant describes the ability of ions to traverse the membrane in a particular state of closing and opening of ion channels. For a given electrochemical gradient, the number of ions crossing a membrane through a single channel depends on how frequently the channel opens and how long the channel stays open each time. The surface area of the membrane is also an important determinant in ion flux, but only when the membrane is significantly permeable to ions.

The movement of ions across a plasma membrane can be analyzed by the placement of microelectrodes into the cytoplasm of cells to measure changes in voltage across the membrane. In an experiment, the voltage across a section of membrane was measured either in the absence of a drug (Figure 1A) or with the same section of membrane in the presence of Drug B (Figure 1B) or Drug C (Figure 1C). The increased movement of ions across the membrane in response to the opening of ion channels is indicated by empty boxes, and the closing of ion channels is indicated by filled boxes.

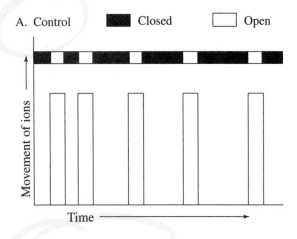

A. Control

☐ Closed ☐ Open

Movement of ions

Time →

B. More frequent opening

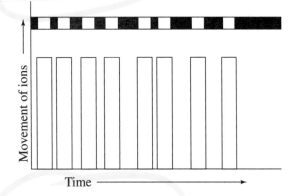

Movement of ions

Time →

C. Longer open interval

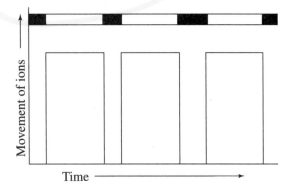

Movement of ions

Time →

Figure 1

1. The difference between Figure 1A and Figure 1B would best support which of the following conclusions?

   A. Net flux of ions is greater in Figure 1B than in Figure 1A.
   B. The transmembrane potential is more negative in the cytoplasm in Figure 1A than in Figure 1B.
   C. The membrane has more ion channels in Figure 1B than in Figure 1A.
   D. The membrane has more inhibitory ion channels in Figure 1A than in Figure 1B.

2. The concentration of K^+ on one side of a membrane populated by potassium leak channels is 1 mM and 10 mM on the other side. Which of the following will increase net potassium ion flux across the membrane?

   I. Increasing the K^+ concentration on one side of the membrane from 10 mM to 11 mM
   II. Increasing the K^+ concentration on both sides of the membrane by 10 mM
   III. Increasing the density of potassium leak channels in the membrane

   A. III only
   B. I and II only
   C. I and III only
   D. II and III only

3. Most animal cells have approximately 27 times more chloride in the extracellular fluid than in the cytoplasm. If the plasma membrane of a postsynaptic neuron is populated with ligand-gated chloride ion channels which open in response to binding of GABA (γ-aminobutyric acid), which of the following will occur upon release of GABA into the synaptic cleft?

   A. The Cl$^-$ concentration in the cytoplasm of the postsynaptic cell will decrease.
   B. The number of GABA receptors in the postsynaptic membrane will increase.
   C. The postsynaptic membrane will be hyperpolarized.
   D. Net ion flux across the presynaptic membrane will increase.

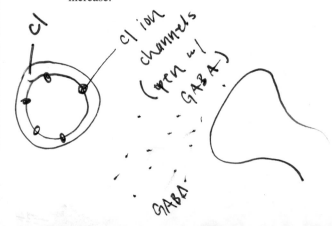

4. Due to the presence of protein channels, ions such as Na⁺, K⁺, Cl⁻, and Ca²⁺ diffuse across plasma membranes at rates that are much faster than would be predicted from:

   A. the fact that they are nonpolar.
   B. concentration differences across the membrane.
   C. their very low solubility in lipids.
   D. net ion flux.

5. Which observation would be the best evidence that active transport was responsible for moving a particular substance into a cell?

   A. An inverse relationship between the amount of substance taken in and oxygen uptake
   B. A transmembrane protein is required for the substance to cross the plasma membrane.
   C. Equal concentrations inside and outside the cell
   D. A correlation between the amount of the substance taken in and ATP hydrolysis

6. The following is a graph of the change in concentration over time of Substance X as it diffuses across the plasma membrane of a cell:

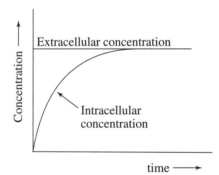

   This curve suggests that:

   A. the plasma membrane is permeable to this substance.
   B. this cell is regulating the influx of Substance X.
   C. efflux is slow at first, and increases over time.
   D. proteins required for Substance X transport are inactivated with increasing time.

7. Neurons often possess acetylcholine-gated sodium channels. If researchers found that the flow of sodium across the membrane of a particular neuron under study is not altered by the presence of acetylcholine, which of the following is the best explanation?

   A. The neuron has a different lipid composition in its plasma membrane.
   B. The gene for the acetylcholine-gated ion channel in the neuron contained a premature stop codon.
   C. The cytoplasm of the neuron contains acetylcholine.
   D. Sodium is present at a higher concentration in the extracellular environment than in the neuron's cytoplasm.

active = requires energy

Passage 31 (Questions 1-5)

Many hormones bind to receptors on the surface of the cell and exert their influence by triggering the adenylate cyclase cascade, a series of reactions that leads to increased levels of cyclic AMP (Figure 1).

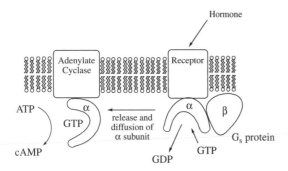

Figure 1 Signal transduction by hormonal activation of the adenylate cyclase cascade

Hormones, including ACTH, epinephrine, glucagon, and vasopressin, bind to cell-surface receptors, activating the α unit of the stimulatory G protein (G_s). The activation stimulates exchange of GDP bound to $G_s \alpha$ for GTP. GTP bound to the α unit is slowly hydrolyzed to GDP, thereby deactivating the cascade. Cholera toxin produced by the Gram-negative bacterium *Vibrio cholerae* blocks the hydrolysis of GTP bound to $G_s \alpha$ in intestinal mucosal cells, causing excess levels of cAMP to be generated.

The adenylate cyclase cascade continues when increased levels of cAMP in the cytosol activate protein kinases. One such kinase in skeletal muscle is phosphorylase kinase, which leads to the breakdown of glycogen in muscle cells.

Signal transduction is also carried out by the phosphoinositide cascade, in which activated hormonal receptors drive the synthesis of intracellular messengers from extracellular signals. One membrane component, phosphatidyl inositol 4,5-bisphosphate (PIP_2), is converted into the second messenger inositol 1,4,5-triphosphate (IP_3). IP_3 causes the release of calcium ions from intracellular stores such as the sarcoplasmic reticulum in smooth muscle. The increased calcium levels are detected by calmodulin, an intracellular protein.

Calcium and cAMP are able to play key roles in signal transduction because of their ability to cause conformational changes upon binding to intracellular proteins. Their binding is also highly selective, eliciting highly coordinated effects within the cell.

1. Adenylate cyclase stimulation takes place after receptors bind hormone because:

   A. of the exchange of GTP for GDP bound to $G_s \alpha$.
   B. of the exchange of GDP for GTP bound to $G_s \alpha$.
   C. adenylate cyclase binds to receptor.
   D. the $G_s \alpha$ subunit converts ATP to cAMP.

2. Activation of skeletal muscle phosphorylase kinase is most likely due to:

   A. parathyroid hormone receptor activation, which results in increased levels of calcium in the blood.
   B. insulin receptor activation, which results in increased levels of sugar in the blood.
   C. glucagon binding of cell receptors, leading to increased blood levels of glucose.
   D. glucocorticoid binding of cell receptors, leading to decreased blood levels of glucose.

3. Increased production of the messenger IP_3 in muscle cells of the gastrointestinal tract can lead to:

   A. excess levels of cAMP.
   B. inactivation of thick filament ATPase subunits.
   C. increased levels of calcium within the smooth muscle cell cytosol.
   D. increased levels of calmodulin within the smooth muscle cell cytosol.

4. Calcium and cAMP cause many intracellular proteins to show increased activity. These substances achieve this by:

   A. causing allosteric changes in target proteins.
   B. increasing feedback inhibition of target enzymes.
   C. cleaving specific target enzyme moieties.
   D. binding to the alpha helix subunit of calmodulin.

5. When the hormone ACTH activates the adenylate cyclase cascade in target cells, the expected result is that blood levels of:

   A. calcium will decrease.
   B. glucose will decrease.
   C. epinephrine will increase.
   D. aldosterone will increase.

Passage 32 (Questions 1-6)
ADVANCED PASSAGE

Vibrio cholerae is a Gram-negative bacillus that causes cholera in humans. The immune response to cholera is entirely humoral; there is no evidence of stimulation of cellular immunity. The bacteria colonize the mucosa of the small intestine and secrete an enterotoxin that binds to receptors on the mucosal epithelium. A subunit of the toxin activates cellular adenylate cyclase, resulting in an intracellular increase of 3′,5′-cyclic adenosine mono-phosphate (cAMP), which activates a protein kinase, cAMP-dependent protein kinase.

The toxin activates adenylate cyclase by ADP-ribosylating the diffusible stimulatory subunit (G_s) of a G protein receptor complex. G_s, located at the inner surface of the cell membrane, binds a molecule of GTP when the receptor complex is activated. With GTP bound, it diffuses to the membrane-bound adenylate cyclase and activates it. Like other G proteins, G_s has an inherent GTPase activity which hydrolyzes the bound GTP to terminate the stimulatory action of G_s. The result of cholera toxins ADP-ribosylating G_s is inhibition of the GTPase activity of G_s. The toxin of *Bordetella pertussis* also causes overactivity of adenylate cyclase, but via a slightly different mechanism. The pertussis toxin ADP-ribosylates G_i, the inhibitory G-protein, which normally attenuates activity of adenylate cyclase by competing with G_s. ADP-ribosylation by pertussis toxin inactivates G_i. Another difference is that *Bordetella* infects only respiratory mucosa, while cholera is a gastrointestinal disease.

The increase in cAMP caused by cholera toxin stimulates an extreme increase in chloride secretion by cells of the Lieberkühn crypts, which are small invaginations of the mucosa between the villi. The massive chloride loss is accompanied by a correspondingly massive loss of water from the crypt cells, because chloride secretion is a physiological mechanism for intestinal mucosal water excretion. The consequent diarrhea can be severe enough to cause life-threatening dehydration.

One strategy for treating cholera consists of combating dehydration by oral rehydration therapy (ORT). Standard ORT solutions contain sodium chloride and glucose. The sugar promotes transport of the salt ions into the villi via the 1:1 sodium–glucose cotransporter, a protein in the mucosal cell membrane. Water follows by osmosis, thus effecting rehydration.

1. Differences between *Vibrio cholerae* and *Bordetella pertussis* include which of the following?

   I. *Vibrio cholerae* infects the intestinal epithelium, while *Bordetella pertussis* infects the respiratory tract.
   II. Cholera toxin increases the concentration of cAMP in the cell, while pertussis toxin decreases cAMP in the cell.
   III. *Vibrio cholerae* increases chloride secretion, while *Bordetella pertussis* decreases chloride secretion.

   A. I only
   B. I and III only
   C. II and III only
   D. I, II, and III

2. Which of the following conclusions can be inferred from the passage?

   A. G_s with GDP bound does not activate adenylate cyclase.
   B. G_s with GDP bound activates adenylate cyclase.
   C. ADP-ribosylation of adenylate cyclase inactivates it.
   D. ADP-ribosylation of adenylate cyclase activates it.

3. The osmolarity of ORT solutions is equal to that of normal blood. What effect would dramatically increasing the glucose concentration of the ORT solution have on fluid uptake by the blood?

   A. Fluid uptake would increase due to an increase in sodium transport.
   B. Fluid uptake would increase due to a decrease in lumen osmolarity, causing water to diffuse into the villi.
   C. Fluid would be lost from the blood to the lumen, due to an increase of lumen osmolarity.
   D. Increased glucose concentration would have no effect on fluid uptake.

4. A further treatment for cholera includes using drugs that inhibit net chloride secretion, thus slowing fluid loss. One such drug, chlorpromazine, has been found to inhibit net secretion *in vivo* and, *in vitro*, to inhibit the activity of protein kinases. What is a likely mechanism of action of chlorpromazine?

    A. Reversal of the effect of cellular cAMP
    B. Increasing uptake of sodium chloride by villi cells
    C. Preventing attachment of cholera bacteria to the intestinal epithelium
    D. Causing increased sodium uptake by the sodium–glucose symport

5. Which of the following would cause the greatest loss of water through diarrhea?

    A. Coinfection with *Vibrio cholerae* and *Bordetella pertussis*
    B. Infection with *Vibrio cholerae* plus ingestion of Gatorade (a solution of NaCl and glucose)
    C. Infection with *Vibrio cholerae* plus ingestion of non-absorbable carbohydrate, such as cellulose
    D. A humoral immune response against *Vibrio cholerae*

6. Overactivity of the cAMP system is usually prevented by which of the following?

    I. Spontaneous hydrolysis of GTP by G_s
    II. Competition of G_s and G_i
    III. cAMP-dependent protein kinase

    A. I only
    B. II only
    C. I and II only
    D. II and III only

Passage 33 (Questions 1-6)

Cancer cells are recognized by their ability to escape normal regulation of cell division, proliferating out of control, and often invading local tissues or metastasizing to distant locations. Most cancers are thought to originate from a single cell which has undergone a change in its genetic sequence. However, many cancers require two genetic aberrations. In these cases a defect in the genome is thought to predispose the cell to malignant transformation, which then takes place only after further genetic disturbance. Tumor progression, whereby a benign tumor becomes a malignant one, is accelerated by mutagenic agents (tumor initiators) and nonmutagenic agents (tumor promoters). Both types of agents affect gene expression, stimulate cell proliferation, and alter the balance of mutant and nonmutant cells.

The following tables show the relative risks (RR) of tobacco and alcohol use for cancer of the endolarynx, epilarynx, and hypopharynx. A relative risk greater than 1.0 indicates increased risk relative to a control group.

RR for Alcohol & Tobacco by Site			
Cigarettes/day	Endolarynx	Epilarnyx	Hypopharnyx
0	1.0	1.0	1.0
1–7	2.5	2.3	5.5
8–15	7.5	6.7	13.7
16–25	14.6	11.0	18.0
26+	17.0	9.4	20.0
g Alcohol/day			
0–20	1.0	1.0	1.0
21–40	0.88	0.87	1.57
41–80	1.08	1.53	3.15
81–120	1.71	5.10	5.59
121+	2.50	10.6	12.5

Table 1

Combined Effect of Alcohol & Tobacco on RR				
g Alcohol per day	Number of Cigarettes per day			
	0–7	8–15	16–25	26+
Endolarynx				
0–40	1.0	7.0	12.9	15.0
41–80	2.8	8.3	16.1	18.7
81–120	4.3	12.8	24.8	28.9
121+	6.3	18.7	36.5	42.5
Epilarynx				
0–40	1.0	12.4	17.7	17.9
41–80	9.1	23.9	33.9	34.4
81–120	20.9	54.6	77.6	78.6
121+	45.2	118.3	168.2	170.5

Adapted from *International Journal of Cancer: Cancer of the Larynx/Hypolarynx, Tobacco and Alcohol,* © 1988

Table 2

1. Based on the passage, tobacco and alcohol would be classified as:

    A. tumor initiators.
    B. tumor promoters.
    C. mutagens.
    D. Cannot be determined from the information given

2. The direct role of tumor initiators is to cause:

    A. changes in the DNA sequence of a cell.
    B. noncancerous cells to become cancerous.
    C. changes in the metastatic potential of a cell.
    D. tumors to develop in normal tissue.

3. The likelihood of cancer in a person who consumes 21–40 g/day of alcohol, compared to the likelihood in a nondrinker, is:

    A. decreased for endolarynx, epilarynx, and hypopharynx.
    B. decreased for endolarynx and epilarynx, but increased for the hypopharynx.
    C. decreased for endolarynx, but increased for epilarynx and hypopharynx.
    D. increased for endolarynx, epilarynx, and hypopharynx.

4. Overall, the combined effects of tobacco and alcohol on the relative risk for cancer are:

    A. additive.
    B. multiplicative.
    C. independent of each other.
    D. mutually antagonistic because alcohol lowers the risk produced by tobacco consumption.

5. What is the relative risk for developing cancer of the epilarynx in an individual who smokes 8–15 cigarettes per day and drinks more than 121 g of alcohol per day (compared to a nonsmoking, nondrinker)?

    A. 6.7
    B. 10.6
    C. 18.7
    D. 118.3

6. Each of the following could cause cancer EXCEPT:

    A. a mutation in the gene coding for a cell surface receptor.
    B. a mutation in the gene coding for a steroid receptor.
    C. an error in translation of a cell-surface receptor.
    D. deletion of the gene coding for a receptor's regulatory subunit.

procarcinogen

Passage 34 (Questions 1-6)

At the molecular level, cancer often begins with the mutation of a cell's genome. Dietary carcinogens act as mutagens, transforming a normal cell to a malignant cell by binding to the DNA of its genome. The cell's normally precise DNA replication is thus disturbed.

The study of a dietary carcinogen begins with laboratory tests for mutagenic behavior. A positive Ames assay, for example, indicates a chemical's tendency to produce mutations in bacterial cell cultures. While tests for mutagenicity are helpful, they fail to provide definitive information about a chemical's carcinogenic activity. While most carcinogens are mutagens, the converse is not true. Many mutagens do not cause cancerous mutations. In addition, some chemicals are neither carcinogens nor mutagens, but still play an important role in the genesis of cancer by acting as promoters. Promoters amplify the effects of carcinogens but do not act as carcinogens on their own. In animal models, a chemical is recognized as a promoter if it worsens the risk of cancer if administered after, but not before, exposure to a known carcinogen.

1. Promoters induce cancer only after the administration of a true carcinogen because they:

   A. are not mutagenic except in the presence of a procarcinogen.
   B. cannot be evaluated according to the Ames assay and related tests.
   C. only augment the effects of genuine carcinogens.
   D. are not ordinarily eaten intentionally.

2. A particular substance increases the risk of cancer in normal rats but does not increase the risk of cancer in rats with liver disease. This may be true because:

   A. the diseased rats have an increased resistance to mutagenicity.
   B. the substance was administered to the diseased rats before the administration of another known carcinogen.
   C. the substance is a procarcinogen that normally requires hepatic conversion to a carcinogen.
   D. the substance is widespread in the rats' normal food supply.

3. If a population of animals has an extremely high dietary intake of several promoters, but ingests no mutagens, its incidence of cancer would likely be:

   A. high, because promoters are known to amplify the incidence of carcinogenicity among populations that consume them.
   B. high, because promoters can be carcinogenic without causing mutation.
   C. low, because animal diets do not, generally, include artificial additives.
   D. low, because promoters do not cause cancer in the absence of mutagens.

4. What is the relationship between mutagens and carcinogens?

   A. All mutagens are carcinogens.
   B. All carcinogens are mutagens.
   C. The Ames test detects carcinogens but not mutagens.
   D. Mutagens cause mutations, while carcinogens cause cancer.

5. Xeroderma pigmentosum is a recessive skin condition that can lead to cancer at an early age. A woman homozygous for the dominant gene and a homozygous man with the condition wish to have a child. What is the probability that the child will get xeroderma pigmentosum?

   A. 0%
   B. 25%
   C. 50%
   D. Cannot be determined

   mitotic division

6. Some cancer cells resemble embryological cells in that they are less determined than those found in normal tissues. Which of the following activities would NOT be associated with these cancer cells?

   A. Rapid DNA synthesis
   B. Elevated rates of translation
   C. Frequent meiotic cell division
   D. Low level of differentiation

   not determined = not differentiated

Passage 35 (Questions 1-6)

Oncogenes are genes that have the potential to cause cancer if activated. *Myc* is an oncogene that has been linked to Burkitt's lymphoma, a group of three cancers, all of which affect B cells. Endemic Burkitt's lymphoma is the most common pediatric cancer in equatorial Africa. This variant is commonly preceded by an infection with the Epstein Barr virus (EBV), which enters B cells and causes dysregulation of the *Myc* gene.

Myc, which is found on chromosome 8, normally produces a transcription factor involved in up-regulating the production of ribosomal RNA and generally driving cell proliferation. It also recruits histone acetyl-transferases, which work to transfer the acetyl group from acetyl-CoA to various conserved lysine residues on histones; this acetylation is typically works to increase gene expression. The activity of *Myc* is regulated posttranslationally via multiple possible modifications, including phosphorylation and ubiquitinylation. A common translocation often converts *Myc* from being a protooncogene to a functioning oncogene; its overproduction outstrips the cell's ability to regulate its activity and thus its impact on cell proliferation is greatly increased.

EBV is a double-stranded DNA virus. After EBV enters the host B cell, the virus will enter either a lytic or lysogenic cycle. Once active, EBV can cause translocation of *Myc* from chromosome 8 most commonly to chromosome 14. The translocation causes the dysregulation of the gene. Burkitt's lymphoma will often affect the jaw and other facial bones, producing a large, disfiguring tumor. The tumor is composed of a conglomeration of the immature, dysfunctional B cells and can enlarge internally as well, potentially restricting the airway. If detected early, Burkitt's lymphoma responds well to treatment with monoclonal antibodies to B cells.

Malaria is a tropical illness caused by the protozoan *Plasmodium falciparum*. Studies have shown that children with recurrent malaria infections are more likely to develop Burkitt's lymphoma.

1. Patients who receive treatment for Burkitt's lymphoma are susceptible to tumor lysis syndrome (TLS), which results in the release of large amounts of electrolytes, including phosphate, when a substantial number of tumor cells are lysed in a short amount of time. Which of the following electrolytes is also likely to be elevated in the serum of a patient suffering from TLS?

    A. Calcium
    B. Potassium
    C. Sodium
    D. Creatine

2. In addition to promoting transcription, which of the following would most enhance *Myc*'s oncogenic effect?

    A. Up-regulating DNA methlyation
    B. Inducing further chromosomal translocations from chromosome 8
    C. Disrupting mitochondrial replication
    D. Downregulating mediators of apoptosis

3. Which of the following is the most likely explanation for why children with recurrent infections with *Plasmodium falciparum* are more likely to develop Burkitt's lymphoma?

    A. Infections increase the production of B cells.
    B. *Plasmodium falciparum* mutates the *Myc* gene.
    C. *Plasmodium falciparum* carries the Epstein-Barr virus.
    D. The stress of infection stimulates latent EBV to become active.

4. Which of the following is/are possible side effects of medications used to treat Burkitt's lymphoma?

    I. Hives
    II. Increased susceptibility to infections
    III. Increased risk of blood clots

    A. I only
    B. II only
    C. I and II
    D. I, II, and III

5. Which of the following structures is most likely to be obstructed in Burkitt's lymphoma?

    A. Pharynx
    B. Trachea
    C. Bronchi
    D. Alveoli

6. Which of the following is NOT a means by which oncogene activation could occur?

    A. Chromosomal rearrangement
    B. Mutation
    C. Genetic amplification
    D. Nondisjunction

Passage 36 (Questions 1-6)

Ewing sarcoma was first described by pathologist James Ewing in 1920. Unlike many of the blood-based cancers that had been identified up to that time, Ewing sarcoma is a bone tumor, typically seen in the pelvis and long bones. It most commonly affects teens and young adults, and patients will often complain of deep pain in the general vicinity of the tumor. Occasionally a patient will be diagnosed with Ewing sarcoma after sustaining a fracture, and the tumor is found on X-ray where it has a characteristic "onion-skin" appearance.

Ewing sarcoma is caused by a translocation between chromosomes 11 and 22, fusing the *FLI1* gene on chromosome 11 with the *EWS* gene on chromosome 22. *FLI1* is considered a proto-oncogene, one that becomes cancer-producing with activation. The protein product of the *EWS/FLI1* combination gene is an oncoprotein that can act as a transcription activator for another gene (*NKX2.2*) on chromosome 20 that codes for a neural transcription factor. The proliferation of this factor is believed to result in the formation of neuroectodermal tumor cells. This common genetic locus creates the classification of the Ewing family of tumors.

Ewing sarcoma is typically treated by a combination of chemotherapy, radiation, and tumor resection. Various chemotherapy agents prevent key cell mechanisms involved in proliferation, such as transcription, translation, and mitosis. Radiation treatment is typically focused on the tumor itself with the clinical goal of decreasing its size. Larger tumors may require amputation of the affected limb.

A bacterial plasmid was created containing the *EWS/FLI1* combination gene as part of an experiment. This plasmid also contained a gene for ampicillin resistance. The plasmid was introduced into a colony of *Staphylococcus aureus* growing on minimal media. After 24 hours, some of the bacteria were transferred to another media plate containing ampicillin. A large colony was observed after another 24 hours. The cells from this colony were lysed and treated with DNase and RNase to allow for isolation of the oncoprotein product for further proteomic analysis.

1. In addition to its role in Ewing sarcoma, *FLI1* is also the oncogenic trigger for some erythroleukemias. What is the most likely impact of *FLI1* on erythrocytes?

   A. Blocking signals for cell proliferation
   B. Diverting cells signals for terminal differentiation to cell proliferation
   C. Increasing regulation on G_1 to S phase transitions
   D. Promoting both terminal differentiation and cell proliferation

2. After amputation of a limb, patients will often feel sensation of pain as though the amputated limb were still attached. These signals can be a result of action potentials in the remaining nerve that are relayed by the spinal cord. Which part of the brain would process phantom pain?

   A. Cerebellum
   B. Frontal lobe
   C. Occipital lobe
   D. Thalamus

3. Children who are successfully treated for Ewing sarcoma generally grow to be shorter than their healthy counterparts. Which of the following is the best explanation for this?

   A. Amputation of the affected leg results in short stature.
   B. Chemotherapy prevents cellular processes necessary for growth.
   C. Radiation causes the patient to shrink.
   D. Ewing sarcoma destroys epiphyseal plates.

4. Actinomycin D is chemotherapy drug that has been shown to limit or prevent transcription and is often used as part of the treatment for Ewing sarcoma. Which of the following enzymes could be inactivated by actinomycin D?

   I. RNA polymerase
   II. Primase
   III. Helicase

   A. I only
   B. I and II only
   C. I and III only
   D. II and III only

5. In a separate experiment, the oncoprotein isolated at the end of the first experiment was added to a liquid culture of bacteria containing the *NKX2.2* gene. Which of the following results is most likely?

   A. The cells in the culture would die because they are sensitive to ampicillin.
   B. The cells in the culture would not be affected by the fluid.
   C. The cells in the culture would increase translation of the *NKX2.2* gene.
   D. The cells in the culture would reproduce uncontrollably.

6. Another translocation involving chromosome 22 with chromosome 9 is associated with different types of leukemia. The locus for this translocation is different from the *EWS* site. What test would best differentiate the two DNA sequences on chromosome 22?

A. ELISA
B. Northern blot
C. Southern blot
D. Western blot

Passage 37 (Questions 1-5)

The remedy for genetic deficiency diseases by the insertion of new DNA into a human genome is the basis for treatments called gene therapy. Gene therapy may have application for both inherited disorders as well as certain acquired diseases, such as cancer.

There are two types of gene therapy: gene replacement therapy and gene addition therapy. In gene replacement therapy, a normal gene is recombined with a cell's defective gene at the site of the affected gene; the exogenous normal gene replaces the defective gene in the cell's genome. In gene addition therapy, the inserted gene does not replace the defective gene, but rather supplements it. Successful treatment requires that cells targeted for gene therapy be actively dividing.

There are two possible routes for application of gene therapy: *in vivo* and *ex vivo*. *Ex vivo* therapy involves removing cells from an affected individual's body, adding new genetic material to them *in vitro*, and then reintroducing the genetically altered cells into the body. *In vivo* therapy involves addition of genetic material directly into an individual's body.

Retroviruses are a convenient vector for the transfer of genetic material into cells targeted for gene therapy. A retrovirus is an RNA virus capable of transcribing its genome into complementary DNA within the cell it infects. The enzyme that catalyzes the manufacture of DNA from an RNA template is reverse transcriptase. The reverse transcript is then incorporated into the cell's own genome, where it replicates along with host genes during the normal cell cycle. When the viral genome is thus assimilated into the host genome, it is termed a provirus. Mutant retroviruses can be engineered to include normal genes homologous to defective human genes and, importantly, to exclude genes important in viral reproduction and virulence.

One drawback to using viruses as gene vectors is their potential to alter the expression of certain genes, such as oncogenes. The amplification of the activity of these genes can lead to tumor formation and cancer. Another potential hazard is insertional mutagenesis. Because it is often difficult to control the site at which genetic material is introduced, serious problems could arise if DNA were inserted in the middle of genes that encode proteins essential to normal cell function.

1. Which of the following cells would be a good candidate for successful treatment by gene therapy?

A. A T cell
B. An intestinal epithelial cell
C. A red blood cell
D. A neuron

2. Huntington's disease is an autosomal dominant genetic disorder. It could not be treated by gene addition therapy because:

A. the defective gene would still be expressed in the treated individual, despite the presence of the inserted normal gene.

B. the added gene would show a faster rate of mutation than other genes, and would soon mutate to the defective allele.

C. Huntington's disease is caused by a retrovirus, and the addition of a new gene by a viral vector would cause an individual to develop the disease.

D. the defective gene would still be present in the individual's genome, and would mutate any genetic material inserted at a nearby locus.

3. The success of gene therapy that uses retrovirus vectors depends on the existence of an appropriate receptor for the virus on the target cell. This receptor most likely consists of:

A. DNA.
B. RNA.
C. protein.
D. phospholipid.

4. One nonviral vector for gene therapy relies on receptor-mediated endocytosis. This approach has proven ineffective in the past because material taken up by the target cell is usually transported to the:

A. lysosomes.
B. endoplasmic reticulum.
C. nucleus.
D. mitochondria.

5. One method of treating cancer with gene therapy is to introduce genes that disrupt DNA replication in malignant tissue. This treatment would be likely to affect tumor cells more than normal cells because tumor cells:

A. contain mutations which are difficult to replicate.
B. divide mitotically at a faster rate than normal cells, and thus would be more affected by the gene product.
C. are more easily infected by viruses, and thus would be easier targets for inserted genes.
D. have larger genomes than normal cells, so it is easier to add new genetic material to them.

Passage 38 (Questions 1-6)

Multiple allelism is the existence of several known alleles of a single gene in a population. Although only two alleles of a gene can exist in a diploid cell, the total number of possible allelic forms that might exist in a population of individuals is very large.

A familiar example of multiple allelism in humans is the ABO blood group locus. The gene codes for cell-surface proteins. These proteins determine the compatibility of donated blood. If the donor has different cell-surface proteins from the recipient, the recipient's immune system attacks the donated red blood cells, with the new cell-surface proteins serving as antigens.

In the ABO allelic series, there is a cell-surface protein formed by the allele I^A and another by the allele I^B. The allele i determines a failure to produce either form of that type of protein. There are thus four possible phenotypes: A, B, AB, and O. The O phenotype corresponds to the genotype ii.

Coat color in rabbits provides another example of multiple allelism. There are four coat-color phenotypes. The Himalayan phenotype is interesting, in that its expression is temperature dependent. Himalayan rabbits are all black when raised at temperatures of about 5°C; white with black ears, forepaws, noses, and tails when raised at normal room temperatures; and all white when raised at temperatures above 35°C.

Adapted from D. Suzuki, A. Griffiths, J. Miller, and R. Lewontin, *An Introduction to Genetic Analysis* ©1981, and H. Curtis, *Biology* © 1983.

1. Antibodies act against foreign particles in which of the following ways?

   I. They may coat a foreign particle so that it is taken up by phagocytic cells.
   II. They may bind to a foreign particle, interfering with its function.
   III. They may elicit a cascade leading to the lysis of foreign cells.

   A. I only
   B. II only
   C. I and II only
   D. I, II, and III

2. A hospital has possibly switched the babies of Couples X and Y. Their blood groups are: Couple X—A and O; Couple Y—AB and B; Baby 1—AB; Baby 2—O. Which baby belongs to which set of parents?

    A. Baby 1 belongs to Couple X, and Baby 2 belongs to Couple Y.
    B. Baby 1 belongs to Couple Y, and Baby 2 to Couple X.
    C. Baby 2 belongs to Couple X, but Baby 1 belongs to neither couple.
    D. Neither baby can belong to either couple.

3. A man whose blood group is AB needs a blood transfusion. Which of the following blood groups would be compatible?

    I.   O
    II. A
    III. AB

    A. I only
    B. III only
    C. II and III only
    D. I, II, and III

4. In which of the following genotypes is codominance operating to produce the phenotype?

    A. ii
    B. $I^A I^B$
    C. $I^A I^A$
    D. $I^B i$

5. Which of the following would best explain the temperature dependence of Himalayan coat color?

    A. The protein governing the deposition of black pigment into hair might only function at temperatures lower than core body temperatures.
    B. The protein governing the deposition of black pigment into hair might only function at temperatures higher than core body temperatures.
    C. Temperature alters the genotype imports of the body.
    D. Multiple allelism is operating in a temperature-dependent pattern.

6. A man of blood type A marries a woman of blood type B. Possible genotypes among their offspring include:

    A. $I^A I^B$ only.
    B. $I^A I^A$ or $I^B I^B$ only.
    C. $I^A i$ or $I^B i$ only.
    D. $I^A I^B$ or $I^A i$ or $I^B i$ or ii.

_____

Passage 39 (Questions 1-6)

The black color coat in hamsters is due to a dominant gene (*B*). A recessive allele (*b*) at this locus results in a brown coat when homozygous. However, neither coat color is expressed when the organism is homozygous for the allele (*a*) at a separate locus. The *a/a* genotype results in a white (albino) coat, regardless of the allele at the *B* locus. The wild-type allele (+) at the (*a*) locus allows normal coat coloration, whether the genotype is +/+ or +/*a*.

The following experiments were performed to better understand these relationships.

Experiment 1:

A female hamster with the genotype *B/B*; +/+ is crossed with a male hamster of genotype *b/b*; *a/a*.

Experiment 2:

Female offspring from the cross in Experiment 1 were backcrossed to the (*b/b*; *a/a*) parent. The distribution of coat coloration among the progeny was as follows: black (66), brown (34), and white (100).

1. Which of the following can be inferred from the passage?

    A. The (+) allele is dominant over the (*B*) allele.
    B. The (*a*) allele is dominant over the (*B*) allele.
    C. The (+) allele and the (*a*) allele are codominant.
    D. The albino gene is epistatic to the *B* gene.

2. A true-breeding strain of black hamsters is available. What is the genotype of this strain?

    A. *B/b*; +/+
    B. *B/b*; +/*a*
    C. *B/B*; +/+
    D. *B/B*; +/*a*

3. A strain of hamsters known to be homozygous (*b/b*; *a/a*) at both loci is available. What is the phenotype of these animals?

    A. Black
    B. Brown
    C. White
    D. A mixture of white and brown

4. What will be the phenotype(s) of the F_1 animals resulting from the cross in Experiment 1?

    A. All black
    B. All brown
    C. All white
    D. Both black and brown

5. Experiment 2 suggests that the two genetic loci discussed in the passage are:

    A. linked.
    B. unlinked.
    C. recessive.
    D. Not enough information to determine linkage

6. Based on the results from Experiment 2, what is the genetic map distance (frequency of recombination) between the two loci discussed in the passage?

    A. 17 centimorgans
    B. 34 centimorgans
    C. 68 centimorgans
    D. Impossible to determine; they are unlinked.

Passage 40 (Questions 1-6)

Populations of organisms can interact through competition, predation, or one of the three types of symbiotic relationships: parasitism, commensalism, or mutualism. Three communities which exemplify these relationships are described below.

Community 1:

Acacia trees of Central and South America have hollow thorns that house the ant *Pseudomyrmex*. The ants feed on sugar and proteins produced in Beltian bodies at the tips of leaflets on the tree. The ants protect the tree by stinging invaders, removing debris, and clipping competing vegetation. Experiments have shown that when the ants are poisoned, the tree cannot compete as well for light and growing space, and is damaged by herbivores.

Community 2:

The cattle egrets of North and South America inhabit the same areas as grazing cattle. The grazing cattle flush insects from vegetation as they move. The egrets benefit from the relationship, whereas the cattle neither benefit nor are harmed.

Community 3:

The *Myxoma* virus was introduced in the 1950s in Australia to control the enormous rabbit population. The first infection killed 99.8% of the rabbits, but the subsequent second and third infections killed only 90% and 50%, respectively, of the remaining rabbits. The rabbit population today has rebounded, due to selection for less virulent strains of the virus and for rabbits better able to resist the virus.

1. The symbiotic relationship of Community 1 would best be classified as:

    A. parasitism.
    B. commensalism.
    C. mutualism.
    D. a predator–prey relationship.

2. In Community 3, the decline of the rabbits' mortality in repeated viral epidemics is an example of:

    A. coevolution.
    B. mutation.
    C. speciation.
    D. competition.

3. Birds that feed on insects would be most like which organism, as described in the passage?

    A. *Pseudomyrmex* ants eating acacia nutrients
    B. Cattle with egrets
    C. *Myxoma* viruses with rabbits
    D. None of the above

4. According to the Hardy–Weinberg law, the frequency of all alleles in the rabbit population would not change, as long as each of the following were true EXCEPT that the:

    A. rabbit population was extremely large.
    B. rabbits were free to migrate to new habitats.
    C. rabbit genome never mutated.
    D. rabbits mated randomly.

5. Most individual species of figs are pollinated by a single host-specific species of wasp which in turn receives nourishment. This host-specificity provides reproductive isolation among both the wasps and the figs that can lead to:

    A. speciation.
    B. intra-species competition.
    C. natural selection.
    D. genetic diversity.

6. Why do predators usually not kill the entire population of their prey?

    A. Because geographical barriers usually prevent this
    B. In order to avoid obliterating their prey
    C. Because prey populations evolve traits that prevent them from being killed
    D. Because when prey become too scarce, the predators begin to die off also

Passage 41 (Questions 1-6)
ADVANCED PASSAGE

At what level does natural selection operate: the individual or the group? This is a central question in the field of sociobiology. In 1962, V. C. Wynne Edwards put forth his revolutionary group selection thesis, which states that animals avoid overexploitation of their habitats, especially with regard to food supply. In his theory, they accomplish this by altruistic restraint on the part of individuals who reduce their reproduction, or refrain altogether, to avoid overpopulation. Thus altruism is favored by natural selection.

For example, small birds of the species *Parus major* typically produce nine or ten eggs per clutch, although they have been observed to produce as many as thirteen eggs per clutch. Data show that a clutch size larger than nine or ten actually produces fewer surviving offspring. See Figure 1; the vertical axis gives the percent occurrence of each brood size, and the numbers labelling the dots indicate the number of known survivors per nest.

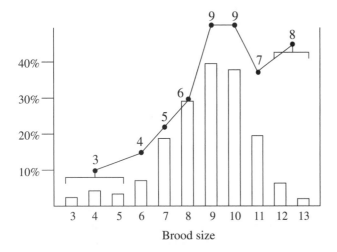

Figure 1

Additional evidence for the group-selection theory is that there appears to be a relationship between reproductive success of individuals and the density of the population. When density is low, mortality is likewise low and reproductive rate high. At high numbers resources are more scarce, and it is more difficult to stay alive and to reproduce, so mortality is high and reproductivity low. Figure 2 shows the number of surviving offspring per mating pair plotted against the number of breeding adults present (the graph covers several years).

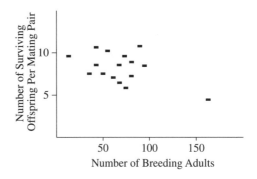

Figure 2

Adapted from R. Trivers, *Social Evolution* © 1985, and D. Barash, *Sociobiology and Behavior* © 1983.

1. According to the passage, which of the following is NOT an accurate statement about the relationship of population size to reproductivity of *Parus major*?

    A. Population numbers tend to increase when low and tend to decrease when high.
    B. Breeding success is inversely proportional to the number of fledglings.
    C. Increased food availability increases reproductivity.
    D. When density is high, difficulty of survival increases, lowering reproductivity.

2. The term "carrying capacity" is often used in ecology. Which of the following is an accurate description of the carrying capacity of a population?

    A. It is best measured in the springtime, when the new offspring are born.
    B. It is the number of individuals that are present over several seasons.
    C. It is the population size during the phase of exponential growth.
    D. It is determined more by reproductive potential than by the environment.

3. Which of the following is an accurate interpretation of the evidence provided by Figure 1?

   A. It neither supports nor contradicts Edwards's theory, because it does not display information about altruism or group versus individual behavior.
   B. It shows that *Parus major* reduces clutch size in response to environmental constraints, because a higher percentage of offspring survive when the clutch size is lower.
   C. It shows that *Parus major* produces as many offspring as possible, regardless of environmental constraints.
   D. It shows that Edwards's theory does not apply to this particular species.

4. Which of the following is NOT an accurate interpretation of the evidence provided by Figure 2?

   A. It may be consistent with Edwards's theory.
   B. It proves Edwards's theory is correct.
   C. It does not contradict the idea that *Parus major* reproduces less when population is very high.
   D. It does not demonstrate a clear linear relationship.

5. Which of the following is most consistent with Darwin's theory of natural selection?

   A. There exists a species of monkey in which adults sacrifice themselves for unrelated youths.
   B. Females suffer higher mortality in some species in order to increase the number of available mates for those who do survive.
   C. Infanticide in langur monkeys serves to regulate the population size.
   D. Parents keep resources away from other unrelated parents within the species in order to provide for their own offspring.

6. Which of the following, if true, would be evidence AGAINST Edwards's theory?

   A. A Native American tribe left its rural homeland to move into a city, and the reproductive rate increased due to the greatly increased availability of nourishment and safe housing.
   B. In most species, all individuals reproduce at the most rapid rate the environment will support.
   C. A sociologist performed a survey of Chinese farmers, and learned that the farmers do not oppose government-imposed population control.
   D. Female lions will nourish the young of unrelated females and not have offspring of their own.

Passage 42 (Questions 1-6)

The following experiment was designed to elucidate the role of Na^+ and K^+ in determining the resting membrane potential (RMP) and action potential (AP).

Experiment:

Cytoplasm from a giant axon (obtained from a squid) was extruded without damaging the plasma membrane. The axon was then perfused with solutions containing various concentrations of K^+ and Na^+ inside ("Int.") and outside ("Ext."). It was then tested for its ability to produce action potentials upon electrical stimulation; the RMP was monitored as well.

$[K^+]$ (mM)		$[Na^+]$ (mM)		RMP (mV)	AP?
Int.	Ext.	Int.	Ext.		
150.0	7.5	15.0	150.0	−80	yes
7.5	150.0	150.0	15.0	+80	no
15.0	15.0	15.0	15.0	0	no
150.0	7.5	15.0	80.0	−80	yes

Adapted from Alberts et al., *Molecular Biology of the Cell*, © 1989.

1. Which of the following increases the speed of conduction of an action potential?

    A. A decrease in axon diameter
    B. Myelination of the axon
    C. Chemical synapses
    D. Even distribution of sodium fast channels down the length of the axon

2. The sympathetic nervous system uses all of the following EXCEPT:

    A. motor neurons to innervate glands.
    B. sensory neurons to innervate blood pressure receptors.
    C. interneurons to facilitate neural control.
    D. motor neurons to innervate skeletal muscle.

3. Based on the experiment, which of the following is necessary to allow an action potential in an electrically stimulated neuron?

    I. ATP
    II. A concentration gradient
    III. A net negative charge in the axonal interior

    A. II only
    B. I and II only
    C. II and III only
    D. I, II and III

4. Which of the following is NOT generally a characteristic of axons?

    A. Presence of protein-synthesizing machinery
    B. Abundance of microtubules and actin filaments
    C. Presence of ion channels in the plasma membrane
    D. Ability to transmit action potentials in one direction only

5. Each of the following conclusions can be drawn from the experiment EXCEPT:

    A. Artificial establishment of concentration gradients opposite those found in nature can reverse the polarity of the action potential.
    B. The plasma membrane of an axon at rest is permeable to K^+.
    C. The concentration gradient of K^+ determines the resting potential.
    D. Reducing the concentration of extracellular sodium does not necessarily alter the resting membrane potential.

6. In order to achieve repolarization during the action potential, which of the following will occur in the squid axon?

    A. Na^+ and K^+ channels must close.
    B. Na^+ channels must close, and K^+ channels must open.
    C. Na^+ channels must open, and K^+ channels must close.
    D. Na^+ and K^+ channels must open.

Passage 43 (Questions 1-6)

Generalized anxiety disorder (GAD) is characterized by excessive, uncontrollable, and often irrational worry about normal life events that is disproportionate to the actual source of worry. Severe GAD may interfere with the activities of daily life; people afflicted with GAD often catastrophise, anticipate a possible disaster, and are overly anxious about matters such as health, money, death, or work difficulties. Most patients with GAD state that the physical, not mental, symptoms of the disease are the most debilitating; these include excessive fatigue, leg/hand shaking and wringing, chronic headaches, nausea and anorexia, muscle tension, difficulty swallowing due to esophageal spasm, excessive sweating, and insomnia. Approximately 6.8 million American adults experience GAD.

Much research has been done recently to uncover the scientific basis of GAD and other mental diseases. Some research focuses on changes in the amygdala, sometimes referred to as the "fear center" of the brain. The amygdala regulates fear, memory, and emotion and coordinates these experiences with heart rate, blood pressure, and other physical responses to stressful events. Some evidence suggests that in people with anxiety disorders, the amygdala is highly sensitive to novel or unfamiliar situations and reacts with a high stress response. Hundreds of other studies suggest that an imbalance of neurotransmitters contribute to anxiety disorders, specifically γ-aminobutyric acid (GABA), serotonin, dopamine, and epinephrine. As many as 40% of patients with GAD have close relatives with the disorder.

GABA is an inhibitor of neurons both pre and post-synaptically. Once GABA is bound to its receptor, ion channels open that allow K^+ to exit the cell while Cl^- enters the cell. There are three types of GABA receptors; types A, B, and C. Receptor types A and C are direct ligand-gated ion channels, whereas receptor type B utilizes G-protein coupling. During fetal neural development, GABA shows both paracrine and autocrine properties. It has the molecular formula $C_4H_9NO_2$ with the chemical structure of an amino acid, and is normally found in its zwitterion form. Low levels of either GABA or GABA receptors have been linked to panic disorders, and prolonged, unrelenting baseline stress has been linked to a decrease in GABA levels. Without enough GABA, the fear centers of the brain are not inhibited sufficiently and panic attacks result. Many drugs have been shown to have GABA-agonistic effects such as benzodiazepines, thus these drugs have anti-anxiety properties.

Serotonin (5-HT) is another important neurotransmitter in the regulation of anxiety. 5-HT is a monoamine neurotransmitter derived from tryptophan. It is made in both CNS neurons and enterochromaffin cells of the GI tract. 5-HT's effects were first noted as a potent vasoconstrictor in the early 1950s. Now, however, it is known that serotonin plays an important CNS role as a neurotransmitter in the modulation of anger, aggression, body temperature, mood, sleep, human sexuality, appetite, and metabolism, as well as stimulating vomiting. Neurons in the raphe nuclei surrounding the brainstem are responsible for the production of CNS serotonin that is eventually shuttled to effector centers of the brain (such as the amygdala and hypothalamus). Individuals deficient in 5-HT are found to have high levels of depression and anxiety symptoms. Drugs such as cocaine, MDMA (ecstasy), tricyclic antidepressants, and selective serotonin reuptake inhibitors (SSRIs) have been shown to prolong the effects of 5-HT. SSRIs inhibit the reuptake of 5-HT into the presynaptic cell, increasing levels of 5-HT within the synaptic cleft.

1. Which of the following best describes the state of a cell shortly after GABA is bound?

   A. Depolarized
   B. At rest potential
   C. Hyperpolarized
   D. At threshold

2. Which of the following is the best example of paracrine function?

   A. Testosterone, secreted from the testes, acts to stimulate growth events, such as muscle growth.
   B. Testosterone, secreted from the testes, acts to stimulate spermatogenesis in seminiferous tubules.
   C. An activated T cell is induced to mature by binding to a peptide:MHC complex on an antigen presenting cell. Upon activation, "low affinity" IL-2 receptors are replaced by "high affinity" IL-2 receptors. The same T cell then releases IL-2 which binds to its own new IL-2 receptors, causing self-stimulation and ultimately a monoclonal population of T cells.
   D. Chief cells of the stomach release pepsinogen that will eventually lead to protein breakdown.

3. Which of the following is the molecular structure of GABA?

A.

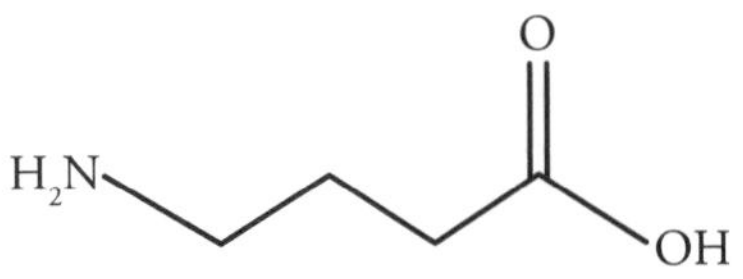

B.

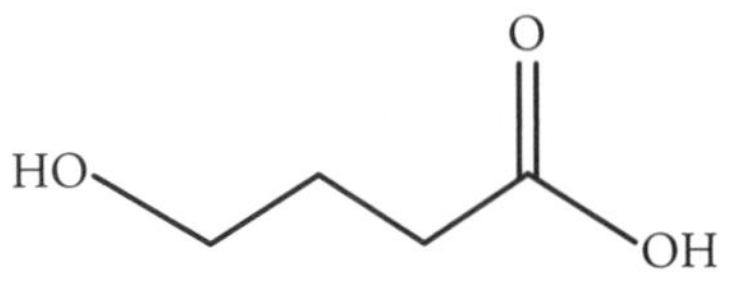

C.

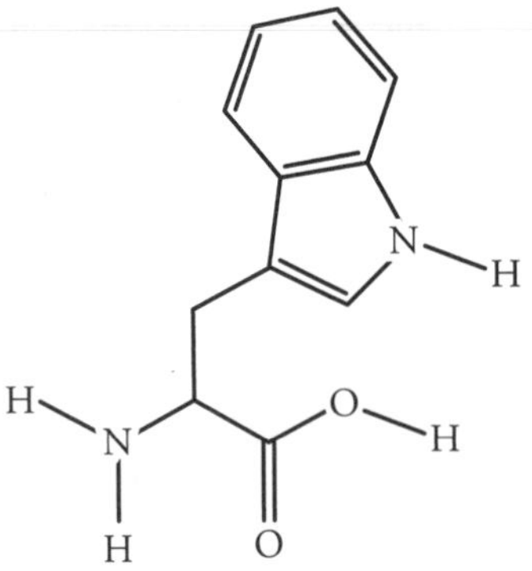

D.

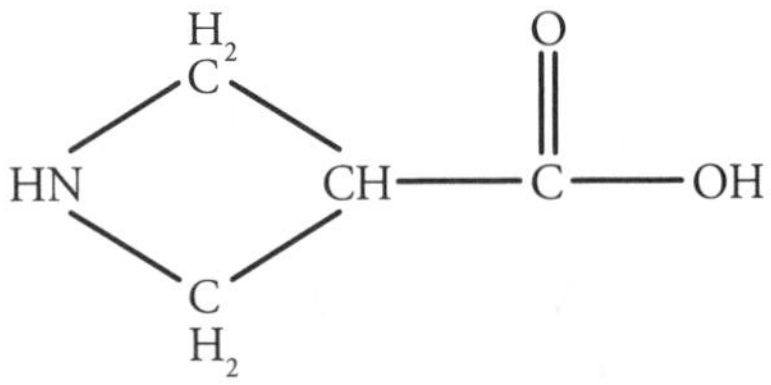

4. Based on the passage above, which of the following drugs is likely a potent anti-vomiting medication?

   A. SSRIs
   B. GABA antagonists
   C. 5-HT receptor inhibitors
   D. Cocaine

5. Which of the following would most likely NOT be seen in an individual having a panic attack?

   A. Bronchodilation
   B. Decreased oral secretions
   C. Vasoconstriction of cutaneous vessels
   D. Pupillary constriction

6. Which of the following drugs produce a similar end result on their target neurotransmitters as SSRIs?

   A. Dopamine
   B. Acetylcholinesterase inhibitors
   C. Monoamine oxidase
   D. Epinephrine

_____

Passage 44 (Questions 1-6)

Learning is one of the most complex functions of the central nervous system. There are two major categories of learning: associative and nonassociative.

Associative learning is a complex process in which a relationship between two or more stimuli is established. The association between (among) stimuli may then influence behavior. For example, the classic experiments of Pavlov showed that the association of a sound with feeding was "learned," so that feeding behavior was elicited by the sound, whether or not the food was present.

Nonassociative learning is a simpler form, not requiring the formation of a predictive relationship between stimuli. Habituation is a type of nonassociative learning that involves a decrease in sensitivity or attention after repeated stimuli. For example, an individual will initially attend to a novel sound, but after hearing the sound repeatedly without any relevant association, this individual will learn not to respond to the sound. Another type of nonassociative learning is sensitization, in which the individual responds to a lesser stimulus than previously experienced. This may occur when the earlier stimulus has been accompanied by a noxious event (pain, for example).

The simple nervous system of the sea snail *Aplysia* provides a model system for the physiological study of nonassociative learning. The neural circuit of the gill- withdrawal reflex demonstrates the neural plasticity that underlies both habituation and sensitization. This circuit is a simple reflex arc in which a sensory neuron from the skin synapses with a motor neuron to the gill. A branch of the sensory neuron also synapses with an excitatory interneuron.

Electrophysiological studies have shown that habituation of the gill-withdrawal reflex to repeated touching occurs at the presynaptic terminals. Repetitive firing of action potentials in the sensory neuron leads to a reduction of the number of functional Ca^{2+} channels in the terminal membrane. The decreased Ca^{2+} influx for subsequent action potentials causes fewer synaptic vesicles to release neurotransmitter which they would do by fusing with the presynaptic cell membrane.

Sensitization involves a secondary presynaptic serotonergic input. Binding of serotonin to the presynaptic terminal results in a series of biochemical events that alter the K^+ channel in such a way as to reduce the repolarizing K^+ current during the action potential. Thus, an action potential of longer duration results, with more neurotransmitter released per spike.

1. When kittens are raised from birth with one eye sutured closed, the neural pathways leading from the optic nerve to the visual cortex show continued synapse formation only on the side contralateral to the active eye. This is an example of:

   A. associative learning.
   B. stimulus-driven neural development.
   C. habituation.
   D. sensitization.

2. Which of the following is the most critical event in repolarizing the neuron back to the resting membrane potential?

   A. All-or-none activation of Na^+ channels
   B. Inactivation of Na^+ channels
   C. Increasing K^+ current
   D. Increasing Ca^{2+} influx

3. Assume that the gill-withdrawal reflex in *Aplysia* is accomplished by a sensory neuron directly contacting a motor neuron, causing contraction of muscles attached to the gill. This is analogous to what process in humans?

   A. The inhibition of contraction of the hamstring muscles which occurs when the knee-jerk reflex is elicited
   B. The contraction of the quadriceps muscle which occurs when the knee-jerk reflex is elicited
   C. The contraction of arm muscles in order to scratch an itch
   D. Running away from a fearful situation

4. Unlike the gill-withdrawal reflex arc in *Aplysia*, the knee-jerk reflex in humans includes a polysynaptic element in which an inhibitory interneuron synapses with the motor neuron to the antagonistic muscle. Which of the following best describes the function of this inhibitory element of the knee-jerk reflex?

   A. It relaxes the antagonistic hamstring muscle to facilitate the knee-jerk movement.
   B. It inhibits stretch receptors in both muscle groups to minimize further reflexes.
   C. It increases tone of the antagonistic muscle to provide support after the reflex.
   D. A single interneuronal synapse is not functionally significant.

5. Synaptic transmission between two neurons requires several important events. Which of the following is (are) common to such synaptic processes, regardless of the neurotransmitter released?

   I. Synaptic vesicles fuse with the presynaptic membrane to release neurotransmitter.
   II. The receptor on the postsynaptic membrane is also an enzyme that degrades the neurotransmitter.
   III. The receptor–ligand interaction on the postsynaptic membrane produces an action potential at the site of this interaction.

   A. I only
   B. II only
   C. I and III only
   D. II and III only

6. If we can generalize from *Aplysia* studies, serotonin in humans may:

   A. bind to postsynaptic neurotransmitter receptors.
   B. alter the strength of response to other neuro-transmitters.
   C. increase the speed at which action potentials propagate along an axon.
   D. increase the rate of presynaptic repolarization.

Passage 45 (Questions 1-6)

Vision is the transduction of light energy into information that the brain integrates to form perceptions. The transduction process occurs in the retina, where photoreceptor cells respond to incident light by decreasing their steady release of neurotransmitter.

The human retina contains two types of photoreceptors: rods and cones. Rods are the most prevalent type. They contain the pigment rhodopsin and are responsible for black-and-white vision. Rods are sensitive transducers and can further adapt to dark conditions to become even more sensitive to very low light intensities. Cones are responsible for color vision. Each cone contains one of three pigments, with greatest sensitivity either in the blue, green, or red region of the visible spectrum. Cones also mediate high-acuity vision and are responsible for much of the vision in daylight.

The photoreceptor cells synapse with bipolar cells (neurons). These are interconnected by a complex network of inhibitory interneurons. The bipolar cells synapse with ganglion cells, which send axons toward the visual cortex of the brain via the optic nerve.

The response of photoreceptors to light can be measured using a microelectrode. Figure 1 shows schematically how a rod cell's voltage can be measured. With a rod cell bathed in its normal medium (vitreous humor) in the dark, the resting membrane potential is –40 mV. As the rod is stimulated by varying intensities of white light, the membrane potential shifts transiently to more negative values; that is, the membrane hyperpolarizes. This hyperpolarization is known as a generator potential. The following experiments were designed to characterize photoreceptors.

Experiment 1:

A rod was stimulated and its responses measured. Figure 2 shows the hyperpolarizations resulting from two light intensities (two separate stimuli are depicted on the same graph). Figure 3 is a plot of intensity versus hyperpolarization (ΔmV).

Experiment 2:

The vitreous humor contains a higher concentration of Na^+ than the rod cytoplasm. When the Na^+ is removed from the bathing medium, the resting membrane potential changes to about –65 mV and remains steady, even during stimulation by light.

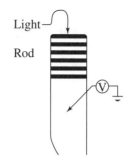

Figure 1

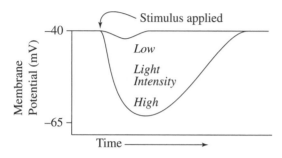

Figure 2

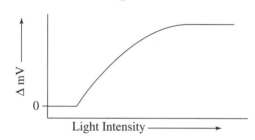

Figure 3

1. When an individual moves from bright daylight into a dimly lit room, her vision will steadily improve over the next several minutes. The process underlying this gradual improvement of vision most likely includes:

    A. pupil dilation.
    B. lens flattening.
    C. photochemical adaptation of rods.
    D. increased excitability of cones.

2. A region of the retina that is irradiated with bright light will inhibit the activity of the surrounding regions through interactions among neuronal cells in the retina. This "surround inhibition" will:

    A. enhance contrast of the image.
    B. improve peripheral vision.
    C. increase cone sensitivity in dim light.
    D. increase the sensitivity of the inhibited region.

3. With the eyes closed, mechanical pressure slowly applied to the side of the eye will stimulate retinal photoreceptors. The sensation thus created will be:

    A. severe pain.
    B. visible light.
    C. altered balance.
    D. no sensation will occur.

4. One can infer from Experiment 2 that the mechanism of light-evoked hyperpolarization is described by which of the following?

    A. Rod cytoplasm quickly transitions from a solution to a gel.
    B. Opening of Na^+ channels in the rod cell membrane increases inward Na^+ current.
    C. Opening of K^+ channels in the rod cell membrane increases outward K^+ current.
    D. Closing Na^+ channels in the rod cell decreases sodium influx.

5. The generator potentials described in the passage are DIFFERENT from neuronal action potentials in that:

    A. only changes in K^+ permeability are involved in the hyperpolarization.
    B. the magnitude of the hyperpolarization is related to the stimulus strength.
    C. they involve changes in the movement of ions across a membrane.
    D. the duration of the hyperpolarization is longer than the stimulus.

6. From Figure 3, one can draw which of the following conclusions about the relationship between the magnitude of the light-evoked hyperpolarization and the intensity of stimulating light?

    I.   They are proportional over a definable range of light intensities.
    II. There is a maximum intensity above which no further increase in response is possible.
    III. They are logarithmically proportional at lower light intensities.

    A. I only
    B. II only
    C. I and II only
    D. II and III only

Passage 46 (Questions 1-6)

The wall of the human eye is composed of three layers of tissue, an outer layer of tough connective tissue, a middle layer of darkly pigmented vascular tissue, and an inner layer of neural tissue. The outer layer is subdivided into the *sclera*, the white portion, and the *cornea*, the clear portion. The inner layer is more commonly known as the *retina* and contains several types of cells.

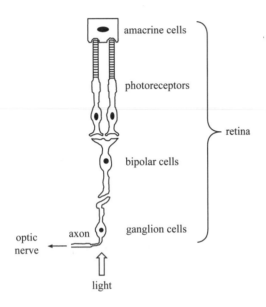

Figure 1 Retina structure

The photoreceptors of the retina include rods and cones which respond to light under different circumstances. Rods are more sensitive to light but cannot distinguish color; cones are less sensitive to light overall, but can respond to different wavelengths. Response to light involves visual pigments, which in all cases consist of a light-absorbing molecule called *retinal* (derived from vitamin A) bound to a protein called *opsin*. The type of opsin in the visual pigment determines the wavelength specificity of the retinal. The specific visual pigment in rod cells is called rhodopsin.

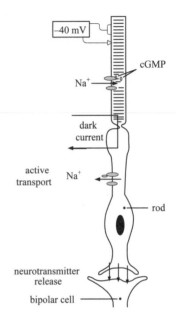

Figure 2 The two forms of retinal

In the absence of light, Na^+ channels in the membranes of rod cells are kept open by cGMP. The conformational change in retinal upon light absorption causes changes in opsin as well; this triggers a pathway by which phosphodiesterase (PDE) is activated. Active PDE converts cGMP to GMP, causing it to dissociate from the Na^+ channel and the channel to close. Until retinal regains its bent shape (helped by enzymes), the rod is unable to respond further to light.

Figure 3 Rod cell in darkness

Visual defects can be caused by abnormal visual pigments or by misshapen eyeballs; for example, *myopia* (nearsightedness) is due to an eyeball that is too long, causing light rays from distant objects to focus in front of the retina so the image appears blurry.

1. Which of the following is NOT a possible explanation for why a person becomes temporarily blind upon walking into a dark movie theater on a sunny day?

   A. The retinal in rod cells has not yet been converted to the 11-*cis* form.
   B. The rod cells are already depolarized.
   C. The cone cells require higher intensity light to be stimulated.
   D. Flow of Na^+ into the rod cells has stopped.

2. At rest, rod cells continuously release neurotransmitter onto the bipolar cells. However, upon stimulation by light, neurotransmitter release from the rod is stopped and the bipolar cell fires an action potential. Which of the following could best explain this?

  A. Both rods and bipolar cells are depolarized at rest.
  B. The neurotransmitter opens Na^+ channels in the bipolar cell.
  C. The neurotransmitter inhibits the bipolar cell.
  D. Light closes Na^+ channels in the bipolar cell.

3. In which other process could PDE be involved?

  A. Protein synthesis
  B. Nucleic acid synthesis
  C. Protein digestion
  D. Nucleic acid digestion

4. Vitamin A deficiency leads to a decrease in the ability to see in dim light. Poor night vision can be corrected by supplementation with this vitamin. Could supplementation with vitamin A also help correct the blurriness due to myopia?

  A. No, myopic blurriness is not due to vitamin A deficiency.
  B. No, vitamin A only helps synthesize rhodopsin and would have no effect on cones.
  C. Yes, increased retinal synthesis would increase sharpness of vision.
  D. Yes, myopic patients can see better in bright light.

5. The middle layer of the eyeball wall most likely contains:

  A. bipolar cells.
  B. photoreceptors.
  C. blood vessels.
  D. collagen fibers.

6. Which of the following would occur when rod cells are stimulated by light?

  I. cGMP levels decline.
  II. All-*trans* retinal is converted to 11-*cis* retinal.
  III. Na^+ enters the rods, and they depolarize.

  A. I only
  B. I and II only
  C. I and III only
  D. II and III only

Passage 47 (Questions 1-6)

The structure of the eye is designed to process images and relay visual stimuli to the brain. In order to transmit a clear image, the eye must first focus the image on the retina. The retina contains photoreceptor cells called rods and cones. The rods and cones have pigment proteins that contain retinal, a derivative of vitamin A. The absorption of a photon of light converts *cis* bonds in retinal to the *trans* configuration. This prompts a series of reactions that alters both the potential of the photoreceptors, and the neurotransmitter release by the cell. These changes are transmitted to the brain via the optic nerve, which travels to the occipital lobe of the brain.

The inability of the eye to focus an image on the retina can cause numerous deficits in vision. One of the most common visual disturbances, myopia, results when the eye focuses the image in front of the retina. Myopia can occur when the eye is too long for its optical power, or if there is too much refraction at the lens. Conversely, having too little refraction at the lens or having an eye that is abnormally short can cause the image to be focused behind the retina. This is called farsightedness, or hyperopia.

In addition, vision can be further impaired by the presence of astigmatism. Astigmatism results from the inability of the eye to focus light at one focal point. Instead, the image is focused at multiple focal points, resulting in an image that is blurred. These focal points can be either behind or in front of the retina (or in the same plane as the retina). The most common form of astigmatism is caused by a misshapen cornea or lens that has two radii. This misshapen eye is commonly described as being shaped like a football instead of a basketball.

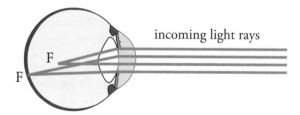

Figure 1 Astigmatism

1. The relay of images to the brain is dependent on the stimulation of which type of receptors?

  A. Nociceptors
  B. Chemoreceptors
  C. Mechanoreceptors
  D. Electromagnetic receptors

2. Which of the following nutritional disturbances is most likely to impair vision?

   A. A vegetarian diet rich in fruits and vegetables, but is lacking in sources of iron.
   B. A deficiency of pancreatic lipase that results in severely impaired fat absorption.
   C. A high protein diet that contains excess vitamin B12.
   D. A deficiency of pancreatic amylase that results in severely impaired carbohydrate digestion.

3. Which of the following best describes the pathway that light takes from the cornea to the retina?

   A. Cornea → anterior chamber → lens → vitreous chamber → retina
   B. Cornea → iris → vitreous chamber → lens → fovea centralis → retina
   C. Cornea → anterior chamber → sclera → vitreous chamber → retina
   D. Cornea → iris → anterior chamber → fovea centralis → vitreous chamber → retina

4. Which of the following best describes how light stimulates rods and cones?

   A. Absorption of a photon opens voltage-gated K^+ channels, hyperpolarizing rods and cones.
   B. Upon absorption of a photon, *trans* bonds in retinal are converted to *cis* bonds, which alters the potential of the photoreceptors in rods and cones.
   C. Absorption of a photon opens voltage-gated Na^+ channels, depolarizing rods and cones.
   D. Upon absorption of a photon, *cis* bonds in retinal are converted to *trans* bonds, which alter the potential of the photoreceptors in rods and cones.

5. Which of the following best describes the location of the focal point in astigmatism?

   A. The focal points are always located behind the retina.
   B. The focal points are always located in front of the retina.
   C. The focal points are always located in the same plane as the retina.
   D. The focal points may be located in front of, behind, or in the same plane as the retina.

6. Which of the following best describes the impact of autonomic nervous system stimulation on the eye?

   A. Sympathetic neurons release acetylcholine which results in constriction of the pupils
   B. Sympathetic neurons release norepinephrine which results in dilation of the pupils.
   C. Parasympathetic neurons release acetylcholine which results in dilation of the pupils
   D. Parasympathetic neurons release norepinephrine which results in constriction of the pupils

Passage 48 (Questions 1-6)

The ear is the site for the transduction of sound waves into nerve impulses that are perceived in the brain. Sound first travels through the outer ear (pinna) and ear canal. The sound waves then cause the tympanic membrane to vibrate. Connected to the tympanic membrane are small bones known as the auditory ossicles, located in the middle ear. They move in response to vibrations of the tympanic membrane, and are connected to the fluid-filled inner ear. Movement of the ossicles causes pressure changes in the inner ear, establishing a traveling wave within a spiral-shaped duct called the cochlea. The cochlea contains hair cells that transduce the traveling wave into nerve impulses. The hair cells rest on the basilar membrane, a thin membrane that runs the length of the cochlea, dividing it into two fluid-filled spaces. The tops of the hair cells are anchored onto an immobile membrane called the tectorial membrane. The basilar membrane moves when a traveling wave passes through the inner ear, creating a shearing force on the hair cells. This causes them to release a neurotransmitter, which causes auditory neurons to fire. The cell bodies of these neurons are located in the spiral ganglion, and their axons travel to the auditory cortex.

The cochlea is arranged in such a way as to permit different sound frequencies to activate different neurons. Low frequencies cause the most vibration in the apical end of the cochlea, the end farthest from the eardrum and ossicles. High frequencies cause vibration only in the basal end, closest to the ossicles. Figure 1 provides a graphical depiction of this.

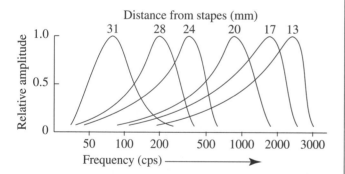

Figure 1

Adapted from *Molecular Biology of the Cell*, by Alberts, et. al., © 1989

1. At what distance from the auditory ossicles would the basilar membrane most strongly respond to sound of frequency 400 cps?

   A. 17 mm
   B. 20 mm
   C. 24 mm
   D. 28 mm

2. In hearing, the sound wave is transduced into a traveling fluid wave in the:

   A. outer ear.
   B. middle ear.
   C. inner ear.
   D. hair cells.

3. Assuming the cochlea to be 100 units long, at what distance from the auditory ossicles would the basilar membrane most strongly respond to sound of frequency 20 Hz, the lowest frequency that the human ear can detect?

   A. 0 units
   B. 20 units
   C. 80 units
   D. 100 units

4. In sensorineural deafness, hearing loss is restricted to a particular frequency range. Which of the following could account for this type of deafness?

   A. Damage to the tympanic membrane
   B. Damage to a group of hair cells
   C. Damage to the auditory ossicles
   D. Blockage of the outer ear canal

5. Place the following statements in the correct sequence in the process of translating a sound wave to a nerve impulse.

   I. Displacement of basilar membrane
   II. Movement of hair cells with respect to the tectorial membrane
   III. Movement of auditory ossicles
   IV. Pressure changes produced within the inner ear

   A. I, III, II, IV
   B. III, I, IV, II
   C. III, IV, I, II
   D. IV, III, I, II

6. Nerve impulses from hair cells traveling to the brain get processed finally in the:

   A. cerebellum.
   B. hypothalamus.
   C. cerebral white matter.
   D. cerebral gray matter.

Passage 49 (Questions 1-6)

The processing of auditory information involves conversion of mechanical waves into electrical signals. The vestibulocochlear nerve, cranial nerve VIII, is responsible for carrying the sound information from the inner ear to the CNS. The cochlea in the inner ear contains a single layer of inner hair cells resting on the basilar membrane within the organ of Corti. The basolateral surface of the hair cells is in contact with the cochlear nerve. When the inner hair cells are depolarized due to the vibration from the waves, glutamate is released at the synaptic junction causing increased number of action potentials in the afferent fibers.

The basilar membrane is tonotopically organized with the base being responsive to high frequency of the travelling sound waves and the apex being responsive to low frequencies. The range of frequencies gradually increases from the base to the apex, starting with 20,000 Hz at the base to 20 Hz at the apex. When a travelling wave of a particular frequency reaches the organ of Corti, it will produce maximum oscillatory response at a specific resonant point that corresponds to that frequency on the basilar membrane. The cochlear nerve transmits information about the frequency (pitch) and the intensity (loudness) of the stimuli to the CNS through selective excitation of the fibers and the impulse frequency within the axons of the fibers.

The cochlear nerve terminates at the cochlear nuclei in the medulla of the brainstem. The auditory information is carried through the brainstem and thalamus before reaching the primary auditory cortex in the temporal lobe. The primary auditory cortex also exhibits tonotopic arrangement, with low to high frequencies represented in rostral to caudal direction.

Sensorineural hearing loss can result from damage to the hair cells in the cochlea, the vestibulocochlear nerve or the cochlear nuclei. If the damage is at the level of cochlea with intact neuronal functioning, cochlear implants can serve to restore certain level of hearing. The implants have an external and an internal part that collects the sound information and converts it into electrical impulses. The impulses are then transmitted to the cochlear nerve through a series of electrodes.

1. The cation channels on the hair cells open due to the mechanical bending of the sterocilia on the hair cells caused by the sound vibrations. This is an example of what type of channel?

   A. Mechanically-gated channel
   B. Ligand-gated channel
   C. Voltage-gated channel
   D. Temperature-gated channel

2. Which of the following can cause sensorineural hearing loss?

    I. Ototoxicity resulting in loss of hair cells
    II. Middle ear infection
    III. Acoustic neuroma (tumor of vestibulocochlear nerve)

    A. I only
    B. II only
    C. I and III only
    D. I, II, and III

3. Will cochlear implants be successful in a patient with a lesion in the cochlear nuclei?

    A. Yes, hearing can be restored as the electrodes bypass the cochlear nuclei through direct transmission of signal to the cochlear nerve.
    B. Yes, hearing can be restored as cochlear nuclei is not involved in the auditory processing.
    C. No, hearing cannot be restored because normal functioning of the neuronal component is necessary for the cochlear implants to transmit the signal.
    D. No, hearing cannot be restored because lesion in the cochlear nuclei results in impairment in the primary auditory cortex.

4. Which one of the following is a function of the ossicles in the middle ear?

    A. Convert the sound waves into neural impulses
    B. Amplify the transmission of the sound vibrations
    C. Decrease sound transmission
    D. Lubricate the middle ear

5. Presbyacusis is loss of hair cells associated with aging. The condition commonly affects the ability to hear high frequency sounds rather than low frequency sounds. Which of the following could explain this observation?

    A. Increased loss of hair cells at the apex of the basilar membrane
    B. High frequency sound waves are harder to transmit than low frequency sound waves
    C. The nerve fibers carrying the high frequency information also undergo atrophy with aging
    D. Increased loss of hair cells at the base of the basilar membrane

6. The vestibulocochlear nerve fibers are bipolar neurons. How do bipolar neurons differ in structure from multipolar neurons?

    A. Bipolar neurons have many dendrites whereas multipolar neurons have only one dendrite.
    B. Bipolar neurons do not contain a soma, unlike multipolar neurons.
    C. Bipolar neurons have one dendrite-like structure whereas multipolar neurons have many dendrites.
    D. Bipolar neurons have many axons whereas multipolar neurons have only one axon.

Passage 50 (Questions 1-6)

The sense of hearing involves the conversion of sound waves to electrical impulses via mechanical intermediates. Sound waves are focused by the outer ear into the ear canal and on to the eardrum. The waves cause the eardrum to vibrate, which results in movements of three ossicles (malleus, incus, and stapes) in the middle ear. These movements are then transmitted to the oval window of the cochlea in the inner ear. The cochlea is filled with fluid called perilymph and also contains multiple tiny hair cells. Movement of the stapes on the cochlea produces waves in the perilymph, causing subsequent movement of the hair cells, which produces action potentials that are transmitted via the eighth cranial nerve to the brainstem.

Sound intensity is measured in decibels (dB). A normal conversation is around 60 dB, while a rock concert is around 120 dB. This is a logarithmic scale, so by being 60 dB greater, the rock concert is actually 10^6 or 1,000,000 times more intense than conversation. Louder sounds will produce greater vibration of the ossicles, which in turn will result in increased frequency and intensity of perilymph waves.

Hearing ability gradually decreases as part of normal aging as the cochlear hair cells die and do not regenerate; the ability to detect high-frequency sounds is the aspect of hearing most affected by this. Multiple studies have shown that exposure to loud sounds accelerates hearing loss. Hair cells are damaged by extremely forceful waves of perilymph and may not be able to heal properly. In addition to decreased auditory acuity, a patient with hearing loss will also complain of *tinnitus*, or ringing in one or both ears. This is a result of the damaged hair cells producing action potentials without external stimulation. Hearing loss can be prevented by wearing protective devices such as earplugs or over-ear-style ear defenders.

An experiment was done to try and determine the extent of hearing loss in ten subjects one hour after attendance of a rock concert. Prior to the concert, all subjects could hear tones at all tested frequencies. After the concert, the following data was obtained:

Subject	Gender	Age (Yrs)	Able to hear 900 Hz tone	Able to hear 7 kHz tone	Able to hear 15 kHz tone
A	M	18	Yes	Yes	Yes
B	M	25	Yes	Yes	Yes
C	M	35	Yes	Yes	No
D	M	45	Yes	No	No
E	M	60	No	No	No
F	F	18	Yes	Yes	Yes
G	F	25	Yes	Yes	Yes
H	F	35	Yes	Yes	Yes
I	F	45	Yes	Yes	No
J	F	60	Yes	No	No

1. Neuromas are nerve tumors that often affect the eighth cranial nerve that can initially manifests as tinnitus (a "ringing" in the ears). Which of the following is the most likely cause of tinnitus in this scenario?

    A. Damaged cochlear hair cells produce spontaneous action potentials without external stimulation.
    B. Normal cochlear hair cells produce spontaneous action potentials without external stimulation.
    C. The tumor produces spontaneous action potentials along the nerve.
    D. The tumor causes spontaneous movement of the cochlear hair cells.

2. The stapes can sometimes become fused to the cochlea. How would this affect hearing ability?

    A. It would improve, because stronger waves in the periplymph are produced.
    B. It would improve, because weaker waves in the perilymph are produced.
    C. It would worsen, because stronger waves in the periplymph are produced.
    D. It would worsen, because weaker waves in the periplymph are produced.

3. An adolescent patient has started working as a landscaper, primarily using a riding lawnmower that produces 90 dB of sound. Based on the information in this passage, would you advise that she wears hearing protection while at work?

    A. Yes, because exposure to loud sounds has been shown to accelerate hearing loss.
    B. No, because hearing loss doesn't start until later in life.
    C. Yes, because the lawnmower produces sound that is 50% greater than normal conversation.
    D. No, because the lawnmower is 1,000 times less intense than a rock concert.

4. Which of the following conclusions can the researchers make based on the data from the experiment?

    I. Older subjects are more adversely affected by loud sounds.
    II. Male subjects are more adversely affected by loud sounds.
    III. The ability to hear low frequency sounds are least affected by exposure to loud sounds.

    A. I only
    B. II only
    C. I and II only
    D. I, II, and III

5. As a result of a recent ear infection, a patient has been diagnosed with a ruptured eardrum. Which of the following offers the best explanation as to why he is having trouble hearing?

    A. Inflammation in the ear canal is blocking sound waves.
    B. The ossicles cannot vibrate properly.
    C. Hair cells were damaged by the loud sound produced when the eardrum ruptured.
    D. The infection damaged the eighth cranial nerve.

6. What type of receptor are the hair cells?

    A. Mechanoreceptor
    B. Baroreceptor
    C. Chemoreceptor
    D. Nociceptor

Passage 51 (Questions 1-6)

Cutaneous receptors are not evenly distributed throughout the body. Body parts for which sensation is a key function are richly endowed with sensory nerve endings and specialized receptors. Correspondingly large areas of sensory (cerebral) cortex are devoted to these parts. The areas of sensory cortex devoted to various areas are arranged in a miniature map of the body, known as the *homunculus* (Figure 1).

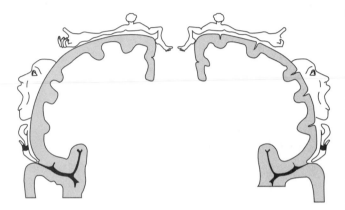

Figure 1

In addition to this topographical organization and functional distribution, the sensory system has other useful features. For example, most sensory cells undergo adaptation, as when our sense of smell adapts to familiar scents until we no longer smell them, or when our touch receptors cease to inform us about our clothing. Some of this adaptation takes place at the level of sensory receptors.

Sensory receptors adapt at varying rates. At one end of this spectrum are cells that adapt almost instantly, known as *phasic*. Those at the other end—cells that essentially never adapt—are called *tonic*. These fire at a continuous rate proportional to the strength of the stimulus. When the stimulus is removed, they will immediately return to the unstimulated state. By contrast, a phasic receptor does not fire at a rate proportional to the stimulus, and it returns to its basal firing rate almost immediately after the onset of stimulation, even while the stimulus continues. In this case, stimulus intensity may be communicated by the number of receptors firing or by the firing of receptors with differing sensitivities. Removal of the stimulus causes phasic cells' firing rates to transiently drop below the basal level, until adaptation to the removal has taken place. See Figure 2.

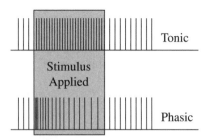

Figure 2

Adapted from W. Keeton and J. Gould, *Biological Science*, © 1986 by W.W. Norton and Company, Inc.

1. The vertical lines in Figure 2 represent:

    A. action potentials.
    B. resting potentials.
    C. the basal firing rate.
    D. the touch of a hot object.

2. In the dermis of mammals, "nets" of nerve fibers surround the bases of hairs. These fibers most likely aid in the detection of:

    A. touch.
    B. pressure.
    C. pain.
    D. heat.

3. Which one of the following has the largest area of the cortex devoted to analysis of its cutaneous sensations?

    A. Thumb
    B. Lips
    C. Neck
    D. Leg

4. Temperature receptors are phasic. A woman places her right hand in hot water and her left hand in cold water for three minutes. Both hands are then placed in lukewarm water. She will feel:

   I. heat with the right hand.
   II. heat with the left hand.
   III. lukewarm temperature with both hands.

   A. I only
   B. II only
   C. III only
   D. I and II only

5. Highly tonic receptor cells are usually found in groups, with nearby tonic receptor cells having different, but slightly overlapping, sensitivity ranges. Regarding this arrangement, then, tonic cells:

   A. respond efficiently over a relatively narrow range of stimulus intensity.
   B. do not change their rate of action-potential firing in response to the magnitude of a stimulus.
   C. provide the best information about the onset and end of stimulation.
   D. are good adaptors.

6. A man's back is touched with two needles at the same time, close together, with equal pressure. He feels only one poke. This is due to:

   A. the failures of phasic receptor cells to detect the second stimulus.
   B. sensory adaptation.
   C. distribution of touch receptors.
   D. a limited range of sensitivities in that area of skin.

Passage 52 (Questions 1-6)
ADVANCED PASSAGE

The giant squid axon has been studied extensively in efforts to understand the mechanism of generation of the resting membrane potential (RMP) and of action potentials. Its large size facilitates stimulation of and recording from the axon, and it is a good model for the mammalian axon.

The RMP in nerve cells is about –70 mV. This potential is created by the activity of the Na^+/K^+ ATPase and the membrane's selective permeability to potassium. Initially the ATPase creates a large concentration gradient for the inward movement of Na^+ and the outward movement of K^+ by pumping 3 Na^+ out and 2 K^+ in for every ATP hydrolyzed to ADP and P_i. Then, because the membrane is fully permeable to potassium but not to sodium, potassium moves passively from inside the cell to outside, down its concentration gradient. Selective permeability derives from the presence of transmembrane ion channels specific for K^+ (these are the K^+ "leak" channels). The exiting K^+ ions carry positive charge out of the cell. The diffusion stops only when the charge imbalance creates a driving force for the movement of positive charge into the cell which outweighs the concentration-gradient-driven K^+ exit. The transmembrane potential at this point is known as the Nernst equilibrium potential for potassium, $EMF(K^+)$, and is defined by the Nernst equation, which applies only when the membrane is permeable to the ion:

$$EMF(i) = (60\,mV) \times \log \frac{[i]_{outside\ the\ cell}}{[i]_{inside\ the\ cell}}$$

where EMF is the electromotive force and i denotes the ion.

In fact, the RMP of –70 mV is smaller (less negative) than that calculated by the Nernst equation for potassium, because the membrane is slightly permeable to sodium (that is, it has a sodium "leak") and for other reasons.

An action potential (AP) is initiated when the membrane is depolarized to about –55 mV. This causes voltage-gated Na^+ channels ("fast channels") to open immediately, allowing Na^+ ions to diffuse passively, that is, to cross the membrane as driven by electrical and concentration gradients. The Na^+ influx further depolarizes the membrane, bringing the transmembrane potential to approximately +35 mV; this massive depolarization is the "spike" portion of an AP. (The potential actually approaches the Nernst potential for sodium, which lies at about +55 mV). The AP spike has three important effects: 1) it causes the fast channels to close; 2) it causes many more K^+ channels to open than are open in the resting state; 3) it causes fast channels down the axon to open. The first two of these effects allow local membrane repolarization and even cause a transient hyperpolarization. The third results in propagation of the AP down the axon.

Adapted from Bullock et al., *The NMS for Independent Study: Physiology*, © 1984 by Harwal Publishing Co.

1. A giant squid axon is placed in a solution identical to the *in vivo* environment. Its RMP is –70 mV. If an excess of K^+ is added to the bathing medium, the RMP will:

   A. become more negative.
   B. become less negative.
   C. not change.
   D. be impossible to predict.

2. In an experiment, all K^+ channels are blocked in a giant squid axon. If the ratio of $[Na^+]_{outside}$ to $[Na^+]_{inside}$ is 10, then what will be the RMP?

   A. –60 mV
   B. 0 mV
   C. 60 mV
   D. It is determined solely by the electrogenicity of the Na^+/K^+ ATPase.

3. A giant squid axon is placed in a solution identical to the *in vivo* environment. Its RMP is –70 mV. If the external concentration of K^+ is decreased, then relative to normal, the depolarization necessary to reach threshold will be:

   A. greater.
   B. smaller.
   C. the same.
   D. the same in magnitude but will have to be applied for a longer period of time.

4. Which of the following correctly characterizes the passive movement of sodium early in an AP?

   I. Electrical forces tend to drive Na^+ out of the cell.
   II. Concentration gradients tend to drive Na^+ into the cell.
   III. Both electrical and concentration-driven forces tend to drive K^+ into the cell.

   A. I only
   B. II only
   C. III only
   D. I and III only

5. The passage states that the actual RMP is less negative than one would predict using the Nernst equation. Why is this?

   I. Many K^+ channels are open.
   II. A few Na^+ channels are open.
   III. The Na^+/K^+ ATPase partially dissipates the RMP.

   A. I only
   B. II only
   C. I and II only
   D. I, II, and III

6. Which of the following accurately describes myelinated axons?

   A. By entirely preventing depolarization in segments of axons, Schwann cells speed action potential conduction.
   B. Myelin inhibits depolarization in axons, and as a result, action potentials may propagate smoothly and more rapidly.
   C. Fast sodium channels are spread evenly down the length of the axon.
   D. Axons transmit information towards the soma.

   _____

Passage 53 (Questions 1-6)
ADVANCED PASSAGE

Guillain-Barré syndrome (GBS) is an acute, remitting neurological illness that results from an immunologic attack on the peripheral nerves. It affects approximately 4000 patients in the United States each year, who present with varying levels of muscular and sensory dysfunction. There are several subtypes of GBS. Some subtypes cause more damage to motor nerves, whereas others predominantly affect sensory nerves. The cause of many cases of GBS was shown to be infiltration of the spinal roots and peripheral nerves by immune cells. The myelin sheath is the specific target structure. Macrophages penetrate the basal lamina surrounding the axon, displace the Schwann cell from the myelin sheath, and then phagocytose the myelin layers. Focal areas of demyelination result in slowed conduction or complete conduction block, depending on the severity of the process. Axon loss also occurs, but it is much less marked. Paralysis has been observed in severe cases.

Researchers have so far been unable to determine exactly why the immune system suddenly becomes sensitized to the myelin sheaths. It has been noted that, when GBS does occur, it is usually seen 2 to 3 weeks after certain common infections. The most common antecedent infection recognized before the onset of GBS is *C. jejuni* enteritis, but it has also been noted to occur after infections with various other pathogens.

The first therapy proved to benefit GBS patients was plasmapheresis, more accurately called plasma exchange. Humoral factors, including antibodies, immune complexes, complement, and other inflammatory mediators of disease are filtered out during plasma exchange. Another treatment of GBS is the infusion of immunoglobulin preparations. Intravenous immunoglobulin (IVIG) is composed of polyspecific immunoglobulin molecules prepared by cold ethanol fractionation of pooled human sera harvested from thousands of donors. IVIG has a broad range of effects on the immune system. For example, IVIG can modulate the immune activity of both CD^{8+} and CD^{4+} T-cells. This has been attributed to the presence of antibodies directed against several T-cell surface molecules such as T-cell receptor, CD4, and MHC.

1. What clinical effect might slowed nerve conduction have?

   A. Inability to move a limb
   B. Hypersensitivity to painful stimuli
   C. Loss of sensation in a limb
   D. Alteration of sensation in a limb

2. A scientist researching GBS hypothesized that some bacteria contain molecules that are very similar to molecules in human myelin. Which of the following would support her hypothesis?

   A. Purified T-cell preparations from patients who suffered from GBS bound to lipopolysaccharide molecules isolated from *C. jejuni*.
   B. Purified antibodies from patients who suffered from GBS bound to lipopolysaccharide molecules isolated from some, but not all, strains of *C. jejuni*.
   C. Purified antibodies from patients who suffered from GBS bound to lipopolysaccharide molecules isolated from all strains of *C. jejuni*.
   D. None of the above information would support her hypothesis.

3. Which of the following suggests why GBS affects the peripheral nervous system?

   A. The blood/brain barrier keeps anti-myelin antibodies from reaching the central nervous system.
   B. The blood/brain barrier keeps bacteria from reaching the central nervous system.
   C. The CNS contains more myelinated neurons than the PNS.
   D. The PNS contains more myelinated neurons than the CNS.

4. A researcher investigating a rat model of GBS noticed that reflex arcs were abnormal in mice with the disease. She discovered that nerves with slowed conduction were unable to excite postsynaptic neurons enough to cause them to fire, even though action potentials were being conducted through the presynaptic neurons. A possible explanation is that sowed action potentials:

   A. depolarize the presynaptic neuron less, which leads to release of fewer neurotransmitter molecules at the synapse and therefore fewer EPSPs.
   B. cause a longer refractory period and the nerves are unable to transmit action potentials.
   C. change the timing of neurotransmitter release in the synapse and affect summation of EPSPs.
   D. cause release of inhibitory neurotransmitters in the synapse.

5. A scientist suggested that the large amount of antibody in IVIG saturates receptors on other immune system molecules, preventing them from destroying myelin. Which of the following would support his hypothesis?

   A. Another researcher shows that after administering IVIG, there is no change in anti-myelin antibody titers.
   B. A study shows that administration of IVIG induces scavenger molecules that destroy excess antibodies.
   C. Another scientist isolates T-cells that attack myelin sheaths from patients with a disease clinically similar to GBS.
   D. Another researcher discovers that IVIG prevents macrophage activation in a disease similar to GBS.

6. The role of potassium in action potential transmission is:

   A. to facilitate release of neurotransmitter molecules at the synaptic cleft.
   B. repolarization of the depolarized neuron.
   C. depolarization of the neuron from resting membrane potential.
   D. temporary, total inhibition of further action potentials.

Passage 54 (Questions 1-6)

The so-called "fight or flight," response in animals occurs as a result of physiological processes that allow an organism to adapt to stressful events. Stressors activate the hypothalamic–pituitary–adrenal axis, commonly known as the stress axis, triggering the release of corticotropin releasing factor (CRF) from the hypothalamus into the anterior pituitary portal vessels.

CRF travels via the bloodstream to the anterior pituitary gland, which is stimulated by CRF to secrete adreno-corticotropic hormone (ACTH). ACTH then induces the release of cortisol from the adrenal cortex. Cortisol is one of the primary hormones involved in the mediation of the stress response.

Cortisol causes an increase in plasma glucose, making extra energy resources available under stressful conditions. Cortisol also increases the rate of protein catabolism, making additional amino acids available for tissue repair. Another function of cortisol is to decrease sensitivity to histamine, thus diminishing pain perception. In addition, cortisol inhibits the tissue inflammatory response, preventing swelling at sites of injury.

The following experiments were conducted to study this chain of events as it occurs in response to both internal and external stresses.

Experiment 1:

Step 1: Experimental animals determined to be in good health were maintained for two weeks under stable laboratory conditions. All external sources of stress were controlled in order to establish baseline levels of hormonal activity.

Step 2: At the end of this period, the experimental group was subjected to a series of gradually increasing electric shocks. Blood was drawn after each stimulus in order to measure cortisol levels.

Results: Cortisol secretion rates increased dramatically in response to electroshock administration. Furthermore, the rate of increase was correlated with the strength and duration of the electrical impulse.

Experiment 2:

Experiment 2 was identical to Experiment 1 except that instead of the administration of electric shocks, animals were subjected to injections of gradually increasing doses of exogenous ACTH. The results paralleled those of Experiment 1. Both groups were observed to exhibit behavioral manifestations of stress including increased heart and respiration rates.

1. High levels of CRF and ACTH would NOT be found in an animal:

   A. receiving an electric shock.
   B. with a wound.
   C. with a cortisol-secreting tumor.
   D. with adrenal glands removed.

2. Which of the following effects is not due to "fight-or-flight" blood levels of cortisol?

   A. Increased resistance to inflammation
   B. Increased supplies of energy
   C. Decreased sensitivity to pain
   D. Decreased response to stress

3. Animals in the second experiment exhibited increased levels of blood lipids because ACTH:

   A. stimulates storage of fats.
   B. increases secretion of cortisol by the adrenal gland.
   C. inhibits the release of cortisol from the adrenal gland.
   D. stimulates the conversion of carbohydrates to fats.

4. Long-term corticosteroids are sometimes used to treat inflammation. This treatment is likely to cause all of the following side effects EXCEPT:

   A. abnormally high blood glucose concentration.
   B. destruction of cellular proteins.
   C. increased destruction of arthritic tissue.
   D. altered fat metabolism.

5. Cortisol is bound to receptor proteins in the cytoplasm of target cells. This binding is necessary for:

   A. the action of cortisol and its receptor in the nucleus.
   B. the action of cortisol at receptor sites in an aqueous environment.
   C. the transport of the hormone molecule through an aqueous environment.
   D. the transport of the hormone molecule through nonpolar liquids.

6. Which of the following can explain the fact that, during administration of one electric shock, cortisol secretion increases and then stabilizes until the stimulus is withdrawn?

   A. Decreased secretion of ACTH is prevented through negative feedback by cortisol.
   B. Increased secretion of ACTH occurs with increasing levels of cortisol.
   C. Electroshock increases the rate of filtrate formation in the kidney.
   D. Electroshock stimulates secretion by the hypothalamus.

Passage 55 (Questions 1-6)

An experiment was conducted to determine the physiologic effects of adrenal corticosteroids in dogs and regulation of these hormones by both the hypophysis (the pituitary) and adrenal gland. The investigator's objective was to study the mechanism by which these organs regulate the release of adrenal corticosteroids. Initial studies had shown that removal of the hypophysis brought about an involution of the adrenal gland.

Dogs similar in age and weight were selected and randomly distributed into three groups. All animals were anesthetized with ether and the following procedures were performed. The hypophysis was removed from one group of dogs (hypophysectomy) and the adrenal gland was removed from a second group (adrenalectomy). A sham operation was performed on the remaining group that was identical to the procedure performed on the other two groups except that no organs were removed.

All animals were housed individually after the operation and conditions were maintained at a high ambient temperature. After a 12-hour recovery period, blood samples were collected to determine plasma levels for various adrenal corticosteroids.

1. Considering the multiplicity of physiologic actions of the adrenal gland, all of the following are examples of its effect, EXCEPT:

    A. regulation of fluid and sodium ions.
    B. increased deposition of glycogen in the liver.
    C. maintenance of normal blood pressure.
    D. regulation of plasma calcium.

2. Which of the following procedures served as control(s) in this experiment?

    I. Sham operation
    II. Adrenalectomy
    III. Hypophysectomy

    A. I only
    B. I and II only
    C. I and III only
    D. II and III only

3. Circulating adrenal corticosteroids bind to specific proteins located:

    A. in the ER of adrenal gland cells.
    B. in the cytoplasm of target cells.
    C. on the cell membrane of target cells.
    D. on the cell membrane of adrenal gland cells.

4. Twelve hours after injection of labeled aldosterone in the adrenalectomized dogs, radioactivity would most likely appear in the:

    A. heart.
    B. kidney.
    C. brain.
    D. adrenal gland.

5. Following adrenalectomy in Group 2 dogs, would there be a rapid rise of ACTH in the blood?

    A. Yes, because of the absence of feedback inhibition.
    B. Yes, because the hypophysis takes over by sending a message to the hypothalamus.
    C. No, because removal of the adrenal gland leads to a decrease in plasma ACTH.
    D. No, because ACTH must always be stimulated by the products of the adrenal gland.

6. Consider an experiment in which normal chimpanzees are injected with extract from the anterior pituitary gland. Which of the following probably would NOT be observed?

    A. Increased production of aldosterone
    B. Increased blood levels of glucocorticoids
    C. Decreased secretion of ACTH by the pituitary
    D. Increased secretion of epinephrine and norepinephrine.

Passage 56 (Questions 1-6)

The term *hypocalcemia* refers to abnormally low levels of calcium in the blood. In humans the condition is known to be associated with kidney failure, convulsions, and tetany of skeletal muscle. The following experiment was designed to investigate the effects of low calcium levels on organ dysfunction.

In a laboratory experiment, the liver, ovary, and parathyroid were excised from a rabbit, and each organ was ground, pulverized and homogenized with salt solution. Three living rabbits were then chosen, and each was given a series of injections of an extract from one of the three homogenized organs. Each series involved three injections of increasing dose. A fourth rabbit was given a series of injections of salt solution. Each rabbit was then tested for blood levels of calcium and phosphate ion.

A fifth rabbit was given a series of injections with parathyroid hormone (PTH), and antibody assays were obtained to determine blood levels of two substances: aldosterone and another substance (Hormone X), known to be involved in calcium metabolism. Measurements of aldosterone and Hormone X were also taken for Rabbit #4.

The results of these procedures are shown in Table 1.

	Extract	Amount Injected	Calcium concentration	Phosphate concentration	Hormone X concentration (mg/ml)	Aldosterone (mg/ml)
RABBIT #1	Liver	5	2	15		
	Liver	10	3	14		
	Liver	20	4	12		
RABBIT #2	Ovary	5	2	12		
	Ovary	10	2	15		
	Ovary	20	2	15		
RABBIT #3	Parathyroid	5	8	12		
	Parathyroid	10	10	6		
	Parathyroid	20	15	2		
RABBIT #4	Salt Sol.	5	2	15	1,000	400
	Salt Sol.	10	2	15	1,000	400
	Salt Sol.	20	3	15	1,000	420
RABBIT #5	Parathyroid	5	8	12	1,200	390
	Parathyroid	10	10	6	1,200	395
	Parathyroid	20	15	2	9,800	410

Table 1

1. Which of the following observations would best explain the convulsions induced by hypocalcemia?

   A. Hypocalcemia increases parathyroid hormone secretion.
   B. Skeletal muscle requires calcium to contract.
   C. Decreased plasma calcium levels increase neuronal membrane permeability to sodium.
   D. Hormone X is secreted in response to low extracellular calcium.

2. Which laboratory procedure(s) served as control(s) in these experiments?

   I. No injection
   II. Injection of saline
   III. Measurement of Hormone X

   A. I only
   B. II only
   C. I and III only
   D. II and III only

3. Based on the data presented in Table 1, Hormone X could be:

   A. L-thyroxine.
   B. calmodulin.
   C. calcitonin.
   D. thyroglobulin.

4. Would an individual without a parathyroid gland be expected to have difficulty breathing?

   A. Yes, because skeletal muscle requires calcium influx into cells during each action potential.
   B. Yes, because decreased calcium induces convulsions and tetany.
   C. No, because the individual would probably have enhanced kidney function.
   D. No, because respiration is influenced primarily by blood concentrations of oxygen and carbon dioxide.

5. The results of the experiments would support the conclusion that the parathyroid gland secretes a substance that:

   A. increases plasma levels of calcium, and decreases plasma levels of phosphate and aldosterone.
   B. decreases calcium levels in the ovary, decreases plasma levels of phosphate, and increases plasma levels of Hormone X.
   C. increases plasma levels of calcium and Hormone X, and decreases plasma levels of phosphate.
   D. decreases plasma levels of calcium and phosphate, and increases plasma levels of Hormone X.

6. An evaluation of Table 1 would justify a researcher in undertaking further research to confirm which of the following hypotheses?

   A. The liver decreases calcium concentration, and calcium stimulates the production of parathyroid hormone.
   B. The liver increases calcium concentration, and calcium inhibits the production of parathyroid hormone.
   C. Parathyroid hormone decreases calcium concentration, and calcium inhibits the production of Hormone X.
   D. Parathyroid hormone increases calcium concentration, and calcium stimulates the production of Hormone X.

Passage 57 (Questions 1-6)

Although Harvey Cushing originally described a pituitary adenoma as the etiologic agent of Cushing's disease, any disease process that causes an overproduction of cortisol is now commonly referred to as "Cushing's syndrome." In a healthy human, three glands control the production of cortisol: the hypothalamus, the pituitary, and the adrenal cortex. The glands themselves are controlled by a negative-feedback loop (Figure 1). A disease process in any one of these areas can lead to the overproduction or underproduction of cortisol. For instance, some pituitary tumors fail to respond to cortisol's negative feedback. Additionally, certain cancers (lung, for example) may produce adrenocorticotropic hormone (ACTH), the same hormone that is released by the pituitary gland, causing the adrenal cortex to grow and to produce an excessive amount of cortisol. However, the most common cause of Cushing's syndrome is iatrogenic, or physician-induced. Iatrogenic Cushing's syndrome results from aggressive treatment of other disease processes such as chronic inflammation with corticosteroids.

Cortisol excess leads to characteristic "Cushingoid" features. These include thin arms and legs, poor wound healing, thin skin, easy bruising, a prominent abdomen with striae (red stripes), a large fat pad on the back known as a "buffalo hump," and a bloated face ("moon face").

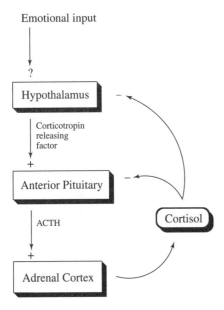

Figure 1 The hypothalamic site for corticotropin releasing factor (CRF) release consists of neurons that release hormones into the hypophysial portal veins, fed by the superior hypophysial artery. CRF in these portal veins leads to pituitary release of ACTH, which in turn causes the release of cortisol and enlargement of the adrenal cortex. Cortisol then provides negative feedback via the systemic vascular supply.

1. A patient with a large hump on the back, red stripes on the abdomen, and elevated laboratory cortisol levels would lead you to first suspect:

    A. that the patient is taking corticosteroids prescribed by another doctor.
    B. hypersecretion of ACTH by the adrenals.
    C. chronic inflammation.
    D. an infection that had led to the destruction of both adrenal glands.

2. ACTH is a medium-sized peptide hormone. When this peptide is incubated with proteolytic enzymes known to break it into fragments, and then injected into rats, they develop a Cushing's-like condition. This implies which of the following?

    A. ACTH is resistant to proteolytic cleavage.
    B. ACTH is a prohormone that is activated by proteolytic cleavage in the gut.
    C. ACTH has a peptide that retains biological activity.
    D. ACTH is a cofactor for an enzyme that is responsible for the release of cortisol.

3. The pituitary adenoma that Cushing originally described may have resulted in cortisol excess because:

    I. it increased the number of ACTH-producing cells.
    II. its cells did not respond to CRF.
    III. its cells did not respond normally to cortisol.

    A. I only
    B. I and III only
    C. II and III only
    D. I, II, and III

4 Corticosteroids are used in the treatment of a variety of autoimmune diseases, including diseases caused by both autoantibody and cell-mediated defects. This implies that steroids inhibit at least:

    A. macrophages.
    B. neutrophils.
    C. B cells.
    D. T cells.

5. Which of the following is true about Figure 1?

   I. Increased CRF and increased cortisol will increase ACTH production.
   II. Increased ACTH will always increase cortisol production.
   III. Increased cortisol will reduce both CRF and ACTH.

   A. I only
   B. I and II only
   C. I and III only
   D. II and III only

6. Based on information in the passage, cortisol exerts its negative feedback via:

   A. increased neural input to the pituitary.
   B. increased releasing hormones.
   C. the superior hypophysial artery.
   D. receptor down-regulation.

Passage 58 (Questions 1-6)

Diabetes mellitus is a syndrome of disordered regulation of the intermediary metabolism of carbohydrates, proteins, and fats. The consequences include hyperglycemia, glucosuria (glucose in the urine), polyuria (abnormally large amounts of urine), polydipsia (abnormally increased thirst), weight loss in spite of polyphagia (increased eating), ketosis (circulating ketone bodies), acidosis, and coma.

These defects are due either to an absence of insulin or to a decreased response to insulin. In the absence of insulin's actions, its principal targets (liver, muscle, and fat) not only fail to appropriately take up glucose but also continue to deliver glucose, amino acids, and/or fatty acids into the bloodstream. The fatty acids are made into ketone bodies by the liver. Ketone bodies (acetone, β-hydroxybutyrate, and acetaldehyde) are normally made only during starvation, when fat breakdown is the only source of fuel. Diabetes thus results in an intracellular nutrient deficiency and an extracellular nutrient excess, a situation that has been called "starvation in the midst of plenty."

Most of the long-term pathology of diabetes results from the extremely elevated blood glucose levels. Proteins and other molecules become glycosylated, disrupting protein structure and function. Diabetics frequently suffer kidney damage, because the excess glucose leads to the destruction of the glomerular basement membrane. Nerve damage results from damage to axons (which is also thought to result from hyperglycemia) and is referred to as "stocking–glove peripheral neuropathy" because the loss of sensation involved is much worse in the hands and feet than in other parts of the body. Another problem caused by elevated glucose levels is the proliferation of certain bacteria which cause disease only infrequently in non-diabetics, such as *Klebsiella*. Finally, vascular defects stemming from direct damage to vessels leads to numerous circulatory problems, including high blood pressure and stroke.

There are two basic types of diabetes mellitus. Type 1 is also known as insulin-dependent diabetes mellitus (IDDM) or juvenile-onset diabetes. Type II is called non-IDDM (NIDDM) or adult-onset diabetes. In IDDM there is no insulin in the blood, while in NIDDM insulin levels are usually normal or high. Treatment of IDDM involves rigorous monitoring of blood glucose and carefully timed insulin injections. NIDDM is usually a less severe disease, but its hyperglycemia is also more difficult to correct. Drugs which lower blood glucose, known as oral hypoglycemics, are given, and sometimes very high doses of insulin are helpful.

1. What is a likely effect of insulin?

   A. To stimulate ketone body production by the liver
   B. To modify the activity of cytoplasmic proteins necessary for the uptake and utilization of glucose
   C. To inhibit glycogen synthesis in the liver
   D. To promote the release of glucose from muscle cells

2. The polyuria in diabetes mellitus is caused most directly by which of the disease's other manifestations?

   A. Peripheral neuropathy
   B. Polyphagia
   C. Hyperglycemia
   D. Glucosuria

3. In the liver, insulin normally acts to promote:

   I. glycogen breakdown.
   II. fatty acid synthesis.
   III. gluconeogenesis.

   A. I only
   B. II only
   C. I and III only
   D. II and III only

4. Which of the following hormones would exacerbate the state of diabetes mellitus?

   I. Insulin
   II. Glucagon
   III. Epinephrine
   IV. Glucocorticoids

   A. I only
   B. II only
   C. III and IV only
   D. II, III, and IV only

5. How might one explain the differences between IDDM and NIDDM?

   A. IDDM is caused by antibodies to glucose, while NIDDM is caused by antibodies to ketone bodies.
   B. IDDM is caused by antibodies to ketone bodies, while NIDDM is caused by antibodies to glucose.
   C. Type I diabetes is caused by antibodies to the β cell, while type II is caused by antibodies to the insulin receptor.
   D. Type I diabetes is caused by antibodies to the insulin receptor, while type II is caused by antibodies to the β cell.

6. Why is the hyperglycemia of IDDM easier to correct than the hyperglycemia of NIDDM?

   A. Oral hypoglycemics used in the treatment of NIDDM are relatively toxic.
   B. Because insulin is a polypeptide, it is easily absorbed from the digestive tract.
   C. The defect responsible for IDDM is easily repaired.
   D. In IDDM, the body's ability to respond to injected insulin is unimpaired.

Passage 59 (Questions 1-5)

Influenza is a contagious, acute respiratory disease, which has caused global epidemics over the past 300 years. The influenza virus envelope is covered with surface spikes of transmembrane glycoproteins of two types: hemagglutinin (H) and neuraminidase (N). The H spike enables the virus to attach itself to susceptible cells, such as those lining the respiratory tract. The N spike, an enzyme, enables the virus to spread from cell to cell. Antibodies to both the H and N spikes distinguish different strains of the influenza virus.

Unlike other viruses, the influenza virus has a segmented genome consisting of eight separate pieces of RNA. The segmentation of the virus allows for genetic recombination or reassortment. The genetic variability of the virus is due to its capacity for genetic reassortment with related strains.

Two types of genetic variation exist in the H and N antigens. Antigenic drift is due to minor genetic changes within a group of similar strains. The other type of genetic variation is antigenic shift. It signifies a radical change in the composition of the H antigen, N antigen, or both. Both antigenic shift and drift have been detected in influenza A viruses, but only antigenic drift has been detected in influenza B viruses.

Despite the proven immunogenicity of specific vaccines, efforts to develop a vaccine that confers immunity have been limited. Although antibodies against the spikes can effectively block infection, their effects have been temporary because the virus with a single mutation of an amino acid can escape neutralization by a monoclonal antibody. The disease continues to defy control by artificial immunization because the vaccine is unable to keep pace with rapid changes in the virus. Vaccines directed at strains that have undergone antigenic drift have been somewhat successful, especially those directed against new strains of the virus. Therefore, the effectiveness of a vaccine depends on the magnitude and the extent of the genetic variation of the viral strain in question.

1. Which of the following would pose the greatest threat to a person NOT infected with the influenza virus?

    A. A substance containing antibodies against the N antigen
    B. A substance containing antibodies against both N and H antigens
    C. A substance containing antibodies against the H antigen alone
    D. A culture containing small amounts of unprocessed influenza virus

2. The same vaccines against influenza virus are NOT used year after year because:

    A. the virus constantly undergoes changes in its antigenic structure.
    B. the virus is less understood than most other microorganisms.
    C. the vaccines only work for individuals who are AB negative.
    D. old vaccines can cause the common cold.

3. Influenza vaccine decreases viral activity by increasing:

    A. levels of acids in the blood.
    B. humoral recognition of double helixes.
    C. immune responses to viral antigens.
    D. translation of viral RNA polymerases.

4. In studying viral synthesis of the H antigen, what findings would a researcher most likely discover?

    A. H antigen contains no amino acids.
    B. mRNA anticodons for the antigen are read backwards.
    C. tRNA must bind to the ribosome before translation can occur.
    D. Viral DNA codes for the synthesis of both proteins and fats.

5. According to the passage, after the influenza virus has invaded respiratory mucosal cells, it must:

    A. activate the H antigen for attachment to other mucosal cells.
    B. express N antigens on its capsid.
    C. undergo rapid *in situ* antigenic shift or drift to provoke immune responses.
    D. recombine the eight RNA fragments to develop immunity to DNA polymerases.

Passage 60 (Questions 1-5)

Blood consists of plasma and cells. The hematocrit is the percent of blood volume that is made up of red blood cells. A hematocrit of 40 indicates that the blood is 40% red blood cells by volume. Red blood cells contain hemoglobin and thus facilitate gas exchange. The red cell count normally correlates with the hematocrit, since it represents the actual number of red blood cells per unit volume of blood.

The viscosity of blood plasma is 1.5 to 2.0 times that of water, but the viscosity of whole blood is considerably greater because the presence of cells increases viscosity. The greater the hematocrit, the more friction there is between successive layers of flowing blood, and this friction largely determines blood viscosity. Therefore, the viscosity of blood increases dramatically as the hematocrit increases. Blood hematocrit is ascertained by centrifuging blood in calibrated tubes such as those shown in Figure 1, which shows hematocrit values for several blood conditions. The calibration allows direct reading of the hematocrit.

Blood flowing in very minute vessels exhibits far less viscosity than it does in large vessels. This difference becomes most apparent when blood vessel diameter falls below 1.5 mm. In vessels as small as capillaries, the viscosity of whole blood is one half that in large vessels. This is probably due to the orderly alignment of the red blood cells as they pass through the capillaries. That is, the red blood cells, instead of moving randomly, line up and move through the capillaries in single file, thus eliminating much of the viscous resistance that occurs within larger vessels.

In small vessels larger than capillaries, the tendency towards low viscosity is probably offset by other factors. The viscosity of blood increases as its velocity decreases. Since the velocity of blood flow in minute vessels is extremely low, often less than 1 mm per second, blood viscosity increases as much as tenfold as the diameter of the vessels decreases. This is presumably caused by adherence of red blood cells to each other and to the vessel walls.

Because of these special effects that occur in the minute vessels of the circulatory system, it has proven impossible to determine the exact manner in which hematocrit affects viscosity in the minute vessels. In these vessels viscosity almost certainly plays its most important role. Because some characteristics of the small vessels tend to cause an increase in viscosity, it is perhaps best at present to simply assume that the overall viscous effects in the small vessels are approximately equivalent to those present in the large vessels.

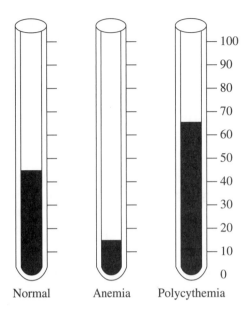

Normal   Anemia   Polycythemia

Figure 1

Figure adapted from Arthur C. Guyton, M.D., *Textbook of Medical Physiology*, Fifth Edition. © 1976 by W. B. Saunders Company.

1. Within the capillaries, blood viscosity tends to be less than it is in larger vessels because:

   A. small vessel size promotes adherence among erythrocytes.
   B. small vessel size promotes alignment of erythrocytes as they pass through the vessel.
   C. large vessel size promotes increased hematocrit.
   D. large vessel size promotes decreased hematocrit.

2. As blood passes from an artery to an arteriole with diameter greater than 1.5 mm, the viscosity:

   A. increases, because pressure decreases.
   B. increases, because pressure increases.
   C. decreases, because velocity decreases.
   D. increases, because velocity decreases.

3. An abnormally low hematocrit would probably be detrimental to a patient's health because it would:

   A. cause the blood to move too rapidly through the capillaries.
   B. impair the blood's ability to deliver oxygen from the lungs to the tissues.
   C. interfere with normal flow of red blood cells.
   D. create an excess of plasma and hence an increased demand for fluid.

4. Patients with polycythemia have a higher than normal hematocrit. This means that in comparison to normal individuals their blood may:

    A. be less viscous.
    B. be deficient in hemoglobin.
    C. consist of more cells by volume.
    D. not be able to carry oxygen adequately.

5. If an accident victim suffers loss of whole blood and receives plasma as replacement, what is his hematologic status?

    A. High hematocrit and low red cell count
    B. High hematocrit and high red cell count
    C. Low hematocrit and high red cell count
    D. Low hematocrit and low red cell count

Passage 61 (Questions 1-6)

Atherosclerosis is one of the leading causes of death in North America. The disease is characterized by the development of plaques within large and medium-sized arteries, resulting in the restriction of blood flow to tissues and organs. Although many of the complex interactions that lead to the pathogenesis of the disease are not very well understood, it has been demonstrated that macrophages infiltrate between the endothelium and smooth muscle tissue surrounding vessels (called the *intima*) where they ingest cholesterol and become *foam cells*. Smooth muscle cells are recruited and migrate to the intima as well; they become fibroblast-like and begin to deposit collagen and lipids extracellularly. Atherosclerotic plaques build up slowly over time, often without noticeable clinical manifestations.

Cardiac muscle has a high metabolic demand, necessitating a rich supply of blood. As a result, formation of an advanced atherosclerotic plaque within a coronary artery can have severe consequences. An initial warning sign is *angina pectoris* (chest pain) noticed during exercise. This exertional ischemic pain (resulting from inadequate blood supply to the heart) is temporary and resolves itself once the activity is ceased and blood supply catches up to the demand. However, should the blood flow to a particular segment of heart tissue be restricted for an extended period, a *myocardial infarction* (death of heart muscle tissue) may occur. Often, these events are the result of a coronary *thrombus* (blood clot) further compromising the flow of blood through atherosclerotic vessels. Essentially, the thrombus is the "straw that breaks the camel's back" when it comes to meeting blood supply demands for myocardial tissue.

Thrombolytic drugs are often utilized in myocardial infarction cases in order to dissolve the thrombus and restore blood flow. However, because of the anti-coagulative effects of these medications there is a risk of internal bleeding and hemorrhagic stroke.

1. Which of the following statements concerning atherosclerosis is true?

    A. People develop atherosclerosis only during excessive exercise.
    B. Plaques often build up in veins, preventing the flow of blood returning to the heart.
    C. It is difficult to diagnose the disease in its early stages.
    D. Thrombolytic drugs can be used to reverse atherosclerosis.

2. Chronic ischemia can lead to the death of large regions of cardiac muscle tissue, leading to an insufficient force of contraction to propel blood through the circulatory system. If blood pressure in the aorta was low, but blood pressure in pulmonary circulation was normal, which region of the heart has likely been affected?

   A. Sinoatrial node
   B. Left ventricle
   C. Right ventricle
   D. Left atrium

3. One would expect cardiac output to increase the most with:

   A. increased levels of antidiuretic hormone and stimulation of the vagus nerve.
   B. increased levels of antidiuretic hormone and inhibition of the vagus nerve.
   C. decreased levels of antidiuretic hormone and stimulation of the vagus nerve.
   D. decreased levels of antidiuretic hormone and inhibition of the vagus nerve.

4. Thrombolytic drugs would NOT be indicated in a patient who has:

   A. a coronary thrombus.
   B. a myocardial infarction.
   C. hemophilia.
   D. elevated levels of platelets.

5. In the interventricular septum, the conduction pathway in the heart splits into a left and right bundle while traveling to the apex of the heart. Which of the following best describes the action potential transmission and muscle contraction of the heart in a patient with a left bundle branch block?

   A. SA node → ventricular contraction → AV node → atrial contraction
   B. SA node → atrial contraction → AV node → ventricles
   C. Atrial contraction → AV node → right ventricular contraction → left ventricular contraction
   D. SA node → atrial contraction → AV node → right ventricular contraction → left ventricular contraction

6. Atherosclerosis can affect the vasculature of many different organs and tissues other than the heart. Ischemic necrosis of peripheral arteries can lead to the death of the tissues supplied by these vessels. This condition, termed *gangrene*, is most similar to:

   A. myocardial infarction.
   B. formation of foam cells.
   C. coronary thrombus.
   D. angina pectoris.

Passage 62 (Questions 1-6)

Shock is a physiological state defined as an imbalance between oxygen delivery and oxygen demand at the cellular level. As tissues become hypoxic, they stop functioning efficiently. Tissue hypoxia leads to organ dysfunction and failure; shock can rapidly progress to multi-organ system failure (MOSF) and death if it is not corrected. Clinically, the most common sign of shock is hypotension (low blood pressure). In a hypotensive state, the body attempts to maintain oxygen delivery by increasing the heart rate. Blood supply to the digestive tract and extremities is reduced to increase blood supply to more vital organs such as the brain or the heart.

Shock can be divided into three categories: *hypovolemic*, caused by a decrease in circulatory volume; *cardiogenic*, due to poor contraction of heart muscle; and *distributive*, in which blood is abnormally distributed throughout the body. Distributive shock can be either *neurogenic*, which can result after injury to the sympathetic nervous system, or *septic*, caused by systemic bacterial infection.

One way of differentiating causes of shock is by comparing hemodynamic variables. A pulmonary artery catheter is useful in this regard. The catheter is threaded into the venous system through a large vein, typically the right internal jugular vein. A balloon is inflated and the catheter passed through the heart and into the pulmonary vasculature. A pressure sensor is used to determine the position of the catheter (Figure 1). The balloon eventually wedges in one of the smaller branches of the pulmonary arteries. At this point, a sensor distal to the balloon is used to measure pressure in the vessel. During diastole, when the mitral valve is open, the sensor can measure the filling pressure of the left ventricle. This pressure, often called the "wedge pressure," is equal to left ventricular end diastolic pressure (LVEDP) or left ventricular preload in a normally compliant ventricle.

With other sensors, the catheter can also measure different variables used to calculate heart function, including cardiac output (CO), pulmonary artery pressures, and central venous pressure (CVP, measured in the right atrium). CVP is a measure of preload of the right ventricle. This determines how much the ventricular muscle is stretched prior to contraction and is one determinant of the force with which the heart will contract.

If the CO and systemic blood pressure gradient (mean arterial pressure) are known, the systemic vascular resistance (SVR) can be calculated from Equation 1:

$$SVR = \frac{Mean\ Arterial\ Pressure}{Cardiac\ Output}$$

Equation 1

Mean arterial pressure (MAP) is the pressure driving blood into the tissues averaged over the entire cardiac cycle. Since diastole lasts about twice as long as systole, the MAP value is weighted toward diastolic pressures. It can be approximated using the following equation, where SP denotes systolic pressure and DP denotes diastolic pressure:

$$MAP = (1/3)(SP + 2 \cdot DP)$$

Equation 2

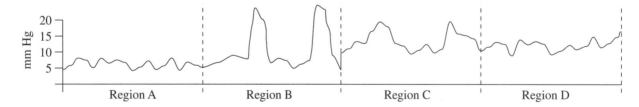

Figure 1 Swan-Ganz tracing

1. One of the treatments for shock is giving intravenous fluid. It has been shown that a liter of *colloid* (an isotonic solution of a high molecular weight substance, such as albumin) is much more effective at raising blood pressure than a liter of *crystalloid* (an isotonic solution of sodium chloride or other salts). Which of the following provides the best explanation for this?

   A. There are more molecules in a crystalloid solution than in a colloid solution, so it has a higher osmolality.
   B. Colloid cannot diffuse out of blood vessels and therefore increases the intravascular osmolarity, helping retain fluid in the blood vessels.
   C. Albumin is a component of blood, but sodium chloride is not.
   D. Colloid contains molecules that activate the sympathetic nervous system and therefore raises blood pressure.

2. In which shock state might one observe low blood pressure and low heart rate?

   I. Hypovolemic
   II. Cardiogenic
   III. Neurogenic

   A. I and II only
   B. II only
   C. III only
   D. I, II, and III

3. Many investigators are looking for better ways to diagnose shock. These would ideally be rapid, inexpensive, and minimally invasive. One such way would be to measure:

   A. hemoglobin O_2 saturation.
   B. central venous pressure.
   C. O_2 content of tissue samples.
   D. blood lactate levels.

4. In patients with septic shock (caused by bacterial infection in the bloodstream), cardiac output increases to several times normal levels. However, the blood pressure is usually low. This could be because:

   A. SVR is low due to activation of the parasympathetic system.
   B. the heart is moving less blood with each beat.
   C. the heart is not beating as rapidly.
   D. SVR is low due to vasodilation caused by inflammatory mediators.

5. Which region of Figure 1 represents the period during which the catheter is in the right ventricle?

   A.

   B.

   C.

   D.

6. According to Equation 1, all of the following would cause an increase in mean arterial pressure *except*:

   A. an increase in stroke volume.
   B. an increase in heart rate with no change in SVR.
   C. a decrease in heart rate and a proportional increase in SVR.
   D. an increase in stroke volume and systemic vasoconstriction.

Passage 63 (Questions 1-6)

The lymphatic circulation is a one-way system that returns interstitial fluid to the bloodstream. It also recovers protein that has leaked through blood capillary walls. The system is composed of a network of interlinked lymphatic capillaries that drain into lymphatic vessels which join to form two lymphatic ducts. These ducts empty into the intersection of the subclavian and internal jugular veins near the heart. The thoracic duct serves all but the right shoulder area and the right side of the head, which are drained by the right lymphatic duct. Most of the tissues that contain blood vessels also contain lymph vessels.

The lymphatic capillaries mark the beginning of the lymphatic system. A cross-sectional representation in Figure 1 shows not only the overlapping endothelial cells, separated by gaps through which interstitial fluid enters into the lymph capillary, but also the valves which facilitate the one-way flow of lymph. It has been shown that the lymph valves create a negative pressure in the interstitial tissue through what is essentially a sucking action, facilitating forward fluid flow into the lymphatic capillary. Fluid is moved forward by the contraction of smooth muscle in the walls of larger lymphatics and of surrounding skeletal muscle.

In injured or infected tissues, damaged cells release proteins that increase the colloid osmotic pressure of the interstitial fluid, favoring filtration. This can overwhelm the lymphatic system, leading to accumulation of fluid. The result is swelling, known as *edema*.

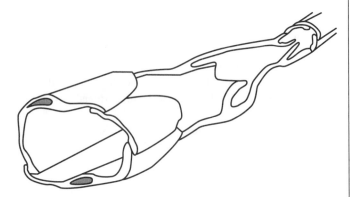

Figure 1 Cross section of a lymphatic capillary

Adapted from *Experimental Biology of the Lymphatic Circulation*, by Miles Johnston, © 1985 by Elsevier. and from *Human Physiology*, by Charles L. Schauf, et al., © 1990 by Times Mirror/Mosby College Publishing.

1. Which one of the following is NOT a significant function of the lymphatic system?

   A. Returning white blood cells to the circulatory system
   B. Returning red blood cells to the circulatory system
   C. Maintaining protein concentrations in the blood
   D. Transporting fats from the digestive tract to the circulatory system

2. Lymph flow is facilitated by:

   I. contraction of skeletal muscle.
   II. contraction of lymphatic smooth muscle.
   III. negative pressure created by valves.

   A. I only
   B. II only
   C. I and III only
   D. I, II, and III

3. Proteins cannot be readily reabsorbed into the blood-stream when they leak out because:

   A. capillaries are completely impermeable to them.
   B. they are positively charged.
   C. concentration and pressure gradients prevent it.
   D. they are degraded in the interstitium.

4. Which of the following would favor edema?

   I. Increased capillary blood pressure
   II. Increased tissue osmotic pressure
   III. Increased numbers of valves in lymphatics

   A. I only
   B. III only
   C. I and II only
   D. I, II, and III

5. Lymph from the left lung returning to the venous blood would pass through at least part of which of the following?

    I. Thoracic duct
    II. Lymphatic capillaries
   III. Right lymphatic duct

    A. I only
    B. II only
    C. III only
    D. I and II only

6. Lymphatic capillaries differ from blood capillaries in that they:

    A. are more muscular.
    B. actively transport proteins.
    C. allow bidirectional flow.
    D. are more permeable to proteins.

Passage 64 (Questions 1-6)

The thymus gland plays a central role in the development of the immune system. Here, T cells mature and "learn" to distinguish self from non-self. This distinction is essential for cell-mediated immune responses such as graft rejection. The following experiments characterize the mechanisms of development of immunological self-tolerance.

Experiment 1a:

The entire pituitary gland was transplanted from one tree-frog larva to another. When both frogs attained adulthood, the transplant was returned to the original donor, and was rejected by the immune system.

Experiment 1b:

The experiment was repeated, but only half the pituitary gland was transplanted. At the end of the experiment, the graft was not rejected.

Experiment 2a:

A rat was thymectomized at birth. It soon became unhealthy and developed a "wasting disease," characterized by weight loss, diarrhea, and poor appearance.

Experiment 2b:

Another thymectomized rat was reared in a sterile environment, and did not develop the disease.

Experiment 2c:

An adult rat was thymectomized and did not develop severe wasting disease. When biomarkers were monitored for several months, a deterioration of cell-mediated immunity became apparent.

Experiment 3:

Adult rat pancreatic islet cells were implanted into another adult rat's thymus gland. The recipient then accepted additional islet cell grafts; that is, it became tolerant to islet cell grafts.

Experiment 4:

Non-identical twin cattle that shared a placenta *in utero* were found to accept skin grafts from one another. Non-identical twins that had separate placentas *in utero* rejected skin grafts from one another.

Adapted from *How the Immune System Learns about Self*, by Boehmer and Kisielow, © 1990 by Boehmer and Kisielow.

1. The results of Experiment 1 support which of the following hypotheses?

    A. The immune system is incapable of reacting against genetically identical tissue.
    B. The immune system must remain immature if immunological self-tolerance is to be maintained.
    C. The organism's immune system is capable of reacting against its own tissue but must be "instructed" not to do so during development.
    D. The organism's immune system cannot accept foreign grafts under any circumstances.

2. Experiment 4 supports the hypothesis that immunological self-tolerance is:

    A. a genetic phenomenon.
    B. passed from mother to offspring.
    C. a characteristic acquired during development.
    D. facilitated by reduced blood flow in a shared placenta.

3. Identical twins who did not share a placenta would be expected to:

    A. reject each other's grafts.
    B. accept each other's grafts.
    C. accept all grafts from non-relatives.
    D. accept grafts from their parents.

4. Rats born without a thymus gland would be expected to:

    A. reject all foreign grafts.
    B. accept all foreign grafts more easily than normal.
    C. accept only grafts from relatives.
    D. reject only grafts from relatives.

5. Which of the following is/are suggested by the passage regarding immune system function?

    I. Recognition of an antigen as self is facilitated by exposure of thymus cells to the antigen.
    II. The immune system is essential for physical growth.
    III. It is possible to induce tolerance to a foreign antigen even in an adult rat.

    A. I only
    B. I and III only
    C. II and III only
    D. I, II, and III

6. The most likely explanation for the result of Experiment 3 is that:

    A. the T cells which recognize foreign islet cell antigens were selectively suppressed or destroyed.
    B. adults are more immunologically flexible than younger animals.
    C. the T cells which recognize islet cell antigens were selectively activated.
    D. the T cell development was nonspecifically blocked.

Passage 65 (Questions 1-6)

In order to carry out essential functions, like the recognition of pathogens or the rejection of xenotissues, the immune system must be able to differentiate "self" tissues from those that are "non-self." In some cases, the immune system is unable to classify "self" and "non-self" tissues correctly, and inaccurately recognizes "self" tissues as foreign. An immune response is then mounted against these tissues, causing a variety of symptoms ranging from inflammation to the complete destruction of one or more tissues. Disorders resulting from these misguided immune responses are called autoimmune diseases.

Many autoimmune diseases are associated with specific human leukocyte antigen (HLA) alleles, called HLA haplotypes. In addition to encoding proteins necessary for the production of complement, HLA genes code for major histocompatibility complexes (MHC) I and II. This unique combination of alleles at each HLA gene is what allows the immune system to recognize cells as either "self" or "non-self." In addition, MHC I and MHC II play a crucial role in immune signaling by presenting foreign peptides to cytotoxic (CD8+) and helper (CD4+) T cells, respectively.

Numerous autoimmune diseases have been associated with specific haplotypes of HLA-DR, a heterodimeric MHC II receptor that is found on the surface of antigen-presenting cells (APCs). The presentation of foreign antigens on HLA-DR elicits a response from T helper (CD4+) cells and results in the formation of antibodies that are specific for the antigen presented on HLA-DR. In the case of autoimmune diseases, the presentation of self-proteins on HLA-DR results in the stimulation of CD4+ cells and the production of antibodies against proteins within an individual's own body.

In an effort to determine which HLA-DR alleles are associated with an increased risk for autoimmune disease development, a researcher conducted an experiment and measured the relative risk (RR) for multiple autoimmune diseases by HLA-DR haplotype. The researcher found that the presence of the HLA-DR3 or HLA-DR4 haplotype increased an individual's RR for numerous autoimmune diseases. The results of the study are presented in Figure 1.

$$RR = \frac{\text{Probability of Disease in individuals with Variant HLA - DR haplotype}}{\text{Probabilty of Disease in individuals with other HLA - DR haplotypes}}$$

Equation 1 Relative Risk

Disease	HLA Allele	Relative Risk
Type 1 Diabetes	HLA-DR3	5
	HLA-DR4	6
	HLA-DR3 + HLA-DR4	15
Autoimmune Hepatitis	HLA-DR3	14
Rheumatoid Arthritis	HLA-DR4	4
Sjögren Syndrome	HLA-DR3	10

Figure 1 Relative Risk and HLA-DR Haplotypes

1. HLA-DR is found on the surface of which of the following cell types:

   I. Macrophages
   II. B cells
   III. Red blood cells

   A. I only
   B. I and II only
   C. III only
   D. I, II, and III

2. An individual with the HLA-DR3 haplotype, who is also lacking the HLA-DR4 haplotype, has the greatest increased risk of which of the following diseases?

   A. Type 1 diabetes
   B. Autoimmune hepatitis
   C. Rheumatoid arthritis
   D. Sjögren syndrome

3. Which of the following cell types interacts directly with MHC I receptors?

   A. Cytotoxic T cells
   B. Plasma B cells
   C. Helper T cells
   D. Memory B cells

4. The probability that an individual who does not have the HLA-DR3 or the HLA-DR4 haplotype will develop type 1 diabetes is 1%. What is the probability that an individual who has both the HLA-DR3 and HLA-DR4 haplotypes will develop type 1 diabetes?

   A. 5%
   B. 6%
   C. 11%
   D. 15%

5. After finding that HLA-DR3 and HLA-DR4 increase the risk of multiple autoimmune disorders, the researcher described in the passage conducted an additional study and found that three non-HLA genes also influence the risk of autoimmune disease development. Which of the following terms best describes this influence of multiple genes on one complex trait?

   A. Pleiotropism
   B. Polygenism
   C. Penetrance
   D. Epistasis

6. Which of the following best describes where T cells are produced and where T cells mature?

   A. T cells are produced in the bone marrow and mature in the thymus.
   B. T cells are produced in the thymus, and mature in the thymus as well.
   C. T cells are produced in the bone marrow and mature in the spleen.
   D. T cells are produced in the lymph nodes and mature in the thymus.

Passage 66 (Questions 1-6)

Malaria is one of the world's oldest known diseases. It involves alternating chills and fever with severe hemolysis (erythrocyte destruction) and liver damage. It is caused by the protozoan parasite *Plasmodium,* which is transmitted by the female *Anopheles* mosquito, which is itself a parasite, requiring a blood meal as a source of protein for egg production. The protist is transmitted from an infected insect to a human host. It completes part of its life cycle in the human, but requires a new *Anopheles* host to complete the cycle. This new host is infected when it bites the infected human. See Figure 1.

A wound the size of a mosquito bite will trigger the primary hemostatic responses which act to constrict blood vessels and seal the wound by platelet aggregation, and also the secondary hemostatic response, coagulation. However, compounds present in mosquito saliva prevent these processes while the parasite is feeding.

Natural selection has made it possible for some individuals to resist malarial infection. A single base-pair change in the gene that codes for hemoglobin results in the substitution of valine for glutamic acid (amino acid #6). Individuals heterozygous for this gene have erythrocytes containing mutant hemoglobin that are resistant to parasitization. However, this hemoglobin tends to clump when the oxygen content of the blood decreases, such as at high altitudes or during strenuous exercise. Erythrocytes then become distorted and sickle-shaped, hence the term *sickle-cell trait*. Individuals homozygous for the defective hemoglobin suffer from *sickle-cell anemia*, in which many sickled red blood cells are destroyed in the spleen.

The course of infection with *Plasmodium* is as follows:

1. Mature sporozoites enter the blood when an infected *Anopheles* mosquito attacks.

2. The sporozoites evade the immune system and migrate to the liver, where they invade hepatocytes. Asexual reproduction occurs and the liver cells are lysed, releasing up to 30,000 merozoites per cell into the bloodstream.

3. Merozoites invade red blood cells and undergo asexual reproduction, eventually lysing the red blood cells and releasing more merozoites.

4. These can then invade more red blood cells. The cycles of chills and fever correspond to the destruction of red blood cells.

5. Some of the merozoites give rise to male and female gametocytes.

6. In order for malaria to be transmitted, a mosquito must bite an infected individual and take the gametocytes up in the blood meal. The *Plasmodium* then completes its life cycle in the mosquito.

7. This begins with fusion of the gametocytes and zygote formation in the gut.

8. & 9. Development proceeds in the gut of the mosquito.

10. Mature sporozoites are released into the body cavity of the mosquito. They migrate to the salivary glands, from where they are released when the mosquito takes her next blood meal.

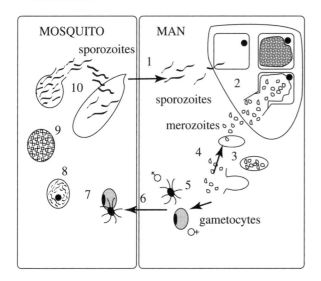

Figure 1 Life cycle of *Plasmodium*

Adapted from: *Malaria: Obstacles and Opportunities*, by Stanley C. Oaks, Jr., Violaine S. Mitchell, Greg W. Pearson and Charles C.J. Carpenter, eds. © 1991 by National Academy Press, Washington, D.C.

1. Platelets do not normally aggregate in the absence of tissue injury because:

   I. platelets are not normally found in plasma.
   II. they are not exposed to compounds present in damaged cells.
   III. circulating T cells prevent aggregation.

   A. I only
   B. II only
   C. I and II only
   D. I, II, and III

2. There are antibiotics which are effective against malaria. Why is this surprising?

   A. Antibiotics are generally not effective on blood-borne diseases.
   B. All strains have developed resistance.
   C. Antibiotics cannot be taken up by cells.
   D. *Plasmodia* are eukaryotes.

3. Malaria can be controlled with drugs such as chloroquine, but it is difficult to cure. What would be the best target for drug therapy for people already sick with malaria?

   A. The sporozoite
   B. The merozoite
   C. The gametocyte
   D. The mosquito

4. What method(s) would be effective in disrupting the cycle of malaria transmission?

   I. Vaccination against the sporozoites
   II. Vaccination against the merozoites
   III. Vaccination against the gametocytes
   IV. Destruction of mosquitoes

   A. I only
   B. IV only
   C. II and IV only
   D. I, II, III, and IV

5. How would the mutation causing sickle-cell anemia affect the characteristics of hemoglobin?

   I. It would change the primary structure.
   II. It would cause abnormal interactions between hemoglobin molecules.
   III. It would change the isoelectric point.

   A. I only
   B. II only
   C. I and III only
   D. I, II, and III

6. If the *Plasmodial* merozoite were viewed as an independent organism, its life cycle would most resemble that of a:

   A. lytic virus.
   B. lysogenic virus.
   C. saprophyte.
   D. predator.

Passage 67 (Questions 1-6)

Modern pregnancy test kits work by detecting the protein human chorionic gonadotropin (hCG) in the urine. The technique used is an immunological assay called the sandwich ELISA (Enzyme Linked Immunosorbent Assay). The manufacture of pregnancy test kits using the ELISA assay requires the production of two different antibodies. The *primary* antibody is produced by injecting the terminal region of hCG into a mouse. Isolation of a white blood cell which is manufacturing an antibody to this region of the hCG molecule and fusion of this cell with a malignant human tumor cell create an immortalized cell that produces large quantities of pure monoclonal mouse anti-hCG.

The *secondary* antibodies are called *conjugated* anti-bodies, because they have enzymes covalently linked to their non-antigen-binding end. The enzymes catalyze a color-producing reaction when a particular substrate is present. The secondary antibodies are generated in rabbits and are capable of binding to different sites on hCG than the primary antibodies.

The test kit is a plastic microtiter well, on which the mouse anti-hCG is immobilized. A small sample of urine is added to the well. If hCG is present in the urine, it will bind to the mouse anti-hCG. Next, the remaining urine is washed away, and the conjugated antibodies are then added. If the hCG/anti-hCG complex is present, the conjugated antibody will "top-off" the "sandwich," that is, it will bind to the hCG molecule at a different site from that already bound by the primary antibody. A second wash is then performed. The three-part complex is visualized when a color change occurs upon the addition of a colorless substrate, which is converted into a colored by-product by the conjugated enzyme.

1. If the second wash in the pregnancy test procedure were eliminated, then:

    A. unbound mouse anti-hCG could be present.
    B. unbound hCG could be present.
    C. the color change would not occur.
    D. conjugated antibodies could be present in the absence of hCG.

2. A lack of color in the microtiter well at the end of a sandwich ELISA assay indicates:

    A. the absence of hCG and the presence of mouse anti-hCG and conjugated antibodies.
    B. the presence of hCG.
    C. the absence of hCG and conjugated antibodies, with mouse anti-hCG present.
    D. that conjugated antibody is bound directly to mouse anti-hCG.

3. Human chorionic gonadotropin is normally NOT:

    A. a protein.
    B. produced during pregnancy.
    C. an antigen.
    D. a hormone.

4. Fibronectin is a protein that has been associated with the onset of premature childbirth, and has been detected in vaginal fluids. What order would be required for the following steps in a sandwich ELISA to detect fibronectin?

    I. Visualizing the enzyme
    II. Trapping the antigen
    III. "Sandwiching" the antigen

    A. I, II, III
    B. II, III, I
    C. III, II, I
    D. II, I, III

5. The antigen-binding site of the mouse anti-hCG is:

    A. a pocket formed by the interaction of the variable regions of a heavy chain and a light chain.
    B. formed by the foldings of the variable regions of the light chains only.
    C. located in the constant region of the heavy and light chains.
    D. in the variable region of either the heavy or the light chain.

6. Which of the following accurately describes the ELISA secondary antibody used in the hCG assay?

   A. It must be made in a different organism from the primary antibody so that the two antibodies will have distinguishable constant regions.
   B. It may be differentiated from the primary antibody by an assay which makes use of fragmented hCG.
   C. It must be bound by the primary antibody in order for the test to work.
   D. It would not be bound by any antibodies if injected into a mouse.

Passage 68 (Questions 1-5)

Cobalamin, more commonly known as vitamin B-12, is essential for many metabolic functions and is not synthesized by humans. Consequently, it must be absorbed efficiently from the diet. The events leading to the absorption of vitamin B-12 are initiated in the stomach where peptic digestion releases dietary cobalamin which then binds to gastric B-12 binding proteins called R-binders. R/B-12 complexes are transported to the duodenum where they are hydrolyzed by pancreatic proteases. The released cobalamin then binds to intrinsic factor (IF) secreted by parietal cells of the stomach. Formation of IF/B-12 complex leads to the absorption of vitamin B-12 in the ileum. The absorbed B-12 is then bound to a transport protein, trans-cobalamin, which delivers it to the liver and other cells of the body.

Most deficiencies in cobalamin are caused not by an insufficient dietary intake, but by a defect in the absorption of the substance. Usually this results from the inadequate production or impaired function of IF. In the disease pernicious anemia, IgG antibodies are present which are specific for the parietal cell. It is assumed that the immune response initiated by these antibodies renders this cell unable to produce IF. There is also evidence that antibodies against IF and the IF/B-12 complex can be formed and produce similar symptoms. Among the many symptoms of pernicious anemia is demyelination of both central and peripheral nerves.

1. According to the passage, one can infer that in the absence of intrinsic factor, cobalamin will:

   A. be absorbed by the blood but not transported to the appropriate cells.
   B. be digested into its constituent amino acids.
   C. not reach the blood.
   D. be attacked by IgG.

2. A patient suffering from pernicious anemia could experience a deficiency in function of all of the following areas of the nervous system EXCEPT:

   A. spinal cord white matter.
   B. sympathetic ganglia.
   C. motor nerve axons of skeletal muscle.
   D. cerebellar white matter.

3. A treatment for pernicious anemia is developed in which antibodies that bind anti-parietal cell IgG are developed and then injected into pernicious anemia patients. The function of these infused antibodies is most likely to:

    A. directly stimulate the parietal cell to produce IF.
    B. bind to and facilitate uptake of IF.
    C. inhibit the patient's own anti-parietal cell antibodies.
    D. prevent dissolution of the IF/B-12 complex.

4. In a normal individual, cobalamin is absorbed within fifteen minutes after it is swallowed. A patient suspected to have pernicious anemia is given radioactive cobalamin orally. In which of the locations would the presence of radioactivity one hour after administration provide the most evidence for this diagnosis?

    A. Digestive tract circulation
    B. The lumen of the large intestine
    C. Ileal epithelial cell cytoplasm
    D. The liver

5. The immune response in pernicious anemia is humoral. The cells that produce these autoantibodies originate from stem cells in the:

    A. bone marrow.
    B. spleen.
    C. thymus.
    D. liver.

Passage 69 (Questions 1-6)
ADVANCED PASSAGE

Immune system cells continuously monitor the contents of the extracellular environment in search of unfamiliar substances. Antigen-presenting cells such as macrophages place fragments of substances they find on the surface of their cell membranes. In addition, all cells in the body display fragments of their own proteins; these fragments are monitored by immune system cells. This is how the immune system detects cancerous cells and cells infected with viruses. A special cell-surface protein complex known as the major histocompatibility complex (MHC) is used to display antigens. Upon encountering foreign antigen bound by MHCs, T cells are activated to protect the host from the antigen's source (usually a bacterium or a virus). The activation process begins when the T cell releases a small amount of calcium into its cytoplasm from intracellular sequestering compartments with a high concentration of the ion.

There are two classes of MHC molecules. Class I presents endogenous protein antigens (made by the cell), and Class II presents exogenous protein antigens (derived from the extracellular environment and internalized by phagocytosis).

Synthesis of all MHC molecules begins with transcription in the nucleus. The RNA coding for MHC polypeptides is spliced, and the resulting mRNA is transported through nuclear pores. In association with special proteins, the mRNA forms ribonucleoprotein molecules and triggers the pores to open. Once outside the nucleus, the mRNA binds to a ribosome, translation begins, and the mRNA, the ribosome, and the nascent polypeptide bind to the endoplasmic reticulum. MHC synthesis is completed here, with MHC polypeptides translocated into the rough ER lumen during translation.

It is inside the ER lumen where the MHC Class I molecule binds a fragment of an endogenous protein. It is not understood how peptide fragments get inside the ER, but it is known that endogenous proteins are constantly monitored by degradation and presentation on Class I MHCs. After some chemical modifications, the peptide–MHC complex is packaged in a vesicle and sent to the Golgi apparatus. From the Golgi lumen, the complex is transported in a vesicle to its destination on the cell surface.

Class II MHCs are sent to the Golgi apparatus without any bound peptide fragment. From the Golgi lumen, they are packaged in vesicles which fuse with endosomes. These contain exogenous proteins obtained from the cell surface by endocytosis and processed into polypeptide fragments. Class II MHC molecules noncovalently bind peptide fragments, and the resulting complexes are expressed on the cell surface when the endosome fuses with the plasma membrane.

Adapted from *Cellular and Molecular Immunology*, by Abul K. Abbas, et al., © 1991 by W. B. Saunders Co.; and from *Molecular Biology of the Cell*, 2nd ed., by Bruce Alberts; © 1989 by Garland Publishing Inc.

1. Cells are infected by a virus and express a cytoplasmic viral antigen. Which of the following describes how the antigen will be presented?

    A. A peptide from the antigen will be expressed on Class I MHC.
    B. A peptide from the antigen will be expressed on Class II MHC.
    C. A peptide from the antigen could be expressed on either class of MHC.
    D. The antigen will evade the immune system and will not be presented.

2. MHC Class II polypeptides enter the rough ER lumen by:

    A. passively diffusing across the ER membrane.
    B. interacting with a signal recognition particle and a signal recognition particle receptor on the ER surface.
    C. being synthesized near regions of ER with large pores.
    D. endocytosis.

3. After T cell activation, the intracellular Ca^{2+} concentration must be restored to its very low resting level. In the absence of ATP, how can Ca^{2+} levels be restored?

    I. An electrochemical gradient causes Ca^{2+} to diffuse into intracellular calcium-sequestering compartments.
    II. Ca^{2+} is actively transported across the inner mitochondrial membrane.
    III. Ca^{2+} can diffuse through a channel in the plasma membrane.

    A. I only
    B. II only
    C. I and II only
    D. II and III only

4. You read in a journal article that the invariant MHC chain is an MHC-related peptide found in cells during MHC synthesis, but not found on the cell surface. The article describes a rat which has the gene for the invariant chain deleted, and reports that endogenous peptides are bound to both classes of MHC in this rat. You infer that the invariant chain:

    A. is a high affinity signal for the transfer of nascent Class I MHC to the ER.
    B. is bound to the peptide-binding region of Class II MHC proteins until they reach the ER.
    C. prevents nascent Class II MHC from binding to the ER.
    D. blocks Class II MHC's peptide-binding region until the MHC leaves the ER lumen.

5. What prevents unspliced mRNA coding for MHC Class I proteins from being translated in the nucleus?

    A. There are no enzymes in the nucleus.
    B. MHC Class I mRNA is passed to the cytoplasm as it is transcribed.
    C. Unspliced RNA lacks the first codon to be translated.
    D. Ribosomes are excluded from the interior of the nucleus.

6. It can be inferred from the passage that:

    A. macrophages do not display antigen using Class I MHC.
    B. macrophages display antigen using Class II MHC.
    C. T cells display antigen using Class II MHC.
    D. B cells do not display antigen.

Passage 70 (Questions 1-6)

After an interval of quiescence during childhood, hypothalamic–pituitary–gonadal activity intensifies in the peripubertal period. The result is increased secretion of gonadal sex steroids, which causes secondary sexual development, fertility, and the pubertal growth spurt (which also requires growth hormone).

The first sign of puberty in the female is an increase in growth. This is accompanied by breast development, which is stimulated by an increase in estrogen levels. Other developmental changes influenced by estrogen include: enlargement of labia minora and majora, dulling of the vaginal mucosa, production of a whitish vaginal secretion prior to menarche, and changes in uterine size and shape. The development of pubic hair is primarily controlled by adrenal and ovarian androgen secretion.

In males, the first sign of normal puberty is an increase in the size of the testes, primarily due to seminiferous tubular development, under the control of follicle stimulating hormone (FSH). The stimulation by luteinizing hormone (LH) of the interstitial cells of Leydig, which secrete androgens, also plays a role in the increase in testicular size. As in females, pubic hair development and other secondary sex characteristics are primarily controlled by adrenal and gonadal androgen secretion. Androgens are also necessary for spermatogenesis.

1. Breast development in females is stimulated by an increase in estrogen secretion. Which of the following hormones must increase in order for this to occur?

    A. Thyroid stimulating hormone (TSH)
    B. Gonadotropin releasing hormone (GnRH)
    C. Prolactin
    D. Progesterone

2. The seminiferous tubules are the site for:

    A. production of sperm.
    B. synthesis of testosterone.
    C. maturation of sperm.
    D. fertilization.

3. The increase in testicular size at puberty is a DIRECT result of the action of:

    I. luteinizing hormone (LH).
    II. follicle stimulating hormone (FSH).
    III. growth hormone (GH).

    A. I only
    B. II only
    C. I and II only
    D. I, II, and III

4. If a young boy had a deficiency of GnRH secretion, what developmental abnormality would occur first?

    A. Failure of the testicles to increase in size
    B. Absence of pubic hair
    C. Failure of the voice to deepen
    D. Diminished or absent growth spurt

5. A tumor was removed from a patient, and its cells were analyzed. A protein was isolated and found to act as a tyrosine kinase, an enzyme which attaches tyrosine residues to exposed hydroxyl groups on other proteins. This tyrosine kinase activity was constant. The same protein was present in normal cells, but tyrosine kinase activity in this case was only observed if intact cells were exposed to growth hormone (GH). Which of the following is most likely to be true?

    A. The protein normally binds GH in the cytoplasm.
    B. The protein is normally controlled by a protein which binds GH at the cell surface.
    C. The protein's tyrosine kinase activity normally limits the effects of GH.
    D. The abnormal constitutive activity of the tyrosine kinase prevented cell division.

6. The hormone that stimulates the production and release of growth hormone is derived from which of the following organs?

    A. Anterior pituitary gland
    B. Posterior pituitary gland
    C. Bone and liver
    D. Hypothalamus

Passage 71 (Questions 1-6)

Some bacteria are pathogens that synthesize toxic substances that give rise to a variety of disease symptoms. For example, certain strains of bacteria cause food poisoning. A common opportunistic organism is *Staphylococcus aureus*, a Gram-positive cocci. *S. aureus* differs from some other bacteria in that it causes illness by producing enterotoxins. The symptoms associated with food poisoning are vomiting and diarrhea.

To identify the organism a test was conducted using the laboratory procedure below:

1. Throat cultures are sampled with lab swabs.

2. Vessels of Robertson's cooked-meat medium containing 7 to 10 mg NaCl were inoculated with the swab contents and incubated overnight.

3. The inoculate is plated on blood agar.

4. The plates are examined to determine if there was partial or complete decolorization of red corpuscles that would indicate red blood cell lysis.

1. *S. aureus* bacteria generally possess the enzymes citrate synthase and pyruvate dehydrogenase. The organism can grow in the presence or absence of free oxygen. *S. aureus* can be classified as:

    I.   an obligate aerobe.
    II. an obligate anaerobe.
    III. a facultative anaerobe.

    A. I only
    B. III only
    C. I and III only
    D. II and III only

2. When pathogens invade tissues, they trigger an inflammatory response which dilates blood vessels. This leads to:

    A. a decrease in body temperature.
    B. a decrease in the number of phagocytic cells.
    C. an increase in oxygen in the capillaries.
    D. an increase in fluids entering the tissues.

3. Based on the symptom of diarrhea, the effect on the digestive system is most likely:

    A. oversecretion of water into the large and small intestine.
    B. lack of water resorption in the stomach.
    C. lack of pancreatic secretion.
    D. lack of parasympathetic stimulation.

4. The delay between ingestion of food and food poisoning would most likely be the result of the time required for:

    A. the bacteria to produce significant levels of enterotoxin.
    B. the bacterial cell walls to lyse.
    C. digestion of the food.
    D. Gram-positive bacteria to reach the stomach.

5. Which of the following enzymes begins the digestion of the carbohydrates in contaminated food?

    A. Pepsin
    B. Trypsin
    C. Lipase
    D. Amylase

6. Which of the following assumptions could justify Steps 3 and 4 of the procedure in searching for *S. aureus*?

    A. *S. aureus* requires blood agar for incubation.
    B. *S. aureus* requires blood agar for reproduction.
    C. *S. aureus* produces an enterotoxin.
    D. *S. aureus* produces hemolysis.

Passage 72 (Questions 1-6)

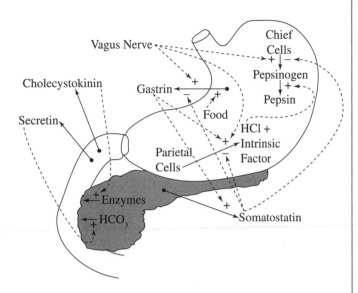

The diagram above displays the complexity of the hormonal and neural regulation of gastrointestinal secretion. It shows the major determinants of gastric and pancreatic secretory activity. Other influences are not shown. For example, the sympathetic nervous system has a generally inhibitory role on both motility and secretion. Cholecystokinin causes the release of bile from the gall bladder. Histamine, released by mast-like cells, binds to H_2 histamine receptors to cause increased parietal and chief cell secretory activity. In fact, the effects of histamine, the parasympathetic nervous system, and gastrin upon the parietal cell are synergistic, meaning that the effect of two of these together is greater than the sum of the individual effects.

Knowledge of these intertwining regulatory mechanisms has facilitated treatment of illnesses such as the duodenal ulcer. Conservative ulcer treatment employs oral antacids. More aggressive treatment has been pursued with vagotomy (sectioning of the vagus nerve). However, this surgical approach has given way to successful pharmacological therapies, involving drugs which block H_2 histamine receptors (cimetidine) or directly inhibit acid secretion (omeprazole).

1. Which of the following does NOT directly stimulate parietal cells to secrete acid?

   A. Gastrin
   B. The vagus nerve
   C. Food in the stomach
   D. Histamine

2. Cholecystokinin functions in digestion to cause the release of:

   I. trypsinogen.
   II. bile.
   III. pepsinogen.

   A. I and II only
   B. I and III only
   C. II and III only
   D. I, II and III

3. Besides functioning in digestion, histamine also:

   A. causes local blood vessel constriction.
   B. mediates B cell clonal selection.
   C. causes inflammation.
   D. plays a role in antibody secretion.

4. It can be inferred from the passage that:

   A. somatostatin antagonizes the sympathetic nervous system.
   B. fatty acids in the duodenum favor gastric acid secretion.
   C. somatostatin stimulates pancreatic secretion.
   D. gastrin inhibits its own release via a negative feedback loop involving somatostatin.

5. Which one of the following CANNOT be inferred from the passage?

   A. The vagus is a parasympathetic nerve.
   B. Somatostatin enters the gastric lumen.
   C. No enzyme is required for the conversion of pepsinogen to pepsin.
   D. Excess gastric acid present in the duodenum stimulates the secretion of secretin.

6. An ulcer patient was given cimetidine, and the gastric H^+ concentration was decreased by a factor of ten. When the ulcer did not improve, a vagotomy was performed. Which of the following resulted?

   A. An increase in gastric pH
   B. A decrease in gastric pH
   C. Increased pancreatic secretion
   D. Increased gastrin secretion

Passage 73 (Questions 1-6)

Essential functions of the kidney include maintenance of electrolyte balance and fluid volume and regulation of blood pressure. The functional unit of the kidney is a microscopic tubule called the nephron. There are approximately 1.3 million nephrons in each human kidney. The nephron is composed of a long tube that begins surrounding a small capillary bed, thus forming a structure called the glomerulus. If the renal tubule is compared to a long balloon, the glomerular capillary bed enveloped by the first part of the tubule can be compared to a fist indenting the end of the balloon. The balloon surrounding the fist is analogous to the epithelial cell layer of the tubule which surrounds the glomerular capillary tuft to form Bowman's capsule. The nephron ends when it empties into a collecting duct, which in turn empties into the calyces of the renal pelvis.

The glomerulus functions by filtering the liquid component of plasma, that is, water and materials smaller than 8 nm in diameter. (By comparison, a red blood cell is 7 μm in diameter.) Filtration is selective not only for small molecules, but also for those with positive charge. This serves to conserve plasma proteins, which tend to be negatively charged. The selectivity is determined mostly by the characteristics of the basement membrane underlying the epithelial cells of Bowman's capsule. The glomerular basement membrane (GBM) is selective because of its small pores and its negative charge. When it is damaged, key plasma components leak into the urine. A classic example is diabetes mellitus, where excess glucose damages the GBM, eventually causing proteinuria (urinary protein loss).

The next step in nephron function after glomerular filtration is selective reabsorption and excretion, performed by the metabolically active columnar epithelium of the proximal tubule. Key reabsorbed substances include glucose, protein, Na^+, Cl^-, and Ca^{2+}. Water passively follows the reabsorbed solutes. Approximately 85% of the filtrate that enters the nephron from the glomerulus is reabsorbed in the proximal tubule. Actively secreted substances include uric acid and drugs. The mechanisms of resorption and excretion can be overwhelmed, as in diabetes mellitus where so much glucose is filtered that it cannot be reabsorbed, and is excreted into the urine along with large amounts of water.

The remaining components of the nephron further modify the contents of the filtrate, according to the body's need to dilute or concentrate plasma and eliminate urea. The hormones ADH (antidiuretic hormone) and aldosterone help control this activity. Aldosterone stimulates the distal tubule to reabsorb Na^+ ions in exchange for excreted K^+. This reabsorption of sodium leads to increased serum osmolarity, thirst, water retention, and increased blood pressure. Aldosterone secretion is stimulated by the renin–angiotensin system, which regulates blood pressure.

ADH is synthesized in the hypothalamus and released by the posterior pituitary in response to increased plasma osmolarity or decreased plasma volume. It causes the cells of the collecting duct (the last part of the nephron) to reabsorb water. The collecting duct is located in an area of the medulla with a very high salt concentration. The walls of the duct are not intrinsically permeable to water. ADH secretion increases the permeability of the duct wall to water, permitting water to flow down the large osmotic gradient. The water thus entering the medulla is carried off by small blood vessels in the interstitium called the vasa recta.

1. Extreme blood loss causes:

    I.   a decrease in the glomerular filtration rate.
    II. an increase in ADH secretion.
    III. an increase in aldosterone.

    A. I only
    B. II only
    C. I and II only
    D. I, II, and III

2. Long-term water deprivation has what effect?

    I.   Decreased glomerular filtration rate
    II. Increased secretion of ADH and aldosterone
    III. Increased Na^+ reabsorption.

    A. I only
    B. I and II only
    C. I and III only
    D. I, II and III

3. Which of the following statements about ADH or aldosterone is correct, based on the passage?

    A. ADH stimulates synthesis of a basolateral Na^+/K^+ ATPase that pumps Na^+ out of the urine and K^+ into the urine.
    B. Aldosterone stimulates synthesis of a basolateral Na^+/K^+ ATPase that pumps Na^+ into the urine and K^+ out of the urine.
    C. ADH stimulates the synthesis of a tubular protein which acts as a channel, permitting H_2O to cross cell membranes.
    D. Aldosterone directly stimulates the release of ADH.

4. In healthy people, secretion and reabsorption in the proximal tubule:

    A. regulates plasma osmolarity.
    B. is inhibited by increased urinary flow.
    C. is directly related to the glomerular filtration rate.
    D. can overcome concentration gradients.

5. It CANNOT be inferred from the passage that:

    A. healthy people have no red blood cells in their urine.
    B. the urine of diabetics would taste sweet.
    C. all negatively-charged substances smaller than 8 nm are excreted in the urine.
    D. red blood cells may be present in the urine of diabetics.

6. How might diabetes first be noticed?

    A. An elevated concentration of urea in the urine
    B. Weight loss and excessive thirst
    C. An abnormally low level of glucose in the urine
    D. Decreased plasma ADH

Passage 74 (Questions 1-6)
ADVANCED PASSAGE

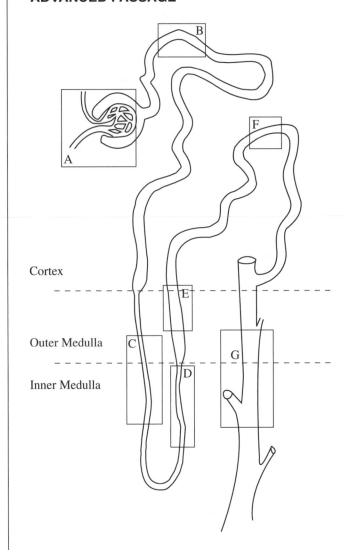

The boxed segments of the nephron are described below.

A. *Bowman's capsule*. Ultrafiltration, due to the high hydrostatic pressure of blood in the glomerular capillary bed, causes nearly 90% of serum fluid to enter Bowman's capsule. The filtrate is composed of water and small solutes such as salts, nitrogenous wastes, glucose, amino acids, and vitamins.

B. *Proximal tubule*. The proximal tubule is permeable to salts, urea, and water, and the fluid within is isosmotic to plasma. Substances actively transported out of the tubule, or reabsorbed, include glucose, amino acids, and Na^+. Water passively follows. Substances actively transported into the tubule, or excreted, include K^+ and H^+. The H^+ excretion results from the action of carbonic anhydrase, which converts CO_2 to H_2CO_3, which in turn dissociates to H^+ and HCO_3^-. Hence, for every H^+ secreted, an HCO_3^- is absorbed.

C. *Descending limb, loop of Henle*. The descending limb is permeable to water and moderately permeable to salt and urea. The urine in the descending loop becomes hypertonic, because water flows out of the tubule, drawn by the high solute concentration of the inner medulla created by mechanisms described below.

D. *Thin ascending limb, loop of Henle*. The thin ascending limb is impermeable to water but permeable to Na⁺, Cl⁻, and urea. These ions flow out of the tubule into the interstitium. The result is an increase in interstitial osmolarity and a decrease in tubular fluid osmolarity.

E. *Thick ascending limb, loop of Henle*. The thick limb is impermeable to urea and water. It is thick because its cells are metabolically active tall columnar cells. They use the energy of ATP to actively pump Cl⁻ out of the tubular fluid. Na⁺ follows this chloride, drawn into the interstitium by the electrical potential created by the movement of large amounts of Cl⁻. The result is a decrease in the osmolarity of the tubular fluid, and most importantly, a great increase in the solute concentration of the medullary interstitium.

F. *Distal Convoluted Tubule*
and
G. *Collecting Duct*. Because of the removal of so much salt from the tubular fluid in the thick segment of the loop of Henle, the fluid arriving at the distal tubule is hypotonic to the original filtrate arriving in the proximal tubule. In contrast to the proximal tubule and loop of Henle, where permeabilities are fixed, the permeability of the distal nephron to water, urea, and salts is under hormonal control. Here the final modifications of urine take place. The influences of ADH (antidiuretic hormone) and aldosterone on this segment are the prime determinants of urinary volume and osmolarity. ADH causes reabsorption of water by making the distal tubule permeable to water. Because of the very high solute concentration of the inner medulla, water will flow by osmosis out of the tubule when the tubule becomes permeable. The solutes concentrated in the medulla are NaCl, derived from the pumping of the thick ascending limb, and urea, which is concentrated in the medulla by a complex mechanism. This reabsorbed water is carried off by the vasa recta, long capillary loops which parallel the renal tubules. Aldosterone causes the reabsorption of sodium and the excretion of potassium. The resulting increase in serum sodium concentration results in thirst, water retention, and increased blood pressure.

1. In order for the loop of Henle to make filtrate more concentrated than plasma, which of the following must be true?

   A. The descending and ascending limbs of the loop of Henle must have the same permeability to water.
   B. The loop of Henle must go deep into the renal medulla, and the medulla must have a very high solute concentration.
   C. The proximal tubule must actively transport glucose, amino acids, and NaCl into the interstitial space.
   D. ADH must not be present.

2. In which region(s) of the nephron is the urine hypertonic compared to plasma?

   I. Descending limb of the loop of Henle
   II. Upper part of thick ascending limb of the loop of Henle
   III. The collecting duct in the presence of ADH

   A. I only
   B. II only
   C. I and III only
   D. I, II, and III

3. Which of the following hormones does NOT play a role in regulation of kidney function?

   A. Antidiuretic hormone
   B. Aldosterone
   C. Parathyroid hormone
   D. Oxytocin

4. A low protein diet is associated with a reduction in the ability of the kidney to concentrate urine. Which of the following is a plausible explanation?

   A. Excess urea is produced
   B. Little urea is produced
   C. Sodium balance is impaired
   D. Potassium balance is impaired

5. The drug acetazolamide inhibits the action of carbonic anhydrase in the kidney, which catalyzes the reaction: $CO_2 + H_2O \rightarrow H_2CO_3$. What effect would the drug have on kidney function?

   A. Decrease plasma pH
   B. Increase plasma CO_2 concentration
   C. Increase urine osmolarity
   D. Increase H⁺ secretion

6. What solutes are responsible for the osmotic gradient in the renal medulla?

   A. Urea and NaCl
   B. NaCl and KCl
   C. Glucose and H^+
   D. H^+ and NaCl

Passage 75 (Questions 1-6)

The muscular activity of the gastrointestinal (GI) tract is important for three reasons: gastric motility helps to fragment and dissolve food, intestinal motility helps to mix food with digestive secretions, and gastrointestinal smooth muscle is essential for the movement of food down the digestive tract.

We have conscious motor control over the beginning and end of the GI tract. Chewing (mastication) is under voluntary motor control, and swallowing (deglutition) is under both voluntary and autonomic control. The motility of the lower esophagus, the stomach, and the entire intestine is under control of the autonomic nervous system. Finally, defecation is under both voluntary and autonomic control; the last ring of muscle in the GI tract is called the external anal sphincter, and it is under voluntary motor control.

Histological studies demonstrate that the digestive tract is composed of four layers (tunics), two of which contain muscle. The innermost layer is the tunica mucosa, composed of columnar epithelium surrounding the lumen of the digestive tract. The mucosa is where absorption of nutrients occurs, and is also the first line of defense against toxic substances in the GI tract. The mucosal cells are continually sloughed off and replaced; this gives the intestines resiliency, but also makes them very vulnerable to inhibitors of cell division, such as anti-cancer drugs. The tunica mucosa also includes a thin layer of smooth muscle. Encircling the tunica mucosa is the tunica submucosa, which contains glands, blood vessels, lymph vessels, and nerves.

The third layer is the tunica muscularis, which consists of an inner layer of circular muscle, a nerve plexus which controls GI motility, and an outer layer of longitudinal muscle. Disordered contraction of the smooth muscle of the muscularis moves food back and forth, facilitating mixing and contact with the mucosa. A more ordered form of contraction, known as peristalsis, propels food down the GI tract. In peristalsis, the circular muscle above the bolus contracts, the circular muscle below the bolus relaxes, and longitudinal muscle surrounding the bolus contracts. In this way, circular muscles act like valves, promoting one-way movement, while longitudinal muscle acts to pull the intestine up over the bolus. The result is that the food moves down relative to the intestinal wall. The outermost layer of the digestive tract is the tunica serosa, composed of connective tissue.

Adapted from: *Human Anatomy and Physiology*, A. P. Spence, Ph.D. and E. B. Brown, Ph.D. © 1992 by West Publishing Co., St. Paul; and from *Essentials of Anatomy and Physiology*, R. R. Seeley, Ph.D., T. D. Stephens, Ph.D. and P. Tate, D. A. © 1991 by Mosby-Year Books, Inc., St. Louis, MO.

1. The muscles involved in mastication are under direct control of the:

   A. autonomic nervous system.
   B. somatic nervous system.
   C. neuroglia cells.
   D. brain stem.

2. Gall stones are crystallized bile acids which may block the bile duct. What do they cause?

   A. Poor digestion of carbohydrates
   B. Poor digestion of proteins
   C. Deficiency of fat-soluble vitamins
   D. Deficiency of water-soluble vitamins

3. All of the following are necessary for movement of food through the GI tract EXCEPT:

   A. sphincter muscles.
   B. longitudinal muscles.
   C. circular muscles.
   D. nerve plexi in the tunica muscularis.

4. Why does chemotherapy for cancer cause diarrhea and malnutrition?

   A. Mucosal cells divide very frequently.
   B. The treatment suppresses the immune system, leading to overgrowth of gastrointestinal bacteria.
   C. Chemotherapy causes psychiatric problems including extreme anxiety and anorexia.
   D. These symptoms result from the cancer, not from the chemotherapy.

5. T tubules are present in muscles responsible for:

   I. mastication.
   II. mixing in the small intestine.
   III. peristalsis.

   A. I only
   B. III only
   C. II and III only
   D. I, II, and III

6. Many toxins are capable of doing more physical damage when inhaled than when ingested. What is the best explanation for this?

   A. It is harder for a toxin to diffuse across the respiratory membrane.
   B. Respiration is a more critical process than digestion.
   C. The digestive system is specialized for absorption.
   D. The cells that line the digestive tract are continuously replaced.

Passage 76 (Questions 1-6)

Compact bone is organized into Haversian systems, each consisting of a central canal surrounded by concentric rings of mineralized matrix. The matrix, made up of collagen and hydroxyapatite (calcium phosphate crystals), is secreted by *osteoblasts*, which gradually become embedded in their own secretions. These imprisoned bone cells can no longer divide and are called *osteocytes*. The other major cell type in bone is the *osteoclast*. This is a multinucleate phagocyte derived from the same stem cells as the blood-borne monocyte (the macrophage precursor cell). Its function is to destroy bone by dissolving it in acidic secretions. Osteoblasts and osteoclasts continually deposit and resorb bone. This process is known as bone remodeling.

Three hormones control the activity of these cells and the availability of calcium and phosphate. Their effects are summarized in the table below. (Renal/intestinal uptake denotes the degree of extraction of the substance from food and the degree of reabsorption from the renal tubular filtrate.) *Calcitonin* is made by the C cells of the thyroid gland. *Calcitriol* is made from vitamin D, which is derived either from the diet or from cholesterol. Cholesterol can be converted to vitamin D by a series of reactions, one of which requires the ultraviolet light of direct sunshine. Parathyroid hormone (PTH) is made in the parathyroid glands. It stimulates the conversion of vitamin D to calcitriol, among other activities.

	—Hormone—		
	Calcitonin	Calcitriol	PTH
Osteoblast Activity	↑	↓	↓
Osteoclast Activity	↓	↑	↑
Renal/Intestinal Ca^{2+} uptake	↓	↑	↑
Renal/Intestinal PO$_4^{2-}$ uptake	↓	↑	↓

Defects in bone fall into two broad categories: *osteomalacia* and *osteoporosis*. Osteomalacia is softening of bone due to defective mineralization; the ratio of hydroxyapatite to collagen is abnormally low. The classic cause of osteomalacia is vitamin D deficiency. In children it is known as *rickets*. The affected child has abnormally soft bones, and the skeleton deforms during growth.

Osteoporosis is weakening of the bone due to an imbalance between resorption and deposition; the ratio of mineral to protein is normal. Osteoporosis is most common in post-menopausal women, in whom estrogen concentrations are much lower than before menopause. It is the reason older women are so prone to spine, hip, and other fractures; it also causes the loss of height

and skeletal deformations which occur in many elderly women. In fact, women lose an average of 1.5% of their bone mass each year after menopause. The explanation is that estrogen promotes both deposition of calcium into bone and renal and intestinal retention of calcium.

Estrogen replacement therapy has proved successful in treatment of osteoporosis in post-menopausal women. Estrogen is given both preventatively and in order to halt the progress of advanced osteoporosis. Exercise and adequate calcium and vitamin D intake throughout life are also essential for prevention and slowing of the disease. Up to age 35, these preventative measures lead to increased bone mass; thereafter, the steady decrease in bone mass which occurs with age can be retarded. Another strategy is the administration of calcitonin, which can stabilize bone. Finally, a new group of drugs, the diphosphonates, may prove capable of reversing or slowing very severe osteoporosis.

1. A vitamin is defined as a chemical which is required in the diet because it is necessary for life but cannot be synthesized. By this definition, vitamin D is:

   A. necessary for the intestinal absorption of calcium.
   B. derived from cholesterol.
   C. really only a vitamin for some people, some of the time.
   D. not required in the diet.

2. It can be inferred from the passage that collagen:

   I. has a normal structure in osteoporosis.
   II. has a normal structure in osteomalacia.
   III. requires vitamin D for proper synthesis.

   A. II only
   B. III only
   C. I and II only
   D. I, II, and III

3. Based on the passage, which of the following is an accurate generalization about the activity of a hormone?

   A. Estrogen's primary function in the female body is to increase bone mass.
   B. Estrogen increases both calcium deposition in bone and calcium uptake by the kidney and the intestine.
   C. Calcitonin's primary function is to increase the amount of calcium deposited into bone.
   D. Parathyroid hormone decreases the amount of calcium in the body.

4. Based on the passage, women in their twenties should be advised to:

   A. ask their doctors about estrogen therapy.
   B. avoid strenuous exercise.
   C. take calcium and vitamin D supplements.
   D. avoid birth control pills if they are concerned about osteoporosis in their later years.

5. Which of the following is/are probably accurate regarding rickets?

   I. It is more prevalent in industrialized societies and in colder climates.
   II. It results from the absence of the effects of calcitriol upon osteoblasts and osteoclasts.
   III. It is very rare in the United States today because of the fortification of milk and other foods with synthetic vitamin D.

   A. I only
   B. II only
   C. I and III only
   D. I, II, and III

6. What are the characteristics of bone in people with osteoporosis and osteomalacia?

   A. Increased density in osteomalacia, decreased density in osteoporosis
   B. Decreased protein in osteoporosis, normal protein in osteomalacia
   C. Increased minerals in osteomalacia, decreased minerals in osteoporosis
   D. More brittle bones in osteomalacia, more flexible bones in osteoporosis

Passage 77 (Questions 1-6)

Parasympathetic innervation of the gastrointestinal (GI) tract involves a long myelinated *preganglionic* neuron, which has its cell body in the spinal cord, and a very short unmyelinated *postganglionic* neuron, which has its cell body in a ganglion and sends its axon to the target organs. A ganglion is a collection of cell bodies and synapses located outside the CNS. The pre- and postganglionic neurons may release different neurotransmitters. Each neurotransmitter has its effect by binding to a particular receptor. Often the same neurotransmitter may bind to one of several different receptor proteins, which are present on different types of neurons. A given receptor can be blocked by drugs that do not block the action of the neurotransmitter at its other receptors. The *nicotinic* receptor, for example, is one of the receptors that binds acetylcholine (ACh). It is found on postganglionic autonomic neurons and on the motor end plates of skeletal muscle.

The following experiments were performed to characterize the neurotransmitters involved in the contraction of GI smooth muscle in response to parasympathetic nerve stimulation. GI smooth muscle in a rat was exposed and subjected to various treatments.

Experiment 1:

An artificial form of ACh was injected systemically (throughout the body), and contraction of the exposed GI smooth muscle was observed.

Experiment 2:

Preganglionic parasympathetic nerves were stimulated electrically. Contraction was observed once again.

Experiment 3:

Tetrodotoxin, which blocks voltage-gated sodium channels, was carefully microinjected into the connective tissue sheath surrounding preganglionic axons so that only they were exposed to the drug. Contraction failed to occur when these preganglionic nerves were stimulated electrically, but did occur when the artificial form of acetylcholine was injected.

Experiment 4:

A drug that blocks the action of ACh at nicotinic receptors was injected systemically. This prevented the exposed smooth muscle from contracting when preganglionic nerves were stimulated electrically but did not prevent contraction upon electrical stimulation of postganglionic nerves or upon systemic injection of the artificial form of ACh.

Adapted from *Human Physiology, 5th edition*, by Arthur J. Vander, James H. Sherman, and Dorothy S. Luciano, © 1990 by McGraw-Hill.

MCAT Science Workbook

1. Experiment 4 was used to prove that:

   A. muscle contraction is not a direct result of ACh acting upon nicotinic receptors at the muscle membrane.
   B. preganglionic sympathetic nerves have nicotinic ACh receptors.
   C. contraction occurs upon parasympathetic nerve stimulation.
   D. nicotinic receptors play no role in stimulating contraction.

2. Chemicals which prevent the degradation of synaptic ACh are known as acetylcholinesterase inhibitors. (Examples include the drug neostigmine and the insecticide malathion.) What effects do they have?

   I. Increased amounts of ACh escaping from synapses into the bloodstream
   II. Immediate and intense involuntary contraction of all skeletal muscles
   III. Increased gastrointestinal motility

   A. II only
   B. III only
   C. I and III only
   D. I, II, and III

3. The function of tetrodotoxin in Experiment 3 was to:

   A. ensure neurotransmitter release.
   B. directly prevent neurotransmitter release.
   C. prevent muscle depolarization.
   D. prevent action potentials.

4. Smooth muscles play the major role in contraction of all of the following EXCEPT the:

   A. uterus.
   B. aortic arch.
   C. heart.
   D. airways of the lungs.

5. Which of the following properties is shared by both smooth and skeletal muscle?

   A. Microscopic banded appearance
   B. Actin–myosin cross-bridging causes contraction
   C. Not under direct voluntary control
   D. Can be excited or inhibited by nerve stimulation

6. The tetrodotoxin used in Experiment 3 might affect each of the following EXCEPT:

   A. postganglionic parasympathetic axons.
   B. skeletal muscle.
   C. axon hillocks.
   D. binding of ACh to its receptor.

Passage 78 (Questions 1-6

A single skeletal muscle is composed of numerous myofibers. Each myofiber is a long multinucleated cell which contains many thick and thin filaments. Thick filaments are composed of the protein myosin, and thin filaments consist of the polymeric protein actin. The filaments are organized into sarcomeres, which form the contractile unit of skeletal muscle and give it its characteristic striated appearance.

In the sliding filament model of muscle contraction, the thin and thick filaments slide along one another in a process which is spontaneous in the presence of ATP and calcium. The contractile process is spontaneous in that the myosin head group has an intrinsic affinity for certain binding sites on the actin polymer, and once it has bound such a site, a myosin head will spontaneously bend inward on itself, pulling the actin chain past. This movement is known as the *power stroke*. After the power stroke, myosin remains bound to actin until an ATP molecule becomes available. Upon binding ATP, myosin releases actin, and then spontaneously unbends itself, hydrolyzing the bound ATP to ADP + P_i in the process. The myosin head is now ready for another cycle of contraction.

1. During or after muscle contraction, each of the following occurs EXCEPT:

    A. the length of the thick and thin filaments decreases.
    B. the thick and thin filaments slide along one another.
    C. calcium is released into the muscle cell cytoplasm.
    D. calcium is actively transported from the cytoplasm into the sarcoplasmic reticulum.

2. Cardiac and skeletal muscle are similar because both:

    A. are striated.
    B. contain intercalated discs between cells.
    C. are multinucleated.
    D. None of the above

3. The amount of ATP stored in muscle can only sustain contraction for less than a second. However, vertebrate muscles contain a large amount of creatine phosphate. Creatine phosphate:

    A. phosphorylates myosin.
    B. contains a high-energy phosphate bond that can be transferred to ADP to make ATP.
    C. catalyzes the formation of ATP from ADP.
    D. can bind the myosin head, breaking cross-bridges.

4. Rigor mortis is a constant contracted state of the musculature which occurs soon after death. It results from the:

    A. destruction of muscle cells.
    B. inability of myosin cross-bridges to move actin molecules.
    C. inability of myosin cross-bridges to bind actin.
    D. inability of myosin cross-bridges to release actin.

5. Which of the following is the most direct effect of an action potential initiated in a skeletal muscle by means of a motor neuron?

    A. Binding of myosin heads to actin filaments
    B. Removal of the tropomyosin/troponin complex from the myosin binding sites on actin
    C. Hydrolysis of ATP bound to myosin
    D. Release of calcium from the sarcoplasmic reticulum

6. Action potentials can travel down a motor neuron frequently enough to cause a smoothly sustained contraction called:

    A. a twitch.
    B. tetanus.
    C. the all-or-none phenomenon.
    D. rigor mortis.

Passage 79 (Questions 1-5)

The sarcomere is the contractile unit of skeletal muscle. It is primarily composed of two proteins: actin and myosin. In solutions of low ionic strength, actin is a monomeric protein with a globular shape. In ionic solutions comparable to a physiological environment, actin polymerizes into a helical filament. Myosin is composed of six polypeptide chains: two identical heavy chains and four light chains.

Electron micrographs reveal the structure of the sarcomere (see Figure 1). The sarcomere is bounded by Z lines, which are composed of α-actinin. Thin filaments, composed of actin, are bound to the Z lines and extend toward the M line with a specified polarity. The polarity of the thin filaments is manifested when myosin binds to them. This complex is called a decorated filament and creates an arrowhead pattern, which points away from the Z line. The thick filament, myosin, is bipolar with the heads of the filament pointing in opposite directions on either side of the H zone. The H zone is the region of the thick filament devoid of myosin heads.

During muscle contraction, the thin and thick filaments slide over one another, causing the Z lines to move closer together. The biochemistry of muscle contraction involves a complex interaction among actin, myosin, ATP, and other components. The following experiments were performed to better understand these biochemical processes.

Experiment 1:

Purified actin and myosin were added to a solution, and the viscosity of the solution increased dramatically. When ATP was added to the mixture, the viscosity decreased.

Experiment 2:

Magnesium ions were added to the solution from Experiment 1. ATP hydrolysis was observed, and the viscosity increased.

Experiment 3:

Magnesium ions and ATP were added to an extract from minced muscle. ATP hydrolysis was not observed.

Experiment 4:

Calcium was added to the extract from Experiment 3. ATP hydrolysis was observed.

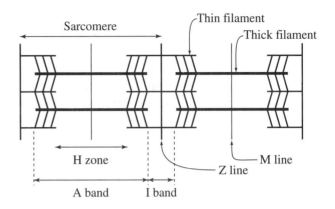

Figure 1

Adapted from *Biochemistry, 5th ed.*, by Lubert Stryer, © 1988 by Walter H. Freeman.

1. Which of the following best explains the results of Experiment 1?

    A. Myosin binds to and spontaneously dissociates from actin filaments over time.
    B. Myosin spontaneously binds to actin, and adding ATP causes actin and myosin to dissociate.
    C. Myosin spontaneously binds to actin, and adding ATP causes actin to depolymerize.
    D. Myosin binds to actin, increasing the viscosity. ATP then binds to actin causing actin and myosin to dissociate, decreasing the viscosity.

2. ATP hydrolysis was not observed in Experiment 3 because:

    A. magnesium is not required for myosin to hydrolize ATP.
    B. magnesium inhibits ATP hydrolysis in cell extracts.
    C. ATP could not bind to myosin.
    D. there was no ATPase present to hydrolyze ATP.

3 Why do muscle fibers stretched beyond a certain point lose the ability to contract?

    A. ATP is no longer available.
    B. The separation of Z lines tears the thick filaments in half.
    C. The thick and thin filaments no longer overlap.
    D. Overstretching muscle does not prevent it from contracting.

4. ATP hydrolysis was observed in Experiment 4 because calcium:

   A. is required for the ATPase to function.
   B. changes troponin's conformation, allowing myosin to bind actin.
   C. binds to myosin, allowing myosin to bind to actin.
   D. binds to actin, causing it to bind to myosin.

5. Creatine phosphate is a molecule with a high-energy phosphate bond which:

   I. is used to generate ATP from ADP.
   II. has a more positive free energy of hydrolysis than ATP.
   III. can be hydrolyzed to creatine + P_i, with $\Delta G > 0$ for the reaction.

   A. I only
   B. I and II only
   C. I and III only
   D. II and III only

Passage 80 (Questions 1-6)

Muscle contraction is governed by several factors, including the availability of intracellular Ca^{2+}. Ca^{2+} levels are themselves dependent on motor nerve impulses that initiate an action potential in the muscle cell membrane.

Two principal proteins interact in skeletal muscle contraction: actin, which is a long helical chain constituting the thin filament of muscle fiber, and myosin, assembled as a double-stranded helix. The myosin molecule has globular heads and helical tails. Together the heads and tails create the thick filament of muscle fiber. Each head contains a distinct actin-binding site and ATP-hydrolyzing site. When actin and myosin are free to interact, thin and thick filaments slide relative to one another and the muscle contracts.

A different set of proteins regulates the sliding of the actin and myosin filaments. These are troponin, with subunits of troponin I, troponin T, and troponin C, and tropomyosin, a filamentous molecule with an α-helical secondary structure. In the relaxed position the troponin is bound to tropomyosin while tropomyosin lies lengthwise across actin in such a way as to cover the binding sites of actin.

Research has revealed that Ca^{2+} binds to a specific site on troponin in skeletal muscle, inducing conformational changes in troponin and tropomyosin that ultimately result in muscle contraction. Research also reveals that troponin and tropomyosin prevent muscle contraction by inhibiting binding between actin and myosin. This suggests that intracellular Ca^{2+} causes muscular contraction by reversing the inhibitory action of troponin and tropomyosin.

To assess the role of intracellular Ca^{2+} in skeletal muscle contraction, Ca^{2+} release in living muscle cells was examined. Aequorin, a protein isolated from a jellyfish, was employed for its bioluminescent properties. Aequorin releases photons when it binds to Ca^{2+}, and thus signals the presence of Ca^{2+}.

Experiment 1:

Step 1: A single intact muscle fiber was carefully isolated from the leg of *Rana pipiens* and bathed in fluid to maintain its function.

Step 2: The muscle fiber was injected with aequorin and stimulated to contract. Changes in light emission were measured with a photodetector.

Results: The muscle fiber emitted a brief flash of light immediately before contraction. Contraction was followed by relaxation.

Experiment 2 was a repetition of Experiment 1 except that the muscle fiber was not permitted to reaccumulate Ca^{2+} after releasing it. The muscle fiber emitted a brief flash of light immediately before contraction occurred. Contraction was sustained; relaxation did not occur.

1. Which of the following could NOT be associated with striated muscle contraction?

   A. Simple reflex arc of the knee
   B. Pumping of the heart
   C. Peristalsis of the digestive tract
   D. Motion of the fingers

2. Which of the following would most likely be abundant in active skeletal muscle cells?

   A. Secretory vesicles
   B. Mitochondria
   C. Gap junctions with neighboring cells
   D. Voltage-gated calcium channels in the plasma membrane

3. In Experiment 2, the muscle cell continued to contract when Ca^{2+} remained in the cell because Ca^{2+} causes:

   A. troponin and tropomyosin to prevent interaction between actin and myosin.
   B. release of actin-myosin inhibition by troponin and tropomyosin.
   C. depletion of ATP within the muscle.
   D. absorption of glucose within the muscle.

4. Which of the following pieces of information, if true, would support the conclusion that interaction between Ca^{2+} and troponin/tropomyosin proteins induces muscle contraction?

   A. Myosin and actin *in vitro* cannot produce contractile action in the absence of troponin/tropomyosin proteins.
   B. Myosin and actin alone produce contractile action *in vitro* which is not affected by calcium.
   C. Ca^{2+} cannot bind to troponin in the presence of myosin and actin.
   D. Contractile action by myosin and actin alone is stimulated by calcium *in vitro* in the absence of troponin/tropomyosin proteins.

5. Intracellular calcium levels in the muscle cell increase as the result of a(n):

   A. action potential, causing influx of Ca^{2+} from adjacent cells.
   B. action potential, causing release of Ca^{2+} from the sarcoplasmic reticulum.
   C. feedback mechanism, causing an increase in sequestering of Ca^{2+} by sarcoplasmic reticulum.
   D. feedback mechanism, causing an increase in ATPase activity in myosin.

6. In Experiment 1, what was indicated by the brief flash of light emitted directly before contraction?

   A. ATP was present.
   B. ATP was degraded.
   C. Ca^{2+} was present.
   D. Ca^{2+} was degraded.

_____

Passage 81 (Questions 1-6)

Skeletal muscles are comprised of different muscle fiber types. The three types of fibers commonly found in humans are type I, type IIa, and type IIb. These fibers have distinct structural and metabolic components to meet their functional needs.

The type I fibers, also called slow oxidative or red slow twitch, have rich capillary network and high concentrations of mitochondria and myoglobin, which makes them appear red in color. They produce ATP though aerobic oxidative processes and use triglycerides as the primary form of energy storage. The myosin ATPase activity is slow in these fibers. Therefore, the myosin head splits ATP at a slower rate. This leads to slow contraction velocity, slow twitch rate and low force generation; however, they have high resistance to fatigue. Hence these fibers predominate in muscles that need to generate slow, constant force for prolonged periods of time.

The type IIb fibers, also called fast glycolytic or fast twitch, appear pink in color due to relatively low capillary density and mitochondrial content. They produce ATP through anaerobic glycolytic processes and therefore, use glycogen as their energy store. The myosin isoform has a fast ATPase activity. This allows for fast contraction velocity, fast twitch rate, and high force generation. These fibers are abundant in muscles that are involved in swift and precise movements. The type IIa fibers, also called fast glycolytic oxidative or fast fatigue resistant, have components of both type I and type IIb.

Skeletal muscles exhibit high level of plasticity. It has been shown that endurance exercise promotes fiber growth and transformation among other cardiovascular changes. The transformation of type IIb fiber to type IIa and/or type I fibers increases muscle performance by increasing force generation and reducing fatigue. It has been shown that cellular changes that contribute to fiber transformation often target transcriptional isotype switching of the myosin heavy chain, which is responsible for the ATPase activity of the myosin.

1. Which of the muscle fibers would be most abundant in the trapezius muscle, one of the major muscles of the back?

   I. Type I
   II. Type IIa
   III. Type IIb

   A. I only
   B. II only
   C. I and III
   D. I, II, and III

2. What is the role of myosin in skeletal muscle contraction?

   A. It is involved in the production of ATP necessary for the contraction.
   B. It allows for muscle contraction through the cross-bridge cycle.
   C. It is a structural protein involved in stabilization of sarcomeric units.
   D. It binds to Ca^{+2} and activates the thick and thin filaments.

3. How can the type I fibers utilize triglycerides to generate ATP?

   A. The triglycerides can undergo catabolism to ultimately yield acetyl CoA and reduced electron carriers, which can feed into the Krebs cycle and the electron transport chain to generate ATP.
   B. Triglycerides can be broken down to produce free glucose, which can undergo glycolysis to produce ATP.
   C. Triglycerides can directly produce ATP via substrate-level phosphorylation.
   D. Triglycerides can be combusted to generate heat, which in turn can drive ATP synthase.

4. Which of the following long-term physiological changes would NOT be observed in individuals involved in regular endurance exercise?

   A. Angiogenesis (generation of new blood vessels) in skeletal muscle to increase blood supply.
   B. Increase in mitochondrial biogenesis in the skeletal muscle tissue.
   C. Increase in the cardiac output by the heart.
   D. Increase in resting heart rate.

5. Which of the following is true regarding myoglobin?

   A. It has a sigmoidal oxygen saturation curve.
   B. It interacts with oxygen via Zn^{+2} at the center of its prosthetic heme group.
   C. It is the major transporter of oxygen in the blood.
   D. It is a monomeric globular protein, which acts as an oxygen storage molecule within muscle tissues.

6. The transcriptional changes involved in isotype switching of myosin heavy chain are carried out by specific transcription factors. How do specific transcription factors influence protein expression?

A. They bind to specific regions on the ribosome and increase the rate of protein translation.

B. They bind and stabilize the mRNA molecule, thereby, decreasing its rate of degradation.

C. They bind to regions on the DNA in a site-specific manner and either increase or decrease transcription of genes.

D. They act as chaperone proteins to enhance the rate of protein folding.

Passage 82 (Questions 1-6)

The plasma membrane is a dynamic barrier that maintains a specific milieu of biomolecules within the cell. The intracellular compartment is drastically different from the interstitium and blood. Concentration gradients across the plasma membrane require energy to establish, but are critical to normal cellular physiology. Dissipation of these gradients, due to either malfunctioning membrane proteins or physical disruption of the lipid bilayer, disturbs cellular processes. Changes in ion concentrations may lead to instantaneous changes in resting membrane potential, muscular contraction, and ultimately, cell death. When very large numbers of cells die at once, the released cell contents mix with the extracellular environment and can alter the concentrations of proteins and ions within the blood. This may lead to systemic imbalances and, if not corrected, the death of the organism.

Traumatic crush injuries of the body destroy muscle tissue. If the injury is extensive, breakdown of myocytes (specifically, skeletal muscle cells) manifests as a group of clinical symptoms referred to as *rhabdomyolysis*. Sequestration of plasma within affected myocytes occurs and may lead to noticeable swelling. In severe cases, the redistribution of fluid from the blood into the muscular compartment causes symptomatic hypovolemia. In addition, the excess fluid increases the pressure within the muscular compartment; this eventually compromises local blood flow, leading to ischemic damage to the muscle and neurological dysfunction. As a result, patients often experience pain and weakness. Injured myocytes release phosphates and sulfates into the blood (which decreases pH), as well as several proteins. If the proteins are small (usually, less than 70,000 daltons), they may filter across the renal glomerular membrane and into Bowman's capsule. In a healthy individual, about 75 percent of myoglobin (16,700 daltons) present in the blood is freely filtered into Bowman's capsule; however, myoglobin concentrations in the blood are normally negligible. Large amounts of this protein will precipitate within the nephron tubules and lead to their damage. Signs of kidney failure may occur within days of the initial insult.

Measuring the levels of intracellular enzymes in the blood is frequently used to detect and monitor the course of disruptive cellular traumas, including rhabdomyolysis. Concentrations of creatine kinase (CK), glutamic-oxaloacetate transaminase, and skeletal muscle-specific aldolase transiently rise and fall following a traumatic event. Rhabdomyolysis produces CK levels that are elevated above the normal range in 100% of cases, often to values 5–10 times greater than normal. Different isoforms of CK exist, and more sensitive laboratory techniques can distinguish between CK originating primarily from skeletal muscle, brain, or cardiac muscle.

While trauma is the most common cause of rhabdomyolysis, any process that compromises the integrity of the myocyte plasma membrane may lead to this phenomenon. Inherited myopathies like Duchene muscular dystrophy and malignant hyperthermia, electrocution, seizure activity, hypothermia, certain viral or bacterial infections, cocaine use, and many prescription drugs may result in this disorder.

1. Which of the following statements is true regarding myoglobin?

    A. Plasma myoglobin levels increase when red blood cells leak intracellular contents.
    B. Myoglobin's quaternary structure allows maximal oxygen delivery to myocytes.
    C. Myoglobin may damage renal tubule cells.
    D. Actively contracting muscles causes a right shift in the myoglobin-oxygen dissociation curve.

2. Which of the following is LEAST likely to occur after extensive disruptive myocyte injury?

    A. Decreased blood flow within the affected muscle tissue
    B. Irregular heart rhythm resulting from increased blood potassium levels
    C. Increased serum levels of lactate dehydrogenase
    D. Decreased ventilation rate due to acid-base disturbances

3. Which of the following features is/are shared among skeletal, smooth, and cardiac muscle cells?

    I. Myofibrils are arranged into sarcomeres.
    II. Calcium plays a regulatory role in contraction.
    III. Acetylcholine binding to muscle plasma membrane receptors is excitatory.

    A. I and II only
    B. II only
    C. II and III only
    D. III only

4. According to information provided in the passage, which of the following assumptions should NOT be made regarding the use of blood CK levels as a tool for diagnosing rhabdomyolysis?

    A. 100 percent of patients with elevated CK levels have some degree of disruptive skeletal muscle injury.
    B. CK will be elevated to some degree in 100 percent of patients with disruptive skeletal muscle injury.
    C. Patients with non-elevated CK levels do not have extensive disruptive skeletal muscle injury.
    D. Patients with elevated CK levels may not have disruptive skeletal muscle injury.

5. Urine from a patient suffering from severe 3rd degree burns (burns that affect the skin and underlying muscle tissue) appears dark brown; analysis reveals the presence of large amounts of a heme-containing protein. Which of the following statements is the most likely rationale for this patient's abnormally colored urine?

    A. Myoglobin is normally too large to filter into Bowman's capsule, but high myoglobin concentrations in this patient's blood have damaged the renal tubules, causing them to become leaky and to allow myoglobin access to the urine.
    B. Myoglobin is small enough to filter into Bowman's capsule and is normally found in large quantities in the urine; the patient's urine is dark because of large amounts of hemoglobin.
    C. Myoglobin is small enough to filter into Bowman's capsule; the patient's urine is dark because there is an abnormally high amount of myoglobin in the blood.
    D. Myoglobin is normally too large to filter into Bowman's capsule; the patient's urine is dark because large amounts of hemoglobin (which is much smaller than myoglobin) has been released from destroyed red blood cells.

6. Skeletal muscle is derived from which embryological germ layer?

    A. Endoderm
    B. Mesoderm
    C. Ectoderm
    D. Neuroectoderm

Passage 83 (Questions 1-6)

The skin is the largest organ in the human body, comprising approximately 15% of total body weight. Its primary roles are to provide a barrier against various harmful agents, to serve as a sensory organ, and to help regulate body temperature and fluid content. Ambient temperature is the main factor influencing the vasculature of the skin. Normal body temperature is a physiological set point; that is, it is maintained by active compensatory processes. Maintenance of the set point is a complex task involving somatic, autonomic, and endocrine systems.

An increase in ambient temperature requires greater heat loss and reduction of heat production. In a warming environment, heat loss is enhanced by sweating (leading to evaporation) and dilation of cutaneous vessels (promoting cooling of the blood by conduction). In addition, heat production is diminished by a decrease in thyroxine secretion by the thyroid which occurs over a period of weeks; this decreases metabolic activity. In the brain, the preoptic region and the anterior hypothalamus mediate responses that result in heat loss.

A decrease in external temperature causes the body to engage in heat production and reduction of heat loss. Hence it elicits shivering and an increase in thyroid hormone over a period of weeks. It also elicits reduction of heat loss by piloerection (the bristling of skin hairs) and constriction of the cutaneous vessels, both of which result from sympathetic nervous activity. The posterior hypothalamus has been found to mediate heat production and conservation.

1. Which of the following is NOT a feature of the epidermal layer of skin?

    A. It consists of stratified squamous tissue.
    B. It consists of closely packed cells arranged in several layers.
    C. Only its innermost layer of cells reproduces itself.
    D. It consists of fibrous connective tissue.

2. The primary mechanism of shivering thermogenesis is:

    A. asynchronous contraction of muscle fibers.
    B. increased metabolism as a hormonal contribution to heat production.
    C. dilation of the cutaneous vessels.
    D. a hormonal contribution to heat conservation by decreasing metabolism.

3. Electrical stimulation of the preoptic region and the anterior hypothalamus is most likely to lead to:

    A. cutaneous vasodilation.
    B. shivering.
    C. increased TSH.
    D. piloerection.

4. Electrical stimulation of the posterior hypothalamus is most likely to result in:

    A. sweating.
    B. piloerection.
    C. cutaneous vasodilation.
    D. increased parathyroid hormone levels.

5. Interleukin 1 is also known as *endogenous pyrogen* because it results in fever during illness. Which of the following is probably NOT true of this chemical?

    A. It is released by T cells.
    B. It causes shivering.
    C. It causes piloerection.
    D. It constitutes an important means of increasing body temperature in cold climates only.

6. Which of the following does the autonomic nervous system use to conserve heat?

    I. Shivering
    II. Piloerection
    III. Constriction of cutaneous vessels

    A. I only
    B. II only
    C. II and III only
    D. I, II, and III

Passage 84 (Questions 1-6)

The following graphs summarize the effects of pH, P_{CO_2}, and P_{O_2} on respiratory control. Graph A shows the increase in relative ventilation (RV) which occurs as the P_{O_2} falls, with P_{CO_2} and pH normal. (Normal P_{CO_2} is 40 mm Hg, and normal pH is 7.4.) An RV of 1 corresponds to the normal minute-ventilation of 7 L/min. The receptors responsible for monitoring the P_{O_2} are the peripheral chemoreceptors, located in the aortic and carotid arteries. (Central chemoreceptors in the brain do not monitor the oxygen level of the blood.) Note that the response stimulated by oxygen deficit does not become significant until P_{O_2} falls below 50 mm Hg.

Graph A:

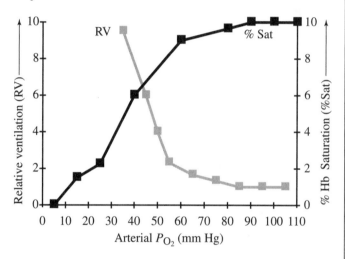

Graph B shows the effect of arterial P_{CO_2} on the response of peripheral chemoreceptors sensitive to P_{O_2}. When the arterial P_{CO_2} rises, the response to decreasing P_{O_2} levels is increased.

Graph B:

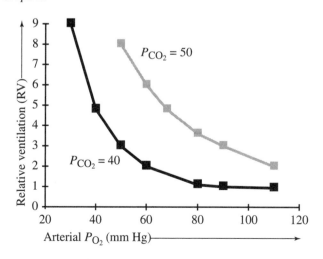

Graph C demonstrates the most sensitive ventilatory control mechanism in the body: the response of peripheral chemoreceptors to changes in plasma pH. Central chemoreceptors also respond to changes in pH, though less sensitively.

Graph C:

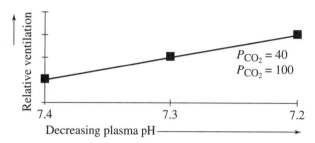

Graph D shows the dependence of ventilation on P_{CO_2} when pH and P_{O_2} are normal (7.4 and 100 mm Hg), and also when pH and P_{O_2} are decreased. The response to P_{CO_2} is mediated by both central and peripheral chemoreceptors.

Graph D:

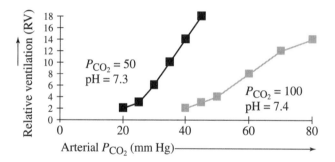

1. The peripheral chemoreceptors respond to changes in arterial:

   I. pH.
   II. P_{CO_2}.
   III. P_{O_2}.

   A. I only
   B. III only
   C. I and II only
   D. I, II, and III

2. At an arterial oxygen pressure of 50 mm Hg, what is the approximate percent saturation of hemoglobin?

   A. 30%
   B. 50%
   C. 80%
   D. 100%

3. Increases in relative ventilation are directly proportional to increases in P_{CO_2} when the P_{CO_2} is:

   A. at any level greater than 30 mm Hg, regardless of P_{O_2} and pH.
   B. greater than 30 mm Hg, but less than 50 mm Hg, regardless of P_{O_2} and pH.
   C. between 30 mm Hg and 40 mm Hg, but only in cases of decreased pH and P_{O_2} levels.
   D. less than 40 mm Hg, but only in cases of decreased pH and P_{O_2} levels.

4. If an individual has an arterial P_{O_2} of 40 mm Hg, a P_{CO_2} of 40 mm Hg, and a pH of 7.4, then the relative ventilation rate is:

   A. normal.
   B. higher than normal and is driven by peripheral chemoreceptors.
   C. higher than normal and is driven by central chemo-receptors.
   D. lower than normal and is driven by peripheral chemoreceptors.

5. Which of the following is true about Graph B?

   I. Relative ventilation is increased by increases in P_{CO_2} at any constant P_{O_2}.
   II. The ventilatory response to decreased P_{O_2} is augmented when the P_{CO_2} is increased.
   III. Increases in the P_{O_2} above normal cause increases in the relative ventilation response.

   A. I only
   B. I and II only
   C. I and III only
   D. II and III only

6. What is the approximate minute-ventilation when the P_{CO_2} is 40 mm Hg, the pH is 7.4, and the P_{O_2} is 35 mm Hg?

   A. 7 L/min
   B. 20 L/min
   C. 31 L/min
   D. 45 L/min

Passage 85 (Questions 1-6)

The thoracic cage is constructed of several components: ribs, costal cartilages, sternum, vertebral column, primary and associated musculature, skin, etc. It houses and protects the heart and lungs, and is important in the mechanics of respiration.

The primary muscle of inspiration is the diaphragm, a large, flat, dome-shaped muscle attaching to the most inferior ribs and costal cartilages and extending laterally to the vertebral column. Upon contraction, it descends into the abdominal cavity, thus expanding the volume of the thoracic cavity. The external intercostals, which connect the ribs to each other, are also inspiratory muscles. They lift the ribs, expanding the chest wall. The ribs form a series of hoops which make the chest barrel-shaped when the hoops are aligned parallel to each other, that is, when the external intercostals contract. In expiration, the hoops are allowed to sag downward; they overlap, and no longer hold the chest wall open.

Accessory muscles of inspiration include two neck muscles (the sternocleidomastoid and the anterior scalene) and the pectoral muscles. The pectorals extend from the anterior chest wall to the proximal humerus; they normally function to pull the arms forward and inward. They function as accessory muscles of inspiration in cases of respiratory dysfunction such as paralysis of the diaphragm. By leaning over with the arms in a barrel shape and the hands locked onto an object (a table, for example), the patient can accomplish chest wall expansion.

Expiration is normally a passive process, driven by the elasticity of the large airways. When an unusually large amount of ventilation is needed, muscles can speed the process of respiration. Contraction of abdominal muscles shrinks the volume of the abdominal cavity, and the contents of this space are pushed into the thoracic cavity; this results in lung compression. The internal intercostals also help by pulling the ribs down, so that they do not expand the chest.

1. The external intercostals cause the pressure in the pleural cavity to:

    A. not change.
    B. become more negative.
    C. become more positive.
    D. approach atmospheric pressure.

2. Which of the following muscles is/are important for respiration only during exercise?

    I. Abdominal muscles
    II. Diaphragm
    III. Expiratory muscles

    A. III only
    B. I and II only
    C. I and III only
    D. I, II and III

3. Hypoventilation has what effect on the composition of gas in arterial blood compared to normal?

    A. Increased P_{CO_2} and decreased P_{O_2}
    B. Increased P_{CO_2} and normal P_{O_2}
    C. Decreased P_{CO_2} and normal P_{O_2}
    D. Decreased P_{CO_2} and increased P_{O_2}

4. Each of the following would tend to prevent expansion of the thoracic cavity EXCEPT:

    A. a large meal.
    B. cutting the nerves to the diaphragm.
    C. a decrease in lung elasticity.
    D. a third-trimester pregnancy.

5. A patient stands leaning over a table and gripping it with both hands. Muscles in his neck can be seen to contract with each attempt to breathe, and his lips appear blue. Which of the following might be responsible for his difficulty in breathing?

    I. Accidental destruction of the nerves to the diaphragm in a recent surgery
    II. Complete paralysis from the neck down
    III. Ingestion of a toxin which prevented smooth muscle contraction

    A. I only
    B. II only
    C. I and III only
    D. II and III only

6. Pleural adhesions are fibrous connective tissue growths which cause the parietal and visceral pleura to adhere to each other. The most likely effect of pleural adhesions on respiration is that they would:

    A. impair inspiration.
    B. impair active expiration.
    C. decrease lung elasticity.
    D. not significantly interfere with breathing.

Passage 86 (Questions 1-6)
ADVANCED PASSAGE

Carbonic acid and bicarbonate form the body's most important buffer system. It is the mechanism whereby the lungs and kidneys minimize changes in pH resulting from diet, metabolism, respiration, or any other cause. The pH of arterial plasma is normally maintained at 7.4. The normal value of P_{CO_2} is 40 mm Hg, and that of $[HCO_3^-]$ is 24 mEq/L.

The two categories of acid–base disturbance are *metabolic* and *respiratory*. Respiratory *acidosis* results from hypoventilation (too little breathing), which causes a build-up of CO_2, which becomes H_2CO_3 in solution. The latter, in turn, dissociates into HCO_3^- and H^+ (hence the drop in pH). Respiratory *alkalosis* is the opposite, resulting from hyperventilation. Respiratory acid–base changes occur very rapidly.

Metabolic acid–base disturbances occur when the kidney retains too much or too little HCO_3^-, when acidic or basic substances are ingested, when H^+ is lost from the stomach (as vomitus), or when HCO_3^- is lost from the intestines (as diarrhea). These changes are more gradual, requiring hours to days to occur.

Figure 1 below shows the relationship between plasma pH and HCO_3^- concentration. Various disturbances (#1, 4, and 7) and compensations (#2, 3, 5, and 6) are indicated by the numbered arrows. At every point on Curves #1 and #4, the P_{CO_2} is 40 mm Hg; that is, Curves #1 and #4 lie on an arterial CO_2 isobar.

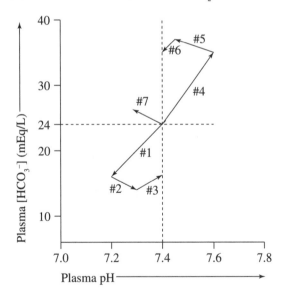

Figure 1

Adapted from *Human Physiology Foundations & Frontiers*, by Charles Schauf et al., © 1990 by Times Mirror/Mosby College Publishing.

1. In a healthy, resting individual, for every H^+ produced by metabolism:

   I. one H^+ is excreted in the urine.
   II. one bicarbonate is reabsorbed from urine as H_2CO_3 dissociates.
   III. two H^+ are excreted in the urine.

   A. I only
   B. III only
   C. I and II only
   D. I, II and III

2. At extremely high altitudes, the low P_{O_2} causes an increase in the rate of breathing. All of the following result from the increased ventilation EXCEPT:

   A. an abnormally low P_{CO_2}.
   B. respiratory alkalosis.
   C. acidic urine.
   D. a very small increase in the amount of oxygen transported.

3. A patient ingests huge amounts of a toxin which depresses respiration, and as a result hypoventilates for four days, during which time his kidneys compensate for the resulting change in plasma pH. If he is placed on a mechanical ventilator, what disturbance of the plasma will be evident within a few hours?

   A. Elevated CO_2
   B. Increased pH
   C. Decreased P_{O_2}
   D. Decreased pH

4. Which line in Figure 1 shows renal compensation for respiratory acidosis?

   A. #1
   B. #2
   C. #3
   D. #6

5. Which line in Figure 1 represents incomplete respiratory compensation after ingestion of acid?

   A. #1
   B. #2
   C. #3
   D. #7

6. Which line in Figure 1 might be seen in near-drowning with large amounts of water entering the lungs?

   A. #1
   B. #4
   C. #5
   D. #7

Passage 87 (Questions 1-6)

The circulation of a fetus differs from that of a newborn infant in several important aspects.

First, unlike an infant's anatomy, fetal anatomy does not provide direct contact between the fetus and the external environment. The lungs of the fetus are collapsed and fluid-filled, and do not function in respiration. Fetal respiration, nutritional and excretory functions are all performed by the placenta, which is essentially composed of interwoven fetal and maternal capillaries. Maternal blood, however, does not normally mix with fetal blood.

Second, both sides of the fetal heart supply blood to the systemic circulation; hence, they work largely in parallel, rather than in series as in an infant. While the lungs are fluid-filled, the pulmonary vascular resistance is higher than the systemic vascular resistance. Shunts between the left and right atria and between the great arteries permit most of the blood to bypass the lungs.

Third, the fetus exists in hypoxic conditions relative to those that exist after birth. To reach the fetal blood, oxygen must diffuse through the placenta from the maternal blood which has already oxygenated a substantial portion of maternal body tissue. The blood that perfuses the fetus is about 67% saturated with oxygen. In the normal person, this is the approximate saturation of mixed venous blood returning to the lungs to be oxygenated. Blood that leaves the lungs of the normal adult is about 95% to 98% saturated with oxygen. The lowest oxygen saturation of blood in the fetal circulation occurs in blood in the lower inferior vena cava. In the fetal lamb, which furnishes a good model for the study of human fetal circulation, oxygen saturation of blood in the lower inferior vena cava is 26%. Blood in the superior vena cava, which comes mostly from the head, is only 31% saturated in the human fetus.

The fetus has two adaptations for surviving relative hypoxia: its cellular enzymes can function at low oxygen tensions, and fetal hemoglobin can deliver oxygen to the tissues despite low levels of oxygen saturation. These special properties are lost within a few days after birth, when normal respiratory activities begin.

The brain of the human fetus is large relative to the rest of the body, and its supply of oxygen is very important. The fetal brain is perfused with highly saturated blood from the left ventricle. The output of the right ventricle, which is less saturated, supplies the limbs and internal organs of the fetus.

1. At the placenta, CO_2 should normally:

    A. diffuse from the fetal side to the maternal side.
    B. diffuse from the maternal side to the fetal side.
    C. be of equal concentration on both the maternal and fetal sides.
    D. be of higher concentration on the maternal side with no net diffusion between the maternal and fetal sides.

2. Some children persist in forming fetal hemoglobin for months or even years after birth. Such children would likely:

    A. be able to withstand environments having low oxygen content.
    B. be able to shunt blood from the right to the left side of the heart.
    C. be unable to survive in the absence of an artificial oxygen supply.
    D. be unable to bear children.

3. A newborn infant is able to survive the loss of fetal hemoglobin within a few days after birth because the infant's:

    A. blood continues to bypass the fluid-filled lungs.
    B. circulatory system is independent of the mother's.
    C. lungs have direct contact with oxygen in the environment.
    D. digestive and excretory systems become active.

4. In a pregnant woman with healthy lungs but impaired circulation, her fetus may be at risk of suffering birth defects because:

    A. the placenta will show increased material perfusion.
    B. the fetus cannot tolerate any compromising of the blood supply to its internal organs.
    C. the maternal alveoli may be deficient in oxygen partial pressure.
    D. fetal oxygen supply depends on maternal circulation.

5. Blood delivered to the fetus has a lower oxygen concentration than does blood leaving the adult lung because, before it reaches the placenta, maternal blood:

   A. mixes with fetal blood of lower oxygen concentration.
   B. releases oxygen to the mother's own tissues.
   C. gives up nutrients to the fetal circulation.
   D. must pass through the right atrium and ventricle.

6. Which of the following chambers of the fetal heart supply blood to the systemic circulatory system?

   A. Right atrium and right ventricle
   B. Right atrium and left atrium
   C. Left ventricle and right ventricle
   D. Left ventricle and right atrium

Passage 88 (Questions 1-6)

The eggs of sea urchins and amphibians have two mechanisms that prevent polyspermy during fertilization, the *fast block* and the *slow block*.

When the cell membranes of the egg and sperm fuse, sodium channels in the egg cell membrane open, and depolarization results. This depolarization prevents other sperm from entering. It is known as the fast block because it occurs very rapidly and also because the depolarization lasts less than a minute.

However, the effects of the depolarization have permanent results. These are due to ion fluxes that are caused by the initial depolarization. First, the depolarization leads to an influx of Ca^{2+}. This, in turn, causes the *cortical granules* to release proteolytic enzymes, which destroy bindin receptors in the vitelline layer. The bindin receptors are the cell surface proteins to which sperm attach, using the acrosomal protein *bindin*. Other proteins exocytosed by the cortical granules crosslink proteins in the vitelline layer, hardening it, and cause the vitelline layer to move away from the plasma membrane of the egg. These permanent changes prevent other sperm from entering the egg, and constitute the slow block to polyspermy.

The second ion flux which results from the initial depolarization is an exit of protons. A Na^+–H^+ exchanger in the plasma membrane exports one proton for each sodium ion it imports. Alkalinization of the egg cytoplasm results. The increase in pH is thought to be responsible for activation of protein synthesis and initiation of DNA replication in the egg. Drugs known to interfere with translation block initial protein synthesis in fertilized eggs, but inhibitors of transcription do not.

1. Where are the bindin receptors located in sea urchin eggs?

   A. Vitelline layer
   B. Jelly coat
   C. Cortical granules
   D. Perivitelline space

2. Primary oocytes are found at what stage of meiosis?

   A. Interphase
   B. Meiotic prophase I
   C. Meiotic anaphase I
   D. Meiotic prophase II

3. Which of the following might result from fertilization in a medium that had an abnormally low Na⁺ concentration?

I. Polyspermy
II. Failure of bindin receptors to be degraded
III. Alkalinization of the cytoplasm of the fertilized ovum

A. I only
B. II only
C. I and II only
D. II and III only

4. What would be the effect of artificially depolarizing the plasma membrane of an unfertilized egg?

A. Polyspermy
B. Inhibition of fertilization
C. Inhibition of postfertilization protein synthesis
D. Adherence of the vitelline layer to the plasma membrane

5. Which of the following can be inferred from the passage about postfertilization events in the sea urchin egg?

A. Messenger RNA coding for proteins which are normally made after fertilization is synthesized before fertilization occurs.
B. Special ribosomes are used for initial post-fertilization protein synthesis.
C. RNA polymerases are in place at the initiation sites for transcription of the mRNA for initial postfertilization proteins before fertilization occurs, and immediately begin transcribing when the fertilized egg becomes alkalinized.
D. Ribosomes are not used in the synthesis of initial post-fertilization proteins.

6. Which of the following is NOT a characteristic of the acrosomal reaction that occurs in sperm of sea urchins during fertilization?

A. Actin is polymerized to create an acrosomal process in the sperm.
B. Hydrolytic enzymes are released that digest the jelly coat.
C. Specific proteins are exposed that can bind receptors on the egg.
D. It is mediated by a decrease in intracellular pH and Ca^{2+} concentration.

Passage 89 (Questions 1-6)

The female reproductive system undergoes a series of regular cyclic changes termed the menstrual cycle. The most obvious of these changes is periodic shedding of the endometrial lining of the uterus. It results primarily from the interaction of hormones derived from the hypothalamus, pituitary gland, and ovaries. In most women during the reproductive years, menstrual bleeding recurs every 25–35 days, with a median cycle length of 28 days. The interval from the onset of menstruation to ovulation is termed the follicular phase of the ovarian cycle. The time from ovulation to the onset of menstrual bleeding is termed the luteal phase. Ovulation normally occurs at about the 14th day of the cycle.

In the normal menstrual cycle, serum concentrations of both luteinizing hormone (LH) and follicle-stimulating hormone (FSH) begin to increase prior to menstruation. FSH concentrations attain maximum levels during the first half of the follicular phase and, with the exception of a brief peak at mid-cycle, continue to fall until the lowest concentration in the cycle is reached during the second half of the luteal phase. The preovulatory decline of FSH is due to the increasing concentration of estradiol. LH levels increase gradually throughout the follicular phase, and at mid-cycle there is a large peak in serum concentration of LH. Subsequently, LH levels gradually decline, reaching their lowest concentration late in the luteal phase.

1. Women treated over a long period of time with relatively large doses of estrogen do not ovulate. This is probably due to:

A. inhibition of gonadotropin secretion by estrogen.
B. direct inhibition of progesterone's actions by estrogen.
C. overstimulation of FSH secretion by estrogen.
D. changes in behavior.

2. Ovulation is most directly caused by:

A. a peak in progesterone secretion.
B. stimulation by the corpus luteum.
C. a peak in LH secretion.
D. a decline in FSH secretion.

3. The preovulatory decline of FSH is due to:

A. positive feedback of estradiol.
B. negative feedback of FSH.
C. negative feedback of estradiol.
D. positive feedback of progesterone.

4. In the absence of pregnancy, menstruation normally occurs. This is due to the decline of which of the following hormone(s) required for maintenance of the endometrium?

    A. Progesterone and estradiol
    B. hCG
    C. FSH
    D. LH

5. Both estradiol and progesterone are produced by which of the following?

    I.   Ovarian follicle
    II. Corpus luteum
    III. Placenta
    IV. Adrenal medulla

    A. I and II only
    B. II and III only
    C. I, II, and IV only
    D. I, II, III, and IV

6. The stimulus for FSH and LH production and secretion is the pulsatile release of gonadotropin releasing hormone (GnRH). Which of the following structures produces GnRH?

    A. Anterior pituitary
    B. Posterior pituitary
    C. Hypothalamus
    D. Pineal gland

Passage 90 (Questions 1-6)

The uterus is a complex reproductive sex organ common to most mammals. In addition to providing structural support to the pelvic and abdominal viscera, it plays a critical role in several aspects of sexual reproduction and development. Anatomically speaking, the human uterus is bordered inferiorly by the cervix (which extends into the vagina), and superolaterally by each of the paired uterine tubes (which lead to the ovaries.) A simplified representation of the thickness of the endometrial lining and its associated arteries is depicted below in Figure 1.

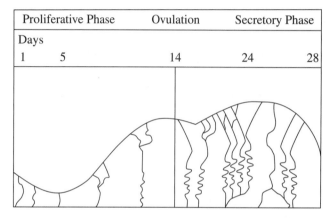

Figure 1 Endometrial Histology

The organ itself is divided into several layers, each of which has a structure well-suited to carrying out its function. The innermost layer, known as the *endometrium*, is an excellent example of this interplay between structure and function. It consists of two different zones: an outer layer adjacent to the muscular myometrium called the *basal layer*, and a variable inner layer in direct contact with the uterine cavity called the *functional layer*. Throughout the female menstrual cycle, the basal layer serves as a source of progenitor cells for the functional layer, which undergoes many changes during the cycle. These changes, which correspond to changes in circulating levels of particular hormones, can be divided into three main uterine phases: menstrual, proliferative, and secretory.

The different uterine phases are directly influenced by a series of hormones released during the menstrual cycle. These hormones are under the influence of the hypothalamic-pituitary-ovarian axis. When the hypothalamus releases gonadotropin releasing hormone (GnRH), it binds to receptors on cells in the anterior pituitary to induce the release of follicle stimulating hormone (FSH) and luteinizing hormone (LH). LH acts on the thecal cells of the ovarian follicle to cause androgen production; the androgens then diffuse into the granulosa cells of the follicle, where FSH induces their conversion into estrogen. Estrogen is the main sex hormone seen during the proliferative phase of uterine development, and is responsible for rebuilding the endometrial lining after menstruation. Its levels peak just before ovulation, which occurs at about Day 14 in a typical cycle. After ovulation, the oocyte enters the fallopian tubes, while the ruptured follicle left behind transforms into the corpus luteum. This structure begins secreting progesterone, which, along with slightly lowered levels of estrogen, is the dominant hormone of the secretory phase of the uterine cycle. Progesterone serves to further build up the endometrial lining of the uterus and increase its glandular secretions, which prepare it for implantation. Progesterone is responsible for maintaining a robust endometrium. If fertilization and implantation occur, then the corpus luteum is sustained by human chorionic gonadotropin (hCG) for 2–3 months, at which time the corpus luteum regresses and progesterone production is taken over by the placenta. If fertilization and implantation does not occur, the corpus luteum regresses within 2 weeks (approximately Day 28 of the cycle), and menstruation occurs.

1. Endometriosis is a condition in which retrograde menstruation occurs into the peritoneal cavity, leading to deposition of endometrial tissue throughout different areas of the body. Which of the following would NOT be a possible symptom of this condition?

    A. Infertility
    B. Increased diameter of the uterine tube lumen
    C. Pelvic pain
    D. Partial or complete adhesion of the fimbriae to one other

2. Which of the following is most directly responsible for the sloughing off of tissue from the uterine lining during Days 1–4 of the menstrual cycle?

    A. Increased estrogen levels
    B. Increased progesterone levels
    C. Decreased estrogen levels
    D. Decreased progesterone levels

3. A tumor affecting the posterior pituitary of a 32-year-old woman would be LEAST likely to directly produce which of the following consequences?

    A. An increase in the production of breastmilk
    B. A decrease in urine volume
    C. An activation of several feedback mechanisms in the hypothalamic-pituitary axis
    D. An increase in circulating levels of vasopressin

4. All of the following will be elevated at one point or another over the course of a regular monthly menstrual cycle in a nonpregnant woman EXCEPT which one of the following?

    A. Estrogen
    B. hCG
    C. FSH
    D. LH

5. During which phase is the basal layer most responsive to ovarian hormones?

    A. During the menstrual phase
    B. During the proliferative phase
    C. During the secretory phase
    D. The basal layer remains unresponsive throughout the cycle.

6. Which of the following statements regarding the uterus and ovaries is false?

    A. A patient with a tumor creating abnormally high levels of estrogen and progesterone is expected to have decreased levels of LH.
    B. High levels of estrogen and progesterone are seen at different times during the course of the menstrual cycle.
    C. The uterine lining's histological changes are directly regulated by FSH and LH.
    D. During menstruation, estrogen and progesterone levels are at their lowest.

Passage 91 (Questions 1-6)

Pluripotent stem cells are capable of differentiating into cells from all the three embryonic germ layers. Therefore, these are of great interest in the field of regenerative medicine. However, it is difficult to obtain and maintain pluripotent stem cells in culture for therapeutic use. Thus a novel approach to reprogramming somatic cells into pluripotent stem cells has become extremely appealing. These cells are termed *induced pluripotent stem cells* (iPSCs). In addition to providing a reliable source of stem cells, they also offer a safer approach for transplantation by using autologous grafting.

Leukemia is cancer of the bone marrow and the current treatment for most chronic cases is hematopoietic stem cell transplant. The screening process includes obtaining a donor with a high antigenic match; however, the rate of rejection of the graft is still high due to minor variations not included in the compatibility tests.

Recently, scientists proposed the following mechanism to induce differentiation of iPSCs into hematopoietic stem cells to use as an allograft.

Step 1: Isolate fibroblast cells from the patient. Endogenously express pluripotency genes using retroviral vectors.

Step 2: Utilize pluripotent transcription factors, such as Oct-4 and Sox2, to drive alternate differentiation. Isolate the iPSCs population based on changes in cell surface marker profiles, in particular ICAM1 and CD44.

Step 3: Redifferentiate the cells toward hematopoietic lineage using cytokine-mediated mechanisms and allow for proliferation in culture. Isolate the hematopoietic stem cells (HSCs) by selecting for CD34+ cells, a cell surface marker specific for HSCs.

Step 4: Irradiate all the hematopoietic stem cells in the bone marrow of the patient and administer immuno-suppressive drugs.

Step 5: Intravenously administer the hematopoietic stem cells and allows few weeks for the HSCs to home into the bone marrow. Follow-up by performing red blood cell and white blood cell counts in peripheral blood.

1. Graft rejection is one of the major concerns in transplants. Which of the following is an important determinant of antigenic compatibility in solid organ or tissue transplants?

    A. Identical ABO antigens on the surface of the graft
    B. Comparable expression of proteins within the graft
    C. Similar major histocompatibility (MHC) molecules on the surface of the graft
    D. Treatment with immune suppressant drugs

2. At what embryonic stage would pluripotent cell first exist?

    A. Zygote
    B. Inner cell mass
    C. Gastrula
    D. Morula

3. In Step 3, why is it necessary to irradiate all the cancerous hematopoietic stem cells in the patient prior to the transplant?

    A. It is important to destroy the cancerous cells in the marrow and also provide space for homing of the newly transplanted cells.
    B. Irradiation of all the HSCs destroys the immune cells, which decreases the chances of rejection of the graft.
    C. The process reduces the rate of metastasis of the tumor cells from the marrow.
    D. Irradiation of the tumor cells relieves some of symptomatic problems associated with leukemia, such as pain.

4. Which of the follow is NOT a difference between adult stem cells and embryonic stem cells?

    A. Adult stem cells are found in certain tissues for the life of the individual whereas embryonic stem cells are only found in prenatal period, until few weeks after fertilization.
    B. Adult stem cells are differentiated further down the spectrum compared to embryonic stem cells.
    C. Adult stem cells do not have self-renewal properties unlike embryonic stem cells.
    D. Adult stem cells can give rise to a more limited range of cells whereas embryonic stem cells can potentially give rise to any cell in the body.

5. A scientist is looking to examine the stages of differentiation induced by Oct-4 and Sox2. What could be added to the cell culture at given time points to stop their effect?

   I. Methylases
   II. Corepressors
   III. Heat-labile RNA polymerase

   A. I only
   B. III only
   C. I and II only
   D. II and III only

6. Which of the following would be a common complication from hematopoietic stem cell (HSC) transplant compared to a solid organ transplant?

   A. In HSC transplant, there is a higher chance of the graft immune cells attacking the recipient's body tissue due to incompatibility versus the in solid organ transplant, the host immune cells attack the incompatible graft.
   B. HSC transplant requires longer period of immunosuppression therapy compared to solid organ transplant
   C. There is a chance of developing an autoimmune disease with HSC transplant whereas there are no risks of autoimmune problems with solid organ transplant.
   D. The rejection of the graft in HSC transplant can lead to life-threatening problems whereas that is not a concern in solid organ transplant.

Passage 92 (Questions 1-6)

During development, cells change in competency, the ability to respond to signals from other tissues. They also change in their ability to induce changes in other cells. These changes are inherited by daughter cells. Experiments in amphibian gastrulas and neurulas have helped determine the developmental timing of these events.

The eye field of the early gastrula contain the cells destined to become the eye. By the neurula stage, the eye field has differentiated into retinal and lens fields, which become the retina and lens, respectively.

The following transplantation experiments were done to investigate embryogenesis in amphibians.

Experiment 1:

The eye field was excised from an early gastrula and placed into culture medium. It divided and formed undifferentiated ectoderm.

Experiment 2:

The eye field was excised from an early gastrula and transplanted into a neurulated embryo. The resulting ectodermal structure depended on the identity of the closest mesodermal tissue. For example, the implanted tissue developed into gills if grafted near the gill slits.

Experiment 3:

When an early gastrula eye field was excised and incubated with tissue excised from neurula eye field, the gastrula tissue differentiated into neural tube.

Experiment 4:

The eye field was excised from an early gastrula and allowed to incubate for 36 hours in culture medium. Then when it was incubated with tissue excised from neurula eye field as in Experiment 3, it differentiated into a lens.

Experiment 5:

The eye field was excised after neurulation had begun, and transplanted into ectodermal tissue of a neurulated embryo. An eye developed regardless of the location of the graft.

Adapted from: 1) *Foundations of Developmental Genetics*. D. J. Pritchard. © 1986 by Taylor and Francis, London. 2) *From Egg to Embryo*. J.M. Slack. © 1991 by Cambridge University press, Cambridge, England. 3) *Pattern Regulation in Defective Embryos of Xenopus laevis*. © 1984. Developmental Biology 101.

1. After the completion of gastrulation, the embryo undergoes:

   A. dedifferentiation.
   B. neurulation.
   C. cleavage.
   D. blastulation.

2. If a portion that is destined to become the heart is excised from an early gastrula and placed in culture medium, what would be expected to form?

   A. Undifferentiated ectoderm
   B. Undifferentiated mesoderm
   C. Undifferentiated endoderm
   D. An eye

3. Judging by the experiments in the passage, each of the following is true of the cells of an early gastrula's eye field EXCEPT that the cells are:

   A. competent.
   B. terminally differentiated.
   C. capable of becoming other ectodermal structures.
   D. derived from the ectodermal layer.

4. What process could account for the difference in results between Experiments 2 and 5?

   A. The differentiation into three germ layers
   B. Mutations in the cells of the eye field
   C. Ongoing development of mesodermal cells
   D. Differentiation of neural tissue

5. The results of Experiments 3 and 4 suggest that during the 36 hours of incubation, the gastrula tissue has:

   I. become mesodermal.
   II. undergone induction.
   III. altered the expression of genes.

   A. I only
   B. II only
   C. III only
   D. II and III only

6. As development proceeded in the various experiments, what changed in the developing cells?

   A. The genetic information which was duplicated with each round of cell division
   B. The composition of polypeptides in the cytoplasm and nucleus
   C. The cytoskeletal elements involved in forming the mitotic spindle
   D. The energy requirements of each cell

   _____

Passage 93 (Questions 1-5)
ADVANCED PASSAGE

The frog *Xenopus laevis* has been a model for the study of development. The egg is a large cell, consisting of an animal pole in which cleavage is very rapid, and a vegetal pole that contains most of the yolk. Very yolky cells from the vegetal pole are ultimately enclosed by the developing gut and digested. Fertilization causes a rotation of the outer layer of animal pole, creating the gray crescent, which will give rise to the dorsal lip of the blastopore. Future stages of development, known as the blastula, gastrula, and neurula, follow this initial event. The following experiments on *Xenopus* study the interactions and fates of tissues in the developing embryo.

Experiment 1:

After the first cleavage, the two blastomeres, or daughter cells, are separated from each other by shaking and allowed to develop. If the gray crescent is equally divided among both blastomeres during the first cleavage, two tadpoles, each from one blastomere, will develop. But, if the first cleavage is asymmetric so that the gray crescent is contained in only one blastomere, only one tadpole results. The blastomere without gray crescent becomes an undifferentiated ball of cells.

Experiment 2:

The dorsal lip of the blastopore of a donor in the early stage of gastrulation is grafted onto another embryo, but in a different position. The host embryo initiates gastrulation at both its own dorsal lip and at the site of the graft, forming a double embryo similar to what is seen in the case of conjoined twins.

Experiment 3:

A blastula is dissociated into free cells in a medium containing calcium and magnesium. The resulting cells form only ectodermal and endodermal cells, but not mesodermal cells. In another blastula, cells from the animal pole are removed and cultured in isolation, giving only ectodermal tissue. When similar animal pole cells are cultured in combination with vegetal pole tissue, mainly mesodermal tissue develops.

Experiment 4:

Skin cells are removed from an adult frog and cultured. The nucleus of one of the cultured skin cells is injected into an unfertilized frog egg, whose own genome was destroyed beforehand by exposure to ultraviolet radiation. A normal blastula and later a normal tadpole develop.

1. Which of the following is/are true about a differentiated cell?

   I. The genome contains a different set of genes than the fertilized egg from which it was derived.
   II. Only a subset of all the genes inherited from the zygote are expressed to give the cell its characteristics.
   III. A differentiated cell need not have undergone the process of determination.

   A. I only
   B. II only
   C. I and III only
   D. II and III only

2. The dorsal lip of the blastopore is:

   I. derived from the gray crescent.
   II. the site of neurulation in the developing zygote.
   III. the site at which gastrulation initiates.

   A. I only
   B. I and II only
   C. II and III only
   D. I, II, and III

3. Which of the following is NOT true about totipotency?

   A. Totipotent cells have the potential to develop into any part of the animal.
   B. Totipotency requires expression of all genes at the same time.
   C. Totipotency is not observed in ectodermal cells.
   D. Totipotency is usually lost by the end of gastrulation.

4. Each of the following is a distinguishing feature of chordates in the embryo stage EXCEPT:

   A. cephalization.
   B. pharyngeal gill slits.
   C. dorsal, hollow nerve cord.
   D. use of lungs for respiration.

5. In Experiment 3, mesodermal tissue develops due to:

   A. induction by animal pole tissue.
   B. induction by vegetal pole tissue.
   C. cell determination.
   D. cell differentiation.

Passage 94 (Questions 1-5)
ADVANCED PASSAGE

Early in the seventh week of gestation, the human embryo has gonads which are bipotential (ovaries are indistinguishable from testes). The internal reproductive structures are also indistinguishable.

During the seventh week, male gonads differentiate into testes. Ovaries remain undifferentiated until late in the second trimester, when many germ cells (oogonia) enter meiosis. They will remain frozen in prophase of meiosis I until puberty. The transition from oogonia to oocytes in the embryonic gonad marks the onset of ovarian differentiation.

Ongoing development in the gonads determines the differential development of male and female reproductive anatomy. In the male, Sertoli cells (the cells which support and nourish developing spermatozoa) secrete a substance which causes female reproductive structures to disappear. This substance is called Müllerian inhibiting factor (MIF), and it causes the Müllerian duct system to involute. In the female, the Müllerian ducts give rise to the fallopian tubes, the uterus, the cervix, and the upper third of the vagina. A different system of ducts develops in the male, under the influence of testosterone secreted by Leydig cells in the testicular interstitium. The male ducts are known as Wolffian ducts, and they give rise to the epididymis, vas deferens, seminal vesicles, and ejaculatory ducts.

Differentiation into functional ovaries is the default; a factor present only in the male is necessary for the switch to male development. This is a protein coded on the distal short arm of the Y chromosome, known as H–Y antigen.

The following experiments were designed to clarify the signals for differential sexual development in the mammalian embryo.

Experiment 1:

Cells were isolated from the gonads of embryonic male mice and placed in a nutritive culture medium. They formed organized structures resembling seminiferous tubules. However, when an antibody to H–Y antigen was added to the culture medium, the cells formed "follicle-like" structures, that is, clumps of cells not associated with tubules.

Experiment 2:

Cells were isolated from the gonads of embryonic female mice and incubated with H–Y antigen. They formed organized structures resembling seminiferous tubules.

1. The Sertoli cells, which produce Müllerian inhibiting factor, are located in the:

   A. seminiferous tubules.
   B. epididymis.
   C. vas deferens.
   D. corpus luteum.

2. Which of the following would probably NOT apply to an individual with a large deletion in the short arm of the Y chromosome?

   A. He would be genetically male.
   B. He would be less likely to suffer from X-linked recessive diseases than developmentally-normal females.
   C. He would have differentiated ovaries.
   D. He would have a normal-appearing vagina.

3. Testosterone is produced by which of the following?

   I. Corpus luteum
   II. Interstitial cells of Leydig
   III. Sertoli cells

   A. I only
   B. II only
   C. II and III only
   D. I, II, and III

4. Treating an XY fetus with an anti-MIF antibody during week 12 of gestation would produce a child with which of the following characteristics?

   A. Normal Wolffian duct derivatives
   B. Normal Müllerian duct derivatives
   C. Internal testes and female external genitalia
   D. All female reproductive organs and structures

5. Daily injections of anti-H–Y-antigen antibodies to an XY embryo at gestational day 80 would result in:

   I. undifferentiated testes.
   II. formation of "follicle-like" structures instead of seminiferous tubules.
   III. no change in testicular development.

   A. I only
   B. II only
   C. III only
   D. II and III only

MCAT
Biochemistry and Biology
Solutions

Passage 1

1. **C** Recall that for a fatty acid containing C carbons the amount of acetyl-CoA produced via beta-oxidation is C/2 and the number of rounds of beta oxidation is C/2 − 1. Thus a 14-carbon fatty acid would produce 14/2 = 7 acetyl CoA in 14/2 − 1 = 6 rounds of beta-oxidation. 1 NADH and 1 $FADH_2$ are produced directly during each round of beta-oxidation, so 6 NADH and 6 $FADH_2$ are produced directly by beta-oxidation for a 14-carbon fatty acid. For each acetyl CoA entering the TCA cycle, 3 NADH and 1 $FADH_2$ are generated. Thus, for a 14-C fatty acid, 7 acetyl CoAs are generated, and 21 NADH and 7 $FADH_2$ will be produced in the TCA cycle. The total amount of NADH produced is 6 + 21 = 27 NADH and the total amount of $FADH_2$ produced is 6 + 7 = 13 $FADH_2$, (choice C is correct; choices A, B, and D are wrong)

2. **B** The passage states that DTE is a reagent that is "known to break disulfide bonds." Disulfide bonds are most easily broken by reduction to their thiol state, and a reducing agent would assist in this reduction (choice B is correct). An oxidizing agent would be responsible for the formation of a disulfide bond from the corresponding thiols (choice A is wrong). Lewis acids act as electron acceptors in complexation reactions (choice C is wrong). Brønsted-Lowry acids act as H^+ donors, and the transfer of a H^+ alone will not break a disulfide bond (choice D is wrong).

3. **D** The passage states that omeprazole is known to react with thiol-containing compounds by forming mixed disulfides, a covalent interaction. Looking at Figure 1, even without the Cys residues to form disulfide bonds, the C-less CACT shows a decreased rate of carnitine uptake in the presence omeprazole (see the "C-less" and the "C-less + omeprazole" lines), which suggests that omeprazole is inhibiting the CACT though some form of non-covalent interaction (choice D is correct). Omeprazole does cause a decrease in the rate of carnitine uptake, and this confirms that the inhibition of CACT by omeprazole involves covalent interactions, but does not prove whether or not the inhibition also occurs through non-covalent interactions (choice A is wrong). The fact that DTE decreases omeprazole's inhibition of carnitine uptake suggests that DTE is reducing the disulfide bonds formed between omeprazole and the CACT (see the omeprazole DTE line). However, the fact that carnitine uptake did not increase to normal under these conditions suggest that there is some other interaction other than covalent taking place (choice B is wrong). The fact that the C-less CACT shows decreased carnitine uptake relative to the WT suggests nothing about the interaction of the CACT with omeprazole (choice C is wrong).

4. **C** Lineweaver-Burk plots invert the standard Michaelis-Menten equation and simplify to derive the equation. Treating as y and as x, we have a linear equation in the form of $y = mx + b$ with a y-intercept of , slope of , and x-intercept of. A Lineweaver-Burk plot (like that of the WT CACT) which shows a series of lines that intersect on the x-axis (same K_m values), but have different y-intercepts (different V_{max} values), is characteristic of noncompetitive inhibition (choices A and B are wrong). A Lineweaver-Burk plot (such as that of the C-less CACT) that shows a series of lines with the same y-intercept (same V_{max}) but different x-intercepts (different K_m values) is characteristic of competitive inhibition (choice C is correct and choice D is wrong).

5. **A** Item I is true: the passage states that omeprazole inhibits a gastric H^+/K^+ ATPase, which suggests that it is active in the acidic environment of the stomach at a low pH (choices B and D can be eliminated). Note that both remaining choices exclude Item III, so Item III must be false and we can focus on Item II. Item II is false: there is nothing in the passage that suggests that omeprazole consists of multiple subunits that would exhibit quaternary structure (choice C can be eliminated and choice A is correct). Note that Item III is false: it is the carnitine/acylcarnitine transporter that acts as the carrier of acyl groups, not omeprazole.

Passage 2

1. **B** An important characteristic of enzymes is their ability to catalyze reactions in a stereospecific manner. Citrate is symmetrical, but isocitrate does not wind up with radiolabel on both ends. Aconitase must be able to catalyze the reaction in a stereospecific manner, acting only on one end of citrate and not the other (choice B, not A). The information given says nothing about rates (eliminating C), and succinate dehydrogenase does not act on α-ketoglutarate (eliminating choice D).

2. **A** In the absence of the Krebs cycle, only the electrons from glycolytic NADH would be supplied to the electron transport chain, resulting in the production of less ATP (choice D is wrong). (Note that the ETC should still be functional; there is no reason to assume conditions have become anaerobic. All we are told is that the Krebs cycle was "suddenly arrested.") To compensate for the reduced ATP production, the cell would have to consume more glucose. The cytochromes (proteins in the ETC) would not be affected (choice B is wrong). Neither would there be an increase in lactic acid; remember, conditions are not anaerobic (choice C is wrong).

3. **D** α-Ketoglutarate loses a CO_2 (decarboxylation), and NAD^+ is converted to NADH, picking up high-energy electrons (it is reduced). Choice D is the answer. In general, the Krebs cycle involves the reduction of NAD^+ and FAD to form high-energy electron carriers (NADH and $FADH_2$), which in turn reduce components of the electron-transport chain.

4. **D** Since the enzyme is stereospecific, it can distinguish one end of citrate from the other. If it were not stereospecific, one would expect the enzyme to treat both ends of citrate equivalently, resulting in half of the label in succinate and half in CO_2.

5. **D** Pyruvate dehydrogenase and the Krebs cycle are located in mitochondria, so the matrix of the mitochondria is the best choice.

6. **D** Citrate has two sides which are the same. It does not have any carbons in which all four substituents are different, so it has no chiral centers and is therefore optically inactive.

Passage 3

1. **B** Insulin is a hormone, not an enzyme. It does not itself catalyze reactions.

2. **C** In hypotonic medium, there will be greater osmotic pressure in the cell than in the medium, tending to draw water into the cell and decrease the interior osmotic pressure (which eliminates choice A). Bacteria with intact cell walls can exist in hypotonic media since the rigid cell wall helps to oppose the osmotic pressure within the cell. In the absence of the cell wall, water will flow into the cell (choice C), and it will burst. There is no reason to assume an increase in ATP consumption (choice B is wrong) or in protein production (choice D is wrong).

3. **B** The NAM and NAG units are linked by β-glycosidic bonds, so this is the type of bond hydrolyzed by lysozyme.

4. **D** Prosthetic groups are not part of the amino acid sequence of proteins, but are nonprotein components of enzymes which are required for enzyme activity. For example, some enzymes contain biotin as a prosthetic group. Statements I, II, and III are all true.

5. **B** In these particular steps, glutamic acid 35 (E35) is donating a proton to the hydrolyzed NAM residue.

6. **A** In Step 3, water supplies a proton to the Glu 35 residue and an OH⁻ which attacks the carbocation. If radiolabeled, water could label the reaction product (hydrolyzed NAG group) and indicate the site of enzymatic cleavage; thus, A is correct. B is false since radioactive Asp 52 would be part of the enzyme and would remain part of the enzyme, providing no information about the reaction. C is wrong because excess Glu 35 does not make sense: This is a part of the enzyme, not a soluble amino acid, and it cannot be added separately in excess. And D is incorrect since we have no specific information about the effect of pH on the lysozyme reaction mechanism. It is likely that low pH would diminish enzyme activity, as it does for most enzymes at lower than physiological pH.

Passage 4

1. **B** The passage states that the ion is attracted to Photosystem 1 by the attraction of opposite charges (positively-charged photosystem and negatively-charged hexachloroplatinate ion).

2. **A** The main result of the light phase, as depicted in Figure 1, is the reduction of NADP⁺ to make NADPH (choice A). Choice B is wrong since NADP⁺ is converted into NADPH, not vice versa. Choice C is incorrect since in any system, mass and charge are conserved. Electrons move from one molecule to another, but they are not created or destroyed in a chemical reaction. Choice D is eliminated since Figure 1 depicts electrons moving from Photosystem 2 to Photosystem 1.

3. **D** The passage states that the light reactions supply the dark reactions with a "high energy substrate". The most likely candidate among the choices is ATP.

4. **B** The light phase makes NADPH, and the dark phase consumes it. In the absence of the dark phase, NADPH will continue to be produced, but none will be consumed, making NADPH levels rise (choice B). Choice C is wrong since the dark phase is responsible for biosynthesis, such as carbohydrate production, so this will decrease, not increase. Choice D can be eliminated since the amount of light and photoactivation should remain the same.

5. **B** Proteins are composed of amino acid residues which are joined together by peptide bonds during the translation process. To split the protein into smaller pieces, proteases and chemical reagents act to hydrolyze the peptide bond, reversing the biosynthetic process.

6. C   A racemic mixture is one which contains equal quantities of two stereoisomers that rotate plane-polarized light in opposite directions. Since there are equal quantities of both, racemic mixtures are optically inactive. Thus, choice C, which states that the sample rotates light, is inconsistent with the conclusion that the sample is racemic and is the correct answer choice. All other choices are consistent with the conclusion that the sample is a racemic mixture of glucose. Carbohydrates, of which glucose is one, are made of only carbon, hydrogen and oxygen (choice A is consistent and can be eliminated), glucose, with six carbons and a carbonyl group on the 6th carbon, is an aldohexose (choice B is consistent and can be eliminated), and racemic mixtures do not rotate light (choice D is consistent and can be eliminated).

Passage 5

1. D   During oxidative phosphorylation, the final electron acceptor from NADH is O_2, but during fermentation, the final acceptor is an organic compound.

2. C   Pyruvate is decarboxylated (it loses a CO_2), and acetaldehyde is reduced by NADH.

3. A   Pyruvate is reduced (accepting electrons), and NADH is oxidized (choice A). Choices B, C, and D are wrong since in fermentation, NADH is oxidized to NAD^+.

4. A   Lactic acid will decrease the pH of plasma. Carbon dioxide dissolved in plasma also decreases the pH through conversion to carbonic acid. The respiratory rate is regulated to increase when the plasma becomes more acidic, getting rid of CO_2 and making the plasma more alkaline again.

5. B   Only in fermentation is NAD^+ regenerated (choice B). Glycolysis consumes NAD^+, converting it to NADH. Under aerobic conditions, oxidative phosphorylation must occur to convert the NADH back to NAD^+ for glycolysis to continue. Choices A, C, and D are incorrect since both fermentation and normal glycolysis result in the oxidation of glucose, with ATP production and transfer of high-energy electrons to NAD^+.

6. B   Muscle cells can produce ATP through aerobic respiration, with glycolysis linked to the Krebs cycle and oxidative phosphorylation. Under anaerobic conditions, muscle cells can produce ATP through fermentation, using NADH to reduce pyruvate to lactic acid and regenerate NAD^+. This is similar to metabolism in facultative anaerobes, which are able to use either fermentation or oxidative phosphorylation, depending on the availability of oxygen. Thus, B is the answer. Choices A and D can be eliminated since muscle cells can use lactic-acid fermentation to survive without using oxygen during periods of strenuous activity, and C is wrong since muscle cells will use aerobic respiration most of the time, except during strenuous exercise which uses oxygen faster than it can be supplied.

Passage 6

Passage 6 is labeled as an "Advanced Passage". This passage (and the other passages labeled similarly) is longer and more difficult than anything you will see on the MCAT, so don't be discouraged! The reasons you are doing these passages are: 1) to improve your test-taking skills, and 2) to improve your mastery of the material. Both of these goals are best met by more difficult practice passages. When you tackle a tough passage like this one, study the explanations to familiarize yourself with the information—don't memorize all the details. More importantly, study the questions and the explanations together to see how you could have answered the question correctly without fully understanding the theory. Though this passage is tougher than your average MCAT passage, you will definitely see a few questions that are this tough, and again, the best way to get good at easy passages is to do hard ones.

1. **A**
   - **A:** **Yes.** This is the correct choice because the equation is balanced and accounts for changes in FAD and NAD^+ redox states and H_2O as a reactant. Remember that the acyl-CoA formed after one turn is two carbons shorter than the acyl-CoA entering the cycle.
   - B: No, this does not account for changes in the redox state of NAD^+ and FAD, and it is not a balanced equation.
   - C: No, this does not account for NAD^+ and FAD as redox reactants.
   - D: No. This equation is not balanced: the left side is missing a CoA and the right side an H^+.

2. **D**
   - A: No. An isomerase rearranges the linkages of atoms between compounds with identical molecular formulas. In this case, two protons are removed as a double bond is created, so the reactant (acyl-CoA) is not an isomer of the product (enoyl-CoA).
   - B: No. The conversion of enoyl-CoA to L-hydroxy acyl-CoA is a hydration reaction. In the hydration of an alkene, water acts as a nucleophile to destroy the double bond and produce an alcohol.
   - C: No, this is an oxidation, in which two C–H bonds are replaced by a C=C double bond. Note that FAD gets reduced, as the reactant is oxidized.
   - **D:** **Yes.** An enoyl consists of a carbonyl group plus a double bond between the α and β carbons. (Recall that the carbonyl carbon is #1; the next carbon, #2, is known as the α carbon; carbon #3 is the β carbon.) Creating a double bond from a single bond is an oxidation. Also, the reduction of FAD to $FADH_2$ (gain of electrons) is a signal that the conversion of acyl-CoA to enoyl-CoA is an oxidation. Remember that oxidations are always accompanied by reductions.

3. **C**
   - A & B: No. Don't forget to add the ATP produced by acetyl-CoA in the citric acid cycle! See C.
   - **C:** **Yes.** In order for a 16-carbon fatty acid to be completely oxidized, 7 turns of the cycle must be completed, which produces 7 $FADH_2$, 7 NADH, and 8 acetyl-CoA. Each acetyl-CoA then goes through the citric acid cycle and produces 3 NADH, 1 $FADH_2$, and 1 GTP; since there are 8 acetyl-CoA, the total is 24 NADH, 8 $FADH_2$, and 8 GTP. The grand total for both β oxidation and the citric acid cycle is 15 $FADH_2$, 31 NADH, and 8 GTP. Each $FADH_2$ produces 1.5 ATP, and each NADH produces 2.5 ATP in oxidative phosphorylation. The total ATP produced is $(15 \times 1.5) + (31 \times 2.5) + (8 \times 1) = 108$ ATP. We subtract the 2 ATP required to activate the fatty acid (from the passage), giving the grand total of 106 ATP.
   - D: No. Don't forget the activation "cost" of 2 ATP equivalents. (Remember, the conversion of 1 ATP to 1 AMP has the same energy cost as the conversion of 2 ATP to 2 ADP.)

4. **D**

   A: No. Synthesis occurs in the cytosol, while oxidation occurs in the mitochondrial matrix.

   B: No. Synthesis requires NADPH, while NAD^+ is produced in oxidation.

   C: No. Like most opposing pathways, different enzymes are involved in fatty acid synthesis and oxidation.

   D: **Yes.** Synthesis builds fatty acids out of acetyl-CoA two-carbon units, while oxidation produces acetyl-CoA.

5. **B**

   A: No. This is phenylpropionate. Knoop's dogs digested it to benzoate. According to the passage, FA's with an even number of carbon atoms in their chains plus a phenyl ring (in this case phenylpalmitate) result in phenylacetate in the urine.

   B. **Yes.** This is phenylacetate. From Knoop's experiment, fatty acids with an even number of carbons produce phenylacetate. The key point here is that either benzoate or phenylacetate will result when any FA with an attached phenyl is digested.

   C: No. This is benzoate, which was produced when fatty acids with odd numbers of carbons were fed to dogs.

   D: No. This is phenol. See B.

6. **B**

   A: No. Citrate is produced when OAA combines with acetyl-CoA in the citric acid cycle.

   B: **Yes.** Under conditions of low carbohydrate availability (i.e., fasting), OAA is used for gluconeogenesis. This lowers its availability to the citric acid cycle. An insufficient supply of OAA, which combines with acetyl-CoA at the beginning of the citric acid cycle, prevents acetyl-CoA from being further oxidized.

   C: No. Acetyl-CoA cannot be converted to glucose. A little glucose is necessary to provide OAA if the citric acid cycle is to run.

   D: No; true but irrelevant.

7. **C**

   A: No, there is a dehydrogenation, not a hydration.

   B: No, this is dehydrogenation, which is an oxidation, not a reduction. See C.

   C: **Yes.** Conversion of an alcohol to a ketone is an oxidative removal of protons, a dehydrogenation. And as noted in #2D, when you see an electron carrier (NAD^+ in this case) get reduced, you know an oxidation has taken place.

   D: No, it is not a transacylation reaction. See C.

8. **C**

   A: No. In the absence of oxygen, the electron transport chain is shut down; this prevents the oxidation of NADH and $FADH_2$ to NAD^+ and FAD. Without NAD^+ and FAD, the β-oxidation cycle would stop, not accelerate.

   B: No. In fact, the availability of CoA would increase because it would be unable to react with fatty acids in the cycle.

   C: **Yes.** The electron transport chain and oxidative phosphorylation normally use oxygen to oxidize NADH and $FADH_2$, thereby regenerating NAD^+ and FAD. Without oxygen, NADH and $FADH_2$ build up.

   D: No. This statement is accurate, but it describes the effect on glucose breakdown, not fatty acid breakdown. When oxygen is scarce, the pyruvate made from glucose is fermented to lactate instead of decarboxylated to an acetyl unit. The role of fermentation is to recycle the NAD^+ necessary for glycolysis.

Passage 7

1. **B** The reaction shown in Figure 1 depicts the transfer of an amine group from alanine to α-ketoglutarate. The transfer of a C-, N-, or P-containing functional group from one molecule to another is catalyzed by a transferase (choice B). Oxidoreductases catalyze redox reactions (choice A is incorrect), isomerases catalyze intramolecular rearrangements (choice C is incorrect), and ligases catalyze bond formations at the expense of a high energy phosphate bond (choice D is incorrect).

2. **C** Glycogen breakdown serves to buffer decreases in dietary intake of glucose in the short term (e.g. during the overnight fast). This occurs in response to elevated serum glucagon (choice C is correct). Glycerol is a substrate for the production of glucose, but it comes from the breakdown of triglycerides and subsequent gluconeogenesis. Triglyceride breakdown doesn't occur until day 2 according to Figure 2, meaning that there will not be significant levels of glycerol available to go through the gluconeogenesis pathway (choice A is incorrect). Most glucose from a meal is stored relatively soon after intake of the meal (on the scale of hours), as indicated by the decreased insulin levels following the overnight fast (choice B is incorrect). Ketogenesis produces ketone bodies, not glucose (choice D is incorrect).

3. **C** Ketone bodies are polar and thus are soluble in aqueous solution (choice A is true and can be eliminated). A key function of ketone bodies is to take the place of glucose in many tissues, including the brain (choice B is true and can be eliminated). Ketone bodies are produced in the liver (choice D is true and can be eliminated) from acetyl-CoA, not glycerol, which enters gluconeogenesis after triglyceride breakdown (choice C is not true and is the correct answer choice).

4. **A** This question offers the possibility to do 2x2 elimination. The gain of a hydrogen atom by 3-hydroxybutyrate indicates that a reduction has occurred (choices B and D can be eliminated), and reductions require donation of a reducing equivalent, in this case in the form of an NADH molecule (choice C can be eliminated and choice A is correct).

5. **B** Consider the differences between serotonin and tryptophan: the presence of a hydroxyl group on carbon 5 of the aromatic ring and the lack of the carboxylic acid group that made up the backbone of tryptophan. Thus Item I is false: no deamination occurred, all amines are still present (choices C and D can be eliminated). Both remaining choices include Item III so it must be true and we can focus on Item II. Item II is true: the loss of the carboxylic acid group from tryptophan represents a decarboxylation (choice A can be eliminated and choice B is correct). Note that Item III is true: the addition of a hydroxyl group represents a hydroxylation reaction.

6. **C** Five days after starting a ketogenic diet, the body will be in a glucose-conserving, highly ketotic state, per Figure 2. Hexokinase and phosphofructokinase are involved in glycolysis, and thus are active in the liver when there is abundant glucose in the blood (e.g. just after a mea, choices A and B can be eliminated). Glycogen phosphorylase is involved in glycogen breakdown. While it was likely active during the overnight fast, all glycogen reserves are also likely exhausted by this point, evidenced by the body's reliance on ketone bodies (choice D can be eliminated). HMG-CoA synthase (hydroxymethylglutaryl-coenzyme A synthase) is involved in ketone body synthesis. Figure 2 shows abundant ketone bodies at the point of the five-day fast, and ketone body synthesis occurs in the liver (choice C is correct). Note that specific knowledge of the action of HMG-CoA synthase was not required to choose the correct answer; only the elimination of the other three enzymes as involved in glucose metabolism.

Passage 8

1. **C** Both DNA and RNA contain phosphate, so choice A is wrong. Only DNA contains thymine, so choice B is wrong. Only RNA contains uracil, so C is the best choice. D-ribose is unique to RNA and not DNA, but deoxyribonucleotides are synthesized from ribonucleotides, meaning that labeled ribose would end up in DNA as deoxyribose, so choice D is wrong.

2. **A** The diploid cell that survived in Experiment 2 was formed by the fusion of two haploid cells: one wild-type and one with mutation No. 136. Thus, the cell contained one copy of the No. 136 mutation.

3. **A** DNA is replicated from DNA, so a change in the DNA genome, such as the mutations shown in Figure 1, must occur during DNA replication.

4. **B** Fitness is measured by the number of offspring in future generations who share an organisms' alleles. If it were true that the mutants reproduce at different rates, that would indicate different fitness, but the passage states that they grow at the same rate; thus, A is eliminated. The answer is B: Since mutant No. 127 is protected against virus while No. 136 is not, No. 136 would be expected to produce fewer offspring in the population and to have a lower fitness as a result. C is wrong since fitness cannot be compared between two different species, and D is wrong since protein length indicates nothing about the fitness of the organism as a whole.

5. **D** Nonsense mutations are those which introduce premature stop codons into a protein, causing translation to terminate early. This is the case for mutant No. 136.

6. **C** A key to speciation is a barrier to reproduction with other species, which is what happened in this case. As long as a population is in contact with other populations and interbreeding, reproductive barriers are not likely to arise, and speciation will probably not occur. Geographic isolation, however, allows a population to change its allelic frequency from other populations and for reproductive isolation to arise.

Passage 9

1. **C**

   C: Yes. One high-energy phosphate bond is required for initiation. For each AA to be added to the chain, two high-energy phosphate bonds are required for "charging" the tRNA with the correct amino acid ($\times$ 100 amino acids = 200). Two high-energy phosphate bonds are required for chain formation—one to carry the AA to the ribosome, one to translocate ($\times$ 99 peptide bonds = 198). Finally, one high-energy phosphate bond is needed for termination. The grand total is $1 + 200 + 198 + 1 = 400$. This can be summarized in the following general equation: # high-energy phosphate bonds = $4n$, where n is the number of amino acids in the peptide.

2.   **C**

Item I: True. First, remember that the code is read from 5′ to 3′. Since we do not know the reading frame, it is possible that the AUG sequence in the original length of mRNA served as a start signal, in which case changing the U would result in failure to initiate translation.

Item II: True. Without knowing the reading frame, we cannot rule out the fact that this change will result in a stop codon (UAA).

Item III: False. No matter what position the original U is in (first, second, or third) changing it will change the amino acid that is being coded for. Note, however, that there are certain code changes which do not change the genetic message, especially in the third position ("letter") of the codon ("word"). For instance, changing AUU to AUC makes no difference, since both code for isoleucine. The code is said to exhibit degeneracy. Remember, however, that any given codon codes for only one amino acid: There is no ambiguity in the genetic code.

3.   **A**

A: **Yes.** Puromycin "looks" like a tRNA. It enters the ribosome, forms one peptide bond, and thus becomes covalently attached to the protein. But, since it cannot be linked to the next amino acid because it lacks a carboxyl, protein synthesis terminates prematurely.

B: No, aminoacyl tRNAs enter at the A site during elongation (see passage, second paragraph).

C: No, puromycin can only form one bond, so protein synthesis stops.

D: No, puromycin causes premature termination. Initiation requires the binding of only a single aminoacyl tRNA (the initiator) to the ribosome, and thus would not be affected.

4.   **C**

C: **Yes.** Ribosomes dissociate between rounds of translation. Hence, at the end of the experiment there would be some all-light ribosomes, some all heavy ones, some with the 30S subunit light and the 50S subunit heavy, and finally some with the 50S subunit light and the 30S subunit heavy. Thus, there would be 4 different densities of 70S ribosomes.

5.   **C**

C: **Yes.** This is directly stated in the passage (first paragraph). In fact, certain cells in our immune system can "sniff out" f-MET and release toxins in the area, where prokaryotes are.

6.   **C**

A: No, it is true that the N-terminal AA is formylated.

B: No, this is true. Since prokaryotic mRNA has no nuclear membrane to cross, its translation can begin even before its synthesis is complete. Remember that this applies only to prokaryotes. Eukaryotic mRNA must be spliced and transported across the nuclear membrane before translation can begin.

C: **Yes.** This is false. It is hydrogen bonds between tRNA and mRNA which are essential for translation. This is stated in the second sentence of paragraph 2 in the passage.

D: No, this is true. It is not spliced, and translation is simultaneous with transcription. The opposite holds for eukaryotes.

Passage 10

1. **C**
   A: No. Lysis is destruction of host cells by the phage. Slight cloudiness appeared before the phage was added to the *E. coli* culture and was due to increasing bacterial density.
   B: No. Lysis is the destruction of host cells by the phage. An increase in turbidity marks an increase in the number of cells, not destruction.
   C: **Yes.** Lysis is destruction of host cells by the phage. The passage states: "1 mL of stock high titer coliphage is added to the culture. After 3 hours the culture appears nearly clear."
   D: No. As stated in the passage, there is a visible change in the culture 3 hours after the phage are added.

2. **D**
   A: No. Colonies on the agar surface indicate *E. coli* growth, not virus.
   B: No. This would occur in the absence of virus.
   C: No. Viral replication can be inferred to produce clear spots in the lawn of *E. coli* growth, since it produced clearing in the broth (see #1C).
   D: **Yes.** The *E. coli* that was added to the soft agar will produce a solid growth, or lawn, covering the agar. Phages lyse the cells; this results in release of more phages; eventually a macroscopic clear spot, or plaque, appears. This indicates large-scale cell destruction.

3. **B**
   A: No. There is no reason to suspect this.
   B: **Yes.** The bacteria must be in a growth phase in order for the phages to replicate efficiently, as they depend on the replication mechanism of their host cells. The overnight culture would be mostly in stationary phase because nutrients and space would have been exhausted.
   C: No. There would be some dead cells in the overnight culture, but if they were all dead, they couldn't grow in the new culture.
   D: No. As in all such microbiological studies, sterile technique would be used to produce the *E. coli* culture, so competing bacteria would not likely be present. Besides, a few contaminating bacteria wouldn't change the culture's gross appearance after massive phage infection. And furthermore, any contaminating bacteria would be transferred right along with the 0.5 mL of *E. coli* culture.

4. **D**
   D: **Yes.** The virus was diluted 1:10 and then 1:10 again, or 1:100 total. From this dilution, 0.1 mL was added with *E. coli* to the plate, yielding 150 plaques. 150 virus in 0.1 mL means that there are 1500 virus per mL in the diluted virus. 1500 virus/mL × 100 dilution factor means there are 1.5×10^5 virus in the original solution.

5. **D**
   Item I: True. The cleaving of the culture indicates the lysis (and death) of bacterial cells.
   Item II: True. Some infected but not yet lysed cells should be present.
   Item III: True. Determining the titer of free phage is the next step in the protocol outlined in the passage.

6. **A**
    - A: **Yes.** Lysosomes are membrane-bound organelles, which prokaryotes (in this case the bacterium *E. coli*) lack.
    - B: No. The peptidoglycan cell wall is one of the defining characteristics of bacteria.
    - C: No. Ribosomes are necessary for protein synthesis. Prokaryotes have them, although they are different from the ones we have (key for antibiotic specificity).
    - D: No. Bacteria have a DNA genome, plus mRNA, tRNA, and rRNA—just like us.

7. **D**
    - A: No. Budding cannot occur in the presence of a cell wall. The cell wall is lysed by a lysozyme, and the host cell bursts, releasing the viruses.
    - B: No. Assembly must be complete before lysis.
    - C: No. Lysozyme is coded by a late gene. It must not lyse the host until the viruses are assembled and ready to go.
    - D: **Yes.** T4 has a DNA genome which is transcribed and translated by the host's machinery.

Passage 11

1. **D**   Choices A, B, and C are wrong because these are all viral proteins, so they will be produced through transcription and translation of the hepatitis B viral DNA genome. Double-stranded DNA, however, is not produced through transcription and translation.

2. **C**   Thymine is not found in RNA. Uracil is used in place of thymine in RNA, and the pre-genome is made of RNA. Radiolabeled thymine would not be found in the pre-genome.

3. **A**   The capsid first forms around the pre-genome RNA, which is then reverse transcribed to make a DNA genome inside the capsid. The virus is then infective and can leave the cell.

4. **A**   HBV is an enveloped virus. When it leaves the cell, its acquires its envelope from the plasma membrane of the infected cell; thus, A is correct. Choice B is wrong since the budding of virus is distinct from endocytosis, in which material enters the cell. Choice C is wrong because there is no mention of IgG production by infected cells; this is part of the immune response mediated by other cells. Choice D is wrong since the pre-genome is packaged in a protein capsid and never comes into direct contact with the plasma membrane.

Passage 12

1. **D**   Ataxia is defined in the passage as "coordination problems." The region of the brain that controls muscular coordination is the cerebellum.

2. **C**   The curves for the prion-free control and prion-free injected mice are essentially the same, indicating that the injection of PrP^{Sc} (abnormal prion) can not be the cause of the ataxia. Furthermore, if there is no normal prion protein to begin with, there is nothing for PrP^{Sc} to convert (choice A is wrong). Normal age-related ataxia appears later in life, at about 74 weeks compared to prion-free ataxia, which appears at about 60 weeks (choice B is wrong). While infection with the West Nile virus could cause encephalitis and ataxia, there is no reason to assume the mice were infected; the

question asks for the most likely explanation (choice C is a better answer than choice D). The passage states that PrP^c (normal prion) is thought to be important in the maintenance of critical brain cells, thus its absence leads to CNS deterioration and ataxia (choice C is correct).

3. **B** The passage states that Creutzfeldt–Jakob disease and fatal insomnia are both caused by mutations, thus they could be inherited (choices A and C are true and eliminated). Hemophilia (although not mentioned in the passage) is an X-linked recessive disorder, and can be inherited (choice D is true and eliminated). Kuru, however, is caused by ingestion of diseased tissue (choice B is false and the correct answer choice).

4. **C** Prion-related ataxia does not appear until approximately 10 weeks after injection (see Figure 2). Since in this case ataxia appeared within one week, it is unlikely that the solution contained abnormal prions (choice A is wrong). Also, abnormal prions are resistant to protease treatment (choice D is wrong). There is no reason to assume an immune reaction would occur upon injection of normal prion proteins (choice B is wrong). The symptoms and the speed with which they develop are consistent with viral infection. This is supported by the fact that treatment with detergent and protease (destroying the viral envelope and capsid) prevents infection (choice C is correct).

5. **B** Statements I and II are clearly stated in the passage as being causes of prion disease, and are therefore true. However the passage states that it is a missense mutation in the prion protein (the mutation of a codon for an amino acid into a codon for a new amino acid), not a nonsense mutation (the mutation of a codon for an amino acid into a STOP codon) that causes disease. Statement III is false.

6. **A** The West Nile virus is a flavivirus which is described in the passage as being enveloped (surrounded by a host-derived lipid bilayer). Only animal viruses can be enveloped, since these are the only cells without a cell wall. Hence yeast (choice A), which have a cell wall, would not be a good choice for culturing this virus. Neurons, osteoblasts, and muscle are all animal cells, and could be acceptable for culturing (choices B, C, and D are wrong).

Passage 13

1. **D** A virus that lacks E1B will not be able to infect and replicate in normal cells that express p53 (choice A is incorrect). Only transformed cells generally lack p53, and these are not normal. Since the virus cannot replicate in normal cells, but only cells that lack p53, it is not likely to cause new tumors (choice B is wrong). In order to prevent tumor response to chemotherapy, the virus must contain the E1B gene so that it can block p53 activity. Since this virus lacks E1B, it cannot suppress response to chemotherapy (choice C is wrong). A virus with E1B deleted can infect and replicate only in cells which lack p53 expression. Therefore, those cells lacking p53 expression would be affected by the virus, while those with normal p53 expression would not (choice D is correct).

2. **C** A virus lacking E1B cannot replicate in cells with p53, since these cells will enter apoptosis. If this same cell line expresses E1B, then this will complement the virus, inactivating p53 to prevent apoptosis, and allow virus lacking E1B to replicate in these cells. Choice A is incorrect since the E1B expressed at high levels will block p53-induced apoptosis. The progeny virus that

are produced from infection by the E1B-lacking virus will still have the same genome and still lack E1B. These cells will be able to replicate in E1B-expressing cell lines, as before, but will remain unable to replicate in cells that do not express E1B but do express p53 (choice C is correct, and B and D are wrong).

3. **B** p53 does not block the signals that stimulate proliferation. It is E1A that causes the signal to proliferate, and the passage does not indicate a connection directly between E1A and p53 (choice A is wrong). The passage states that p53 induces apoptosis in the event of aberrant DNA replication, such as induction of proliferation by virus (choice B is correct). p53 can help to prevent the development of cancer, since it is a tumor-suppressor gene, but it will not prevent infection by wild-type adenovirus, which possesses wild-type E1B to inactivate p53 (choice C is wrong). And in no way does p53 increase the risk of viral infection (choice D is wrong).

4. **D** Rb and p53 are both tumor-suppressor genes, but this does not necessarily mean that they both have the same function in the cell. There are many different mechanisms that help to regulate the cell cycle (choice A is wrong). Since Rb and p53 do not necessarily have the same mechanism, there is no reason to believe that they will both interact with E1A (choice B is wrong). There is no information suggesting that the two tumor-suppressor gene products interact physically in any way (choice C is wrong). It is stated that E1A and E1B in combination are much more efficient at inducing transformation that either protein alone. Since these products interact with Rb and p53 to inactivate them, this suggests that inactivation of Rb and p53 together increases the transformation efficiency (choice D is correct).

5. **D** The scale on the vertical axis is logarithmic, meaning that Mutant B produced at least 10 times more virus, not twice as much (choice A is wrong). The data indicate that virus cannot replicate efficiently in the absence of E1A. Replication in the absence of both E1A and E1B was not tested in this experiment, so no conclusion about this can be drawn, although based on the passage, the functions of the proteins are complementary, not antagonistic, so it is unlikely that E1A is not required if E1B is absent (choice B is wrong). There is a significant difference in the replication of virus lacking E1B depending on the presence of p53, indicating that p53 is active and probably can induce apoptosis. The data certainly do not support the opposite conclusion, that p53 cannot induce apoptosis (choice C is wrong). Wild-type adenovirus appears to replicate the same in the presence or absence of p53, indicating that choice D is the best response.

Passage 14

1. **C** Prion plaque formation results from protein-protein interactions between prion precursor proteins, in this case the protein Aβ. Protein-protein interactions are an example of quaternary structure, and thus involve noncovalent interactions between subunits. Hydrophobic interactions (choice A), hydrogen bonding (choice B), and salt bridges (choice D) are noncovalent interactions and thus may be affected during plaque formation. The amino acid sequence (choice C) does not change based on noncovalent interactions as it is built via peptide bonds.

2. **B** Item I is true: Figure 2 shows that the hippocampus, which is involved in the encoding of new memories, is strongly affected by amyloid plaques in Alzheimer's disease (choice C can be eliminated). Item II is false: the occipital lobe, which is involved in the processing of visual information including color, is not affected by Alzheimer's. While the thalamus is also involved in routing incoming visual information, there is no reason to believe that amyloid plaques there would

lead to color vision loss specifically (choice A can be eliminated). Item III is false: Figure 2 shows that the precentral gyrus (motor cortex) is not affected in Alzheimer's, so there is no reason to believe that paralysis would occur (choice D can be eliminated and choice B is correct).

3.   **A**   This question offers the possibility to do a 2x2 elimination. In order for prions to cause production of plaques, they must cross the blood-brain barrier. Figure 1 shows that no disease results when plaques are introduced intravenously. Thus, Figure 1 indicates that they do not cross the blood-brain barrier (choices C and D can be eliminated). Small, neutrally charged molecules cross the blood-brain barrier, while larger charged molecules do not. Choice B thus presents a reason that amyloid plaques would be able to cross the blood-brain barrier and thus can be eliminated. The passage states the amyloid plaques are comprised of multiple proteins of molecular weight of 42 kDa, a very large size. Thus, choice A offers a plausible explanation and is therefore correct.

4.   **A**   The passage states that there are two forms of Aβ, a benign lower molecular weight form of 40 kDa (Aβ40) and a pathological higher molecular weight form of 42 kDa (Aβ42), both derived from the same precursor of 135 kDa (APP). The gel in this question shows that digestion with protease produces two fragments: a smaller (more electrophoretically mobile) fragment which can be presumed to be the Aβ cleavage product and a larger (less electrophoretically mobile) fragment which is the remainder of the APP precursor. Cleavage with Protease 1 produces the larger version of the smaller fragment, presumed to be Aβ42. Thus, a mutation that enhances expression of Protease 1 would produce more Aβ42 and would make the patient more likely to develop Alzheimer's, according to the passage (choice A is correct). A mutation resulting in more production of Aβ40 would not have any pathological consequences (choice B is incorrect). The Shine-Dalgarno sequence is the ribosome binding site in prokaryotic RNA and would not be found in eukaryotes (choices C and D are wrong).

5.   **A**   Prions are highly stable aggregates of misfolded protein. Protein-protein interactions that allow prion aggregation are a result of tertiary and quaternary structure. It is plausible that these interactions are sufficiently strong that they could prevent denaturation of the prion upon heating (answer A is correct). Heat treatment denatures proteins; it does not proteolytically degrade them (answer B is incorrect). Proteins usually cannot spontaneously refold following denaturation (answer C is incorrect). Prions form as a result of noncovalent interactions, so there are no covalent bonds between subunits (answer D is incorrect).

6.   **D**   The initial inflammatory reaction following intracerebral injection provides a hint that the rabbits' immune systems are responding against the foreign Aβ plaques. A treatment which decreases the rabbits' immune response thus could circumvent destruction of the foreign plaques. Corticosteroids cause systemic immunosuppression (choice D is correct). Intracerebral injection with an antibody against Aβ42 would decrease the amount of Aβ42 available to form plaques and thus decrease the chances of developing Alzheimer's (choice A is incorrect). The permeability of the blood-brain barrier is not a factor here because the purified Aβ plaques are injected directly into the brain (choice B is incorrect). While some of the immune response involves proteolytic breakdown of foreign proteins, a key feature of prions is that they are highly resistant to proteolysis because of their stable structures; a protease inhibitor also would not suppress the initial antibody-mediated neutralization of the foreign Aβ plaques (choice C is incorrect).

Passage 15

1. **D**

    General: The plasmid has genes that encode proteins providing antibiotic resistance. Inserting the *nrd*⁺ into the *Eco*RI site will disrupt the chloramphenicol resistance gene and leave bacteria sensitive to that antibiotic. At the same time, bacteria containing the recombinant plasmid will gain resistance to hydroxyurea.

    A: No. The sensitivity to chloramphenicol and resistance to hydroxyurea are not shown.

    B: No. Resistance to hydroxyurea is not shown.

    C: No. Resistance to chloramphenicol is not shown.

    D: **Yes; amp and tet resistance are not changed, but chloramphenicol resistance is lost, and hydroxyurea sensitivity is gained.**

2. **B**

    B: **Yes.** Plasmid pBR325 has one cutting site for each of these enzymes (see Figure 1), so cutting with both will create two fragments. The size of the fragment can be estimated from the map or calculated precisely from the description following Figure 1. A kbp is 1000 base pairs. The distance between the *Hind*III site and the *Sal*I site, moving clockwise, is $1800 - 1100 = 700$ bp, so this must be the size of one fragment. The second fragment is the rest of the plasmid: $6000 - 700 = 5300$ bp.

3. **C**

    Item I: False. Plasmids are extrachromosomal circular DNA molecules, not organelles. Organelles are membrane-bound cellular components present only in eukaryotes.

    Item II: True. Like the bacterial genome, plasmids are found free in the cytoplasm, i.e., they are not membrane-bound. Hence, ribosomes can translate plasmid mRNA while it is being transcribed.

    Item III: True. Plasmids rely on bacterial machinery for replication (and transcription).

4. **D**

    A: No. It is transcription of the *nrd*⁺ gene that is the key to the question. Plasmid replication is ensured by a bacterial origin.

    B: No. The *nrd*⁺ gene is present in both orientations, indicating that its expression does not depend on a plasmid promoter. See D below.

    C: No. The bacteria are raised in the presence of hydroxyurea and would not survive without the *nrd*⁺ gene.

    D: **Yes.** The *nrd*⁺ gene is 28 kb long, and the pBR325 plasmid is 6 kb long, so the total size of the recombinant plasmid is 34 kb. The *nrd*⁺ gene can insert in two different orientations into the *Eco*RI site. If the *nrd*⁺ gene contains its own promoter, then either orientation will produce gene product and provide resistance to bacteria. If transcription of *nrd*⁺ requires a plasmid promoter, only one orientation will produce resistance. In this case, bacteria carrying the other orientation will not survive, and this orientation will not be observed. If there were only one orientation, only two fragments would be observed, with a total size of 34 kb. However, there are four fragments, with $23 + 11$ adding up to 34 kb, and $28 + 6$ also adding up to 34 kb, so the bacterial population includes both orientations. This means that the *nrd*⁺ gene contains its own promoter.

5. **C**

A: No. Ligases will only ligate sticky ends that base pair properly with each other.

B: No. Plasmid DNA is double stranded.

C: **Yes.** The sequences recognized by most restriction enzymes are inverted repeats that read the same if flipped 180°. The sticky ends of both ends of a fragment are the same if the fragment is rotated in either orientation, so it does not matter to the ligase which orientation occurs.

D: No, this is irrelevant. The correct matching of sticky ends in either orientation is the key.

6. **C**

A: No. This is the size of the *nrd*+ gene alone.

B: No. This would be the size of the recombinant plasmid if only one cut were made, but *Eco*RI will cut twice, on both sides of the *nrd*+ gene.

C: **Yes.** The *nrd*+ gene will simply be cut out of the plasmid.

D: No. This would be the product of *Eco*RI cleavage of the entire phage genome. The question asks for the results of cleavage of a recombinant plasmid containing only the *nrd*+ gene plus the original pBR325.

Passage 16

1. **B**

B: **Yes.** Since the colony can grow with only lactose as a carbon source (Plate B), it is Lac+. Since it can grow without arginine (Plate D), and leucine (Plate C), but cannot grow without threonine (Plate E), it is also Arg+ Leu+ Thr−.

2. **C**

Item I: True. This bacterium could grow on only minimal medium plus a carbon source, i.e., glucose or lactose. Arg+ Leu + Thr+ just means it could grow without arginine, leucine, or threonine.

Item II: False. Arg− means arginine is required for growth, and plate D lacks arginine.

Item III: True. Plate D supplies glucose, leucine, and threonine, just what this bacterium needs for growth, since it can't make leucine or threonine and can't metabolize lactose.

3. **A**

A: **Yes.** This is a definition and, essentially, a freestanding question. Auxotrophs have a mutation preventing them from growing on minimal media. (Aux-o-troph = requires an auxiliary trophic substance. Trophic means "relating to nutrition.")

B: No. Prototrophs are wild-type, i.e., can grow on minimal media. "Proto," means "first in time."

C: No, a heterotroph is an organism which grows using energy derived from another organism's metabolism. "Hetero," means other or different. Plants are generally autotrophs, animals are heterotrophs, and bacteria can be either.

D: No. Chemotrophs derive their energy from an inorganic carbon source (a chemical source).

4. **D**

A: No. This is true, but irrelevant. Polycistronic refers to the expression of bacterial genes on a single RNA in an operon.

B: No. They are replicated by the same method during conjugation.

C: No, this would obscure the results.

D: **Yes.** One assumes all cells in a given strain will transfer their genomes in the same order and at the same rate. The transfer is then interrupted at various times, and by matching the genes transferred to the length of time necessary for the transfer, the genes are mapped.

5. **B**

 B: Yes. In Experiment 3, after 5 minutes colonies grew on media lacking Leu. After 15 minutes, colonies grew on media lacking Arg. Not until after 30 minutes did colonies grow on media lacking Thr. Therefore, the Leu gene must be the first transferred, Arg second, and Thr last.

6. **C**

 C: Yes. The survivors from the mixed culture grow on minimal media, so their genotype must be wild-type; they are not auxotrophic for any nutrient. This is explained by the fact that Colony 3 bacteria gave Colony 6 bacteria the enzymes they were missing in Hfr transfer events, or vice versa.

Passage 17

1. **D** The mutations alter the ability of bacteria to grow in the absence of exogenous amino acids. Without the ability to make specific amino acids, these bacteria are dependent on an outside source. If this source is removed, then protein synthesis (choice D) will run out of the amino acid. The other choices can be eliminated since the ability to make phenylalanine or histidine are not directly related to RNA or DNA synthesis.

2. **A** If both types of cells had the same mutation, then the fused cell would have two copies of the same defective gene and would have the same properties as haploid cells. If the haploid cells complement each other, however, they must each have a different mutation.

3. **D** This is the simplest test to see if a cell can grow in the absence of exogenous amino acid. If cells grow on media which lack phenylalanine, they must be able to make their own.

4. **B** The cells which were used to start the experiment grew on His⁻, Phe⁻ media and so could make both of these amino acids themselves. To conclude that normal cells have the same phenotype, these cells must represent normal-type Chlamydomonas. If the cells had undergone mutations affecting His or Phe biosynthesis prior to their placement on the master plate, then this assumption is not true.

5. **A** A fusion of two haploid cells to form a diploid zygote is sexual reproduction (choice A). The other choices describe asexual reproduction through mitosis, in which haploids undergo morphological changes to produce new haploid gametes.

6. **D** Meiosis in this species starts with the diploid cell and ends up in the haploid state. The fusion of these haploid gametes constitutes sexual reproduction. DNA replication occurs in the diploid cell in meiosis. In mitosis, DNA replication occurs in haploid cells (choice D). The other choices describe events in meiosis.

Passage 18

1. **D** Prokaryotes lack all subcellular membrane-bound organelles, including nuclei.

2. **C** The complete oxidation of glucose yields 2 ATP and 2 NADH through glycolysis, 2 GTP in the Krebs cycle (equivalent to ATP in energy), 2 NADH from pyruvate dehydrogenase, 2 $FADH_2$ from the Krebs cycle, and 6 NADH from the Krebs cycle. In oxidative phosphorylation, each NADH yields 2.5 ATP, and each $FADH_2$ yields 1.5 ATP. This all totals up to 32 ATP per glucose. (In eukaryotes, the answer is 30 ATP per glucose, due to the fact that electrons from glycolytic NADH [in the cytoplasm] must be shuttled to the electron transport chain [in the mitochondria]; they bypass the first proton pump, just like $FADH_2$, and yield only 1.5 ATP, just like $FADH_2$.)

3. **B** The growth curve for this bacteria will have the three phases of growth: A slow phase of biosynthesis, a log phase, and a stationary phase at the end when growth slows.

4. **A** Bacteria reproduce asexually in a process of simple cell division termed binary fission. The DNA and other contents of a cell are replicated, then divided equally between two daughter cells (so I is true). Transformation and conjugation can alter the genetic content of a bacterial cell but are not involved in cell division or reproduction (thus, II and III are false).

5. **B** Tryptophan is an amino acid and is most likely to be found in proteins.

Passage 19

1. **D** Protozoans are unicellular eukaryotes (eliminating A and C), mostly heterotrophic (eliminating B), and in many cases can reproduce either sexually or asexually. Thus, choice D is the correct response.

2. **C** Failure of the drug to enter the bloodstream or degradation in the liver would prevent the drug from acting at all, not only on particular stages (eliminating A and B). The described action of the drug is to insert in DNA. A drug that inserts in DNA would be likely to disrupt DNA replication and, therefore, cell division (choice C). D is not likely since the drug alleviates the symptoms of malaria, which include fever.

3. **A** By inserting in plasmoidal DNA, chloroquine can affect both transcription and DNA replication. Merozoites grow and multiply, meaning they will require transcription and replication, so choice A is correct. Choice B is incorrect since chloroquine alters DNA structure, not membranes. Choices C and D can be eliminated since there is no information that chloroquine has any effect on translation or release of progeny.

4. **D** In the erythrocytic stage, the malaria parasite "digests hemoglobin" to acquire required amino acids. Digestion of hemoglobin would be catalyzed by a protease, so a protease inhibitor would block the erythrocytic stage.

5. **B** Chloroquine has one chiral center:

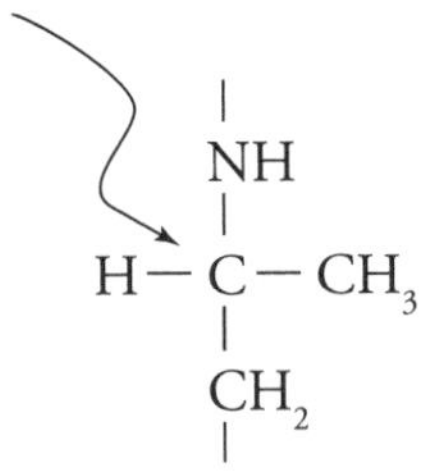

Passage 20

1. **B** As explained in the passage, the difficulty is the length of time required to observe growth. This would best be explained by a long period between rounds of cell division. Some bacteria can replicate every 30 minutes, so 2 days per cell division is slow by comparison (choice B). There is no reason to believe that oxygen is a limiting factor since the atmosphere is oxygen rich (eliminating choice A). The bacillus is resistant to desiccation (eliminating choice C) and stains readily (eliminating choice D).

2. **C** Tuberculosis is caused by a bacillus (rod-shaped) that stains in an acid-fast manner with this procedure.

3. **B** Choice B is correct since it is stated that tuberculosis bacteria require an oxygen-rich environment. Choices A and C can be eliminated because there is no information provided about sensitivity to pH changes, and choice D is wrong because it is stated that although tuberculosis usually starts in the lungs, the disease can spread to other tissues.

4. **A** The passage describes how the sulfated glycolipid of the bacterial cell wall prevents lysosomes from fusing with the phagosome containing the bacteria ingested by macrophages.

5. **B** Human cells do actively divide (eliminating choice A) and do have RNA polymerase (eliminating choice D). And the drug must be absorbed if it is efficacious in treating the disease (eliminating choice C). If the drug is not toxic to humans, then their RNA polymerase must be different from that of the tuberculosis mycobacterium (choice B).

6. **B** Since the disease resides primarily in the lungs, the air (choice B) is the most likely means of transmission. Choice A can be eliminated since skin is a good passive barrier against infection, and there is nothing stating that the bacterium is found in blood. As for C and D, there is no reason to believe that the disease has anything to do with food or sexual contact.

Passage 21

1. **D**   It sounds counterintuitive, but the passage specifically states that bacteria with incomplete cell walls survived, while 95% of those with normal cells died.

2. **B**   Choices A, C, and D can all be eliminated: For the 5% that survive, the cells are altered genetically, so the resistance is a property of the cells, not the penicillin. It is not simply a matter of insufficient penicillin. The correct answer is choice B: The resistant cells pass on the resistance to future generations, meaning that the change is genetic. The passage describes penicillinase as an enzyme that inactivates penicillin, making increased expression of this enzyme a likely genetic change to confer resistance to cells.

3. **C**   Penicillin blocks the last step in bacterial peptidoglycan cell wall function, disrupting cell wall formation.

4. **C**   Normally, osmotic pressure drives water into bacterial cells through the plasma membrane, but the rigid cell wall opposes this pressure, preventing the cell from swelling. In the absence of the cell wall, the osmotic pressure is unopposed, and water flows into the cell to lyse the bacteria.

5. **A**   Instability in acid would most likely make the drug ineffective if given orally, since the drug would be likely to break down in the stomach. Intravenous administration, however, would avoid the stomach.

Passage 22

1. **B**   The radioactive label is used as a means to detect the amino acid. If the radiolabeled amino acid does not behave in the same manner as the normal amino acid, then the results observed will not reflect the normal transport mechanism; thus, B is correct. Choices A, C, and D indicate that the radiolabel alters transport, which would make any conclusions based on radiolabel invalid.

2. **D**   Both aerobes and anaerobes have a proton gradient. Aerobes use electron transport to produce the proton gradient, which is used in turn to drive ATP synthesis. Anaerobes, however, consume ATP to produce a proton gradient, as depicted in Figure 1. This supports choice D. A is wrong because both types of cells must allow for protons to both exit and enter the cell to maintain balance. Choice B seems to state that phosphorylation of the ATP synthetase protein regulates its activity, but no information is presented to support this statement. Choice C states that ATP synthetase functions in the same manner in both aerobes and anaerobes, while the figure depicts the enzyme functioning in an opposite manner in the two types of cells.

3.   C   Glycolysis requires NAD$^+$ to proceed at the glyceraldehyde 3-phosphate dehydrogenase step (choice C), where it is a cofactor for this enzyme and is converted to NADH. Oxygen is not directly required for glycolysis (eliminating A), but for oxidative phosphorylation. Lactic acid can sometimes be produced as a fermentation product during glycolysis in anaerobic circumstances, but it is not required for glycolysis to occur in the first place (eliminating B).

4.   A   Proteins that transport ions through the membrane are generally highly selective in the ions they transport. One ion cannot typically substitute for another in a transport process. Proteins responsible for cotransport of sodium with lysine or other substances will not recognize magnesium, so lysine uptake would decrease (supporting choice A but not choice B). Choice C is wrong since there is no information linking flagella movement with the Na$^+$ gradient. Choice D is wrong, since uptake of other substances dependent on sodium cotransport will also decrease.

5.   D   Absence of radiolabel indicates that lysine import failed to occur. Both aerobic and anaerobic bacteria import lysine, so lack of import does not indicate the mode of respiration; this eliminates choices A and B. Choice C is incorrect since there is no information suggesting that ATP must be added to the medium; cells make their own. The answer is D: The cotransport of sodium is essential for lysine import, but other factors must also be present.

6   C   Both aerobic and anaerobic bacteria use a proton gradient to drive lactose import. Making the medium more acidic will increase the proton gradient and increase cotransport of lactose and other substances; thus, C is correct. Choice A is wrong because an increased proton gradient will also increase ATP synthesis, and B is wrong since lactic acid can be the result of anaerobic fermentation, but its presence would not induce anaerobic fermentation. As for choice D, uncoupling is induced by substances which carry protons through the membrane, reducing the proton gradient without generating ATP, and there is no reason to believe that lactate does this.

7.   B   The passage states that the bacteria are hypotonic in saltwater. Since fresh water contains no solutes, whereas the bacteria do, they must be hypertonic in fresh water.

Passage 23

1.   B   Oogenesis is the formation of the egg, not what happens during early development (eliminating A). DNA replication is very important in early development, in which the DNA must be replicated many times very rapidly during the early cell cleavages, so B is the best choice. C is wrong since little transcription occurs during early cleavages. The early cell divisions are so rapid that there is no time for transcription. RNAs are stored in the egg and translated during the early stages. Double-helix formation is an inherent feature of DNA and will not change during embryo development (eliminating D).

2.   D   The amount of mitosis-inducing protein present seems to be the key variable affecting the rate of embryonic development in these experiments. The most likely explanation is that the rate of translation of this protein must be affected in some way by irradiation (choice D). Choices A and B are inherent features of DNA, not affected by irradiation. Although replication could be affected, it is not the key variable described in this experiment (eliminating C).

3.   B   The zygote divides rapidly while having little time to perform biosynthesis. Up to the blastula stage, there are many more cells, but essentially the same total amount of cytosol, meaning there is less cytosol per cell.

4. **A**   The amino acid sequence of the protein in B-1 was examined and found to be the same as in the control. If the amino acid sequence is the same, then the difference in activity cannot be explained as a mutation in the gene, but must be associated with the amount of protein expressed (choice A). Choice B is wrong since Hardy–Weinberg applies to population genetics, not to embryo development. Choice C is wrong because the effect of A-1 protein on the controls is irrelevant to the B-1 sample. While it is true that these samples did not develop into normal embryos (according to the passage), this does not address the role of mutation in the rate of early B-1 development (eliminating choice D).

5. **A**   B-1 developed slowly with low levels of inducing protein, while A-1 developed rapidly and had high levels of the protein. Controls developed more rapidly when exposed to the same levels of inducing protein that A-1 had. The fact that the controls increased their developmental rate in response to A-1 levels indicates that A-1 levels do not slow development in the controls; thus, A is correct. And while choices B, C, and D may be true, they do not address the question.

6. **B**   Choice A is eliminated because the experiment appears to demonstrate that embryological development is affected by protein induction. Choice B is correct: If the alterations in development are caused by mutations in DNA, then they must not be due to changes in translation activity. Choice C is not true, and choice D is eliminated because only one gene is relevant as far as we know, so this assumption does not have to be correct in order for mutation to play a role in these observations.

Passage 24

1. **B**   Choice B is correct since the secretory pathway for a secreted protein is Rough ER → Golgi → secretory vesicle → extracellular environment. Choice C is wrong since it places the Golgi before the ER. Choices A and D can be eliminated since lysosomes are not in the pathway for proteins that are secreted.

2. **A**   Transcription is the reading of genes in DNA by RNA polymerase to make mRNA. All transcription takes place in the nucleus.

3. **B**   Proteins that are transported to the lysosome are first transported to the rough ER, the Golgi, and then the lysosome. Choice A is wrong because the acidic pH is in the lysosome only, choice C is incorrect because endocytosis does not bring newly synthesized proteins into the lysosome, and choice D is wrong because inhibition of signal peptide cleavage is not part of normal lysosomal targeting.

4. **C**   Pepsin's activity is optimized in the stomach's acidic environment. Choice A can be eliminated because signal peptidase functions in the ER, not an acidic environment. Choices B and D are wrong because trypsin and pancreatic lipase are both secreted enzymes that function in the small intestine, not an acidic environment.

5. **A**   M6P is the signal that a protein is destined for the lysosome. In the absence of M6P, lysosomal proteins will not be targeted correctly to the lysosome, and the lysosome will not be able to carry out its normal activity in the hydrolysis of macromolecules. Choices B, C, and D are wrong because M6P is not involved in targeting to other organelles, including the ER, mitochondria, or Golgi.

6.   C   The interior of the ER (the lumen) corresponds to the interior of the Golgi, the interior of secretory vesicles, and the extracellular environment in turn. The other choices can be eliminated since these spaces are separated from the contents of the ER at all stages of the secretory pathway.

Passage 25

1.   **B**

    B: **Yes.** Cytochalasin blocks cytokinesis and amoeboid motility. Cytokinesis occurs after metaphase, indicating that cells progressed through metaphase. Metaphase requires microtubules for sister chromatid separation, so the drug does not affect microtubules. Microfilaments are required for amoeboid motility and contractile processes, such as contraction of the cleavage furrow to complete cytokinesis. Thus, the drug blocks microfilaments but not microtubules.

2.   **A**

    Item I: True. The centromere is the organizing center of each chromosome, while the centrioles, at the center of the microtubule organizing center, are the organizing poles of the dividing cell. The polar fibers cause separation of sister chromatids during anaphase. The entire bundle of fibers, including the polar fibers and the two asters, is called the spindle.

    Item II: False. It is microfilaments, not microtubules, that are responsible for contraction of the cleavage furrow. The passage states that microfilaments are responsible for contractile processes.

    Item III: False. Recombination occurs only during *meiosis*.

3.   **C**

    A: No. This describes the appearance of microtubules during interphase, when a pair of centrioles can be seen near the nucleus. Each centriole has a set of radiating fibers known as the aster.

    B: No. Since the distribution of proteins is not even throughout the cell, staining won't be uniform either.

    C: **Yes.** Microfilaments, composed of actin, are found in the cytoplasm as part of the cytoskeleton.

    D: No. The cytoskeleton is excluded from the nucleus.

4.   **D**

    A & B: No. As stated in the passage, microtubules are responsible for intracellular organelle movement and spindle formation.

    C: No. This is not relevant to actin.

    D: **Yes.** From the passage you know that the dynamic equilibrium between monomers and polymerized forms of actin is important for amoeboid motion. Therefore, stabilizing actin in the polymerized form would have the same affect as the drug cytochalasin.

5.   **A**

    A: **Yes.** Flagella of prokaryotes are fundamentally different from those of eukaryotes. Choice B describes eukaryotic flagella. Prokaryotic flagella are formed from chains of a protein called flagellin, and are attached to the cell surface (as opposed to being cytoplasmic extensions).

    B, C, & D: No, all are true.

6   **B**
   A: No. This describes a cell in anaphase, just before cytokinesis.
   B: **Yes.** This describes metaphase, when the chromosomes are lined up on the metaphase plate.
   C: No. This is early prophase, when the chromosomes are appearing and the nuclear membrane is disappearing. The table in the passage indicates that all Group C cells will be past prophase.
   D: No. This describes a cell in interphase.

Passage 26

1.   **D**
   D: **Yes.** Since only the nucleus is transplanted, and it was previously not active, the control must come from somewhere else within the cell, that is, in the cytoplasm.

2.   **C**
   A: No. The formation of the nuclear membranes of daughter nuclei occurs during telophase.
   B: No. The nuclear membrane disappears in late prophase, after the visible condensation of the chromosomes.
   C: **Yes.** There is a visible condensation of the chromosomes at the beginning of mitosis, during prophase. This is the best sign of the onset of mitosis.
   D: No. The centromeres do not split until early anaphase, when they prepare to move towards the opposite poles of the spindle.

3.   **A**
   Item I: False. Primary spermatocytes undergo meiosis to form secondary spermatocytes.
   Item II: True. The cells of the bone marrow do indeed undergo mitosis quite frequently, in the production of cells found in blood.
   Item III: False: Erythrocytes are terminally differentiated and lack a nucleus in humans. They are incapable of mitosis and must be continually replenished by stem cells in the marrow.

4.   **D**
   A: No. This is a feature unique to meiosis. As a result of crossing over, the daughter cells have combinations of chromosomes different from those in the parents. In mitosis the daughter cells are identical to the parent cell.
   B: No. Mitosis can occur in haploid cells, unlike meiosis, which can only occur in diploid cells.
   C: No. In mitosis there is only one division, producing two daughter cells, whereas meiosis has two divisions, to produce four.
   D: **Yes.** In both mitosis and meiosis, replication of chromosomes occurs prior to the beginning of cell division with prophase.

5.   **B**
   A: No. The S phase is the time when cellular chromosomal material is replicated.
   B: **Yes.** The passage states that organelles are produced during G_1. Replication of organelle DNA is not coupled to replication of the nuclear genome, so it probably occurs during G_1.
   C: No. There is no synthesis of cytoplasmic organelles during mitosis.
   D: No. There is no synthesis of cytoplasmic organelles during cytokinesis.

6. **A**
   A: **Yes.** Use the mnemonic "PMAT." (Or you can use your knowledge of word elements to take a guess. All of the beginnings of the names of the phases are learned borrowings from the Greek meanings. "Pro" means before and "telo" means end, placing prophase first and telophase last, making A the only viable answer.)

Passage 27

1. **B** Yeasts and molds are both fungi. General characteristics of fungi include the following: they are eukaryotes, haploid for most of the life cycle, and produce spores. This eliminates choices A, C, and D. Choice B is correct since molds are multicellular, while yeasts are unicellular.

2. **C** Choices A, B, and D all deal with meiosis, which is not involved in these experiments. Since nothing specific is indicated about the mechanism by which mutations disrupt the cell cycle, the mitotic cell division mutants may not be relevant to meiotic cell division. The answer must be choice C: Once the mutant cells are blocked at the end of mitosis, they will not be able to reinitiate DNA replication.

3. **C** If all of the mutant cells are blocked at the same place in the cell cycle, regardless of the time at which they are placed in the high temperature, then there must be a defect in a specific stage of the cell cycle which the cells cannot get past (choice C). Choice A is incorrect since the behavior of wild-type cells does not indicate anything about the cell-cycle block in the mutants. B is wrong because the behavior of the mutants at the permissive temperature is apparently normal, without a block, so this does not indicate anything about the stage of the block. As for choice D, it is not clear how the added regulatory proteins allow the mutant cells to grow.

4. **D** The question asks about evidence of competitive advantage for wild-type yeast. The best evidence would come from placing the yeast in an environment where they can compete and see after a time which yeast predominates; thus, D is the best choice. It is true that the mutant cannot grow at high temperatures (choice C), and this is likely to lead to a competitive disadvantage, but choice D addresses the question of competition directly.

5. **B** During interphase, biosynthetic activity produces enough material in the cell to form two separate cells, including replication of the genome during interphase (which includes the G_1, S, and G_2 phases). If the cell cannot go through interphase, there will be no replication of the DNA genome (choice B). There is no evidence to support any of the other choices. (Note: The cells will completely lack DNA replication but may still synthesize protein, so A is incorrect.)

6. **A** The two haploid cells will form a diploid cell with one copy of the wild-type allele and one copy of the recessive mutant allele (the genotype will be heterozygous). Since the mutant is recessive, its phenotype will not be observed in the diploid cell, making the phenotype wild-type.

Passage 28

1. **C** In Experiment 1, both glucose and sodium concentrations decrease in the medium and must be increasing inside the cells. This suggests that a sodium concentration gradient was driving the transport of glucose into the cells (thus, choice C is correct). In Experiment 2, the sodium concentration remains the same as glucose is transported, but ATP in the medium is decreasing, suggesting that the cells are importing ATP and using ATP hydrolysis to maintain the Na^+ gradient to drive glucose transport even further, essentially to completion. Choices A and B are incorrect because there is no evidence for exchange of either ATP or sodium for glucose. Both ATP (in Figure 2) and sodium (in Figure 1) decrease in the medium at the same time that glucose is decreasing, suggesting that they are being transported in the same direction as glucose. Choice D also cannot be correct, since extracellular ATP does not increase in these experiments.

2. **C** As evidenced by Figures 1 and 2, both the sodium concentration gradient and the ATP hydrolysis that maintains this gradient are forms of energy that drive glucose transport (choice C). Choices A, B, and D all make false statements, so they cannot be correct.

3. **A** ATP maintains extracellular Na^+ at a high level in Experiment 2, indicating that it will cause the extracellular Na^+ to increase back to this high level after it has been depleted through co-transport with glucose. As the Na^+ gradient is restored, glucose concentration in the medium will decrease further with the additional energy provided. Thus, choice A is correct. Choice B depicts ATP as having no effect on glucose, which is not supported by Figure 2. (ATP drives extracellular glucose to a lower level than is observed in the absence of ATP.) The linear depletion of glucose in choice C does not agree with either Figure 1 or Figure 2. And in choice D, extracellular glucose increases, which is not observed in either experiment.

4. **C** The energy to drive glucose transport is from the sodium concentration gradient. When the sodium concentration is the same inside as outside the cell, there is no gradient, and thus no energy to drive glucose transport further. Transport will stop, and the extracellular glucose concentration will level off, so choice C is correct. As for choices A and B, the sodium in the medium decreases in Figure 1. And choice D is wrong because the sodium in Figure 1 decreases but levels off before it reaches zero.

5. **B** Adding more sodium to the medium increases the sodium gradient, and a larger gradient means that more glucose can be transported before the sodium gradient is depleted. The curve will be similar to Figure 1, therefore, but will level off at a lower concentration of extracellular glucose, so choice B is correct. Choice A is incorrect because the final glucose concentration in this case is the same as it appears in Figure 1. Choice C is wrong because it represents less glucose transport, not more. As for choice D, there is no reason to believe that glucose will reverse direction of transport and go back up again.

6. **D** Choice **A** is wrong because there are no secreted proteins involved in the transport process. Choices B and C are incorrect since ATP hydrolysis is not catalyzed by the Na^+/glucose cotransporter, but the Na^+/K^+ ATPase that produces the Na^+ gradient in the first place. D is the only possible choice here: A membrane protein must bind sodium and glucose in the extracellular side of the membrane prior to transport.

Passage 29

1. **B**
    A: No. Osmotic pressure in the cell is regulated by the transport of ions across the plasma membrane, not proteins.
    B: **Yes.** Without ouabain, the Na^+/K^+ ATPase creates a net movement of sodium ions out of the cell. If the Na^+/K^+ ATPase is inhibited, then the concentration of ions inside the cells is higher than normal, driving water to enter the cell by osmosis, bursting cells.
    C: No. Potassium transport into the cell will be decreased by ouabain, not increased.
    D: No. Leak channels are always open.

2. **B**
    B: **Yes.** The Na^+/K^+ ATPase pumps K^+ ions into the cell against a gradient, and potassium channels allow K^+ ions to diffuse back out of the cell down a gradient. The Na^+/K^+ ATPase alone creates a small negative potential in the cellular interior since only 2 K^+ are pumped into the cell for every 3 Na^+ pumped out, but most of the resting membrane potential, with negative charge in the cellular interior, is due to the leakage of potassium through leak channels. Blocking leak channels will not make the membrane potential more negative, but less. It will not make the cellular interior positive, however, since this would require net movement of positive ions into the cell, which is not what happens.

3. **C**
    Item I: True. Hydrophobic amino acids are essential components of membrane-spanning domains, because they must interact with the hydrophobic lipid tails of the membrane interior.
    Item II: False. Basic amino acids are positively charged, and thus hydrophilic. They are found on the exterior of proteins in aqueous environments.
    Item III: True. Nonpolar amino acids are hydrophobic (see above.)

4. **A**
    A: **Yes.** The Na^+/K^+ ATPase is very specific for pumping sodium out.
    B: No. The fact that other ions can substitute for potassium suggests the external binding site is not specific.
    C: No. If this were the case, the pump would not be able to function at all in the presence of these ions, but we know it can pump them into the cell and continue working (we have no reason to suspect it quits working).
    D: No. Cellular pumps are generally very specific about which ions they carry. The fact that the external site is not specific is unusual.

5. **A**
    A: **Yes.** ΔG and equilibrium are related functions. If ΔG is negative, then the reaction will move forward toward equilibrium spontaneously. Coupling ATP hydrolysis to a reaction alters the overall ΔG and will also change equilibrium.
    B & C: No. It is not possible to alter either equilibrium or ΔG without changing both.

6. **C**

Item I: False. The pump has distinctly different intracellular and extracellular portions. Since there is only a single pump in the artificial membrane, the ATP hydrolyzing side of the pump will be located on one side only.

Item II: False. The side where ATP hydrolysis occurred would be equivalent to the intracellular side, where potassium would accumulate.

Item III: True. Sodium would accumulate on the side equivalent to the extracellular surface, that is, the side opposite that where ATP hydrolysis occurred.

Passage 30

1. **A**

A: **Yes.** All other things being equal, since the same section of membrane is measured in all three experiments, the difference between A and B is that ion channels are open more frequently in B than A. The net flux of ions will be greater in B than in A.

B. No. We do not know the type of ion channels that are opening or the effect on transmembrane potential.

C: No. It is the same section of membrane in both experiments, so it will have the same number of channels. It is changes in the frequency of ion movement that are measured (the horizontal axis in the figures is the time axis).

D: No. We do not know the type of ion channels that are opening.

2. **C**

Item I: True. The net flux is related to the concentration gradient across the membrane. Increasing the concentration of potassium from 10 mM to 11 mM will increase the concentration gradient and therefore increase the net flux.

Item II: False. If the concentration is increased equally on both sides of the membrane, then the concentration gradient is not changed, and the net flux will not change.

Item III: True. The more leak channels that are present, the more ions that will diffuse across the membrane per unit of time.

3. **C**

A: No. The concentration gradient drives chloride movement into the cell, so when chloride channels open, the chloride concentration in the cytoplasm increases.

B: No. There is no information given about expression of the receptor gene.

C: **Yes.** When chloride enters the postsynaptic cell, relative to the extracellular environment, and is therefore hyperpolarized.

D. No. There is no reason to believe that ion flux across the *presynaptic* membrane will change at all.

4. **C**

A: No. Just the opposite—they are highly polar; see C.

B: No. Once a channel is open, ion flux is predictably determined by this factor and also by potential differences.

C: **Yes.** The interior of the lipid bilayer is formed by the hydrophobic tails of membrane phospholipids. It is an excellent barrier to hydrophilic substances any larger than water. Remember that though K$^+$ (for example) is only a single atom, in aqueous solution it carries with it a huge solvation shell of H$_2$O molecules.

D: No. Net ion flux is a measure of ion movement, not a predictor of it.

5. **D**

   A: No. Active transport is powered by the hydrolysis of ATP. ATP in turn is derived from oxidative phosphorylation, which requires oxygen uptake. So the relationship would be direct, not inverse.

   B: No. Proteins are involved in facilitated diffusion as well as active transport.

   C: No. This would be most consistent with a freely permeable membrane and passive diffusion.

   D: **Yes.** Chemical energy is transferred directly from ATP to membrane carrier proteins during active transport, so a correlation with ATP hydrolysis would be good evidence of active transport.

6. **A**

   A: **Yes.** The fact that the intracellular concentration approaches the extracellular concentration suggests that the membrane of the cell is permeable to Substance X.

   B: No. The cell may be regulating Substance X transport, but this cannot be determined from the information given.

   C: No. This is stated backwards. Influx is rapid at first, and then slows as the concentration gradient lessens.

   D: No. A simpler explanation is that equilibrium is reached between the inside and outside of the cell.

7. **B**

   A: No. Varying the fatty acids in phospholipids and the quantity of cholesterol will vary membrane fluidity, but the membrane will remain very hydrophobic in the interior and impermeable to sodium ions.

   B: **Yes.** The most likely explanation out of those presented is that the neuron lacks functional receptors for acetylcholine and so does not respond to acetylcholine by opening sodium channels.

   C: No. Acetylcholine in the cytoplasm has no effect. Acetylcholine must be in the extracellular fluid to bind to its receptor and cause ion channels to open.

   D: No. This is true for all cells in the body due to the activity of the Na^+/K^+ ATPase.

Passage 31

1. **A** When hormone binds to receptor, G_s α releases GDP and binds GTP. As long as it has GTP bound, it stimulates adenylate cyclase activity to produce cAMP (supporting choice A and eliminating choice B). Adenylate cyclase does not interact with receptor directly (so choice C is wrong), and the G protein does not catalyze cAMP production (so choice D is wrong).

2. **C** The breakdown of glycogen will release glucose. This is likely to occur to supply glucose when blood glucose is low. Since parathyroid hormone is unrelated to glucose metabolism, choice A is wrong. Choice B is wrong since insulin acts to decrease, not increase blood glucose, and choice D is wrong since glucocorticoids act on nuclear receptors, not cell-surface receptors, and act to increase, not decrease blood glucose. The answer is C: Glucagon is a hormone secreted by the pancreas in response to low blood glucose, which increases glucose levels.

3. **C** It is stated in the passage that IP_3 acts to release calcium from the sarcoplasmic reticulum in smooth muscle cells.

4. **A** The passage states that calcium and cAMP exert their effects through inducing conformational changes in proteins to which they are bound. Allostery is the propagation of conformational

changes through a protein's structure to more distant parts of the protein; thus, A is the answer. Choice B is wrong because the question asks how protein activity is increased, not decreased. Choice C is incorrect since calcium and cAMP are not themselves enzymes and cannot hydrolyze proteins, and choice D can be eliminated because only calcium binds to calmodulin, and the specifics of this interaction are not given.

5.   **D**   ACTH stimulates the adrenal cortex to produce cortisol and aldosterone.

Passage 32

1.   **A**
    Item I: True. The passage states this difference explicitly in the last sentence of the second paragraph.
    Item II: False. Both toxins increase cAMP in the cell, although by different mechanisms.
    Item III: False. Both toxins increase cAMP in the affected cells, which activates cAMP- dependent protein kinase, which in turn stimulates chloride secretion.

2.   **A**
    A: **Yes.** G_s with GTP bound activates adenylate cyclase to make cAMP. Hydrolysis of the bound GTP terminates the stimulation of adenylate cyclase by G_s, so it is reasonable to conclude that G_s with GDP bound does not activate adenylate cyclase.
    C & D: No. The toxins ADP-ribosylate G proteins to alter adenylate cyclase activity; they do not ADP-ribosylate adenylate cyclase directly.

3.   **C**
    A: No. Dramatically increasing glucose concentration without a concomitant increase in sodium concentration would not lead to an increase in activity of the 1:1 sodium-glucose contransporter.
    B: No, just the opposite. Increasing glucose concentration increases osmolarity.
    C: **Yes.** Increasing glucose concentrations much above the osmolarity of blood would cause the villi to lose water into the lumen by osmotic forces.

4.   **A**
    A: **Yes.** As stated in the passage, cAMP has its effects via the activation of cAMP-dependent protein kinase. If chlorpromazine were to inhibit the activity of this protein kinase, it would thus reverse the effect of cAMP.
    B: No. Nothing in the passage indicates that NaCl uptake is dependent on a protein kinase. Note, however, that if NaCl uptake were dependent on a protein kinase, this choice would be correct, because the question asks about decreasing "net" secretion, which includes both decreases in secretion and increases in the rate of uptake. When you see "net" secretion, remember that it includes both secretion and uptake.
    C: No. This has nothing to do with protein kinase activity.
    D: No. This is not related to the activity of any protein kinase.

5.   **C**
    A: No. As regards the intestinal mucosa, this is no different from cholera alone, since *Bordetella* infects only the respiratory tract (as noted in the passage).
    B: No. This is equivalent to cholera plus oral rehydration therapy, which is designed to decrease water loss.
    C: **Yes.** Ingestion of nonabsorbable carbohydrates increases lumenal osmolarity and thus draws ad-

ditional water into the lumen from the intestinal wall (also see 4C). This, in addition to cholera infection, would cause the greatest loss of water.

D: No. This is not related to water loss.

6.   **C**

Item I: True. The passage states that the GTPase activity of G_s is necessary for termination of activation of adenylate cyclase.

Item II: True. The passage states that G_s normally serves to attenuate adenylate cyclase activation by competing with G_s.

Item III: False. Cyclic AMP-dependent protein kinase is activated by cAMP. When the cAMP system is overactive, it is overactive too.

Passage 33

1.   **D**

A, B, & C: No. The passage tabulates the relative risk (increased chance) of cancer in smokers and drinkers, but does not discuss the mechanisms of the increased risk.

D: Yes. The passage never tells us whether tobacco and alcohol cause mutations (tumor initiator, mutagen), or nonmutagenic changes (tumor promoter). If the question had not said, "Based on the passage," you would have been correct in thinking that the answer was "Both." Cigarette smoke does function as both a tumor initiator and a tumor promoter. But you could not infer this from the passage.

2.   **A**

A: Yes. According to the passage, tumor initiators cause mutations, or changes in the DNA sequence of a cell.

B, C, & D: No. These are secondary effects. The only direct effect is mutagenesis.

3.   **B**

B: Yes. A relative risk greater than 1 indicates an increased likelihood, and a relative risk less than one indicates a reduced likelihood. According to Table 1, 21–40 g of alcohol per day actually decreases the risk of cancer for both endolarynx (88% the chance of a nondrinker) and epilarynx (87%), but increases it (1.57 times the risk) for the hypopharynx.

4.   **B**

B: Yes. The easiest way to figure out the relationship between alcohol and tobacco is to see what happens to relative risk at the higher doses (the lower doses combined almost look addictive, but not so at the higher doses). For the 26+ cigarettes/day and 121+ g of alcohol/day the relative risk is 42.5 for endolarynx. This is much greater than the sum of 17 and 2.5 but is exactly their product. This holds true also for the epilarynx.

D: No, alcohol only lowers the tobacco risk at levels where by itself it lowers the relative risk of cancer. Overall, the combined effect is multiplicative.

5.   **D**

D: Yes. Reading Table 2, find the 8–15 cigarettes/day column and go down until you meet the 121+ alcohol row.

6. **C**

    A, B, & D: No. Cancer often results from a change in the gene coding for a receptor. Receptors are proteins which allow hormones to exert control over individual cells. Receptors which do not respond normally to their ligands can result in an out-of-control cell.

    C: **Yes.** Errors in translation do not have significant effects on cellular function. Only mutations in DNA cause permanent changes in a cell's behavior and are passed down to daughter cells.

Passage 34

1. **C**   The answer is C since promoters are described in the passage as compounds that are not carcinogens on their own but which can increase the carcinogenic activity of known carcinogens when added to them. Choice A is wrong because promoters are never mutagenic, B is wrong because there is no information that promoters can or cannot be assayed in the Ames assay or related tests, and D is wrong since the source of exposure is irrelevant to the mechanism of action.

2. **C**   The liver plays an important role in detoxifying chemicals by transforming them through oxidation and conjugation into more polar structures. In some cases, however, the biotransformation catalyzed by the liver results in more toxic (or carcinogenic), rather than less toxic, compounds. Choice A can be eliminated since a diseased liver will probably lose functions, not confer increased protection from mutagens. Choices B and D are wrong since they do not address the difference between diseased and normal rats.

3. **D**   By definition, promoters are not carcinogenic on their own, and there is no reason to believe that mixing them will result in cancer; thus, choices A and B are false. Choice C is irrelevant, so D is the best response. Promoters only increase carcinogenesis, so they will have no activity in the absence of mutagens (or carcinogens).

4. **D**   The passage describes that there is not a 100% correlation between mutagens and carcinogens. Most carcinogens are mutagens, but not all, and not all mutagens are carcinogens; thus, A and B are false. Choice C is also false: The Ames Test detects mutagens through mutation of bacteria. It does not determine if something is a carcinogen. Choice D is correct: The essential difference is, by definition, that mutagens cause mutations, while carcinogens cause cancer. The two sets of compounds are likely to overlap significantly, but not completely.

5. **A**   If the mother is homozygous dominant (dominant is the wild-type normal allele), then all of her children will receive a normal allele from her and a recessive allele from their father. They will all be heterozygous, and since the disease is caused by a recessive allele, none of them will express the disease.

6. **C**   Cancer cells are growing rapidly and dividing through mitosis frequently; thus, A and B are true. If cells are not determined, then they will not be differentiated; thus, choice D is true. Choice C is false (and therefore the correct response) since cancer cells divide mitotically, not through meiosis.

Passage 35

1. **B**   Potassium is maintained in relatively high intracellular concentrations by the Na^+/K^+ ATPase. Lysis of cells will cause this potassium to be released, thus causing an increase in extracellular potassium (choice B is correct). The extracellular concentrations of calcium and sodium are already high relative to intracellular concentrations of these ions, so lysis of cells would not cause a significant increase in the extracellular calcium or sodium concentrations (choices A and C are wrong). Creatine is primarily found in muscle tissue and its role is to aid in the regeneration of ATP. The amount of creatine in B cells is negligible, so the concentration of this would not change with the lysis of those cells (choice D is wrong).

2. **D**   Apoptosis is programmed cell death; by downregulating apoptotic mediators, *Myc* is able to perpetuate activity in a cell that would normally be destroyed for its unregulated growth (choice D is correct). Since DNA methylation works to prevent gene expression, this would work against the oncogenic activity of *Myc* (choice A is incorrect). Though the passage specifies that the *Myc* gene is on chromosome 8, there is nothing to indicate that further translocations from the same chromosome would increase this effect (choice B is incorrect). While interfering with the production of new mitochondria might impact the cell's ability to divide, choice C does not address the question directly and should be eliminated.

3. **D**   The passage states that active EBV causes disregulation of the *Myc* oncogene which results in the rapid, uncontrolled proliferation of B cells, causing Burkitt's lymphoma. The passage also states that EBV can be lysogenic; as such, stressors (such as infection with another organism) could activate EBV (choice D is correct). Although infections do lead to an increase in the production of B cells, this does not explain why people develop Burkitt's lymphoma (choice A is incorrect). The protozoan does not affect the host DNA, nor is it a carrier of EBV (choices B and C are incorrect).

4. **C**   Item I is true: hives are a symptom of an allergic reaction, which is a possible side effect of any medication (choice B can be eliminated). Item II is true: the passage states that Burkitt's lymphoma is treated with antibodies to B cells, rendering them inactive. By having B cells inactivated, the patient is more susceptible to infections (choice A can be eliminated). Item III is false: B cells do not play a role in the clotting cascade, so antibodies to B cells would not affect clotting (choice D can be eliminated and choice C is correct).

5. **A**   The passage states that Burkitt's lymphoma often affects the jaw and other facial bones. The pharynx, and specifically the nasopharynx, lies posterior to the maxilla, one of the bones of the face. A tumor in the maxilla that grows internally will directly compromise the pharynx (choice A is true). None of the other structures listed are bordered by bones of the face, and are thus less likely to become obstructed in Burkitt's lymphoma (choices B, C, and D are incorrect).

6. **D**   Nondisjunction refers to the failure of homologous chromosomes or sister chromatids to separate properly during meiosis. Though this can create non-viable or compromised gametes, it is not a trigger for oncogenes (choice D is incorrect and is therefore the correct answer). Translocation is a type of chromosomal rearrangement and is referenced in the passage as the way *Myc* converts from being a protooncogene to being fully oncogenic (choice A is correct and is eliminated). Mutation can alter the activity of any gene (choice B is correct and is eliminated). Finally, one of the issues with protooncogenes is that their function in the cell is necessary, but their overall activity typically needs to be tightly regulated. For example, the cellular expression and proliferation triggered by *Myc* is part of normal cellular activity, but only to a certain point. Increasing the expression of the gene, even without other changes, can lead to an oncogenic effect (choice C is correct and is eliminated).

Passage 36

1. **B** Oncogenes are triggers for dysregulated cell growth; switching signals from terminal differentiation to proliferation is an example of increased, dysregulated cell growth (choice B is correct). Blocking proliferation or increasing regulation on G1 to S phase transitions would limit cell growth (choices A and C are wrong), and while the proliferation described in choice D would work, promoting terminal differentiation at the same time would not (choice D is wrong).

2. **D** The thalamus acts as a relay for sensory input from the body to the appropriate part of the brain. Sensory stimuli from the body will be transmitted via the spinal cord to the thalamus and from there to the cerebral cortex (choice D is correct). The cerebellum is in the lower posterior portion of the brain and plays an important role in balance and coordination. It does receive proprioceptive input from the body via the spinal cord, but not pain (choice A is wrong). The frontal lobe is involved in problem solving and reasoning and is not directly involved in the processing of pain signals (choice B is wrong). The occipital lobe plays an important role in vision, not in pain processing (choice C is wrong).

3. **B** The passage states that chemotherapy can inhibit processes such as mitosis, transcription, and translation. Thus growth cannot occur while these medications are active (choice B is correct). Although amputation is used as a possible treatment for Ewing sarcoma, amputating a single limb will cause a patient to be lighter, not shorter (choice A is wrong). Radiation causes the tumor to shrink, not the whole patient (choice C is wrong). The epiphyseal plate (or growth plate) is near the end of long bones and is where lengthening of bones occurs. Even if Ewing sarcoma were to destroy the epiphyseal plate, typically only one limb is affected, so that would not likely result in an overall short stature (choice D is wrong).

4. **C** Item I is true: transcription of DNA to RNA is catalyzed by RNA polymerase (choice D can be eliminated). Item II is false: unlike DNA replication, RNA transcription does not require a primer (choice B can be eliminated). Item III is true: helicase catalyzes unwinding of DNA, which is an important preliminary step in both replication and transcription (choice A can be eliminated and choice C is correct).

5. **B** Some of the original bacteria underwent transformation (the took up the plasmid) and those that did not died when transferred to the media containing ampicillin. The surviving transformed bacteria were grown and lysed, which released all their intracellular contents, including proteins and nucleic acids. The DNase and RNase would break down their respective nucleotide polymer, including the plasmid DNA, and the oncoprotein was purified. If this protein were somehow introduced into the actual individual cells in the liquid colony, it might have an effect, but simply adding a protein to the liquid culture is unlikely to cause any changes as random proteins are typically not taken up by bacteria and cannot cross the cell walls and membranes (choice B is correct). The passage states that the EWS/FLI1 oncoprotein acts as a transcription activator for the *NKX2.2* gene; if it could get into the cells it might lead to increased translation of the *NKX2.2* product and uncontrolled growth, but since it can't, it won't (choices C and D are wrong). Ampicillin is not produced by the transformed bacteria, so it is not transferred with the lysate (choice A is wrong).

6. **C** Southern blots are a way to detect specific DNA sequences in a sample. DNA fragments are separated by electrophoresis and matched to a DNA probe. ELISAs are used to detect antibodies or antigen, something protein-based (choice A is wrong). The methods for Northern and Western blots are similar to Southern blots; however, Northern blots are a way to detect specific RNA sequences (choice B is wrong) and Western blots are a way to detect specific proteins (choice D is wrong).

Passage 37

1. **B** At the end of paragraph 2, it is stated that for gene therapy to succeed, the target cells must be dividing actively. Intestinal epithelial cells are continually dividing and being replaced, so B is the best choice. T cells are not always actively dividing; they must be stimulated by antigen along with the appropriate chemical signals in order to begin proliferating (choice A is not the best choice). Finally, red blood cells and neurons are terminally differentiated and arrested in the cell cycle; they do not divide, so these are not good targets (choices C and D are wrong).

2. **A** In gene-addition therapy, a correct copy of a gene is added to cells which already contain at least one defective gene copy responsible for disease. In a disease caused by a recessive allele, the addition of even one wild-type copy should mask the effect of the recessive allele and reverse the disease. A dominant allele, however, cannot be masked by a wild-type allele, so that even after the gene addition therapy, cells will continue to express the disease allele. Choice B is incorrect since genes inserted in the host cell genome must replicate at the same rate as the rest of the genes in the cell. Choice C is wrong because the disease is genetic, not caused by a virus. Choice D is wrong since the disease allele does not cause mutation, but is itself caused by a mutation.

3. **C** All viruses gain entry into the cell through recognition of cell-surface proteins (receptors) by viral proteins.

4. **A** Endocytosis results in material being internalized into the endosome and lysosomes for destruction.

5. **B** Only choice B addresses the question: Why would tumor cells be more sensitive to a virus that disrupts replication? The answer is that tumor cells divide more often and therefore replicate their genome more often, so they will be more sensitive than normal cells to treatments that disrupt DNA replication.

Passage 38

1. **D**

    Item I: True. Antibodies serve as markers, causing phagocytic cells to engulf and destroy foreign particles or cells.

    Item II: True. For example, an antibody can inactivate a virus.

    Item III: True. The complement system is a biochemical cascade which leads to the lysis of cells. It can be initiated by an antibody binding to the cell surface.

2. **B**

    A: No. Baby 1 having AB blood, must come from parents having an I^A and an I^B allele among their genotypes. Couple X's blood types are A and O, so they could not be the parents—they do not have an I^B allele between them. Baby 2 could not belong to Couple Y, because to have blood type O, both parents must have an i allele. Couple Y includes an AB blood type, which cannot possibly donate the i allele.

B: **Yes.** Couple X could produce a baby of blood type O, since the A-type parent could have the I^Ai genotype and donate the i allele to combine with an i allele from the O-type parent. Couple Y could produce a baby of blood type AB if the AB-type parent donated an I^A allele, and the B-type parent donated an I^B allele.

C: No. Baby 1 could belong to Couple Y. See explanation for A.

D: No. See explanations for A and B.

3. **D**

Item I: True. Type-O donor cells will have neither the A antigen nor the B antigen.

Items II & III: True. The man has both antigens, A and B, in his bloodstream. His immune system will not recognize either as foreign.

4. **B**

A: No. See B. The ii genotype does not fit this definition, as there is only one allele present: i.

B: **Yes.** Codominance is the phenomenon in which the effects of both alleles at a particular locus are apparent in the phenotype of the heterozygote. In this case, there are two alleles, I^A and I^B, and both will be expressed in the phenotype, which will be blood type AB.

C: No, see B. The I^AI^A genotype does not fit this definition, as there is only one allele present: I^A.

D: No, see B. Genotype I^Bi is a case of simple dominance, not codominance. The I^B allele is dominant to the i allele, and together they will produce a blood type B phenotype.

5. **A**

A: **Yes.** Many enzymes are thermolabile, that is, they do not function at higher temperatures, even within the normal physiological range. Coat color in Himalayan rabbits is one example.

B: No. In the data given, black pigment shows up only at lower temperatures, not higher ones.

C: No. The genotype will not vary. The environment must produce a change in gene expression or activity of a gene product.

D: No. Temperature dependence is a property of the "Himalayan" allele, not a property of the notion of multiple allelism.

6. **D**

A & B: No. Since a person of blood type A could have an i allele, and, similarly, a person of blood type B could have an i allele, the offspring could have an i allele.

C: No. Offspring with the ii or I^AI^B genotype could result.

D: **Yes.** The man's genotype could be I^AI^A or I^Ai, and the woman's could be I^BI^B or I^Bi, which would allow for all of the possibilities given.

Passage 39

1. **D**

A & B: No. One allele can only be dominant over another allele at the same locus. The (+) allele allows the coat color gene to be expressed; this is known as epistasis.

C: No. The (+) allele is dominant; refer to the last sentence of the first paragraph of the passage.

D: **Yes.** Epistasis refers to the situation where one gene controls the expression of another. (*Epi* means "upon," and *stasis* means "standing.") Do not confuse this with dominance and recessivity, which only apply to alleles at the same locus. Dominant and recessive are relationships between alleles; epistatic is a relationship between genes (loci).

2. **C**

    C: **Yes.** True-breeding means that the phenotype does not change from generation to generation. Since this was a true-breeding strain of black hamsters, the genotype must have been homozygous at both loci. Therefore, the correct answer would be *B/B; +/+*.

3. **C**

    C: **Yes.** These animals must be white (albino), since they are homozygous for the albino allele (a).

4. **A**

    A: **Yes.** The F$_1$ generation is the first generation of offspring from an experimental cross. All of the F$_1$ hybrids will be black, since they must all have the genotype *B/b; +/a*.

5. **A**

    A: **Yes.** Assume both of the genes in question are on the same chromosome (linked), and very close together. The F$_1$ hamster has the genotype (*B/b; +/a*). It has two chromosomes containing the genes in question, and they are arranged like this: B—+ and b—a. We know this because each chromosome came from a parent with a known genome. For example, the parent that passed the B gene also passed the + gene. If the two genes are very close together on the chromosome, they will never be separated, so all progeny resulting from Experiment 2 will be either *B/b; +/a* or *b/b; a/a*. The corresponding phenotypes would be half black offspring and half albino offspring.

        Now assume the genes are on different chromosomes (unlinked). In this case, the progeny resulting from Experiment 2 may have any of four genotypes, namely the ones given above plus *B/b; a/a* and *b/b; +/a*. All four of these genotypes should appear with equal frequency. In this case we would see half albino hamsters, 1/4 black ones, and 1/4 brown.

        Now assume the genes are on the same chromosome, but not too close together. In this case, sometimes they will be separated by recombination during the formation of gametes by meiosis in the parents' germ cells. Depending on just how far apart they are, we would see the second pair of genotypes given above more or less frequently.

        Let's look at the actual results of Experiment 2. We got half albino hamsters, and the remaining offspring were 2:1 black:brown. This indicates that the *B/b; +/a* genotype was twice as frequent as the *b/b; +/+* genotype (these are the only possible genotypes of non-albino offspring, given the parental genomes). Hence, the genes are linked.

    C: No. A gene (locus) cannot be recessive. Dominance and recessivity are relationships between alleles; these words are not used to describe genes. When one gene takes precedence over another it is said to be epistatic (see 1D).

6. **B**

    B: **Yes.** If no crossover took place in the heterozygous organism, you would expect to see half of the offspring albino (*b/b; a/a*) and half of the offspring black (*B/b; +/a*), with no brown offspring at all. In other words, the brown hamsters resulting from this cross are "crossover" (recombinant) offspring. Each crossover event will produce one brown hamster. However, we should also see recombinant hamsters with this genotype: *B/b; a/a*. These crossover-type offspring are lost in the crowd of albino hamsters which arise from non-crossover events. Since they cannot be identified individually, we must assume that there are just as many of them as there are brown recombinants, so the total number of crossover-type offspring in this test-cross must be 2 × 34 = 68.

        Now we can calculate the genetic map distance between the two loci. The map distance between two genes is defined as the frequency of crossover events between those genes. This is simply the number of recombinant offspring divided by the total number of offspring: 68/200, which equals 34%, or 34 centimorgans. (For you genetics buffs: 34% is actually the minimum distance. The actual genetic distance is probably greater, since double recombinations between loci this far apart will result in some apparently unrecombinant offspring.)

Passage 40

1. **C**
   A: No. Parasitism is a symbiotic relationship in which one species is harmed while the other benefits. A parasite is an organism which derives its nourishment from the body fluids of its host. Parasitism is contrasted with predator prey relationships in that parasites are smaller than their hosts, and are usually species-specific. The *Myxoma* virus in Community 3 is an example of a parasite.
   B: No. Commensalism is characterized by one species benefiting while the other is neither helped nor hurt (Community 2).
   C: **Yes.** Mutualism is characterized by both species benefiting from the interaction (Community 1).
   D: No. In predation, the predator usually feeds upon prey smaller than itself, and on many different species of prey.

2. **A**
   A: **Yes.** Coevolution occurs when the characteristics of one species influence the evolution of another species. At first glance, selection of a less virulent strain of virus might not seem like "evolution," but rather a thwarting of the virus' evolution. However, in the long run, a less virulent strain is better because it will not kill off its host. Besides, "evolution" is not a valuative term, that is, it does not imply "progress"; it just refers to change in a lineage over time.
   B: No. Mutation may have occurred, but the passage indicates that selection was primarily at work to drive coevolution (see A).
   C: No. Speciation is the origin of a new species, and the new generations of rabbit were not new species.
   D: No. Competition results when organisms from the same or different species overlap in their utilization of insufficient resources. Better surviving a disease is not "out-competing," because no resource is competed over.

3. **D**
   A: No. The relationship in Community 1 is a mutualistic one.
   B: No. The relationship in Community 2 is a commensal one.
   C: No. Viruses are parasites.
   D: **Yes.** Birds feeding on insects are a predator-prey relationship. Predators are larger than their prey and usually feed upon many species of prey. In contrast, parasites are smaller than their hosts, and are usually species-specific.

4. **B**
   A, C, & D: No. The Hardy–Weinberg law states that the frequency of all the possible alleles at a given locus will remain the same over time, as long as five conditions are met. These are three of the conditions; the fourth is that no migration occurs (see choice B), and the fifth is that no natural selection occurs.
   B: **Yes.** If migration occurs, the gene pool does not remain constant, in which case Hardy–Weinberg does not apply.

5. **A**

    A: **Yes.** Reproductive isolation is one way species diverge to create new species.

    B: No. Reproductive isolation actually relieves intra-species competition by creating new species.

    C: No. Natural selection arises from competition rather than reproductive isolation.

    D: No. On the contrary, such a specific mutualism would probably result in stabilizing selection. This is selection against extreme variants, in favor of average ones. For example, wasps which were unusually small or large might not do as well as medium-sized wasps.

6. **D**

    A: No. There is no basis for this generalization.

    B: No. This is anthropomorphic reasoning, attributing rationale to the process of evolution. In evolution nothing happens "in order" that something else may happen or not happen.

    C: No. This does not necessarily take place.

    D: **Yes.** This leads to the establishment of population cycles, in which the predator population increases while the prey population falls, until the prey gets too scarce. The predator population then begins to drop and the prey population increases, and so forth.

Passage 41

This passage is unusually difficult for two reasons: 1) It is very theoretical, not factual. 2) It presents an illegitimate theory and uses graphs which do not accomplish what the author intended them to. The MCAT is filled with the unexpected.

1. **B**

    A: No. This is stated in the passage (third paragraph).

    B: **Yes.** Breeding success is the number of fledglings born to each adult. Figure 1 shows that the relationship between clutch size and number of surviving offspring is not a simple inverse proportionality. In fact the relationship is a direct proportionality at clutch sizes between seven and nine.

    C & D: No. Both statements are consistent with paragraph 3 of the passage.

2. **B**

    A: No. Some of these new offspring will die during the year, so it is better to measure later. In fact, measuring during just one year is not correct at all, as carrying capacity is defined as the number at which a population stabilizes over several years.

    B: **Yes.** Carrying capacity is defined as the number at which a population stabilizes after several years. It is the number of organisms the environment can support in the long term, or "carry."

    C: No. You should realize that the population size is changing during the exponential growth phase, and "capacity" suggests a fixed number. The carrying capacity is the population size during the stationary phase.

    D: No. Carrying capacity is determined by the environment, which puts constraints on reproductive potential.

3. **A**

    This question challenges you to identify what sort of argument a graph makes. It is important that you be comfortable with the graph as a tool for information display. The basic graph consists of an independent variable (usually on the *x* axis) and one or more dependent variables (usually on the *y* axis). The graph tells us how the dependent variables change in response to changes in the independent variable. The independent variable in this graph is "Brood Size," or the number of eggs hatched. (The meaning of "brood size" can be inferred from paragraph 2 of the passage.) There are two dependent variables. Bar height represents the dependent variable, "% Occurrence of Each Brood Size." The distance of dots from the x axis represents the dependent variable, "Number of Known Survivors per Nest."

  A: **Yes.** The author of the passage provides Figure 1 in an attempt to support Edward's theory, but the information in the figure does nothing to confirm or refute the theory. The theory states that animals behave altruistically. Figure 1 does not say anything about animal behavior. It just shows that when too many eggs are laid in a given clutch, fewer birds survive.

  B: No. The figure does not say anything about any deliberate reduction of clutch size. Stated mathematically, clutch size is the independent variable in this graph; we are given no information as to when and why a particular clutch size is produced, but rather only the results of a given clutch size.

  C: No. We are not told anything about the birds' decision-making about how large a clutch to produce, and we are not shown any relationship between environmental conditions and clutch size.

  D: No. the graph neither supports nor refutes the theory (see above).

4. **B**

    As with Figure 1, Figure 2 does not serve the author's purpose very well. The data are vague because no clear relationship is evident. In other words, the graph does not give very convincing evidence that increased numbers of breeding adults lead to decreased clutch size. It does give weak evidence that this is the case, because the one data point at a high number of breeding adults (on the far right) shows a low number of fledgling pairs. However, this is statistically insignificant data, because only one data point provides evidence in support of one conclusion or the other.

  A: No. "Consistent with" simply means "not contradictory." The data in Figure 2 do not contradict the idea that animals deliberately reproduce less when population is high.

  B: **Yes,** though the data do not disprove the theory, they certainly do not prove it. First of all, the data in Figure 2 are weak (statistically insignificant). Secondly, we cannot conclude that the birds deliberately, altruistically regulated their population to produce the data, which is what the theory argues.

  C: No. It supports this idea.

  D: No. This is true. The plotted points are quite scattered, too scattered for one to draw a straight line and conclude that there is a clear linear relationship.

5. **D**

Always be aware of MCAT key words like "most consistent." They notify you that you will have to make a subtle, often subjective, choice between alternatives which are difficult to separate. Darwin's theory of natural selection is best paraphrased as "Survival of the fittest." The main idea is that evolution does not occur "in order to fill a need." Rather, because of mutation and genetic recombination, differences between individuals just happen to exist; the fittest individuals are then most likely to survive and produce offspring.

A: No. Darwinian fitness is determined by the ability to pass on one's own alleles. Allowing unrelated animals to survive does not increase one's own fitness.

B: No. This describes altruistic behavior without an increase in the passing of alleles to future generation.

C: No. Regulation of population size was not a component of Darwin's theory.

D: **Yes.** This is an example of competition. The parents who are most effective at getting resources will have healthier offspring and pass on their alleles more frequently.

6. **B**

A: No. According to the passage, Edward's theory stated that animals reproduce more when more food is available, and the question states that the availability of nourishment was increased. If you chose this answer, you probably did so because the tribe moved into a presumably more crowded city, and Edwards's theory says that animals reproduce less when the environment is more crowded. But the passage states that "animals avoid overexploitation of their habitats, especially with regard to food supply." The availability of nourishment (and safe housing) is greatly increased.

B: **Yes.** This does not describe altruistic sacrifice for the good of the population.

C: No. The farmers are agreeing to limit their own reproductive rate for the good of all. This is altruistic behavior, which is consistent with Edward's theory.

D: No. This is consistent with the theory.

Passage 42

1. **B**

A: No. Larger axons conduct more rapidly.

B: **Yes.** Myelination causes the action potential to jump from node to node by saltatory conduction (jumping conduction), which is much faster than conduction down the axon in a continuous manner.

C: No. Chemical synapses are the slowest part of the chain of transmission. A single long axon is much faster than several nerve cells connected by chemical synapses.

D: No. This describes unmyelinated axons, which are slower. In myelinated axons, the fast sodium channels are concentrated at the nodes. This is part of saltatory conduction (see A).

2. **D**

A: No, this is true. Remember that "motor" neurons are simply neurons that carry information from the CNS. "Motor" does not necessarily refer to a nerve that innervates a muscle.

B & C: No, each is true.

D: **Yes.** Striated skeletal muscle is innervated only by the somatic nervous system.

3. **C**

    Item I: False. There is no ATP present in the experiment. The chemical gradients are created artificially, by perfusion of the inside and outside of the neuron with different solutions.

    Item II: True. The correct concentration gradient is essential, as shown by the fact that either absence of the gradient or reversal of the gradient prevents action potentials.

    Item III: True. Reversal of the gradient prevents an action potential (−80 vs. +80 mV).

4. **A**

    A: **Yes.** Axons do not have a nucleus, ER, Golgi apparatus, or ribosomes.

    B: No. These are essential for axonal transport and cytoskeletal structure, respectively.

    C: No; this is why axons exist!

    D: No. Action potentials are only transmitted in one direction.

5. **A**

    A: **Yes.** The experiment proves this statement false. Making the intracellular concentration of sodium high and that of potassium low, while creating the opposite pattern extracellularly, led to no action potentials (second row of data in the table). It did reverse the polarity of the RMP (but the question asked about action potentials, not the RMP). You should know, by the way, that the gradients found in nature are: K^+—high inside, low outside; Na^+—the opposite (as determined by the Na^+/K^+ ATPase).

    B & C: No, these are true. The experiment shows that reversing the Na^+ and K^+ gradients reverses the RMP. Also, when $[Na^+]$ is varied and $[K^+]$ is held constant, the RMP remains constant (last row of the table). Hence, it is K^+, not Na^+, which determines the RMP.

    D: No. There is no reason to believe that this is true.

6. **B**

    B: **Yes.** Na^+ channels must close to end the influx of sodium, and K^+ repolarization channels must open to facilitate rapid return to resting membrane potential. The depolarization that constitutes the action potential (that is, the spike) triggers both of these occurrences. The Na^+ channels open very rapidly when the neuron is first depolarized to threshold. Then these channels are slammed shut very rapidly when the action potential spike occurs. Hence, the Na^+ channels are referred to as "fast channels." The potassium repolarization channels are opened by the action potential spike too, but they take longer to open. In fact, they do not open until just the right time for repolarization to begin (otherwise they would mess up the action potential spike).

Passage 43

1. **C**   With K^+ ions exiting the cell and Cl^- ions entering, the cell will become hyperpolarized (membrane potential more negative than rest potential, choice B is wrong) until the GABA ion channels are closed and the Na^+/K^+ ATPase can restore the cell to resting potential. Choices A and D both describe states where the membrane potential is more positive that rest potential; they can be eliminated.

2. **B**   Paracrine function is defined as one cell releasing a signal (e.g., a hormone, a chemical, a protein, a cytokine) that will affect other, nearby cells. Since interstitial cells (Leydig cells, the testosterone producers) are found right next to seminiferous tubules, the stimulation of spermatogenesis

by testosterone is a good example of paracrine function (choice B is correct), while the stimulation of muscle growth by testosterone is too distant to be paracrine (choice A is wrong). A situation where a cell can stimulate changes within itself using its own chemokines and receptors is an example of autocrine function (choice C is wrong), and the release of chemicals that act on non-cell substances (such as protein digestion by pepsinogen) is an example of exocrine function (choice D is wrong).

3. **A** The "butyric" aspect of the name suggests a four carbon backbone. The "gamma-amino" portion of the name suggests that there will be an amino group on the 4th carbon. The passage states that GABA has the structure of an amino acid, thus there will be a carboxylic acid group attached to the 1st carbon. Therefore, choice A is the only possibility.

4. **C** The passage states that 5-HT can stimulate vomiting. Therefore a 5-HT receptor blocker should be effective in inhibiting vomiting (choice C is correct), while drugs that prolong the effects of 5-HT (such as SSRIs and cocaine) would worsen vomiting (choices A and D are wrong). The passage states that GABA agonists have anti-anxiety properties, thus it can be assumed that GABA antagonists would worsen the symptoms of anxiety, one of which is nausea. Thus, if anything, GABA antagonists may in fact worsen vomiting (choice B is wrong).

5. **D** While not explicitly stated, the physical manifestations of a panic attack are the result of uninhibited overstimulation of the sympathetic nervous system (the "stress response" discussed in the passage). A person experiencing a panic attack feels quite the same effects at a person running away from a salivating lion. Sympathetic stimulation leads to bronchodilation (choice A would be seen and can be eliminated), decreased oral secretions (choice B would be seen and can be eliminated), and vasoconstriction of skin vessels (choice C would be seen and can be eliminated). However, pupillary *dilation* would be expected with sympathetic stimulation, not constriction (choice D would not be seen and is the correct answer choice). Picture a stressed, scared person; they are breathing deeply, have dry mouth, and are pale.

6. **B** As stated in the passage, SSRIs prolong the presence of serotonin in the synaptic cleft. Acetylcholinesterase inhibitors have the same end result on ACh, although the mechanism is different (choice B is correct). By inhibiting the enzyme that breaks down ACh, they allow the effects of ACh to last longer. Dopamine and epinephrine are simply other types of neurotransmitters (choices A and D are wrong), and monoamine oxidases break down monoamines. The passage states that serotonin is a monoamine, thus these drugs would reduce the time that serotonin spends in the synaptic cleft, blunting its effect (choice C is wrong). In fact, there is a class of drugs called *monoamine oxidase inhibitors* (MOAIs) that are also used as anti-anxiety medications because they can prolong the effects of some neurotransmitters.

Passage 44

1. **B**

    This question is a little tricky because development was not discussed in the passage. The key is knowing what the things discussed aren't.

    A: No. No two stimuli are associated in this scenario, and the passage defines associative learning as a pairing of stimuli.

    B: Yes. Monocular vision demonstrates the development of neural pathways that were not present at birth. Activity of the sensory nerve drives synapse formation along the pathway. In the absence of stimulation, normal development did not occur.

    C: No. Habituation is described as a reduced response by existing neurons. The question describes sensory input as creating more synapses.

    D: No. Sensitization, although similar to stimulus-driven development in that it leads to an increased response, is different in that it involves numbers of receptors, not numbers of synapses.

2. **B**

    A: No. This causes depolarization.

    B: Yes. The membrane's impermeability to sodium is essential to the resting potential. Regardless of what else happens, if the membrane is permeable to sodium, it will not be repolarized.

    C: No. As discussed in B, if sodium channels are open, the membrane will not be polarized, regardless of what potassium does. Furthermore, even if the potassium current remained small, the membrane would eventually repolarize as long as it remained impermeable to sodium.

    D: No. This is key for neurotransmitter release, but is not a major determinant of polarity.

3. **B**

    A: No. This is an example of a polysynaptic reflex. An inhibitory interneuron is required for the stimulus (striking reflex hammer) to cause inhibition of contraction of the hamstring. In the knee-jerk reflex, an example of a deep tendon reflex, the quadriceps contracts and its antagonist, the hamstrings, relax. This combination leads to the foot kicking out (that is, to the extension of the leg).

    B: Yes. This is an example of a monosynaptic reflex, in which a sensory neuron synapses with a motor neuron, directly causing contraction.

    C: No. Scratching an itch is a complicated process involving conscious control of many muscles. One does not scratch an itch involuntarily.

    D: No. This too is a complex, cerebrally-controlled action. It involves many muscles, and though it may seem "involuntary," it is not reflexive.

4. **A**

    A: Yes. Relaxation of the knee flexors allows extension to take place unimpeded. The quadriceps is the active muscle in the reflex, while the hamstrings are the inactivated antagonists.

    B: No. This simply does not occur.

    C: No. The antagonistic muscle is relaxed during the reflex, not contracted afterward.

    D: No. This is simply not true.

5. **A**

    Item I: True. This accurately describes neurotransmitter release into the synapse.

    Item II: False. The receptor molecule does not generally degrade the neurotransmitter. This is usually done by enzymes in the synaptic cleft or bloodstream. Some neurotransmitters (norepinephrine, for example) are not degraded but rather reclaimed by the presynaptic terminal from which they were released.

    Item III: False. Action potentials begin at the axon hillock, not at the dendritic spine where the neurotransmitter has its effect. Also, not all neurotransmitters are excitatory, and even if they are, they do not directly cause action potentials, but membrane depolarization.

6. **B**

    A: No. Serotonin in *Aplysia* acts on the presynaptic cell.

    B: **Yes.** Serotonin alters the amount of neurotransmitter released by the presynaptic cell, amplifying the response.

    C: No. The speed of propagation depends on other factors, such as myelination.

    D: No. Serotonin decreases the rate of repolarization.

Passage 45

1. **C**

    A: No. The iris adapts to light in a fraction of a second.

    B: No. The refractive power of the lens has nothing to do with light adaptation.

    C: **Yes.** As stated in the passage, rods are responsible for dark vision.

    D: No. Cones are responsible for visual acuity and color vision, not night vision.

2. **A**

    A: **Yes.** An active area inhibiting surrounding areas more highly defines the edges of the active area, thereby enhancing contrast. This is why a straight dark line on a white page appears distinct, and not just as a nondescript smear.

    B: No. Peripheral vision lacks acuity, and there is no reason to suppose that surround inhibition will change this.

    C & D: No. The neuronal inhibitions of a region of the retina has no effect on the photoreceptor sensitivity.

3. **B**

    A: No. Although pain may result from pressure on the eye, it will not result from stimulation of photoreceptors.

    B: **Yes.** Vision is the only sensory function mediated by the photoreceptors.

    C: No. The photoreceptors are not directly involved in balance. Then again, if you saw the walls of a room begin to move, you might indeed lose your balance, but B is clearly a better choice.

    D: No. The question states that photoreceptors are activated.

4. **D**
   A: No. Nothing in the passage suggests this.
   B: No. Inward movement of sodium depolarizes cells.
   C: No. This would hyperpolarize the cell, but would not explain the effect of removing Na^+ from the medium.
   D: **Yes.** We can infer from Experiment 2 that the photoreceptor has open sodium channels in the resting state. We know this because removing sodium from the medium led to increased polarization—there was less sodium outside the cell to flow in and depolarize it.

5. **B**
   A: No. As discussed in the solution to question 4, sodium is also involved.
   B: **Yes.** The action potential is an all-or-none phenomenon, the magnitude of which is not related to strength of the stimulus, whereas the generator potential described in the passage is proportional to stimulus strength (see Figures 2 and 3). Also, neuronal action potentials involve depolarization, not hyperpolarization.
   C: No. Both types of potentials change ion movement.
   D: No. This is not stated, nor is it true.

6. **C**
   Items I & II: True. In the early part of the graph (low light intensities), we see a direct proportionality between light intensity and hyperpolarization (ΔmV). After a point, however, increasing the light intensity can no longer increase ΔmV.
   Item III: False. They are directly proportional at low intensities, not logarithmically.

Passage 46

1. **B** When in bright light (such as outside on a sunny day) virtually all of the retinal in rod cells is in its all-*trans* form. Once it is converted back to its 11-*cis* form by the enzymes in the rod cells, it is almost immediately straightened again by light; this straightening is referred to as "bleaching." Thus, in bright light the majority of the rods are inactive (bleached) and are unable to respond upon first entering a darkened theater (choice A is a possible explanation and can be eliminated). The passage states that cone cells are less sensitive to light, and the relatively dim light of a movie theater is not enough to stimulate them (choice C is a possible explanation and can be eliminated). If Na^+ flow into the rods has been stopped, it is because the cells have been activated by light (bleached) and cannot respond (choice D is a possible explanation and can be eliminated). However, rod cells are normally depolarized at rest (when not responding to light). In the absence of light, cGMP keeps the Na^+ channel open, and Na^+ flows into the cell, down its gradient, causing the cell to be depolarized. When light strikes the retinal, a series of events occur that cause the channel to close, which stops Na^+ from entering. This causes the stimulated rod cell to hyperpolarize. So, if the rod cells are already depolarized, that means they are at rest and are ready to respond to light. This cannot be a possible explanation for the temporary blindness, making choice B the correct answer choice.

2. **C** If the neurotransmitter were inhibitory, then its continuous release from the rod cell in the absence of light would prevent the bipolar cell from firing action potentials. Then, when light strikes the rod cell and the release of neurotransmitter is stopped, the bipolar cell is no longer inhibited and can fire action potentials. If the bipolar cell were also depolarized at rest (the time during which neurotransmitter is released), then the cessation of transmitter release would cause

the cell to hyperpolarize and prevent an action potential from occurring (choice A is wrong). If the neurotransmitter opened Na^+ channels in the bipolar cell, then its release during rest would cause action potentials, not the other way around (choice B is wrong). There is no reason to assume that light has any effect on a bipolar cell; in any case, if light did close Na^+ channels in the bipolar cell, the cell would stop firing action potentials (choice D is wrong).

3. **D** Phosphodiesterase is an enzyme that breaks phosphodiester bonds, such as are found in nucleic acids. Thus, PDE could be involved in the breakdown (digestion) of nucleic acids (choice D is correct and B is wrong). Recall that nucleotide monomers are held together with phosphodiester bonds to form the nucleic acid polymer. Proteins are polymers of amino acids, held together by peptide bonds, upon which PDE has no effect (choices A and C are wrong).

4. **A** Myopia (nearsightedness) is caused by a misshapen eyeball (in this case it's too long). Vitamin A is a precursor to retinal, which is part of the visual pigment; however, vitamin A supplementation cannot change the shape of the eyeball, and so would have no effect on the blurriness of myopia. Retinal (derived from vitamin A) is found in both rods and cones (choice B is wrong), and increased retinal synthesis would increase sharpness of vision by increasing the ability of the photoreceptors to respond to light, however this is irrelevant since in myopia, bad photoreceptors are not the problem (choice C is wrong). Anybody can see better in bright light since cones are activated, but again, this is irrelevant to the question (choice D is wrong).

5. **C** The first paragraph of the passage describes the wall of the eye, and the middle layer is described as being pigmented (colored) and vascular (contains blood vessels). Photoreceptors and bipolar cells are essentially specialized neurons and would be found in the retina (the inner layer; choices A and B are wrong). Collagen fibers are strong fibers found in connective tissue and would most likely be found in the tough outer layer of the eyeball (choice D is wrong).

6. **A** When rod cells are stimulated by light, 11-*cis* retinal is converted to the all-*trans* form (Item II is false), opsin is activated, transducin is activated, PDE is activated, and cGMP levels fall (Item I is true). In the absence of cGMP, the Na^+ channels close, Na^+ stops entering the rod cell, and the cell hyperpolarizes (Item III is false).

Passage 47

1. **D** Stimulation of rods and cones, which are electromagnetic receptors, allows for the transmission of visual stimuli to the brain (choice D is correct). Nociceptors are pain receptors (choice A is incorrect). Chemoreceptors detect chemicals, such as odors or food chemicals (choice B is wrong), and mechanoreceptors detect physical stimuli, such as vibration (choice C is wrong).

2. **B** As stated in the passage, retinal is a vitamin A derivative. Vitamin A is a fat soluble vitamin, and severe impairments in fat absorption would impair vitamin A absorption, decreasing the availability of the vitamin for conversion to retinal. A diet that is rich in fruit and vegetables would likely be high in vitamin A (choice A is incorrect). High protein diets, vitamin B12, and carbohydrate digestion are all irrelevant to vision (choices C and D are wrong).

3. **A** When light strikes the cornea, it then moves through the anterior chamber, the lens, the vitreous chamber, and the retina (choice A is correct). Choices B, C, and D all place the items in the wrong order.

4. **D** Correctly identifying that light stimulates rods and cones through retinal allows for the elimination of both choices A and C. Choice B is incorrect because it states that *trans* bonds are converted to *cis* bonds. In reality, *cis* bonds are converted to *trans* (choice D is correct).

5. **D** The information needed for this question is located in the passage. The passage states that the focal point in astigmatism may be in front of, behind, or in the same plane as the retina (choice D is correct).

6. **B** Sympathetic neurons release norepinephrine (choice A is wrong) and parasympathetic neurons release acetylcholine (choice D is wrong). Norepinephrine leads to pupil dilation (choice B is correct), while acetylcholine leads to pupil constriction (choice C is wrong).

Passage 48

1. **C**
   C: Yes. Figure 1 shows six curves, each of which represents the amplitude of vibration of regions of the cochlea. The curve for the part of the cochlea 24 mm away from the stapes peaks at approximately 400 cps.

2. **C**
   A: No. Sound merely travels through air in the outer air.
   B: No. The middle ear is comprised of the ossicles.
   C: Yes. The passage states that the inner ear is the site where the sound wave becomes a traveling wave.
   D: No. The hair cells transduce the impulse in the traveling wave into a nervous impulse.

3. **D**
   D: Yes. The passage states that low frequencies cause the most vibration at the apical end, farthest from the eardrum.

4. **B**
   A: No. This would cause conduction deafness, and hearing loss would be uniform over all frequencies.
   B: Yes. Since hair cells in different locations along the basilar membrane record sound of different frequencies, damage to a portion of hair cells would cause only hearing loss from a portion of the sound frequencies.
   C: No. Again this would cause hearing loss over all sound frequencies (conduction deafness).
   D: No. This would also affect all frequencies (conduction deafness).

5. **C**
   C: Yes. The first step of those listed is the movement of the auditory ossicles (which are in the middle ear). The second step is pressure changes of the inner ear (caused by ossicle movement). Third is the displacement of the basilar membrane (caused by pressure changes of the inner ear). And last but not least is the movement of the hair cells that are attached to the basilar membrane. This information is given in the passage.

6. **D**
   A: No. The cerebellum is the site of coordination of movement and balance.
   B: No. The hypothalamus is the site of the regulation of homeostasis.
   C: No. The cerebral white matter is comprised of myelinated axons (it is the lipid-rich myelin which makes it white). It is not considered a processing center but rather an area of complex intertwining pathways leading from one processing center to another (for example, from cerebellum to cortex).
   D: Yes. The cerebral cortex is composed of nerve cell bodies, and appears gray. The cerebral cortex processes "higher" information such as speech, sound, sight, learning, etc., and is the seat of consciousness. Also, the passage states that the hearing nerves of the spiral ganglion send their axons toward the auditory cortex.

Passage 49

1. **A** The cation channels on hair cells are mechanically-gated, that open due to the stretching caused by the movement of the stereocilia (choice A is correct). Ligand-gated channels are opened or closed by the binding of a ligand to a receptor (choice B is wrong), voltage-gated channels by changes in membrane potential (choice C is wrong), and temperature-gated by changes in temperature (choice D is wrong).

2. **C** Item I is correct: the loss of hair cells is associated with damage to the cochlea and would lead to sensorineural hearing loss (choice B can be eliminated). Item II is incorrect: infection of the middle ear generally does not affect the cochlea or any of the neuronal components of the auditory system. It can affect the ability to transmit the vibration and could therefore cause conductive hearing loss, but not sensorineural (choice D can be eliminated). Item III is correct: a tumor on the cochlear nerve will cause sensorineural hearing loss (choice A can be eliminated and choice C is correct).

3. **C** As stated in the passage, cochlear implants can only restore hearing loss if the impairment is in the cochlea. The cochlear nerve and the nuclei must be functioning in order for the electrodes from the implant to transmit the signal to be carried to the cortex.

4. **B** The function of the auditory ossicles (the three bones of the middle ear; malleus, incus, and stapes) is to efficiently amplify and transmit sound waves when transitioning from air-filled space to a fluid-filled ear cavity.

5. **D** Presbyacusis is associated with loss of hair cells (choices B and C can be eliminated). The loss of the hair cells mostly at the apex of the basilar membrane would cause inability to hear low frequency sounds (choice A can be eliminated). The loss of hair cells at the base would affect the ability to hear high frequency sounds (choice D is correct).

6. **C** All neurons have a soma and one axon (choices B and D can be eliminated). Multipolar neurons have many dendrites (choice A can be eliminated) whereas bipolar neurons have one dendrite-like structure, often referred to as a peripheral process (choice C is correct).

Passage 50

1. **C** The passage reviews the auditory pathway from the external ear to the brainstem. The auditory nerve is the second-to-last structure in this pathway. A tumor of this nerve would not affect structures before this, so choices A, B and D are wrong and can be eliminated, leaving choice C as the correct answer. Note that choice A is explicitly mentioned in the passage as a cause of tinnitus associated with exposure to loud sounds, but this is not the case in this scenario.

2. **D** This is a 2x2 question, where both components of the choice need to be true in order for it to be correct. The passage states that movements of the auditory ossicles are transmitted to the oval window of the cochlea. If the stapes is fused to the cochlea, it would not be able to move as well, and if it cannot move as well, then weaker waves of perilymph are produced (choices A and C can be eliminated). The passage also states that louder sounds result in waves of perilymph in greater frequency and intensity. Waves in this situation are not strong, thus the sound is not perceived as well (choice B is wrong and choice D is correct).

3. **A** The second paragraph of the passage states that exposure to loud sounds accelerates hearing loss, and 90 dB can be considered loud, especially with prolonged exposure. Although hearing loss is part of normal aging, cochlear hair cells can be damaged at any age (choice B is wrong). The lawnmower is 30 dB higher than normal conversation, so it is 10^3 or 1000 times more intense than normal conversation, not 50%; thus choice C is wrong. Although the lawnmower is 1000 less intense than the rock concert, it should still be considered as loud, and protective devices would be recommended during use, making choice D is wrong.

4. **D** Item I is true: the data shows that subjects C, D, E, I, and J all experienced varying degrees of hearing loss, while A, B, F, G, and H did not. The difference between these groups is age, demonstrating that the older subjects experienced hearing loss (choice B can be eliminated). Item II is true: comparing subjects C to H, D to I, and E to J, the men experienced more hearing loss compared to women of the same age (choice A can be eliminated). Item III is true: looking at the columns, only subject E cannot hear the lowest frequency 900 Hz tone, so this ability appears to be the least affected (choice C can be eliminated and choice D is correct).

5. **B** The first paragraph of the passage highlights the auditory pathway. The vibration of the eardrum will produce vibration of the ossicles, and if the eardrum is ruptured, it will not vibrate properly. Thus the ossicles will not vibrate properly either (choice B is correct). Although the ear canal can be blocked, it is typically by earwax or a foreign object, and not by inflammation (choice A is wrong). Although exposure to loud sounds does cause hearing loss, the rupturing of eardrum does not produce a loud sound. Even if it did, exposure to a single loud sound has not been shown to lead to hearing loss (choice C is wrong). The infection is not likely to damage the cranial nerve (choice D is wrong).

6. **A** The passage mentions that waves of perilymph will cause the hair cells to move, producing an action potential. This describes a mechanoreceptor (choice A is correct). Baroreceptors detect changes in pressure, and as there is no change in pressure in the cochlea, choice B is wrong. Chemoreceptors detect changes in electrolytes, and since there are no changes in the electrolytes in the perilymph, choice C is wrong. Nociceptors detect painful or noxious stimuli, and sound is typically not a painful or noxious stimulus (choice D is wrong).

Passage 51

1. **A**

    A: **Yes.** The vertical lines represent the firing of a receptor cell. You can infer this from the fact that there are more when the stimulus is on. This firing is an action potential, the basic unit of communication in nerves.

    B: No. Nerve cells generally spend most of their time at the resting membrane potential, which is represented by the steady horizontal baseline.

    C: No. The vertical lines before the "stimulus applied" box represent the basal firing rate, but in general the vertical lines just represent action potentials.

    D: No. There is no indication given that the stimulus is the touch of a hot object. This is a type of sensory stimulus, but we have no reason to suppose it is the one involved here.

2. **A**

    A: **Yes.** The movement of hairs which are embedded in these neural nets will stimulate firing of the neurons and send a signal that touch has occurred. What would a hair be useful in sensing if not movement?

    B: No. Pressure is sensed deeper in the skin, by the Pacinian corpuscle and other receptors. Dermal hairs are much more efficient for the detection of touch.

    C: No. Pain is sensed by free nerve endings in the dermis, not by hairs. Dermal hairs are much more efficient for the detection of touch.

    D: No. Hairs would not be effective in the detection of heat.

3. **B**

    A: No. Refer to Figure 1. The thumb has a large area of the sensory cortex devoted to it, but not as large at the lips.

    B: **Yes.** As shown in Figure 1, the area labeled lips is definitely the largest of the options given.

    C & D: No. As examination of the top of Figure 1 will show, only a small area of the sensory cortex is devoted to the neck and the leg.

4. **B**

    Items I & III: False. See discussion of Item II.

    Item II: True. The passage states (and Figure 2 shows) that phasic receptors adapt. It is also stated (and shown) that phasic receptors drop their firing rate below a basal level when a long-standing stimulus is removed. Hence, while the woman has her hands in hot and cold water, she will soon stop feeling hot and cold. Then, when her hands are placed in lukewarm water, the adapted receptors will transiently drop their firing rate below the basal level, and she will feel the opposite of what she felt before. Then the receptors will adapt once again, and she will stop having any temperature sensation while her hands remain in the warm water.

5. **A**

    A: **Yes.** Each tonic receptor cell in such a series measures with great precision but has a restricted intensity range over which it is sensitive since it cannot adapt to strong stimuli. A series of receptor cells with different but overlapping ranges can measure over a large range with great accuracy. This can be inferred from the question, which states that the receptors "have different, but slightly overlapping, sensitivity ranges." Also, you can eliminate the other choices based on information in the passage.

    B: No. The passage states that tonic cells fire to a degree proportional to the stimulus, thus providing good information about the magnitude of the stimulus.

    C: No. Nothing in the passage explicitly states which receptor type provides better information about the onset or end of stimulation.

    D: No. As stated in the passage, it is the phasic cells that adapt to stimulus, not the tonic cells.

6. **C**

    A: No. This is not adaptation.

    B: No. Sensory adaptation will not cause the initial stimulus not to be felt.

    C: **Yes.** Cutaneous receptors are located at specific points in the skin and are relatively sparsely distributed on the skin of the back. This is why it is possible to feel only one needle touch when there are actually two; both needles poke within the domain of a single receptor.

    D: No. The question states that the needles are applied with equal pressure. Only one sensitivity is needed. Also, no indication is given that pain receptors respond to a limited range of intensities.

Passage 52

1. **B**

    B: **Yes.** The RMP is created by the outward diffusion of potassium down its concentration gradient. If K^+ is added to the extracellular fluid, this gradient will be decreased, and thus so will the RMP.

2. **D**

    A, B, & C: No. The passage states that the Nernst equation only applies when the membrane is permeable to the ion in question. The giant squid axon is impermeable to sodium.

    D: **Yes.** The Nernst equation is only applicable when the membrane is permeable to the ion in question—it can't be used here, since the membrane is impermeable to sodium, and there are no resting channels for this ion. Normally the nerve cell membrane is permeable to potassium due to specialized channels, and it is potassium's efflux through these channels which creates the RMP. If they are blocked, the only significant source of a transmembrane potential would be the electrogenicity of the ATPase. This refers to the fact that the pump exports 3 Na^+ for every 2 K^+ it imports; this results in a negative charge inside the cell relative to outside (same polarity as the RMP). Remember, though, that this is not the major source of the RMP–K^+ efflux through channels is.

3. **A**

    A: **Yes.** Decreasing $[K^+]_{outside}$ will increase the RMP (more negative) by causing a greater concentration-driven efflux of potassium. Hence a greater depolarization will be necessary to trigger the voltage-sensitive sodium fast channels.

4.   **B**

Item I: False.

Item II: True. Both electrical- and concentration-driven forces drive sodium into the cell. The Na$^+$/K$^+$ ATPase has pumped sodium out of the cell (creating the concentration gradient), and the negative RMP tends to draw positive ions into the cell.

Item III: False. Concentration gradients tend to drive K$^+$ out of the cell, because it is pumped in by the Na$^+$/K$^+$ ATPase. It is true that electrical gradients tend to drive K$^+$ into the cell. This is explained on the latter half of the second paragraph of the passage.

5.   **B**

Item I: False. The membrane is fully permeable to K$^+$, with many leak channels.

Item II: True. The passage directly explains that the RMP is less negative than predicted "because of the presence of a slight permeability to sodium." You should know that an ion like Na$^+$ could never cross the membrane without a channel or transporter, that the membrane itself is 100% impermeable to sodium.

Item III: False. The ATPase is electrogenic, because it pumps 3 Na$^+$ out for every 2 K$^+$ it pumps in. But this would tend to increase the negativity of the RMP, not make it less negative.

6.   **A**

A: **Yes.** Myelin, which consists of Schwann cell membranes, prevents an action potential from occurring within a segment of an axon. As a result, the action potential must leap from one node of Ranvier to the next. There is no myelin at the nodes, so depolarization can occur there. This jumping process is known as saltatory conduction, and it greatly increases the action potential propagation rate.

B: No. Myelin blocks depolarization in segments only, and conduction in myelinated axons is always saltatory.

C: No. They are concentrated at the nodes of Ranvier.

D: No. Dendrites do this. Axons conduct away from the soma (nerve cell body).

Passage 53

1.   **D**   Slowed conduction implies that conduction still occurs. Thus, a person would maintain sensory and motor function, although they would be weaker (choices A and C are wrong). However, since the impulses traveling through that nerve are delayed compared to impulses traveling through undamaged nerves, the brain has trouble interpreting the late sensory data and the person has an alteration in sensation. This is known as paresthesia. Note that pain sensations would be altered as well, making choice B too specific of an answer. Affected individuals might well be hyposensitive to painful stimuli.

2.   **B**   Because GBS responds to plasmapheresis, this suggests that GBS is caused by an antibody to myelin (which then signals macrophages to attack the myelin sheaths). Remember that T-cells attack directly; B-cells secrete antibodies (choice A is wrong). The passage states that *C. jejuni* is a common infection, but GBS is not very common (4000 cases/year in the U.S.). That implies that only certain strains of *C. jejuni* contain an epitope which is also found in human myelin (choice C is wrong).

3. **A** Although B and C are both true, they do not explain why GBS affects peripheral but not central nerves. The passage states that GBS results from an immunologic attack on nerves (it is not caused by bacteria, so B is not the answer). C is true, but since the target in GBS is myelin, one would then expect to see more involvement of the CNS. D is a false statement.

4. **C** A single action potential at a synapse does not cause the release of enough neurotransmitter to bring the postsynaptic cell to threshold. This requires the summed effect of several action potentials in a short period of time; EPSPs from each action potential will build on one another until threshold is reached in the postsynaptic cell. If conduction were slowed, action potentials would arrive less frequently at the synapse, preventing the EPSPs from building up to threshold. Action potentials are "all or nothing"—nerve cells depolarize to about +30 mV with every action potential (choice A is wrong). The speed of the action potential does not affect the refractory period; also, the question states that action potentials were being transmitted (choice B is wrong). Neurons release only one category of neurotransmitters (choice D is wrong).

5. **D** Although all of these findings have actually been made, only D directly supports our scientist's hypothesis. The passage states that macrophages phagocytose the myelin sheaths, but remember that macrophages need a signal to know where to attack. That signal probably comes from the attachment of anti-myelin antibodies to the myelin sheath. Choice A only indirectly supports the hypothesis by showing that IVIG does not lead to destruction of anti-myelin antibodies. Choice B suggests that administering IVIG leads to destruction of anti-myelin antibodies (a different mechanism than our scientist suggested). Choice C concerns T-cells, which do not produce antibodies.

6. **B** After the cell has been depolarized, voltage-gated K^+ channels open. This allows the efflux of potassium, thereby repolarizing the cell. Calcium, not potassium, facilitates release of neurotransmitter molecules at the synaptic cleft (choice A is wrong). The influx of sodium ions is responsible for the initial depolarization of the cell from its resting membrane potential (choice C is wrong). The total inhibition of further action potentials is due to the absolute refractory period, which is a property of the voltage-gated sodium channels, and which is not affected by potassium (choice D is wrong).

Passage 54

1. **C** CRF and ACTH secretion are associated with stress. Choices A and B are stressful conditions which would lead to increased secretion of these hormones. In choice D, there would be no cortisol present, and in the absence of feedback inhibition, CRF and ACTH levels would be very high. Thus, the answer is choice C: High levels of cortisol would be present in the blood and would repress CRF and ACTH secretion by feedback inhibition.

2. **D** Cortisol tends to protect against stress in several ways, including inflammation (eliminating A), increasing the energy available for action and tissue repair (eliminating B), and decreasing the sensitivity to pain (eliminating C). Choice D is correct since cortisol is a response to stress and does not decrease the response to stress.

3. **B** The site of ACTH action is the adrenal gland, to increase secretion of the adrenal hormones, supporting choice B and eliminating C. Choices A and D are incorrect because ACTH is not itself directly responsible for any of the metabolic effects associated with stress and corticosteroids.

4. **C** Choices A, B, and D are all effects of cortisol. High levels of corticosteroids reduce inflammation. The tissue damage of arthritis is associated with chronic inflammation, and is reduced, not increased, by corticosteroids.

5. **A** Cortisol is a steroid hormone. Hormones of this class act by binding to intracellular receptors which regulate gene transcription in the nucleus.

6. **D** Choices **A** and **B** can be eliminated because it is cortisol secretion, not ACTH secretion, that must be explained (besides, they're both false statements). Choice C is wrong because it also does not address the changes in cortisol secretion. Choice D is correct: If the shock causes the hypothalamus to increase CRF secretion, then cortisol secretion will increase and then decrease again once the shock is removed.

Passage 55

1. **D** The adrenal glands produce aldosterone and cortisol in the cortex and epinephrine in the medulla. Aldosterone regulates the retention of salt and water in the kidney, acting to increase extracellular fluid volume and blood pressure, eliminating choices A and C. Cortisol induces gluconeogenesis and glycogen formation in the liver, thus eliminating B. The answer is D: Plasma calcium is regulated by parathyroid hormone from the parathyroid gland, by vitamin D, and by calcitonin from the thyroid gland.

2. **A** The sham is a control to ensure that any changes observed are due to the removal of a specific organ and not to the act of surgery itself.

3. **B** Steroid hormones passively diffuse through the plasma membrane to bind to receptors located in the cytoplasm and nucleus, which can subsequently regulate transcription of specific genes through binding to DNA in promoter and enhancer regions.

4. **B** The site of action for aldosterone is the kidney. In this tissue, it will concentrate in the nuclei of target cells, due to the mechanism of action for this hormone.

5. **A** The adrenal glands make cortisol in response to ACTH from the pituitary. In normal regulation, this cortisol represses ACTH (feedback inhibition). In the absence of the adrenal gland, cortisol levels will fall rapidly, and ACTH will increase due to the lack of feedback inhibition by cortisol in the plasma.

6. **D** The anterior pituitary secretes ACTH, which induces secretion of aldosterone and cortisol. Injection of anterior pituitary extract will include ACTH, which will induce aldosterone and cortisol secretion by the adrenal cortex; this eliminates A and B. The elevated cortisol secretion caused by ACTH will in turn feed back to inhibit the secretion of additional ACTH, so C is eliminated. Epinephrine and norepinephrine are secreted by the adrenal medulla in response to stimulation by the sympathetic nervous system and will not be greatly influenced by hormones from the anterior pituitary. Thus, choice D is the correct response here.

Passsage 56

1. **C**   Choices A and B are true statements, but they do not explain the convulsions observed. (In fact, B would imply that decreased extracellular calcium would decrease muscle contraction.) Choice D is not true, as the data in the table show. The answer must be C. Convulsions are caused by uncontrolled stimulation of skeletal muscle by motor neurons. If the low extracellular calcium levels increase sodium permeability in neurons, then more sodium will enter the cell, depolarizing the membrane and causing uncontrolled action potentials.

2. **B**   Statement I is false: None of the animals received no injection (this would not make a good control even if they were treated in this manner). Statement II is true: A good control has everything identical to the test animals, except for the key variable being tested. And Statement III is false: Hormone X was indeed measured in at least some of the animals, but this was not the control. It was a parameter that was being studied.

3. **C**   Hormone X secretion appears to increase in response to increased plasma calcium. Calcitonin is a hormone secreted by the thyroid gland which acts to decrease plasma calcium, and whose secretion is increased by elevated plasma calcium.

4. **B**   In the absence of parathyroid hormone, plasma calcium drops and hypocalcemia results. The hypocalcemia in a person with complete absence of PTH would probably be severe, resulting in convulsions and tetany as described in the first paragraph of the passage. Respiration requires properly functioning nervous stimulation and muscle function, and would be impaired by convulsions.

5. **C**   This information is read from the table, with either parathyroid hormone extract or PTH itself.

6. **D**   There is no information provided that suggests that the liver regulates plasma calcium, thus eliminating choices A and B. Parathyroid hormone increases, not decreases, plasma calcium, and this in turn increases Hormone X production (supporting choice D and eliminating C).

Passage 57

1. **A**
   A: Yes. The passage directly states that the most common cause of Cushing's disease is a prescription.
   B: No. The adrenals do not make ACTH.
   C: No. Inflammation is treated with corticosteroids; it is not the cause of their elevation.
   D: No. This would cause a deficiency of cortisol.

2. **C**
   A: No. The question states that the proteolytic enzymes used are known to fragment ACTH.
   B: No. ACTH is secreted directly into the bloodstream by the pituitary, not eaten!
   C: Yes. ACTH must have a portion that is biologically active and will exert its biological effects when cleaved from the larger molecule.
   D: No. Protein hormones such as ACTH exert their effects by way of a cell-surface second messenger system; they are not cofactors, which act in concert with enzymes within cells.

3. **B**

Item I: True. An adenoma is a benign hyperproliferation of cells. Too many ACTH-producing cells lead to too much ACTH.

Item II: False. If the cell didn't respond to CRF, it would release less ACTH.

Item III: True. According to the passage, pituitary tumors may fail to respond normally to negative feedback.

4. **D**

A: No. Because it does not have a central role in the regulation of the immune response, inhibiting the macrophage would not be efficacious in the treatment of so wide a variety of immune disorders. Recall that the macrophage is a key phagocyte and is also important in antigen presentation.

B: No. The neutrophil is a key player in the inflammatory response and is an essential phagocyte. However, as noted regarding the macrophage, it does not have so central a role in the immune response that its inhibition could explain such a wide range of treatment efficacies.

C: No. Inhibiting B cells would not block cell-mediated immunity, which is carried out by T cells.

D: **Yes.** Via the production of interleukins and other chemicals, the T cell is the central player in the regulation of the immune response. Inhibiting the T cell is the quickest way to knock out the entire immune system: both the humoral and cell-mediated responses (as in AIDS).

5. **D**

Item I: False. The negative feedback of increased cortisol on the pituitary would oppose stimulation by CRF.

Item II: True. Refer to the diagram and follow ACTH down to cortisol. You can see that as long as there is a high level of ACTH, no other factor illustrated here can shut down cortisol production.

Item III: True. This can be inferred by following the negative-feedback loops from the adrenal gland to the hypothalamus and pituitary.

6. **C**

A, B, & D: No, these cannot be inferred from the information provided.

C: **Yes.** The annotation to the diagram states that the superior hypophysial artery supplies the hypophysial portal system. You must come to the conclusion that since cortisol is released into the general circulatory system ("systemic vascular supply"), it must get back to the ACTH producing cells via this route.

Passage 58

1. **B**

A: No. This occurs in the absence of insulin signaling.

B: **Yes.** This is just what it does. Insulin is a peptide hormone which binds to a cell-surface receptor, leading to changes in the activity of cytoplasmic proteins. For example, the enzyme responsible for glycogen synthesis is activated, and the enzyme responsible for glycogen degradation is inhibited.

C: No. Insulin is normally released when blood sugar is elevated. It functions to lower blood sugar by promoting glucose uptake and storage. It promotes glycogen synthesis and inhibits glycogen breakdown.

D: No, just the opposite. As illustrated by the description of diabetes in the passage, insulin is necessary for the uptake of glucose into cells, not the opposite.

2. **D**

   A: No. "Peripheral neuropathy" refers to problems with peripheral nerves (see third paragraph of passage). It can cause incontinence (loss of control of the time and place of urination), but not polyuria (increased urine volume).

   B: No. The polyphagia of diabetics results from two factors: the loss of so much glucose in the urine, and the intracellular glucose deficit resulting from absence of insulin's effects.

   C: No. Hyperglycemia causes glucose to be lost in urine. The glucose loss in urine in turn causes polyuria.

   D: **Yes.** The excess blood glucose overwhelms the proximal tubule's ability to resorb glucose from the urine. The resulting high urinary glucose concentration (glucosuria) draws excess water into the renal tubules by osmosis.

3. **B**

   Item I: False. Insulin does just the opposite; it inhibits glycogen breakdown and promotes glycogen synthesis. Thus, blood glucose is stored as glycogen.

   Item II: True. Insulin is secreted when there is plenty of glucose and causes this glucose to be stored as glycogen and fat.

   Item III: False. Since insulin is secreted when there is plenty of glucose, it would be a useless positive-feedback loop for it to cause glucose synthesis. It actually inhibits gluconeogenesis while promoting glycogen synthesis.

4. **D**

   Item I: False. The whole problem with diabetes is that insulin is not functioning.

   Item II: True. Glucagon is the hormone of hunger. It does the opposite of nearly everything insulin does. For example, in the liver it stimulates glycogen breakdown and release of glucose into the bloodstream.

   Item III: True. Epinephrine also stimulates glycogen breakdown in the liver. It helps to increase blood glucose during the sympathetic "fight or flight" response.

   Item IV: True. Glucocorticoids stimulate gluconeogenesis. Cortisol actually causes muscle protein to be broken down and made into glucose in the liver. Muscle wasting and obesity result.

5. **C**

   A: No. Ketone bodies are a result of diabetes, not the cause of it.

   B: No; see A.

   C: **Yes.** In IDDM, the β cells are destroyed, so no insulin is present. In NIDDM, insulin is made but does not have the effects it should. Destroying insulin receptors would mimic this response.

   D: No; see C.

6. **D**

   A: No. This is not true, and more importantly, there is nothing in the passage which suggests that it is true.

   B: No. Because insulin is a polypeptide, it is easily digested by the digestive tract. Hence, it must be injected and cannot be taken orally.

   C: No. IDDM is generally caused by antibodies to the β cells of the pancreatic islets of Langerhans. Loss of these cells cannot be corrected (yet).

   D: **Yes.** It is easy to control the extreme hyperglycemia of IDDM because the body responds normally to injected insulin. There's nothing wrong with the insulin receptor, just a failure of the pancreas to make insulin.

Passage 59

1. **D** Antibodies against viral antigens will protect against viral infection, while live virus carries a risk of causing the disease.

2. **A** The passage describes the difficulty in developing effective vaccines due to the propensity of the virus to mutate surface antigens to escape immune detection, so choice A is correct. Nothing similar to B, C, or D is true or hinted at in the passage.

3. **C** Vaccines provide protection by stimulating specific clones of immune cells that recognize antigen to proliferate. B cells which respond against a vaccine will proliferate and provide protection against future infection by the same virus.

4. **C** Choice A is wrong because H antigen is a protein composed of amino acid residues. Choice B is wrong because mRNA for viral or cellular proteins will be translated in the same way, since the virus must utilize cellular machinery for translation. Choice D is wrong because fats are not encoded by DNA, only proteins. Thus, only choice C is a viable option (although this statement would be true of any translated protein, not just this specific viral antigen).

5. **A** The passage states that H antigen is required for a virus to attach itself to susceptible cells, such as those of the respiratory tract lining. Note that the N antigen is also required for the spread of the virus, but choice B states that the N antigen is expressed on the capsid, while the passage states that the virus is enveloped.

Passage 60

1. **B** Choice B is the answer because viscosity is caused by interactions between cells, which are very orderly in the capillaries (thereby reducing viscosity). Choice A is wrong because it would increase viscosity (and does not apply to capillaries), and C and D can be eliminated because they suggest that hematocrit varies with the vessel size, which is not true. Hematocrit reflects the number of red blood cells per unit volume of blood, which is constant in an individual throughout their circulatory system.

2. **D** As velocity decreases, viscosity increases (and vice versa). The velocity in vessels larger than capillaries (that is, greater than 1.5 mm in diameter) is very slow, without the orderly flow found in capillaries, thus corresponding to a rise in viscosity. No information is presented linking pressure with viscosity, eliminating choices A and B.

3. **B** A low hematocrit indicates fewer than normal red blood cells in blood. Red blood cells contain hemoglobin, which carries oxygen in blood, so a low hematocrit indicates poor oxygen-carrying capacity in blood.

4. **C** With greater than normal red blood cells, there will be more than normal hemoglobin and greater than normal oxygen-carrying capacity (eliminating choices B and D). The blood will also be more viscous (eliminating choice A) since it has more cells per volume.

5. **D** With just plasma used to replace whole blood, the red blood cells in circulation will be more diluted, producing a lower red cell count and a lower hematocrit.

Passage 61

1. **C** The passage describes atherosclerotic plaques as building up "slowly over time, often without noticeable clinical manifestations." This would be consistent with the assertion that the disease is difficult to diagnose, particularly early in its progression (choice C is true). The passage says that the initial warning sign of atherosclerosis (chest pain) may be initially noticed during bouts of exercise, but it does not say that exercise contributes to the development of atherosclerosis (choice A is false; note also that this answer option is too extreme because of the word "only"). The first paragraph says plaques develop in arteries (not veins), and obstruct the flow of blood to tissues and organs (not the return to the heart; choice B is false). Although thrombolytic drugs are discussed in the passage, they are described as a treatment for blood clots in coronary arteries that have been rendered vulnerable due to atherosclerotic plaques. They are not used to treat atherosclerosis itself (choice D is false).

2. **B** Low blood pressure in the aorta (the major artery leading to the systemic circulation) indicates that blood flow has been compromised. Since the left ventricle is responsible for pumping blood into the aorta, this is most likely the affected region (choice B is correct). The sinoatrial node is responsible for the rhythm of the heart, but has nothing to do with pressure generation beyond affecting heart rate, and in any case, if the SA node were affected, the pressure in both the aorta and the pulmonary circulation would be low (choice A is wrong). If blood travelling through pulmonary circulation (i.e., to the lungs) is normal, then the right ventricle (which pumps blood to the lungs) is probably not affected (choice C is wrong). The left atrium receives blood returning from the pulmonary circulation. It is not responsible for the large pressures generated to pump blood through the aorta and the systemic circulation (choice D is wrong).

3. **B** This is a two-by-two question, where two decisions must be made to get to the right answer. ADH acts at the kidneys to increase water retention. This results in an increase in total blood volume, an increase in stroke volume (due to the Frank-Starling mechanism), and an increase in cardiac output (CO = SV × HR, choices C and D can be eliminated). The vagus nerve decreases both the heart rate and the force of contraction; thus, to increase cardiac output, the vagus nerve must be inhibited (choice B is correct and choice A is wrong).

4. **C** A patient with hemophilia already has difficulty clotting their blood; treating such a patient with thrombolytic drugs would not be helpful in any way, and could be seriously detrimental to the patient (thrombolytics would not be indicated in choice C, and this is the correct answer). The passage describes the use of thrombolytics in the treatment of myocardial infarction, typically caused by a coronary thrombus (choices A and B could be treated via thrombolytics and can be eliminated). Platelets are an important mediator in the clotting process; elevated platelet levels could lead to more frequent and/or severe blood clots. Thrombolytic drugs could be utilized in order to prevent development of these potentially life-threatening clots (choice D could be treated with thrombolytics and can be eliminated).

5. **D** Action potentials in the heart are generated at the SA node (choice C is wrong), then transmitted through the atria (causing their contraction; choice A is wrong) before being delayed at the AV node and finally traveling to the ventricles and causing their contraction. The action potential must travel via the left and right bundles in the interventricular septum in order to reach the ventricular muscle. With a left bundle branch block, conduction to the left ventricle is diminished, resulting in delayed left ventricular contraction (choice D is better than choice A).

6. **A** The question describes a condition in which blood flow is restricted, resulting in an inability of oxygen supply to meet oxygen demand (ischemia) and tissue death. This is what occurs in the case of a myocardial infarction, as described in the passage; blood flow is restricted to cardiac muscle tissue, resulting in tissue death (choice A is correct). The formation of foam cells is the beginning of atherosclerosis, and does not involve tissue death (choice B is wrong). A coronary thrombus can cause myocardial infarction, but is only a clot, not actual tissue death (choice C is wrong), and angina pectoris is a symptom of atherosclerosis and possible myocardial infarction, but again, is not itself tissue death (choice D is wrong).

Passage 62

1. **B** Colloid is used to increase the osmotic draw of the intravascular space. The large molecules are unable to diffuse out of the blood vessels, unlike the small, ionic sodium and chloride molecules which rapidly equilibrate. Choice A is incorrect; if the crystalloid solution had a higher osmolality than the colloid, it would be more effective at drawing water into the blood vessels and raising blood pressure. Choices C and D are both false statements; sodium and chloride are components of blood and colloid molecules do not activate the sympathetic nervous system.

2. **C** According to the passage, neurogenic shock is caused by an injury to the sympathetic nervous system. It is safe to assume the injury would lead to malfunction of this system, thus a loss of sympathetic tone, which results in vasodilation (leading to low blood pressure) and a slow heart rate (due to overriding parasympathetic tone). Statement III is true. Cardiogenic and hypovolemic shock are characterized by low blood pressure along with an increase in heart rate, since loss of sympathetic function does not occur in these instances. Statements I and II are false.

3. **D** Hb O_2 saturation is only a good measure of hemoglobin O_2 saturation. It tells us nothing of how much O_2 is actually reaching the tissues (choice A is wrong). Although knowing the oxygen content of a tissue sample would be useful, it is very invasive and would take a long time to process (choice C is wrong). CVP is a useful measure of shock, but it is more invasive than simply measuring blood lactate levels (choice B is wrong). Remember that as cells become hypoxic, they will switch to anaerobic metabolism and generate more lactic acid.

4. **D** The parasympathetic system does not innervate blood vessels and thus does not affect SVR (choice A is wrong). If the heart moved less blood with each beat (i.e., the stroke volume decreased) or if the heart rate decreased, cardiac output would be reduced, not increased as is described in the question (choices B and C are wrong). A systemic inflammatory response occurs in septic shock and causes dilation of almost all blood vessels, leading to very low blood pressures.

5   A   This question stumps many a medical resident, "floating the swan" for the first time. It's really not that difficult, but the graphs can be confusing, especially in real time. You can answer the question without Figure 1 if you think it through; the graph is of course in the order that the catheter passes through the heart! Region A (choice D) is the right atrium. Region B (choice A) is the right ventricle. Region C (choice C) is the pulmonary artery. Region D (choice B) is the wedge tracing. Region B is the correct region because systolic pressures are high and diastolic pressures are equivalent to CVP (right atrial pressure, Region A), as discussed in the passage. In Region C, note that the diastolic pressure has risen due to elasticity of the pulmonary artery and the fact that the pulmonic valve has closed. In Region D, the pressures are no longer pulsatile, and the catheter has equilibrated with the return flow to the left side of the heart.

6.   C   Equation 1 relates mean arterial pressure to cardiac output and SVR (total peripheral resistance). The relationship is directly proportional; the equation can be rearranged so that this is more obvious (MAP = CO × SVR). Thus, changes in CO or SVR will result in corresponding changes in mean arterial pressure. An increase in stroke volume would lead to an increase in cardiac output (recall that CO = stroke volume × heart rate), and thus an increase in MAP (choice A is true and eliminated). If this were accompanied by systemic vasoconstriction (in other words, an increase in SVR) the pressure would rise even higher (choice D is true and eliminated). Similarly, an increase in heart rate would raise CO, and without a corresponding decrease in SVR, MAP would increase (choice B is true and eliminated). A decrease in heart rate, however, would decrease cardiac output and blood pressure. If this were accompanied by a proportional increase in SVR, then MAP would remain unchanged (choice C is false and the correct answer choice).

Passage 63

1.   B
A: No. White blood cells escape blood vessels (using amoeboid motility), conduct their business in the tissues, and can return to the blood circulation by lymphatic flow, stopping at lymph nodes en route.
B: Yes. This is the correct choice here, because it is a false statement. The lymphatic system has no role in the circulation of red blood cells. They do not escape blood vessels, because they are large and lack the amoeboid motility of white blood cells.
C: No. The lymphatic system does maintain protein concentrations in the blood by returning leaked proteins from the interstitium to the blood circulation (this is covered in the passage).
D: No. This is true; the lymphatic system does transport fats from the digestive tract to the circulatory system, in the form of chylomicrons.

2.   D
Items I, II, & III: True. These facts are directly stated in the passage.

3.   C
A: No. They managed to get out, so the impermeability must not be absolute.
B: No. Most plasma proteins are negatively charged, and charge would make no more sense than size anyway (if it prevented them from getting in, wouldn't it prevent them from getting out?).
C: Yes. Blood pressure is much higher than interstitial fluid pressure, and the concentration of protein is also much higher in the blood. Hence, proteins tend to leak out of vessels and cannot diffuse back in.
D: No. In fact, many proteins are returned to the circulation intact (via the lymphatic system).

4. **C**

Item I: True. Increasing capillary hydrostatic pressure will tend to drive fluid out. (Edema is defined in the last sentence of the passage.)

Item II: True. Increasing tissue osmotic pressure will tend to draw fluid out of the bloodstream. The large osmotic gradient between the blood and the interstitial space is key for retention of fluid in the vascular space. In the case of liver disease or protein deficiency, the concentration of plasma proteins (i.e., albumin) falls and edema results. (Edema is defined in the last sentence of the passage.)

Item III: False. As discussed in the passage, lymphatic valves are important in maintaining lymph flow.

5. **D**

Item I: True. As discussed in the passage, the thoracic duct drains the entire left side of the body.

Item II: True. Lymphatic capillaries are the starting point of lymph return to the blood.

Item III: False. The right lymphatic duct drains only the right shoulder area and the right side of the head, as stated in the passage.

6. **D**

A: No. Neither capillary type has muscle.

B: No. Neither capillary type transports proteins actively.

C: No. Flow is unidirectional in both types of capillary and is determined by the difference in pressure between upstream and downstream fluids. In the case of blood, upstream arterioles have higher pressure than downstream venules. In the case of lymphatics, as discussed in the passage, valves create a negative downstream pressure.

D: **Yes.** Lymphatic capillaries are more permeable. They are "meant" to uptake proteins, whereas blood capillaries were "designed" to retain proteins.

Passage 64

1. **C**

A: No. In Experiment 1a, the rejected tissue (pituitary gland) is genetically identical to the rejecting organism, since it was originally part of that organism. But since none of this tissue was present during maturation of the immune system, the tissue is recognized as foreign. The explanation is that the expression of genes in pituitary tissue gives rise to cell-surface markers not present on other tissue types.

B: No. The passage states that the frogs attained adulthood. The correct interpretation is that a cell type must be present during maturation if it is to be recognized as self, not that maturation cannot occur for this recognition to take place.

C: **Yes.** The antigens in the pituitary tissue must be present during development if they are to be recognized as "self."

D: No. One cannot generalize about foreign grafts from Experiment 1, because the graft was not foreign.

2. **C**
   A: No. Nonidentical twins have the same degree of genetic similarity as non-twin siblings, regardless of whether they share a placenta or have separate ones. Hence it is not genetics, but rather the developmental environment, which explains scenarios like that described in Experiment 4.
   B: No. If this were the case, why would the number of placentas matter?
   C: **Yes.** Something about developing within a single placenta makes nonidentical twins immunologically co-tolerant. A shared blood supply is the explanation; each twin is exposed to antigens from the other throughout gestation.
   D: No. This would not affect immunological tolerance.

3. **B**
   B: **Yes.** This is a bit tricky if you just read the explanation to question 1. In that question, genetic identity did not ensure self-recognition because the graft (pituitary tissue) expressed cell-surface antigens not present in the host (all cells of the tissue type had been removed), even though the graft originally came from the host and was thus genetically identical to it. In the present question, every cell is genetically identical, every tissue type present in one identical twin is present in the other, and *every normal tissue is present throughout development.* They both share the same self-tolerance acquired during development, so the twins can interchange tissue.
   C & D: No. There is no reason to suppose that identical twins would be more likely than non-twins to accept grafts from any random source or from their parents. The twins are merely tolerant of *each other's* antigens (since they share all antigens).

4. **B**
   B: **Yes.** Without a thymus, the rat's T cells do not develop normally. The rat will fail to reject not only grafts, but also pathogens, causing susceptibility to infection and the wasting illness described in Experiment 2.
   C & D: No. Normally, animals are more likely to accept grafts from relatives, and the absence of the thymus would not change this.

5. **B**
   Item I: True. Experiment 4 suggests that exposure to an antigen is essential for the recognition of that antigen as self, and Experiment 3 shows that the thymus is the critical location where the "learning" takes place.
   Item II: False. The immune system has no direct role in physical growth. Experiment 2 does describe a wasting disease, but this is due to infection, not the thymus directly.
   Item III: True. Experiment 3 shows this to be true.

6. **A**
   A: **Yes.** This question presupposes some knowledge of immune system function. Selection of T cells in the thymus is a process whereby T cells "programmed" to destroy self antigens are eliminated. It is also possible to eliminate T cells specific to a non-self antigen if the antigen is thrust directly into the self-selection center, the thymus.
   B: No, the opposite is true. If a graft is implanted *anywhere* in a very immature animal, it will be recognized as self. This can be inferred from the fact that the transplant in Experiment 1 remained with the recipient until adulthood.
   C: No, the opposite is true; they were selectively destroyed (see A).
   D: No. There is nothing in Experiment 3 to suggest that this is true in general; the only information given is that a particular graft was accepted. Choice A is best.

Passage 65

1. **B** The passage states that HLA-DR is a type of MHC II receptor. MHC II is found on the surface of antigen-presenting cells (APCs). Item I is true: macrophages are APCs, and thus would contain HLA-DR (choice C can be eliminated). Item II is also true, as B cells are also APCs (choice A can be eliminated). Item III is false: red blood cells are not APCs, and would not have MHC II on their surface (choice D can be eliminated and choice B is correct).

2. **B** The information required for this answer is found in Figure 1, which includes the relative risk (RR) of various autoimmune disorders by HLA-DR haplotype. The table states that HLA-DR3 is associated type 1 diabetes, autoimmune hepatitis, and Sjögren syndrome. Choice C is eliminated because HLA-DR4 is associated with rheumatoid arthritis, not HLA-DR3. The RR of type 1 diabetes for someone who has HLA-DR3, but not HLA-DR4, is 5. The RR of autoimmune hepatitis is 14, and of Sjögren syndrome, 10. This makes choice B (autoimmune hepatitis) the correct choice.

3. **A** MHC receptors interact with T cells, not B cells (choices B and D can be eliminated). Helper T cells interact with MHC II receptors, so choice C can be eliminated as well. As is stated in the passage, MHC I receptors interact with cytotoxic (CD8+) cells (choice A is correct).

4. **D** According to Figure 1, someone who has both HLA-DR3 and HLA-DR4 has a relative risk of type 1 diabetes of 15. Plugging this RR into Equation 1, along with the risk of 1% (0.01) for those who do not have HLA-DR3 or HLA-DR4 shows that the probability that someone with HLA-DR3 and HLA-DR4 will develop type 1 diabetes is 0.15, or 15%. This corresponds to choice D. Choice A accurately describes the probability that someone with HLA-DR3, but not HLA-DR4, will develop type 1 diabetes. Conversely, choice B describes the probability that someone with HLA-DR3, but not HLA-DR4, will develop type 1 diabetes. Adding the RR associated with HLA-DR3 and HLA-DR4, without using the accurate RR from the table, would provide the final incorrect answer, choice C.

5. **B** Polygenism (choice B) describes a situation where multiple genes influence one phenotype. Pleiotropism refers to one gene that influences multiple phenotypes, and the question asks for the opposite (choice A is incorrect). A gene's penetrance describes the likelihood that someone with that genotype will express the expected phenotype (choice C is incorrect). Epistasis describes a situation where the expression of one allele is dependent on the presence of a specific allele at a second gene (choice D is incorrect).

6. **A** This is a 2x2 question: where are T cells are produced and where do T cells mature? T cells, like all blood cells, are produced in the bone marrow (choices B and D can be eliminated) and mature in the thymus, in fact the "T" in "T cell" stands for "thymus" (choice C can be eliminated and choice A is correct). The spleen filters the blood, is the site of immune interactions, and destroys aged red blood cells, but is not involved in T cell maturation.

Passage 66

1. **B**

    Item I: False. Platelets are always present in plasma.

    Item II: True. Platelets bind to exposed collagen in damaged tissue to trigger clotting.

    Item III: False. T cells play a role in immunity, *not* in hemostasis.

2. **D**

    A: No. Antibiotics are carried in the bloodstream, and this is where they have most of their effects.

    B: No. There is no reason to conclude this.

    C: No. Many antibiotics work by killing bacteria which spend much of their time inside our cells (such as *M. tuberculosis*). They either enter infected cells or affect the bacteria when they move from one cell to another.

    D: **Yes.** Antibiotics are generally used for bacterial infections. They are such valuable drugs because they are imminently fatal to bacteria but generally harmless to us. This results from the great differences between the prokaryotic cell and the eukaryotic cell. The challenge in treating cancer and viral and eukaryotic infections is to kill the abnormal cell type without killing healthy cells.

3. **B**

    A: No. item 4 above Figure 1 states that the chills and fever of malaria are caused by merozoites. A drug against sporozoites might help with prevention, but would not be curative.

    B: **Yes.** Item 4 above Figure 1 states that the chills and fever of malaria are caused by merozoites infecting and lysing RBCs. Killing merozoites would halt the progress of the disease.

    C: No. Killing the gametocyte could only prevent spread of the disease. It is the merozoites which cause the actual illness.

    D: No. The mosquito only transmits the disease. It plays no role in the illness itself.

4. **D**

    Item I: True. This would prevent infection and thus prevent reproduction.

    Item II: True. This would not prevent infection, but it would thwart the development of the proto-zoan, and would thus thwart reproduction.

    Item III: True. This would prevent transmission of the disease to a new insect host and would thus disrupt the protist's life cycle.

    Item IV: True. This is one of the most effective ways of combating malaria. The problem is that mosquitoes can develop resistance to insecticides (as *Plasmodia* can develop resistance to drugs).

5. **D**

    Item I: True. Primary structure refers to the sequence of amino acids comprising a polypeptide. (Re-fer to the third paragraph of the passage.)

    Item II: True. This is precisely the problem in sickle-cell anemia. The abnormal valine residue is hydrophobic and replaces a hydrophilic residue (glutamate) on the surface of the folded poly-peptide. Hydrophobic interactions between the abnormal residues on the protein's surface lead to the formation of gigantic macropolymers (many Hb molecules stuck together) which become so large that they distort red blood cells.

    Item III: True. This change also affects the charge of the protein and would thus change the isoelec-tric point.

6. **A**

    A: **Yes.** Lytic viruses infect the host cell and soon lyse it and release many progeny viruses which go on to infect other cells.

    B: No. Lysogenic viruses infect the host cell and then enter a dormant phase in which the viral genome is integrated into the host genome. No such process is described for *Plasmodium*.

    C: No. A saprophyte is an organism which derives its nourishment from dead organisms. The host cell of the merozoite is the red blood cell.

    D: No. A predator is an organism which eats living organisms smaller than itself. The merozoite is a parasite, not a predator, because it infects red blood cells which are larger than itself.

Passage 67

1. **D**

    A: No. The mouse anti-hCG is bound to the plastic well before the pregnancy test kit is used. Some could indeed be present, but it wouldn't matter—the secondary (conjugated) antibody will bind only to a site on hCG, not to the primary antibody.

    B: No. Unbound hCG is washed away with the first wash.

    C: No; see D.

    D: **Yes.** The purpose of the second wash is to remove any unbound (excess) conjugated antibody. Without this step, a false positive would result when the color-producing substrate was added (the color change would occur even without hCG to bind the secondary antibody).

2. **C**

    A: No. Without hCG to fill the "sandwich," there is nothing for the conjugated antibody to bind to.

    B: No. A lack of color indicates an absence of the three-part complex containing mouse anti-hCG, hCG, and conjugated antibody. The assay was designed to detect hCG by the appearance of color.

    C: **Yes.** Mouse anti-hCG is present, because it is initially bound to the plastic of the test well. Conjugated antibody enzyme and hCG are absent, because if present they would have led to a color change. Absence of color change is how the test indicates absence of hCG and thus of pregnancy.

    D: No. The conjugated antibody is specific for hCG. It cannot bind directly to the mouse antibody. Besides, if it did, a color change would occur on addition of the color-producing substrate.

3. **C**

    A: No. It is a protein.

    B: No. It is always produced during pregnancy; this is why pregnancy tests work by detecting it.

    C: **Yes.** An antigen is a substance capable of eliciting an immune response. In the rabbit, hCG functions as an antigen, but in humans, it is a normal host molecule and is thus recognized as "self" by the immune system.

    D: No. It is a molecule produced by glands and acting at a distant site which it reaches via the bloodstream (that is, a hormone).

4. **B**
    The correct order of the steps given is:

    II: Trapping the antigen. In this case the antigen is fibronectin. An antigen is a foreign substance with which an antibody specifically combines. In the pregnancy test the antigen was hCG.

    III: "Sandwiching" the antigen. After the antigen is bound to the primary antibody, it is "sandwiched" by the addition of the secondary antibody.

    I: Visualizing the enzyme. This is the last step in the detection of an antigen. The secondary antibody is linked to an enzyme that catalyzes a color change in a substrate which is added at the end of the test. The color change occurs only if the enzyme–antibody complex has not been washed away. It is not washed away when the antigen is present, allowing the formation of a "sandwich."

5. **A**
    A: **Yes.** Antibodies are composed of two identical light chains and two identical heavy chains. Each chain has a constant and a variable region. Each antibody has two antigen binding sites, each one consisting of a pocket formed by the interaction of the variable regions of a heavy and a light chain.

    C: No. The constant region is common to all antibodies of a particular antibody class (such as IgM). The binding site (which is unique to a particular idiotype of antibody) is formed by the interaction of the variable regions of one light and one heavy chain.

6. **B**
    A: No. The passage does not give a reason for the use of rabbits in the synthesis of the secondary antibody. It is conceivable that a mouse could have been used. The ELISA test depends on the binding specificity of the antigen-binding regions of both the primary and the secondary antibodies (both are specific for hCG).

    B: **Yes.** The passage states that the primary and secondary antibodies bind to different sites on hCG. Hence, fragmenting hCG and isolating different portions would allow differentiation of the antibodies.

    C: No. If the antibodies bound each other, the test would fail. The whole point is that both antibodies bind hCG and only hCG.

    D: No. If a rabbit antibody is injected into a mouse, it will be recognized as foreign and be bound by mouse antibodies. The reason is that the large constant region of the antibody differs from organism to organism.

Passage 68

1. **C**   Intrinsic factor (IF) binds to cobalamin in the stomach and is required for cobalamin to be absorbed into the blood in the intestine. Therefore, choice C is correct and A is not. Choice B is wrong because cobalamin is not a protein, and, since it is not itself recognized by any of the antibodies described in the passage, choice D is wrong.

2. **B**   White matter is white because of myelin, and the motor nerve axons are also myelinated. Thus, choices A, C, and D are all wrong. Ganglia are collections of cell bodies, which are not myelinated, so choice B is correct.

3.   C   Antibodies against intrinsic factor cause pernicious anemia. If these antibodies could be removed, this would alleviate the disease. One way to remove the anti-IF IgG would be to provide
IgG which binds the anti-IF IgG (using one antibody to neutralize another).

4.   B   In pernicious anemia, cobalamin is not absorbed in the intestine, due to a lack of an essential
factor or disruption of the process. Thus, the ingested cobalamin will pass through the small
intestine (site of absorption) into the large intestine.

5.   A   All immune cells, both B and T cells, originate from stem cells which reside in the bone marrow.

Passage 69

1.   **A**
   A: Yes. The antigen will be treated as an endogenously-synthesized protein, because it is free in the
cytoplasm, just like many truly endogenous proteins which are constantly sampled, according
to the passage. Class II MHC molecules only bind antigens which are internalized from the
extracellular space. Remember that the extracellular environment is contiguous with the space
inside vesicles, inside the Golgi, inside the ER, and between the two nuclear membranes.

2.   **B**
   A: No. Lipid bilayers are impermeable to polypeptides.
   B: Yes. Note that this question cannot be answered from the information given in the passage.
Secreted and membrane-bound proteins have a special signal sequence at their amino terminus.
When mRNA bound to a ribosome in the cytoplasm is translated, translation pauses at the sig-
nal sequence. A signal recognition particle (SRP) binds to the signal sequence. The SRP binds
to an SRP receptor on the ER surface. The signal sequence is inserted into the membrane, and
translation resumes. This applies to MHC proteins as well as all proteins destined for secretion
and the cell surface.
   C: No. The ER membrane has no pores large enough for the passage of a large protein.
   D: No. Endocytosis only refers to the invagination and pinching off of the cell membrane to internalize material from the exterior.

3.   **B**
   Item I: False. The passage states that only a small amount of calcium is released from compartments
packed with the ion. Hence, it must move *up* a concentration gradient to get back inside (so it
would not diffuse in). Note that in most eukaryotic cells, only mitochondria create a non-ATP-
dependent electrochemical gradient (a proton gradient dependent upon electron transport).
   Item II: True. The mitochondrial proton gradient which is normally used for ATP synthesis can be
used to actively transport calcium into mitochondria when the intracellular calcium concentration reaches abnormally high levels, which occurs in the absence of ATP. This is an example of
active transport not directly or indirectly dependent on ATP hydrolysis. This question requires
you to eliminate the wrong choices based on their implausibility and then to realize that item II
is plausible, even though you may not have heard it before.
   Item III: False. Facilitated diffusion would not remove all the calcium from the cytoplasm (because
calcium is present in the extracellular fluid), and it cannot pump against a gradient.

4. **D**

A: No. Both classes of MHC must enter the ER lumen to be transported to the cell surface. The question implies that the invariant chain is necessary for the differentiation of the two classes, since deleting the invariant chain made Class II act like Class I (binding endogenous proteins).

B: No. If the invariant chain dissociated from Class II molecules before they reached the ER, it could not play a role in blocking the peptide binding site. In that case, it could not be responsible for differentiating the roles of MHC I and MHC II. Also, the majority of the protein will not be synthesized before it reaches the ER.

C: No. As stated in the passage, all MHC proteins must enter the ER.

D: **Yes.** You must infer that the invariant chain prevents MHC II from binding endogenous peptides, since when the invariant chain is absent, MHC II does bind endogenous peptides. The invariant chain blocks the peptide binding region of the Class II molecule in the ER. This is why only Class I molecules can bind endogenous proteins in the ER. After Class II molecules leave the ER, the invariant chain dissociates, allowing the MHC II to bind exogenous peptide fragments in endosomes.

5. **D**

A: No, there are many enzymes in the nucleus (polymerases, for example).

B: No, it must be spliced first.

C: No. The RNA contains all protein-coding sequences prior to splicing.

D: **Yes.** Ribosomes are made and *partially* assembled in the nucleolus within the nucleus. Assembly is completed in the cytoplasm, and the large ribosomal assemblies are then excluded from the nucleus.

6. **B**

A: No. In the first paragraph it is stated that all cells in the body present endogenous antigens. Later in the passage (4th paragraph) it is stated that MHC I is used to display endogenous antigens. Macrophages display antigen in both MHC I and MHC II.

B: **Yes.** The passage states that macrophages find antigens in the extracellular space and present them on their cell surfaces (first two sentences). Later in the passage it is stated that MHC II is used by antigen-presenting cells to display exogenous antigens.

C: No. Nothing in the passage indicates that T cells use MHC II to present antigens.

D: No. B cells are not discussed in the passage. The question explicitly asks you to infer from the passage.

Passage 70

1. **B**

A: No. TSH plays no role in reproductive development.

B: **Yes.** Estrogen secretion by the ovaries is under the control of gonadotropins (LH and FSH) secreted by the anterior pituitary. The production and release of the gonadotropins, in turn, is under the influence of hypothalamic GnRH. Therefore, estrogen production and secretion is dependent on the secretion of GnRH.

C: No. Prolactin plays no role in the control of estrogen secretion and breast development, though it plays an important role later in inducing milk secretion.

D: No. Progesterone plays no role in promoting estrogen secretion.

2. **A**

   A: **Yes.** The seminiferous tubule, located in the testes, is the site for sperm production. Under the influence of FSH and testosterone, spermatogonia develop into spermatozoa. Further maturation occurs in the epididymis.

   B: No. As stated in the passage (third paragraph), testosterone is secreted by the interstitial cells of Leydig.

   C: No. Maturation occurs in the epididymis.

   D: No. The seminiferous tubules are the site of sperm production in the male. Fertilization occurs in the fallopian tube, which is, of course, in the female.

3. **C**

   Items I & II: True. The last paragraph of the passage directly states that both hormones cause increased testicle size—FSH via seminiferous tubule development and LH via stimulation of the interstitial cells of Leydig.

   Item III: False. GH, from the anterior pituitary, stimulates somatic growth, particularly skeletal growth. It causes increases in the length of long bones until the epiphyses fuse at the time of puberty. It does not have a role in testicular development.

4. **A**

   A: **Yes.** The third paragraph of the passage begins, "The first sign of normal puberty is an increase in the size of the testes." Hence, even though it would not be as noticeable as abnormalities which would occur later, this would occur first.

   B, C, & D: No. Each of these would occur later (see A). These are caused by reduced androgen levels, a secondary effect.

5. **B**

   A: No. GH and all the other pituitary hormones are peptide hormones, which bind their receptors at the cell surface.

   B: **Yes.** GH and all the other pituitary hormones are peptide hormones, which function by binding to a cell-surface receptor; this in turn leads to changes in the activity of intracellular proteins via signal transduction. Tyrosine kinase activity is an example of a signal-transduction system. In normal cells, kinase activity is not observed unless cells are exposed to hormone, indicating the kinase is regulated by a GH receptor.

   C: No. A cancer (unregulated growth) resulted when the kinase attained constitutive (unregulated) activity. It would appear that the tyrosine kinase activity caused growth, not inhibited it.

   D: No. Again, a cancer (too much growth and cell division) resulted from the abnormal activity.

6. **D**

   A: No. GH itself comes from the anterior pituitary; the question asked about GH-releasing hormone.

   B: No. The posterior pituitary only stores ADH and oxytocin from the hypothalamus.

   C: No; see A and D.

   D: **Yes.** The primary stimulus for GH secretion is GH-releasing hormone derived from the hypothalamus.

Passage 71

1. **B** These enzymes are part of the Krebs cycle and would only be present in an organism that uses aerobic metabolism to produce ATP. The organism can also live in the absence of oxygen, so it must be able to switch to anaerobic energy production, such as fermentation. Thus, it is a facultative anaerobe. An obligate aerobe could not survive in the absence of oxygen, and an obligate anaerobe could not survive in the presence of oxygen.

2. **D** The dilation of blood vessels in inflamed tissue increases the pressure in capillaries, increases their permeability, and increases the flow of fluid out of the plasma into the extracellular space in surrounding tissues.

3. **A** The large intestine has a maximal capacity for water resorption. If this capacity is exceeded by secretion of abnormally large quantities of water, diarrhea will result. Thus, A is the best choice.

4. **A** The enterotoxin is required for symptoms to develop. This will take time, both for the bacteria to proliferate and release toxin (choice A). Choices B and C are irrelevant, and D is a trivial period of time compared to the time required for bacteria to proliferate and release toxin.

5. **D** Whether the food is contaminated or not is irrelevant. Pepsin and trypsin hydrolyze proteins, and lipase hydrolyzes triglycerides. Amylase is responsible for hydrolysis of starches into simpler sugars, however.

6. **D** The test is designed to distinguish *S. aureus* from other bacteria. The bacteria can apparently grow and reproduce during incubation in meat broth (eliminating A and B). Enterotoxin (choice C) is irrelevant; it will not have an effect in culture. The passage states, however, that lysis of red cells (choice D) is being examined.

Passage 72

1. **C**
   A, B, & D: No. Each of these stimulates acid secretion, as shown in the diagram or stated in the passage.
   C: **Yes.** Food stimulates acid secretion, but only indirectly, via its stimulation of gastrin secretion (refer to the diagram).

2. **A**
   Item I: True. The diagram shows that cholecystokinin causes the release of pancreatic enzymes, a key example of which is trypsin, stored as trypsinogen.
   Item II: True. This is stated in the passage.
   Item III: False. Pepsinogen is released in response to stimulation by the vagus nerve (refer to the diagram).

3. **C**
   A: No. It causes vasodilation and increased vascular permeability. The result is redness and swelling (inflammation).
   B: No. Histamine has no role in B-cell development.
   C: **Yes.** The vasodilation caused by histamine leads to the redness, heat, and swelling of the inflammatory response.
   D: No. Histamine has no role in the development or function of B cells, the cells responsible for antibody synthesis.

4. **D**
   A: No. Since somatostatin inhibits acid secretion, which the parasympathetic system promotes, it acts in concert with the sympathetic system (which antagonizes the parasympathetic).
   B: No. The passage gives no information about the effect of duodenal fatty acids upon gastric acid secretion. (The fact is that they inhibit it.)
   C: No. There is no link indicated between somatostatin and pancreatic secretion.
   D: **Yes.** As shown by the dashed arrows in the diagram, gastrin stimulates the secretion of somatostatin, and somatostatin in turn inhibits gastrin secretion. This is a negative-feedback loop.

5. **B**
   A: No. This can be inferred. The diagram shows the vagus promoting the secretion of acid, pepsin, and gastrin. Promoting gastrointestinal activity is a parasympathetic function.
   B: **Yes.** Somatostatin is a hormone which is secreted into the bloodstream.
   C: No. The diagram shows that HCl is responsible for the conversion of the zymogen pepsinogen to the active form, pepsin.
   D: No. The diagram shows that secretin causes the secretion of bicarbonate by the pancreas. You should be able to infer that this serves to neutralize excess gastric acid, and from that inference to conclude that secretin is released when the duodenal pH is low.

6. **A**
   A: **Yes.** The parasympathetic system stimulates acid secretion via the vagus nerve. Cutting the vagus nerve decreases acid, increasing the pH.
   C: No. The parasympathetic system stimulates pancreatic secretion.
   D: No. Gastrin secretion will be reduced (refer to the diagram).

Passage 73

1. **D**
   Item I: True. Extreme blood loss would cause a decrease in blood volume and a subsequent decrease in blood pressure. This would lower the hydrostatic pressure driving fluid from the glomerular capillaries into the nephron, reducing the glomerular filtration rate.
   Item II: True. As stated in the passage, ADH is secreted in response to reduced plasma volume.
   Item III: True. The passage states that aldosterone increases sodium reabsorption, which leads to increased water retention and blood pressure. This is just what is needed after blood loss.

2. **D**

 Item I: True. Decreased water intake leads to decreased blood pressure, which leads to decreased filtration (see #1, Item I).

 Item II: True. As explained in the passage, both ADH and aldosterone cause water retention.

 Item III: True. This results from the increased aldosterone (see above).

3. **C**

 A: No. ADH stimulates the syntheses of a tubular protein that acts as a channel. ADH does not affect the pumping of Na^+ and K^+.

 B: No. Aldosterone stimulates synthesis of a basolateral Na^+/K^+ ATPase which pumps Na^+ out of the urine and K^+ into the urine.

 C: **Yes.** This is how ADH has the effect discussed in the passage (permitting water to flow according to osmotic gradients across an otherwise impermeable cell layer).

 D: No. Aldosterone increases sodium reabsorption, which increases blood osmolarity, which in turn stimulates the release of ADH, but this is an indirect effect.

4. **D**

 A: No. The proximal tubule does not play a role in regulating plasma osmolarity. It functions to reclaim useful molecules such as glucose from the filtrate.

 B: No. The secretion and reabsorption of various substances must be independent of urinary flow so that it can be accomplished regardless of changes in flow.

 C: No. As discussed in B, control of substances by the proximal tubule must not be affected by changes in urinary flow.

 D: **Yes.** The proximal tubule can absorb essentially all the glucose from the glomerular filtrate of a healthy person. To do so, concentration gradients must be overcome.

5. **C**

 A: No. This can be inferred from the passage's discussion of the GBM.

 B: No. It is directly stated in the passage that the diabetic's urine has a lot of glucose. [Many years ago, diabetes was actually diagnosed by the physician only after he tasted (!) the urine.]

 C: **Yes.** It can be inferred that all such substances pass through the GBM, but many of them will be reabsorbed in the proximal tubule. (An example is phosphate.)

 D: No. This makes sense, based on the passage's description of the destruction of the GBM in diabetes.

6. **B**

 A: No. If anything the urea concentration in the urine would be decreased due to the large urinary volume.

 B: **Yes.** The passage states that a lot of glucose is lost; this can cause weight loss. It also states that excess urine is produced; this can cause both dehydration and weight loss.

 C: No. It is directly stated in the passage that there is a lot of glucose in the urine.

 D: No. If someone is dehydrated, he or she will have an elevated level of ADH in the blood.

Passage 74

This passage is unusually long, generally longer than what you'll see on the MCAT. It tests your ability to use the passage as a reference. The ideal way to attack this passage is to rapidly skim it over to see what information it contains. Even this is barely necessary since there are clear subheadings for each paragraph. As you move on to each new question, return to the passage with the goal of extracting information as efficiently as possible.

1. **B**
   A: No. As stated in the passage, the ascending and descending limbs have very different water permeabilities.
   B: **Yes.** The key to concentrating urine is that the ascending and descending limbs both pass through the medullary osmotic gradient, and that they are close together to achieve a counter-current exchange system with the vasa recta.
   C: No. This is true but irrelevant to the concentrating ability of the loop of Henle.
   D: No. ADH acts on the distal tubule and collecting duct, not the loop of Henle.

2. **C**
   Item I: True. The passage states that the urine becomes hypertonic in the descending limb.
   Item II: False. In the thick ascending limb, ions are pumped out, but water is left in filtrate, creating hypoosmotic filtrate.
   Item III: True. ADH causes water to be reabsorbed in the distal tubule and collecting duct.

3. **D**
   A & B: No. Quoting the passage (middle of last paragraph): "The influences of ADH (antidiuretic hormone) and aldosterone on this segment are the prime determinants of urinary volume and osmolarity."
   C: No. PTH's most important action on the kidneys is promoting reabsorption of Ca^{2+}; it also promotes excretion of PO_4^{2-}. This information cannot be found in the passage, and it is important to know.
   D: **Yes.** The posterior pituitary releases ADH and oxytocin. Only ADH plays a role in regulating kidney function. Oxytocin is important for letdown of milk from the breasts and for uterine contraction during labor.

4. **B**
   B: **Yes.** Urea is a by-product of protein metabolism. It is a carrier of nitrogen which can be excreted. The high concentration of urea in the renal medulla is essential for the reabsorption of water in response to ADH.
   C & D: No. There is no reason to suppose that electrolyte balances would be impaired.

5. **A**
   A: **Yes.** The mechanism of H^+ excretion is discussed in the passage. It can be inferred that without carbonic anhydrase, the proximal tubule's ability to secrete H^+ is inhibited; increased urine pH results. Another consequence is that if H^+ is not secreted into urine, then it will remain in the plasma, thereby decreasing plasma pH at the same time that urine pH increases.
   B: No. CO_2 is easily eliminated by the lungs.
   C: No. Acid secretion is not the major factor in determining urine osmolarity.
   D: No; see A.

6. **A**

    A: **Yes.** Quoting from the middle of the last paragraph: "The solutes concentrated in the medulla are NaCl derived from the pumping of the thick ascending limb, and urea, which is concentrated in the medulla by a complex mechanism."

    B: No. K^+ does not play a significant role in establishing the medullary gradient (see A).

    C: No. Glucose is reabsorbed by the proximal tubule, which does not lie in the medulla.

    D: No. H^+ does not play a role in establishing the medullary gradient (see A).

Passage 75

1. **B**

    A: No. Chewing is voluntary.

    B: **Yes.** The passage states that chewing (mastication) is under voluntary, or somatic, motor control.

    C: No. These are cells which provide structural support for nerve cells.

    D: No. The brain stem generally controls the autonomic nervous system. The somatic motor system is controlled by the cerebral cortex.

2. **C**

    A & B: No. These *may* result if secretions from the pancreas, as well as secretions from the liver and gall bladder (bile), are blocked. But this only occurs if the gall stone forms an obstruction so low in the bile duct that the pancreatic duct is blocked too (the two ducts empty into the duodenum through the same hole, the hepatopancreatic ampulla). Pancreatic amylase and pancreatic proteases are essential for the digestion of carbohydrates and proteins. (Pancreatic lipase is necessary for the digestion of fats, but plays no role in the absorption of vitamins.)

    C: **Yes.** Micelles formed from bile acids are essential for the absorption of fats and fat-soluble vitamins.

    D: No. Water-soluble vitamins are absorbed without the aid of bile.

3. **A**

    A: **Yes.** Sphincter muscles prevent movement of the contents of a part of the GI tract.

    B: No. The last paragraph of the passage describes peristalsis, including the role of longitudinal muscle. The best way to think about the role of the longitudinal muscle is that it pulls the intestine over its contents much as you pull your sock over your foot (imagine pulling your sock up and the seeing it contract).

    C: No. The last paragraph of the passage describes the essential role of circular muscle in peristalsis.

    D: No. Nerve plexi are complex networks of nerves which control GI motility, as stated in the third paragraph of the passage.

4. **A**

    A: **Yes.** The passage states that the rapid turnover of mucosal cells makes them susceptible to inhibitors of cell division such as anti-cancer drugs. The reason this is true is that they divide frequently. This is discussed in the passage: frequent mitosis allows constant replacement of the mucosa. Chemotherapeutic agents disrupt DNA synthesis, thus destroying rapidly dividing cancer cells. The problem with chemo is that it also destroys normal cells which divide frequently, such as mucosal and hair follicle cells. The result is diarrhea, baldness, etc.

    B: No. This statement is actually true, because the cells of the immune system also divide rapidly (see A). But the biggest reason chemo patients get diarrhea is that given in A. Plus the passage indicates A to be true, while saying nothing about the immune system.

C: No. This is sometimes true, but choice A is correct based on the passage, and is also the main reason chemo patients have diarrhea and malnutrition.

D: No. The passage gives no reason to conclude this, and it is not usually true (sometimes it is).

5. **A**

Item I: True. Mastication (chewing) is a voluntary process, and thus involves skeletal muscle, which has sarcomeres, T tubules and the troponin-tropomyosin complex.

Item II: False. the passage states that mixing of GI contents is under autonomic control, and is thus accomplished by smooth muscle. Smooth muscle cells are thinner than skeletal muscle cells. They are so thin, in fact, that they do not require a T-tubule system to transmit action potentials into the center of the cell.

Item III: False. The passage explains that peristalsis is an autonomic function, thus involving smooth muscle; see Item II.

6. **D**

A: No. The respiratory epithelium is a very thin, delicate membrane which is specialized to facilitate diffusion. The intestinal mucosal cell is thick, and absorbs substances by active transport, for the most part.

B: No. Both respiration and digestion are critical. Plus this has nothing to do with the extent of physical damage caused.

C: No. This does not determine why toxins have less effect.

D: **Yes.** This is stated in the passage. Sloughing of the intestinal mucosa is a normal process. (Alveolar lining cells are replaced too, but at a rate nowhere near the rate at which mucosal cells are replaced.)

Passage 76

1. **C**

A & B: No. These statements are accurate but have nothing to do with the definition of a vitamin the question asks about.

C: **Yes.** The passage states (end of the second paragraph) that vitamin D can be derived either from the diet or from cholesterol by a reaction requiring sunlight. Hence, the chemical is only required in the diet (a true vitamin) when sunlight is scarce.

D: No. This is true for people living in sunny areas, but does not address the question. The question asks for a completion of the sentence that begins with "By this definition…" The fact that vitamin D may not actually be required in the diet does not follow.

2. **C**

Item I: True. The passage explains that osteoporosis is due to an imbalance between resorption and deposition of bone. There is nothing to indicate any abnormality in the structure of collagen.

Item II: True. The passage explains that osteomalacia results from an abnormal ratio of hydroxyapatite to collagen. There is nothing to indicate any abnormality in the structure of collagen.

Item III: False. Vitamin C is required for proper collagen synthesis. The question asks you to infer from the passage, and the passage says nothing about collagen synthesis.

3. **B**   Based on information given in paragraph 4, estrogen promotes deposition of calcium into bone as well as renal and intestinal retention of calcium. This, however, is not its primary function in the female body, which is to maintain female secondary sex characteristics and to promote endometrial growth (choice A is wrong). Calcitonin is described as having several functions, one of which is to increase the amount of calcium deposited into bone (by stimulating osteoblast activity), however this is not listed as its primary function, and nothing else in the passage indicates that this function is more important than its other functions (choice C is wrong). Parathyroid hormone's function is to increase calcium in the body, not decrease it; hence the stimulation of osteoclasts (to break down bone and release calcium into the blood) and the increased renal and intestinal calcium uptake (choice D is wrong).

4. **C**
    A: No. The passage explains that estrogen replacement therapy is used for post-menopausal women (women who have ceased menstruating).
    B: No. The passage states that along with adequate calcium and vitamin D intake, exercise is an important way to combat osteoporosis.
    C: **Yes.** The last paragraph of the passage states that this is a way to preventatively and curatively combat osteoporosis and that bone mass can be increased up to the age of 35.
    D: No. Birth-control pills do generally consist of estrogen (with or without added progesterone), but nothing in the passage indicates that they lead to osteoporosis in later life.

5. **C**
    Item I: True. This describes settings in which children are less likely to be exposed to adequate sunlight. The passage states that vitamin D can be made from cholesterol in a series of reactions, one of which requires the ultraviolet light of direct sunshine.
    Item II: False. The table shows that calcitriol stimulates osteoclasts and inhibits osteoblasts. This would lead to bone resorption, not bone deposition/strengthening. Hence, rickets must result from the absence of calcitriol's effects upon the gut and the kidney (increased calcium uptake).
    Item III: True. This makes perfect sense and is in fact true. (The question asks you to choose statements which are "probably" accurate, indicating that you don't necessarily have to find the answer in the passage.)

6. **B**
    A: No. The density is decreased in both diseases. In osteoporosis it is decreased because more bone is resorbed than is deposited, so a given bone gradually gets eaten away. In osteomalacia, density is decreased because the ratio of minerals to protein is lower than normal.
    B: **Yes.** In osteoporosis, bone is being destroyed by resorption, so both mineral and protein content are decreased. In osteomalacia, the only problem is that mineralization is not proceeding normally. One expects the protein structure of bone to be normal.
    C: No. The minerals are decreased in both diseases (decreased relative to protein in osteomalacia, absolutely decreased in osteoporosis).
    D: No, just the opposite. As discussed in the passage, fractures are very frequent in people with osteoporosis, sue to the brittleness of bone. In osteomalacia, the problem is that the amount of hydroxyapatite crystal is abnormally low, with a normal amount of protein. If anything, you'd expect bone to be more flexible (the passage uses the word "soft").

Passage 77

1.   **A**
     A: **Yes.** Experiment 4 suggests that ACh released by the preganglionic neuron binds to a nicotinic receptor, but that the ACh released by the postganglionic neuron does not require nicotinic receptors. We can draw this conclusion from the fact that a nicotinic *antagonist* (specific blocker of nicotinic receptors) prevented contraction in response to preganglionic stimulation, but did not prevent contraction in response to direct postganglionic stimulation or injected artificial ACh.
     B: **No.** The receptors on the preganglionic neurons were not tested for in Experiment 4; these neurons were stimulated electrically. In any case, preganglionic neurons *release* ACh; they do not have nicotinic ACh receptors. Those receptors are found on the *post*ganglionic neurons, on which the ACh from the preganglionic neurons is released.
     C: **No.** This was known going into the experiment.
     D: **No.** the point is the nicotinic receptor is not directly responsible, although it does play a role. It is necessary for information to get from the CNS to the postganglionic neuron.

2.   **C**
     Item I: True. If ACh is not degraded in the synapse, it will diffuse into the interstitial fluid and bloodstream.
     Item II: False. It is true that the ACh released by motor neurons will stay around longer if it is not degraded normally. However, ACh will only be released by motor neurons upon deliberate activation of specific motor units. Hence, though it is conceivable that blood-borne ACh might stimulate a few muscle cells, it is not predicted that "immediate and intense involuntary contraction of all skeletal muscles" would occur.
     Item III: True. ACh released by the parasympathetic nervous system causes increased GI motility. Unlike the somatic motor nervous system, which is quiescent until activated specifically, the autonomic nervous system has *tone*, which is a basal level of activity. The duration of action of ACh released at this basal level would be increased by acetylcholinesterase inhibitors.

3.   **D**
     A: No. It *prevented* neurotransmitter release.
     B: No. It had this function *indirectly* by preventing action potentials which cause neurotransmitter release *via calcium influx* at the axon terminal.
     C: No. Contraction depends on muscle depolarization and still occurred in Experiment 3. This is because the drug was "carefully microinjected" so as not to affect any cells besides the nerves close to the site of injection.
     D: **Yes.** Action potentials depend on the opening of voltage-gated sodium channels, which would be nonfunctional in the presence of tetrodotoxin.

4.   **C**
     Whether or not you are sure about A, B, and D, you should definitely be able to pick C as the correct answer.
     A: No. Sheets of smooth muscle surround various hollow organs and tubes, and the uterus is one of these.
     B: No. The aorta contains a thick smooth muscle layer.
     C: **Yes.** Cardiac muscle is unique in the body, similar in some ways to skeletal muscle and in others to smooth muscle. It is important for you to understand the main differences between the three types of muscle: smooth , skeletal, and cardiac.
     D: No. The airways contain much smooth muscle.

5. **B**

   A: No. Only skeletal and cardiac muscle have this banding, also called striation. Striation is due to the presence of ordered arrangements of actin and myosin known as sarcomeres. Smooth muscle lacks sarcomeres, and thus lacks striation; this is why it is called "smooth." Instead, it's actin and myosin filaments are scattered throughout the cytoplasm in a poorly organized manner.

   B: Yes. Both smooth and skeletal muscle generated force by this mechanism.

   C: No. Smooth muscle is controlled by the parasympathetic nervous system, a portion of the autonomic nervous system, and is thus not under voluntary control. Skeletal muscle, on the other hand, is controlled by somatic motor nerves, which are voluntary. You can deliberately wiggle your finger, not your uterus.

   D: No. This is true of smooth and cardiac muscle, but not of skeletal muscle, where the only direct effect of nerve stimulation is excitation.

6. **D**

   A & B: No. Sodium "fast-channels" are responsible for propagating the action potential in nerves and skeletal muscles. The opening of the fast channels causes the classic spike potential. Sodium fast channels are also important in cardiac muscle, but here calcium "slow channels" also play an important role. In smooth muscle, only the calcium slow channels are important (few if any sodium fast channels are present).

   C: No. This is where the action potential normally starts.

   D: Yes. The binding of neurotransmitters to their receptors is a specific high-affinity reaction which has nothing to do with whatever events may ensue thereafter. Action potentials causing neurotransmitter release and action potentials resulting from neurotransmitters binding to receptors would be inhibited by tetrodotoxin, but the actual binding of ACh to its receptor would be unaffected.

Passage 78

1. **A**

   A: Yes. The myofilaments do not shorten, they merely overlap more.

   B: No. Shortening is achieved by the filaments sliding along one another so that they overlap more.

   C: No. When the action potential arrives at the neuromuscular junction, calcium is released from the sarcoplasmic reticulum, causing the conformational change in the tropomyosin-troponin complex, allowing muscle contraction to begin.

   D: No. The SR sequesters calcium after contraction. This is necessary so that the cytoplasmic calcium concentration is low enough for contraction not to occur spontaneously (that is, low enough for troponin to allow tropomyosin to block the myosin-binding sites on actin).

2. **A**

   A: Yes. Cardiac muscle is uninucleate, striated, and contains intercalated disks between cells. Skeletal muscle is striated, but is multinucleate and lacks intercalated disks.

3. **B**

   A: No. The myosin head specifically binds and hydrolyzes ATP.

   B: Yes. Creatine phosphate stores energy in the form of a high-energy phosphate bond. This energy can be transferred to ATP with the aid of an enzyme.

   C: No. It is an energy-storage molecule, not an enzyme.

   D: No. Again, the myosin head *specifically* binds and hydrolyzes ATP.

4. **D**

    A: No. Muscle cells are not destroyed until later.

    B & C: No. Both of these processes take place spontaneously, in the absence of ATP.

    D: Yes. As stated in the passage, ATP is necessary for the release of actin by the myosin cross-bridges. After death, metabolism stops, and cells run out of ATP.

5. **D**

    (Note: You are asked for the most direct influence. Thus, you must choose the one most closely connected in time to contraction. Always be on the lookout for words like "direct" and "always.")

    D: Yes. Calcium is the mediator of signal transduction (excitation-contraction coupling), by which information in the form of a nerve impulse is converted into a mechanical phenomenon. The order of events in muscle contraction is D-B-A-C.

6. **B**

    A: No. A twitch is a single muscle contraction.

    B: Yes. Tetanus results when there is insufficient time between action potentials for the intracellular calcium to be cleared. As a result, contraction continues indefinitely.

    C: No. The all-or-none principle describes the fact that a skeletal muscle contraction can either occur or not occur; the force of contraction cannot be varied by ionic or hormonal influences. In cardiac and smooth muscle, there are different degrees of contraction, depending on such influences as extracellular ionic concentrations and hormonal influences.

    D: No. As stated in question 6, this refers to a state of constant contraction resulting from failure of myosin cross-bridges to release actin due to a deficit of ATP. (*Rigor* means hardness, or contractedness; *mortis* refers to death [as in "mortal"].)

Passage 79

1. **B**

    A: No. Myosin does bind to actin, but it does not spontaneously dissociate; it dissociates only when ATP is added.

    B: Yes. Myosin binds to actin, which increases the viscosity. When ATP is added, it binds to the myosin heads causing them to dissociate from the actin filaments. This decreases the mixture's viscosity.

    C: No. ATP does not depolymerize actin.

    D: No. ATP does not bind to actin.

2. **C**

    A: No. Magnesium is required for myosin's ATPase function to be effective.

    B: No. Magnesium does not inhibit ATP hydrolysis.

    C: Yes. In muscle tissue, actin and myosin are complexed with other proteins. In particular, the troponin-tropomyosin complex mediates calcium's regulation of muscle contraction. In the absence of calcium, the complex blocks myosin from binding to actin. If myosin cannot bind actin, it will not release its bound ADP and will therefore by unable to bind a new ATP and hydrolyze it. ATP hydrolysis could occur in Experiment 2, because there the actin and myosin had been purified (so troponin and tropomyosin were not present).

    D: No. Myosin is an ATPase.

3. **C**
   A: No. There is no reason to think ATP would no longer be available.
   B: No. The Z lines are not attached to the thick filaments, so they will not tear them in half.
   C: **Yes.** If the filaments do not overlap, contraction cannot occur.
   D: No. The question states that they do, and C is a plausible explanation.

4. **B**
   A: No. Calcium is not required for the ATPase to function, as seen in Experiment 2.
   B: **Yes.** Calcium binds to troponin, which causes a conformational change that allows tropomyosin to shift its position, exposing the myosin binding site on actin.
   C & D: No. Calcium binds to troponin.

5. **A**
   Item I: True. Creatine phosphate is a high-energy buffer, because it maintains the level of available high-energy phosphates. During intense muscular exertion, creatine phosphate replenishes the muscle's ATP by transferring its phosphate group to ADP.
   Item II: False. In order to spontaneously transfer its phosphate group to ADP, creatine phosphate's free energy of hydrolysis must be more negative than ATP's. (The lower the ΔG, the more favorable the reaction.) Creatine phosphate's free energy of hydrolysis is –10.3 kcal/mol compared to ATP's –7.3 kcal/mol.
   Item III: False. This is a reaction which will proceed spontaneously ($\Delta G < 0$).

Passage 80

1. **C** Choices A and D involve skeletal muscle, and B requires cardiac muscle, all of which are striated. Only smooth muscle, such as that found in the GI tract, is not striated. The striations are caused by regularly spaced arrays of actin–myosin filaments.

2. **B** Choice A is wrong because muscle would contain few secretory vesicles, since this is not secretory tissue. C is incorrect since gap junctions are not found in skeletal muscle; these would allow transmission of action potentials between cells, which occurs in cardiac muscle but not in skeletal muscle. And choice D is wrong because voltage-gated calcium channels are also found in cardiac but not in skeletal muscle. Choice B is correct: muscle contraction requires a lot of energy, so muscle contains a large number of mitochondria.

3. **B** Calcium links excitation with contraction. The action potential causes calcium release from the sarcoplasmic reticulum. This calcium then causes troponin and tropomyosin to release actin, revealing myosin binding sites so that myosin can bind to actin and catalyze sliding of filaments past each other. As long as calcium remains present, myosin will bind actin, and the muscle will remain contracted.

4. **B** Troponin and tropomyosin inhibit contraction, except in the presence of calcium. Actin and myosin do not require troponin and tropomyosin to contract, only to display calcium-sensitive contraction. Choice A is eliminated since it would not support the involvement of calcium in relieving troponin/tropomyosin inhibition, and both C and D are wrong since they would indicate that troponin is not involved in the link between calcium and muscle contraction.

5. **B** Only choice B is true and relevant here. (Note: choice A does not occur in skeletal muscle, in which cells are multinucleated, but isolated electrically from each other.)

6. **C** The flash of light was caused by the fluorescent protein aequorin, which emits light when it binds calcium.

Passage 81

1. **A** The trapezius is one of the upper back muscles and is involved in postural maintenance. It needs to generate slow, constant force to maintain the shoulder and upper back in its position. Thus only Item I is correct and choice A is correct.

2. **B** The role of myosin is to bind to the actin thin filaments and pull them towards the M line using ATP as the sources of energy. This entire process is known as the cross bridge cycle.

3. **A** Breakdown of triglycerides yields fatty acids and glycerol. The fatty acid can undergo beta-oxidation to produce acetyl CoA, NADH, and $FADH_2$. These moieties can act as substrates for Krebs cycle and ETC to produce ATP via oxidative phosphorylation. This is the reason type I fibers are described as oxidative.

4. **D** Endurance exercise strengthens the skeletal muscle and cardiovascular systems. It achieves this by increasing blood supply to skeletal muscle to promote growth and function (choice A is correct and can be eliminated). The changes with in skeletal muscle fibers include increase in the number of mitochondria to enhance aerobic oxidative processes (choice B is correct and can be eliminated). The cardiac output is increased due to increased contractility of the heart among other changes, which is a result of a larger and supple heart produced from endurance training (choice C is correct and can be eliminated). The resting heart rate is generally lower in these individuals due to the increased efficiency of the heart, which is capable of pumping higher volume of blood per cycle with decreased effort (choice D is incorrect and is the correct answer choice).

5. **D** Myoglobin is similar to hemoglobin with some key differences. Myoglobin consists of a single subunit (monomeric protein) and has a hyperbolic oxygen saturation curve (choice A is incorrect). Similar to hemoglobin, it binds to oxygen via Fe^{2+} coordinated at the center of the heme group (choice B is incorrect). Hemoglobin is the major transporter of oxygen in the blood (choice C is incorrect), whereas myoglobin is found prominently in skeletal muscle tissue to serve as a reservoir for oxygen during times of increased demand (choice D is correct).

6. **C** Transcription factors are proteins that bind to DNA at specific sequences (choices A and B are wrong) and influence the rate of transcription by stabilizing or destabilizing the transcription machinery (choice C is correct). Protein folding occurs after translation and would not be affected by a transcription factor (choice D is wrong)

Passage 82

1. **C** According to the passage, myoglobin released from injured myocytes precipitates in renal nephrons, damaging them and causing kidney failure (choice C is true). Red blood cells contain hemoglobin, not myoglobin (choice A is wrong), and unlike hemoglobin, which is made up of four globular protein subunits, myoglobin consists of a single protein subunit. As a result, myoglobin has no quaternary structure (choice B is wrong) and it cannot participate in cooperative binding (choice D is wrong).

2. **D** According to the passage, injured myocytes swell with fluid, sometimes increasing pressures to the point where blood flow is compromised (choice A is likely and can be eliminated). Intracellular potassium concentrations are normally much higher than extracellular levels. When large numbers of myocytes lyse, they release enough potassium to alter total blood potassium levels. This may lead to life-threatening changes in heart rhythm (choice B is likely and can be eliminated). Lactate dehydrogenase is an intracellular enzyme found in the cytoplasm of muscle cells. It helps to convert pyruvate to lactic acid when the muscle must function in anaerobic conditions. Just like other enzymes mentioned in the passage, lactate dehydrogenase levels will increase when myocytes are disrupted (choice C is likely and can be eliminated). The passage states that the release of certain phosphates and sulfates decreases blood pH. This would trigger an increase in ventilation rate in order to help increase blood pH back to normal (choice D is unlikely and is the correct answer choice).

3. **B** Item I is false: Cardiac and skeletal muscle cells are described as *striated* because the regular arrangement of their protein filaments into sarcomeres produces a regular banding pattern along the cell. Smooth muscle lacks this feature; remember that myosin and actin need not be organized into sarcomeres for physical interaction to occur (choice A can be eliminated). Item II is true: In all types of muscle, calcium binds to tissue-specific regulatory molecules (choice D can be eliminated). Item III is false: Acetylcholine is released from all neurons innervating skeletal muscle, and the binding of ACh to skeletal muscle receptors is excitatory (leads to contraction). However, ACh is also released from parasympathetic effector neurons, and is not always excitatory in those cases. ACh released by parasympathetic neurons onto cardiac muscle tissue is also inhibitory, reducing both the rate and force of contraction (choice C can be eliminated and choice B is correct).

4. **A** According to the passage, "rhabdomyolysis produces CK levels that are elevated above the normal range in 100 percent of cases" (choices B and C are fair assumptions and can be eliminated). The passage also states that multiple isoforms of CK exist. Thus, a patient with cardiac muscle injury or brain injury will also present with elevated CK levels, even though they have undergone NO skeletal muscle injury (choice D is a fair assumption and can be eliminated). In other words, not all patients with elevated CK have skeletal muscle injury (choice A should not be assumed and is the correct answer choice).

5. **C** The passage states that proteins < 70,000 daltons are small enough to be freely filtered into Bowman's capsule; thus, myoglobin, at 16,700 daltons, can enter the capsule (choices A and D are wrong). The passage further states that under normal conditions (e.g., no injury), myoglobin concentrations in the blood are negligible (choice B is wrong). Only when large numbers of cells become damaged (as in a burn victim) can myoglobin proteins access the circulation and, subsequently, the urine. In particular, this patient is described as having severe burns that affect the skin and underlying muscle tissue (choice C is correct).

6. **B** You should memorize the basic tissues and structures that are derived from each of the three germ layers. The mesoderm forms not only muscle tissue, but also bone, blood vessels, and nongland organs. The endoderm forms the inner linings of the digestive system, the urinary system, and the respiratory system, as well as glandular organs such as the liver and pancreas. The ectoderm forms the skin, hair, and fingernails, as well as all nervous system structures (note that "neuroectoderm" is not an embryonic germ layer).

Passage 83

1. **D**
   A: No. It is true that the epidermis is composed of stratified squamous epithelium.
   B: No. Stratified squamous epithelium is made up of layers of closely packed flat cells.
   C: No. It is true that only the basal layer, or stratum germinativum, undergoes cell division. As new cells are produced here, the old cells are pushed outward, become keratinized, and eventually die and are sloughed off.
   D: **Yes.** It is false that the epidermis is composed of fibrous connective tissue.

2. **A**
   A: **Yes.** Shivering is an asynchronous contraction of muscle fibers and the primary mechanism for thermogenesis in adult humans. Infants and many animals utilize non-shivering thermogenesis, whereby heat is produced by increased metabolism, as in the "burning" of brown adipose tissue.
   B: No. As noted in A, this is non-shivering thermogenesis.
   C: No. This leads to heat loss.
   D: No. Decreasing metabolism decreases the amount of heat the body produces.

3. **A**
   A: **Yes.** The passage states (end of second paragraph) that the preoptic region is responsible for heat loss. Stimulating this region will result in cutaneous vasodilation, which increases heat loss through convection, and other heat-losing processes.
   B: No. This increases heat (see A).
   C: No. Increased TSH leads to increased thyroxine (thyroid hormone, TH), which the passage says causes increased metabolic activity and thus increased heat production.
   D: No. This provides an insulating layer of air and thus conserves heat.

4. **B**
   A: No. The posterior hypothalamus is involved in heat production and conservation (end of third paragraph of passage). Lesions here eliminate heat-production responses and lead to hypothermia. Electrical stimulation produces shivering, a method of heat production. Sweating is a heat-dissipation response.
   B: **Yes.** The passage states that the posterior hypothalamus is responsible for heat maintenance. Piloerection (bristling of skin hairs) creates an insulatory layer of air, which facilitates heat retention.
   C: No. The passage states that the posterior hypothalamus causes cutaneous vasoconstriction, not vasodilation.
   D: No. Read carefully! Stimulating the posterior hypothalamus increases thyroid hormone levels, not parathyroid hormone levels. Parathyroid hormone has nothing to do with temperature regulation (its function is to raise the serum calcium level).

5. **D**
   - A: No. This is true. (Remember that interleukins are the chemicals used for communication between ["inter"] white blood cells ["leukocytes"].)
   - B & C: No. These are both heat-generation/conservation mechanisms, and thus both function in the elevation of temperature known as fever.
   - D: **Yes.** The question states that interleukin 1 increases body temperature during illness. As discussed in the passage, body temperature is normally regulated by shivering, piloerection, cutaneous vasodilation, and thyroid hormone. Interleukin 1 is only important during illness, and climate should have no bearing on this.

6. **C**
   - Item I: False. Shivering is the contraction of skeletal muscles, which are part of the somatic, not autonomic, nervous system.
   - Item II: True. Piloerection is a sympathetic autonomic response which helps to conserve heat by maintaining an insulatory layer of air (see paragraph 3 of the passage).
   - Item III: True. This too is a sympathetic autonomic response which conserves heat (it prevents heat loss by convection). See the third paragraph of the passage.

Passage 84

1. **D**
   Items I, II, & III: True. The passage states that the peripheral chemoreceptors are sensitive to each.

2. **C**
   - C: **Yes.** Only Graph A gives information about the % Sat. At a P_{O_2} of 50, the % Sat is about 80%.

3. **C**
   - A & B: No. Refer to graph D. In order for the graphed variables to vary proportionally in a certain range, the graph must be linear. Between 40 and 50 mm Hg on the pH = 7.4 graph there is an obviously nonlinear region.
   - C: **Yes.** Refer to Graph D, because this is the only plot of P_{CO_2} versus ventilation. The linear portion is on the line on the left (pH = 7.3) from 30 up to 40 mm Hg. In every other region of the graph, the slope changes from data point to data point.
   - D: No. Less that 40 mm Hg would include the nonlinear range of this graph.

4. **B**
   - A: No. Refer to Graph A. At a P_{O_2} of 50 mm Hg, the ventilation rate is increased (remember that 100 mm Hg is normal).
   - B: **Yes.** Peripheral chemoreceptors respond dramatically to P_{O_2} values lower than 50 mm Hg, increasing the ventilation rate (Graph A).
   - C: No. Central chemoreceptors do not respond to oxygen levels (first paragraph of passage), and the question states that the P_{CO_2} and pH (to which central chemoreceptors do respond) are normal.
   - D: No. The ventilation rate will be higher, not lower, than normal. When the P_{O_2} is low, increasing the ventilation rate serves to blow off CO_2 faster, which increases the fraction of is oxygen in the alveolus (the alveolar P_{O_2}).

5. **B**

   Item I: True. Choose any P_{O_2} on the graph for $P_{CO_2} = 40$ mm Hg. Then switch to the $P_{CO_2} = 50$ mm Hg graph. How does the relative ventilation change? It increases.

   Item II: True. Going from a P_{O_2} of 100 to 80 mm Hg significantly increases the RV only on the $P_{CO_2} = 50$ mm Hg graph. On the $P_{CO_2} = 40$ mm Hg graph, you have to drop the P_{O_2} way down to see any effect.

   Item III: False. Nothing in the passage indicates that increasing P_{O_2} above normal will affect the relative ventilation response.

6. **D**

   D: Yes. Only Graphs A and B give any information about a P_{O_2} of 35 mm Hg. On either graph, this corresponds to an RV of just under 7. The passage explains the RV by saying that an RV of 1 corresponds to the normal minute-ventilation of 7 L/min. Hence an RV of 2 would correspond to 14 L/min, etc. An RV of just under 7 would correspond to a minute-ventilation of a little less than 7×7, or about 45.

Passage 85

1. **B**

   B: Yes. *Pleura* refers to sheets of connective tissue that line the inside of the chest wall (parietal pleura) and the outside of the lungs (visceral pleura). The pleural space is the space between the two pleural layers. Due to lung elasticity and chest wall expansion, this space is negatively pressurized. When the chest wall expands in preparation for inspiration, the negative pressure in the parietal space increases; as a result, the lungs are sucked open. The passage states that the external intercostals expand the chest wall (paragraph 2).

   C: No. The opposite is true (see B). When the pleural space pressure is increased, the lungs are compressed.

   D: No. The pressure in the pleural space will become more negative when the eternal intercostals contract (see B).

2. **C**

   Item I: True. The passage states (last paragraph) that active expiration occurs only when an unusual increase in ventilation is necessary (that is, during exertion), and that the abdominal muscles function to compress the lungs.

   Item II: False. The diaphragm is important for lung expansion at all times.

   Item III: True. Again, the passage states that expiration is active only during exertion.

3. **A**

   A: Yes. Hypoventilation (decreased breathing) causes one to blow off less CO_2, so P_{CO_2} increases. Hypoventilation both lowers P_{O_2} and increases P_{CO_2}.

4. **C**

   A: No. This will increase the contents of the abdominal cavity, which will make descent of the diaphragm more difficult.

   B: No. The diaphragm is the main muscle of inspiration.

   C: Yes. Lung elasticity tends to draw the chest inward. If lung elasticity decreases, chest expansion is easier.

D: No. In a third-trimester pregnancy, the size of the uterus forces abdominal contents upwards making the descent of the diaphragm more difficult.

5. **A**

Item I: True. This is a description of a patient using accessory muscles to breathe. Refer to the third paragraph of the passage.

Item II: False. The question states that the patient is standing and gripping a table!

Item III: False. The muscles of respiration are skeletal muscles. This includes the diaphragm. Even though breathing happens automatically, we can control it; it is a voluntary motor function.

6. **D**

D: **Yes.** The pleural space normally contains negative pressure. The result is that when the chest cavity expands (via contraction of the diaphragm and external intercostal muscles), so do the lungs; when the chest cavity reduces in size (via relaxation of the diaphragm and contraction of the internal intercostal muscles), they do too. Pleural adhesions do not change this relationship.

Passage 86

1. **C**

Item I: True. The kidneys compensate for acidic products of metabolism by excreting acid.

Item II: True. This is the mechanism by which the kidneys excrete acid. They combine H_2O and CO_2 into H_2CO_3 (using the enzyme carbonic anhydrase); the H_2CO_3 then dissociates into H^+ and HCO_3^-. When the proton is excreted in the urine, the bicarbonate must be retained, or no net acid secretion would have occurred.

Item III: False. The goal is to maintain pH balance. This would lead to a net increase in plasma pH.

2. **C**

A: No, this is true. Increased ventilation results in an increase in the amount of CO_2 expired; a lowered arterial P_{CO_2} results.

B: No, this is true. An abnormally low P_{CO_2} (see A) will result in respiratory alkalosis, since less CO_2 is present to turn into bicarbonate plus protons.

C: **Yes.** When the plasma pH is too high (see B), the kidney will create alkaline urine to compensate.

D: No, this is true. Since oxygen is quite insoluble in water, it must be carried by hemoglobin. Hb is a very efficient scavenger of oxygen in the lungs; it becomes saturated with oxygen easily. Hence, changes in the respiratory rate do not tend to change the amount of oxygen carried in the blood much. (Because CO_2 is water soluble, much of it is carried free in the blood. Thus, an increase in ventilation, which lowers the P_{CO_2} in the alveoli, will lead to much more CO_2 leaving the blood. So changes in respiration do affect the plasma CO_2 level, even though they do not affect the O_2 level.)

3. **B**

B: **Yes.** Before the patient is put on the ventilator, he will be in a state of metabolically compensated respiratory acidosis. This is a state where the lungs retain CO_2, causing acidosis, and the kidneys then gradually adapt to retain HCO_3^- and excrete H^+. On the ventilator, the hypoventilation will suddenly cease. As a result, the plasma concentration of CO_2 will fall, but the kidney will continue to excrete protons and retain bicarbonate. A secondary alkalosis results. The second and third paragraphs state that respiratory changes are fast and metabolic changes slow.

For Questions 4, 5, and 6:

#1) Sudden increase in acidity. Possible cause: increased lactic acid due to exertion.

#2) The respiratory system attempts to compensate by blowing off CO_2

#3) The kidneys kick in, excreting acid. The pH is returned to normal.

#4) Sudden increase in pH. Possible cause: loss of HCl due to vomiting.

#5) The respiratory system attempts to compensate by retaining CO_2 (hypoventilation).

#6) The kidneys kick in, retaining acid. The pH is returned to normal.

#7) Hypoventilation. Fluid in the lungs, for example, results in a failure to eliminate CO_2. Plasma CO_2 increases and pH falls.

4. **C**

A: No. Line #1 shows decreasing pH and decreasing bicarbonate at a constant P_{CO_2}, which indicates increasing metabolic acidosis with no respiratory or renal compensation.

B: No. Line #2 shows a change in P_{CO_2}, which indicates respiratory compensation is occurring.

C: **Yes.** Line #3 parallels the isobar (constant P_{CO_2}—refer to the end of the passage), indicating that it represents a process occurring at constant P_{CO_2}. Hence respiratory compensation is not taking place. Meanwhile, the pH is returning to normal while the bicarbonate level increases. This indicates renal retention of bicarbonate, that is, metabolic compensation for acidosis. Also note that #3 came after #2, which would indicate that #3 was probably metabolic (slower).

D: No. In #6 we see a drop in pH from an initially high value toward normal; this is compensation for an alkalosis.

5. **B**

A: No. Line #1 shows only decreasing pH and decreasing bicarbonate at a constant P_{CO_2}, which indicates increasing metabolic acidosis with no respiratory or renal compensation.

B: **Yes.** Line #1 represents the ingestion of acid: falling pH at constant P_{CO_2}. Line #2 shows the lungs blowing of CO_2 to compensate.

C: No. See 4C.

D: No. As indicated above, line #7 represents poor ventilation causing respiratory acidosis.

6. **D**

A: No. Line #1 shows decreasing pH and decreasing bicarbonate at a constant P_{CO_2}, which indicates increasing metabolic acidosis with no respiratory or renal compensation.

B: No. Line #4 represents the onset of respiratory alkalosis.

C: No. Line #5 represents initial respiratory compensation for metabolic alkalosis.

D: **Yes.** Fluid in the lungs impairs gas exchange, resulting in CO_2 retention and respiratory acidosis.

Passage 87

1. **A** CO_2 and oxygen passively diffuse through membranes. Passive diffusion always occurs down a concentration gradient. In the placenta, fetal plasma CO_2 must be higher than the maternal circulation in the placenta, forcing CO_2 to move down a gradient from the fetal circulation into the maternal circulation.

2. **A** Since oxygen and carbon dioxide diffuse passively in the placenta, the fetal oxygen must be lower than maternal oxygen in the placenta. Fetal hemoglobin is adapted to bind oxygen more avidly than adult hemoglobin, to provide sufficient oxygen to fetal tissues under these reduced-oxygen conditions. This adaptation would allow resistance to low oxygen content after birth as well. Choice B is wrong because this change in circulation is related to decreased resistance in the pulmonary circulation. Choice C is incorrect since this is the opposite of what would be expected, and choice D is wrong because no connection to fertility or survivability is indicated.

3. **C** The external atmosphere is richer in oxygen than the maternal circulation, which is depleted of oxygen by maternal tissues. The infant therefore no longer requires the higher affinity oxygen binding of fetal hemoglobin to saturate its hemoglobin with oxygen and deliver oxygen to tissues. Choice A is false, choice B is true but not does explain the change, and choice D is true but irrelevant.

4. **D** The question states that the lungs are normal but the circulation impaired in the mother. Choice D is the most relevant response. Even if the maternal lungs are perfectly healthy, the fetus will not receive sufficient oxygen if the maternal circulatory system is functioning sub-optimally. Choices A and B can be eliminated because there is no indication that the placental barrier is compromised or that fetal circulation is impaired, and choice C is wrong because it describes impaired lung function, which the question excludes.

5. **B** Maternal blood must supply oxygen to maternal tissues before reaching the placenta. Choice A is incorrect because there is no mixing of maternal and fetal blood, and choices C and D are wrong because they are irrelevant to oxygen content in blood.

6. **C** Since blood mixes in the fetus between the pulmonary artery and the aorta through the ductus arteriosus, both ventricles pump blood to the systemic circulation. In the adult, only the left ventricle pumps blood to the systemic circulation. The other choices are wrong because the atria deliver blood only to the ventricles, not the systemic circulation.

Passage 88

1. **A**
   A: Yes. In fertilization, the *acrosomal reaction* allows the sperm to penetrate the *jelly coat* to reach the *vitelline layer*, in which the bindin receptors are located. The third paragraph in the passage describes "bindin receptors in the vitelline layer."
   B: No. The jelly coat is the layer just outside the vitelline layer.
   C: No. Cortical granules are located inside the plasma membrane of the egg. It is stated in the passage that substances from the cortical granules degrade the bindin receptors, so how could these be located in the granules?
   D: No. The perivitelline space is the space between the plasma membrane and the vitelline layer.

2. **B**
   B: Yes. Primary oocytes are arrested for years at meiotic prophase I, from birth until ovulation.

3.   **C**

Item I: True. The passage explains that both the fast block and the slow block depend on the influx of Na^+ from the media. Therefore, removal of Na^+ from the medium would directly prevent the fast block and indirectly prevent the slow block. Polyspermy could result.

Item II: True. The passage explains that a calcium influx results from the sodium influx, and that this calcium influx leads to release of enzymes from the cortical granules which degrade bindin receptors. In a low-sodium medium, the sodium influx and all of its results would fail to occur.

Item III: False. This normally results from the sodium influx, through the action of a sodium-proton exchanger. As discussed in I and II above, the sodium influx would be reduced if the external sodium concentration were abnormally low.

4.   **B**

A: No. Such a depolarization would make the egg "think" it had been fertilized, and the mechanisms discussed in the passage would kick in to prevent fertilization (see B).

B: **Yes.** As discussed in the passage, depolarization constitutes the fast block to polyspermy, and also leads to some of the elements of the slow block (all the elements of the slow block that depend on depolarization, not a sodium influx, *per se*). Artificially depolarizing the membrane would activate both the fast block and the slow.

C: No. Again, such a depolarization would make the egg "think" it had been fertilized. If anything, we would expect postfertilization protein synthesis to be stimulated.

D: No. The passage states that depolarization causes the slow block to polyspermy, and that one of the components of the slow block is movement of the vitelline layer *away from* the plasma membrane. This is what we would expect to see in the case of artificial depolarization.

5.   **A**

A: **Yes.** The last sentence of the passage states that *translation-blockers but not transcription-blockers* prevent initial postfertilization protein synthesis. This indicates that the mRNA is already present and need only be translated for the proteins to be made.

B: No. Nothing in the passage suggests this to be the case.

C: No. This implies that transcription must occur in order for initial protein synthesis to proceed. But as discussed in A, the passage implies that this is not the case.

D: No. Ribosomes are responsible for all protein synthesis. They are necessary for the complex interaction of tRNA and mRNA, which allows translation of the genetic code.

6.   **D**

A: No, this is true.

B: No, this is accurate.

C: No, these are known as *bindins*.

D: **Yes.** The acrosomal reaction is actually accompanied by an increase in pH and calcium. If you didn't know that this was false, you could have eliminated the other choices, since they are all important facts about the acrosomal reaction.

Passage 89

1. **A**
   A: **Yes.** Estrogen acts at the hypothalamic and pituitary levels to inhibit the secretion of GnRH from the hypothalamus, and FSH and LH from the anterior pituitary. This is a classic negative feedback loop.
   B: No. Estrogen and progesterone generally work together. Although they do have opposite effects in certain situations (which you don't need to worry about), one does not ever directly inhibit the other.
   C: No. As stated in A above, estrogen inhibits LH and FSH secretion.
   D: No. There is no information linking ovulation with behavior.

2. **C**
   A & B: No. Progesterone and the corpus luteum play a role in the luteal phase, not ovulation.
   C: **Yes.** The preovulatory LH surge is essential for ovulation.
   D: No. The passage does state that FSH declines prior to ovulation, but this is not the cause of ovulation.

3. **C**
   A: No. Positive feedback would favor secretion, not inhibit it.
   B: No. The hypothalamic-pituitary negative feedback axis works by the inhibition of secretion of hypothalamic and pituitary hormones by their products, not by the hormones themselves.
   C: **Yes.** The passage states, "The preovulatory decline of FSH is due to the increasing concentration of estradiol." Estrogen inhibits FSH by negative feedback.
   D: No. Positive feedback would favor secretion, not inhibit it.

4. **A**
   A: **Yes.** Progesterone is responsible for the changes in the endometrium that result in the secretory phase, namely an increase in vascularization and the storage of lipids and glycogen. Estrogen is responsible for the proliferative phase of the endometrial cycle, and is also necessary for the secretory phase, along with progesterone.
   B, C, & D: No. FSH, LH, and hCG act on the ovaries, not the endometrium.

5. **B**
   Item I: False. The ovarian follicle produces estradiol but not progesterone.
   Items II & III: True. The corpus luteum and the placenta are the only two structures that produce both estradiol and progesterone.
   Item IV: False. The adrenal medulla produces catecholamines (epinephrine and norepinephrine).

6. **C**
   A: No. FSH and LH are produced in the anterior pituitary.
   B: No. The posterior pituitary is the site of release of ADH and oxytocin.
   C: **Yes.** The hypothalamus produces GnRH. It produces most of the releasing and inhibiting hormones that act on the anterior pituitary.
   D: No. The pineal gland is thought to secrete melatonin. It has no significant role in the menstrual cycle.

Passage 90

1. **B** "Retrograde" means "opposite to normal," thus retrograde menstruation must mean the flow of menstrual fluid opposite to its normal course. The question text states that the flow is into the peritoneal (abdominal) cavity, and the only entrance from the uterus to this cavity is via the uterine tubes. This could lead to deposition of endometrial tissue in the uterine tube, reducing the diameter of its lumen (choice B is not a symptom and is the correct answer choice). If the tube narrows too much or closes completely, infertility could be the result; oocytes would not be able to migrate toward the uterus and sperm would not be able to migrate toward the ovary (recall that fertilization occurs in the uterine tube, choice A is a possible symptom and can be eliminated). Deposition of endometrial tissue in the peritoneal cavity near the pelvis can cause inflammation and pain in that region (choice C is a possible symptom and can be eliminated). Deposition of endometrial tissue on the fimbriae could cause them to stick together (note that this could also cause infertility if the oocyte cannot enter after ovulation; choice D is a possible symptom and can be eliminated).

2. **D** The passage states that progesterone, made by the corpus luteum, is responsible for maintaining the endometrium after ovulation. It also states that the corpus luteum will regress and disappear if pregnancy does not occur, and when this occurs, menstruation follows immediately after. Thus, the presence of the progesterone made by the corpus luteum is what keeps the endometrium thickened. Without the corpus luteum, progesterone levels fall and the endometrial lining degenerates and sloughs off (menstruation; choice D is correct and choice B is wrong). Increased estrogen is seen mainly during the follicular phase and is responsible for rebuilding the endometrium after menstruation (choice A is wrong). Lastly, decreased estrogen, although occurring before menstruation, is not the main trigger for menstruation (choice D is better than choice C).

3. **A** A tumor in the posterior pituitary could lead to an increase in the hormones normally released from it, namely, vasopressin (ADH) and oxytocin (choice D is likely and can be eliminated). An increase in vasopressin would cause the kidneys to retain water, thus decreasing urine volume (choice B is likely and can be eliminated). Increased levels of vasopressin and oxytocin would feedback to the hypothalamus and pituitary, thus initiating compensatory activity (choice C is likely and can be eliminated). However, lactogenesis (milk production) is under the control of prolactin, a hormone of the anterior pituitary. It would not be affected by a tumor in the posterior pituitary (choice A is unlikely and is the correct answer choice).

4. **B** The passages states that "if fertilization and implantation occur" (i.e., pregnancy), "the corpus luteum is sustained by human chorionic gonadotropin." This suggests that hCG is present only when pregnancy occurs (choice B is not found in nonpregnant women and is the correct answer choice). The passage discusses the importance of the hypothalamic-pituitary-ovarian axis in controlling the monthly menstrual cycle and describes the effects of the hormones on that cycle. Estrogen is elevated during the cycle as it is necessary to stimulate the rebuilding of the endometrium during the proliferative phase of the uterine cycle (choice A would be elevated in nonpregnant women and can be eliminated). The hypothalamus releases GnRH, which stimulates the release of both FSH and LH; both of these hormones are needed to stimulate development of the ovarian follicle (including estrogen release; choices C and D would be elevated in nonpregnant women and can be eliminated).

5. **D** The passage states that the basal layer serves as the source of progenitor cells for the functional layer. In other words, it is the layer responsible for adding cells to the functional layer during the proliferative and secretory phases. This layer would thus have to remain unaffected by ovarian hormones so that it could continuously serve as a "stem cell-like" layer of undifferentiated cells. If the basal layer was equally influenced by these hormones, it too could be thickened and sloughed off, and if this were to occur, then there would be no progenitors to restart the next cycle. Only the differentiated cells, which are in the functional layer, can be influenced by ovarian hormones.

6. **C** The changes in the uterine lining that occur during the menstrual cycle are controlled directly by estrogen and progesterone, which are controlled by FSH and LH. Thus, the uterus is only indirectly controlled by FSH and LH (choice C is a false statement and the correct answer choice). The hypothalamic-pituitary-ovarian axis is controlled by a negative feedback mechanism, wherein high levels of target hormone (estrogen and progesterone) will feed back on the hypothalamus and pituitary to control the release of the tropic hormones FSH and LH. Thus, high levels of estrogen and progesterone would be expected to decrease LH (choice A is true and can be eliminated). The passage states that estrogen is elevated during the proliferative and secretory phases of the cycle, while progesterone is elevated during the secretory phase of the cycle (choice B is true and can be eliminated). Menstruation is the body's response to low levels of progesterone and estrogen; these hormones are what build up the uterine endometrium in the first place, thus withdrawal of this influence causes the endometrium to collapse and slough off (choice D is true and can be eliminated).

Passage 91

1. **C** MHC molecules are the key markers involved in determining antigenic compatibility in transplants. A graft with dissimilar or incompatible MHCs will cause the immune cells in the patient, especially T-cells, to attack the graft and destroy the tissue. This will lead to rejection of the tissue and potentially life-threatening complications. Choice C best describes this situation and thus is the correct answer. Choices A and B, while providing some similarities between donor and host, are not as thorough a screening as using the MHC proteins. Immune suppressant drugs are typically administered after the graft, and are not part of the screening for antigenic compatibility (choice D is wrong).

2. **B** The inner cell mass specifically gives rise to all of the tissues of the body and thus is thethe first occurrence of pluripotent stem cells (choice B is correct). The zygote is formed from the fusion of an egg and sperm cell and thus is totipotent rather than pluripotent; this means it can also form the extra-embryonic structures like the placenta (choice A is wrong). The gastrula has three layers, but is not the first occurrence of the pluripotent cells (choice C is wrong). The morula is composed of more cells than the zygote, but is still totipotent rather than pluripotent (choice D is wrong).

3. **A** Leukemia patients, similar to patients with other cancers, undergo chemotherapy and radiation with the intent to kill all the tumor cells. This also clears up space in the bone marrow, which is limited and can hold only certain amount of cellular population (choice A is correct). While it is true that irradiation will destroy the patient's immune cells, this is not the intent of the procedure as the patient will be treated with immunosuppressants (choice B is wrong). While reducing the rate of metastasis benefits the patient, this does not the issue around transplantation and thus does not answer the question (choice C is eliminated). Similarly, the removal of tumor cells and reduction of pain benefits the patient, but is not inherently related to the transplant (choice D is eliminated since it does not directly answer the question).

4.   **C**   Choices A, B and D all describe valid differences between adult and embryonic stem cells and can be eliminated. However adult stem cells in tissues, such as bone marrow, skin epithelium and testes, are capable of self-renewal in order to maintain these cellular populations for the lifetime of the individual. In these tissues, constant production of the mature cells is required and the stem cells are capable of giving rise to only one type or a few types of mature cells (choice C is not a difference between adult stem cells and embryonic stem cells and is the correct answer choice).

5.   **C**   Item I is correct: Oct-4 and Sox2 are transcription factors involved in triggering and controlling differentiation. Methylases would induce methylation of the genome thus blocking their ability to interact with the DNA (choices B and D can be eliminated). Item II is correct: similar to the effect of methylases, corepressors would prevent interaction with the DNA binding sites for the transcription factors (choice A can be eliminated and choice C is correct). Item III is incorrect: the process is cell culture rather than a technique like PCR so the susceptibility of an enzyme to heat is not relevant to the question..

6.   **A**   In an HSC transplant, the graft is the source of the immune cells so incompatibility is likely to cause destruction of host body tissues by reactive immune cells (graft-versus-host disease). In solid organ transplant, the host's immune cells recognize the transplanted organ as being foreign, which leads to rejection and destruction of the graft (host-versus-graft disease; choice A is correct). The similar length of immunosuppression therapy, risk of developing autoimmune disease and potentially life-threatening consequences exist in both type of transplants thus eliminating choices B, C, and D.

Passage 92

1.   **B**
   A: No. Once a cell is differentiated, it will never dedifferentiate unless it is a cancerous cell.
   B: **Yes.** Neurulation and organogenesis follow gastrulation. Gastrulation is when the three primary germ layers become distinct.
   C: No. Mitosis will indeed continue throughout development, but cleavage is a specific term reserved for the first few cell divisions in which the zygote gives rise to the morula. During these cell divisions, no growth occurs, so that the morula does not take up any more space than the zygote did.
   D: No. Blastula formation comes before gastrulation.

2.   **B**
   A: No. Ectoderm gives rise to skin, nervous system, retina, lens, etc.
   B: **Yes.** You need to know that mesoderm gives rise to the entire circulatory system and muscle (and most of the other stuff between the gut and the skin, excluding the nervous system).
   C: No. Endoderm gives rise to the inner lining of the gut.
   D: No. An eye is unlikely, and there is no information to support this.

3.   **B**
   A: No. Competency is defined in the first line of the passage. From Exp. 2 we can see that the cells in question can be influenced by their surroundings, so they are competent.
   B: **Yes.** The cells can assume several different fates and are not yet terminally differentiated.
   C: No. The cells can become other ectodermal tissue, such as gills.
   D: No. Exp. 1 tells us this.

4. **D**

    A: No. The three germ layers are formed prior to gastrulation.

    B: No. Nothing in the passage indicates that any of the cell types used in the experiments are abnormal. The idea behind the experiments was to move normal cells to abnormal places as they developed to see when their fates became fixed.

    C: No. Exp. 2 does state that the closest mesodermal tissue determines development of grafted ectodermal tissue. But in Exp. 5 no mention is made of mesoderm. It is the *ectodermal* cells which are differentiating. In Exp. 5 they are more differentiated and have lost competence.

    D: **Yes.** The transplanted neural tissue is more developed in Exp. 5.

5. **C**

    Item I: False. Nervous tissue is ectodermal. The tissue started and finished ectodermal.

    Item II: False. While the cells were isolated in a culture medium for 36 hours, there were no cells there to induce them.

    Item III: True. The cells respond differently but have the same genome, so it must be the way genes are expressed which has changed.

6. **B**

    A: No. All cells in the body at all stages of development have the same genes! (With a couple of exceptions, such as B and T cells.)

    B: **Yes.** It is gene expression which changes as development proceeds, and proteins are the product of gene expression.

    C: No. These are microtubules. The structures involved in mitosis do not change during development.

    D: No. There is no reason to suspect a systematic change in energy requirements.

Passage 93

1. **B**

    Item I: False. The genome remains intact during development, with no loss or gain of genes. (B and T cells of the immune system are an exception.)

    Item II: True. Differential *expression* of genes is what gives cells their different characteristics.

    Item III: False. Determination is what destines a cell to differentiate into whatever specific type it is going to be.

2. **D**

    Item I: True. This is stated in the passage.

    Item II: True. The dorsal lip tissue eventually develops into the neural plate. (If you did not know this already [you definitely wouldn't have to for the MCAT] you should have chosen D because there's no way to choose I and III only.)

    Item III: True. From Experiment 2, you can see that the dorsal lip causes gastrulation to occur.

3.   **B**
   A: No. By definition, a totipotent cell is one that still retains the ability to develop into any part of the developing zygote.
   B: Yes. This is false; all genes are never expressed at one time in a cell.
   C: No; this is true. If cells are ectodermal, then they have already narrowed down their developmental options and are unlikely to form endodermal or mesodermal tissues.
   D: No. This is true. By late gastrulation, cells have lost their totipotency and are fated to develop into certain cells.

4.   **D**
   A: No. Cephalization, the possession of a well-developed head region, is shared by all chordates, and is obvious during gestation.
   B: No. All chordates possess pharyngeal gill slits early in gestation.
   C: No. A dorsal hollow nerve cord is a chordate feature.
   D: Yes. Chordates have lungs but do not use them for respiration until after birth (during embryonic development they are collapsed and contain fluid).

5.   **B**
   A: No. The animal tissue is *induced* to become mesoderm.
   B: Yes. The vegetal pole cells induce the animal pole cells to become mesoderm. From Exp. 3, one can infer that animal tissue becomes ectoderm except in the presence of vegetal pole tissue, in which case it becomes mesoderm.
   C: No. It is apparent from Experiment 3 that the vegetal pole cells are essential for the transformation to mesoderm. The animal pole cells are not intrinsically determined to become mesoderm, but rather are "instructed" by the environment (i.e., the vegetal pole cells nearby).
   D: No. Cell differentiation refers to the process of cells developing. In this case, the animal pole cells differentiate into mesodermal cells. Differentiation is the process itself, not the cause of the process.

Passage 94

1.   **A**
   A: Yes. The passage states (third paragraph, second sentence) that Sertoli cells are the cells which support and nourish developing spermatozoa. Since sperm develop in the seminiferous tubules, Sertoli cells must be located here. In fact, their cell bodies extend from the base of the tubule into the lumen. In addition to producing Müllerian inhibiting factor, they provide nutrients to the developing sperm.
   B: No; see A. The epididymus is where sperm mature.
   C: No. This is the duct through which sperm pass en route to the ejaculatory duct.
   D: No. This is the remnant of the ovarian follicle that is left behind after ovulation has occurred.

2. **B**
   - A: No. Anyone with a Y chromosome is genetically male (unless multiple copies of the X chromosome are present, in which case the individual is not simply "male" or "female").
   - B: **Yes.** Males are more likely to suffer from an X-linked recessive disease, because if they have an abnormal X chromosome, it is their only copy. Females have two X chromosomes, one donated by each parent, and are thus very unlikely to have two copies of a defective X chromosome. Defects on the Y chromosome would not change this.
   - C: No. The passage explains that female development is the default, and that male development only occurs when the Y chromosome is present. A large deletion on the short arm of the Y chromosome would likely disrupt the gene for H-Y antigen, which determines male development.
   - D: No. Again, since female anatomy is the default, absence of H-Y antigen would result in female structures.

3. **B**
   - Item I: False. The corpus luteum makes estrogen and progesterone.
   - Item II: True. The interstitial cells of Leydig are the testosterone-producing cells, located in the testes, outside of the seminiferous tubules. (Refer to the third paragraph of the passage.)
   - Item III: False. The Sertoli cells do not make testosterone (and nothing in the passage suggests they do), although they modify it by converting it to dihydrotestosterone.

4. **A**
   - A: **Yes.** According to the passage, testicular differentiation occurs after 43–50 days of gestation and MIF has already taken effect. Therefore, the fetus will develop a Wolffian duct system and male external genitalia, as determined by testosterone secreted by the Leydig cells.
   - B, C, & D: No; see A. The baby will be born male.

5. **C**
   - Items I & II: False. Note that I and II are equivalent—the "follicle-like" structures represent undifferentiated seminiferous tubules. Since there is no way to choose both I and II, neither can be correct.
   - Item III: True. According to Experiment 1, treatment of neonatal XY testes with anti-H-Y antigen results in the failure of seminiferous tubules to develop. *But*, the passage states that testicular differentiation occurs during the seventh week of gestation. Anti-H-Y antigen should not have an effect at this late stage of development.

MCAT Psychology and Sociology

Passages

Passage 1 (Questions 1-6)

Social support is broadly defined as the emotional and instrumental resources that an individual receives from his or her social network that help the individual manage stress. Researchers have observed that the support networks of men and women tend to differ in structure and function. While women tend to have a larger and more expanded variety of people who serve several functions in their networks, men tend to have more limited and denser networks, and rely on their spouses for most of their support. Further studies show that women receive more health and well-being advantages from their social support resources than do men.

Although most research has demonstrated distinct sex differences in support networks, some findings suggest a lack of sex differences in support networks. One study in particular aimed to observe quantitative and qualitative measures of social support.

This study included a sample of 200 men and 200 women, each of whom was married and had at least one child. Participants were asked to list "all of the names of the people that you consider closest to you." The participants were given a questionnaire, which asked a series of questions about the quantitative and qualitative aspects of social support that participants receive from and provide to others. Results demonstrated that women have larger support networks than men do. Also, men in the study indicated that they were much more satisfied with their marriages than the women were. Figure 1 and Figure 2 show the percentages of respondents who reported receiving social support from others (Figure 1) and providing social support to others (Figure 2).

	Spouse		Children		Friends	
	Male	Female	Male	Female	Male	Female
Confiding	93.2	69.3	45.4	60.9	11.7	18.9
Reassuring	72.4	61.8	34.9	49.0	11.3	17.7
Sick care	88.9	70.1	66.7	78.1	10.3	13.6
Talk when upset	75.4	51.6	22.0	34.9	12.8	20.3
Talk about health	73.0	54.2	29.4	37.3	8.8	16.0

Figure 1 Percentage of respondents receiving social support from others

	Spouse		Children		Friends	
	Male	Female	Male	Female	Male	Female
Confiding	85.4	62.0	59.2	67.2	13.4	21.9
Reassuring	79.2	58.3	63.0	69.5	10.2	24.3
Sick care	93.8	82.5	68.9	71.6	18.3	28.8
Talk when upset	79.9	58.4	56.9	62.4	9.7	22.3
Talk about health	80.1	60.7	38.1	53.7	11.5	21.0

Figure 2 Percentage of respondents providing social support to others

Adapted from T. Antonucci & H. Akiyama. *An examination of sex differences in social support among older men and women.* © 1987 by Plenum Publishing Corporation

1. Which of the following is true regarding social networks?

   I. Men tend to utilize their strong ties more than their weak ties while women tend to utilize their weak ties more than men do.
   II. Women tend to utilize their strong ties more than their weak ties while men tend to utilize their weak ties more than women do.
   III. Social networks are an example of symbolic culture.

   A. I only
   B. II only
   C. I and III only
   D. II and III only

2. If it is true that women receive more benefits from their support networks than men, then women have more:

   A. human capital.
   B. cultural capital.
   C. social capital.
   D. symbolic capital.

3. Which of the following statements is true about the relationship between social support and mortality rates?

   A. Mortality rates are likely to increase if people have high amounts of social support.
   B. Mortality rates are likely to decrease if people have high amounts of social support.
   C. Mortality rates are likely to decrease if people have low amounts of social support.
   D. There is no definite relationship between social support and mortality rates.

4. About fifty years ago, men and women provided social support more than they received it, on average. Today, men and women receive social support more than they provide it, on average. Which of the following sociological concepts explains this scenario?

   A. Symbolic interactionism
   B. Conflict theory
   C. Social constructionism
   D. Deviance

5. Which of the following conclusions can be drawn from Figure 1?

   I. Females received more social support from their friends than did men in all five aspects of social support.
   II. Females received more social support from their spouses than from their children in all five aspects of social support.
   III. Men received more social support by confiding in their friends than they received by talking about their health to their friends.

   A. I and II only
   B. I and III only
   C. II and III only
   D. I, II, and III

6. Comparing Figure 1 and Figure 2, what can be concluded?

   A. Women receive and provide social support to their spouses in all five aspects more than men do.
   B. Friends provide sick care for men more than men provide sick care for their friends.
   C. Women reassure their spouses more than their spouses reassure them.
   D. Mothers provide social support to their upset children more than children provide social support to their upset mothers.

Passage 2 (Questions 1-6)

The Pew Research Center conducted public opinion and demographic research to better understand the response to widespread social changes affecting family structure in the United States. The center collected survey responses from a nationally representative participant sample (n = 2,693 adults). First, to gather information on public opinion, respondents were asked to consider seven demographic trends and indicate whether they considered the social consequence of each trend to be positive, negative, or neither ("no impact"). The seven trends studied were as follows: (1) More unmarried couples raising children; (2) More gay and lesbian couples raising children; (3) More people living together without getting married; (4) More mothers of young children working outside the home; (5) More people of different races marrying each other; (6) More women not ever having children; and (7) More single women having children without a male partner to help raise them.

The results suggested a three-cluster solution reflecting a sharp division in public opinion on the sweeping changes in family structure, this three-cluster solution divided the respondents into the following groups: Acceptors (32% of respondents), Skeptics (36.5%), and Rejecters (31.5%).

Acceptors were the most tolerant of structural changes and most likely to view the trends as socially good rather than bad; Skeptics were less tolerant of structural changes and more likely to view the trends as socially bad rather than good; and Rejecters were the least tolerant of structural changes and most likely to view the trends as socially bad rather than good. The division between the Acceptors and the Skeptics is driven primarily through a single trend ("More single women having children without a male partner to help raise them"); in fact, the difference in response is so significant that, in removing this item, the two groups merge into a single cluster. Two percent of Acceptors reported this trend as "bad for society"; greater than 99% of Skeptics, and 98% of Rejecters, reported the same. For the remaining six trends, Figure 1 reports the percentage of respondents who described the change as a negative development for society.

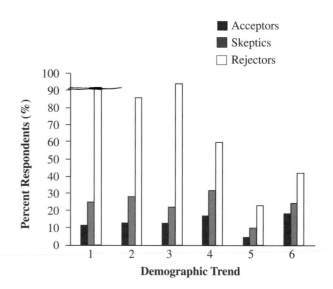

Figure 1 Percent of respondents describing demographic trends 1-6 as bad for society

Next, respondents provided information that allowed investigators to determine demographic differences between the three groups. The center collected information on respondent gender, race, age, geographic location, marital status, political affiliation, voter registration status, and religious observance (both attendance and affiliation). Selected data is presented in Figure 2.

	Percent Accepters	Percent Skeptics	Percent Rejecters
Gender			
Men	27	38	35
Women	38	34	28
Race			
White	32	34	34
Black	29	44	27
Hispanic	43	41	16
Age			
18-29	40	45	15
30-49	35	35	30
50-64	31	35	34
65+	21	33	46
Church Attendance			
Weekly or more	22	26	52
Monthly or less	30	46	24
Seldom or never	50	37	13

Figure 2 Percent of respondents defined as Acceptors, Skeptics, and Rejecters by demographic category

Adapted from P. Taylor, R. Morin, & W. Wang. The public renders a split verdict on changes in family structure. © 2011 by *Pew Research Center: Social & Demographic Trends*

1. In the United States, there are a number of formal rules and regulations affecting family relationships. Political activists have argued that these regulations create limitations on the definition of family. For example, anti-miscegenation laws prevented the legal recognition of interracial unions in the United States until 1967. These laws were found to be unconstitutional and are best described as an example of:

   A. discrimination.
   B. privilege.
   C. stereotyping.
   D. prejudice.

2. Which of the following conclusions is NOT supported by the results presented?

   A. The greatest percentage of Rejecters believes that the increased rate of premarital cohabitation is a socially negative trend.
   B. The greatest percentage of Acceptors believes that the decrease in the number of women who have children is a socially negative trend.
   C. Rejecters are less likely to believe that the increased rate of interracial marriage is bad for society than any other trend.
   D. Acceptors are less likely to believe that the increase in employment rate among women is bad for society than any other trend.

3. The ability of politicians to lobby for legislation against same-sex marriage represents which component of social stratification?

   A. Power
   B. Class
   C. Status
   D. Prejudice

4. Based on the information provided, which of the following can be concluded about the group referred to as Skeptics?

   I. The social opinions of young adults are most likely to be clustered into this group.
   II. The largest proportion of respondents overall reflected opinions that fit this category.
   III. Respondents in this group are less likely to advocate for adoption by single mothers than for other social trends.

   A. I and II only
   B. I and III only
   C. II and III only
   D. I, II, and III

5. A social institution is a structure that functions to maintain social order, often through the creation of central norms or formal laws that influence individual behavior. The family is an example of an institution. Which of the following identifies the expected Durkheimian view of the family?

   A. The structure of the family serves to maintain the power of men in patriarchal societies.
   B. The relationship between married partners reflects inequalities between social groups.
   C. The specific social roles of the husband, wife, and children are necessary to maintain solidarity in the family.
   D. The amount of communication between parents and their children is reflective of the levels of familial trust.

6. According to the passage, which demographic characteristic produces the biggest difference in positive views of the changing structure of families in the United States?

   A. Respondent's geographic location
   B. Respondent's religious service attendance
   C. Respondent's racial identification
   D. Respondent's gender

Passage 3 (Questions 1-6)

Television advertisements contain symbols that convey a specific message to the target audience. Researchers have observed that television programs and advertisements are intentionally correlated with one another in order to provide viewers with advertising content that is targeted to them, based on the type of television program they are watching. Furthermore, advertisers paint an idealized reality, one where the notion of what is "normal" or "average" might be rather skewed. Advertisements, therefore, contribute to the process of gender stereotyping because they portray men and women in certain societal roles.

Researchers examined how gender differences are currently portrayed in television advertisements by analyzing a variety of advertisements aired from 2008 to 2011 compared to previous data from 1956-1960 (which often portrayed men as the bread-winners in a widespread variety of occupations while women were often portrayed as the caretakers of the family). Researchers collected 1,900 television advertisements from 25 of the most popular television programs from the years 2008 to 2011. The popular television programs were selected based on five target audiences: older individuals (aged 60 or higher), men (aged 20-59), working women (aged 20-59), women (aged 20-59), and youths (aged 19 or below). Researchers then devised a set of variables that were used to categorize and analyze the advertisements in a way that showed the gender stereotype qualities common in the United States. The results demonstrate that although more women have appeared in television advertisements compared to data from 1956-1960, there has not been a huge change in the way advertisements portray gender differences regarding family, work, and attitude in advertisements (Figure 1).

Variables	Women Percentage (N)	Men Percentage (N)
Major characters in commercials	45.0 (850)	55.0 (1040)
Behavior displayed		
Active/instrumental	30.7 (261)	61.1 (635)
Passive/emotional	35.3 (300)	27.5 (286)
Sex objectification	34.0 (289)	11.4 (119)
Race		
White	88.0 (748)	79.4 (826)
Non-White	12.0 (102)	20.6 (214)
Work status		
Worker	24.5 (208)	56.9 (592)
Not Worker	75.5 (642)	43.1 (448)
Job authority		
Taking Orders	80.3 (167)	58.3 (345)
Giving Orders	19.7 (41)	41.7 (247)
Occupational Category		
Service/clerical (Pink-collar)	40.4 (84)	20.8 (123)
Trades/craft/operative (Blue-collar)	1.9 (4)	14.4 (85)
Managerial/professional (White-collar)	24.5 (51)	34.0 (201)
Performer/artist (Yellow-collar)	33.2 (69)	30.9 (183)

Figure 1 Percentage and number (N) of characters in 2008-2011 television advertisements by gender for the analyzed variables

Adapted from S. Coltrane and M. Adams. Work-family imagery and gender stereotypes: Television and the reproduction of difference. ©1997 by *Academic Press*

1. All of the following could be reasonably concluded about television advertisements, EXCEPT:

   A. they utilize the concept of conformity to encourage people to purchase a given product.
   B. they act as agents of socialization in society.
   C. they employ peer pressure by using models and attractive actors within specific age groups to target certain demographics.
   D. they act as agents of social facilitation within society.

2. Which of the following statements portrays gender differentiation?

   I. Men are independent while women are intuitive.
   II. Boys play with toy cars while girls play with dolls.
   III. Men have XY chromosomes while women have XX chromosomes.

   A. I and II only
   B. I and III only
   C. II and III only
   D. I, II, and III

3. Suppose that in the 1960s, there was a television program that showed a husband who worked in a pink-collared job while the wife worked in a white-collared job. From the perspective of society in the 1960s, this program would be:

   A. considered an example of labeling.
   B. a clear demonstration of conformity to the social norms of the time period.
   C. an example of deviance.
   D. demonstrating clear discrimination.

4. According to Figure 1, the variable "race: white" had the highest overall percentage for both women and men. If most advertisers believe that White culture is superior in America, and this is reflected in most advertisements, which sociological principle does this scenario most accurately demonstrate?

   A. Ethnocentrism
   B. Social exclusion
   C. Global inequality
   D. Cultural relativism

5. Based on Figure 1, which of the following is FALSE about the major characters in the television advertisements?

   A. Women are more passive/emotional than men, while men are more active/instrumental than women.
   B. It is more likely to find a woman in a pink collared job than a man in a white collared job.
   C. There are more non-working women than there are working men.
   D. Women are taking orders more than giving orders while men are giving orders more than taking orders.

6. What can be concluded about the relationship between television ads and gender equality?

   A. Because gender inequality is gradually declining in society, media has successfully portrayed gender equality in the workforce and family.
   B. Because gender inequality is gradually declining in society, media strives to portray gender equality in the workforce and family.
   C. Although gender inequality is gradually declining in society, media is doing little to portray gender equality in the workforce and family.
   D. Although gender inequality is gradually declining in society, media plays absolutely no role in portraying gender equality in the workforce and family.

Passage 4 (Questions 1-6)

Measures of the physician-patient relationship, such as trust and communication, have been considered in studies analyzing the disparities in healthcare outcomes, such as patient satisfaction. An important dimension of this relationship is concordance, defined as demographic similarities between the physician and patient (e.g., similarities based on age, race, or sex). Previous research on the effects of concordance has lead to equivocal results. The mechanism behind the relationship between concordance and outcomes is also unclear; research has not measured the role of mediating variables, such as cognitive and affective processes, to determine the process through which concordance has its effects.

In response to the gaps in the literature, public health investigators developed a research design to better understand the role of racial and sexual concordance. The purpose of this research was to examine the role of demographic concordance in patient perceptions of similarities to their physician, as well as the influence of these similarities on patient ratings of their medical care. The cross-sectional research method involved recruiting participants from ten primary care clinics in both public and private medical settings. Overall, a total of 29 physicians participated in the research; the median number of participant patients per physician was 7 ($n = 214$ patients for the purpose of final analyses).

The main source of data was patient-completed questionnaires. The first questionnaire was completed before a medical consultation and collected information on patient demographics. Researchers determined racial and sexual concordance through a comparison of patient and physician self-reports. The mean age (years) was 41.1 and 56.6 for physicians and patients, respectively; further demographic information is shown below (Figure 1).

	Physicians	Patients
Gender		
Male	59	38
Female	41	62
Ethnicity		
White	33	40
Black	27	49
Hispanic	0	11
Asian	40	0
Education		
Less than high school	0	15
High school	0	27
Some college	0	37
College degree (or more)	100	21

Figure 1 Self-reported demographic characteristics of participant physicians and patients (% reported)

The second questionnaire was completed after the medical consultation and collected information on perceived similarities to the provider, as well as outcome measures. Because the perception of similarities is a multidimensional concept, researchers created a similarities scale that included 10 measures, later divided into two groups: personal similarities (those in thinking, values, and communication) and ethnic similarities (those in race and community). The effects of racial concordance on perceived relational similarities are presented in Figure 2; sexual concordance was not found to be related.

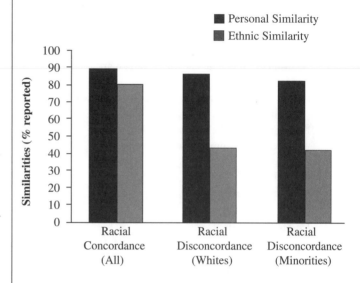

Figure 2 Racial concordance and patients' self-reported perceptions of perceived similarities to the physician

Outcome measures included patient self-reports of trust in the physician, satisfaction with care, and intent to follow treatment recommendations. Perception of personal similarities was a strong predictor of positive outcome reports; however, perception of ethnic similarities was not related to outcomes. Furthermore, controlling for other demographic characteristics and perceptions of similarities, racial and sexual concordance had minimal effects on outcome measures.

Adapted from R. Street, K. O'Malley, L. Cooper, & P. Haidet. Understanding concordance in patient-physician relationships: Personal and ethnic dimensions of shared identity. © 2008 by *Annals of Family Medicine*

1. The results included five potential sample groups of patients based on racial concordance. These groups could include all of the following EXCEPT:

   A. white patients in racial concordance with their providers.
   B. black patients in racial disconcordance with their providers.
   C. white patients in racial disconcordance with their providers.
   D. Hispanic patients in racial concordance with their providers.

2. Based on the results, participants of which demographic group could relate most to providers of different ethnic backgrounds?

   A. Patients reporting an ethnic background of "White"
   B. Patients reporting an ethnic background of "Black"
   C. Patients reporting an ethnic background of "Hispanic"
   D. Patients reporting an ethnic background of "Asian"

3. Human conditions are transformed to medical conditions, which are thus to be defined, diagnosed, and treated, through a process described as medicalization. The medicalization of mental health issues is controversial, and the approach to diagnosis and treatment is dependent on social and cultural factors. For example, different cultures have conflicting understandings of what constitutes optimal biological and psychological functioning, as well as the sources of mental health disorders. Symbolic interactionists would offer the explanation that mental illness is:

   A. defined in order to uphold social values about conforming behavior.
   B. the result of societal reactions rather than individual behavior being problematic.
   C. a label applied more often to those with the fewest social resources.
   D. needed to create regulations that separate acceptable and deviant behaviors.

4. The researchers were also interested in methods that could be used to transcend issues of racial and sexual concordance or discordance. In addition to the questionnaires described above, researchers also collected audio records of communications between participant patients and providers, which were later coded for results. Research assistants considered three components of provider communication to gauge patient-centeredness, rating the degree to which the provider was informative, used supportive communication, and engaged in partnership-building. It was found that these measures were correlated in a direct pattern with one another. This suggests that:

   A. providers who were more informative are less expected to use supportive communication.
   B. providers who were more supportive are less expected to engage in partnership-building.
   C. providers who were less engaged in partnership-building are less expected to be informative.
   D. providers who were less informative are more expected to have strong communication skills.

5. The authors proposed that patient perception of similarities are modifiable and better results could be achieved through appropriate interventions, such as focusing on patient-centered communication in medical settings. According to this perspective, providers could best benefit their patients through communication that addresses issues of:

   A. race.
   B. culture.
   C. ethnicity.
   D. spirituality.

6. In general, demographic characteristics are immutable. However, social class is less fixed; one's position in the social stratification structure can change. In the process of completing their medical education and training and beginning their careers in practice, it is expected that the participant providers experienced:

   A. upward mobility.
   B. downward mobility.
   C. intergenerational mobility.
   D. intragenerational mobility.

Passage 5 (Questions 1-6)

In a research project on the effect of social stratification on health and wellbeing, researchers examined health disparities in a Haitian immigrant group in Olympia, Washington. In this study, researchers visited the neighborhood where the majority of this community lived. The community members arrived gradually over the past 20 years, and while residents mentioned valuing being close to family members and having a tight-knit community, there were persistent health disparities affecting this group. Their average life expectancy was 75 years, compared to the Washington state average of 79.9 and an average of 77.5 years for African Americans in Washington state. From the interview data, the researchers concluded that many of the premature deaths in the community were due to a lack of preventive and primary medical care across the lifespan, as well as difficulty accessing health care in Olympia.

The researchers also gathered information about the community's integration into the existing Olympia community, composed primarily of Washington-born white Caucasians. They found that the immigrants were in a curious situation: they experienced only partial integration in the surrounding community. The interviewees explained that this was because the existing residents of Olympia saw the immigrants as threats to their jobs and a drain on the local social services. These negative feelings were expressed through giving the Haitian community the cold shoulder—stares at the grocery store, reluctance to hire community members, and exclusion from local politics. It was generally possible for community members to get under-the-table, contingent employment, like yard work and kitchen work, but steady, full-time employment remained much more difficult to obtain. Many community members reported their search for work to be very stressful, and the researchers found higher than average rates of heart disease, depression, and substance abuse in the Haitian community. When community members were able to find work, employers often didn't offer health insurance. Researchers compared the rates of on-the-job injury between Haitians and their white counterparts in Olympia and found that the Haitians had a fourfold increased chance of being injured at work.

Now that the community was well into their second generation as Olympia residents, health researchers were interested in tracking the health status of the children born on American soil. Their survey of the community's children found the following:

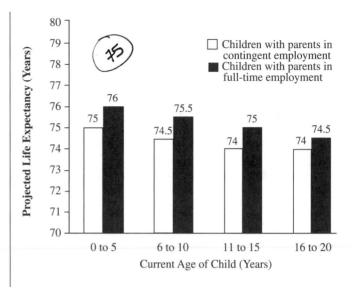

Figure 1 Projected life expectancy for children with parents in contingent and full-time employment, by current age

1. What is the best interpretation of the study results as presented in Figure 1?

    I. Both groups of children aged 0-5 indicate increases in projected life expectancy within the second generation.
    II. The gains of children with steadily employed parents outpaced the gains of children with contingently employed parents.
    III. Childhood age is a better predictor of life expectancy than parental employment.

    A. I only
    B. II only
    C. I and II only
    D. II and III only

2. Identities (race, gender, class, age, immigrant status, sexual orientation, etc.) combine in non-additive ways to produce unique social positions for individuals. For example, the lived experience of an African American woman cannot be understood through separate considerations of her race and gender—her identities must be understood together. The sociological name for an approach that analyses the lived experience of these multiple identities instead of trying to isolate individual aspects of identity for separate analysis is known as:

    A. symbolic interactionism.
    B. social identity theory.
    C. intersectionality.
    D. social constructionism.

3. Based on the information given in the passage, what can you conclude about the status of the Haitian community?

A. The Haitians had high social support and low social capital.
B. The Haitians had high social support and high social capital.
C. The Haitians had low social support and low social capital.
D. The Haitians had low social support and high social capital.

4. Which sociologist is known for his theory of capital?

A. Karl Marx
B. Emile Durkheim
C. George Herbert Mead
D. Max Weber

5. In communities that are socially excluded, such as the Haitians in the passage above, health disparities usually increase. All of the following will increase as a result of social exclusion, EXCEPT:

A. crime rates.
B. employment rates.
C. substance abuse rates.
D. forced assimilation.

6. What best explains why the researchers might be interested in the health of the children of the original Haitian immigrants to Olympia?

A. The health of the Haitian population could affect the health of other Olympians.
B. The researchers are interested in the children's coping strategies.
C. The disadvantage the Haitian parents face can carry over to the next generation.
D. Olympia-born whites will try to exclude the immigrants' children.

Passage 6 (Questions 1-6)

The construction of a stable and established self-identity is integral to development. During this critical period of psychosocial growth, individuals strive to figure out their personal identities. This may include where they fit with their peers, their aspirations for the future, and their opinions on politics or religion. Identity establishment may also coincide with the development of an internal set of values and goals. Although these values often originate from the values established by parents, an individual exploring their identity will often strive for autonomy in deciding who they are.

Psychologist James Marcia theorized beyond Erik Erikson's stages of psychosocial development to further explain the challenging period of identity establishment. Figure 1 demonstrates the four categories of identity statuses that are possible during this stage, dependent upon whether an individual is settled in their identity and whether they have explored their identity options.

	Identity Settled	Identity not settled
Have explored Identity Options	Identity Achievers	Identity Moratoriums
Have not explored Identity Options	Identity Foreclosures	Identity Diffusions

Figure 1 Marcia's Identity Status Model

Researchers have hypothesized that the mechanism by which identity exploration develops is in the generation of possible selves. In other words, individuals may explore and imagine themselves in different roles or identities, to investigate future possibilities. In an experiment examining this hypothesis, 100 participants were given a questionnaire designed to identify their current identity and separate each participant into one of four identity status groups based on the results of the questionnaire.

In addition, the researchers measured the types of possible selves, and categorized them as positive, negative or neutral. Prior studies have demonstrated that identity exploration is positively correlated with anxiety and self-doubt. In addition, the types of possible selves may have an impact on mood, such that those who have a higher percentage of negative selves may also have higher levels of negative affect. Figure 2 displays the number of participants in each group, and the number of possible selves measured for each group.

	n	Mean number of selves	Negative Selves	Positive Selves	Neutral Selves
Moratoriums	30	80	40	20	20
Achievers	25	60	20	20	20
Foreclosures	25	40	15	10	15
Diffusions	20	30	10	7	13

Figure 2 Participants, mean number of selves, positive selves, negative selves and neutral selves in sample

Source: Adapted from J.C. Dunkel. Possible selves as a mechanism for identity exploration. © 2000 by *Journal of Adolescence*

1. Which stage of Erik Erikson's theory of psychosocial development pertains to adolescents?

    A. Initiative vs. Guilt
    B. Industry vs. Inferiority
    C. Identity vs. Role Confusion
    D. Generativity vs. Stagnation

2. According to the passage and the study presented, which of the following statements is correct?

    I. There is a relationship between percentage of negative selves and mood
    II. A higher number of negative selves causes someone to have anxiety
    III. Identity exploration causes a person to doubt themselves

    A. I only
    B. I and II only
    C. II and III only
    D. I, II, and III

3. Based on the information provided in the passage, was this an experimental study design and why or why not?

    A. Yes, because the participants were randomly assigned to groups and the independent variable was manipulated.
    B. Yes, because the participants were not randomly assigned to groups and the variables were not manipulated.
    C. No, because the participants were randomly assigned to groups and the independent variable was manipulated.
    D. No, because the participants were not randomly assigned to groups and the variables were not manipulated.

4. Moral development is considered to be an important factor in identity development. According to Kohlberg's Stages of Moral Reasoning, teenagers are typically thought of to have progressed into the Conventional Morality stage. Which of the following is characteristic of the Conventional Morality stage?

    A. The morality of an action is based on its direct consequences, and is characterized by self-interest in seeking reward or avoiding punishment.
    B. Social conventions and rules are used as guidelines for appropriate moral behavior.
    C. An individual in this stage considers rules and laws as relative and based on abstract principles.
    D. An individual in this stage recognizes that those in the world hold different opinions, rights and values, and rules are based on compromises between those opinions.

5. According to the passage and the results of the study presented, which group would be associated with the highest level of anxiety and negative mood?

    A. Identity achievers
    B. Identity moratoriums
    C. Identity foreclosures
    D. Identity diffusions

6. Researchers have studied the way self-identity varies by culture. In general, which of the following statements is true concerning the differences between identity in western and eastern cultures?

    A. There is no difference between Eastern and Western concepts of self-identity.
    B. Western cultures place a greater value on defining the self in terms of group membership and goals, while Eastern cultures do not.
    C. Eastern cultures place more emphasis on community identity while Western cultures place more emphasis on self-identity.
    D. Western cultures place more emphasis on community identity while Eastern cultures place more emphasis on self-identity.

Passage 7 (Questions 1-6)

The "foot-in-the-door technique" asserts that people who comply with a small initial request will be more likely to comply with a later, larger request than would those asked only for the larger one. This technique has been hypothesized to work because the first request may create a bond between the requester and the person to whom the request was made. In one experiment, subjects were phoned and asked to complete a survey about household soap use. Two days later, the subjects who agreed to complete the survey were asked to allow a group of men to come and inventory all the products in their homes. A control group of comparable individuals was asked only for the second, larger request. Those who agreed to the smaller request (survey) were significantly more likely to comply with the larger request (in-home inventory) than were those who were only asked for the larger request.

Research suggests that the foot-in-the-door technique is most effective with individuals who rank high in "self-concept clarity," defined as the consistency with which one identifies and thinks of oneself. Another study sought to determine whether self-concept clarity was a factor in susceptibility to the foot-in-the-door technique. Study subjects consisting of 112 male and female undergraduates were pre-screened for self-concept clarity using a personality assessment. Per the assessment results, 52 subjects (30 female and 22 male) were placed in the high self-concept clarity group and 60 subjects (28 female and 32 male) were placed in the low self-concept clarity group. Subjects in both groups were then randomly assigned into one of two conditions: the foot-in-the-door condition or the control condition.

Subjects in the foot-in-the-door condition were asked to sign a petition for the homeless; all but two of the subjects in this condition agreed to sign (the two who did not sign were excluded from the study). All of the subjects were contacted three days later, by an experimenter blind to treatment and control conditions, and asked whether they would be willing to volunteer three hours of their time for a homelessness-related cause (the target request; results in Figure 1). Statistical analyses by gender determined that there was no significant difference in outcome for males vs. females in either of the conditions.

	High Self-Concept Clarity	Low Self-Concept Clarity
Foot-in-the-Door	39%	0%
Control	16%	32%

Figure 1 Percent of participants agreeing to target request (to volunteer three hours of their time for a homelessness-related cause)

1. In the first study, the effect of "foot-in-the-door" on the second request may be confounded by:

   A. the fact that some individuals were only asked the second request.
   B. the possibility that those willing to agree to completing a survey might also be inherently more willing to agree to allow strangers into their homes.
   C. the social norm that most have a tendency to mistrust strangers who ask personal questions.
   D. the amount of preparation required of the subjects for the second request.

2. Suppose that an individual has just agreed to compete a short survey and is then praised for being so "helpful" and "generous with her time." This individual is then asked to complete a much longer and more in-depth survey. This individual really doesn't want to complete the second survey, but does believe that she is a helpful person in general. Therefore, she agrees to the second survey. While the foot-in-the-door technique might explain why she agrees to the second survey, what is another potential explanation for her actions?

   A. Cognitive dissonance theory
   B. Social learning theory
   C. The social facilitation effect
   D. Groupthink

3. Suppose that the low self-concept clarity control subjects were each asked to volunteer while they were in the same room with three confederates who all readily agreed to volunteer. If true, the results appearing in the table could then best be explained by:

   I. conformity.
   II. group pressure.
   III. in-group bias.

   A. I only
   B. I and II only
   C. II and III only
   D. I, II, and III

4. Which of the following serves as the best example of self-concept clarity, as it is described in the passage?

    A. A restaurant worker blames stress and long hours for the initial difficulty she had quitting cigarette smoking.
    B. An honors student at a local high school is also nominated swim-team captain.
    C. A normally stingy man donates a very large amount of money to charity to avoid tax penalties.
    D. An office worker, cajoled into donating to an employee pool, later refuses to purchase a raffle ticket from a co-worker selling raffle tickets for her son's soccer team.

5. Suppose that someone's belief in helping others is a core value. He is always willing to help others and feels that this personality trait is central to who he is as a person. For this person, helpfulness would be considered part of his:

    A. self-schema.
    B. self-esteem.
    C. self-efficacy.
    D. social identity.

6. Which of the following most exemplifies foot-in-the-door principles, as they are described in the passage?

    I. An individual drives his friend to the airport and then agrees to pick him up from the airport three days later.
    II. A passerby gives a panhandler a small amount of money after the panhandler requests and receives a cigarette from him.
    III. A neighbor has agreed to complete all of the yard work for an elderly disabled man for the summer, and then agrees to a one-time request to move the elderly man's car out of the driveway.

    A. II only
    B. III only
    C. I and III only
    D. II and III only

Passage 8 (Questions 1-6)

The fundamental attribution error (FAE) is defined as the tendency to overestimate dispositional factors, and to underestimate situational factors, as causes for an individual's behavior.

A group of researchers in Iowa City, Iowa were interested in testing this theory. A group of 300 undergraduates from a nearby university were invited to participate in what they believed was a focus group. Participants were shown a "documentary" and were then asked to discuss the behaviors of the main "character" of the documentary. Participants were split into two groups ($N = 150$): for one of the groups, the main character in the documentary behaved in prosocial ways (holding open the doors for strangers, saying "please" and "thank you," smiling and waving at friends and neighbors, etc.); for the other group, the main character behaved in more antisocial ways (yelling out expletives while driving on the freeway, slamming doors, scowling and frowning, etc.). In each group, participants were subdivided into two further groups ($N = 75$): for each documentary "theme," there was one group who participated in a lecture on the FAE, and another who participated in a lecture on research methods. The FAE groups acted as the experimental groups, whereas the research methods groups acted as control groups. All lectures occurred prior to watching the documentary.

After viewing the documentary, all participants filled out a paper-and-pencil measure to identify the causes of the character's behaviors. Participants were to answer a series of questions attributing the character's behaviors to either situational or dispositional factors. These scores were then combined and averaged across all of the subjects in the experimental and control groups as composite percentages for both situational and dispositional factors. Higher percentages indicated that these factors were likely more responsible for the character's behaviors (e.g. a situational score of 87% means that participants' survey results indicated that situational factors were causing the 87% of the character's behaviors; Table 1).

	Situational	Dispositional	p
Prosocial Control	36%	64%	.08
Prosocial Experimental	42%	58%	.07
Antisocial Control	16%	84%	.09
Antisocial Experimental	27%	73%	.10

Table 1 Average scores for behavioral causes ($N = 300$); *$p < .05$

642 | © TPR Education IP Holdings, LLC

1. Based on the data in Table 1, what can be concluded?

   A. Control participants were more likely to attribute prosocial behaviors to dispositional factors than experimental participants were.
   B. Experimental participants were more likely to attribute antisocial behaviors to situational factors than control participants were.
   C. Participants in the prosocial groups were more likely to attribute the character's behaviors to dispositional factors than participants in antisocial groups were.
   D. None of the situational and dispositional attributions within groups were significantly different.

2. What is the purpose of using control groups in this study?

   A. To isolate the effects of the experimental variable and to rule out alternative explanations
   B. To intensify the effects of the experimental variable
   C. To nullify the effects of the experimental variable
   D. To ensure that the results would be statistically significant.

3. One potential explanation for the FAE is the "just world phenomenon." What is the basic idea behind this phenomenon?

   A. People get what they deserve
   B. People tend to attribute an observed effect to potential causes that capture their attention
   C. People are unable to take both behavioral and situational information into account simultaneously
   D. People selectively attend to information that confirms their preconceived biases

4. Which of the following is an example of a self-serving bias?

   A. An individual does poorly on an exam and blames the professor for not teaching the material well enough in class
   B. An individual does poorly on an exam and believes it is because he did not study hard enough
   C. An individual does well on an exam and believes it is because the exam was really easy
   D. An individual does well on an exam and believes it is because his tutor is excellent at her job

5. Which of the following is NOT one of the factors we consider when attributing someone's behavior to internal or external causes?

   A. Consistency
   B. Consensus
   C. Persuasion
   D. Distinctiveness

6. A particularly attractive professor arrives late to class, yells at a student when his cell phone goes off during the lecture, and rants about how poorly the entire class did on a recent exam. Despite all this negativity, you still very much admire this professor, and hold her in a very high esteem. Which cognitive error is this an example of?

   A. Self-serving bias
   B. Correspondence bias
   C. Cognitive dissonance
   D. Halo effect

Passage 9 (Questions 1-6)

People who hold strong opinions on complex social issues are likely to examine relevant empirical evidence in a biased manner. They are apt to accept "confirming" evidence at face value while subjecting "disconfirming" evidence to critical evaluation, and, as a result, draw undue support for their initial positions from mixed or random empirical findings. Thus, the result of exposing contending sides of a social dispute to an identical body of relevant empirical evidence may be not a reduction of disagreement, but rather an increase in polarization.

This "polarization hypothesis" can be derived from the simple assumption that data relevant to a belief are not processed impartially. Instead, judgments about the validity, reliability, relevance, and sometimes even the meaning of proffered evidence are biased by the apparent consistency of that evidence with the perceiver's theories and expectations. Thus, individuals will dismiss and discount empirical evidence that contradicts one's initial views, but will derive support from evidence that is no more probative, but seems consistent with one's views. Through such a biased assimilation, even a random set of outcomes can appear to lend support for an entrenched position, and both sides in a given debate can have their positions bolstered by the same set of data.

To test the polarization hypothesis, 48 undergraduate students, consisting of 24 "proponents" (in favor of capital punishment) and 24 "opponents" (opposed to capital punishment), were recruited to participate in the experiment. Upon entering the experiment, mixed groups of proponents and opponents were seated at a large table, and an experimenter, blind to the students' attitudes, presented them with index cards containing the results of a fictitious study. All of the index cards provided identical prodeterrent information, which advocated for the efficacy of capital punishment. After reading one of these "result cards," subjects answered two sets of questions about changes in their attitudes toward capital punishment and their beliefs about the deterrent efficacy of the death penalty. Following completion of these questions, the entire procedure was repeated: students were presented with the results of a second fictitious study, which brought the efficacy of capital punishment into question (antideterrent). As before, subjects were asked to report their attitudes towards capital punishment and efficacy of capital punishment laws. Changes in student attitudes after each study are presented in Figure 1.

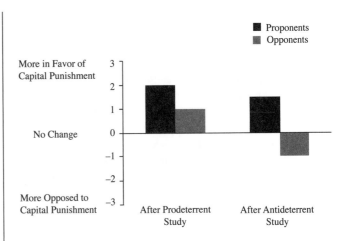

Figure 1 Changes in attitudes toward capital punishment relative to start of experiment as reported across time by proponents and opponents of capital punishment

Adapted from C. G. Lord, L. Ross, & M. R. Lepper. Biased assimilation and attitude polarization: The effects of prior theories on subsequently considered evidence. © 1979 by *Journal of Personality and Social Psychology*

1. Which of the following concepts is most opposite of the "polarization hypothesis," as it is described in the passage?

   A. The bystander effect
   B. Group polarization
   C. The availability heuristic
   D. Social loafing

2. A follow-up study documented that "proponents" who were shown photos of death row inmates multiple times became more likely to oppose capital punishment. Their attitude change could be explained by:

   A. cognitive dissonance theory.
   B. persuasion cues.
   C. self-perception theory.
   D. mere-exposure effect.

3. Opponents of capital punishment reported that many of their friends and family members also opposed the death penalty. These findings suggest that:

   A. cognitive dissonance plays a role in attitude formation.
   B. social learning plays a role in attitude formation.
   C. in-group bias plays a role in attitude formation.
   D. prejudice plays a role in attitude formation.

4. Which conclusion is best supported by Figure 1?

    A. Presenting students with the results of both studies increased group polarization

    B. Presenting students with the results of both studies decreased group polarization

    C. After reading the results of the prodeterrent study, opponents became more opposed to capital punishment

    D. Proponents' attitudes towards capital punishment remained unchanged after reading the results of the prodeterrent study.

5. The tendency to seek evidence and reach conclusions that are consistent with our existing beliefs is known as:

    A. informal reasoning.

    B. representativeness heuristic.

    C. confirmation bias.

    D. availability heuristic.

6. In addition to assessing mean attitude scores for the proponent and opponent group, the researchers wanted to calculate the average difference between each score and the mean of the group. This statistic is known as:

    A. Range

    B. Median

    C. Standard deviation

    D. Variance

Passage 10 (Questions 1-6)

Even though racism has acquired a negative social stigma in America, researchers suggest that racism against blacks continues to exist in today's society. Surveys show that over 50% of blacks report encountering racism in the workplace, as well as while participating in public activities, such as shopping. Based on recent research, it appears that society condemns the *idea* of racism more than the racist act itself. Aversive racism theory posits that individuals with egalitarian beliefs (they believe all people are equal) subconsciously have a negative attitude towards blacks when they interact with them. Though most people think that they would take a stand against racism should they witness a racist act, individuals often overestimate the level of offense they would feel towards racism in the moment.

Wanting to study how people from a non-target group (any race other than black) react to racism against blacks (the target group), researchers designed a study and recruited 200 participants, who were randomly assigned to be the "forecaster" or the "experiencer" in the study. The forecasters were the participants who indirectly witnessed a racist act occur and predicted how they would react to it; the experiencers were the participants who directly witnessed the racist act. Researchers hypothesized that forecasters would exaggerate their predicted responses to the racist act compared to the actual responses of the experiencers.

Participants in the "experiencer" group were individually led into a room by a researcher, and introduced to one black and one white male who pretended to be other participants in the study, but were actually confederates. When the researcher left, the black "participant" bumps into the white "participant" on his way to use the restroom. Each experiencer was randomly assigned to one of three comment conditions: (1) no racist comment from the white man, (2) a moderately racist comment from the white man (i.e. a generalized comment about "black people"), and (3) an extremely racist comment from the white man (i.e. a specific racial slur and insult). Once the black male returned to the room, the researcher entered and instructed everyone to complete a short survey that assessed how they were currently feeling on a scale from 1-10 (1 being scaled as low emotional distress and 10 being scaled as severe emotional distress). The researcher then asked the experiencer to choose between the two males as a partner for the experiment. Meanwhile, participants assigned as "forecasters" watched video footage of one of the three comment condition situations, completed the same emotional distress survey, and privately choose which of the two males they would have chosen as partners. The results of this study are shown in Figure 1 and Figure 2.

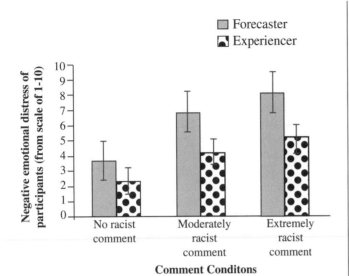

Figure 1 Self-reported emotional distress of forecasters and experiencers on a scale of 1 to 10

Comment Conditions	White partners chosen (in percentage)	
	Forecaster	Experiencer
No racist comment	75%	55%
Moderately racist comment	29%	68%
Extremely racist comment	8%	77%

Figure 2 Percentage of forecasters and experiencers who chose white partners during the study

Adapted from K. Kawakami, E. Dunn, F. Karmali, and J. Dovidio. Mispredicting affective and behavioral responses to racism. © 2009 by *American Association for the Advancement of Science*

1. Suppose that a group of people watch gang members brutally beat an individual in public because of his race; the witnesses do not do anything to stop them. This scenario most accurately portrays:

    A. social loafing.
    B. the bystander effect.
    C. peer pressure.
    D. attribution theory.

2. Aversive racism theory can also be described as an individual showing:

    A. discrimination against the out-group.
    B. prejudice against the out-group.
    C. ethnocentrism against the out-group.
    D. cultural relativism against the out-group.

3. Researchers conducted a second part of this experiment where participants were asked to fill out a survey to assess their views about an out-group; the results showed that some participants valued egalitarianism, while other participants valued elitism (they believe that certain groups should have more power over others). Participants were put into small groups and asked to discuss a series of social issues and come up with a resolution to each issue. At first, the participants shared their own opinions about the issues; however, as the participants continued to interact, researchers observed that all of the unanimous decisions revolved around an elitist point of view, especially when one of the elitist participants fulfilled the role as the leader of the group. On a follow-up survey, participants who valued egalitarianism explained that even though they did not agree with the resolution, they valued the group's uniformity rather than their own opinions about the matter and wanted to avoid "rocking the boat." Which of the following concepts most accurately describes why this is occurring?

    A. Group polarization
    B. Social facilitation
    C. Groupthink
    D. Social exclusion

4. Based on the study mentioned in the passage, which of the following groups would researchers most likely avoid choosing as experiencers and forecasters for the experiment?

    A. Black participants because they are considered the target population for the experiment.
    B. White participants because they are more likely to choose the white "participant" over the black "participant."
    C. Older participants because their generation considers racism against blacks to be more socially acceptable.
    D. Younger participants because their generation is less tolerant of racism against blacks.

5. Which of the following most accurately demonstrates the relationship between the severity of the racial comment and the percentage of white partners portrayed in Figure 2?

A.

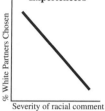

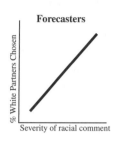

B.

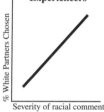

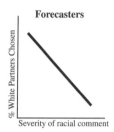

C.

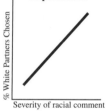

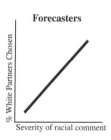

D.

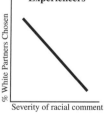

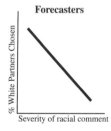

6. What can be concluded based on Figure 1 and Figure 2?

    I.   The results support the hypothesis of the study.
    II. Between forecasters and experiencers, there is a wider gap in the percentage of white partners in the moderately racist comment compared to the percentage of white partners in the no racist comment.
    III. Figure 1 demonstrates that experiencers and forecasters have a negative correlation between negative emotional distress of participants and the degree of severity of the racial comment.

    A. I and II only
    B. I and III only
    C. II and III only
    D. I, II, and III

Passage 11 (Questions 1-6)

In 1921, Carl Gustav Jung published his highly influential book *Personality Types*. A foundation for Jung's theory of personality is the distinction between introverts and extraverts. Somewhat different from the popular understanding of the two terms as shyness or social outgoingness, Jung defined extraverts as people who have a predominant orientation towards objectivity and objective environmental factors (e.g., friends, wealth, and possessions) in contrast to introverts, whom he saw as orientated towards subjectivity and subjective factors within the self (e.g., one's moods, thoughts, and feelings).

In addition to the primary categorizations of introversion vs. extraversion, Jung defined four subtypes: thinking, feeling, sensation, and intuition. This set up three dichotomies: introversion/extraversion, thinking/feeling, and sensation/intuition. In addition to being either introverted or extraverted, each individual could display one of the four subtypes as their dominant orienting function and one as an auxiliary, or complementary, type. In Jung's view, certain dominant subtypes tended to pair well within an individual with corresponding auxiliary types, such that intuition usually complemented thinking and sensation usually paired with feeling. Thus a typical personality within Jung's typology would be Introverted Thinking Intuitive. Jung believed that personality type was innate, but that certain individuals became pressured through external sources or psychic illness to assume a different type, to the detriment of their psychological well-being. Table 1 shows each of the four subtypes with a brief description.

Later in the 20th century, Hans Eysenck made lasting contributions to the theory of personality and subdivision of traits. Eysenck extended many of Jung's ideas, including the distinction between introversion and extraversion. He helped develop reliable psychometric instruments to measure these traits, and his findings contributed to the Five-Factor Model of Personality, developed by Paul Costa and Robert McCrea in 1985.

Thinking	Feeling	Sensation	Intuition
Uses logical analysis to orient towards the subject or object. Concerned primarily with cause and effect and formulating descriptive schema using rationality.	Uses emotional valence to orient towards the subject or object. Concerned primarily with the circumstantial impact of the internal and external environment on moods and feelings.	Uses the senses as the primary orienting function. Concerned with ephemeral qualities of the environment and the ongoing affirmation of existence through the natural senses.	Uses an understanding of the potentialities of a situation and an object's dynamic flux as the orienting function. In lieu of current realities, concerned primarily with past and future possibilities.

Table 1 Description of four Jungian personality types

1. Which of the following scenarios best describes an individual who scores very high on the personality trait for openness to experience?

   A. A patient diagnosed with a rare autoimmune disease does not trust his doctor and seeks multiple second opinions.
   B. A young physical therapy patient works very hard on her daily exercises and is diligent to comply carefully with her doctor's and physical therapist's orders.
   C. A patient diagnosed with a rare form of cancer volunteers to try a new experimental procedure that has never been tested on humans.
   D. An older physician refuses to try the newer treatment protocols, despite the fact that they have been producing much better results.

2. A patient enters a medical clinic hoping to receive treatment for an unspecified physical ailment. However, the patient is hostile to many of the diagnostic methods used and becomes irritable when asked to answer personal health questions. Which factor would this patient most likely score highly on?

   A. Extraversion
   B. Agreeableness
   C. Conscientiousness
   D. Neuroticism

3. A psychometric evaluation of Jung's typology asks individuals to rate their agreement to the following statement: When solving a problem you consider the rational approach the best. Which Jungian dichotomy is this question most likely evaluating?

   A. Introversion/Extraversion
   B. Thinking/Feeling
   C. Thinking/Intuition
   D. Judging/Perceiving

4. Introverts often score lower on psychometric evaluations of happiness. Based on Jung's personality theory, which of the following could explain this discrepancy?

   A. Introverts are also more likely to display neuroticism and become anxious more easily.
   B. Extraverts are more social and outgoing and therefore report more positive experiences.
   C. Society often places high value on extraverted traits, leading many innate introverts to assume extraverted characteristics.
   D. Introverts lack openness to experience and willingness to try new things.

5. Studies show that higher scores in neuroticism are associated with structural changes in the gray matter of the amygdala. Based on the functional anatomy of the amygdala, which of the following could help explain the correlation between neuroticism and the amygdala?

   A. The amygdala's control of emotion regulation could lead to less emotional stability.
   B. The amygdala's role in fear responses could lead to greater anxiety.
   C. The amygdala's role in releasing serotonin could reduce positive moods.
   D. The amygdala's relaying of superego function could encourage self-pitying.

6. Jung believed that individuals of opposing types, in spite of their different psychological mechanisms for making sense of the world, tended to marry and cohabit. However, many others theorize the opposite is true. Which of the following characteristics have been demonstrated to foster human attraction?

   I. Similarity
   II. Proximity
   III. Appearance

   A. I and II only
   B. I and III only
   C. II and III only
   D. I, II, and III

Passage 12 (Questions 1-6)

In one study on motivation, researchers used chocolate as a sensory stimulus to determine what specific parts of the brain are associated with motivation to eat chocolate. They compared brain activity, motivation, and pleasure in a pool of twenty-eight young adults between the ages of 18 and 35. Based on the theory that a desire increases if it is not satisfied and that the same desire decreases when fulfilled, subjects ate pieces of chocolate to beyond satisfaction (or past the point at which the subjects wanted more chocolate). Prior studies found that eating five chocolate pieces within 30 minutes was the average amount required to reach satiety. The study subjects were fed nine pieces of chocolate within a 30-minute timeframe. They then rated the reward value and motivation to eat after each piece on an affective rating scale from –5 to 5, with 5 being delicious (the most pleasant) and wanting another piece (the most motivated) and –5 being awful (the least pleasant) and feeling sick if they had another piece (the least motivated). After each piece of chocolate, an H215O-PET scan was also performed to measure activity in different parts of the brain.

The subjects were instructed to keep eating chocolate until they reached nine pieces, even if they were no longer motivated to eat another piece before reaching nine pieces. Because subjects were instructed to eat beyond their satisfaction (0 on the motivation affective liking scale), eating chocolate was no longer enjoyable and the reward value (based off the pleasantness affective rating scale) turns into a punishment. The same act of chocolate consumption is first rewarding and then later punishing to the subject. Figure 1 displays the average affective liking ratings subjects gave after each chocolate condition.

Using the results of the affective rating scales described above, the researchers established a relationship between each subject's rating of motivation and pleasantness and their brain activity (measured using the $H_2^{15}O$-PET scans). A regression of the $H_2^{15}O$-PET scans with the affective liking rating results showed that one part of the brain was responsible for motivation when subjects experienced high motivation/pleasantness (a rewarding experience) and another part of the brain was responsible for motivation when subjects experienced low motivation/pleasantness (a punishing experience).

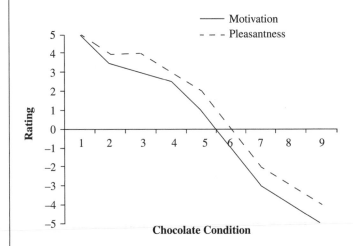

Figure 1 Average affective liking ratings across nine chocolate conditions

Adapted from D. M. Small, R. J. Zatorre, A. Dagher, A. C. Evans, and M. Jones-Gotman. Changes in brain activity related to eating chocolate. © 2001 by *Brain* and M. R. Lepper, D. Greene, and R. Nisbet. Undermining children's intrinsic interest with extrinsic reward; A test of overjustification hypothesis. © 1973 by *Journal of Personality and Social Psychology*

1. What is an example of extrinsic motivation?

    A. A student wanting to receive a high grade in class.
    B. A student wanting to learn more about a topic covered in class because they are interested in the topic.
    C. A student joining the soccer team because they find it enjoyable.
    D. A student determined to finish a puzzle because they find the challenge engaging and fun.

2. Assuming that the slopes of the solid line (motivation) and the dotted line (pleasantness) are the same, what does Figure 1 indicate?

    I. Motivation causes pleasantness.
    II. Pleasantness causes motivation.
    III. There is a correlation between motivation and pleasantness.

    A. I only
    B. III only
    C. I and II only
    D. I, II, and III

3. The results of the study described in the passage best support which hypothesis?

   A. There are two separate motivational systems in the brain: one coordinates extrinsic motivations and the other intrinsic motivations.
   B. There are two separate motivational systems in the brain: one coordinates conscious behaviors and the other unconscious behaviors.
   C. There are two separate motivational systems in the brain: one coordinates approach behaviors and the other avoidance behaviors.
   D. There is only one motivational system in the brain that controls all behaviors.

4. In the study described in the passage, which of the following accurately describes the variables?

   A. Independent variable: amount of chocolate consumed; dependent variables: activity of brain, affective liking for both satisfaction and reward value
   B. Independent variables: amount of chocolate consumed and brain activity measured by the $H_2^{15}O$-PET scan; dependent variables: affective liking for both satisfaction and reward value
   C. Independent variable: brain activity on $H_2^{15}O$-PET scan; dependent variables: amount of chocolate consumed, affective liking for both satisfaction and reward value
   D. Independent variable: affective liking rating for both satisfaction and reward value; dependent variable: amount of chocolate consumed

5. What is the region of the brain responsible for motivation?

   A. Parietal lobe
   B. Orbitofrontal cortex
   C. Occipital lobe
   D. Temporal lobe

6. What theory is the study described in this passage based on?

   A. Drive-reduction theory
   B. Self-determination theory
   C. Attribution theory
   D. Cognitive dissonance theory

Passage 13 (Questions 1-6)

In 2013, the *Diagnostic and Statistical Manual of Mental Disorders* published its most recent edition, abbreviated DSM-5. The DSM-5 included numerous new classifications and disorders, including hoarding disorder (HD). HD involves three components: (1) excessive collection of items as a result of excessive acquisition and/or the failure or inability to discard items, regardless of their true value; (2) subsequent disturbance of the living space as a result of the items; and (3) subsequent distress or problems as a result of the items.

Excessive hoarding behavior can cause harmful effects for both the individual and their support system, including emotional, physical, social, financial, and legal issues. Thus, a "clean out" is not enough for the treatment of HD, although professional cleaners can assist in the recovery process. Reasons for hoarding often include beliefs that individual items are useful, sentimental, or irreplaceable, leading to high levels of anxiety and/or stress upon attempts to decrease the amount of one's possessions.

It is estimated that 1.2 million people in the United States, and up to 5% of the world's population, suffer from HD. Research has revealed trends in hoarding by age, gender, income, and other demographic characteristics. Hoarding behaviors begin early, between 11-20 years of age, and appear to be a lifelong struggle. However, the disorder becomes more prominent after age 40, and the average age for those seeking treatment is 50. HD appears to be more common among women, who constitute 78% of sufferers. Figure 1 demonstrates income characteristics of those suffering from HD.

Income	Incidence
< $15,000	33.6%
$15,000-30,000	23.2%
$30,000-45,000	10.6%
$45,000-60,000	13.7%
$60,000-75,000	5.2%
> $75,000	13.7%

Figure 1 Income of diagnosed hoarders in the U.S.

Research on hoarding behaviors has called for potential sociological explanations, which has lead to an evaluation of consumer culture. Consumerism is a social and economic order that encourages the consumption of goods and services and, thus, the accumulation of possessions. While consumerism is a relatively new social invention resulting from the rise of the capitalist economy, media culture has presented consumerism as natural, making the issue of hoarding relevant to current times. Although consumption is an individual behavior, social factors influence the action. In a consumer culture, an individual's possessions are a measure of their social position; consumption is a means of obtaining happiness and acceptance in society. Hoarding, then, can be viewed as an extreme form of consumption, a process otherwise viewed as a social norm. Finally, it has been suggested that social factors, such as isolation, socioeconomic status, and the aging process, can influence hoarding behavior.

1. A cognitive behavioral therapy approach to HD would include:

    A. a thorough analysis of an individual's past childhood traumas.
    B. reprogramming behaviors with conditioning.
    C. a restructuring of thought patterns and tools to engage in less acquisitive behaviors.
    D. an approach that allows the individual with HD to self-actualize through an empathetic relationship with her or his therapist.

2. If researchers at the National Institutes for Health were to design a study on hoarding disorder, which of the following hypothesis would NOT be supported by the passage?

    A. Diagnosis of HD will be more common among adults than children.
    B. Prevalence of HD will be directly inversely proportional to income level.
    C. Participants with HD will have more possessions than the average surveyed American.
    D. HD will be more common among participants of the lowest income bracket.

3. New research suggests that the brain activity of individuals with HD and individuals with OCD is quite different. What sort of brain scan would be used to observe the brain activity of individuals with HD and OCD while trying to make decisions?

    A. a PET scan
    B. MRI
    C. a CT scan
    D. X-ray

4. Decluttering as a result of the interventions by third parties might cause an increase in:

    A. sympathetic nervous system functioning and an increase in glucocorticoid levels.
    B. sympathetic nervous system functioning and a decrease in glucocorticoid levels.
    C. parasympathetic nervous system functioning and an increase in glucocorticoid levels.
    D. parasympathetic nervous system functioning and a decrease in glucocorticoid levels.

5. Hoarding disorder, as a mental illness, can be studied as a form of social deviance. Which of the following correctly pairs the sociological theory with its potential evaluation of hoarding disorder?

    I.   Functionalist theory; including HD in DSM-5 reinforces social order through the definition of socially acceptable behavior and consumerism.
    II. Conflict theory; HD is expected to be more common among those with less access to social resources, including medical interventions.
    III. Symbolic interaction theory; HD, like many categories of mental illness, is likely the result of biological abnormalities.

    A. I only
    B. I and II only
    C. II and III only
    D. I, II, and III

6. There is a growing awareness of hoarding disorder as the result of recent media exposure. Three proposed causes of clinical hoarding are family, evolution, and genetics. Research indicates that 50% of hoarders were raised by a family member with hoarding behaviors. These family members can be defined as:

    A. primary group members.
    B. secondary group members.
    C. out-group members.
    D. reference group members.

Passage 14 (Questions 1-6)

Schizophrenia is one of the most pervasive psychopathological disorders, with over 2 million patients diagnosed in the United States, as well as an additional 2 million new cases diagnosed annually around the world. Most cases are chronic and characterized by both positive symptoms and negative symptoms. Current literature suggests that both genetic and environmental factors contribute to the etiology of schizophrenia, making the disorder a prime example of a multifactorial condition. Genetic risk factors for schizophrenia have been measured broadly through twin studies and the identification of specific gene loci is a continuing area of interest in research. Two important environmental variables that have been linked to schizophrenia are urbanicity and cannabis abuse.

Urbanicity represents the extent to which an individual's development took place in an urban setting. While plenty of variables contribute to this quality, most analyses point to social "fragmentation" as the primary driver for relative risk of psychotic outcomes. Defined broadly as an indicator of social maladjustment among individuals or within a community, social fragmentation is characterized by the breakdown of social institutions that comprise the basis for cohesion within a group. For example, some of the variables that have been measured include single parent family status, residential instability, and illicit drug use—all of which tend to be more common in urban areas. Intriguingly, longitudinal studies have found that moving from an urban to a rural environment in childhood brings about a corresponding decrease in risk for psychotic outcomes.

Studies show that delta-9-tetrahydrocannabinol IV, the main psychotropic component of cannabis, causes psychotic symptoms in healthy volunteers while also increasing the severity of symptoms in psychiatric patients, including those diagnosed with schizophrenia. The association between cannabis use and psychotic outcomes has been demonstrated in cognitive performance measures, neuroanatomic phenotypes, as well as subclinical behavioral expression. Of potentially primary importance are the independent conclusions that both schizophrenia and cannabis use are associated with decreased cortical thickness in the brain. These findings suggest that decreased cortical thickness may provide a neuroanatomic explanation for the cognitive deficits observed in schizophrenia patients and cannabis users.

Various studies have compared individuals who possess genotypes that are believed to be consistent with an increased risk for psychotic disorder (group G+) to those who lack a genetic profile for increased risk (group G–). Figures 1-4 demonstrate the results from several such studies that provide evidence for possible interactions between genetically predisposing factors and the environmental variables considered here (urbanicity and cannabis abuse).

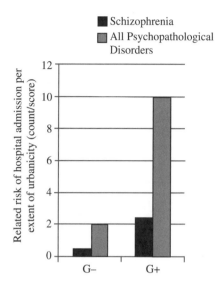

Figure 1 Related risk of urbanicity on hospital admission for schizophrenia compared to all other psychopathological disorders

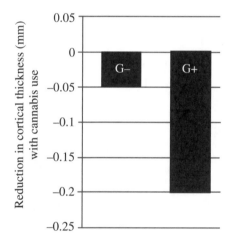

Figure 2 Effect of cannabis use on reduction in cortical thickness

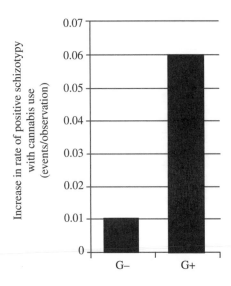

Figure 3 Effect of cannabis use on positive symptomatology in schizophrenia

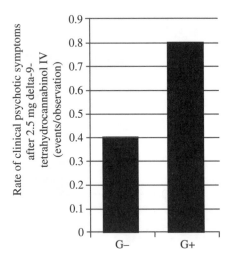

Figure 4 Rate of psychotic symptoms with cannabis use

Adapted from J. van Os, G. Kenis, B.P.F. Rutten in Nature.
© 2010 Macmillan Publishers Limited

1. Which of the following is the best definition for a positive symptom and negative symptom of schizophrenia, respectively?

   A. Positive symptoms are neither normally experienced by healthy individuals nor present in the disorder; negative symptoms are normally experienced by healthy individuals and diminished or absent in affected individuals.
   B. Negative symptoms are neither normally experienced by healthy individuals nor present in the disorder; positive symptoms are normally experienced by healthy individuals and diminished or absent in affected individuals.
   C. Negative symptoms are not normally experienced by healthy individuals but are present in the disorder; positive symptoms are normally experienced by healthy individuals but are diminished or absent in affected individuals.
   D. Positive symptoms are not normally experienced by healthy individuals but are present in the disorder; negative symptoms describe a diminished or absent normal emotion or behavior.

2. Based on the information provided in the passage, which of the following sets of conditions would we expect to most minimize the risk of psychotic outcomes?

   I. Moving to an urban setting during childhood
   II. Being born and raised in a rural setting
   III. Avoiding cannabis use

   A. I only
   B. III only
   C. I and III only
   D. II and III only

3. Which of the Figures most strongly supports the statement that there are interactions between environmental and genetic variables in psychopathology?

   A. Figure 1
   B. Figure 2
   C. Figure 3
   D. Figure 4

4. A large prospective cohort study is conducted in which cognitive performance is assessed for patients diagnosed with schizophrenia as well as their healthy siblings. Which of the following statements would most likely be true about the results of this study?

A. Non-twin male siblings of schizophrenics would exhibit diminished cognitive function with respect to female siblings.
B. Non-twin female siblings of schizophrenics would exhibit diminished cognitive function with respect to male siblings.
C. Monozygotic twin siblings of schizophrenics would exhibit enhanced cognitive function with respect to dizygotic twins.
D. Dizygotic twin siblings of schizophrenics would exhibit enhanced cognitive function with respect to monozygotic twins.

5. Which of the following can be most reasonably concluded?

A. Genetic factors appear to have a greater effect on related risk due to urbanicity for all psychopathological disorders rather than for schizophrenia only (Figure 1)
B. Cannabis abuse reduces cortical thickness in individuals with increased genetic risk only (Figure 2)
C. The increase in rate of symptoms of schizophrenia due to cannabis use is positive for both low- and high-risk groups (Figure 3)
D. The rate of clinical psychotic symptoms in the high-risk group was twice that of the low-risk group (Figure 4)

6. According to the information provided in the passage, all of the following statements are true, EXCEPT:

A. community building may help mitigate the development of psychopathology.
B. the results of this study demonstrate that social fragmentation and urbanicity have a strong, direct correlation.
C. growing up in a rural area decreases risk for psychotic outcomes.
D. cannabis abuse can induce psychotic symptoms in healthy individuals.

Passage 15 (Questions 1-6)

A number of studies have indicated that insomnia and depression are often concurrent. However, ascertaining which disorder arises first is difficult due to the nature of the disorders: it is unethical and unfeasible to deprive healthy subjects of sleep, and then assess depression. Consequently, many studies have focused on observational epidemiology and retrospective studies, but these approaches have limitations.

For example, one study of men and women between 20 and 90 years of age assessed self-reported measures of health, difficulty falling asleep (sleep onset insomnia), difficulty staying asleep (sleep maintenance insomnia), depression, and anxiety. People with combined insomnia (both onset and maintenance insomnia) were more likely to have clinically significant depression than did people with only onset or maintenance insomnia, and were 13.58 times as likely to have clinically significant depression as people without insomnia. African Americans were 4.2 times more likely to have clinically significant depression than Caucasians, and women were more likely to be clinically depressed than were men (Figure 1).

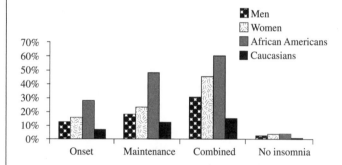

Figure 1 Percentage of respondents with clinically significant depression

In a separate Epidemiologic Catchment Area study (a survey of samples of the general population at five sites across America) of participants interviewed at baseline and 1 year later about sleep complaints and psychiatric symptoms, 13% and 5% noted insomnia and hypersomnia (excessive daytime sleepiness), respectively, at the first interview. Forty-two percent of those with insomnia and 51% of those with hypersomnia had a psychiatric disorder compared with 17% of those with no sleep complaints. The risk of developing new major depression was much higher in those who had insomnia at both interviews compared with those without insomnia, while the risk of developing new major depression was much less for those who had insomnia that had resolved by the second visit.

The data from these studies conforms to others that support the idea that insomnia may be causing or exacerbating depression. Because insomnia in these studies is a quasi-independent variable (the researchers are not controlling insomnia status), it is hard to be sure that some other factor was not instigating both conditions.

Adapted from Depression and sleep. © 2013 by *National Sleep Foundation;* R. Benca & M. Peterson. Insomnia and depression. © 2008 by *Sleep* Medicine; D. Taylor. Insomnia and Depression. © 2008 by *Sleep*; H. Morphy, K. Dunn, M. Lewis, H. Boardman, & P. Croft. Epidemiology of insomnia: a longitudinal study in a UK population. © 2007 by *Sleep*; and D. E. Ford & D. B. Kamerow. Epidemiologic study of sleep disturbances and psychiatric disorders. An opportunity for prevention? © 1989 by *Journal of the American Medical Association*

1. Which of the following is true regarding sleep?

    A. Sleep disorders do not develop until puberty or later.
    B. Sleep onset is linked to falling melatonin levels.
    C. Periods of slow-wave deep sleep are shortest right after sleep onset and longest just before waking.
    D. The duration of total sleep and proportion of REM sleep both decrease gradually throughout one's lifetime from infancy to old age.

2. According to Figure 1, which respondents would be LEAST likely to have depression concurrent with a sleep disorder?

    A. African-American men
    B. African-American women
    C. Caucasian men
    D. Caucasian women

3. Suppose that, in the first study, participants with insomnia in the control group completed certain basic tasks at their initial interview and then completed the same task at the second interview. Comparing their performance on the task at each testing session would show evidence of the task's:

    A. reliability.
    B. homogeneity.
    C. standardization.
    D. validity.

4. Which of the following is NOT true regarding depression?

    A. Depression is a mood disorder
    B. Symptoms mimicking clinical depression can be caused by alcohol or drug withdrawal
    C. Clinical depression is more common in men than in women
    D. Major depressive disorder is characterized by at least one major depressive episode lasting at least two weeks, as well as some or all of the following: depressed mood or decreased interest in activities, significant increase or decrease in weight or appetite, excessive or insufficient sleep, speeded or slowed psychomotor activity, fatigue or loss of energy, feelings of low self-worth or guilt, impaired concentration or decision-making, and thoughts of death or suicide

5. If the second study were modified to investigate the correlations between insomnia and changes in participants' cognitive functioning and incidence of increased risk for developing depression, how would this change the design of the study?

    A. A new independent variable would be added
    B. A new dependent variable would be added
    C. All the variables would be quasi-independent
    D. The study would become a cross-sectional study

6. Insomnia:

    I.   causes an overall reduction in REM sleep.
    II. are part of the broader category of sleep disorders called parasomnias.
    III. is also a common symptom of generalized anxiety disorder.

    A. I only
    B. I and III only
    C. II and III only
    D. I, II, and III

Passage 16 (Questions 1-7)

Albert Bandura's social learning theory (SLT) encompasses several cognitive constructs that reflect a bold departure from the highly mechanistic classical and instrumental learning models of Pavlov and Hull. One of the key features of Bandura's theory was the notion of self-efficacy, which has been the subject of much research. In the field of educational psychology, some researchers have explored how the notion of self-efficacy can be applied to the achievement of greater academic outcomes. One approach that may contribute towards enhancing students' self-efficacy is the implementation of social-emotional learning (SEL) programs. These comprehensive, school-based programs incorporate sets of values and practices that reflect the fundamental attitude that social and emotional skills are as important as academic skills. The *Responsive Classroom* (RC) is an example of an SEL program, and, as part of its social-emotional repertoire, it features an emphasis of mastery rather than performance. In other words, the application of effort is itself considered an academic success, regardless of the performance outcome. The program includes principles such as, "How children learn is as important as what they learn," and "The greatest cognitive growth occurs through social interaction."

In light of evidence suggesting that student performance during the middle school years has long term consequences for future academic opportunities and success, one group of researchers examined how the RC approach impacts the dynamic between anxiety and self-efficacy in sixth grade math and science students. Part of the theoretical basis for their investigation was the assertion that students interpret their anxiety about math and science as evidence of their inability to succeed in those subjects. Accordingly, they were interested in understanding how RC practices may affect that process. For this study 26 elementary schools in the state of Florida were included; 14 of those schools were already employing the RC approach, and the 12 that were not comprised the control group.

To determine the quality of RC practices in the RC schools, and to account for unofficial RC practices in the control group schools, all teachers in both groups were given the Responsive Classroom Adherence Probe (R-CAP), which is a 30-item questionnaire about RC principles and practices. Students' anxiety was assessed with the School Anxiety Scale (SAS), which presents students with ten statements regarding anxiety symptoms and behaviors. Similarly, all students completed the Self-Efficacy Assessment Tool for Students (SEATS), which presented students with 12 statements relating to self-efficacy.

The researchers split the schools into low and high RC groups by using the mean of scores falling below and above the quartiles of the score distribution. Students' anxiety levels were divided into low, medium and high based on whether they fell below the lower quartile, within the interquartile range, or above the upper quartile. Mean self-efficacy scores for both math and science were calculated for each group of students falling into each of those categories. The integration of RC quality, students' anxiety, and students' self-efficacy were plotted to clarify the impact of RC practices on the anxiety/self-efficacy dynamic. These data appear in Figure 1. In addition to this primary question, the researchers also sought to learn if, after controlling for anxiety, RC practices predict higher self-efficacy in math and science. Accordingly, mean self-efficacy scores were calculated for all students in each RC group after accounting for anxiety as a covariate. These data appear in Figure 2.

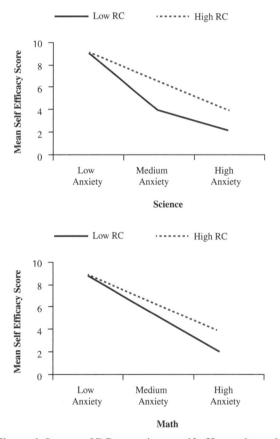

Figure 1 Impact of RC on anxiety – self-efficacy dynamic

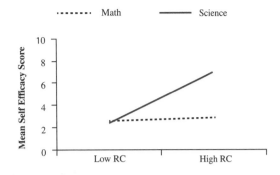

Figure 2 Association between different levels of RC
and math and science self-efficacy scores

Adapted from M. S. Griggs, S. E. Rimm-Kaufman, E. G. Merritt, &
C. L. Patton. The Responsive Classroom Approach and Fifth Grade
Students' Math and Science Anxiety and Self-Efficacy. © 2013 by
School Psychology Quarterly

1. According to the researcher's model:

   A. low self-efficacy causes unwarranted anxiety.
   B. particular appraisals of physiological stress lead
      to less persistence in math and science.
   C. deficits in the superego undermine self-efficacy.
   D. environment has little impact on children's learning.

2. Which of the following serves as a reasonable explanation
   for the data in Figure 2?

   A. The concrete operational nature of science activities
      allows students to demonstrate observable effort
      more easily than the more formal operational
      problem solving required by math word problems.
   B. The concrete operational nature of abstract math
      problems allows students to demonstrate effort more
      easily than the more formal operational nature of
      science activities.
   C. The concrete operational nature of science activities
      makes it easier for students to earn higher grades
      than to demonstrate actual effort.
   D. Math requires less sensorimotor intelligence than
      physics.

3. To ensure that teachers' impression management does not
   compromise the construct validity of the R-CAP, it would
   be critical that:

   A. R-CAPs earn consistently similar scores by multiple
      teachers who employ similar classroom practices.
   B. teachers are observed by the principal without prior
      notice.
   C. teachers' identities remain confidential.
   D. R-CAP items accurately reflect the principles and
      practices of the *Responsive Classroom* program.

4. Which of the following conclusions can be drawn from
   the results depicted in Figure 1?

   A. In schools with high RC programs, students' science
      anxiety is less than that of students in schools with
      low RC programs.
   B. In schools with high RC programs, students' anxiety
      has a more detrimental effect on math self efficacy
      than in schools with low RC programs.
   C. In schools with high RC programs, students' anxiety
      has a less detrimental effect on science self efficacy
      in than in schools with low RC programs.
   D. In schools with high RC programs, increasing levels
      of anxiety are not associated with decreased self
      efficacy.

5. The shift in focus from performance to mastery as
   described in the passage allows students to:

   A. emphasize academics over social learning.
   B. avoid the consequences of reciprocal determinism.
   C. develop an external locus of control rather than
      internal locus of control.
   D. develop an internal locus of control rather than
      external locus of control.

6. Which of the following RC practices is most relevant to the Sapir-Whorf hypothesis?

   A. Collaborative problem solving (strategies for peaceful conflict resolution)
   B. Positive teacher language (teachers use words that express warmth and support)
   C. Academic choice (opportunities are provided for students to focus on topics of their own interest)
   D. Working with families (guidelines for collaborating with students' parents or guardians)

7. Suppose a school calculated the mean score earned by the sixth grade girls on their most recent math exam to be 75 out of 100. Based on the results, teachers determined that the typical fifth grade girl possesses mediocre math ability. If a histogram of the actual scores was constructed and the distribution was negatively skewed, it would seem that:

   A. the sixth grade girls' achieved status surpasses their ascribed status.
   B. the sixth grade girls' achieved status falls sharply below their ascribed status.
   C. the sixth grade girls' achieved status is highly consistent with their ascribed status.
   D. the sixth grade girls performance is likely to have severely negative consequences on their self efficacy level.

Passage 17 (Questions 1-6)

BF Skinner invented the operant conditioning chamber (now called the "Skinner Box"), in order to conduct animal research on the principles of reward, punishment and behavior. The box contained lights, a loudspeaker, and a food dispenser. In addition, the animal in the box had access to a response lever, which Skinner used to test how animals responded under different reinforcement schedules. Skinner was interested in four types of reinforcement schedules: variable ratio, fixed ratio, variable interval, and fixed interval (Table 1). From various experiments, Skinner found specific response patterns for the four different reinforcement schedules.

	Fixed	Variable
Ratio	Reinforcement presented after a fixed number of responses (e.g. food released for every 10 responses)	Reinforcement presented after a variable number of responses (e.g. food released after a randomly varying number of responses from 3-20)
Interval	Reinforcement presented after a fixed Interval period of time (e.g. food released every 3 minutes)	Reinforcement presented after a variable period of time (e.g. food released after a randomly varying period of time from 5-15 minutes)

Table 1 Skinner's four reinforcement schedules

Skinner became interested in responses during fixed intervals, since the presentation of reinforcement under this schedule did not depend on the behavior of the animals in the Skinner Box. In a study with pigeons, Skinner found what he saw as an animal correlate of human superstitious behavior. Namely, even though presentation of food did not depend on the pigeons' behavior, they nevertheless developed responses that they repeated in hope of gaining access to food. One pigeon even consistently turned three times counterclockwise, even though food dispensation occurred on a fixed schedule. Even after the behavior was extinguished, reconditioning of the idiosyncratic response (such as turning) occurred on a fixed interval reinforcement schedule.

Adapted from B. F. Skinner. Superstition in the pigeon. © 1948 *Journal of Experimental Psychology*

1. Part of Skinner's experimental method was to starve the pigeons until they reached less than 90% of their healthy weight. Which theory best explains why the starved pigeons would be very motivated to engage in behavior that might lead to the presentation of food?

   A. Drive-reduction theory
   B. Conflict theory
   C. James-Lange theory
   D. Cannon-Bard theory

2. How would the superstitious behavior of turning in a circle described in the second paragraph become extinguished?

   A. If a shock was administered every time the target behavior occurred
   B. If a timed reinforcement of an alternate behavior (like sitting still) was applied
   C. Food dispersal ceased until the pigeon stopped exhibiting the target behavior
   D. The environment was shifted and the length of time between reinforcements was increased

   [handwritten: extinction = absence of reinforcement]

3. Which of the following brain regions is most directly involved with a pigeon's ability to respond to new reinforcement schedules?

   A. Pons
   B. Hypothalamus
   C. Thalamus
   D. Hippocampus

4. There was a lag in responses by pigeons in the Skinner box because they:

   A. were on a variable schedule of reinforcement and could not predict when the next reinforcement would come.
   B. were on a fixed schedule of reinforcement and could predict when the next reinforcement would come.
   C. were on a fixed schedule of reinforcement and could not predict when the next reinforcement would come.
   D. were on a variable schedule of reinforcement and could predict when the next reinforcement would come.

5. What would Skinner have most likely said contributes to the human phenomenon of superstition?

   A. A period of regression to childish beliefs results from failure to confront psychogenic conflicts.
   B. A lack of resources and education due to poverty causes unscientific beliefs to persist.
   C. A correct guess is reinforced from time to time by chance, and the individual continues to misattribute cause.
   D. Through observation of an individual's social network, the person takes on the idiosyncratic beliefs of others.

6. What type of behavior is most commonly observed when organisms are rewarded on a fixed ratio schedule?

   A. Superstitious behavior
   B. Procrastination; the organism is very slow to respond just after receiving the reward, and then responds quickly to get the next reward
   C. Slow, steady, and consistent rate of response
   D. Behavior is very slow to extinguish and will persist for a very long time even after the reward is no longer given.

Passage 18 (Questions 1-6)

Researchers have long studied the causes of memory loss and damage. Traumatic brain injury occurs when a part of the brain has been damaged through an accident of some kind; this could include a concussion caused by blunt trauma to the skull, or a stroke caused by a blocked artery which results in a lack of blood flow to a localized part of the brain. In contrast, in some diseases of the brain there is a diffuse breakdown of cells, neurons, and/or connections throughout the entire brain, such as is the case in Alzheimer's disease. However, whether the cause of the memory loss is biological or accidental, a group of researchers are attempting to take the treatment of memory loss into the technological age.

This group of researchers from universities and research facilities around the United States are getting close to developing a device that could be implanted into the brain to assist in the conversion of short-term memories into long-term memories. This implant would be placed near the hippocampus, and could one day allow individuals with certain types of brain damage to improve their memory. In time, the researchers hope to "bypass the hippocampus" entirely. The researchers state, however, that this device would only be practical to use with individuals who had localized brain damage, and not widespread damage.

If this brain implant works, researchers hypothesize that the results of a study examining the differences between stroke survivors with implants, stroke survivors without implants, and normal controls on memory performance would be represented by the data in Figure 1. The future implications of this research are important to the many individuals who have suffered memory loss from brain damage.

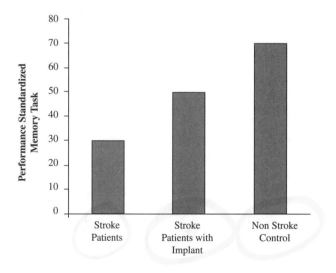

Figure 1 Hypothesized effectiveness of brain memory implant on memory performance in stroke survivors

Adapted from M. Acey. Brain implants: Restoring memory with a microchip. © 2013 by *CNN*

1. Suppose that an individual with a traumatic brain injury was found to have developed anterograde amnesia, but his memory retrieval remains intact. Which of the following would NOT illustrate this patient's condition?

   A. The patient remembers his birthday two years ago, but has trouble remembering his most recent birthday, which occurred after his accident.
   B. The patient remembers what he did yesterday and today, but has trouble remembering his birthday from two years ago, which occurred before his accident.
   C. The patient has difficulty learning new information presented to him after the accident.
   D. The patient remembers the names of his childhood friends, but has difficulty remembering the names of people he has just met.

2. Based on the hypothesized results, what would be an example of a future implication of the research study outlined in the passage?

   A. Individuals who have suffered localized brain damage will be able to regain some of their memory function, but may not be able to achieve premorbid levels of functioning.
   B. Individuals who have suffered localized brain damage will be able to regain all of their memory function.
   C. Individuals who have suffered widespread brain damage will be able to regain some of their memory function, but may not be able to achieve premorbid levels of functioning.
   D. Individuals who have suffered widespread brain damage will be able to regain all of their memory function.

3. What is the function of the hippocampus and where is it located?

 A. The hippocampus is integral in the process of memory consolidation, the changing of long-term memories into short-term memories, and it is located in the medial temporal lobe of the brain.

 B. The hippocampus is integral in the process of memory consolidation, the changing of short-term memories into long-term memories, and it is located in the medial temporal lobe of the brain.

 C. The hippocampus is integral in the process of memory consolidation, the changing of long-term memories into short-term memories, and it is located in the medial parietal lobe of the brain.

 D. The hippocampus is integral in the process of memory consolidation, the changing of short-term memories into long-term memories, and it is located in the medial parietal lobe of the brain.

4. Working memory is generally restricted to a limited number of items that can be remembered and subsequently manipulated. According to Baddeley's model of working memory, which of the following is NOT a component of working memory?

 A. Phonological loop
 B. Visuospatial sketchpad
 C. Short-term store
 D. Episodic buffer

5. Which of the following correctly describes the different types of memory?

 A. Explicit memory includes the ability to recall personal events, like what you had for dinner yesterday, while implicit memory includes factual information, like important historical dates.
 B. Explicit memory includes both personal and factual information, while implicit memory involves the ability to complete certain tasks, like driving or running.
 C. Explicit memory is unconscious while implicit memory is conscious.
 D. Implicit memory, also known as nondeclarative memory, includes recollection of personal and factual information, while explicit memory, also known as declarative memory, include the recollection of how to complete certain tasks.

6. The experiment proposed in Figure 1 was repeated, but instead of using patients who have suffered a stroke, they used patients with Alzheimer's disease. The new groups would be Alzheimer's patients without the implant, Alzheimer's patients with the implant, and a non-Alzheimer's control group. Based on the information about Alzheimer's disease and the brain implant presented in the passage, which figure below would most likely represent the results of this study?

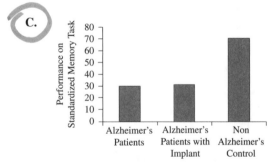

Passage 19 (Questions 1-6)

As an individual progresses through the various of stages of life, it becomes quite obvious that some memories are embedded more strongly than others. For example, one might not remember what he ate for breakfast last Tuesday, but will always remember the time he got mugged at knifepoint in college. One might not remember the name of her elementary school gym teacher, but will always remember the moment her now-husband proposed to her thirty years ago. Many laypersons might argue that this is because getting mugged or accepting a proposal are overwhelmingly more important life events to remember than an everyday breakfast or a teacher from long ago, but many scientists are beginning to detect a link between memory encoding and the neurotransmitter epinephrine. Many scientists hypothesize that emotionally significant experiences activate hormones and brain regions that regulate the consolidation and encoding of newly acquired memories, thus making these highly emotional events easier to remember at a later date.

Researchers in Tampa, Florida put this hypothesis to the test. A total of 300 students from a local university were recruited to participate in a study about memory. All participants were given a list of 100 words, which they were instructed to memorize to the best of their ability. However, one-third (100) the participants were injected with a shot of epinephrine prior to being given the list of words. Another third received an injection of a sterile saline to act as a placebo. The final third received no injection at all, and served as the control group. Research assistants were not made aware of which participants were in which group. All participants were given thirty minutes to memorize the list, then took an unrelated online quiz, and then were asked to recite as many of the words as they could remember to a research assistant.

One week later, all participants were asked to return for a follow-up trial. Again, participants were asked to recite as many of the words from the list as they could remember to a research assistant. The results can be viewed in Table 1, below.

Participants	Immediate Recall	One Week Follow-up Recall
Epinephrine	87	66[a]
Placebo	84	61[b]
Control	80	42[a,b]

In each row, values with the same superscript are significantly different at the $p < 0.05$ level

Table 1 Average participant immediate and follow-up recall of word list ($N = 300$)

1. What conclusions can be drawn from the data presented in Table 1?

   A. Participant immediate recall in the epinephrine group was significantly higher than that in the control or placebo groups.
   B. Participant immediate recall in the placebo group was significantly lower from that in the epinephrine or control groups.
   C. Participant one week follow-up recall in the epinephrine and placebo groups was significantly higher than that in the control group.
   D. Participant one week follow-up recall in the control and placebo groups was significantly lower than that in the epinephrine group.

2. What is the emotion most closely linked to the release of epinephrine?

   A. Happiness
   B. Depression
   C. Fear
   D. Anger

3. What was the purpose of the quiz participants took after studying the word list, but before recalling the words to the research assistant?

   A. Deception
   B. Decoy
   C. Extinction
   D. Distraction

4. Also known as "flashbulb memories," these memories are very clear and are often of unique and highly emotional events, such as where you were when you heard about the 9/11 terrorist attacks. What is another term for these types of memories?

   A. Eidetic memory
   B. Explicit memory
   C. Implicit memory
   D. Episodic memory

5. The passage above indicates that the research assistants were not aware of which participants were in which group. This is an example of what type of study?

   A. Case study
   B. Double-blind study
   C. Meta-analytic study
   D. Naturalistic observation

6. Which of the following structures is involved in the emotional component of memory formation?

   A. Thalamus
   B. Hippocampus
   C. Amygdala
   D. Prefrontal lobe

Passage 20 (Questions 1-6)

Zoo animals need yearly vaccinations for both bacterial and viral diseases in order to stay healthy. However, it is not always easy for zoo veterinarians to administer the vaccinations. Wild canids (domestic dogs, wolves, and foxes), in particular, show resistance, such as barking, growling, and clenching their jaws, when they sense their annual shots. The canids' reluctance can be very troublesome and tedious for veterinarians who need to reach the vaccination site on the back of the animals' necks. Other animals, such as primates, are much more willing to comply and tend to present their limbs quietly during their shots.

Researchers were interested to see how operant conditioning principles could increase the wild canids' compliance of presenting their necks during their vaccinations. They conducted two separate experiments to observe the effects of operant conditioning on two groups, which were comprised of 60 wild canids. However, instead of administering actual vaccinations, the researchers injected the canids with a placebo solution. Therefore, they were able to have repeated trials with no adverse effects on the health of the zoo animals. The researchers defined the canids' compliance as them permitting the veterinarians to access their injection site within fifteen seconds from the start of the trial.

During experiment one, 30 wild canids were randomly assigned to group A and received a treat every time they willingly presented their vaccination site to the veterinarian within fifteen seconds. The other 30 canids were randomly assigned to Group B, which did not receive a treat after being injected with the placebo solution. For experiment one, the researchers measured the percentage of canids from groups A and B that allowed the veterinarian to inject the solution in their necks within the allowed time frame.

Six months later, the researchers returned to the testing sites and conducted their second experiment. Similarly, 30 canids were assigned to group A and the remaining wild canids were randomly designated to group B. Group A still received a treat for every occurrence of the correct behavior. However, for experiment two, the group B canids were sometimes, in a random manner, given a treat for allowing the veterinarian to access their necks. In experiment two, the researchers were interested in the number of trials, on average, it took for the canids to learn the desired behavior.

Results for experiment one indicated that the wild canids from group A were significantly more compliant and presented their injection sites in less time than the canids from group B. Furthermore, in experiment two, the canids from group A learned the correct behavior in a significantly shorter number of trials, on average, than their counterparts in group B (Table 1).

	Experiment 1: Compliance (Correct Behavior Within Fifteen Seconds)	Experiment 2: Average Number of Trials to Learn Behavior
Group A	90%	3
Group B	58%	9

Table 1 Vaccination compliance and learning the correct behavior in wild canids

1. Which of the following operant conditioning principles did the researchers implement during their two studies?

   A. Negative reinforcement; administration of a treat is a primary reinforcer
   B. Negative reinforcement; administration of a treat is a conditioned reinforcer
   C. Positive reinforcement; administration of a treat is a primary reinforcer
   D. Positive reinforcement; administration of a treat is a conditioned reinforcer

2. Experiment two in the passage was repeated, but instead of determining the average number of trials needed before the wild canids' performed the correct behavior, researchers measured how long it took for the canids to stop executing the desired behavior after the administration of treats ceased. Which group, A or B, would be expected to continue demonstrating the compliance behavior for a longer period of time even after the canids stopped receiving treats?

   A. Group A
   B. Group B
   C. Group A and B would continue to do the behavior for same amount of time
   D. Cannot be determined

3. The researchers decided to conduct a third experiment on the wild canids. Once again they randomly assigned thirty dogs to groups A and B. The group A canids were given a treat after performing the compliance behavior five times. Meanwhile, the group B canids received the treat after conducting an unpredictable amount of compliance behaviors. Which of the following are the schedules the researchers implemented for group A and group B, respectively?

   A. Fixed ratio and variable ratio
   B. Continuous and variable ratio
   C. Variable ratio and fixed ratio
   D. Fixed ratio and continuous

4. Which of the following statements is/are true concerning experiments one and two, as described in the passage?

   I. The wild canids were all the same species.
   II. The injections had no effect on the zoo animals' health.
   III. The wild canids received a treat sometimes when they did not perform the compliance behavior.

   A. I only
   B. II only
   C. I and II only
   D. II and III only

5. Which of the following correctly describes negative reinforcement?

   A. A mother gives her child dessert right after he finishes his vegetables at dinner.
   B. A teacher takes away recess from a student after she finds out the student failed to complete the homework assignment.
   C. A car stops beeping once the driver has fastened his seatbelt.
   D. A father gives his son extra chores for getting detention.

6. The researchers returned to the zoo to conduct another experiment on the canids. The new experiment was similar to experiment two, but rather than giving treats to group B in a random fashion, they gave the treat after every three occurrences of the compliance behavior. Group A still received a treat every time they performed the desired behavior and the researchers were still interested in the average number of trials it took for the canids to learn the behavior. Which of the following best approximates the average number of trials it now took for the group B canids to learn the compliance behavior?

   A. 2
   B. 5
   C. 9
   D. 10

Passage 21 (Questions 1-6)

According to the physical attractiveness stereotype, people assume that attractive strangers are more trustworthy than their unattractive counterparts. Several studies have demonstrated that experimental subjects overwhelmingly tend to rate statements made by an attractive confederate as more reliable than those made by a less attractive one. Complementary research has found physical attractiveness to be positively correlated with personal income, confidence, and social skills.

Research has also demonstrated that people act differently when watched. In studies that require experimental subjects to divide, donate, or otherwise give money, subjects behave more generously when they believe others can see them, even when researchers merely display a picture of eyes. In one experimental example, contributions to a communal coffee fund box nearly tripled when a picture of flowers on the box was replaced with a picture of eyes.

In a recent study, 82 college psychology students were recruited as subjects to play a financial trust game that they were told involved two subjects (but in actuality, the second "subject" was an experimenter-controlled image). The financial trust game asks subjects to choose one of two options: option 1 allowed subjects to split a small sum of money between themselves and the "partner," in whatever way the subject wanted. Option 2 allowed subjects to trust the "partner" to split a much larger sum of money between them, in whatever way the "partner" wanted. Previous studies using the financial trust game have demonstrated that subjects are more likely to trust a physically attractive partner. For this study, prior to asking subjects to pick either option 1 or option 2, the researchers took pictures of the subjects' faces and told them that their "partner" would see their photos, but only in certain rounds of the game. This study was designed to determine whether physically attractive subjects, perhaps sensing their appearance to be an asset, would be more trusting when they believed their "partners" could see them.

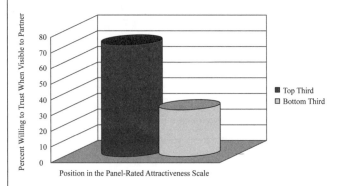

Figure 1 Percent of subjects, rated by the panel in terms of attractiveness, willing to trust "partner" to divide a sum of money when they believed they could be seen by the partner

The subjects' attractiveness was quantified by subjects' self ratings and ratings from a panel of 10 people unfamiliar with the subjects. All used an attractiveness rating scale of 1 to 7. The experimenters found that "top third" subjects were 71% more likely to trust a "partner" to divide the larger sum of money when told that the "partner" could see the subject's photo than when told no photo would be shown. In contrast, the "bottom third" subjects trusted their "partner" to divide a larger sum of money approximately 30% of the time when told that the "partner" could see the subject's photo. Although there was a positive correlation between the subjects' self ratings and those of the panel, the results held only for the panel ratings.

Adapted from F. G. Smith, L. M. Debruine, B. C. Jones, D. B. Krupp, L. L. M. Welling, and C. A. Conway. Attractiveness qualifies the effect of observation on trusting behavior in an economic game. © 2009 by Evolution and Human Behavior

1. If a majority of other research finds that one's own perceived attractiveness primarily drives one's tendency to trust others, what impact would that have on the experimenters' findings?

   A. None, because the researchers incorporated subjects' self-ratings into their experimental design.
   B. It would call into question the higher correlation between the panel ratings and the subjects' willingness to trust.
   C. It would bolster the researchers' finding that objective measures of attractiveness were more reliable in attaining the experimental results described in the passage.
   D. It would suggest that self ratings of attractiveness are more reliable than those provided by others.

2. If it were discovered that people considered attractive by others are significantly less likely to suffer performance issues in public than are their less attractive counterparts, which of the following statements helps explain this finding?

   I. Less attractive people have more social ties than do their more attractive counterparts.

   II. Evaluation apprehension, the tendency of the presence of others to affect one's performance, is exacerbated by concerns about one's appearance.

   III. Society tends to expect less from people who are less attractive.

   A. I only
   B. II only
   C. I and III only
   D. II and III only

3. Which of the following, if true, would most undermine the researchers' results?

   A. 40% of the subjects rated as attractive by the panel believed themselves to be unattractive.
   B. Attractiveness is influenced by social and cultural norms.
   C. Some subjects rated less attractive by the panel thought themselves to be very attractive.
   D. Subjects who rated themselves as attractive were more likely to do so after seeing the experimenters' photographs of them than before they were shown those photos.

4. Which of the following conclusions can be drawn from the study results?

   A. Self-perceived attractiveness is a strong honesty motivator.
   B. People may subconsciously believe their attractiveness higher than they would otherwise state.
   C. Male subjects would be more likely to trust attractive female partners than less attractive ones.
   D. People considered unattractive are potentially less trusting of others than are attractive people.

5. If the experiment were changed so that subjects first had to grant permission to the experimenter to take their photos, then had to grant permission to their "partners" before the "partner" could see their photos, which of the following accounts for a higher tendency among those who granted permission to both of the smaller requests to also agree to let their partners divide the money?

   A. Foot-in-the-door phenomenon
   B. Self-serving bias
   C. Groupthink
   D. The bystander effect

6. Which of the following would best increase the external validity of the experimental results?

   I. Excluding of all of the least attractive (score of 1) and most attractive (score of 7) participants' data from the final results.

   II. Averaging the participants' self ratings with the panel ratings before dividing participants into three attractiveness groups.

   III. Repeating the experiment with a much larger sample of randomly selected adults.

   A. III only
   B. I and II only
   C. II and III only
   D. I, II, and III

Passage 22 (Questions 1-5)

While sociocultural factors are widely assumed to impact body image among young girls, researchers also hypothesize that biological and psychological variables can predict levels of body esteem among both young girls and boys. Researchers at Smith-Jones University devised a longitudinal study in order to measure the impact of body mass index (BMI), socioeconomic status (SES), and perception of autonomy on body esteem across time. The one constant for all participants was reported regular (3-4 times/week) exposure to media images that emphasize appearance.

In Phase 1 of the study, participants were split into groups by sex (150 10-year-old girls and 150 10-year-old boys), and completed the Body-Self Relations Questionnaire (BSRQ), which yielded Body Esteem Assessment (BEA) scores. An attitudinal assessment tool, the BSRQ poses a series of questions designed to measure Appearance and Fitness Evaluations, which combine to yield BEA scores. High BEA scores indicate strong body-esteem, while lower scores indicate decreased body-esteem. Low body esteem is typically understood to be a risk factor in the development of eating disorders. The BSRQ, it should be noted, relies on a self-report inventory of feelings, rather than a descriptive method of classification, which relies on a combination of self-report data and external observations of behavior.

The BEA scores were then correlated with the BMI, SES, and autonomy perception data, which were measured for each participant using standard methods. Three years later, in Phase 2 of the study, the same participant groups completed the BSRQ again, and their scores were again correlated with the BMI, SES, and autonomy variables. The results presented in Figure 1 indicate that, when sociocultural factors are held constant, BMI, SES, and low autonomy all predict a decrease in BEA among girls; high autonomy correlates with unaffected BEA in both genders; SES does not appear to affect BEA among boys; and above average BMI predicts low BEA in boys.

Note: this study has been criticized for its use of the BMI, which only measures height and weight. BMI is increasingly being replaced with body-fat percentages (BF%), which is believed to more accurately account for interactions between variables like height, bone structure, and muscle versus fat composition. Consequently, BF% is thought to more precisely assess obesity-related health risks than BMI.

Variables	Phase 1 (10 yrs, girls)	Phase 2 (13 yrs, girls)	Phase 1 (10 yrs, boys)	Phase 2 (13 yrs, boys)
Average BMI	32	26	35	34
Above Average BMI	29	20	33	25
Low SES	29	20	30	31
High SES	38	28	43	42
Low autonomy	27	20	32	25
High autonomy	30	29	34	32

Figure 1 Body Esteem Assessment (BEA) scores (range 0-40)

1. From the results in Figure 1, the researchers conclude that interactions between gender and gender norms are a significant variable in predicting the likelihood of low body esteem. They explain that the lower incidence of decreased BEA in boys is related to the fact that the primary focus of media images is on female appearance, and therefore, young girls are more likely to internalize ideals of female appearance than are males to internalize male ideals. With which theory of adolescent development is this explanation most aligned?

   A. Latency stage (Freud)
   B. Gender socialization theory
   C. Imaginary audience (Piaget)
   D. Physiological revolution (Erikson)

2. Which graph represents the correlation between low SES and BEA across time for both participant groups?

A.

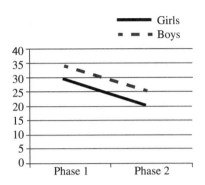

B.

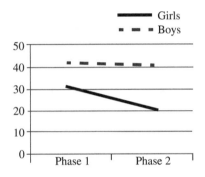

C.

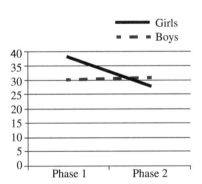

D.

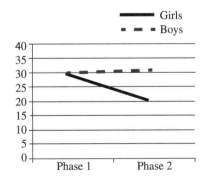

3. Consider if this experiment were repeated with the two following changes: the two groups are both comprised of female participants, and one of the two groups would receive a weekly class on media literacy skills and body image awareness (deemed the "media group"). The class reinforced principles of health as a measure of well being rather than appearance through a combination of educational videos and self-reflective writing exercises that identified negative thoughts similar to those in popular media. During Phase 2, BEA scores remained the same or increased for all variables in the media group only. Which approach to attitudinal change most closely accounts for these results?

A. Social cognitive theory
B. Cognitive-behavioral therapy
C. Classical conditioning
D. Operant conditioning

4. The researchers did not report the racial composition of the participants. A review of the results reveals that a disproportionate number of Above average BMI, Low SES, and Low autonomy participants are of Aboriginal descent. What impact does this have on the researchers' conclusion that gender identity and gender norms predict BEA?

A. It calls into question the results; the experiment should be repeated and experimental groups formed along gender and racial/ethnic categories.
B. It has no impact on the results; race is an extraneous variable.
C. It has no impact on the results; race is a dependent variable.
D. It completely nullifies the results and renders this experiment unethical and unscientific.

5. Which of the following conclusions can be supported by findings in Figure 1?

A. Media images of ideal gender norms predict low self-esteem in young girls
B. Above average BMI predicts low BEA
C. Low SES predicts low BEA
D. Autonomy is not a variable that influences BEA

Passage 23 (Questions 1-5)

Research has shown that memories can be made stronger and more enduring via spontaneous reactivation of brain activity patterns, which can be externally signaled by sensory cues such as smells or sounds related to the particular memory. For example, a memory of a deceased loved one might be made stronger if a person sleeps on a pillowcase spritzed with the loved one's signature perfume or cologne. Could similar methods be employed to suppress or weaken bad or traumatic memories in individuals suffering from post-traumatic stress disorder (PTSD)? For example, could sleeping while being exposed to a smoky smell help ease the PTSD symptoms of a person who's home burned down? Researchers hypothesis that pairing a smell associated with a traumatic event with the seemingly calm and non-stressful act of sleeping might reduce fear response when the individual is exposed to other trigger stimuli.

Researchers were interested in investigating the possibility of reducing traumatic memories, but on a smaller scale. For this, 100 college students from a nearby university were recruited for a study on fear. The participants were split into two equal group; an experimental group and a control group. During Phase 1, subjects in both groups were shown a series of "benign" images, such as flowers, trees, or grasses, all of which were presented on either a blue or green background. Participants in both groups were delivered a mild, but uncomfortable, electric shock every time an image was presented on a blue background, and their heart rate and skin conductance were recorded as objective measures of a physiological fear response. It is widely believed that scent is the sense most closely tied to memory, so researchers elected to include this as a component as well. In the experimental group only, the smell of lemon was piped into the room while the subjects were viewing the images. No smell was present for the control group.

After this phase, participants were dismissed. Participants in the experimental group were given a lemon-scented air freshener and asked to place it near the head of their bed when they went to sleep that night. Control participants were dismissed with no additional instructions. Researchers hypothesized that in the experimental group, by pairing the lemon scent associated with a feared event (being shocked) as well as with a non-feared event (sleep), the experimental participants might better extinguish their fear response than the control participants. The next day, all participants returned and underwent the same procedure as on the previous day. However, in Phase 2, no electric shocks were delivered for either group. The experimental group was again exposed to the lemon scent during the trial. The average physiological fear response (based on a standardized calculation using heart rate and skin conductance measures) is presented in Figure 1.

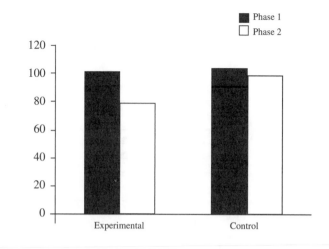

Figure 1 Average physiological fear response (calculated using heart rate and skin conductance) during fear conditioning task for experimental and control participants ($n = 100$)

Adapted from D. Oudiette, J. W. Antony, and K. A. Paller. Fear not: Manipulating sleep might help you forget. ©2014 by *Trends in Cognitive Science*

1. Based on the information provided in the passage and presented in Figure 1, what might the researchers most logically conclude and what might be the biggest methodological criticism of this conclusion?

    A. The presence of the lemon trigger scent while sleeping may be associated with a reduced fear response in the experimental group during Phase 2; however, critics of this study might be skeptical of this conclusion given that the lemon scent was introduced at three different time points for the experimental group, thus it would not be possible to determine that the researcher's hypothesis is correct.

    B. The presence of the lemon trigger scent during Phase 1 and Phase 2 may be associated with an increased fear response in the experimental group due to the close association between the amygdala and the olfactory bulb; however, study skeptics might disregard this conclusion because the images that were associated with the shock during Phase 1 were also presented on a different colored background, so it is not possible to determine if the colored background or the presence of a scent is responsible for the fear response in the experimental group.

    C. The control participants had an overall greater fear response during Phase 2 because they were not subject to the odor treatment, thus the lemon scent itself is responsible for the reduced fear response in the experimental group; however, it could be argued that since the subjects were not tested for innate fear responses before being placed into the experimental and control groups, it is possible that the experimental group had a much higher fear response tolerance thus invalidating the study results.

    D. The researchers would most likely conclude that their hypothesis was correct, and that "odor treatment" would be an effective cure for more systematic fear responses, such as phobias and PTSD; however, critics would argue that reduction or extinction of a simple fear response, such as that generated by a mild electric shock, is not generalizable to more extreme and complex fear responses.

2. The limbic system is a collection of brain structures that support a variety of functions, including (but not limited to) memory and olfaction, which is why many researchers believe that scent is the sense most closely tied to memory. Which of the following are part of the limbic system?

    I. Amygdala
    II. Hippocampus
    III. Medulla oblongata

    A. I only
    B. II only
    C. I and II only
    D. I, II, and III

3. Sigmund Freud is one of the psychologists most closely associated with dream analysis. According the Freud, the latent content of a dream contains which of the following?

    A. Experiences and preoccupations from the day's events
    B. Unconscious drives and wishes
    C. Psychic visions of the future
    D. Scenes from previous lives

4. In the experimental groups' trials, participants were exposed to a lemon scent to manipulate their emotional memories of the electric shocks. Researchers had to be careful in applying the scent, making sure that it was not an overwhelming odor, but strong enough that participants would notice it. What is the term used to describe the point when something becomes noticeable to the senses?

    A. Absolute threshold.
    B. Difference threshold.
    C. Just-noticeable difference.
    D. Threshold potential.

5. Trauma adversely affects many areas of the brain, including shrinkage in the volume of the hippocampus. Which of the following symptoms would this cause?

    A. Difficulty verbally expressing thoughts and feelings
    B. Frequent feelings of fear regardless of the situation
    C. Difficulty regulating emotions
    D. Memory loss

Passage 24 (Questions 1-7)

As researchers have sought to identify and explain emotions, they have found that a number of emotions are universal, meaning they are found in all humans across cultures. Furthermore, they have identified three distinct components of emotional experience. The first is the physiological component: emotional experiences are often associated with some sort of bodily response. The second is cognitive: our thoughts are often powerful influencers of our emotions. Lastly, emotions appear to have a behavioral component: what we do can influence how we feel, and vice versa.

In order to examine the roles of each of these three components, researchers constructed the following experiment. For this study, 100 college-aged males who were touring a nature park were approached by an attractive female and asked to participate in a study. In the park there were two bridges: one very secure, solid and safe perched just a few feet above a creek while the other was a narrow plank bridge suspended more than 200 feet above a canyon. The attractive female approached each man as he walked across the bridge. She asked them to fill out a survey and tell a short story based on a neutral picture of a woman sitting on the floor. At the end of their interaction, the woman gave the men her phone number and let them know they could call her with any questions about the study.

The researchers were exploring an idea known as "misattribution of arousal," which examines how the brain can interpret similar physical sensations (e.g. elevated heart rate, increased respiratory rate, feeling flush) differently depending on the circumstances, and wanted to study how this might influence behavior. The researchers measured two dependent variables to evaluate misattribution. They hypothesized that college-aged males may interpret their physiological arousal as attraction to the female researcher. Therefore they measured number of stories that contained sexual content as an immediate measure. Then, they measured how many participants called the researcher afterward to ask her on a date. The results for those two items have been summarized in Figure 1.

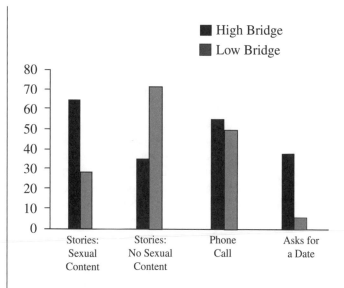

Figure 1 Responses of participants measured for misattribution of arousal

1. All of the following are among the universal emotions, EXCEPT:

   A. Anger
   B. Surprise
   C. Curiosity
   D. Disgust

2. In formulating the hypotheses for the study described in the passage, the researchers consulted different theories of emotion. What would the James-Lange theory of emotion predict about the content of the stories told by participants on the high, narrow bridge?

   A. Most of these stories would involve danger or frightful content
   B. The participant will almost always include himself in the story
   C. There would be a mix of stories featuring different emotions for different people
   D. All of the stories would be about bridges

3. Which of the following best states the researchers' null hypothesis for this study?

   A. The participants on the high, narrow bridge will have more sexual content in their stories than participants on the low, safe bridge.
   B. The people on the high, narrow bridge will have the same amount of sexual content in their stories as participants on the low, safe bridge.
   C. The high, narrow bridge will cause more physiological arousal than the low, safe bridge.
   D. The high, narrow bridge will cause a similar amount of physiological arousal than the low, safe bridge.

4. The arousal felt by participants in this study is a product of the:

   A. enteric nervous system.
   B. parasympathetic nervous system.
   C. somatic nervous system.
   D. sympathetic nervous system.

5. After completing their first study, the researchers returned to the nature park to conduct a second study using these same two bridges. In the new study they asked people to complete simple cognitive tasks (e.g. complete a block puzzle, solve a series of logical word problems, etc.) while on one of the bridges, either the high, narrow one or the low, safe one. The researchers found that people on the high bridge performed significantly better on these cognitive tasks than people on the low bridge. Which of the following might best explain these results?

   A. The social facilitation effect
   B. Cognitive priming
   C. The Yerkes-Dodson law
   D. The Cannon-Bard theory

6. According to the figures above, what did the researchers find in their study?

   A. Participants did not misattribute their arousal from the bridge.
   B. Participants' misattribution of bridge-related arousal to sexual attraction lasted beyond the time spent on the bridge.
   C. Participants misattributed their bridge-related arousal as sexual attraction to the researcher but only while on the bridge.
   D. Individual differences among participants overpowered any possible differences from the bridges.

7. The idea of misattribution of arousal could be explained by which theory(s) of emotion?

   I. Schachter-Singer theory
   II. Cannon-Bard theory
   III. James-Lange theory

   A. I only
   B. II only
   C. II and III only
   D. I, II, and III

Passage 25 (Questions 1-6)

Recently, a study investigated the effects of pet ownership on the health and stress levels of 100 older adults. Participants were generally healthy adults ages 65 or older who were broken into three groups based on pet ownership: those who owned one or more cats ($n = 37$), those who owned one or more dogs ($n = 40$), and those who did not own any pets at all ($n = 23$). Relative health was measured by number of scheduled and unscheduled (emergency) medical appointments over a period of six months. All participants were on Medicare, so cost of appointments and ability to pay were not factors. Stress levels were measured by number of stressful life events (e.g., death of a loved one, divorce, major illness of self or one's spouse, being a victim of a crime) over that same time period, and this information was collected in survey form.

For individuals who reported zero or one stressful life events, there was no significant difference in health between the three groups. Among those who reported two stressful life events, owners of both dogs and cats showed significantly fewer medical appointments than those who did not own pets, though no significant difference emerged between dog and cat owners. Among those participants who reported three or more stressful life events over the past six months, dog owners demonstrated significantly fewer medical appointments than cat owners, who demonstrated significantly fewer medical appointments than participants who did not own any pets. Since investigators measured relative health by the number of medical appointments over a six-month period, they concluded that pet ownership, particularly dog ownership, was correlated to improved health in elderly individuals under greater stress. While the caretaking of any animal can improve one's sense of purpose and therefore potentially one's well-being, it is hypothesized that the difference between the health of dog owners and cat owners who are experiencing greater life stress is due to the increased amount of physical interaction that occurs between an owner and his or her dogs.

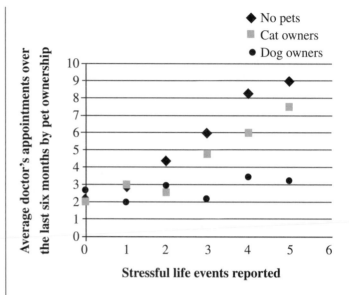

Figure 1 Average number of doctor's appointments scheduled over the past six months among cat owners, dog owners, and individuals with no pets with varying amounts of stress

Adapted from J. M. Siegel. Stressful life events and use of physician services among the elderly: The moderating role of pet ownership. © 1990 by *Journal of Personality and Social Psychology*

1. Which statement is NOT compatible with the hypothesis that elderly adults who are exposed to numerous stressful events and own dogs are healthier than those who own cats because the dog owners interact physically with their pets more than cat owners?

    A. Elderly adults who owned a fish and experienced three or more stressful life events in the last six months attended more medical appointments than elderly dog owners who experienced three or more stressful life events in the last six months.

    B. Elderly adults who owned a fish and experienced three or more stressful life events in the last six months attended as many medical appointments as elderly dog owners who experienced three or more stressful life events in the last six months.

    C. Elderly cat owners in the study spent half as much time petting their cats as the elderly dog owners did petting their dogs.

    D. Elderly dog owners leave their houses more often than elderly cat owners.

2. In the wild, animals will often behave in a manner that allows for their kin to survive even if it does not directly benefit them. This behavior is known as:

A. inclusive fitness.
B. genetic drift.
C. adaptation.
D. natural selection.

3. Certain dogs can be trained to predict seizures in an owner with epilepsy. In a clinical setting, seizures are best studied using:

A. functional MRI.
B. structural MRI.
C. EEG.
D. CT.

4. Which hormone, thought to be involved in social bonding, is released when an individual touches another person or pets an animal?

A. Oxytocin
B. Dopamine
C. Serotonin
D. ACTH

5. Which of Erik Erickson's stages of development is associated with old age?

A. Autonomy versus shame and doubt
B. Generativity versus stagnation
C. Industry versus depression
D. Integrity versus despair

6. The presence of a pet is also correlated with a calmer demeanor and fewer outbursts in Alzheimer's patients. Structural MRI and autopsies show that, compared to a healthy brain of the same age, the brains of Alzheimer's patients usually have:

A. enlarged gyri and enlarged vesicles.
B. enlarged gyri and shrunken vesicles.
C. shrunken gyri and enlarged vesicles.
D. shrunken gyri and shrunken vesicles.

Passage 26 (Questions 1-5)

Many bodily sensations are associated with anxiety, such as increased heart rate, increased perspiration, feelings of dizziness, and increased respiration. For people suffering from chronic anxiety, it has been hypothesized that the perception of these bodily sensations may be distorted. For example, when an individual with an anxiety disorder experiences the symptom of increased heart rate, he may perceive a heart attack coming on, or when he experiences dizziness, he might believe he is going to faint.

Researchers in Little Rock, Arkansas were interested in testing this hypothesis. College students from an introductory psychology course at a nearby university were recruited to participate, and each was asked to complete the Hamilton Anxiety Rating Scale (HAM-A). Participants were divided into groups based on their scores on the HAM-A. Participants with scores between 0-17 were placed in the "low anxiety" group, those with scores between 18-25 were placed in the "moderate anxiety" group, and those with scores between 19-30 were placed in the "severe anxiety" group. Each group contained 60 participants, for a total of 180 participants.

Participants were then asked to complete a task: a difficult psychology test that the students believed would affect their grade in the course from which they were recruited (but in actuality had no impact on their course grade). For each group, heart rate and respiration rate were measured before and after the task. Heart rate was measured in beats per minute, with the average resting heart rate for an adult ranging anywhere between 60-100 beats per minute. Respiration was measured in breaths per minute, with the average resting respiration rate for an adult ranging between 12-18 breaths per minute. Participants were asked to estimate their physiological responses, without being shown the actual results. Researchers hypothesized that individuals who scored higher on the HAM-A would be more likely to overestimate their physiological responses to stress. Results can be viewed in Tables 1, 2, and 3, below.

	Pre-Task			Post-Task		
	Actual	Perceived	p	Actual	Perceived	p
Heart Rate	59	65	.09	81	90	.06
Respiration Rate	14	15	>1	20	26	.07

Table 1 Low anxiety participants' average physiological response and perception of response to stress ($n = 60$), $*p \leq .05$

	Pre-Task			Post-Task		
	Actual	Perceived	*p*	Actual	Perceived	*p*
Heart Rate	63	70	.05	74	92	.08
Respiration Rate	15	18	>1	22	29	.08

Table 2 Moderate anxiety participants' average physiological response and perception of response to stress ($n = 60$), *$p \leq .05$

	Pre-Task			Post-Task		
	Actual	Perceived	*p*	Actual	Perceived	*p*
Heart Rate	65	77	.04*	77	98	.04*
Respiration Rate	17	25	.04*	24	32	.05*

Table 3 Severe anxiety participants' average physiological response and perception of response to stress ($n = 60$), *$p \leq .05$

Adapted from A. Steptoe & C. Vogele. Individual differences in the perception of bodily sensations: The role of trait anxiety and coping style. © 1992 by *Behaviour Research and Therapy*

1. What conclusions can be drawn from the data presented in Tables 1, 2, and 3?

   A. The actual post-task anxiety levels for the low anxiety group were higher than for the moderate and severe anxiety groups, a result that contradicted the researchers' hypothesis.
   B. There was no significant difference between the post-task perceived anxiety levels for the moderate anxiety group and the low anxiety group.
   C. The researchers' hypothesis was supported because the severe anxiety group demonstrated a statistically significant difference between their average actual and perceived responses to stress.
   D. The moderate anxiety group demonstrated the least accurate overall estimations of their own anxiety, on average.

2. An individual in the high anxiety group is just informed that she will have to take an exam that will impact her grade. Immediately, she begins to feel hot and starts perspiring. Her heart suddenly feels like it is beating out of her chest, and all of her muscles feel very tense. Which of the following receptors are likely involved in her ability to detect these physiological changes?

   I. Mechanoreceptors
   II. Baroreceptors
   III. Thermoreceptors

   A. III only
   B. I and II
   C. II and III
   D. I, II, and III

3. Which school of psychology focuses on an individual's sensation and perception?

   A. Humanistic
   B. Gestalt
   C. Psychodynamic
   D. Social

4. The process of constructing perceptions from sensory input by drawing on one's own experience and expectations is called what?

   A. Top-down processing
   B. Bottom-up processing
   C. Serial processing
   D. Transfer-appropriate processing

5. What is a perceptual set?

   A. A set of strongly held beliefs in favor of or against a certain thing, person, or group as compared to another.
   B. The response of a whole organism involving physiological arousal, expressive behaviors, and conscious experience.
   C. A set of mental tendencies and assumptions that greatly affect what one perceives.
   D. All the mental activities associated with thinking, knowing, remembering, and communicating.

Passage 27 (Questions 1-6)

As adults age, they tend to experience declines in various domains of neurological and cognitive functioning, including hearing loss. Researchers have attempted to identify which lifestyle factors, both across the lifespan and within older age, predict better cognitive functioning in the elderly. Years of formal education, involvement in cognitively stimulating activities, and exercise have all been correlated with stronger cognitive performance. In this vein, researchers have begun to examine possible correlations between musicianship, or playing a musical instrument, and cognitive strength.

While musicianship entails many cognitive operations, including working memory and psychomotor coordination, one group of researchers sought to study the specific impact of musicianship on auditory processing in aging adults. The researchers hypothesized that consistent, long-term musicianship enables individuals to build a cognitive reserve such that cognitive processing of auditory signals is consolidated into a highly efficient process. In turn, more cognitive resources are available to compensate for age-related deficits in auditory processing. To test this hypothesis, the researchers recruited 140 participants, ranging in age from 20 to 90 (52% female), from London and surrounding suburbs. To meet criteria for the study, participants had to qualify as either a non-musician (less than 1 year of formal training and a maximum of 1 hour of average weekly time playing a musical instrument) or musician (at least 5 years of formal training and a minimum of 10 hours of average weekly playing time). Those with musical experience that exceeded the non-musician criteria but fell short of the musician criteria were excluded from the study.

The study had three distinct targets, including cochlear functioning, gap detection, and speech in noise detection. Cochlear functioning is critical for basic auditory reception, and this was assessed with the pure-tone measure. During this test, a participant pressed a lever each time he or she heard a tone. The tones were played at a progressively lower amplitude until the participant no longer responded, and the amplitude of the preceding tone was established as the threshold. Gap detection is required to distinguish between phonemes in words. This was assessed with the gap detection task (GDT) in which two tones were played sequentially. One contained a short gap, ranging from 15 ms to 0.8 ms. A participant pressed a button to indicated which tone contained the gap, and the gap was progressively shortened until the threshold was established. Speech-in-noise detection is necessary to distinguish speech within a noisy context, which is fundamental to interpersonal communication. This ability was measured by the language-in-noise (LIN) task. During this task, a participant listened to a recording of 16 sentences embedded in background speech babble. For each sentence, six keywords were identified. Following each sentence, a participant was asked to recall the sentence, and he or she received one point for each keyword correctly recalled. The total possible number of points was 48.

Following the study, researchers analyzed the data in search of any significant effects of age, musicianship, and age x musicianship interaction. Regression model trends (data points excluded) for the pure-tone and gap detection measures are depicted in Figures 1 and 2. The LIN data revealed a trend similar to the GDT.

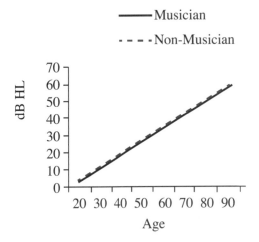

Figure 1 Pure-tone measure correlation model

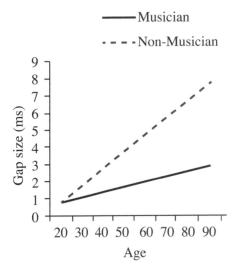

Figure 2 Gap detection task correlation model

Adapted from B. R. Zendel and C. Alain. Musicians Experience Less Age-Related Decline in Central Auditory Processing. © 2011 by *Psychology and Aging*

1. Suppose the LIN task was customized for each participant by including the participant's name in several of the prerecorded sentences. Assuming that the cocktail party phenomenon would influence performance, researchers might erroneously conclude that, as age increases:

   A. non-musicians detect speech-in-noise better than they actually do.
   B. non-musicians do not detect speech-in-noise as well as they actually do.
   C. intoxication interferes with speech-in-noise detection.
   D. non-musicians exhibit stronger cochlear functioning than they actually possess.

2. The study described in the passage could best be characterized as:

   A. a cross-sectional study exploring gender differences among musicians.
   B. a repeated-measures design evaluating dominant age-based stereotypes.
   C. a longitudinal study examining the effects of musicianship at various stages over the lifespan.
   D. a cross-sectional study examining the effects of musicianship on cognitive functioning.

3. Which of the following conclusions can be drawn from a comparison of the pure-tone task results and the LIN task results?

   A. Auditory processing associated with the peripheral nervous system is affected by musicianship x age interaction, but auditory processing associated with the central nervous system is not.
   B. Auditory processing associated with the central nervous system is affected by musicianship x age interaction, but auditory processing associated with the peripheral nervous system is not.
   C. Auditory processing associated with both the central and peripheral nervous systems is affected by musicianship x age interaction.

   D. Auditory processing associated with both the central and peripheral nervous systems is affected by musicianship alone but not by age alone.

4. Bill, a 75-year-old male, has always believed that all older people suffer equally from hearing problems regardless of their life history. If Bill were to read a journal article reporting the results of the LIN measure, he would find evidence of:

   A. in-group homogeneity.
   B. out-group homogeneity.
   C. in-group differentiation.
   D. out-group differentiation.

5. In order to avoid errors resulting from classical conditioning during the GDT, researchers would have:

   A. frequently alternated the sequence of the tones with and without the gap.
   B. always presented the tone containing the gap first.
   C. avoided giving praise after a correct response.
   D. denied participants the opportunity to engage in vicarious learning.

6. Which of the following would support the notion that elderly musicians' performance on the LIN task is the result of musicianship rather than genetically-influenced self-selection?

   A. A superior performance on a timed music reading measure by the musicians, as compared to the non-musicians
   B. Longitudinal neuroimaging studies show a steady increase in the temporal lobe brain mass of musicians over time.
   C. There are lower rates of hearing aid prescriptions among musicians as compared to non-musicians.
   D. Eighth-grade music instructors report highly positive evaluations of participants' instrumental proficiency.

Passage 28 (Questions 1-7)

Aside from posing severe health risks, narcotics interfere significantly with multiple aspects of addicts' lives. Major disruptions in work and family relationships are characteristic consequences of drug addiction. One interpretation of these disruptions is that addiction to powerful drugs results in a devaluation of natural rewards. Thus, the natural pleasure of professional success or intimate relationships diminishes in comparison to the potent effects of drugs. To better understand the phenomenon of devaluation in cases where a natural reward predicted an even greater reward, researchers have conducted studies using rats. Two of these studies entailed three stages, including the application of lesions to the brains of the rats.

The two studies were identical with regard to the procedure for the first two stages. During the first stage, rats were presented with a slightly sweet saccharin (which is sugar-free and non-nutritive) solution for four minutes once a day for eight days. The amount of saccharin solution consumed each day was recorded. In stage two, the rats were again presented with the saccharin solution. However, three minutes later, rats in the experimental groups were also presented with a very sweet sucrose solution, injected with a highly pleasurable morphine solution, or injected with illness-inducing lithium chloride (LiCl) solution. In a fourth group, rats were presented with a second serving of the saccharin solution. The rats in each group were again monitored for eight days and consumption of saccharin (first solution) was recorded. In all of the experimental groups, the rats consumed less saccharin after three days of pairing with the sucrose, morphine, or LiCl. Saccharin consumption (first serving) in the saccharin-saccharin group did not change.

With regard to the third stage, the two studies differed. In the first study, a lesion was made in a region of each rat's thalamus known as the thalamic taste area (TTA). Then, in stage four, the rats were again given the same pairings as in stage two and were monitored for eight days. In this experiment, rats in the saccharin-sucrose and saccharin-morphine groups consumed as much saccharin per day as they did in stage 1, but rats in the saccharin-LiCl group did not increase their saccharin consumption. Rats in the saccharin-saccharin group continued to consume the same amount of the first serving of saccharin as they did in stages 1 and 2.

In the second study, stage three entailed a lesion in a region adjacent to the TTA known as the trigeminal orosensory area (TOA). Again, in the fourth stage, the rats were monitored for eight days and their consumption of the saccharin was recorded. The average amount of saccharin consumed per day in each stage of the second study is depicted in Figure 1.

	Treatment Groups			
Experimental Stages	**Saccharin-Saccharin (Control Group)**	**Saccharin-Sucrose (Experimental Group 1)**	**Saccharin-Morphine (Experimental Group 2)**	**Saccharin-LiCl (Experimental Group 3)**
Stage 1	Presented with saccharin solution for 4 minutes once a day for 8 days	Presented with saccharin solution for 4 minutes once a day for 8 days	Presented with saccharin solution for 4 minutes once a day for 8 days	Presented with saccharin solution for 4 minutes once a day for 8 days
Stage 2	Presented with saccharin solution followed by a second serving of saccharin solution once a day for 8 days; amount of first serving of saccharine consumed recorded	Presented with saccharin solution followed by sucrose solution once a day for 8 days; amount of saccharine consumed recorded	Presented with saccharin solution followed by morphine injection (pleasure-inducing) once a day for 8 days; amount of saccharine consumed recorded	Presented with saccharin solution followed by LiCl injection (illness-inducing) once a day for 8 days; amount of saccharine consumed recorded
Stage 3	Rats in Study 1: lesion to TTA Rats in Study 2: lesion to TOA	Rats in Study 1: lesion to TTA Rats in Study 2: lesion to TOA	Rats in Study 1: lesion to TTA Rats in Study 2: lesion to TOA	Rats in Study 1: lesion to TTA Rats in Study 2: lesion to TOA
Stage 4	Stage 2 repeated for rats in both studies; amount of first serving of saccharine consumed recorded	Stage 2 repeated for rats in both studies; amount of saccharine consumed recorded	Stage 2 repeated for rats in both studies; amount of saccharine consumed recorded	Stage 2 repeated for rats in both studies; amount of saccharine consumed recorded

Table 1 Experimental design overview

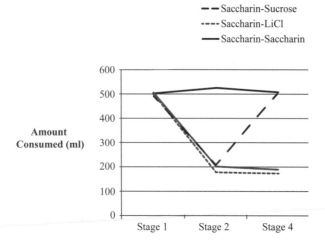

———— Saccharin-Morphine
– – Saccharin-Sucrose
---- Saccharin-LiCl
———— Saccharin-Saccharin

Figure 1 Average amount of saccharin (presented first) consumed per day in each pairing group of rats with TOA lesion

1. Based on the data in Figure 1, which of the following is indicated by the results obtained in the second study?

   A. The TOA can influence an organism's interest in gustatory stimuli after comparing those stimuli with the rewards they predict.
   B. The application of lesions to the TOA of rats results in a preference for morphine over sucrose.
   C. Rats experience more pleasure by consuming greater amounts of saccharin than by consuming a combination of saccharin and another solution.
   D. Contrary to researchers' expectations, rats found LiCl as rewarding as sucrose.

2. Based on the information provided in the passage, which of the following accounts for differences in results between the two studies?

   A. The dependent variables in the third stage differed between studies.
   B. An independent variable employed in the third stage differed between studies.
   C. The first study measured only a sample, while the second study measured the entire population.
   D. Saccharin consumption was measured less frequently in the second study.

3. Which of the following does NOT limit researchers' ability to generalize the studies' findings to a drug addict's devaluation of naturally rewarding interpersonal relationships?

   A. Only natural rewards involving the gustatory pathway are examined.
   B. The studies do not provide evidence of the concept of devaluation beyond situations involving the gustatory pathway.
   C. The TTA is not associated with emotional processing.
   D. Rewarding interpersonal relationships do not necessarily predict drug use.

4. The behavior of the rats in the saccharin-LiCl group is most likely the result of:

   A. devaluation.
   B. avoidance conditioning.
   C. aversion conditioning.
   D. tolerance.

5. Which of the following would likely hasten a devaluation process in Stage 2 of the studies?

   A. Decreasing the interval between the presentation of the saccharin and the presentation/injection of the second substance.
   B. Increasing the interval between the presentation of the saccharin and the presentation/injection of the second substance.
   C. Eliminating the second substance altogether.
   D. Reversing the order of the saccharin and the second substance.

6. Suppose some researchers argued that, due to the delay between the saccharin and the morphine, the behavior of the rats in the saccharin-morphine group during the second stage was a function of aversion conditioning rather than devaluation. According to this interpretation, which of the following phenomena would represent the unconditioned stimulus?

   A. Intoxication
   B. Potentiation
   C. Chemoreception
   D. Withdrawal

7. Which substance used in the experiment is most closely associated with the neurotransmitter dopamine?

   A. Saccharin
   B. Sucrose
   C. Morphine
   D. Lithium chloride

Passage 29 (Questions 1-6)

A significant portion of the population experiences a phenomenon known as synesthesia, in which stimulation of one sensory modality involuntarily and simultaneously activates a different sensory modality. Synesthetes, for example, report hearing sounds that accompany certain colors, tasting flavors when specific non-culinary words are spoken, and seeing colors for different numbers. Although scientists can confirm that many individuals are synesthetes through a battery of available tests, it is thought that a large percentage of people who may have synesthesia-like experiences do not even notice it themselves. Figure 1 shows a test for grapheme-color synesthesia, a type of synesthesia that results in a perception of color with letters and numbers.

Figure 1 A test for grapheme-color synesthesia

When presented the arrangement of numbers in Figure 1, a non-synesthete would perceive the black and white image on the left, while a synesthete who perceives colors when they see the numbers two and five can see patterns such as the triangle made up of the number twos on the right side of Figure 1. Non-synesthetes will typically have a much more difficult time identifying such patterns.

Three constructs that attempt to explain the neural mechanism for synesthesia are called hyperbinding, direct cross-activation, and disinhibited feedback. Hyperbinding is a process by which the neural information transmitted through one modality is linked with the second modality in the parietal lobe, the region of the brain affiliated with unification of disparate sensory features. Cross-activation involves direct stimulation of perceptual neural networks in both sensory modalities simultaneously, occurring in the part of the brain affiliated with processing the sensory modalities in question. Finally, the disinhibited feedback model, which may be compatible with hyperbinding, suggests that there is an over-activation of areas in the brain through limitations in the inhibition mechanism at the spot where different modalities converge.

Much of the research to support these three theories, however, has been limited to experiments with grapheme-color synesthetes. More recent studies have been interested in brain connectivity in music-color synesthetes (where the perception of sound or a specific tone triggers the perception of color). Since the linked modalities in this type of synesthesia are hearing and sight, researchers hypothesized that there might be structural differences in the brain and perhaps extra connectivity between the regions involved in processing the modalities involved.

In one study, it was found that the group of music-color synesthetes, with respect to the controls, showed a higher degree of fractional anisotropy (FA), a scalar value from zero to one that measures how constant diffusion is relative to orientation. FA values approaching zero demonstrate low anisotropy, meaning matter is diffused equally in all directions. FA values approaching one demonstrate high anisotropy, meaning diffusion tends to occur along one dimensional axis and is restricted in other directions. Table 1 shows mean FA in each hemisphere for control and experimental groups. Results like these precipitated the advancement of a fourth working model of synesthesia that postulates higher integration between the corresponding sensory processing centers in the brain for each modality.

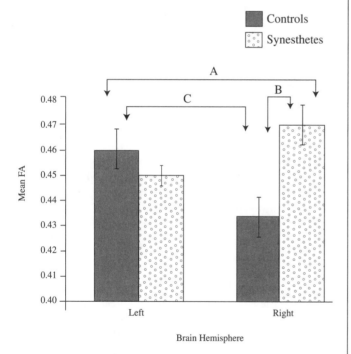

Figure 2 Functional anisotropy in subjects with color-music synesthesia (A = 0.05 significance level; B = 0.01 significance level; B = 0.001 significance level)

Adapted from A. Zamm, G. Schlaug, D.M. Eagleman, P. Loui. Pathways to seeing music: Enhanced structural connectivity in colored-music synesthesia. © 2013 by *Neuroimage*

1. The scientists studying music-color synesthesia hypothesized that there would be extra connectivity between brain regions. The two brain regions most likely involved are the:

   A. frontal lobe and the occipital lobe.
   B. parietal lobe and the occipital lobe.
   C. temporal lobe and the occipital lobe.
   D. frontal lobe and the parietal lobe.

2. Lexical-gustatory synesthesia is one of the more rare types of synesthesia that involves the perception of taste or smell when hearing spoken or reading written language. Which of the following is potentially the most logical locus of cross-activation for lexical-gustatory synesthesia?

   A. Amygdala
   B. Brainstem
   C. Broca's area
   D. Cerebellum

3. Of the four models of synesthesia discussed in the passage, the one most reliant on parallel processing is:

   A. hyperbinding.
   B. disinhibited feedback.
   C. cross-activation.
   D. high integration between processing centers.

4. Some studies have found that synesthetes often perform higher on tests of working memory recall that engage their linked modalities. This is most plausibly explained by:

   A. an emotional association with the task aiding the retrieval process.
   B. the neural plasticity of their brains.
   C. the process of long term potentiation.
   D. their ability to encode across multiple interfaces due to multimodal processing.

5. A young student displays synesthetic tendencies and tells his friends at school about it. They make fun of him and call him weird and crazy, thinking he is imagining the experience. For the first time, the child begins to have a negative opinion about his own synesthesia, which is an example of:

   A. symbolic interactionism.
   B. social constructionism.
   C. functionalism.
   D. the actor-observer bias.

6. The findings in Figure 1 suggest that:

   A. functional anisotropy is more lateralized in individuals with synesthesia.
   B. individuals with synesthesia, on average, had higher levels of functional anisotropy.
   C. functional anisotropy in the brain fully explained the prevalence of synesthesia.
   D. controls had significantly higher functional anisotropy in the left hemisphere than they did in the right hemisphere.

Passage 30 (Questions 1-6)

Human language is a mysterious phenomenon that has intrigued mankind for centuries. Numerous debates have since centered on the topic of second language acquisition. Today, many researchers argue that multilingualism comes with a wide array of benefits, including delayed onset of Alzheimer's disease (AD).

In order to determine whether bilingualism is associated with a delay in the onset of AD, researchers conducted a six-year retrospective study at a memory clinic in India. The sample included 700 patients with a mean age of 66. Of the 700 patients, approximately 62% spoke two or more languages fluently, and were considered to be in the "bilingual" group; the rest of the patients spoke only one language, and were therefore in the "monolingual" group. Researchers collected demographic information, including: education level, occupation, urban vs. rural dwelling, family history of dementia, and patient health history. Several types of dementia were included in this study: AD dementia, dementia with Lewy bodies (DLB), frontotemporal dementia (FTD), vascular dementia (VaD), and mixed dementia (see Figure 1).

Statistical analysis demonstrated that bilingual patients tended to develop dementia significantly later than monolingual patients, by nearly five years. A significant difference in age of onset was apparent across all five of the subtypes of dementia. No additional benefits were observed in those participants who spoke more than two languages. Literacy (the ability to read and write) in one or more languages did not impact the results. Further statistical analysis demonstrated that the effect of bilingualism on age of dementia onset was independent of the potentially confounding demographic variables listed above.

Dementia Subtype	Monolingual ($n = 267$)		Bilingual ($n = 433$)	
AD Dementia	101	(37.9%)	153	(35.3%)
DLB	7	(2.6%)	58	(13.4%)
FTD	58	(21.7%)	77	(17.8%)
VaD	82	(30.7%)	106	(24.5%)
Mixed	19	(7.1%)	39	(9%)

Figure 1 Distribution of dementia subtypes

Adapted from S. Alladi, T.H. Bak, V. Duggirala, B. Surampudi, M. Shailaja, A.K. Shukla, J.R. Chaudhuri, and S. Kaul. Bilingualism delays age at onset of dementia, independent of education and immigration status. © 2013 by *Neurology*.

1. Which of the following symptoms is/are indicative of damage to Broca's area of the brain?

   I. Slurred speech
   II. Clearly spoken but unrelated words strung together to form meaningless sentences
   III. Ability to understand language

   A. I only
   B. II only
   C. I and III only
   D. I, II, and III

2. Based on the evidence presented in the study mentioned above, which of the following is best supported by the study results?

   A. A monolingual would develop AD approximately five years after a bilingual.
   B. A trilingual would be more likely to develop AD later than a bilingual.
   C. A literate bilingual would probably develop AD later than an illiterate bilingual.
   D. An illiterate bilingual would be more likely to develop AD later than a literate monolingual.

3. Suppose a university student studied the Spanish language in high school, but claims to have forgotten nearly everything that she learned. Her friend, who happens to be studying Spanish currently, asks her if she remembers the Spanish word for *egg*. She shakes her head and forgets about the question. A few weeks later, while vacationing in Costa Rica, she picks up a breakfast menu and remembers that *huevo* is the Spanish word for egg. This is an example of:

   A. recall.
   B. recognition.
   C. relearning.
   D. recollection.

4. A mother enrolls her young son in Mandarin Chinese classes so that he will become bilingual and ultimately have an edge over his competitors in the real world. He is reluctant to attend classes and cries each time he is dropped off at the institution. The mother tells her son she will take him for ice cream after each class. His attitude suddenly changes and he goes on to excel in his classes. Which theory of motivation describes the mother's tactic?

   A. Drive-reduction theory
   B. Cognitive dissonance theory
   C. Incentive theory
   D. Needs theory

5. Despite its proven benefits, bilingualism is still viewed negatively by some. For instance, in an American classroom, a majority of monolingual English-speaking students may perceive minority students who are bilingual in English and Haitian Creole unfavorably. The bilingual students might be excluded from certain activities because they are seen as being different. In this case, the monolingual students would believe the bilingual students comprise:

   A. the in-group.
   B. the out-group.
   C. the reference group.
   D. the association group.

6. According to Figure 1, which of the following can be concluded about the patients included in this retrospective study?

   A. DLB was the least common subtype of dementia among both monolinguals and bilinguals.
   B. Bilinguals were more likely than monolinguals to experience VaD.
   C. AD Dementia is more likely to occur among bilinguals than it is among monolinguals.
   D. VaD was the second most common type of dementia among both monolinguals and bilinguals.

Passage 31 (Questions 1-5)

In the United States, there are detailed policies to prevent child abuse and formal structures exist to support the protection of children, such as the Child Protective Services (CPS). However, there is a lack of consensus among professionals regarding classifications of abuse and neglect. For example, corporal punishment (CP) involves the deliberate infliction of pain as a form of punishment (e.g., "spanking" a child with a belt). The United Nation's prohibits CP as a form of degrading punishment, extending the definition of child abuse to cases of discipline. There are 34 countries in the world where CP is made illegal through formal policies, but in most of the United States, this form of violence is legal. Nonetheless, there is evidence of a multitude of negative consequences of CP.

Despite the fact that most prefer receiving help from personal sources of support, parents often use professionals, such as medical professionals or religious leaders, as a source of parenting advice in situations where it is difficult to manage their children's behavior. Investigators at a large urban research institution in the Southern United States conducted a project to better understand the influence of these professionals and their discipline recommendations, in particular those regarding CP. The participant sample (n = 550 parents) was randomly selected to create a final sample comparable to the local population in demographics. The sample was 62% black and 38% white and 71% women and 29% men. Interested adult parents (aged 18 or older) with at least one child below the age of 16 were eligible for participation. The index child for research in families with more than one child was the child closet to the age of four (the peak age for parental use of CP). Measures included the specific professional source of parenting advice that parents used most often, the source whose advice parents followed most often, the use of corporal punishment, and demographics, including religious measures. Participants also provided data later used to consider parenting risks linked with the use of CP, such as parenting stress.

Researchers considered four professional sources: pediatricians, religious leaders, mental health professionals, and other professionals. Pediatricians were the preferred source of professional advice for the participant parents (49%), as well as the most followed source (Figure 1).

	Pediatricians	Religious Leaders	Mental Health Professionals	Other Professionals
Use of CP				
Never	52	16	19	13
< 1 use in the past 6 months	40	26	27	7
> 1 use in the past 6 months	21	37	16	26
Demographics				
Gender				
Female	49	21	19	11
Male	48	17	19	16
Race				
Black	43	29	19	9
White	57	7	18	18
Religious Characteristics				
Service Attendance				
Never	62	1	17	20
< 1 time per month	52	14	21	13
= 1 time per week	50	20	19	11
> 1 time per week	25	49	17	9
Importance of Religious Beliefs				
Very important	44	27	19	10
Less important	59	4	19	18

Figure 1 Family Characteristics by their Preferred Professional Source of Advice (%)

Adapted from C. Taylor, W. Moeller, L. Hamvas, & J. Rice (2012). Parents' professional sources of advice regarding child discipline and their use of corporal punishment. © 2012 by *Clinical Pediatrics*

1. Parents who use corporal punishment as a method of discipline demonstrate adherence to:

    A. authoritarian parenting.
    B. authoritative parenting.
    C. permissive parenting.
    D. rejecting parenting.

2. In order to make comparisons between the different sources of parenting advice, researchers provided a list of 15 relevant sources. Then, participants were asked how probable it was that discipline-related advice from each source would be followed. This response was rated using a range from 1 = very likely to 5 = very unlikely. The results showed that 10 of these sources received an average score near 2. Researchers were correct in their predictions for the source with the average closest to 1. Based on the information provided, this source is expected to be:

    A. the parent's spouse.
    B. the parent's religious leader.
    C. the child's pediatrician.
    D. the child's school teacher.

3. Parenting decisions regarding discipline have important implications for the children. Much evidence exists for the link between corporal punishment and negative outcomes for children, such as mental disorders. Thus, there are awareness campaigns that encourage the use of other forms of discipline, such as positive reinforcement or time out. For example, the United Nations Children's Fund (UNICEF), despite distinguishing between corporal punishment and other forms of abuse, is against the use of corporal punishment. It thus strives for constructive changes to methods of discipline that do not use violence, and thus do not inflict pain on children. The participants most expected to refer to the resources available on the UNICEF website are:

    A. black mothers.
    B. black fathers.
    C. white fathers.
    D. white mothers.

4. Based on the passage, professionals in which of the main three categories are LEAST expected to advise against the use of corporal punishment?

    A. Pediatricians
    B. Religious leaders
    C. Mental health professionals
    D. It cannot be determined

5. Religion is one of the most influential social institutions. In regards to the use of corporal punishment, which of the following can be concluded about the participants who reported the most frequent use of corporal punishment?

    I. These parents consulted religious leaders for suggestions about child discipline.
    II. These parents reported the most frequent attendance of religious events.
    III. These parents reported the highest levels of religiosity.

    A. I only
    B. I and II only
    C. II and III only
    D. I, II, and III

Passage 32 (Questions 1-5)

A decline in cognitive function in late adulthood has been well documented in the clinical literature. Some of the changes noted have been a decline in memory recall, although recognition ability tends to remain relatively intact. Information processing abilities as well as time-based tasks also tend to slow progressively in one's later years. However, the precise mechanisms involved in this cognitive slowing are still not known. As a result, many researchers are focusing their efforts on trying to identify these mechanisms.

One study wanted to determine if there is some sort of internal timing mechanism responsible for age-related cognitive decline. Researchers compared how younger and older participants performed on tasks that involved spontaneous motor tempo, processing speed, and working memory. Of the 60 volunteers, 20 ranged from ages 21 to 35 (younger group), 20 ranged from ages 65 to 80 (older group), and 20 ranged from ages 81 to 95 (very old group). All the participants were reported to be in good physical health.

All the participants engaged in tasks ranging from finger-tapping on a plastic block (a rhythmic task) to comparing symbols to assess whether they were identical (a speed test of symbol comparison) to three tasks to assess working memory involving memorizing letters, words, and sentences. Table 1 shows the average scores and standard deviations for each of the three groups on each test. The results suggest that the scores decline significantly with age, in accordance with the previous literature. The researchers also noted that older people used a slower tapping rate in the first test, indicating the possibility of a slower internal clock, confirming the researchers' hypothesis.

Tests	Younger		Older		Very Old	
	M	(SD)	M	(SD)	M	(SD)
Spontaneous Motor Tap (interval btwn taps in ms)						
Session 1	650	(190)	1100	(395)	1175	(500)
Session 2	640	(180)	1050	(220)	1100	(380)
Session 3	670	(208)	1060	(330)	1095	(400)
Processing speed (item # in 30 sec)						
Digit symbol	24	(3)	17	(3)	12.5	(2.5)
Symbol	26	(3.5)	16	(3)	10	(3)
Motor speed	56	(5)	41	(7)	30	(5)
Working speed (item # in 30 ms)						
Alphabetic span	16	(2)	11	(2.5)	9	(2.5)
Running span	27	(4)	19	(4.5)	16	(4)
Reading span	24	(5)	16	(5)	13	(6.5)

Table 1 Average scores for each age group on three cognitive tests.

Adapted from A. Baudouin, S. Vanneste, & M. Isingrini. Age-Related Cognitive Slowing: The Role of Spontaneous Tempo and Processing Speed. ©2004 *Experimental Aging Research*.

1. Which of the following memory tasks is usually more challenging for people in late adulthood?

   A. remembering to do important things in the future.
   B. remembering meaningful things from the distant past.
   C. remembering trivial things from the immediate recent past.
   D. remembering people and places from anywhere in the past.

2. Which of the following is/are examples of cognitive changes typical in later adulthood?

   I. Difficulty in being able to remember what a person looked like.
   II. An older driver taking longer to break when he sees a pedestrian crossing against a light.
   III. Difficulty recognizing a familiar face in a crowd.

   A. I only
   B. III only
   C. I and II only
   D. I, II, and III.

3. Which of the following are most characteristic of Alzheimer's disease?

   A. Difficulty initiating movement
   B. Reduction of dopamine-producing neurons in the brain
   C. Neurofibrillary tangles in the brain
   D. Increased hippocampal activity

4. The Older and Very Old groups in this study would be predicted to have reached which of Erikson's psychosocial stages?

   A. Identity vs. role confusion
   B. Generativity vs. stagnation
   C. Integrity vs. despair
   D. Intimacy vs. isolation

5. If the investigators of this study wanted to further research cognitive slowing, based on their results in this study, they would most probably choose to examine the link between cognitive processing speed decline and:

   A. internal clock slowing.
   B. memory recall.
   C. memory recognition.
   D. slowed reaction times.

Passage 33 (Questions 1-7)

Educational psychologists have reported several intriguing findings regarding the effects of academic tracking. One of these findings is called the Big Fish in a Little Pond Effect (BFLPE). According to the BFLPE, the academic self concept (ASC) of students in lower instructional tracks is actually higher than that of students in higher instructional tracks. To explain this effect, some theorists propose that when relatively low-achieving students compare themselves to other students within the same general achievement level, they feel more capable than when comparing themselves to a broader spectrum of students, including some with significantly higher achievement capabilities.

One study examining the BFLPE measured the ASC of students in high-level versus low-level tracks. The students remained in their assigned tracks throughout the term of the study. Measurements were taken at the end of ninth grade and again at the end of 11th grade. The researchers found that students in the low-level track showed an initial increase in ASC, but that the ASC of both groups of students dropped over the term of the study.

In a second study, a group of researchers explored how changing from a higher to a lower track impacts students' ASC and achievement scores. Nine-hundred students from three Australian public high schools were administered an ASC questionnaire at the conclusion of each year from the 9th through 12th grades. Additionally, the students' scores on end-of-year standardized achievement tests were obtained for each year of high school. The ASC questionnaire contained items reflective of a strong academic self-concept and it used a 10-point likert scale ranging from 0 (completely disagree) to 9 (completely agree). The achievement score scale ranged from 20% to 100%. Approximately one-third of the sample remained in the same academic track throughout high school; one-third dropped down one track at the beginning of 10th grade (drop-track 1); and one-third dropped down one track at the beginning of 11th grade (drop-track 2). The data for ASC ratings and achievement scores from this study are depicted in Figures 1 and 2, respectively.

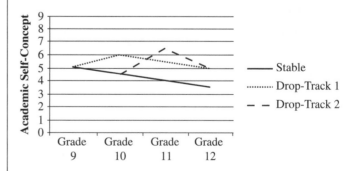

Figure 1 Mean academic self-concept over time

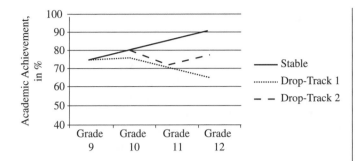

Figure 2 Mean academic achievement test scores over time

Adapted from S. Wouters, B. De Fraine, H. Colpin, J. Van Damme, and K. Verschueren. The Effect of Track Changes on the Development of Academic Self-Concept in High School: A Dynamic Test of the Big-Fish–Little-Pond Effect. © 2012 by *Journal of Educational Psychology.*

1. Which of the following conclusions can be drawn from the data in Figures 1 and 2?

    I.   Students who drop one track in tenth grade will show a similar pattern of change in both ASC and achievement by the time they reach twelfth grade.
    II. Stable-track high school students try to compensate for their low ASC by improving their achievement scores.
    III. For students in the stable track and those who drop a track in 11ᵗʰ grade, the data show a consistently negative correlation between ASC and achievement scores.

    A. I only
    B. II only
    C. I and II only
    D. I and III only

2. In contrast to the first study described in the passage, the second study employs:

    A. a longitudinal design.
    B. a between-groups design.
    C. a within-group design.
    D. a cross-sectional design.

3. Raymond Cattell developed the standard view of intelligence widely used in intelligence testing today, one of the constructs that he defined was termed Crystallized Intelligence, which he used to refer to intelligence that is:

    A. previously acquired knowledge.
    B. the ability to reason with known facts.
    C. unchanging ability.
    D. based on physical abilities.

4. Which of the following statements about ASC is supported by the data?

    A. Moving a student from a relatively high-achieving reference group to a relatively lower-achieving reference group does not negatively impact the student's ASC when compared to a stable-track peer.
    B. By twelfth grade, the rate of change in ASC is the same for students who dropped tracks in 10ᵗʰ grade as for those who dropped tracks in 11ᵗʰ grade.
    C. Dropping tracks later yields smaller initial gains in ASC.
    D. Depending on the tracking group, some students experience a continuous increase in ASC while others do not.

5. Which of the following findings support the argument for the importance of understanding what underlies the BFLPE?

    A. Educational outcomes are unrelated to the way in which students view their ranking among their peers.
    B. Academic self-concept predicts achievement test scores.
    C. Students' psychosocial health is determined by the quality of their interactions with peers.
    D. Schools that track typically have a smaller average class size than those that do not track.

6. Which of the following would NOT account for mixed findings regarding the impact of tracking on students' self concepts?

    A. Variety of grouping patterns and associated reference groups
    B. Different definitions of ASC employed by different researchers
    C. Disparate scores on ASC measures as reported by participants
    D. Different ages of samples

7. A primary implication of the explanation of BFLPE stated in the first paragraph is that:

   A. Piaget's stages of cognitive development are dependent on the affordances of the curriculum.
   B. Festinger's social comparison theory applies to the school context.
   C. Bandura's notion of self-efficacy is relevant to academic outcomes.
   D. Asch's findings on conformity do not apply in schools that track their students.

Passage 34 (Questions 1-6)

Science, technology, engineering and math (STEM) fields are growing quickly and are central to the U.S. knowledge economy. Jobs such as computer science and computer programming are well paid and offer job security and career advancement opportunities. Yet, of all STEM fields, occupational sex segregation is most apparent in computer science—only approximately 25% of college degrees in computer science are earned by women. Like jobs more generally, women have little maternity leave, encounter a work climate that is often not accommodating of women's dual role as employees and mothers, and women are paid less for their work than men. Furthermore, although it is common in two-parent households for both parents to work outside the home, mothers still take on a "second shift"—unpaid housework after the day's paid work is done. This can result in lost sleep, a subtle form of gender inequality. However, one thing is clear: women's absence from computer programming is not due to gender differences in raw intelligence. Because of this, educational researcher are now developing tactics to get women more interested in computer science so that they can enter the workforce and help achieve gender parity in the STEM fields.

To do this, the educational researchers are starting young—they found that while young girls believe they are "good at math," this number steadily decreases, particularly during middle school. There are several reasons for this, primarily that there are enduring stereotypes that boys are better at math because they are naturally more spatial thinkers, while girls are naturally better at reading and writing. The researchers therefore planned an interventional initiative to teach 4th and 5th grade girls the basics of computer coding so that they could have a fun entrée into computer science before they internalized the stereotype that they should be "worse" at math and science than the boys. Three afternoons a week for 6 weeks, the girls met after school with computer science students from a nearby college. Over the course of the 6 weeks, the girls learned the basics of website design and game design. At the end of the course, they gave presentations on their work to their families and celebrated their successes with a party. Pre- and post-intervention assessments suggested that the girls increased significantly on measures of self-confidence and wanting to pursue a career in computer science.

1. Professional women often find that they cannot advance beyond a certain level in their company, while their male peers do continue to receive promotions. Sociologists call this phenomenon:

   A. the wage gap.
   B. stratification.
   C. the glass ceiling.
   D. downward mobility.

2. During which sleep stage can "sleep spindles" be observed on an electroencephalogram (EEG)?

   A. Stage 2 sleep
   B. Stage 3 sleep
   C. Stage 1 sleep
   D. REM (rapid eye movement) sleep

3. A woman computer scientist goes to visit the doctor and complains of a stressful work environment, trouble sleeping, chronic nervousness, and poor concentration; which of the following diagnoses would be the most appropriate?

   A. Panic disorder
   B. Generalized anxiety disorder
   C. Acute stress disorder
   D. Obsessive-compulsive disorder

4. If a person perceives herself to be in a situation that is out of her control, she may respond with passivity because she feels that she can have no impact on the outcome, especially if she has experienced a similar situation in the past. This phenomenon is known as:

   A. Internal locus of control
   B. Low self-esteem
   C. Learned helplessness
   D. Self-efficacy

5. Which sociology concept best describes the teacher's propensity to perpetuate cultural stereotypes in the classroom?

   A. Self-fulfilling prophecy
   B. Prejudice
   C. Teacher expectancy theory
   D. Stratification

6. Computer enrichment courses for girls, such as the one described in the passage, contribute to the girls':

   A. cultural capital.
   B. social capital.
   C. meritocracy.
   D. privilege.

Passage 35 (Questions 1-5)

Using the Five Factor Model (FFM) of personality, researchers have been able to prospectively predict divorce and/or relationship dissolution in committed couples a decade or more into the future. Research has demonstrated that Conscientiousness, Neuroticism, and Ageeableness are the best predictors of divorce, with better predictive power than IQ or socioeconomic status. Low levels of Conscientiousness and Agreeableness, and high levels of Neuroticism have been associated with relationship failure. It has been theorized that personality traits impact the relationship's overall quality by impacting the day-to-day interactions of the couple which can shape the level of relationship satisfaction. It was theorized that relationship dynamics are influenced by personality traits of the members of the couple from the beginning of the relationship onward, and that personality traits influence reactions to negative life events, which can then negatively impact relationship satisfaction.

In order to more fully elucidate the mechanisms by which personality impacts relationship longevity, a longitudinal study was designed to assess which personality factors most strongly influence relationship dissolution and how the mechanism operates. Two thousand adults, in opposite- or same- sex couples, were asked to complete a self-report measure assessing personality, and to describe the status of their current committed relationship. The study authors hypothesized that the couple members' personality traits (particularly Neuroticism) would predict relationship satisfaction without considering the length of the relationship. They predicted that high levels of Neuroticism would lead to lower levels of relationship satisfaction. Next, the researchers predicted that changes in the level of satisfaction over time would be associated with specific personality traits, namely that higher Neuroticism would lead to greater negative changes in satisfaction while Agreeableness would cushion the common decrease in relationship satisfaction over time. Five measurements of relationship satisfaction, relationship dissolution, and significant life events, were taken over the course of five years.

Agreeableness, conscientiousness, openness to experience, and neuroticism were all found to be predictors of relationship dissolution. Couple members low in agreeableness and conscientiousness were more likely to have their relationships dissolve, as were those high in neuroitcism and openness to experience. It appears that those qualities contribute to negative communication patterns which negatively influence relationship satisfaction thereby leading to dissolution.

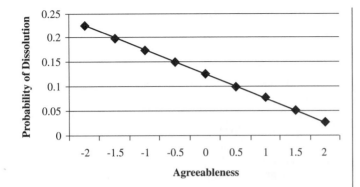

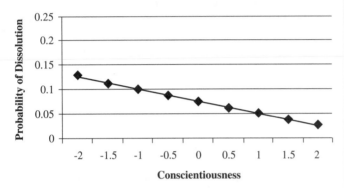

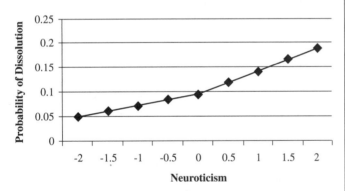

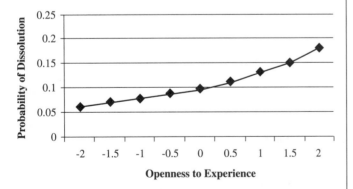

Figure 1 Likelihood of relationship dissolution for each trait; presented as z scores.

Variable	*b*	Odds ratio
Openness	0.25*	1.22*
Agreeableness	-0.02	0.95
Conscientiousness	0.03	1.01
Neuroticism	0.11*	1.12*
Sex	-0.02	0.99
Relationship duration	0.82*	0.47*
Religious identification	.29*	1.33*
Income	-0.18*	.88*
Education	-0.30*	.68*
De facto relationships	0.17*	1.21*
Marriages	0.28*	.67*

*$p < 0.05$

Table 1 Personality Traits Predicting Relationship Dissolution

Adapted from: B. C. Soloman & J. J. Jackson. Why Do Personality Traits Predict Divorce? Multiple Pathways Through Satisfaction ©2014 by American Psychological Association.

1. Which one is NOT a trait of the Five Factor Model?

   A. Neuroticism
   B. Openness to Experience
   C. Amenableness
   D. Extraversion

2. Is the study described a true experiment?

   A. Yes, because the couples were collected randomly.
   B. Yes, because there is one independent and several dependent variables.
   C. No, because it was a longitudinal study.
   D. No, because there is no random assignment to groups.

3. Which factors contribute to the likelihood of relationship dissolution:

    I. Increased Education
    II. High Neuroticism
    III. High Openness to Experience

    A. II only
    B. I & II only
    C. II & III only
    D. I, II, & III

4. Personality is defined as:

    A. inherited, biological traits that determine people's reactions to events.
    B. enduring, characteristic patterns of behavior, thinking, and feeling.
    C. ephemeral reactions which change from situation to situation.
    D. the typical behavior of an individual.

5. Based on the results of this study, who is more likely to have a relationship dissolve:

    A. a person who scores one standard deviation above the mean on Neuroticism.
    B. a person who scores one standard deviation below the mean on Conscientiousness.
    C. a person who scores one and a half standard deviations above the mean on Openness.
    D. a person who scores one and a half standard deviations below the mean on Agreeableness.

Passage 36 (Questions 1-6)

Research on how attention works has demonstrated that for many tasks, full attention to one task is superior than divided attention to many.

A study looking to examine if divided attention is always a distraction attempted to replicate the results of previous research. In prior studies, researchers showed participants a sequence of pictures with a small square superimposed in the center. If the square was white, the subjects were instructed to press the space bar—an infrequent occurrence—and if the square was black, the subjects were instructed to do nothing, and focus only on encoding the pictures. These prior studies demonstrated that the images encoded with the white squares were actually remembered *better*—which was dubbed the attentional boost effect—despite the divided attention situation. In fact, subjects were able to remember the images with the white squares as well as the control group, which only had the images presented without any squares.

In the current study, 100 participants were asked to memorize words presented on a computer screen. For the control group (full attention), this was the only task; for the experimental group (divided attention) there was a second task: they were also asked to attend to the color of a small circle underneath each word. Participants in the divided attention group had to press the space bar each time they saw the infrequent red circle instead of the frequent green circle.

Figure 1 shows the percentage of words recalled correctly by subjects in the divided attention (DA) condition compared to percentage of words recalled correctly by subjects in the full attention (FA) condition, who were able to memorize the list without distractions.

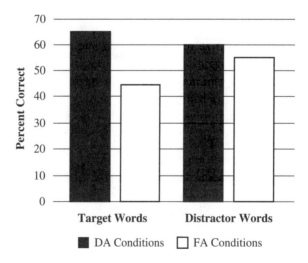

Figure 1 Percent of words recalled correctly for divided attention and full attention groups.

Adapted from P. Spataro, N. W. Mulligan, & C. Rossi-Arnaud. Divided Attention Can Enhance Memory Encoding: The Attentional Boost Effect in Implicit Memory. ©2013 *Journal of Experimental Psychology*.

1. The resource model of attention states that:

    A. in order to focus their full attention, individuals must "shine a spotlight" on the particular resource on which they wish to focus.
    B. humans have the resources to fill in any missing information and thus do not need to attend to everything.
    C. humans selectively filter out unnecessary information according to their resources.
    D. humans have a limited amount of resources for attention when performing tasks.

2. Based on the research about divided attention, how might the researchers have changed the methodology to make it harder for the participants to memorize the lists of words?

    A. Instead of a red or green circle, the researchers used circles the same color as the word so the shapes became harder to spot.
    B. Instead of a red or green circle underneath the word, the researchers put another word in red or green as the "distractor."
    C. Instead of a red or green circle, the researchers used two different abstract shapes, one with round edges, and one angular.
    D. The researchers put the words in red if there was a green circle or green if there was a red circle.

3. Which of the following multitasking situations is most likely to produce results similar to those in Figure 1?

    A. Writing a term paper while listening to instrumental music
    B. The bystander effect
    C. The Stroop effect
    D. Studying in a calm environment with sound-canceling headphones

4. If a person went to a sold-out baseball game that was very noisy, but was still able to hear her name yelled out from many seats away, this would be an example of:

    A. Treisman's attenuation model of selective attention.
    B. Broadbent filter model of selective attention.
    C. the cocktail party effect.
    D. selective priming.

5. How might Treisman's model account for the results in this research?

    A. Words and circles enter the central executive, go through phonological loop, then visuospatial sketchpad, and episodic buffer, and then into working memory.
    B. Words and circles enter a sensory store, go through selective filter, and hit a bottleneck, and only the words go through to higher level processing and then working memory.
    C. Words and circles enter a sensory store, go through an attenuating filter, hit a bottleneck, volume turns up on words and down for circles, and words get stored in working memory.
    D. Words and circles enter a sensory store, go through a phonological filter, hit a bottleneck, and both words and circles reach working memory.

6. If the results showed that the participants in the FA group scored higher than the DA group, this might have been caused by all of the following reasons, EXCEPT:

    A. the second task was too easy.
    B. the second task was too difficult.
    C. the second task was too similar.
    D. the second task required too much practice.

Passage 37 (Questions 1-5)

Several factors contribute to the degree of tolerance individuals have toward ethnic groups, including religious and political affiliations, the deprivation of resources in society, and social mobility. The stability of the individuals' religious and political affiliations as well as the degree of life-satisfaction can result in a higher ethnic tolerance.

Three types of controls that predict hostile inclinations towards ethnic groups are: external control, conscience control, and rational self-control. External control occurs when outside factors (i.e. institutions, peers) have influence over the individual's beliefs and behavior. Unlike external control, conscience control occurs when individuals are not threatened by external forces, but have internalized beliefs that are both partly conscious and partly rational. In contrast, rational self-control deals with irrational beliefs purely through internalized rational control. Though the types of controls differ, it is common for them to coexist with one another.

Researchers hypothesized that those who experienced upward mobility are more likely to have a higher ethnic tolerance compared to those who experienced downward mobility. For this study, 250 U.S. war veterans were encouraged to express their opinions about major ethnic groups (Blacks and Jews) during an interview. Those who belonged in the aforementioned minority groups were not included as participants of the study. Participants were classified into three groups based on their responses: tolerant veterans (no stereotyped beliefs mentioned about ethnic group), stereotyped veterans (both positive and negative stereotyped beliefs mentioned about ethnic group when asked during the interview), and intense veterans (hostile opinions about the ethnic group before the topic was mentioned during the interview). The first part of the interview gave participants the chance to voluntarily talk about their opinions on minority groups while the second part of the interview involved researchers asking direct questions about Blacks and Jews. Figure 1 shows the degree of tolerance the veterans had for both Jews and Blacks respectively in relation to the social mobility of the participants during their lifetime.

	Downward Mobility		No Mobility		Upward Mobility		Total Participants	
	No.	Percent	No.	Percent	No.	Percent	No.	Percent
Anti-Semitic:								
Tolerant	6	16%	38	28%	48	62%	92	37%
Stereotyped	10	27%	62	46%	25	32%	97	39%
Intense	21	57%	35	26%	5	6%	61	24%
Anti-Black:								
Tolerant	7	19%	20	15%	31	40%	58	23%
Stereotyped	12	32%	73	54%	24	31%	109	44%
Intense	18	49%	42	31%	23	29%	83	33%
Total..............	37	....	135	....	78	....	250	....

Figure 1 Results of veteran's degrees of tolerance towards ethnic groups in relation to their social mobility in society

Adapted from B. Bettelheim & M. Janowitz. Ethnic Tolerance: A Function of Social and Personal Control. ©1949 by The University of Chicago Press

1. During the interview, the veterans' stereotypical responses about major ethnic groups are considered acts of:

   A. discrimination.
   B. prejudice.
   C. institutional discrimination.
   D. stereotype threat.

2. Which of the following relationships is most accurate?

   A. There is a positive correlation between the stability of group affiliations and ethnic tolerance, while there is a negative correlation between the satisfaction of the individual's lifestyle and ethnic hostility.
   B. There is a negative correlation between the individual's lifestyle and ethnic tolerance, while there is a positive correlation between stability of group affiliations and ethnic hostility.
   C. There is a positive correlation between the stability of group affiliations and ethnic tolerance as well as the individual's lifestyle and ethnic hostility.
   D. There is a negative correlation between the stability of group affiliations and ethnic hostility as well as the individual's lifestyle and ethnic tolerance.

3. Respectively, external control, conscience control, and rational self-control are most analogous to:

   A. id control, superego control, and ego control.
   B. id control, ego control, and superego control.
   C. social control, superego control, and ego control.
   D. social control, ego control, and superego control.

4. Suppose that an individual originally embraces the ideals of the Republican Party to avoid any societal disapproval. Eventually, the individual began to accept the ideals of the Democratic Party because he personally considers them as absolute values of behavior, no longer having fear of being rebuked by his peers. Which of the following types of control were described in the scenario?

   I. External Control
   II. Rational Self-control
   III. Conscience Control

   A. I only
   B. I and II only
   C. I and III only
   D. II and III only

5. Which of the following statements most accurately portrays Figure 1?

   A. Participants who remained static in mobility were the least likely to harbor ethnic stereotypes.
   B. Overall, more participants had hostile opinions towards Jews than Blacks.
   C. Participants who experienced downward mobility were more likely to express ethnic tolerance compared to those who experienced upward mobility.
   D. The highest amount of participants was categorized as those who experienced no social mobility and expressed positive and negative stereotypes about Blacks.

Passage 38 (Questions 1-5)

Evolutionary Psychology is a theoretical branch of psychology that examines traits like memory, perception, and language from a modern evolutionary framework. It attempts to identify human psychological traits that are evolved adaptations—those that are functional products of natural selection or sexual selection. A core tenet in Evolutionary Psychology is the belief that traits that occur across all humans are good indicators of evolutionary adaptation. If an adaptation is independently exhibited by distant cultures with minimal interaction, then it is likely to have a deep evolutionary foundation. Traits that demonstrate such cross-cultural universality are the ability to infer the emotions of others (intuition), the ability to discern kin from non-kin, the ability to identify and prefer healthy mates, and the ability to cooperate with others.

Evolutionary Psychology involves a fusion of many scientific disciplines: it is rooted in cognitive psychology and evolutionary biology, but also draws on behavioral ecology, artificial intelligence, genetics, ethology, archaeology, biology and zoology. There are many examples of various types of mechanisms: language-acquisition modules, incest-avoidance mechanisms, foraging mechanisms, alliance-tracking mechanisms, among others. Some (not all) mechanisms fall into one of two categories: domain-specific mechanisms deal with adaptive problems within a limited scope but cannot be generalized to solve broader evolutionary challenges while domain-general mechanisms can adapt to solve novel problems and situations. For example, cones are a domain-specific adaptation to perceive color, whereas the evolution of language is a domain-general adaptation that allows for communication and schematic representations to analyze and solve new evolutionary problems.

Traits of organisms can fall into one of several categories in Evolutionary Psychology: these are: adaptations, exaptations, by-products, and random variations. An adaptation is a trait designed to solve an ancestral problem; it shows complexity and a specific functionality. An exaptation is an adaptation that has been "re-designed" to solve a different evolutionary problem. A by-product is a subsidiary function of an adaptive mechanism with no current or ancestral function. A random variation is a change that is due to statistical randomness and not a specifically selected for feature.

1. Which of the following is an example of a trait that is thought to demonstrate cross-cultural universality?

   A. Certain emotions, like fear and anger
   B. Monogamous pair-bonding
   C. Social norms for making eye-contact
   D. Intelligence

2. Some theorists suppose that bird feathers originally adapted for insulation. If this is the case, they are an example of which kind of trait?

   A. Adaption
   B. Exaptation
   C. By-product
   D. Random variation

3. The theory of parental involvement suggests that if there is asymmetry in parental involvement, the more involved sex will be more sexually selective. Which of the following studies would NOT be considered an exploration of parental involvement?

   A. A study that measures the reported willingness of mothers to engage in a casual sexual relationships; maternal involvement as the independent variable
   B. A study that measures self-reported willingness of adult males to provide resources (food, shelter) to a photograph; face similarity to the male himself as the independent variable
   C. A study that identifies levels of competition over an attractive opposite-sex actor; gender as the independent variable
   D. A study that examines the likelihood that teenagers will help an actor; previous helpfulness of the actor as the independent variable

4. The mammalian heart contains four chambers and is the most complex in the animal kingdom. This is an example of:

   A. A domain-specific adaptation
   B. A domain-specific exaptation
   C. A domain-general adaptation
   D. A domain-general exaptation

5. The subject of group evolution is a topic of debate among many researchers. Group selection occurs when evolutionary constraints result in survival being dependent on differences between groups of organisms rather than between individual organisms within a group. Which of the following traits is most likely to have evolved due to group selection?

   A. Muscle mass
   B. Language
   C. Epidermal tissue
   D. Intelligence

Passage 39 (Questions 1-5)

The nature versus nurture debate has raged for centuries. Much of what psychologists and other researchers have learned in this quest for evidence has come from research with twins, both identical and fraternal. Twin research provides psychologists with a natural way to try and determine the effect of environment and genetic makeup on traits.

One area in which this research is particularly important is on how children develop their capacities to relate to others. Additionally, one area particularly important to children's relationships with others is peer difficulties, starting from an early age. Much of the literature on peer relationship difficulties suggests that these experiences are passing phases caused by victimization and rejection. However, more chronic issues seem to be rooted in some combination of environmental and developmental factors. This is where twin studies can be of great help—they can control for the genetic factors.

One longitudinal study on monozygotic (MZ) twins examined the question of how twins dealt with peer relationship difficulties upon entry into school. This study involved 700 families of MZ twins, followed at 5, 20, 30, 50, and 60 months, from kindergarten through grade four. Researchers asked the children to circle the pictures of classmates who they liked and also whom they did not like, as well as classmates who might be treating them badly, such as attacking them physically or verbally. Teachers also evaluated these measures, noting which students were treated badly by which other students. Table 1 shows the correlation coefficients for twin pairs and their teachers for difficult relationships in each of three grades.

	Peer rating of victimization	Teacher rating of victimization	Self-rating of victimization
Kindergarten	.18	.26	.10
Grade 1	.22	.31	.11
Grade 4	.46	.33	.15

Table 1 Correlations between peer difficulty assessments among twins in kindergarten, grade 1 and grade 4

The results show that correlations between self-assessment and external assessment of victimization and peer-relationship difficulties increased as the children got older, which also seems to indicate an increase in overall peer-relationship difficulties, according to the researchers, which they attribute to genetic factors.

Adapted from M. Botvin, M. Brendgen, F. Vitaro, G. Dionne, A. Girard, D. Perusse, & R. E. Tremblay Strong Genetic Contribution to Peer Relationship Difficulties at School Entry: Findings From a Longitudinal Twin Study. ©2013 *Child Development*.

1. MZ twins:

    A. are assumed to share 100% of their genes and most of their environment.
    B. allow for studies on the effect of genes on shared traits, but not on the effects of environment on shared traits.
    C. allow researchers to completely control for both prenatal and postnatal environmental differences.
    D. share about 50% of their genes and most of their environment.

2. If the researchers wanted to understand more about the genetic link between monozygotic twins and peer-relationship difficulties, what other variables might be important to study?

    I. The peer-relationship difficulties of the twins' biological siblings and parents.
    II. The twins' academic difficulties.
    III. The teachers' role in mediating these peer-relationship difficulties.

    A. I only
    B. III only
    C. II and III only
    D. I and III only

3. According to the biopsychosocial model of disease:

    A. psychological disorders are both diagnosable and treatable.
    B. all diseases have an underlying genetic component.
    C. both nature and nurture are important elements in the development of disease.
    D. social factors become more relevant to the onset of disease as individuals age.

4. How do adoption studies change "classic" twin research?

    A. Adoption studies make it harder to control for genetic factors.
    B. Adoption studies focus only on the genetic angle of the research.
    C. Adoption creates two groups: genetic relatives and environmental relatives, so it adds another dimension to the research.
    D. Adoption adds confounding variables such as personality traits, additional family members, and multiple environments.

5. Which of the following would be an argument against a genetic link in peer relationship difficulties?

   A. If the peer relationship difficulties occurred because of a one-time incident.

   B. If the peer relationship difficulties occurred with both twins.

   C. If the peer relationship difficulties are stable and continuous over time.

   D. If the peer relationship difficulties occurred in an unstable environment.

Passage 40 (Questions 1-5)

Perhaps one of the greatest mysteries of the human brain is what motivates people to act the way they do. One place this plays out most clearly is in the classroom, especially the high school classroom. How does a teacher get his or her students to do their best work? How does a teacher convince their students to pay attention in class, to do their homework, to show up for tests, or even to put down their cell phones?

Psychologists have put forth various theories about motivation over the years—that it has to do with instincts, drives, needs, or incentives. The theories integrate physiological and sociocultural factors. However, in the end, the picture is still fuzzy.

To try to begin to clarify the picture, a group of researchers decided to compare students' and teachers' beliefs about high school students' motivation and see how much those beliefs were or were not in alignment. The researchers surveyed 400 high school students and 100 high school teachers in Midwestern high schools. They asked the students and teachers to rank, on a scale of 1 ("strongly disagree") to 6 ("strongly agree"), various statements such as "I am motivated so I can have a good future," "I am motivated when I like the teacher," and "Students are motivated when the teacher takes a personal interest in the students."

Researchers grouped results based on standard categories for types of motivation: goal activation, intrinsic and extrinsic motivation, self-efficacy, and social goals, as well as teacher characteristics and teaching abilities. Figure 1 shows the variations between student perceptions of the importance of these measures versus teacher perceptions.

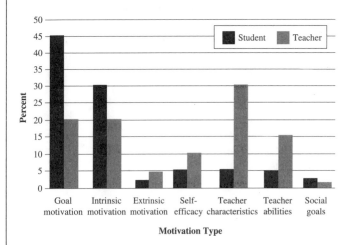

Figure 1 Student and teacher perceptions of motivational factors.

Adapted from J. Wiesman Student Motivation and the Alignment of Teacher Beliefs. ©2012 *The Clearing House*.

1. What is the correct order for these needs according to Maslow's hierarchy of needs?

   A. Need to feel safe, need to feel love, need to achieve, need to self-actualize
   B. Need to feel safe, need to self-actualize, need to achieve, need to feel love
   C. Need to feel love, need to feel safe, need to achieve, need to self-actualize
   D. Need to self-actualize, need to feel love, need to achieve, need to feel safe

2. The results above suggest that students attribute their own motivation and willingness to achieve to more intrinsic factors, while teachers seem to attribute motivation to what the teachers themselves do rather than the students. This would be an example of what social psychology principle?

   A. Fundamental attribution error.
   B. Self-serving bias.
   C. Optimism bias.
   D. Just world phenomenon.

3. If the researchers wanted to look at more interactional factors influencing how students are motivated and what role, if any, teachers have in the process, how might the researchers adapt the study?

   I. Use descriptive questions, which ask how the teachers or students motivate one another.
   II. Include more detailed survey questions focusing on student-teacher interactions.
   III. Increase the gradations on the Likert scale, by adding more number options, so participants can more accurately describe exactly how much they agree or disagree with a statement.

   A. I only
   B. III only
   C. I and II only
   D. I, II, and III

4. Which of the following is NOT a biologically or psychologically based theory of human motivation?

   A. Incentive theory
   B. Human instinct
   C. Homeostasis
   D. Drive reduction theory

5. Which of the following is NOT true regarding adolescent development?

   A. The brain, especially the prefrontal cortex, which is responsible for abstract thought and anticipating consequences, is still developing throughout the teenage years.
   B. It is a time of confusion over identity roles.
   C. Puberty causes changes in primary sex characteristics.
   D. The limbic system is developing more rapidly than the prefrontal cortex.

Passage 41 (Questions 1-5)

Postpartum depression (PPD) is a clinical disorder that can affect both men and women following birth. The most common characteristics of PPD include insomnia, loss of appetite, overwhelming fatigue, and severe mood swings. These issues often interfere with the person's role of providing for their infant. PPD is more severe than the baby blues, which last less than two weeks, but the signs are often similar at first, such as sadness, decreased concentration, and other less intense and short-lived issues. PPD is less severe than postpartum psychosis, which is a rare condition that often develops in the first two weeks after birth and is characterized by much more severe symptoms than those associated with PPD, including disorientation, hallucinations, and paranoia. The prevalence rate of PPD is unclear due to methodological differences in existing studies, but reported estimates range from 5-25%. PPD can be measured through self-reported questionnaires, such as the Edinburgh postnatal depression scale (EPDS), which contains ten items that correspond to various signs of the disorder.

The causes of PPD are not well understood, and much previous research centers on the presence of antenatal depression. However, there is also evidence to support self-reports of antenatal anxiety disorders as a predictor of depression in the postnatal periods. Previous studies have found that the likelihood of developing PPD is three times higher for those reporting such disorders. Researchers at an institution in the United Kingdom were interested in the effects of specific anxiety disorders on concurrent depression with a specific focus on the effects of generalized anxiety disorder (GAD) and social anxiety disorder (SAD), also known as social phobia, at the distinct phases of infant development. Potential participants were recruited at the hospital during their visit for a routine antenatal scan (20 weeks) and the screening process contained multiple steps including an initial questionnaire to assess the presence of an anxiety disorder and a full length diagnostic interview to determine the absence or presence of an anxiety disorder based on DSM-IV criteria. The total sample (n = 250) included women with (1) GAD (n = 55), (2) SAD (n = 70), (3) both GAD and SAD (n = 30), and (4) neither GAD nor SAD (n = 95) for comparison purposes. Data were collected using the EPDS at four specific time points post-delivery: 10-14 days; 10-12 weeks; 12 months; and 18 months. The detailed results are shown in Figure 1 below.

	Postpartum time point			
	10-14 days	10-12 weeks	12 months	18 months
GAD	37	18	33	28
SAD	25	12	26	19
Both	30	15	29	20

Figure 1 The relationship between antenatal anxiety disorders and the development of postpartum depression (percentage of participants who scored a 12 or higher on the EPDS, the diagnostic cut-off for PPD)

Adapted from H. Coelho, L. Murray, M. Royal-Lawson, and P. Cooper. Antenatal anxiety disorder as a predictor of postnatal depression: A longitudinal study. ©2011 by *Journal of Affective Disorders.*

1. In industrialized nations, such as the United Kingdom, most women report positive birth experiences. However, this is not the case for all new mothers. Those who suffered distress during birth are said to have had a traumatic birth. This distress might have resulted from birth complications, such as abnormal presentation of the fetus in preparation for delivery, and injuries can be significant after the birth. In such a situation, PPD can be said to be the result of which of the following stressors?

   A. A chronic stressor
   B. A catastrophe
   C. A daily hassle
   D. A significant life change

2. Postpartum depression can have serious implications for the parent-infant relationship. According to sick role theory:

   A. this type of diagnosis is not an instance of deviance.
   B. a new mother is obligated to return to her normal societal functions, despite a legitimate diagnosis of PPD.
   C. if a women does not bond with her infant during the crucial newborn phase, the child will be more likely to develop fixations later in life.
   D. a woman experiencing PPD should have the desire to feel better and bond with her infant.

3. Based on the findings presented in the passage, which of the following conclusions are supported?

   I. PPD occurred at the greatest rate for most participant groups 10-14 days postpartum.
   II. PPD occurred at the highest levels in most time periods for those with GAD.
   III. Those with both GAD and SAD experienced PPD at a rate most similar to those with GAD only.

   A. I and II only
   B. I and III only
   C. II and III only
   D. I, II, and III

4. Mothers often experience significant tension in their attempt to balance the roles of being a parent to their child and a partner to their spouse. This phenomenon is called:

   A. role conflict.
   B. role exit.
   C. role strain.
   D. role tension.

5. Generalized anxiety disorder is characterized by:

   A. panic attacks.
   B. psychosis.
   C. chronic nervousness and tension.
   D. the presence of a traumatic experience.

Passage 42 (Questions 1-5)

The role of social influence on behavior cannot be understated when examining such phenomena as stereotypes. Simply defined, stereotypes are a set of beliefs about a group of people. Stereotyping, as it is commonly perceived, mainly relates to how people view other people who are typically not a part of their in-group. Although the act of stereotyping others can lead to instances of discrimination or misunderstanding, stereotypes can also have a negative impact on individuals when they project stereotypes upon themselves.

Stereotype threat occurs when an individual unintentionally conforms to a stereotype. This is true of any group that may experience a stereotype, including stereotypes about gender, race, ethnic or cultural groups. For instance, a woman who is interviewing for a job in the technology field may become more aware of the stereotype that men are better at engineering and tech jobs. This cognitive shift may actually hinder the woman's performance during the job interview. On the other hand, one study found that individuals of Asian descent that were primed for the stereotype of being good at mathematics actually improved performance on a test of mathematics, and effect known as stereotype boost.

Logical considerations of stereotype threat reveal some underlying constructs that may help understand the functionality of this process. One could consider harsh self-judgment as an underlying factor in stereotype threat. An individual who tends to judge themselves harshly may be more likely to fall prey to stereotype threat. Consequently, if this relationship is true, an individual who learns to engage with their thoughts with less self-judgment may present with lower levels of stereotype threat.

Mindfulness is a way to train oneself to attend to the cognitions of the present moment with complete non-judgment. Consider a hypothetical study that looks at the relationship between Self-Judgment and Stereotype Threat, as well as the implications of mindfulness training on Stereotype Threat. Women were randomly assigned into two groups, control and treatment. Both groups received Stereotype Threat priming at two measurement points, pre and post group training. The level of Self-Judgment was also measured at the pre-group training. The control group participated in a neutral group training activity, while the treatment group participated in mindfulness training. The results of the study are presented in Figures 1 and 2.

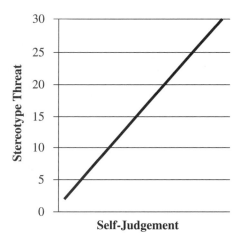

Figure 1 Correlational relationship between Self-Judgment and Stereotype Threat at pre-group training measurement

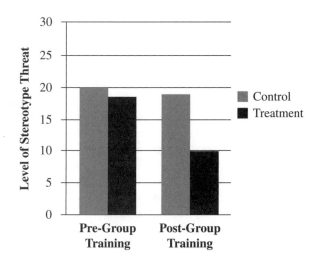

Figure 2 Level of Stereotype Threat with mindfulness training

1. A concept related to stereotype threat is the self-fulfilling prophecy. Which of the following is an example of the self-fulfilling prophecy?

   A. Shirley has a big math test coming up. She tells herself, "I'm no good at math anyway" and spends the week texting her friends and watching TV instead of studying. When she takes her math test on Friday, she receives a failing grade.
   B. Marco wakes up in the morning thinking, "today is going to be a terrible day." When he gets to school, he goofs around with his friends and ends up having a rather pleasant day.
   C. Robert knows he is good at physics. He is so confident that he spends the week playing video games and chatting online with his friends. When he takes his physics test on Monday, he receives a failing grade.
   D. Felicia is not confident about her Biology exam. However, she takes time during the week to study and review her notes on cell mitosis. She ends up receiving an A+ on her exam.

2. Figure 1:

   A. indicates that mindfulness training causes a decrease in stereotype threat.
   B. demonstrates a positive correlation between Self-Judgment and Stereotype Threat.
   C. suggests that those experiencing stereotype boost will have low levels of self-judgment.
   D. proves the null hypothesis correct.

3. Of the following scenarios, which outcome is least likely a result of Stereotype Threat?

    A. Gina, a woman who has a PhD in physics, is a contestant on a reality show where the contestants participate in "challenges" that often involve puzzles. Gina is the one chosen to work the puzzle for her team instead of the intelligent man on her team, Zachary. The puzzle mostly tests spatial relations and is difficult. She performs poorly at solving the puzzle and the team loses the challenge.

    B. Black students at Central High School performed worse than the white students on the mid-term exam when their teacher told them that the test was measuring their academic abilities. The next year, the teachers told the students that the test was not measuring their academic abilities and that it was just a practice test. This time, the black students performed just as well as white students.

    C. Ned is taking an aptitude test for a job placement. The other applicant is a well-dressed East Asian man also taking the test. Ned performs poorly on the aptitude test, even though he was well suited for the job and was confident about the test earlier that day.

    D. Jennifer, a staunch Democrat, is worried that her opinions are too radical for her family, who are more conservative. In order to not start any fights over Thanksgiving, she keeps her opinions to herself.

4. Based on the results of the study shown in Figure 2, what can be concluded?

    A. Mindfulness is not effective at reducing stereotype threat.

    B. Mindfulness is effective at reducing stereotype threat.

    C. There is no relationship between Mindfulness and Stereotype Threat.

    D. The neutral group training activity worked better at reducing stereotype threat than the Mindfulness training group.

5. What is the dependent variable in the experimental study mentioned in the passage?

    A. Self-Judgment
    B. Mindfulness
    C. Stereotype Threat
    D. Self-Fulfilling Prophecy

Passage 43 (Questions 1-6)

Although parent-child interactions have long been shown to predict a child's future relationship dynamics, researchers have begun to explore the impact of genetics on these statistical relationships. One group of researchers set out to test the differential susceptibility hypothesis (DSH) in the context of parent-child interactions. The DSH posits that certain alleles are responsible for moderating one's sensitivity to environmental influences such as hostility or positive emotional engagement. Accordingly, a greater number of such alleles yield an overall greater plasticity, or sensitivity, to both positive and negative experiences. The researchers hypothesized that individuals with higher plasticity will show greater associations between the degree of hostile and positive emotional engagement with parents and the degree of hostile and positive emotional engagement with romantic partners later in life.

The primary participants, referred to here as targets, were observed as adolescents in their interactions with parents. On three occasions over the course of one year, trained observers presented family members with various tasks designed to elicit conflict or positive interaction. The observers categorized behaviors into one of two categories, namely hostility or positive emotional engagement, and rated each behavior on a scale of 1 (minimally hostile/positive) to 6 (extremely hostile/positive). The ratings from the three observation points were averaged to produce a composite score for each category of interaction. Fifteen years later, the targets were observed in their interaction with a romantic partner, and an identical rating system was used. Subsequently, targets' saliva was analyzed for the presence of three different alleles shown to have plasticity effects. A given participant could have none, one, or two of each allele for a minimum of 0 and a maximum of 6. The researchers used the combined number of alleles to construct a plasticity index. One set of results from the study is depicted in Figure 1.

In conducting their study, the researchers also hoped to obtain data that would support or contradict a distinction between two versions of the DSH. In one version, known as the "strong" DSH, plasticity alleles totally control one's sensitivity to hostility or positive engagement, while according to the "weak" DSH, sensitivity to such factors is amplified by, but not dependent upon, plasticity.

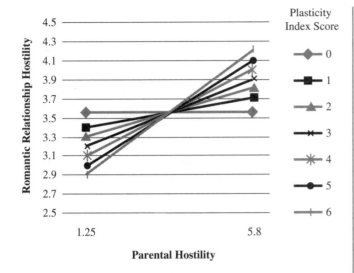

Figure 1 Associations between parental hostility and romantic relationship hostility

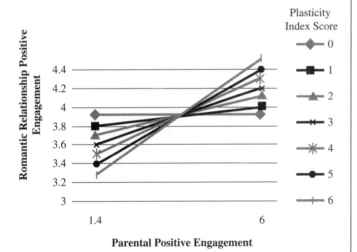

Figure 2 Associations between parental positive engagement and romantic relationship positive engagement

Adapted from A. S. Masarik, R. D. Conger, M. B. Donnellan, M. C. Stallings, M. J. Martin, T. J. Schofield, T. K. Neppl, L. V. Scaramella, A. Smolen, and K. Widaman. For Better and for Worse: Genes and Parenting Interact to Predict Future Behavior in Romantic Relationships. ©2014 by *Journal of Family Psychology.*

1. If the weak DSH hypothesis is true, in a household where parents regularly demonstrate hostility, Mary Ainsworth's "strange situation" experiments would predict that children raised in this type of household would:

    A. be more likely to demonstrate an insecure attachment.
    B. demonstrate greater sensitivity to cortisol.
    C. also display a great deal of hostility, due to social learning.
    D. avoid romantic interactions as adults.

2. The saliva analysis was performed for the purpose of:

    A. phenotyping.
    B. genotyping.
    C. human genome mapping.
    D. trait detection.

3. The construction of the plasticity index reflects the researchers' conceptualization of the alleles as having what type of relationship to the phenotype under study?

    A. Dominant
    B. Recessive
    C. Autosomal
    D. Cumulative

4. Assuming it applies to men and women, the differential susceptibility hypothesis could be described as which of the following?

    A. An exception to the cognitive-behavioral model
    B. A sex-linked chromosomal model
    C. An augmentation of the diathesis stress model
    D. An alternative to the gene x environment model

5. The data shown in Figure 1 confirms which of the following hypotheses?

    I. The weak differential susceptibility model
    II. The strong differential susceptibility model
    III. Slope of phenotype increases as a function of greater numbers of plasticity alleles

    A. I only
    B. II only
    C. I and III only
    D. II a III only

6. All of the following findings support the notion that parent-child interactions predict later relationship dynamics, EXCEPT:

A. Monozygotic twins raised in different homes with different levels of hostility had similar scores on measures of sociability.

B. Monozygotic twins raised by different sets of parents with different levels of responsiveness showed differential rates of aggression in high school.

C. Dizygotic twins raised by different sets of empathic parents exhibited higher regard for classmates' feelings than those raised by aggressive parents.

D. Dizygotic twins raised by the same set of withdrawn parents showed higher rates of social anxiety in college than those raised by gregarious parents.

Passage 44 (Questions 1-5)

Emotional disorders that can be attributed to diseases of the nervous system are called neuro-psychiatric disorders. These disorders are distinguished from neurocognitive and neurodegenerative disorders. Tourette's syndrome (TS) is an inherited neuropsychiatric disorder classified as part of a spectrum of tic disorders, which include disorders that cause sudden, rapid movements that are repeated non-rhythmically. Tics are preceded by an urge and cannot be easily controlled. Tics can be described in two ways and the *Diagnostic and Statistical Manual of Mental Disorders* (DSM) defines tic disorders based on whether the relevant tics are motor or phonic and the duration of the tics. Motor tics cause movements of the body (such as blinking) and vocal tics cause a person to make sounds with his or her voice (such as humming). Furthermore, few body parts are involved in simple tics (such as sniffing) while several different body parts are involved in complex tics (such as pulling at clothes).

Research suggests both environmental and genetic influences on TS, but scientists have not identified an exact cause. TS is often associated with comorbid conditions. Reports suggest that as low as 40% of TS patients have pure TS, defined as the absence of common comorbid conditions. The most common related condition is attention deficit hyperactivity disorder (ADHD). Of children diagnosed with TS, 63% have also been diagnosed with ADHD. TS is also associated with mood and anxiety disorders, learning disorders, and other problems in children.

Adapted from A. S. Carter, D. A. O'Donnel, R. T. Schultz, L. Scajill, J. F. Leckman, and D. L. Pauls. Social and emotional adjustment in children affected with Gilles de la Tourette's syndrome: Associations with ADHD and family functioning. ©2000 by the *Journal of Child Psychology and Psychiatry.*

1. The passage states that most common co-occurring diagnosis for those with TS is ADHD, but it also suggests the diagnosis of which of the following disorders?

A. Depression
B. Generalized anxiety disorder
C. Conversion disorder
D. Obsessive-compulsive disorder

2. Negative emotions, such as sadness due to the loss of a close relative, can worsen the signs of TS for individuals with tics though the relationships and mechanisms are not clear. Research on emotional states, for example, found that tics were least severe during periods of happiness. The area of the frontal lobe with the greatest role in emotion is the:

   A. precentral cortex.
   B. prefrontal cortex.
   C. premotor area.
   D. motor area.

3. Prevalence of TS is not clear, but estimates range from a low of .05% to a high of 2.9% based on the sample and the diagnostic measures. This is a small fraction of the total number of people who meet criteria for a psychological disorder in the U.S., which is roughly:

   A. 1 in 10 Americans.
   B. 1 in 4 Americans.
   C. half of Americans.
   D. two-thirds of Americans.

4. TS is classified as part of a spectrum of tic disorders; all of the following are also considered psychological disorders that lie along a spectrum, EXCEPT:

   A. autism.
   B. mood disorders.
   C. sexual orientation.
   D. psychotic disorders.

5. Which of the following is also expected to be classified as a neuroemotional disorder?

   A. Self-injurious behavior
   B. Parkinson's disease
   C. Alzheimer's disease
   D. Delirium

Passage 45 (Questions 1-5)

Self-Determination Theory (SDT) proposes a spectrum of six types of motivation that drive a person's decisions to engage in a particular behavior or experience. Three types are considered non-self-determined, including amotivation, external regulation, and introjected regulation. Amotivation refers to a lack of conscious motivation, as the individual has difficulty understanding why he/she engages in a given behavior. External regulation is motivation to obtain rewards, avoid punishment, or receive recognition, and introjected regulation is motivation to satisfy the pressures one imposes on him/herself or to achieve self-worth through a given behavior. The three self-determined motivations include identified regulation, integrated regulation, and intrinsic motivation. Identified regulation is motivation to achieve a valued goal, while integrated regulation is motivation to fulfill ones deepest values. Finally, intrinsic motivation is motivation to engage in a behavior for its own sake, as that behavior offers an inherent sense of satisfaction. Prior research indicates that, at least in the realm of behavior, self-determined motivations predict positive consequences, while non-self-determined motivations predict negative consequences.

Like behaviors, a person's affiliation with a group can have positive or negative consequences. To explore what accounts for these divergent manifestations of group identity, one group of researchers applied SDT to the issue of social identity. They recruited a sample of undergraduate college students and administered questionnaires about the six SDT motivation dimensions as they pertained to the students' identification with their school. Participants also completed questionnaires containing items reflecting either positive or negative consequences of their school group identity. Positive consequences included psychological wellbeing and identity quality, which reflected one's emotional attachment to the school group identity. Negative consequences included in-group bias and school superiority relative to other schools. In addition, researchers measured each participant's identity strength. All items employed a 6-point likert scale ranging from 0 (completely disagree) to 5 (completely agree), and all items were scored such that a high score reflected strong endorsement of the construct. Table 1 shows the correlations of the SDT motivation types with the various consequences.

	Psychologi-cal Well-being	Identity	12 months	18 months
Amotivation	−.18*	−.05	−.14	.04
External Regulation	−.21*	.06	.26*	.33*
Introjected Regulation	−.09	−.14*	.05	.25*
Identified Regulation	.07	.09	−.09	−.03
Integrated Regulation	.29*	−.02	.06	.09
Intrinsic Regulation	.12	.27*	.09	.12

*Indicates statistical significance

Table 1 Correlations of SDT dimensions and consequences of school identity

Adapted from C. Amiot and S. Sansfaçon. Motivations to Identify With Social Groups: A Look at Their Positive and Negative Consequences. ©2011 by *Group Dynamics: Theory, Research, and Practice.*

1. Which of the following assumptions underlie the study described in the passage?

   A. The operational definitions of "positive" and "negative" consequences, as applied to behavior, can be meaningfully applied to outcomes of social identification.
   B. Social Identity Theory is a corollary of SDT.
   C. Positive or negative consequences of social identification are a function of identity strength rather than the quality of identification.
   D. The outcomes of social identification are predicted by the dimensions of self-determination theory.

2. Based on the data in Table 1, a student with a high Psychological Wellbeing score would probably have:

   A. a high introjected regulation score.
   B. a high amotivation score.
   C. a low amotivation score.
   D. a low integrated regulation score.

3. Suppose that one member of a group behaves in way that is counter to the group norm, and another group member attempts to ostracize that individual. Assuming that SDT predicts social identity consequences as it does behavior consequences, someone with which of the following characteristics would be most likely to treat another group member as an outcast?

   A. Low identity strength score
   B. Low external regulation score
   C. High integrated regulation score
   D. High introjected regulation score

4. To ensure validity of statistically significant correlations between motivations and consequences, researchers would need to determine correlations:

   A. after accounting for variance due to identity strength.
   B. after accounting for variance due to integrated regulation.
   C. before accounting for variance to identity strength.
   D. before accounting for variance due to in-group bias.

5. Suppose Linda, a participant in the study described in the passage, hears about a competing school's victory in a soccer tournament. Assuming Linda received a high score on the external regulation items, her response to the news would likely reflect:

   A. poor identity quality.
   B. high out-group bias.
   C. the ultimate attribution error.
   D. a strong self-serving bias.

MCAT Psychology and Sociology

Solutions

Passage 1

1. **C** Item I is true: According to the passage, women have larger, more expanded networks while men have denser, more limited networks. This means that women are more likely to utilize their weak ties more than men because weak ties in social networks allow individuals to connect with a wide range of people. On the other hand, men are more likely to utilize their strong ties more than women because strong ties in social networks are considered to be limited because of how dense the network is (choice B and choice D can be eliminated). Item II is false: Men utilize their strong ties more than weak ties and women utilize their weak ties more than men do (choice B and choice D can be eliminated). Item III is true: Symbolic culture refers to the non-tangible culture that exists in society, such as norms, beliefs, and ideas; social networks are a non-material concept (choice A can be eliminated and choice C is the correct answer).

2. **C** Social capital refers to the expected benefits that individuals receive from their social networks; receiving more benefits from a social network translates into greater social capital (choice C is correct). Human capital focuses on an individual's skills, knowledge, and experiences that are considered valuable to society (choice A is wrong). Cultural capital means the non-financial resources that can help an individual's social mobility, such as appearance, language, and dress (choice B is wrong). Symbolic capital refers to the resources given to an individual due to power or prestige, and which can be seen as valuable in society's culture (choice D is wrong).

3. **B** Social support is positively correlated to health and negatively correlated to mortality rate (meaning the higher the amount of social support, the less likely that the individual will be at risk of dying at an early age). Therefore, mortality rates decrease if individuals have higher amounts of social support, which improve overall wellbeing (choice B is correct; choices A, C, and D are wrong).

4. **C** Social constructionism occurs when traditional norms are created by the consensus of a particular society. In the scenario in the question, the norm of providing more social support than is received changed to the norm of receiving more social support than is provided over a period of time (choice C is correct). Symbolic interactionism explains the way people interact and respond to others based on individuals' interpretations of the interactions; this concept focuses on interactions, while the scenario in the question focuses on a change in social norms for a particular society (choice A is wrong). Conflict theory is the idea that inequality occurs when an uneven distribution of power and resources is present in society (choice B is wrong). Deviance occurs when a social norm is violated; even though the social norms did change within fifty years, the scenario in the question indicates that both ideas were considered social norms in the society, rather than violations of them (choice D is wrong).

5. **B** Item I is true: In Figure 1, in the Friends column, percentages are higher for females than males in confiding, reassuring, sick care, talk when upset, and talk about health (choice C can be eliminated). Item II is false: Comparing the Spouse, Female column to the Children, Female column, females received more social support from their spouses than from their children in all aspects of social support *except* in sick care (choice A and choice D can be eliminated). Item III is true: The Friends, Male column indicates that men received more social support by confiding (11.7%) than they did by talking about health (8.8%); therefore, choice B is the correct answer.

6. **D** Compare Figure 1 and Figure 2: 62.4% of mothers provide social support to their upset children while only 34.9% of upset mothers receive social support from their children (choice D is correct). Figure 1 and Figure 2 indicate that males receive and provide social support in all five aspects to their spouses more than females do (choice A is wrong). Figure 2 shows that 18.3% of males took care of their sick friends, while Figure 1 shows that only 10.3% of the males' friends took care of them when they were ill (choice B is wrong). 61.8% of women's spouses reassured them while 58.3% of the women respondents reassured their spouses (choice C is wrong).

Passage 2

1. **A** Anti-miscegenation laws are an example of institutional discrimination or racism (choice A is correct). Discrimination is defined as behavior, usually negative, directed toward a specific social group (e.g., based on a demographic characteristic such as race, sex, and/or social class). Privilege is defined as advantage provided to dominant or majority group members, often at the expense of target or minority group members (choice B is wrong). A stereotype is defined as a single belief, usually distorted, which is applied to all individuals of a social group (choice C is wrong). Prejudice is defined as an unjustified attitude, usually negative, toward a social group (choice D is wrong). Prejudiced thoughts can lead to discrimination, but this is not necessarily the case. The question more accurately describes discrimination, an action against a social group (e.g., the implementation of the law), not prejudice, an attitude against a social group (e.g., an individual's internal rejection of interracial unions).

2. **D** The results of respondent opinions on individual trends are presented in Figure 1; additionally, the trends are described in the first paragraph. This question can be answered using the process of elimination. According to Figure 1, Rejecters show the highest level of negative response to Trend 3, compared to the other trends, which is listed as "More people living together without getting married" (choice A is supported and can be eliminated). Acceptors show the highest level of negative response to Trend 6, compared to the other trends, which is listed as "More women not ever having children"; this can be restated to "less women having children" (choice B is supported and can be eliminated). Rejecters show the lowest level of negative response to Trend 5, compared to the other trends, which is listed as "More people of different races marrying each other" (choice C is supported and can be eliminated). Acceptors also show the lowest level of negative response to Trend 5, compared to the other trends, not to Trend 4 (choice D is not supported and the correct answer).

3. **A** Weber's three-component theory of stratification includes the components of class, power, and status; prejudice is not a component of stratification (choice D is wrong). According to the question, legislation prohibiting same-sex marriage continues to be relevant despite activism in favor of its legalization. This is an example of politicians using their power (choice A is correct). Power is defined as the ability to implement one's decisions despite opposition, such as that posed through pro-same-sex marriage political activism. Politicians often have the advantages of class and status as well, but this does not describe their ability to maintain legislation; instead, class and status help facilitate their power (choices B and C are wrong). Class is defined as one's economic position in society; status is defined as one's reputation, often associated with their class.

4. **D** Item I is true: According to Figure 2, the highest percent of respondents aged 18-29 (45%) fit into the Skeptic group (choice C can be eliminated). Item II is true: According to Paragraph 2, the highest percent of respondents overall (37%) fit into the Skeptic group (choice B can be eliminated). Item III is true: According to Figure 2, the highest levels of negative response among Skeptics was to Trend 4, which is defined as "More mothers of young children working outside the home" in paragraph 1 (choice A can be eliminated and choice D is correct).

5. **C** Emile Durkheim is a founding figure in the field of sociology. He is most associated with the functionalist sociological perspective. Structural functionalism is concerned with the relationship between the individual parts of society, which function together to promote social order (choice C is correct). Conflict theory is concerned with the power relationships and inequalities in society (choices A and B reflect a conflict theory perspective and can be eliminated). Symbolic interactionism is concerned with the symbolic meaning behind social interactions (choice D reflects an interactionist perspective and can be eliminated).

6. **B** Figure 2 presents the demographic characteristics of the three groups. The question stem specifies concern with positive views, which is best represented within the Acceptors category. According to the data, the biggest difference in opinion is the result of differences in church attendance (choice B is correct). The difference between the most represented demographic (those who attend services seldom or never) and the least represented demographic (those who attend services at least once a week) is 28%. Data on geographic location is not presented in the passage; therefore, conclusions cannot be made (choice A is wrong). Data on race shows lower differences in opinion (choice C is wrong). The difference between the most represented demographic ("Hispanic") and the least represented demographic ("Black") is 14%. Data on gender also shows lower differences in opinion (choice D is wrong). In fact, gender produces the smallest difference in views; the difference between men and women is 11%.

Passage 3

1. **D** Social facilitation is the concept that an individual performs better in activities when they are being watched as opposed to when they are alone; this is unrelated to the question stem (choice D is false and therefore, the correct answer). Conformity occurs when an individual follows an established social norm; television advertisements display social norms on screen for viewers to conform to a "normal" society and purchase the advertised product (choice A is true and can be eliminated). Television advertisements are accurately portrayed as an agent of socialization because the passage describes advertisements as transmitting socially constructed gender differences (choice B is true and can be eliminated). Peer pressure involves peers encouraging one to conform to similar social norms; individuals are influenced by actors that they either relate to (because they are portrayed as peers) or see as role models, which makes them more inclined to want to purchase the product (choice C is true and can be eliminated).

2. **A** Item I is true: Gender is a social construct. Independence for men and intuition for women are both qualities that are ascribed to either men or women by society (choice C can be eliminated). Item II is true: Growing up, children are often given gender-specific toys that society believes boys or girls should play with (choice B can be eliminated). Item III is false: Though it is true that men have XY chromosomes and women have XX chromosomes, this is a biological difference, not an example of gender differentiation because it is not a social construct (choice D can be eliminated and choice A is the correct answer).

3. **C** The question stem indicates that the program was aired in the 1960s, which means that gender inequality was much more prevalent. Deviance is an act that violates the accepted social norms in society; during the 1960s, it was out of the norm for husbands to be in pink-collared jobs while their wives worked in white-collared jobs (choice C is correct). Labeling occurs when others place an individual into a certain group until they feel pressured into fulfilling that specific role; the program does not mention anyone putting a label on either the husband or wife (choice A is wrong). Conformity is the opposite of deviance; the program breaks away from the social norms of the 1960s, so it is not demonstrating conformity (choice B is wrong). Discrimination is the unjust treatment of a particular group of people; there is no indication that the characters are being treated unfairly in the television program (choice D is wrong).

4. **A** Ethnocentrism is the idea that a particular ethnic or cultural group is superior above any other groups; this is the idea that advertisers in this question stem promoted (choice A is correct). Social exclusion occurs when certain groups are excluded from particular rights or opportunities; according to Figure 1, there were still a certain amount of non-whites who were cast as main characters for television commercials, so this concept does not most accurately explain the scenario described in the question stem (choice B is wrong). Global inequality deals with inequalities on a global scale; the inequality in the scenario presented in the question stem is only focused on the United States (choice C is wrong). Unlike ethnocentrism, cultural relativism is the idea of believing that no superior group exists and encourages the mindset of being unbiased to all kinds of groups (choice D is wrong).

5. **D** Figure 1 shows that it is true that women are taking orders (80.3%) more than giving orders (19.7%). However, it is not true that men give orders more than take orders; 58.3% of men take orders while 41.7% of men give orders (choice D is false and therefore, the correct answer). 35.3% of women are passive/emotional while 27.5% of men share the same attitude; in addition, 61.1% of men are active/instrumental while only 30.7% of women behave that way in the advertisements (choice A is true and can be eliminated). 40.4% of women work in pink-collared jobs while 34.0% of men work in white-collared jobs (choice B is true and can be eliminated). 75.5% of women do not work while 56.6% of men work (choice D is true and can be eliminated).

6. **C** The final paragraph states that "the results demonstrate that although more women have appeared in television advertisements compared to data from 1956-1960, there has not been a huge change in the way advertisements portray gender differences regarding family, work, and attitude in advertisements;" therefore, there is not much evidence to show that advertisements are proactively prioritizing the display of gender equality (choice C is correct). Gender inequality still exists in recent years, so it is unlikely for media to distinguish it completely (choice A is wrong). Media strives to portray the social norms of society in their advertisements, even if it is not completely gender equal (choice B is wrong). The answer choice claims for media to have "absolutely no role" in depicting gender equality; this statement is too extreme since it is still able to influence some form of gender equality message to certain viewers (choice D is wrong).

Passage 4

1. **D** Patient self-reports of demographic characteristics are presented in Figure 1. According to the results shown, both white and black patients and providers were included in the participant sample. It is thus expected that the research would be able to consider racial concordance and disconcordance between white and black participants and their providers (choices A, B, and C are potential sample groups and can be eliminated). However, the researchers were unable to recruit participant providers of Hispanic origin ($n = 0$). Because of the absence of Hispanic providers, all Hispanic patients (11 percent of participants) were in racial disconcordance with their providers; racial concordance was not possible and thus the research could not consider this sample group (choice D is correct). The five sample groups of patients were white patients in racial concordance (choice A is wrong), black patients in racial concordance, white patients in racial discordance (choice C is wrong), black patients in racial discordance (choice B is wrong), and Hispanic patients in racial discordance (with their providers). It is important to note that no patients identified as Asian.

2. **A** The question stem specifies that the patient and providers of interest are those of different ethnicities; thus, the point of concern is racial discordance. Figure 2 presents the percentages of patients in each patient sample that reported similarities to their provider. It appears that a greater percentage of white patients in racial discordance with their providers reported similarities when compared to patients of racial minorities (choice A is correct; choices B, C, and D are wrong). Furthermore, no patients identified as Asian (Figure 1).

3. **B** Symbolic interactionists argue that social interaction is a process through which social meaning is created and maintained. This perspective considers mental illness to be a social, rather than a biological, phenomenon. People are seen as having a medical condition because social interactions construct mental illness as a symbol of deviance from the social norm (choice B is correct). Structural functionalists and conflict theorists are expected to maintain different views of mental illness. Structural functionalists argue that the purpose of individual structures is to contribute to the stability of the whole society. This perspective considers mental illness to be important to social functioning because it defines what is acceptable and unacceptable in the society (choices A and D are wrong). Conflict theorists argue that power differentials and social inequalities contribute to producing social order. This perspective considers mental illness to be a result of these inequalities (choice C is wrong).

4. **C** Correlation is described as direct, or positive, when two variables move in the same direction. Thus, based on the results, the three components of provider communication should move in the same direction; an increase in one measure should cause an increase in the others and a decrease in one measure should cause a decrease in the others. This direct relationship supports the claim that providers with less engagement in partnership-building would also be less informative (choice C is correct). The other answer choices can be eliminated because the relationships described suggest an inverse, or negative, correlation (choices A, B, and D are wrong).

5. **D** The final paragraph explains that patient perception of similarities is important for patient outcomes when the similarities are personal, rather than ethnic, in nature. Patients would thus benefit from provider efforts to communicate measures of personal similarities (defined as similarities in thinking, values, and communication in paragraph 4). The best measure of personal similarities would be similarities in spiritual beliefs (choice D is correct). Race, culture, and ethnic background would be measures of ethnic similarities, which is defined as similarities in race and community (choices A, B, and C are wrong).

6. **A**   The answer choices are the four main examples of social mobility, which refers to movement in social position. In the transition to independent practice, it is probable that the participant providers experienced changes in social stratification. The most expected change is an upward move in social class or socioeconomic status due to an increase in income, as well as in terms of power and prestige. This change describes upward mobility, an increase in social class, as opposed to downward mobility, a decrease in social class (choice A is correct and choice B is wrong). Based on the minimal information provided, it is more difficult to claim intergenerational or intragenerational changes in social class (choices C and D are wrong). Intergenerational mobility is defined as social mobility, upward or downward, when compared to family members of a different generation (e.g., differences between parents and children); intragenerational mobility is defined as social mobility, upward or downward, when compared to family members of the same generation (e.g., differences between siblings).

Passage 5

1. **C**   Item I is true: the graph shows that younger children have greater projected life expectancy than the older children; thus, both groups of children are showing gains in projected life expectancy. Item II is also true: the shaded bars, which represent children with parents in full-time employment, are higher in each age group than the unshaded bars, which represent children with parents in contingent employment (choice C is correct). Item III is false: while the younger children have higher projected life expectancy than the older children, this is not a better predictor of life expectancy than parental employment because within each age group, the children with employed parents have higher life expectancy than those who don't. Because Item III is incorrect, choice D can be eliminated. Because both Item I and Item II are correct, choice A and choice B can be eliminated.

2. **C**   Intersectionality is an analytical perspective within sociology that holds that the lived experience of individuals cannot be distilled down to only one of their multiple identities; rather, lived experience must be understood as the the intersection of multiple, cross-cutting identities (choice C is correct). Symbolic interactionism is a tradition within sociology that holds that people act towards things based on the meaning that they hold with reference to these things (choice A is wrong). Social identity theory is also a theory of social interaction, and it describes the way that individuals shift between personal and social identities in their interactions with others (choice B is wrong). Social constructionism is a theoretical orientation within sociology that considers all things to be imbued with meanings that they gain from their embeddedness in social groups; in this perspective, things do not have stable meanings in and of themselves, but rather they gain meaning from those who create and use them (choice D is wrong).

3. **A**   Social support comes from being part of a supportive social network and feeling cared for and assisted. This can include tangible and intangible forms of support, such as advice, emotional support or financial support. Social capital means being embedded in a social network that has value (capital). When one has social capital, it can be leveraged in pursuit of other types of capital. The Haitians had high social support from within their community, but were not embedded in networks that could translate well to economic capital—they were largely excluded from steady work and socially excluded from the larger Olympia population (choice A is correct). Because the passage states that the Haitians valued being close to family members and having a tight community (paragraph 1), the Haitians did not have low social support (choice C is wrong, choice D is wrong). Because the Haitians were often unable to integrate themselves into the Olympia network enough to get steady jobs, and because their own social network didn't give them many opportunities to accumulate capital, they did not have high social capital (choice B is wrong).

4. **A**   Karl Marx wrote extensively on the nature of capital, he was primarily concerned with economic capital (choice A is correct). Emile Durkheim is known for his studies of early religious behavior, the effect of religion on social solidarity, and his description of the modern division of labor (choice B is wrong). George Herbert Mead is known for his foundational studies in pragmatism and symbolic interaction (choice C is wrong). Max Weber is known for his theories of social structure, economy and religion (choice D is wrong).

5. **B**   Employment is a sign of social inclusion; the lack of employment is one of the main signals of social exclusion that the passage highlights (choice B is correct). Crime rates are positively correlated with social exclusion because as people are excluded from the formal labor market, they are pushed into the informal economy. Activities in the informal economy are usually criminalized, such as theft or prostitution, and so social exclusion could result in an increase in crime rates (choice A is wrong). Similar to crime rates, substance abuse rates are also positively correlated with social exclusion (choice C is wrong). Assimilation is the process by which one social group relinquishes some or all of its distinctive traits and habits and replaces them with those of the dominant group; assimilation increases social integration and inclusion, but forced assimilation describes a pattern in which excluded groups are forced from the dominant social group to give up their culture and values (choice D is wrong).

6. **C**   The passage notes that the researchers are conducting a study of social stratification. One of the tenets of social stratification is that it can carry over from generation to generation; in other words, disadvantage can accumulate across generations (choice C is correct). The health of the Haitian population could theoretically affect the health of other Olympians, but this is unlikely and does not align with the researchers' concerns (choice A is wrong). Likewise, there is no information in the passage that indicates that the researchers are interested in the children's coping strategies (choice B is wrong). Although the Olympia-born whites are excluding the adult immigrants, there is no information in the passage that indicates that they will try to exclude the children. Classical assimilation theory would suggest the opposite, in fact; second generation immigrants, having grown up in American society, are better integrated (choice D is wrong).

Passage 6

1. **C**   Erik Erikson's theory of psychosocial development separates the life-span into eight stages which involves a particular psychosocial crisis. Initiative vs. Guilt pertains to early childhood, where individuals attempt to take initiative and become independent (choice A is wrong). Industry vs. Inferiority pertains to late childhood through puberty, where individuals focus on accomplishing goals, developing self-confidence, and discovering personal interests (choice B is wrong). The next stage, Identity vs. Role Confusion, pertains to adolescents from puberty through adulthood (choice C is correct). This stage is integral in identity formation and achieving a sense of self and future direction. Generativity vs. Stagnation pertains to adulthood, where the focus is on satisfying personal and family needs, as well as contributing to society (choice D is wrong).

2. **A**   The study described in the passage and the results presented are correlational, therefore there is no causality that can be determined amongst the variables. The passage states that identity exploration is positively correlated with anxiety and self-doubt, but that does not mean that identity exploration causes self-doubt (choices C and D can be eliminated). Similarly, we cannot make a causal attribu-

tion between the association between higher percentage of negative selves and anxiety, we simply know that they are correlated (choice B can be eliminated), so saying that there is a relationship between percentage of negative selves and mood would be accurate (choice A is correct).

3. **D**   An experimental study design is one in which participants are randomly assigned to groups, and the independent variable is manipulated. In a correlational study, participants are not randomly assigned, and variables are not manipulated; they are simply observed. In the study detailed in the passage, the participants were assigned to groups based on their responses to a questionnaire, not randomly assigned, and there were no variables manipulated (choices A and C are wrong). Which means that the study design was not experimental (choice B is wrong) and it was instead correlational (choice D is correct).

4. **B**   Kohlberg's theory of moral reasoning has three stages. The first stage, Preconventional Morality, is characterized by self-interest in seeking reward or avoiding punishment, and is based on the direct consequences of the behavior (choice A is wrong). The second stage, Conventional Morality, regards social conventions and rules as guides for appropriate moral behavior (choice B is correct). The third stage, Postconventional Morality, considers rules and laws as relative and abstract (choice C is wrong). In addition, Postconventional Morality is also characterized by the recognition that everyone has their own opinion, rights, and values, and that the rules that govern us are a compromise of those opinions (choice D is wrong).

5. **B**   The passage states that identity exploration is positively correlated with anxiety, which means that groups with higher levels of identity exploration would be associated with the highest level of anxiety. These would include the two identity statuses that include identity exploration, Achievers and Moratoriums. The groups with lower levels of identity exploration would have lower levels of anxiety: including the Foreclosures and the Diffusions (choices C and D are wrong). The passage also states that the groups with the highest percentage of negative selves would be associated with higher levels of negative affect (which includes anxiety). Identity Achievers have 33% of negative selves (20 negative selves in relation to their 60 possible selves), while Identity Moratoriums have 50% of negative selves (40 negatives selves in relation to their 80 possible selves). Identity Moratoriums have a higher percentage of negative selves than Identity Achievers (choice A is wrong), which would indicate that they would be associated with higher levels of anxiety and negative affect (choice B is correct).

6. **C**   It is well established that there are cultural differences in the concept of self-identity (choice A is wrong). Western cultures are more individualistic, where the personal identity, goals and attributes are of a greater value than group identity, goals and attributes. It is Eastern cultures that place greater value on defining the self in terms of group membership and goals, not Western cultures (choice B is wrong). Likewise, Western cultures do not place more emphasis on community identity and Eastern cultures do not place more emphasis on self-identity (choice D is wrong). Eastern cultures are more collectivist, placing emphasis on community identity, while Western cultures are more individualistic, placing more emphasis on self-identity (choice C is correct).

Passage 7

1. **B** Internal validity assumes that the control group participants were not significantly different from those in the foot-in-the-door condition. There is potential sampling bias: subjects who agree to the larger request may simply be people more likely to agree with either request. One potential confounding factor is the possibility that those more willing to complete a survey might also be more willing to allow strangers into their homes (choice B is correct). The fact that some individuals were only asked the second request is an integral part of the experimental design, as these subject make up the control group, the use of which helps to strengthen the results, not confound them (choice A is wrong). The social norm of mistrusting strangers who ask personal questions is a central tenet of the experimental design that theoretically applies to all participants (choice C is wrong). The second request was meant to require a larger commitment fro the subjects (as per the tenet of the foot-in-the-door technique), but preparation is not really relevant to this experiment, and does not represent a confounding factor (choice D is wrong).

2. **A** Cognitive dissonance theory suggests that people often change their behavior to match their actions when there would otherwise be a disconnect between the two; since the individual wants to be seen as helpful and generous with her time, cognitive dissonance theory might explain why she aligns her behavior to this cognition by taking the second survey, even though she does not want to (choice A is correct). Social learning theory asserts that behavior can be learned purely through observing the behavior of others, even without performing the behavior one's self or receiving any sort of direct reinforcement for the behavior. There is no indication in the question stem that this individual is modeling her behavior after someone else (choice B is wrong). The social facilitation effect suggests that people will perform simple, well-practiced tasks better in front of others; this effect does not help to explain why this individual might agree to a longer survey even though she doesn't want to (choice C is wrong). Groupthink occurs when a group of individuals are attempting to make a decision and the desire for harmony and conformity within the group potentially cloud the decision-making process. Since there is no indication in the question stem that this individual is conferring with a group, groupthink does not logically explain her behavior (choice D is wrong).

3. **B** A scenario in which each control subject from the low self-concept clarity group was asked to volunteer while in a room with several confederates (people who are in on the experiment but the subject does not know are in on the experiment) who all readily volunteered is most similar to Solomon Asch's conformity experiments. Item I is true: therefore, conformity, which is the tendency to match one's attitudes, beliefs or behaviors to that of the group, helps to explain the 32% agreement rate for the low self-concept clarity control group members in Figure 1 (choice C can be eliminated). Item II is true: group pressure (or peer pressure) is the influence that a group can exert over an individual's attitudes or behaviors; group pressure often influences an individual to conform to the group norm. Therefore, group pressure also helps to explain the 32% agreement rate for the low self-concept clarity control group members in Figure 1 (choice A can be eliminated). Item III is false: in-group bias refers to a tendency to favor members of one's in-group over out-group members. This does not explain the results in Figure 1 because there is not enough information to conclude that control group members felt that the confederates were part of their in-group, nor does in-group bias explain why someone might be more willing to volunteer if others around them are agreeing to volunteer (choice D can be eliminated; choice B is correct).

4. **D**   Self-concept clarity is "the consistency with which one identifies and thinks of oneself," suggesting that people use what they believe about themselves to guide future actions. If an office worker, after being cajoled into donating to an employee pool, later refuses to purchase a raffle ticket from a co-worker, she is demonstrating internal consistency, since her reluctance to donate to the office pool is consistent with her later behavior (choice D is correct). Blaming stress and long hours for an inability to quit smoking, on the other hand, involves outside factors affecting a person's behavior, not personal consistency (choice A is wrong). An honors student also being nominated swim-team captain is not necessarily about consistent behavior either, since it's not clear whether the honors student's academic behavior affected the team captain nomination (choice B is wrong). Because the man is described as "normally stingy" (which would imply that he does not give his money away), yet behaves in a way that is inconsistent, but donating a large sum to charity, this scenario demonstrates the opposite of self-concept clarity, since the main is behaving inconsistently with how he normally behaves (choice C is wrong).

5. **A**   A self-schema is a long lasting and stable set of beliefs, experiences and generalizations about the self that is important to one's own self-definition (choice A is correct). For the person described in the questions stem, helpfulness is a self-schema because he believes that it is central to who he is. His self-schema for helpfulness may include general self-categorizations ("I am helpful") and beliefs about how he would act in certain situations ("if someone needed help, I'd help"). Self-esteem is the overall emotional evaluation of one's own worth. It is a judgment of oneself as well as an attitude toward the self. Self-esteem encompasses beliefs and emotions; even if the individual described in the question stem did judge himself *based on* his helpfulness, his actual personality trait of helpfulness is not considered part of his self-esteem (choice B is wrong). Self-efficacy is the belief in one's own ability to succeed at a given task. Though this individual's ability to offer to help to another might impact his self-efficacy, his actual personality trait of helpfulness is not considered part of his self-efficacy (choice C is wrong). Social identity includes all of the social-defined attributes of who one is; this includes such socially-defined characteristics as gender and race, but helpfulness is more of a personally-defined attribute (choice D is wrong).

6. **A**   Item I is false: the individual is essentially agreeing to a request (picking his friend up from the airport in three days) that is roughly equal to the initial task (driving his friend to the airport). The foot-in-the-door technique includes agreeing to a more substantial request after a smaller request is fulfilled, which does not apply to this scenario (choice C can be eliminated). Item II is true: a passerby fulfilling a larger request (giving money) after first agreeing to a smaller request (giving a cigarette) is an example of the foot-in-the-door technique (choice B can be eliminated). Item III is false: if the neighbor first agrees to a large request (completing all of the man's yard work for the entire summer) and then to a much smaller request (moving the man's car out of his driveway once), this does not exemplify the foot-in-the-door technique (choice D can be eliminated; choice A is correct).

Passage 8

1. **D**   Although in all conditions across all groups, it *appears* that participants were slightly more likely to attribute behaviors to dispositional factors, there were no significant differences between situational and dispositional attributions within any of the groups (indicated by the fact that none of the p-values were below 0.05, which was, according to the note below the Table, the experimental cut-off for statistical significance for this study). Therefore, the only conclusion one can make from

these data is that none of the situational and dispositional attributions within groups were significantly different (choice D is correct). According to Table 1, the differences in scores for situational versus dispositional factors in the prosocial groups is not statistically significant; therefore, it cannot be concluded that control participants were more likely to attribute prosocial behaviors to dispositional factors than experimental participants were (choice A is wrong). Similarly, both control and experimental participants in the antisocial groups *appear* more likely to attribute the character's behaviors to dispositional factors, rather than situational factors, but these results are also not statistically significant (choice B is wrong). When comparing prosocial and antisocial groups, both overwhelmingly chose dispositional factors as the likely cause of the character's behaviors, but this none of these groups demonstrate statistical significance (choice C is wrong).

2. A   The purpose of using a control group (or groups) in a scientific study is to isolate the effects of the experimental variable (in this case, knowledge of the fundamental attribution error) and to rule out alternative explanations (choice A is correct). Use of a control group ultimately has no direct effect on the experimental variable, but rather is a measure of what might occur without the experimental variable present (choices B and C are wrong). The use of control groups cannot assure statistical significance; indeed, the data in Table 1 indicate that there is no statistical significance within any of the groups (choice D is wrong).

3. A   The just world phenomenon suggests that people get what they deserve, which leads people to believe that an individual's behavior may actually be causing a particular situation to occur via some sort of karmic retribution; e.g. a "good" person will have good things happen to them, and a "bad" person will have bad things happen to them (choice A is correct). The idea that people tend to attribute an observed effect to potential causes that capture their attention is the idea behind "salience of the actor," another potential explanation for the FAE. This means that our attention is more focused on the "actor" or individual, rather than the "background" or situation, and thus it is easier to attribute the behaviors to the individual (choice B is wrong). The theory that people are unable to take both behavioral and situational information into account simultaneously is the idea behind the "lack of effortful adjustment" explanation for FAE. This theory suggests that, much like the salience of the actor idea, we take into account the individual first, and the situation later, and thus the individual is more present in our minds (choice C is wrong). The idea that people selectively attend to information that confirms their preconceived biases, while generally believed to be true, is not a part of the just world phenomenon (choice D is wrong).

4. A   Self-serving bias is part of the FAE, wherein we are more likely to attribute our successes to dispositional factors, but our failures to external or situational factors. According to the self-serving bias, if an individual did poorly on an exam and blames it on the professor, this is because the individual would rather blame external factors than take personal responsibility for the failure (choice A is correct). If the individual does take personal responsibility for the failure, this would not be an example of the self-serving bias (choice B is wrong). In terms of successes, if the individual did well on the exam and patted himself on the back for being so smart, this would be an example of the self-serving bias. However, attributing his successes to the ease of the exam or to his excellent tutor would not fit the definition of the self-serving bias (choices C and D are wrong).

5. C   Attribution theory suggests that individuals reason backward from the observation of a behavior to a judgment about its cause. John Kelley's identified three sources of information people can use in analyzing covariance (in behavior and cause of behavior over time) to arrive at a cause. Kelley suggested that individuals form causal beliefs by analyzing the consistency, consensus, and distinctiveness of a response or behavior. Observations of a behavior across time provide in-

formation about consistency (choice A is wrong). For example, does a patient express dissatisfaction every time he or she come to the clinic or only on some occasions? Observations of different people allow judgments to be made about consensus (choice B is wrong). Do all patients at the clinic express dissatisfaction or is it just one the one patient who indicates unhappiness? Finally, observations of behavior in multiple situations provides information about the distinctiveness of a response (choice D is wrong). Does patient express dissatisfaction only when getting a shot or when getting any sort of treatment at the clinic? Persuasion is not one of the three factors involved in making attribution (choice C is correct).

6. D The halo effect is an attributional error or bias in which one's judgments of a person's character can be influenced by one's overall impression of that person. In this scenario, you have a good impression of the professor because she is so attractive, and consequently you judge her as having good character, despite her extremely negative behaviors (choice D is correct). The self-serving bias is a cognitive error or bias in which one attributes success to one's own dispositional factors, but failures to situational factors. This might have been the case had you blamed the professor for her poor teaching abilities when she ranted about the class's poor grades on the exam (choice A is wrong). The correspondence bias is another term for the fundamental attribution error, and refers to the phenomenon in which individuals tend to attribute one another's behaviors primarily to dispositional factors, rather than situational factors. Had you concluded that this professor is an inherently mean person, you might have committed this error (choice B is wrong). Cognitive dissonance is the discomfort experienced when simultaneously holding two or more conflicting ideas or beliefs, which might occur if you found this professor to be extremely physically attractive but personally vile (choice C is wrong).

Passage 9

1. B According to the second paragraph, the polarization hypothesis can result in people using neutral information to support their stance and this can result in parties on both sides becoming more entrenched in their opinion, and thus becoming more polarized (or far apart) from each other. In other words, the polarization hypothesis suggests that two opposing sides become more opposing. The concept that is the most opposite of this is group polarization, which occurs when a group of like-minded people come together to discuss something, and the average group opinion becomes even more extreme (for example, if more of the people in the group were moderately in favor of something before discussion, they will be extremely in favor after). Therefore, group polarization is the most opposite of the polarization hypothesis (choice B is correct). The bystander effect predicts that if there are many people around when someone is in need of help, no one will come to their rescue because everyone assumes that someone else will help, so no one ends up helping. The bystander effect is not most opposite to the polarization hypothesis (choice A is wrong). The availability heuristic predicts that we often make choices or judgments based on the information that is most available in our minds; again, this is not most opposite to the polarization hypothesis (choice C is wrong). Social loafing occurs when working together in a group, each individual exerts less effort than he or she would have exerted if working alone (choice D is wrong).

2. D Several studies have documented that individuals develop more positive attitudes towards an object/individual with more frequent exposure. This phenomenon is commonly referred to as the "mere-exposure" effect. Mere exposure effect explains why individuals sometimes come to like products and political candidates after viewing their ads several times (choice D is cor-

rect). Cognitive dissonance theory asserts that attitude change is driven by efforts to reduce the discrepancy between an individual's attitudes and his/her behaviors. The question stem did not mention any specific behaviors, nor did it describe any discrepancies between "proponents" attitudes and their behaviors (choice A is wrong). Persuasion cues are characteristics individuals attune to when the peripheral route to attitude change is activated. These cues emphasize characteristics of the person delivering the message, such as confidence and attractiveness, rather than the content of the message itself. The question stem does not mention any persuasion cues or activation of the peripheral route to attitude change (choice B is wrong).   Daryl Bem's self-perception theory suggests that attitudes can change as people evaluate their behaviors in certain situations and make inferences about their attitudes based on the aforementioned behaviors. This process helps individuals align their attitudes with their behaviors. Attitude change due to self-perception is most likely to occur when individuals are unsure of their attitudes, which is not the case in this question (choice C is wrong).

3. **B** Attitude formation begins in early childhood and continues throughout an individual's lifetime. Individuals aren't born with a certain set of attitudes, instead, they gather relevant cues from the people around them through the process of social learning. Thus, what people learn from their parents, friends, and peers, often plays a major role in attitude formation (choice B is correct). Cognitive dissonance refers to an inconsistency between an individual's attitudes and his/her behaviors. For example, an alcoholic who believes that drinking is unhealthy is likely to experience cognitive dissonance because his/her attitudes and behaviors contradict each other. Cognitive dissonance theory does not explain why people's attitudes are often similar to those of their friends and family members (choice A is wrong). In-group bias is the tendency to favor members of one's group (in this case, proponents) over members outside of one's group (in this case, opponents). The question stem did not mention differences in attitudes towards in-group versus out-group members (choice C is wrong). Prejudice is a positive or negative attitude toward an individual based simply on membership in some group. There is no evidence that "opponents" develop positive or negative attitudes towards anyone based solely on group membership (choice D is wrong).

4. **A** Group polarization is the tendency towards extreme decisions and viewpoints by groups. The differences in attitudes towards capital punishment were exacerbated after reading the results of both studies, as represented by the graphs in figure 1. Thus, presenting students with the results of both studies did, in fact, increase group polarization (choice A is correct). The differences in attitudes between the two groups (proponents and opponents) increased after reading the results of both studies, which increased group polarization (choice B contradicts the figure and can therefore be eliminated). Figure 1 indicates that opponents became more supportive of capital punishment after reading the results of the prodeterrent study (choice C contradicts the figure and can therefore be eliminated). According to Figure 1, proponents favored capital punishment more after reading the results of the prodeterrent study (choice D is wrong).

5. **C** Confirmation bias is the tendency to selectively attune to evidence in support of one's hypothesis, rather than to evidence that refutes that hypothesis (choice C is correct). Informal reasoning, also known as inductive reasoning, is the process of evaluating evidence of a conclusion, theory, or course of action based on the believability of evidence. Informal reasoning doesn't necessarily lead to confirmation of existing beliefs (choice A is wrong). Representativeness heuristic is a mental shortcut that involves judging whether something belongs in a given class based on how similar it is to other members of that class. Although this mental shortcut can produced biased thinking, it doesn't predispose individuals to confirm their existing beliefs (choice B is wrong). Availability heuristic involves judging the likelihood of an event or the correctness of a hypoth-

esis based on how easily the hypothesis or event comes to mind. The availability heuristic often leads people to overestimate how often shark attacks and plane crashes occur, due to the attention these types of events receive in the media. Nevertheless, availability heuristic doesn't cause people to seek out evidence that confirms their existing views (choice D is wrong).

6.　C　The average difference between each score and the mean of the group is known as the standard deviation. Standard deviation describes the variability in a dataset, with higher standard deviation scores indicative of greater distance from the mean, or more variability within the data set (choice C is correct). Variance is the average of the squared differences from the mean, rather than the raw difference between each score and the mean of the group (choice D is wrong). Range is the difference between the highest and lowest values in a data set; it does not provide information about how much each score deviates from the mean (choice A is wrong). The median is the halfway point in a data set, with half of the scores falling above the median and half below. The median provides no information about the mean of the dataset, nor the variability in a set of scores (choice B is wrong).

Passage 10

1.　B　The bystander effect occurs when individuals witness a troubling situation (e.g. a person in distress) and do not proactively do anything to intervene or help. Paradoxically, this is more likely to occur the more witnesses are present. Therefore, the group of people who did not try to stop the gang members from beating the individual is an example of the bystander effect (choice B is correct). Social loafing is the phenomenon in which individuals put forth less effort because they are working with a group than they would if they were working alone; this is not relevant to the question stem (choice A is wrong). There is no indication in the question stem of individuals pressuring one another to avoid helping the person being beaten (choice C is wrong). Attribution theory occurs when an individual attempts to explain the causes behind the behaviors and actions of others; the question stem does not describe a scenario in which an individual tries to explain the behavior of the gang members nor bystanders (choice D is wrong).

2.　B　According to the passage, aversive racism theory suggests that individuals have subconscious negative attitudes towards blacks; prejudice against the out-group is the biased opinion about another group, and is the mostly synonymous with aversive racism theory (choice B is correct). Discrimination is an unjust action against someone as a result of negative attitudes about that individual's group affiliation; aversive racism theory focuses on the subconscious *attitudes* of individuals rather than unjust actions (choice A is wrong). Ethnocentrism occurs when someone judges another based on the belief that one's own cultural values are superior to another person's cultural values; there is no information in the passage indicating that aversive racism theory involves individuals feeling their own culture is superior to anyone else's (choice C is wrong). Cultural relativism is unrelated to aversive racism theory because it involves accepting other cultural groups and viewing them relative to their own social context (choice D is wrong).

3.　C　Groupthink is the likelihood for individuals in a group who share similar attitudes or opinions to establish a consensual viewpoint that is often more extreme than the opinions of individual group members, and without being open to alternative perspectives. Even though there were participants who valued egalitarianism, participants who valued elitism were the majority in the study; because of this, the group's decisions were unanimous and elitist even though some participants may not fully agree with the decisions (choice C is correct). Group polarization normally occurs when like-minded individuals begin to make extreme acts and decisions once they are in a group; the study shows that participants had differing values in the beginning of the study (choice A is wrong). Social facilitation occurs when an individuals' performance is enhanced when they perform with or in front of a group of people; this is unrelated to the question stem (choice B is wrong). Social exclusion occurs when individuals are denied the rights and opportunities that members in society should normally have; the study does not mention any participants denied from their own opinions during the group discussion (choice D is wrong).

4. A   The passage mentions that the researchers' goal is to observe individuals from the "non-target group." Researchers would avoid choosing black participants for this particular study because they are considered the target population (the group that researchers are interested in researching) for this experiment. If they were to be assigned experiencers and forecasters to the moderately racist and extremely racist comment condition, they are more inclined than non-target groups to take the comment personally (choice A is correct). There is not enough information in the passage to prove that researchers would avoid white participants, older participants, and younger participants for the study due to the reasons respectively listed for each of them (choices B, C, and D are wrong).

5. B   The graph for forecasters should illustrate a negative correlation between the two variables; according to Figure 2, as the severity of the racial comment increases, the percentage of white partners chosen decreases. Unlike forecasters, the graph for experiencers should illustrate a positive correlation between the two variables; as the severity of the racial comment increases, the percentage of white partners chosen increases as well (choice B is correct; choices A, C, and D are wrong).

6. A   Item I is true: The hypothesis for the study was that forecasters would have exaggerated emotional distress scores compared to experiencers. Both Figure 1 and Figure 2 show that forecasters had a higher emotional distress scores along with being more inclined to choose the black "participant" over the white "participant" for the more severe comment conditions (choice C can be eliminated). Item II is true: According to Figure 2, the "no racist comment" condition has a 20% gap between forecasters and experiencers while the "moderately racist comment" condition has a 39% gap between forecasters and experiencers; therefore the "moderately racist comment" condition has a wider percentage gap compared to the "no racist comment" condition (choice B can be eliminated). Item III is false: Although forecasters had higher distress results than experiencers, they both showed a positive correlation between the severity of the comment and the emotional distress scores, as demonstrated by the increasing bar height from left to right for both groups in Figure 1 (choice D can be eliminated and choice A is therefore, the correct answer).

Passage 11

1. C   On average, people who register high on the personality trait of openness to experience are intellectually curious, open to emotion, and willing to try new things. Therefore, a patient who is diagnosed with a rare form of cancer and volunteers to try a new experimental procedure that has never been tested on humans is the scenario that best demonstrates high openness to experience (choice C is correct). A patient who does not trust his doctor and seeks multiple second opinions most likely demonstrates a low score on the personality trait of agreeableness, which measures willingness to go along with what others, including authority figures like doctors, say (choice A is wrong). A young physical therapy patient who works complies with orders is most likely high

on the personality trait for conscientiousness (choice B is wrong). An older physician who refuses to try the newer treatments is likely low on the personality trait for openness to experience (choice D is wrong).

2. **D** The passage indicates that neuroticism is characterized by being anxious, tense, and worrying; therefore, the individual described would likely score highly on this personality modality (choice D is correct). The other answer choices list types (extraversion, agreeableness, conscientious) that are not directly connected to the behavior listed (choice A, choice B, and choice C are wrong).

3. **B** The particular item asks about taking a rational approach, which is very similar to the table 1 description of thinking: "uses logical analysis to orient towards the subject or object." In addition, a thinking type could also display an auxiliary type of intuition simultaneously, so this item could not distinguish between those two types, whereas thinking and feeling form a dichotomy (choice B is correct and choice C is wrong). Either an introvert or an extravert could be a thinking type, thus this question could not differentiate someone between these two (choice A is wrong). Judging and perceiving are not Jungian dichotomies and the question states that the item was used to differentiate Jungian typology. (choice D is wrong).

4. **C** The passage states that an individual may assume a personality type which is not their innate predisposition, to their psychological detriment. Thus, according to Jung, if someone was innately introverted, but was pressured into behaving like an extravert due to sociological pressures, this would have negative psychological consequences (choice C is correct). Although some studies have found that neuroticism may be related to introversion, Jung's theory did not draw this connection, and neuroticism was not part of Jung's personality theory (choice A is wrong). Jung also did not directly influence the formulation of openness as a significant personality modality, and this is mentioned later in the passage as a contribution of Eysenck (choice D is wrong). The passage states that Jung did not place heavy emphasis on sociability as a distinguishing feature for introversion/extraversion, and his theory did not connect sociability with happiness (choice B is wrong).

5. **B** The amygdala is implicated prominently in the processing of fear and the fight or flight response. High amygdala activation could lead to activation of the fear response in inappropriate situations, and this could lead to increased anxiety (choice B is correct). The amygdala, although involved in emotions, does not control emotion regulation, which is accomplished mainly in the prefrontal cortex choice A is wrong). The amygdala is not the chief mechanism of release for serotonin pathways. Although serotonin modulation could affect mood, the amygdala is not heavily connected with regulating serotonin (choice C is wrong). The amygdala, likewise, is not responsible for superego function (choice D is wrong).

6. **D** Item I is true: Similarity between people fosters attraction (despite Jung's theory). Friends and partners are more likely to share common values, beliefs, interests, and attitudes. The more alike people are, the more their liking for each other endures over time (choice C can be eliminated). Item II is true: Proximity (or nearness) is the most powerful predictor of attraction. People are more inclined to like, befriend, and even marry others that they are in close proximity to. This can also be demonstrated by the mere exposure effect, which demonstrates that people prefer repeated exposure to the same stimuli (choice B can be eliminated). Item III is true: Appearance also has a powerful impact on attraction; studies show that people rate physically attractive people higher on a number of characteristics and traits, indicating that physically attractive people are somehow more likeable (choice A can be eliminated; choice D is correct).

Passage 12

1. **A** Extrinsic motivation is a driving force from outside of an individual. Receiving a high grade in class is an external reward, so this is an example of extrinsic motivation (choice A is correct). A student wanting to learn more about a topic because of interest means that the student will learn the topic regardless of whether or not they will receive an external reward, such as a good grade; therefore, this is an example of *intrinsic* motivation (choice B is wrong). A student joining soccer or a student who wants to finish a puzzle because they find these activities fun are also internal drives, or motivations that come from within an individual; therefore, these are also both examples of intrinsic motivation (choice C and choice D are wrong).

2. **B** In research, two parallel lines on a graph do not necessarily imply causation. There may be other explanations for the correlation between motivation and pleasantness, such as a third unknown factor causing both the pleasantness and motivation to decrease separately. Item I is false: while the variables may be shown to vary together, causation cannot be inferred (choices A, C and D can be eliminated). Item II is false: similarly, just because the slopes for both motivation and pleasantness are the same, this does not prove causation. Item III is true: Assuming the slope is the same, motivation decreases as pleasantness decreases, demonstrating a correlation (choice B is correct).

3. **C** The dichotomy of reward and punishment is most commonly associated with the approach versus avoidance theory. Approach motivation is the motivation to experience a positive outcome, while avoidance motivation is the motivation to not experience a negative outcome (choice C is correct). Extrinsic motivations are driving forces that come from outside of an individual, such as rewards, while intrinsic motivations are driving forces that come from inside of an individual, such as the desire for autonomy; this study was not looking at intrinsic and extrinsic motivations, so there is no evidence that this study found two separate motivational systems in the brain, one coordinating extrinsic motivations and the other intrinsic motivations (choice A is wrong). Conscious motivations are driving forces that can be explicitly declared, while unconscious motivations are driving forces that an individual is not aware of; this study was not looking at conscious and unconscious behaviors, so there is no evidence that this study found two separate motivational systems in the brain, one coordinating conscious behaviors and the other unconscious behaviors (choice B is wrong). According to the $H_2^{15}O$-PET and affective liking rating regression described in the final paragraph, as the act of eating switches from reward to punishment, two different structures were recruited (choice D is wrong).

4. **A** Independent variables are conditions that do not rely on another variable. Dependent variables are conditions whose value depends on another variable. The amount of chocolate consumed was manipulated by the experimenter and does not depend on another variable; therefore, this is an independent variable (choices C and D can be eliminated). However, the activity of the brain and the affective liking rating for both satisfaction and reward value are all variables that depend on the amount of chocolate eaten (choice A is correct, choice B is wrong).

5. **B** The orbitofrontal cortex is located in the frontal lobe and is responsible for managing emotional impulses, facial expression interpretation, and motivation (choice B is correct). The parietal lobe is responsible for sensation and movement (choice A is wrong). The occipital lobe, located in the back of the brain, is responsible for vision (choice C is wrong). The temporal lobe is responsible for language, memory, emotion, and hearing (choice D is wrong).

6. **A**   The drive-reduction theory asserts that a desire increases if it is not satisfied and that the same desire decreases when fulfilled. In the study described in the passage, the subjects had a lower motivational affective rating after fulfilling their desire for more chocolate thus supporting the drive-reduction theory (choice A is correct). The self-determination theory describes the idea that achievement requires active stimulation from the environment and focuses on the intrinsic motivations of human behavior; this theory does not apply because the study was not looking at extrinsic motivation (choice B is wrong). Attribution theory describes the process by which an individual finds reasons to explain their experiences and rationalizes their failures, which also does not apply to this study (choice C is wrong). Cognitive dissonance theory describes the feeling of discomfort that is the product of an inconsistency between an individual's views on the world and their actions, which also does not apply to this study (choice D is wrong).

Passage 13

1. **C**   Cognitive behavioral therapy (CBT) includes both treatment for maladaptive behaviors and thoughts; therefore, it would most likely include both restructuring of thought patterns and tools to engage in less acquisitive behaviors for an individual with hoarding disorder (choice C is correct). A thorough analysis of an individual's past childhood traumas is most indicative of the psychoanalytic approach to therapy, not CBT (choice A is wrong). An approach that utilized reprogramming behaviors with conditioning but did not include a cognitive component of therapy is most likely stemming from the behavioral approach to treatment (choice B is wrong). Humanistic therapy involves personal growth through self-insight; the aim of humanistic therapy is to help the client develop a stronger, healthier sense of self, which is also called self-actualization (choice D is wrong).

2. **B**   To answer this question, it is important to consider support for each conclusion. The passage states that the average age of those receiving treatment for hoarding disorder is age 50; therefore, while hoarding behaviors can begin in childhood, the passage suggests that clinical diagnosis would be more common among adults (choice A is supported by the passage and can be eliminated). Figure 1 reports incidence of hoarding disorder by income bracket. According to the results, individuals in the lowest income bracket show the highest levels of HD and individuals in the highest income bracket show some of the lowest levels of HD. However, while this suggests a relationship, there is not sufficient evidence to support a claim of significant proportionality; for example, the absolute lowest incidence is among individuals in the $60,000-75,000 income bracket (choice B is not supported by the passage and is the correct answer). The passage introduces and defines HD as a condition that involved excessive collections; by definition, it would be expected that participants with HD would have more than an average amount of possessions (choice C is supported by the passage and can be eliminated). Finally, according to Figure 1, those in the lowest income bracket show the highest levels of HD (choice D is supported by the passage and can be eliminated).

3. **A**   Cognitive behavioral therapy (CBT) addresses disordered thinking and behaviors through a systematic procedure that asserts that problematic behaviors cannot be solved through rational thought alone and thus suggests specific strategies. Hoarding disorder contains both a thinking component (e.g., excessive attribution of value to items) and an action component (e.g., excessive acquisition of items), and those suffering from the disorder are most likely to benefit from CBT (choice A is correct). Interpersonal psychotherapy is a treatment method in which individuals

consider the effect of their relationships on their feelings, thought processes, and actions. More generally, psychotherapy, or talk therapy, refers to the process of therapeutic interaction between a trained professional and a client, which aims to address problems as well as their causes, triggers, and resolutions. IRP is often used to treat disorders such as anxiety and depression; however, the treatment of HD generally necessitates a more involved therapeutic technique that specifically addresses problematic behaviors, and research has found psychotherapy to be generally ineffective in treating HD (choice B is wrong). Meditation techniques, such as mindfulness-based stress reduction, are often used as a method to help alleviate stress. While mediation might have health benefits for those with HD, it is not likely to be sufficient for treatment as the disordered thinking leads to an excessive levels of stress (choice C is wrong). Pharmaceutical interventions are often used to treat depression and anxiety disorders by targeting neurotransmitter levels in the brain. Currently, however, there has been little research on the neurological mechanisms behind hoarding behavior, as reported in the passage, and drug therapies have lead to mixed results at best (choice D is wrong).

4.   **A**   This question can be answered using the two-by-two technique. First, decluttering is discussed in the second paragraph, which explains that attempts to discard items can cause high levels of stress for those with hoarding disorder. The mechanism of stress is associated with the sympathetic nervous system or "fight or flight"; in fact, it is thought to counteract the parasympathetic nervous system or "rest and digest" (choices C and D can be eliminated). Second, cortisol, a glucocorticoid, is often referred to as the stress hormone, and is released as a physiological response to stress. Thus, third party interventions, by causing stress, would lead to an increase in glucocorticoid levels (choice A is correct and choice B is wrong).

5.   **B**   Item I is true: Functionalist theory, or structural functionalism, studies the effect of social structures and functions on promoting social order. Defining mental illness also suggests what is and is not socially acceptable; the clinicalization of hoarding disorder sets limits on consumer behavior which then serves to promote social order (choice C can be eliminated). Item II is true: Conflict theory studies the effect of inequality in society, emphasizing the roles of power differentials. Thus, it is expected that a conflict theorist's evaluation of hoarding disorder would consider health disparities and inequalities in resource distribution (choice A can be eliminated). Item III is false: Symbolic interaction theory studies the effect of social interaction on the creation of social meaning. A symbolic interactionist would be expected to view mental illness, and other forms of deviance, as symbolic in nature. Hoarding disorder would then be considered a mental illness as a result of socialization and the failure to meet social norms *not* a product of biology (choice D can be eliminated and choice B is the correct answer).

6.   **A**   Members of primary groups, which are usually small social groups, share personal and lasting relationships; in general, family members fit this definition (choice A is correct). Members of secondary groups, which are usually large social groups, share impersonal and often short-term relationships (choice B is wrong). An out-group is a social group that an individual identifies negatively with; conversely, an in-group is a social group that an individual identifies positively with, which is the more expected description of family members (choice C is wrong). A reference group is a social group which is used for individual reference and comparison, and is less applicable here (choice D is wrong).

Passage 14

1. **D** Positive symptoms of schizophrenia (such as delusions, hallucinations, disorganized speech, and disorganized or catatonic behavior) are *novel* deviations from normal functioning; healthy individuals will not have hallucinations on a regular basis, while many schizophrenic patients do. Therefore, positive symptoms are not normally experienced by healthy individuals but are present in the disorder (choices A, B, and C can be eliminated; choice D is correct). Negative symptoms (such as flattened affect, social withdrawal, lack of motivation, and lack of speech or thought) are comprised of normal attributes that are diminished or absent entirely in the condition; healthy individuals normally interact socially, while schizophrenics will exhibit diminished interaction with others. Therefore, negative symptoms describe a diminished or absent normal emotion or behavior (choices B and C can be eliminated; choice D is correct).

2. **D** Item I is false: according to the second paragraph and Figure 1, urbanicity appears to increase the risk of schizophrenia (as well as all other psychopathological disorders), particularly in genetically susceptible individuals; therefore, moving to an urban area during childhood should be expected to increase (not minimize) the risk of psychotic outcomes (choices A and C can be eliminated). Item II is true: based on the information in the passage, being born and raised in a rural setting does appear to minimize the risk of psychotic outcomes (choice B can be eliminated). Item III is true: according to the passage and Figures 2, 3, and 4, avoiding cannabis use will also minimize the risk of psychotic outcomes (choice D is correct).

3. **A** Figure 1 indicates that urbanicity increases risk of hospitalization across all psychopathological disorders including schizophrenia and that the introduction of genetically predisposing factors *enhances* this risk several-fold (choice A is correct). In addition, the passage notes that "urbanicity" is a quality that can include increased risk for illicit drug use, a category which includes cannabis. While the passage also states that cannabis use is an "environmental" variable, it is important to recognize that it has a substantial biological domain. Thus, while Figures 2, 3, and 4 also support the claim that there are interactions between environmental and genetic variables in psychopathology, they do not provide the *strongest* evidence for this conclusion (choices B, C, and D are wrong).

4. **D** There is a substantial genetic component in psychopathological disorders, specifically, schizophrenia. Siblings that are most genetically similar to schizophrenics would be expected to perform the worst on neuropsychological testing. Monozygotic twins come from the same fertilized eggs while dizygotic twins come from two separate fertilized eggs. So, since dizygotic twins are less genetically similar than monozygotic twins, we would expect them to perform better on neuropsychological testing (choice D is correct; choice C is wrong). Since "male siblings" and "female siblings" include non-twin siblings, these groups, overall, will be less genetically similar to schizophrenia patients than exclusive twin groups (choices A and B are wrong).

5. **D** Figure 4 demonstrates that, with cannabis exposure, the rate of psychotic symptoms in the high-risk group (G+) is double that of the low-risk group (G−); therefore, it can be most reasonably concluded that the rate of clinical psychotic symptoms in the high-risk group was twice that of the low-risk group (choice D is correct). Both subgroups in Figure 1, "All Psychopathological Disorders" and "Schizophrenia," experience the same fourfold increase in related risk due to urbanicity between the low-risk and high-risk groups; therefore, it does *not* appear that genetic factors have a greater effect on related risk due to urbanicity for all psychopathological disorders

rather than for schizophrenia only (choice A is wrong). Figure 2 demonstrates that, while different in magnitude, *both* low-risk (G−) and high-risk (G+) groups experience a decrease in cortical thickness due to cannabis use (choice B is wrong). Figure 3 only shows the effect size for *positive* symptoms associated with schizophrenia—i.e., not *classic* symptoms—which would include both positive and negative symptoms (choice C is wrong).

6. **B**   While the passage (specifically paragraph 2) does suggest that there is a positive correlation between urbanicity and social fragmentation, it is not possible to determine either the strength of this correlation, nor is this relationship the one analyzed in the study described in the passage (choice B is false, so it is therefore the correct answer). The passage states that social "fragmentation" is probably a key driver in psychotic outcomes; thus, community-building initiatives would reduce social fragmentation as well as the risk of psychotic outcomes (choice A is true, so it is therefore wrong). The passage focuses on growing up in an urban setting as a key driver of psychotic outcomes (choice C is true, so it is therefore wrong). The passage explicitly states that cannabis abuse can induce psychotic symptoms in healthy individuals (choice D is true, so it is therefore wrong).

Passage 15

1. **D**   The amount of total sleep decreases from about 16 hours (on average) a day in newborns to about six hours a day (on average) in older age, and REM sleep shifts from about 50% of total sleep time in newborns to about 25% of total sleep time in old age; therefore, it is true that the duration of total sleep and proportion of REM sleep both decrease gradually throughout one's lifetime (choice D is correct). It is not true that sleep disorders do not develop until puberty or later; in fact, children are much more likely to experience sleep disorders during slow-wave sleep, particularly somnambulism (sleepwalking) and night terrors (choice A is wrong). Sleep onset is linked to rising (not falling) melatonin levels. Melatonin is a hormone made by the pineal gland. During the day the pineal is inactive, but when it is dark outside, the pineal is "turned on" by the suprachiasmatic nucleus (of the hypothalamus) and begins to actively produce melatonin, which is released into the blood. As a result, melatonin levels in the blood rise sharply and you begin to feel less alert (choice B is wrong). Periods of slow-wave deep sleep are actually longest right after sleep onset and essentially disappear the closer you get to waking. REM sleep, on the other hand, has periods that get gradually longer as sleep progresses (choice C is wrong).

2. **C**   The study represented by Figure 1 shows data for Men, Women, African Americans, and Caucasians. For every insomnia type (onset, maintenance, combined, and no insomnia), women were more likely than men to have clinically significant depression (choices B and D can be eliminated), and for every insomnia type, African Americans were more likely than Caucasians to have clinically significant depression (choice A can be eliminated). Therefore, the respondents LEAST likely to have depression concurrent with a sleep disorder would be Caucasian men (choice C is correct).

3. **A**   In psychometrics, reliability is used to describe the overall consistency of a measure. A measure is said to have a high test-retest reliability if it produces similar results under consistent conditions. Therefore, comparisons of the same task performed by the same population at different times would yield a measure of reliability (choice A is correct). Homogeneity is a condition in which elements share the same qualities, parts, or nature. Since the proposed task would be

purposefully identical in each instance of implementation, homogeneity would be established at the outset, and there would be no need to compare performance for evidence of the task's homogeneity (choice B is wrong). Standardization, which means to cause methods or materials to conform to one template, may also seem attractive, as the task is identical. However, as with homogeneity, there would no need to compare outcomes to asses the task's standardization, as the task is already implemented in an identical fashion: standardization comes pre-established (choice C is wrong). A valid measure is one that measures what it is intended to measure. Comparing two outcomes of the performance of one task is not sufficient to indicate whether a test is valid, since a test can be reliable without being valid (choice D is wrong).

4. **C** Clinical depression is twice as common in women as in men (choice C is not true of depression, and is therefore correct). Depression is a mood disorder (choice A is true and therefore incorrect). Withdrawal from prolonged alcohol or drug use can cause symptoms mimicking clinical depression (choice B is true and therefore incorrect). Major depressive disorder is in fact characterized by at least one major depressive episode lasting at least two weeks, as well as some or all of the following: depressed mood or decreased interest in activities, significant increase or decrease in weight or appetite, excessive or insufficient sleep, speeded or slowed psychomotor activity, fatigue or loss of energy, feelings of low self-worth or guilt, impaired concentration or decision-making, and thoughts of death or suicide (choice D is true and therefore incorrect).

5. **B** The question proposes that the study, which currently investigates the likelihood of developing depression according to what sleep disorders are present, also investigate concurrent changes in participants' cognitive functioning. In this study, the risk of developing depression (the observed effect) is correlated according to the presence or absence of insomnia (the hypothesized cause). Observing yet an additional effect—changes in cognitive functioning—would be adding a new dependent variable (choice B is correct). In this study, insomnia is the independent variable, which is tested to determine whether it is causing an effect. In the proposed change, the researchers would not be adding a new independent variable, but would instead be observing changes in cognitive functioning as a result of the independent variable (insomnia), making this an additional dependent variable (choice A is wrong). Even though insomnia is termed quasi-independent in the passage, adding another effect to observe would not make *all* the variables quasi-independent (choice C is wrong). A cross-sectional study collects data from a population at a single point in time. The second study collected data at two points in time, and the proposed addition would not alter this design (choice D is wrong).

6. **B** Item I is true: Insomnia causes an overall reduction in REM and slow-wave sleep (choice C can be eliminated). Item II is false: insomnia is part of the broader category of sleep disorders called dysomnias (abnormalities in the amount, timing, or quality of sleep); parasomnias (abnormal behaviors that occur during sleep) include somnambulism (sleep-walking) and night terrors (choice D can be eliminated). A person with generalized anxiety disorder (GAD) feels tense or anxious much of the time about many issues, but does not experience panic attacks. Symptoms of GAD may include restlessness, tiring easily, poor concentration, irritability, muscle tension, and insomnia or restless sleep (choice A can be eliminated; choice B is correct).

Passage 16

1. **B** The second paragraph of the passage refers to the researchers' assertion that "students interpret their anxiety about math and science as evidence of their inability to succeed." This derives from Bandura's principle that people misinterpret anxiety as evidence of their lack of ability, or inefficacy. Part of the definition of self-efficacy is a belief in one's capacity to succeed in spite of challenges. Thus, a misappraisal of anxiety would undermine a student's self-efficacy, leading to less persistence in subjects that cause the anxiety (choice B is correct). Although a logical argument could be made that lower self-efficacy is correlated with anxiety, this was not mentioned as a basis for the researchers' study, and causation cannot be assumed from the experimental results (choice A is wrong). The superego refers to Sigmund Freud's structural theory in which he describes the superego as that aspect of one's psyche that embodies ideal moral principles and expectations. The superego is considered to be in conflict with the id, which embodies a person's animalistic drives and ambitions. The passage does not discuss any relevance of this concept to self-efficacy (choice C is wrong). The notion that the environment has little impact on learning is fundamentally contrary to Bandura's social learning theory and therefore cannot be compatible with the researchers' approach (choice D is wrong).

2. **A** A knowledge of Piaget's stages of cognitive development is required for this question, and it must be integrated with the data presented in Figure 2. Piaget posited four stages of development, including the sensorimotor stage in which infants learn to manipulate the physical environment; the preoperational stage in which toddlers learn to symbolize the world using language; the concrete operational stage in which grade-school age children learn to engage in complex problem solving about physically observable things; and the formal operational stage in which adolescents begin to learn how to solve problems in a purely abstract manner. The data in Figure 2 indicate that high RC classrooms predict higher self-efficacy in science but not math, and the correct answer must reflect that finding. Science activities entail concrete problem solving, which lends itself to the demonstration of observable effort that characterizes the mastery approach to learning. Math word problems, however, are less concrete as they draw more heavily on formal operational thinking (choice B is wrong), and so it is more difficult to demonstrate observable effort. Accordingly, this distinction would be a reasonable explanation for the results in Figure 2 (choice A is correct). Earning higher grades rather than demonstrating effort is inconsistent with the mastery approach of RC programs and therefore would not be a reasonable explanation for increased self efficacy (choice C is wrong). As noted above, sensorimotor intelligence is a capacity developed in infancy; it is irrelevant to distinctions between middle school academic subjects and has no bearing on the study of physics (choice D is wrong).

3. **C** Impression management refers to the way in which people attempt to portray themselves in order to be liked or respected by others. Construct validity of a measurement tool refers to the tool's accuracy in measuring the construct it is intended to measure, which is a function of the measurement tool's items and their interpretation. If teachers' identities were disclosed, they might engage in impression management to portray themselves as complying with RC practices, which would compromise the interpretation of the R-CAP and render the results invalid (choice C is correct). Although the R-CAP items would need to accurately reflect RC principles in order to demonstrate construct validity, this necessity is unrelated to the issue of impression management (choice D is wrong). The issue of obtaining consistent results by multiple scorers is known as inter-rater reliability, and, by definition, addresses the issue of reliability rather than

construct validity (choice A is wrong). While unannounced observation by a principal may prevent dishonest impression management with regard to teaching performance, it is unrelated to the R-CAP measurement tool (choice B is wrong).

4. C   In both graphs in Figure 2, mean self-efficacy scores are represented on the y-axis, while categorical anxiety levels are represented on the x-axis. Accordingly, the graphs portray the relationship between self-efficacy and varying levels of anxiety. Specifically, they illustrate that, although self efficacy scores decline with increasing anxiety in low RC and high RC in both math and science, the mean self efficacy score declines less dramatically in high RC classrooms than in low RC classrooms, which is an effect known as attenuation (choice C is correct; choice B is wrong). Nevertheless, in both high RC and low RC, the direction of the lines indicate that self efficacy decreases as anxiety increases (choice D is wrong). Also, the graphs do not portray the relationship between low RC or high RC and anxiety levels (choice A is wrong).

5. D   An external locus of control means that an individual's goals are subject to factors outside his/ her control, while an internal locus of control means that the attainment of one's goals is within one's direct control. The shift from performance to mastery enables students to achieve success through effort alone, and thus facilitates the development of an internal locus of control (choice D is correct). This is contrast to defining success by performance, which may depend on cognitive or intellectual limitations beyond one's control, which reflects an external locus of control (choice C is wrong). The passage explicitly states that RC programs give social learning and academics equal weight (choice A is wrong). Reciprocal determinism is Bandura's term for the concept that one's personal attributes, one's behavior, and the environment affect each other in an endless cycle. Shifting focus from performance to mastery does not avoid this process (choice B is wrong).

6. B   The Sapir-Whorf hypothesis is the sociological perspective that the nuances of a culture's language significantly impact people's decisions and interpretations of the world around them. Accordingly, positive teacher language is most relevant to this idea as it relates to the micro-culture of a classroom (choice C is correct; choices A, C, and D are wrong).

7. A   This question requires an understanding of the statistical concept of skew, as well as of the distinction between ascribed status and achieved status. A frequency distribution is skewed when scores cluster above or below the mean rather than around the mean. Skew is expressed in terms of the tail, or "thinner" end of the distribution. Thus, a distribution is positively skewed when the scores cluster at the lower end, which leaves the tail at the higher, or positive, end. A distribution is negatively skewed when scores cluster at the upper end, and the tail is left at the lower, or negative, end. Conceptually, skew indicates that the mean is less reliable as a reflection of the tendency of scores, because, by definition, the scores are not clustered around the mean in a skewed distribution. If the distribution of exam scores had a negative skew, it would indicate that the tail was at the lower, or negative, end, and that most scores actually clustered above the mean. In sociological terms, ascribed status refers to the way a group is perceived, while achieved status refers to the degree of a group's actual accomplishments. In this question, a negative skew indicates that the students' achieved status surpassed their ascribed status, because their ascribed status was based upon the mean score, which was lower than the bulk of the scores (choice A is correct; choices B and C are wrong). Negative skew does not refer to the psychosocial consequences of a test result (choice D is wrong).

Passage 17

1. **A** Drive reduction theory states that individuals are motivated by primary physiological needs such as hunger, thirst, and sex. The individual will then attempt to reach a state of homeostasis in which the need is not present (choice A is correct). In Sociology, conflict theory investigates how different power structures in a society contribute to tensions in which high power groups exploit groups with less power. This theory does not deal with drive or motivation, but social structures (choice B is wrong). The James-Lange theory and Cannon-Bard theory are both theories of emotion. The former stipulates that emotion originates in the presence of a stimulus and the latter focuses on how neural pathways and physiological changes govern emotion (choice C and choice D are wrong).

2. **C** Behavior is extinguished—or becomes extinct—when the reinforcement for that behavior stops occurring, which therefore reduces the target behavior. So ceasing food dispersal should extinguish the superstitious behavior of the pigeon turning in circles, after enough time (choice C is correct). A shock punishment may reduce the behavior but extinction, by definition, must occur because of an absence of reinforcement or punishment (choice A is wrong). Timed reinforcement of an alternate behavior also does not fit the criterion of extinction (choice B is wrong). Shift of environment and removal of discriminative stimulus alone would not be sufficient for extinction to occur. The definition of extinction can only be met when there is an absence of reinforcement of the target behavior (choice D is wrong).

3. **D** The hippocampus is essential to learning and memory; therefore, this region is essential to an animal's ability to learn how to alter its behavior in response to new reinforcement schedules (choice D is correct). The pons is part of the lower brain along with the medulla oblongata and is predominantly implicated in maintaining physiological homeostasis; the pons is not involved in learning (choice A is correct). The hypothalamus is implicated in metabolic processes within the automatic nervous system but is not involved with learning (choice B is wrong). The thalamus, among many other functions, helps regulate alertness and sensation processing. It is therefore less directly implicated in learning than the hippocampus (choice C is wrong).

4. **B** Response lags occur when an individual on a reinforcement schedule can predict when the next reinforcement will come, or that reinforcement will not come for a certain period of time. The individual ceases the target behavior for a period of time after delivery because it knows that there will not be another immediate reinforcement (in this case, food dispersal). This is a 2x2 question, so any responses that say "could not predict" can be eliminated (choice A and choice C are wrong). Variable schedules do not allow individuals to predict when reinforcement will come because they are unpredictable, for both ratio and interval schedules, with each delivery (choice D is wrong). Therefore, individuals on a fixed schedule demonstrate a lag in behavior immediately after receiving the reinforcement (demonstrated in Figure 1 for the fixed ratio and fixed interval schedules), because the individual can predict that the next reinforcement won't occur for awhile (choice B is correct).

5. **C** Skinner and other Behaviorists believe that learned behavior is a result of reinforcement schedules contingent on the occurrence of the behaviors in question. A strict Behaviorist would believe that any human or animal behavior could be predicted if we knew the relevant contingency history and reinforcement schedule; therefore, Skinner would assert that an individual's correct guess is reinforced from time to time by chance, and the individual continues to misattrib-

ute cause of the reinforcement to the correct guess (choice C is correct). Regression and childhood conflicts are of interest to psychoanalytic and humanistic psychologists, among others, but do not fit into a behaviorist framework (choice A is wrong). Poverty and social opportunity are aspects of sociological theory, regarding which behaviorists have very little to say outside of punishment and reward schema (choice B is wrong). Observational learning is also viewed with skepticism among strict behaviorists like Skinner, and he would not have believed learning could take place without external reward (choice D is wrong).

6.   **B**   When organisms are rewarded on a fixed ratio schedule, they receive a reward after a fixed number of instanced of the behavior. For example, if a dog gets a treat after he sits ten times in response to a command, this would be a fixed ratio schedule. The type of behavior is most commonly observed with a fixed ration schedule is a lull in behavior right after the reward is received, which is thought to be similar to procrastination (choice B is correct). Superstitious behavior, as it is described in the passage, is the results of a fixed interval schedule of reinforcement, not a fixed ratio schedule (choice A is wrong). A slow, steady, and consistent rate of response is most characteristics of a variable interval reinforcement schedule (choice C is wrong). The reinforcement schedule that produces the slowest rate of extinction is variable ratio, not fixed ratio (choice D is wrong).

Passage 18

1.   **B**   Anterograde amnesia is the inability to create new memories from the time of the trauma that caused the amnesia, while memory retrieval brings information from long term memory back into short term memory. Therefore, the patient would have no difficulty remembering events that happened before the accident (before the onset of his anterograde amnesia, which prevents him from encoding new memories), but will have difficulty remembering things after the accident, which will not get encoded into long term memory. Therefore, the patient will remember his birthday before the accident, but will have trouble remembering his birthday after the accident (this does illustrate his condition, choice A can be eliminated). On the other hand, the patient will not remember what he did yesterday and today due to the anterograde amnesia (which causes an inability to form new memories), but will not have trouble remembering his birthday from two years ago, before the accident (this does not illustrate his condition, so choice B is correct). Similarly, the patient would have difficulty learning new things after the accident (choice C can be eliminated), as well as difficulty remembering the names of people he just met, which is also after the accident (choice D can be eliminated).

2.   **A**   The passage states that the brain implant would only be useful for individuals with localized brain damage, not widespread brain damage (choices C and D are wrong). Figure 1 shows that researchers hypothesize that the brain implant will improve memory functioning, but it will not return memory back to what it was before the damage, also known as a "premorbid level" (choice B is wrong). The researcher hypothesize that memory will be improved with the implant, but will not function as well as before the damage (choice A is correct).

3.   **B**   The passage states that the researchers are attempting to help the brain convert short term memories into long term memories. The next sentence states that the brain implant would be placed next to the hippocampus in the medial temporal lobe. This implies that the function of the hippocampus is to convert short term memories into long term memories instead of the opposite

(choice A and C is wrong). The hippocampus is located on the medial temporal lobe, not the medial parietal lobe (choice D is wrong). Therefore, the hippocampus is integral in the conversion of short-term memory into long-term memory, and it is located on the medial temporal lobe (choice B is correct).

4. **C** According to Baddeley's model of working memory, working memory is comprised of Phonological Loop, Visuospatial Sketchpad, and Episodic Buffer. This is an alternative to the short-term store description of working memory delineated by the Atkinson–Shiffrin model (choice C is correct). Phonological Loop is the part of working memory that deals with sound or phonological information (choice A is wrong). Visuospatial Sketchpad is the part of working memory is where we hold information about what we see (choice B is wrong). Episodic Buffer is the part of working memory that links information across domains to form integrated units of visual, spatial, and verbal information with time sequencing (choice D is wrong).

5. **B** Explicit memory (also known a declarative memory) includes information that can be consciously recalled, such as personal and factual information; implicit memory (also known as nondeclarative memory) includes the memory for how to perform motor skills and actions, such as driving or running (choice B is correct; choice D, which reverses these two, is wrong). Explicit memory includes *both* the ability to recall personal events and factual information; implicit memory include motor memory, not factual information (choice A is wrong). Explicit memory is largely conscious while implicit memory is unconscious (choice C is wrong).

6. **C** The passage states that the brain implant would only be useful for individuals with localized brain damage, not widespread brain damage. Individuals with Alzheimer's disease have widespread damage to their brain. Therefore, the results of a hypothesized study examining the effectiveness of the brain implant in patients with Alzheimer's disease would not show any significant difference between the Alzheimer's with implant and Alzheimer's without implant groups. The Alzheimer's with the implant group would not perform as well as the control group (choice A is wrong) and would not show a significant improvement over the Alzheimer's without the implant group (choice B is wrong). Similarly, the Alzheimer's without the implant group would not perform as well as the control group (choice D is wrong). According to the passage, the implant would not have much effect on the performance of the Alzheimer's with the implant on a standardized memory task compared to the Alzheimer's without the implant, and both groups would perform worse than the control group (choice C is correct).

Passage 19

1. **C** Based on Table 1, the "a" superscript for the epinephrine and control groups and the "b" superscript for the placebo and control groups indicates that at the one-week follow-up, recall for the epinephrine group is significantly higher than for the control group (indicated by the "a" superscripts), and recall for the placebo group is significantly higher than for the control group (indicated by the "b" superscripts; choice C is correct, choice D is wrong). Given that there are no

superscripts for any of the values in the immediate recall column, there were no significant differences between any of the groups during this phase of the study (choices A and B are wrong).

2. **C** The overwhelming majority of research has been done linking epinephrine to fear, which includes the study of the fight-or-flight response (choice C is correct). The emotion of happiness is most closely linked with the release of the neurotransmitter dopamine, which is involved in what is colloquially known as the "pleasure pathway" (choice A is wrong). Depression has most frequently been linked with a deficit of the neurotransmitter serotonin, although recent studies are beginning to debunk this theory (choice B is wrong). In addition to depression, serotonin is also thought to play a part in anger and aggression (choice D is wrong).

3. **D** The purpose of the quiz participants took after memorizing the word list, but prior to reciting it back to the research assistant, was most likely a use of the distraction technique, wherein researchers attempted to redirect the brain so that the memory of the words had time to encode into short-term memory (choice D is correct). Deception is the research equivalent of lying to participants, frequently used to mislead participants so that they do not learn what the actual purpose of the research may be (choice A is wrong). A decoy is often used as part of deception, generally to intentionally mislead or confuse participants (choice B is wrong). Extinction is a social learning term, which is when an individual has "forgotten" the link between two stimuli (choice C is wrong).

4. **D** Episodic memory, also known as flashbulb memories, are clear memories of unique and often highly emotional events, such as where you were and what you were doing during the 9/11 terrorist attacks (choice D is correct). The ability to perfectly recall images, sounds, or objects without the use of memory aids, such as mnemonics, is referred to as eidetic memory, or photographic memory (choice A is wrong). Explicit memory, or declarative memory, is a type of long-term memory that requires conscious thought to recall, such as remembering a loved one's birthday (choice B is wrong). Implicit memory, or procedural memory, is a type of long-term memory that does not require conscious thought to recall, such as riding a bike (choice C is wrong).

5. **B** Based on the design of the study, wherein research assistants were not made aware of which participants were in which group, this would be classified as a double-blind study (choice B is correct). A case study is a descriptive analysis of an individual, group, or an event, and would not involve various experimental groups (choice A is wrong). A meta-analysis involves contrasting and combining results from different studies, with the aim of finding patterns among the results that might bring about new information (choice C is wrong). A naturalistic observation involves the "participants" being unaware of their participation, as they have no interaction with the researchers, and there is rarely any experimental manipulation (choice D is wrong).

6. **C** The amygdala has been implicated in encoding and storing memories that include intense emotional themes, and works in concert with the hippocampus and other limbic areas to store long-term memories (choice C is correct). The prefrontal lobe stores information on an extremely temporary basis (anywhere from several seconds to several minutes), and thus is highly involved with short-term memory (choice D is wrong). The thalamus is responsible for sensory and motor action, and is not typically associated with memory (choice A is wrong). The hippocampus plays a major part in constructing, integrating, and then storing information from short-term memory into long-term memory, and thus plays a greater role in long-term memory than short-term (choice B is wrong).

Passage 20

1. **C** The researchers were trying to increase the wild canids' compliance behavior towards vaccinations. Reinforcement increases behavior, while punishment decreases the occurrence of a behavior. The researchers added a desirable stimulus, a treat, to increase the desired behavior, which is an example of positive reinforcement. Negative reinforcement *removes* an undesirable stimulus to obtain the preferred behavior; for example, if the canids had a painful choke collar removed upon performance of the desired behavior, this would be an example of negative reinforcement (choices A and B are wrong). A primary reinforcer is a stimulus that is desirable or integral to the survival of the subject. Since the wild canids desire treats and food is necessary for their survival, the treat is a primary positive reinforcer (choice B is correct). Conditioned reinforcers are neutral stimuli that must be paired with primary reinforcers in order to be conditioned (choice D is wrong).

2. **B** The researchers implemented different reinforcement schedules for group A and group B during experiment two. Group A received a continuous schedule, which permitted them to receive a treat every time they conducted the compliance behavior. However, group B canids were given an intermittent schedule, in which the performance of the compliance behavior were sometimes reinforced with a treat. A continuous schedule not only leads to rapid behavior acquisition, but also quick behavior extinction once the reinforcement is removed (choices A, C, and D are wrong). Nevertheless, an intermittent reinforcement schedule leads to gradual behavior acquisition and a greater perseverance of the behavior once the reinforcement is discontinued (choice B is correct).

3. **A** A continuous reinforcement schedule occurs when the subjects receive the reinforcement, a treat, after *every* occurrence of a behavior and is the schedule used for group A in experiment two, not in the third experiment described in the question stem (choices B and D are wrong). A fixed ratio schedule results in the subjects receiving the reinforcement after a set number of instances of the desired behavior and describes group A's schedule in experiment three (choice C is wrong). A variable ratio schedule occurs when the subjects receive the reinforcement after preforming the behavior an unpredictable number of times and describes group B's schedule in experiment three (choice A is correct).

4. **B** Item I is false: The passage did not specify the species of wild canids being studied. Therefore, it cannot be assumed that they were all the same species (choices A and C can be eliminated). Item II is true: the passage states that the injection was a placebo solution, which would not affect the health of the canids. Item III is false: the wild canids *only* received a treat if they performed the desired behavior (choice D can be eliminated; choice B is correct).

5. **C** Negative reinforcement describes a situation in which an undesirable stimulus, such as the repetitive beeping in a car, is removed after conducting the correct behavior (choice C is correct). Positive reinforcement is when a subject receives a desirable stimulus, such as dessert, right after preforming a desired behavior, like finishing the vegetables at dinner (choice A is wrong). Negative punishment is when a subject has a desirable stimulus taken away, such as recess, when they commit an incorrect behavior (choice B is wrong). Positive punishment occurs when a subject is given an undesirable stimulus, chores, when they do an incorrect behavior (choice D is wrong).

6. **B** In the new experiment the researchers give a fixed ratio schedule to the canids in group B. A fixed ratio schedule will lead to faster learning process than a completely random schedule.

However, the fastest learning process occurs from a continuous schedule, which describes group A's condition. Therefore, the average number of trials to learn from the fixed ratio schedule should lie between three and nine (choice B is correct). A continuous schedule leads to faster learning and thus two trials is incorrect because group A learned the behavior in three trials (choice A is wrong). The group B canids would learn quicker than they would have in experiment two because of the fixed ratio schedule (choices C and D are wrong).

Passage 21

1. **B** According to the last sentence of the passage, the "results held only for the panel ratings," yet the study's outcome suggests that attractive people act as though they know their attractiveness is an asset, in turn suggesting that the self-ratings should be a more reliable predictor than the panel ratings. Furthermore, the question stem corroborates this by stating, "other research finds that one's own perceived attractiveness primarily drives one's tendency to trust others." Therefore, this new information negatively impacts the experimenters' finding of a higher correlation between the panel ratings and the subjects' willingness to trust (choice B is correct; choice A is wrong). Rather than bolster the experimenters' finding that objective measures of attractiveness are more reliable, the new information actually undermines this finding (choice C is wrong). While the new information in the question stem does suggest that self ratings of attractiveness are more reliable than those provided by others, this does not explain the impact of this on the experimenters' finding (choice D is wrong).

2. **B** Item I is false: Having more social ties does not help to explain why individuals considered attractive by others are significantly less likely to suffer performance issues in public than are their less attractive counterparts because social ties are unrelated to performance anxiety (choices A and C can be eliminated). Item II is true: If attractive people were found to suffer fewer performance issues in public, that would suggest that being attractive is correlated with less worrying about how one may be judged when performing tasks. Item III is false: if less is expected of people who are not attractive, then those people would be less likely to feel pressure performing tasks in public, the opposite of what should be true based on the information in the question (choice D can be eliminated, choice B is correct).

3. **A** The researchers designed the study "to determine whether physically attractive subjects, perhaps sensing their appearance to be an asset, would be more trusting..." About two-thirds of the subjects rated attractive by the panel were willing to trust. If 40% (a larger quantity than the less trusting one-third) of those subjects did not believe themselves to be attractive, then at least some of the "attractive" subjects did not see their looks as an asset the way the researchers expected (choice A is correct). Though it is true that attractiveness is influenced by social and cultural norms, this does not undermine the researchers' results (choice B is wrong). Even if some "unattractive" subjects thought themselves to be very attractive, they could be among the ones in the "unattractive" group who were willing to trust when their pictures could be seen (choice C is wrong). If self-ratings of attractiveness were influenced by photographs taken that day, that would not contradict the experimenters' expectation, since there was a positive correlation between the self and panelist ratings (choice D is wrong).

4. **D** The researchers "sought to determine whether physically attractive individuals who thought they could be seen would be more trusting in others," so it can be concluded from the study results

that the less attractive subjects trusted "partners" less than did the more attractive ones(choice D is correct). This study was designed to test honesty, not trust; therefore, it cannot be concluded that self-perceived attractiveness is a strong honesty motivator (choice A is wrong). The study design and results do not provide information that would support any of the following conclusions: people may subconsciously believe their attractiveness higher than they would otherwise state (choice B is wrong) or that male subjects would be more likely to trust attractive female partners than less attractive ones (choice C is wrong).

5. **A** Increased likelihood of agreeing to larger request after first agreeing to a smaller one is known as the foot-in-the-door phenomenon (choice A is correct). The self-serving bias pertains to the tendency to attribute success to internal factors and failure to external ones (choice B is wrong). Groupthink explains the tendency for people in groups to concur about decisions, even if those decisions are wrong, because they desire harmony within the group (choice C is wrong). The by-stander effect explains a reduced tendency to help someone in need when there are more people around (choice D is wrong).

6. **A** External validity describes the extent to which the results of a study can be generalized to other situations and to other people. The experimental subjects were all undergraduate volunteers, so the sample is neither random nor representative of the larger population. Item I is false: Excluding some of the participants' data from the final results will not impact the external validity (choice B and choice D can be eliminated). Item II is false: Averaging the participants' self ratings with the panel ratings before dividing participants into three attractiveness groups will not impact the external validity (choice C can be eliminated). Item III is true: repeating the study with a larger sample of randomly selected adults will increase the external validity by increasing the extent to which the study can be generalized to other situations and to other people (choice A is correct).

Passage 22

1. **B** The key assumption underlying the conclusion of the study is that socially constructed norms shape gender expression, which is the central tenet of gender socialization theory (choice B is correct). Freud's latency stage describes the moment when a child begins to identify with and emulate the parent of the same sex, but it does not address appearance (choice A is wrong). While Piaget argued that adolescents imagine they are being watched and evaluated, his theory of imaginary audience does not address appearance and gender expression specifically (choice C is wrong). Erikson's physiological revolution refers only to a period of significant physical change in adolescence that prompts a search for stable identity formation; it does not address interactions with social norms (choice D is wrong).

2. **D** Only choice D accurately represents decreased BEA in girls and maintenance of BEA scores in boys across the two phases of the study. The slope of the line for boys in choice A represents the change in above average BMI for boys, not low SES (choice A is wrong). The slope of both the lines in choice B reflects the BEA scores high (rather than low) SES data (choice B is wrong). The slope of the line for girls in choice C plots BEA scores for high SES for girls (choice C is wrong).

3. **B** The focus of cognitive-behavioral therapy is identifying dysfunctional or maladaptive thoughts and changing them through re-education and goal-oriented behavioral changes. The media group attends a class that employs this dynamic of education and self-analysis, so cognitive-behavioral therapy principles best explain these results (choice B is correct). Social cognitive theory stipulates

that behavior and thoughts are learned or modified through observation and modeling, but does not account for the self-analysis in the study described in the question stem (choice A is wrong). The study described in the question stem does not pair conditioned and unconditioned stimuli in order to elicit automatic conditioned responses as in classical conditioning; the goal of the education and self-analysis is to reveal unconscious conditioning (choice C is wrong). Similarly, operant conditioning involves the reinforcement or punishment of a desired behavior; the subjects in the study are informed participants in the process of attitudinal change (choice D is wrong).

4.   A   The new demographic information exposes a flaw in the experiment: the racial composition of the participant pool is an independent variable to be controlled for at the design stage of the experiment; therefore, it calls into question the results and the experiment should be repeated with a more representative sample of subjects (choice A is correct). Race is neither an extraneous variable (choice B is wrong) nor a dependent variable (choice C is wrong; BEA is the dependent variable). However much these new findings might call into the question the results of this study, this information does not render the experiment void, unethical, and unscientific (choice D is wrong).

5.   B   Only the statement that "above average BMI predicts low BEA" accurately summarizes the results in Figure 1, which show that above average BMI in both genders correlates negatively with BEA scores (choice B is correct). According to the final sentence of the first paragraph, exposure to media images is a constant variable across all groups, rather than an independent variable (choice A is wrong). The conclusion that low SES predicts low BEA is only partially correct; it is true for girls but not for boys, according to Table 1 (choice C is wrong). Similarly, the conclusion that autonomy is not a variable that influences BEA is incorrect because it generalizes to both low and high autonomy; BEA is unaffected by high autonomy across genders, but it is affected by low autonomy in both genders (choice D is wrong).

Passage 23

1.   A   Based on the information presented in the passage and the data in Figure 1, the researchers might most logically conclude that odor manipulation (the presence of the lemon trigger scent) may be associated with a reduced fear response between phases 1 and 2 in the experimental group. However, the fact that the lemon scent was introduced at three time points (during Phase 1 while the experimental participants were receiving shocks, overnight with the lemon-scented air freshener, and then again during Phase 2, when the images were presented without shocks) makes it perhaps more challenging to determine that the lemon scent is responsible for the reduced fear response. Therefore critics of this study might be skeptical of this conclusion given that the lemon scent was present during Phase 2 (choice A is correct; choice B is wrong). Testing the subject for innate fear response is not a viable criticism because the researchers were applying slightly painful electric shocks, which will produce some degree of fear response in everyone (choice C is wrong). Based on the results of this study alone, it would be quite premature for researchers to conclude that PTSD can easily be treated by classical conditioning. Although conditioning is frequently used in PTSD treatments such as exposure therapy, shock therapy is not currently an evidence-based treatment for PTSD, and is used very rarely to treat other disorders when other treatments have failed (choice D is wrong).

2.   C   Item I is true: The amygdalae (plural of amygdala) are two almond-shaped areas located deep within the temporal lobes. They are a part of the limbic system involved in signaling the cortex regarding motivationally significant stimuli (such as rewards, punishments, fear stimuli, and sexual stimuli); they are also involved in emotion and memory (choice B can be eliminated).

Item II is true: The hippocampus is a part of the limbic system involved in the formation of long-term memories, and is also implicated in the maintenance of cognitive "maps" (choice A can be eliminated). Item III is false: the medulla oblongata is the lower half of the brainstem and is continuous with the spinal cord; it is responsible for transmitting information to the brain, and also regulates autonomic functions like respiration and vomiting (choice D can be eliminated; choice C is correct).

3.   B   According to Freud, the latent content of your dreams consists of your unconscious drives and wishes, including sexual and aggressive themes (choice B is correct). Experiences and preoccupations from the day's events would fall into the dream's manifest content (choice A is wrong). Freud did not openly believe in psychic abilities to see into the future (choice C is wrong), nor did he openly express beliefs regarding past lives (choice D is wrong).

4.   A   The absolute threshold is defined as the point at which something becomes noticeable to the senses, e.g. the softest sound a person could hear, the slightest touch a person could feel, or the minimal amount of scent a person can smell (choice A is correct). The difference threshold is defined as the amount of change needed for an individual to recognize that a change has occurred; since the question stem is asking for the minimum amount of scent that becomes barely noticeable to the senses, the difference threshold does not apply (choice B is wrong). Similarly, the just-noticeable difference is defined as the measurable amount of the change itself, which occurs within the difference threshold; for example, if humans can only detect a difference between a 10 lb. weight and a 12 lb. weight, then 2 lbs. is the just-noticeable difference (choice C is wrong). The threshold potential refers to the critical level to which a membrane potential must be depolarized in order to initiate an action potential (choice D is wrong).

5.   D   Shrinkage in volume of the hippocampus would most likely be the cause for memory loss, a common symptom of PTSD (choice D is correct). Difficulty verbally expressing thoughts or feelings is also a common symptom of PTSD, caused by trauma's adverse effects on the prefrontal lobe, which is responsible for linguistic function (choice A is wrong). Frequent feelings of fear regardless of the situation, or hypervigilance, is due to the medial prefrontal cortex's inability to properly regulate itself following a traumatic experience (choice B is wrong). Difficulty regulating emotions, another common symptom of PTSD, is the result of the amygdala going into "overdrive" post-trauma (choice C is wrong).

Passage 24

1.   C   The six basic emotions are anger, fear, disgust, happiness, surprise and sadness. Thus, curiosity is not one of these basic emotions (choice C is not a basic emotion and therefore the right answer; choices A, B, and D are wrong).

2.   A   The James-Lange theory of emotion states that emotions are the direct product of physiological arousal, making the emotion merely a secondary response to the primary stimulus of bodily arousal. In the study in the passage, the participants on the scary bridge would be feeling fear as a result of their bodily arousal that began when they walked onto the bridge, and the brain would not be able to re-label or re-interpret that bodily arousal as sexual arousal or attraction. Therefore, the stories told by participants would most likely include some content involving fear or frightening things (choice A is correct). The James-Lange theory is focused on bodily arousal and does not

have anything to say about whether the person would put themselves in a story (choice B is wrong). Because the James-Lange theory attributes emotions to the physiological arousal, if all participants are in a setting that involves physiological arousal, their emotional responses should be similar. They should not have a wide range of emotional content (choice C is wrong). The James-Lange theory is concerned with emotions and therefore would make no prediction about the basic components of participants' stories; they could involve a bridge or not involve a bridge and the theory would not be able to make a prediction either way (choice D is wrong).

3.   **B**   This study was seeking to measure the misattribution of arousal. Therefore, their hypotheses must contain an explanation for how the participants might misattribute their physiological arousal. The null hypothesis is typically the reverse of the researchers' hypothesis and disproving it is how researchers can claim that there is a difference between measured groups. Therefore, the statement that there will not be a difference between the groups in the amount of misattribution that occurs, in this case measured as sexual content, is the appropriate null hypothesis (choice B is correct). By disproving this null hypothesis, the researchers can show that the participants likely misattributed their non-sexual arousal from the frightening bridge to sexual attraction to the researcher. Their actual hypothesis is that there *is* a difference in sexual content; therefore, this cannot also be the null hypothesis (choice A is wrong). The researchers are not studying the arousal itself; the difference in arousal levels between the bridges is assumed and, in fact, in this study is treated as an independent variable (choice C is wrong; choice D is wrong).

4.   **D**   The sympathetic nervous system is a subset of the autonomic nervous system that controls arousal (choice D is correct). It functions below the level of consciousness and can influence emotional states along with the other components of autonomic nervous system. The enteric nervous system is another part of the autonomic nervous system that controls the gastrointestinal system (choice A is wrong). The parasympathetic nervous system is the final part of the autonomic nervous system controls resting and relaxing and is how humans return to baseline after periods of arousal (choice B is wrong). The somatic nervous system is not part of the autonomic nervous system. It controls voluntary movement and is consciously, rather than unconsciously, operated (choice C is wrong).

5.   **C**   Stress is well studied and has been shown to have both beneficial and deleterious effects on people. At low levels, stress is a powerful motivator and helps people to be more engaged and active with their environment. At high levels, it is debilitating and can completely impair performance on tasks. The principle that describes the varying effect of stress on performance is known as the Yerkes-Dodson law. Because the people on the high bridge performed significantly better on the simple cognitive tasks, it can be assumed that the high bridge supplied some degree of arousal that caused an improved performance, which is best accounted for by the Yerkes-Dodson law (choice C is correct). The social facilitation effect also refers to a change in performance on simple tasks. According to the social facilitation effect people will perform better than their average on simple tasks when other people observe them. This experiment was conducted at a park with similar levels of observers on both bridges, therefore the social facilitation effect does not best explain why those on the high bridge performed significantly better (choice A is wrong). Cognitive priming occurs when an individual is exposed to an idea or concept. This exposure predisposes the person to think of things related to the primed idea. The researchers did not use priming in this study (choice B is wrong). The Cannon-Bard theory attempts to explain emotions. It states that the mental experience of emotions and the physiological experience of arousal associated with those emotions occur simultaneously. The study described in the question does not deal with emotions and so this would not apply (choice D is wrong).

6. **B** Figure 1 shows clear differences between the low-bridge group and the high-bridge group. The researchers measured the number of stories with sexual content as well as the number of participants that called the researcher to ask her out on a date. As shown in the figures, the participants who were interviewed on the arousal-inducing bridge clearly had more instances of sexual stories and follow-up date invitations after the survey. They misattributed their arousal and that misattribution persisted even after the experiment (choice B is correct). The figures show significantly different levels between the groups, so the different bridges must have had an effect (choice A is wrong). If the misattribution stopped once the participants left the bridge, we would expect to see a high amount of sexual content in the stories collected on the bridge, but no difference in the number of people who later called the researcher to ask her out on a date (choice C is wrong). Lastly, if individual differences were more influential than the independent variable of the bridge, the differences would not meet the level of significance. The figures indicate a significant difference between the groups, meaning that the likelihood of the difference being chance is very, very small (choice D is wrong).

7. **A** Item I is true: the Schachter-Singer theory of emotions states that emotions are the product of physiological arousal combined with cognitive labeling. Emotions have a conscious thought-based component as well as physiological component. According to the theory, physiological arousal could become mislabeled by the brain, meaning that this theory encapsulates the idea of misattribution of arousal (choices B and C can be eliminated). Item II is false: the Cannon-Bard theory states that physiological arousal and emotions happen simultaneously. There isn't a moment for the brain to misinterpret bodily arousal, according to this theory, so it is not compatible with misattribution of arousal (choice D can be eliminated). Item III is false: the James-Lange theory of emotions does not allow for a cognitive component. All emotions are a direct result of physiological arousal without the opportunity to interpret those stimuli (choice A is correct).

Passage 25

1. **B** The statement that elderly fish owners who experienced three or more stressful events in the last six months attended the same number of medical appointments as the elderly dog owners with a comparable level of stress conflicts with the proposed hypothesis that dog owners are healthy because of increased physical interaction with their pets. As one does not physically interact with pet fish, it would be expected that the fish owners would have more medical appointments (or worse health) if the hypothesis were true (choice B is correct; choice A is wrong). If cat owners spent half as much time petting their animals as dog owners did, this would contribute to the explanation that dog owners are healthier because of this interaction (choice C is wrong). The passage makes no mention of how much participants left their house (e.g., to walk their dogs), but the statement that elderly dog owners leave the house more than cat owners still does not conflict with the hypothesis regarding physical interaction (choice D is wrong).

2. **A** Inclusive fitness occurs when an organism behaves in a manner that allows for its genes to continue to be passed on via its relatives and sometimes is even done at the sacrifice of the organism itself (choice A is correct). Genetic drift is the change in frequency of a particular allele for a trait in a population that tends to occur by chance (choice B is wrong). Adaptation refers to the changes that happen in a population over time due to selection of a certain trait (choice C is wrong). Natural selection is the overarching term for the process in which particular traits are selected over others but does not specifically refer to organisms attempting to keep kin alive (choice D is wrong).

3. C   Seizures are generally studied with electroencephalograms (EEG) because they provide very specific information about timing of neural events and relatively specific information about the location of neural events (choice C is correct). Functional MRI (fMRI) is generally considered too slow to be useful in studying seizures as they occur, providing information only every two seconds (choice A is incorrect), and while structural MRI can provide insight as to where damaged tissue is, it does not necessarily indicate which tissue is epileptic, and it cannot provide any functional data (choice B is wrong). Computerized tomography (CT) is a series of X-rays of the brain, which also do not provide functional data (choice D is wrong).

4. A   Oxytocin is the hormone that is released during physical interactions (such as touching, nursing, and sexual intercourse) that is said to increase bonding between individuals (choice A is correct). It increases trust and may increase generosity, and it also has been shown to improve cognitive function. Dopamine is a neurotransmitter that is involved with many aspects of functioning, including motor control and impulsivity, but it is not implied in bonding (choice B is wrong). Serotonin plays a major role in mood but not necessarily in bonding (choice C is wrong). Adrenocorticotropic hormone (ACTH) is produced in response to stress, not bonding activities (choice D is wrong).

5. D   Erik Erickson's theory of development breaks the entire life cycle into stages and the internal conflict that occurs during each. Old age, generally defined as 65 years old until death, is defined by the conflict of integrity versus despair, wherein individuals must reflect on their life with a sense of fulfillment or else they will suffer a sense of failure and despair (choice D is correct). Autonomy versus shame and doubt occurs during early childhood (ages two to three) as one gets toilet trained (choice A is wrong), and generativity versus stagnation is the conflict of middle adulthood (40 to 65 years) as individuals hope to be successful at jobs and parenting (choice B is wrong). Industry versus depression is not a stage of Erickson's theory (choice C is wrong).

6. C   Brains of Alzheimer's patients consistently show shrunken gyri as well as enlarged vesicles and therefore a significant decrease in the amount of cortex compared to a healthy brain (choice C is correct). Gyri would not be enlarged in this situation (choices A and B are wrong), and an excess of cerebrospinal fluid would not permit shrunken vesicles (choice D is wrong).

Passage 26

1. C   According to Table 3, the p values for the severe anxiety group for both heart rate and respiration rate are less than or equal to 0.05, meaning that there was a significant difference between the actual and perceived physiological response to stress for this group—a result that supports the researchers' hypothesis (choice C is correct). The researchers hypothesized that severe anxiety individuals would be more likely to overestimate their physiological responses to stress, so the study results are comparing results *within* groups, not between group. Therefore, there is not enough information to conclude that the actual post-task anxiety levels for the low anxiety group were higher than for the moderate and severe anxiety groups (because these between groups measured were not analyzed; choice A is wrong). Again, even though the heart rate and respiratory data in Table 1 and Table 2 may *appear* similar, there were no between group comparisons made, so there is no statistical evidence to support that there was no significant difference between the post-task perceived anxiety levels for the moderate anxiety group and the low anxiety group (choice B is wrong). The severe anxiety group (not the moderate anxiety group) demonstrated the least accurate overall estimations of their own anxiety, on average, a finding

which is supported by the fact that this group demonstrated statistical significance between actual and perceived stress, whereas the moderate anxiety group (with p values of 0.08) did not demonstrate significance (choice D is wrong).

2. **D** Item I is true: mechanoreceptors called muscle spindles located in the skeletal muscle would be involved with the perception of muscle tension described in the question stem (choice A and choice C can be eliminated). Item II is true: baroreceptors (a type of mechanoreceptor) are located in the blood vessels and are involved with detection of changes in blood pressure, which can be influenced by rapid changes in heart rate; therefore, baroreceptors are likely involved with the perception of increased heart rate described in the question stem. Item III is true: thermoreceptors located in the skin respond to changes in temperature, and would be involved with the perception of feeling hot described in the question stem (choice B can be eliminated, choice D is correct).

3. **B** The Gestalt school of psychology focuses greatly on an individual's sensation and perception. The principle behind Gestalt psychology is that the human eyes see objects in their entirety before perceiving their individual parts, thus suggesting that the whole is a sum of its parts (choice B is correct). Humanistic psychology emphasizes the individual's inherent drive toward self-actualization (choice A is wrong). Psychodynamic psychology focuses on revealing the unconscious content of the individual's psyche to alleviate "psychic tension" (choice C is wrong). Social psychology studies how people's thoughts, feelings, and behaviors are influenced by the presence of others, whether it is actual, implied, or imagined (choice D is wrong).

4. **A** Top-down processing is defined as constructing perceptions from sensory input by drawing on our own experience and expectations (choice A is correct). Bottom-up processing is defined as starting at the sensory receptors and working up to the higher levels of processing (choice B is wrong). Serial processing is a form of processing involved in memory, and is defined as the act of attending to and processing one memory at a time (choice C is wrong). Transfer-appropriate processing is a type of state-dependent memory, which shows how a memory is encoded and retrieved is a large part of how strongly the memory stays with an individual (choice D is wrong).

5. **C** A perceptual set is defined as a set of mental tendencies and assumptions that greatly affect what one perceives. For example, when shown a blurry photo of something in the water, one's perception set will determine whether an individual sees a floating log, or the Loch Ness monster (choice C is correct). Bias is defined as a set of strongly held beliefs in favor of or against a certain thing, person, or group as compared to another (choice A is wrong). Emotion is defined as the response of a whole organism involving physiological arousal, expressive behaviors, and conscious experience (choice B is wrong). Cognition is defined as all the mental activities associated with thinking, knowing, remembering, and communicating (choice D is wrong).

Passage 27

1. **A** The cocktail party phenomenon is the tendency for people to detect their name when it is spoken in an otherwise unintelligible, noisy environment. Thus, this tendency would improve performance on the LIN task, which could lead researchers to conclude that aging non-musicians detect speech-in-noise better than they actually do (choice A is correct; choice B is wrong). The cocktail party phenomenon is unrelated to the effects of alcohol consumption (choice C is wrong). The passage explains that cochlear function is assessed by the pure-tone task, not the LIN task (choice D is wrong).

2. **D** Cross-sectional studies compare groups, and the particular study at hand compares musicians and non-musicians of different ages to determine the effects of musicianship on cognition (choice D is correct). Males and females were not isolated as distinct variables, and so the study cannot examine gender differences among musicians (choice A is wrong). A repeated-measures design entails subjects taking the same test at multiple stages over the course of a study, which did not occur in the study at hand (choice B is wrong). Longitudinal studies collect data from the same sample of participants over the course of time in order to compare data from different points in time. In this study, although people of different ages were included in the study, no participant was monitored over time (choice C is wrong).

3. **B** The correlational model depicted in Figure 1 reflects the results of the pure-tone measure. The figure shows a similar starting point for each group's trend, which indicates that musicianship alone does not predict a difference in pure-tone detection. Further, the slope of the line is the same across both groups, which suggests that the threshold for pure-tone detection increased comparably among musicians and non-musicians alike. In other words, the interaction between the variables of age and musicianship (age × musicianship interaction) do not predict a significant difference in performance on this task. As stated in the passage, pure-tone detection reflects functioning of the cochlea, which is a structure of the inner ear. Since the inner ear is not part of the brain or spinal cord, it is considered a component of the peripheral nervous system (PNS). With regard to the LIN task, the passage states that the data followed a trend similar to that of the gap detection measure, which is depicted in Figure 2. Here, the correlational model shows a divergence of the lines representing musicians and non-musicians such that aging musicians exhibit lower thresholds than their non-musician counterparts (age × musicianship interaction). In contrast to pure-tone detection, gap detection is dependent on cognitive processing in the auditory cortex. Since the auditory cortex is part of the brain, it is considered a component of the central nervous system. Therefore, a comparison of the data from the pure-tone measure and GDT suggest that central auditory processing is influenced by an age × musicianship interaction, while peripheral auditory processing is not (choice B is correct; choices A and C are wrong). Since the starting points of both groups is similar in the pure-tone measure and the GDT (and, by extension, the LIN task), musicianship alone is not indicated as a predictor of better auditory processing (choice D is wrong).

4. **C** The passage states that the data trend on the LIN measure was similar to that of the GDT, which reflects that aging musicians detect gaps better than their non-musician counterparts. Accordingly, Bill would find evidence of distinctions even among the elderly. Since Bill is also elderly, this group of people would be considered Bill's in-group, while non-elderly would be considered his out-group. When a person becomes aware of differences within his or her own in-group, this is known as in-group differentiation (choice C is correct). When one views his or her in-group as primarily the same, this is called in-group homogeneity (choice A is wrong). Viewing the individual members of one's out-group as essentially different is called out-group differentiation (choice D is wrong), while viewing them as essentially the same is called out-group homogeneity (choice B is wrong).

5. **A** Classical learning theory emphasizes the association of a given response with a particular stimulus. If the tone with the gap was always presented in the same sequential position (either first or second), or even if it was not alternated frequently enough, participants may begin to automatically associate that tone (either the first or second) with the response behavior of pushing the button. If so, a participant's response might be the result of conditioning rather than of actual detection, which could lead to false positives (if the sequence was always the same) or even false

negatives (if it was not alternated frequently enough). To avoid this problem, it would be important for researchers to frequently alternate the sequence of the tone with the gap (choice A is correct; choice B is wrong). Praise, or reward, is associated with operant (also known as instrumental) learning theory (choice C is wrong), while vicarious learning is associated with social learning theory (choice D is wrong).

6. **B** One way to demonstrate that musician's performance on the LIN task is the result of musicianship would be to find evidence of neural plasticity over time. This would suggest that musicianship actually results in an increase in brain mass of the auditory cortex (temporal lobe), which affords greater cognitive functioning for tasks such as speech-in-noise detection (choice B is correct). Timed music reading measures assess acquired skills rather than speech-in-noise detection, and so they could not be used to interpret the LIN results (choice A is wrong). Hearing aids facilitate the functioning of the ear's physical structures rather than cognitive functioning such as speech-in-noise detection. Further, a lack of need for hearing aids, as well as instrumental proficiency in eighth-grade, may very well be the result of genetic advantages rather than musicianship (choices C and D are wrong).

Passage 28

1. **A** The chart in Figure 1 shows the amount of saccharin consumed across each stage of the study. Specifically, it shows that rats in the saccharin-saccharin group consumed roughly the same amount of saccharin across all three stages, but that consumption varied by stage in the remaining three groups. In the saccharin-sucrose, saccharin-morphine, and saccharin-LiCl groups, consumption declined when the second substance was introduced. At least in the case of the saccharin-sucrose and saccharin-morphine groups, this observation is consistent with the notion of devaluation as described in the passage, because sucrose and morphine are more rewarding than saccharin. Next, consumption in the saccharin-sucrose group remained relatively low even in the third stage. Since lesions were applied to the TOA in the third stage, it can be inferred that the lesions of the TOA did not interfere with the process of devaluation. In the saccharin-morphine group, however, saccharin consumption levels increased in the third stage. This suggests that lesions of the TOA did interfere with the process of devaluation. Accordingly, it seems that, in some cases, the TOA contributes to an organism's devaluation of natural rewards, which means that the TOA can influence interest in gustatory stimuli such as saccharin after comparing those stimuli with the rewards they predict, such as a morphine high (choice A is correct). As noted, the chart in Figure 1 depicts consumption of saccharin, not of the other substances (choices B and D are wrong). In addition, the assertion that rats experience more pleasure by consuming greater amounts of saccharin than by consuming a combination of saccharin and another solution is contradicted by the data, because, in stage 2, saccharin consumption. If the animals preferred saccharin more than any other substance, they would not have consumed less saccharin simply because another substance was introduced. Also, aside from the rats in the saccharin-saccharin group, rats in the other groups were never conditioned to receive two servings of saccharin, so they could not expect that less consumption of saccharin (when paired with another substance) would yield more saccharin in place of the second substance (choice C is wrong).

2. **B** In the third stage of each study, lesions were applied to the rats' brains. In the first study, the lesion was applied to the TTA region of the thalamus, while, in the second study, a lesion was applied to the TOA region. Applying lesions to the rats' brains represents the manipulation of a factor con-

trolled by the experimenters, which is called an independent variable (choice B is correct). While saccharin consumption varied across groups in the third stage, this represents a factor that is not controlled by the experimenters, which is called a dependent variable (choice A is wrong). Both studies measured a sample of rats and not a population, which would required them to have studied every rat on earth (choice C is wrong). Other than the location of the lesions applied in the third stage, the passage describes both studies as identical (choice D is wrong).

3. **B** The passage describes devaluation as a model used to explain why drug addicts forfeit natural rewards. In conducting their studies, the researchers assumed this model to be true; the purpose of the studies was to examine the neural mechanisms that contribute to it. Since the question stem also assumes the notion of devaluation to be true, a lack of evidence of the process of devaluation in contexts other than those involving the gustatory pathway does not constitute a limitation of the study (choice B is not a limitation and is correct). Since the study only addresses natural rewards involving the gustatory pathway (saccharin), the results cannot be generalized to other types of natural rewards in the form of relationships, because emotional processing is not associated with the thalamus (choices A and C are limitations and are wrong). Further, even if the natural rewards were in the form of sensory stimuli, which does pertain to the thalamus, the particular centers incurring lesions are associated with the gustatory pathway only. Thus, no evidence exists with regard to the impact of lesions on other locations of the thalamus that process other forms of sensory information. Finally, the experiments only address the process of devaluation in situations where the natural reward is actually a conditioned predictor of the more powerful reward (such as sucrose or morphine), whereas interpersonal relationships or interactions are not necessarily conditioned predictors of drug use.

4. **C** The rats in the saccharin-LiCl group consumed less saccharin in both stages two and three. Devaluation would not seem to explain this behavior, because LiCl is less rewarding than saccharin (choice A is wrong). Rather, the behavior would be best explained by the classical conditioning concept of aversion, which refers to conditioning whereby a stimulus (saccharin) that previously yielded a particular conditioned response (saccharin consumption) is associated with an aversive stimulus (such as LiCl, which causes illness). In turn, this leads to an aversion response that replaces the original response (choice C is correct). Avoidance conditioning refers to an operant conditioning concept whereby subjects learn to actively make a particular response in order to avoid an unpleasant stimulus. In the studies above, the rats did not actively respond in order to avoid the LiCl; rather, they simply consumed less saccharin (choice B is wrong). Tolerance refers to the body's resilience toward the effects of drugs, which often leads to an addict seeking to increase the amount of stimulation through greater quantities or more powerful drugs

5. **A** Stage 2 of the studies involves the pairing of saccharin with another substance. If devaluation is a function of a natural reward's association with an even more rewarding substance (e.g. sucrose or morphine), then this phenomenon should be hastened by strengthening the association between the two stimuli. From a classical conditioning perspective, an association is strengthened by decreasing the temporal distance between two stimuli (choice A is correct; choice B is wrong). Eliminating the substance altogether would make it impossible to associate the two stimuli (choice C is wrong). If the order of the substance were reversed, then the less rewarding substance (saccharin) would no longer predict the greater reward (choice D is wrong).

6. **D** As noted above, aversion conditioning refers to the pairing of an unpleasant unconditioned stimulus with a pleasurable conditioned stimulus, which leads to the subject's avoidance of the conditioned stimulus. The delay between the saccharin and the morphine could be understood to elicit feelings of withdrawal, which refers to the unpleasant sensations associated with craving a drug. Thus, withdrawal would represent the unconditioned stimulus (choice D is correct). Intoxication refers to the overwhelming effects of a drug (choice A is wrong), while potentiation refers to mixing alcohol with other drugs to enhance its effect (choice B is wrong). Chemoreception is the process executed by gustatory and olfactory receptor genes in response to sensory stimuli. In chemoreception, chemical reactions dilute molecules of the stimulus in a solution which triggers the depolarization of receptor cells. In turn, neurotransmitters are fired from the receptor cells to the thalamus for further processing (choice C is wrong).

7. **C** Dopamine is implicated in the reward pathway of the brain, and would therefore be associated with pleasure-inducing drugs, such as morphine (choice C is correct; choices A, B, and D are wrong).

Passage 29

1. **C** The sensory modalities involved in music-color synesthesia are vision and sound. Vision is processed in the occipital lobe and sound is processed primarily in the temporal lobe. The passage states that the scientists hypothesized that structural differences would be found in regions involved in processing the modalities involved (choice C is correct). The parietal lobe is mentioned in the passage as the location where hyperbinding possibly takes place, however this region is not primarily involved in perceiving sound or vision. Therefore, answer choices containing the parietal lobe can be eliminated (choice B and choice D are wrong). The frontal lobe is involved in higher cortical functions and regulation, and it does not conduct primary processing of vision or sound (choice A is wrong).

2. **A** According to the passage, cross-activation occurs when both senses involved in the synesthetic experience are activated simultaneously despite sensory information being available for only one. Since lexical-gustatory synesthesia involves sight (for written language) or hearing (for spoken language) and taste or smell, the correct answer must be a brain region involved in perceiving one of these senses. The amygdala is an important link in the olfactory network, so it is the most logical potential locus in cross-activation out of the choices provided (choice A is correct). The primary function of the brainstem is to regulate automated processes such as heartrate and respiration and is not involved prominently in sight, taste, or smell (choice B is wrong). Broca's area is the area in the brain that is involved with speech production; since lexical-gustatory synesthesia involves the perception of taste or smell when hearing spoken or reading written language, but not when producing language one's self, it does not make logical sense that Broca's area would be locus of cross-activation for lexical-gustatory synesthesia (choice C is wrong). The cerebellum, principally implicated in movement and spatial orientation, is also not involved in processing the relevant modalities (choice D is wrong).

3. **C** Parallel processing is the brain's ability to process different types of information simultaneously. Cross activation is, according to the passage, direct stimulation of perceptual neural networks in both sensory modalities simultaneously. Without parallel processing, the brain could not have both sensory networks activated concurrently (choice C is correct). Hyperbinding is a pro-

cess by which the neural information transmitted through one modality is linked with the second modality in the parietal lobe. This means it is possible for the information to be processed in one sensory pathway, followed by hyperbinding in the parietal lobe linking the second sense, without parallel processing (choice A is wrong). Disinhibited feedback is similar to hyperbinding, differing in that it operates through limitations in the inhibition mechanism at the spot where different modalities converge. This could occur without parallel processing in a similar mechanism to hyperbinding (choice B is wrong). High integration between processing centers does not explicitly depend on parallel processing, as the theory is viable if the integration occurs in a sequential order and not in parallel (choice D is wrong).

4. **D** The figure shows that Encoding of memories is facilitated by learning across multiple platforms or learning the same information using different parts of the brain. A synesthete in a working memory task would therefore have an advantage in encoding that involved the paired sensory modalities (choice D is correct). If information is enriched with emotional salience it is retrieved more easily, however synesthesia is not known to involve an increase of emotional salience (choice A is wrong). Neural plasticity is the brain's ability to change or adapt to new experiences. This is essential for learning among both synesthetes and non-synesthetes (choice B is wrong). Long term potentiation is a long term enhancement in signal transmission between two neurons. This is beneficial for long term memory, not working memory, or short term memory, as in the question (choice C is wrong).

5. **A** Symbolic interactionism states that people construct reality through interactions with others, and adapt their views of the world based on these interactions. Also, symbolic interactionism involves change in behavior or outlook based on the new adaptation, as the boy does in the question stem and the focus is on micro-interactions between individuals and small social groups (choice A is correct). Social constructionism also highlights the importance of society in helping an individual construct reality, but highlights social constructs on a more macro, institutional scale (choice B is wrong). Functionalism also skews towards a more macro-level investigation of societies. It is especially interested in the role that institutions play in helping an individual construct identity (choice C is wrong). The actor-observer bias occurs when people are more likely to attribute their own actions to the particular situation, but attribute the behavior of someone else to their overall disposition rather than to situational factors. Since the boy in the question stem does not appear to attribute his peers' actions to anything, but rather internalizes their comments, which negatively impact his opinion about his own synesthesia, the actor-observer bias is not occurring here (choice D is wrong).

6. **D** The "C" between the two bars on the graph representing the controls indicates that the difference among controls in functional anisotropy between left and right hemispheres was significant at the 0.001 level, which is very significant (choice D is correct). The figure does not show that functional anisotropy was more lateralized in synesthetes, as the differences between right and left hemispheres are similar for both groups and there is no indication of a statistically significant difference indicated (choice A is wrong). Individuals with synesthesia had higher functional anisotropy in the right hemisphere, however the figure does not indicate if this was true for the brain as a whole (choice B is wrong). The study does not have the experimental power to provide a full explanation for synesthesia, as connectivity is only one aspect involved in the explanation of synesthesia (choice C is wrong).

Passage 30

1. **C** Item I is true: Broca's area is a region of the brain located in the frontal lobe that is responsible for speech production. Damage to this area often results in Broca's aphasia, whereby individuals have difficulty producing words. Therefore, slurred speech is indicative of damage to Broca's area (choice B can be eliminated). Item II is false: Wernicke's area is responsible for language comprehension; damage to this area would result in clearly spoken but unrelated words strung together to form meaningless sentences, a sign of Wernicke's aphasia, not Broca's aphasia (choice D can be eliminated). Item III is true: While individuals with Broca's aphasia have trouble producing speech, they are generally able to understand the words of others (choice A is wrong can be eliminated; choice C is correct).

2. **D** As the passage explained, literacy did not impact results. Therefore, a bilingual who was not literate would still be more likely to develop Alzheimer's later than a literate monolingual, based on the study results (choice D is correct). The study found that monolinguals tended to develop Alzheimer's nearly five years *earlier* (not later) than bilinguals (choice A is wrong). The third paragraph noted that for those persons who knew more than two languages (i.e., three or more) the study did not find any additional benefits; therefore, the age of onset would not likely vary much between a bilingual and trilingual, according to the study results (choice B is wrong). Since the study results demonstrated that literacy did not appear to have an impact on the age of onset of dementia, the conclusion that a literate bilingual would probably develop AD later than an illiterate bilingual is not supported (choice C is wrong).

3. **B** Recognition refers to the idea that a sensory cue will prompt the individual to remember something. Upon seeing the word *huevo*, the student was able to remember the meaning of the word (choice B is correct). Recall occurs when one is able to retrieve something from memory without any kind of cue. When she was asked if she knew the Spanish word for *egg*, she had no cue and was unable to remember it (choice A is wrong). Relearning occurs when someone attempts to relearn something he or she has learned in the past; the question stem does not indicate that she attempted to relearn this word (choice C is wrong). Recollection involves rebuilding a memory from partial memory by adding further detail in order to make it complete (choice D is wrong).

4. **C** The incentive theory rests on the assumption that a tangible reward will facilitate a desired behavior. In this case, the mother offered ice cream as a reward for attending Mandarin Chinese classes. The child responded positively to this incentive and went on to excel in class (choice C is correct). Drive-reduction theory focuses on maintaining equilibrium and balance in terms of the human body. For instance, a person will drink a glass of water when he or she feels thirsty. The child mentioned in the question stem does not need either the language class or the ice cream to maintain homeostasis (choice A is wrong). The cognitive dissonance theory involves conflicting beliefs or attitudes; there is no indication in the question stem that learning Mandarin Chinese involves any sort of conflict of interest within a child (choice B is wrong). The needs theory is based on Maslow's hierarchy of human needs, which begins with the most fundamental human needs. Learning a second language is not considered a basic human need, especially for a child (choice D is wrong).

5. **B** The out-group refers to a group of people who are viewed as being on the outside because they are different in some way. In the scenario described in the question stem, the bilingual students are a minority and are excluded from some activities because they are viewed as being different

(choice B is correct). Conversely, the in-group is the group with which individuals identify. Thus, the monolinguals see themselves as belonging to the in-group while the bilinguals form the out-group (choice A is wrong). The reference group is the group to which another group is compared when striving to meet a certain standard. Since the monolinguals are the majority, they would make up the reference group (choice C is wrong). The association group is a group of people who meet regularly to achieve a common goal. An example might be a support group that meets weekly to discuss issues and challenges. There is no indication of an association group in the question stem (choice D is wrong).

6. **D** According to Figure 1, VaD was the second most common subtype of dementia to occur among monolinguals (30.7%) and bilinguals (24.5%), and AD Dementia was the most common subtype among both groups (choice D is correct). While DLB was least common among monolinguals (2.6%), it was not the least common subtype among bilinguals (13.4%). With a percentage of just 9%, mixed dementia was the least common subtype among bilinguals (choice A is wrong). Whereas 106 (24.5%) of bilinguals experienced VaD, 82 (30.7%) of monolinguals experienced the same subtype. The incidence of VaD was higher among monolinguals compared to bilinguals (choice B is wrong). Again, although a greater number of bilinguals (153) experienced AD Dementia than monolinguals (101), a greater percentage of monolinguals (37.9%) experienced the condition than did bilinguals (35.3%). Thus, if a larger number of monolinguals had participated in the study, a larger number of subjects among this group would have likely experienced AD Dementia (choice C is wrong).

Passage 31

1. **A** There are three main approaches to parenting: authoritarian, authoritative, and permissive (choice D can be eliminated). Authoritarian parenting attempts to control children with strict rules and often uses punishment as a form of discipline (choice A is correct). These parents tend to be less responsive to their children and provide less nurturing, in line with the idea of corporal punishment. Authoritative parenting balances the independence of children with adherence to the rules of the household through some limits on behavior and often uses fair and consistent forms of discipline as a consequence of children failing to meet these behavioral expectations (choice B is wrong). This parenting is considered the "best" as it has the best results for children. Permissive parenting is the least involved, with lenient parents, and disciplined is rare and inconsistent (choice C is wrong).

2. **A** Based on the second paragraph, it can be predicted that the parent's personal contacts would top the list in terms of influence on their parenting behaviors (choice A is correct). These personal sources of supports, such as one's own parent or spouse, seem to be the default; professionals are consulted in response to more specific concerns. In terms of the professionals, pediatricians were a close second and researchers did consider religious leaders and other professionals (such as school teachers and child care providers). However, the question is not specific to professional resources (choices B, C, and D are wrong).

3. **C** It is important to understand that the resources provided on the internet do not fit into one of the three main categories; thus, this question is concerned with the "other professionals" listed. The question can then be answered through two separate considerations of the data presented in the passage. First, discussion with other professionals is more common among whites (choices A and B can be eliminated). Next, it is also more common among males (choice D can be eliminated and choice C is the correct answer).

4. **D** The research presented in the passage is cross-sectional in nature; the investigators studied prevalence through observations of the participant sample at one specific point in time. The consequent data are descriptive in showing correlations but cannot be used to determine cause-and-effect relationships. Remember that correlation does not necessitate causation. Thus, the perspective of the professionals cannot be determined (choice D is correct). For example, despite the fact that the use of corporal punishment is highest amongst those who depend on advice from religious leaders, according to Figure 1, the data does not support the notion that this occurs because religious leaders do not advise against the use of corporal punishment (or even support its use); instead, it is also possible that parents who use corporal punishment more prefer to consult religious leaders, perhaps because these same parents also reported being more religious.

5. **B** First, it is important to determine which group of participants reported the most frequent use of corporal punishment. Measures of the use of corporal punishment provided information on how often parents used corporal punishment, and this information is shown in the figure with use divided into three categories. Based on the question, we are interested in the use of corporal punishment at least once per month as this is the most frequent use listed. Item I is true: The use of corporal punishment at least once per month was higher for parents who consulted religious leaders as opposed to other professionals (choice C can be eliminated). Item II is true: Reports of the most frequent religious service attendance (more than once per week) were higher for parents who consulted religious leaders as opposed to other professionals (choice A can be eliminated). Item III is false: Religiosity describes the extent to which one's religion influences their life. This measured through the item on the importance of religious beliefs. Reports of the highest level of religiosity (very important) were higher for parents who consulted pediatricians not religious leaders (choice D can be eliminated and choice B is the correct answer).

Passage 32

1. **A** Prospective memory, or remembering to do things (which are often important) in the future, is a recall task and thus typically more challenging for people in late adulthood, as recall declines with age (choice A is correct). Memory for the distant past depends on the strength of the networks of nodes and associations, which are often quite strong and complex with meaningful things (choice B is wrong). While the network of nodes and associations for trivial things from the immediate recent past may not be as complex or strong, remembering trivial things that happened quite recently can be quite variable for people in late adulthood depending on their activity level and cues around them (choice C is wrong). Memory for people and places from anywhere in the past would also be variable depending on whether it was a recognition or recall task—recall would be more challenging than recognition—or how distant in the past or how strong the memory (choice D is wrong).

2. **C** Item I is true: difficulty in being able to remember what a person looked like is an example of recall, which is one aspect of memory that is thought to decline as part of normal cognitive changes in late adulthood (choice B can be eliminated). Item II is true: pausing for longer while driving describes a situation in which a driver demonstrates a slowing in reaction time, which is another cognitive change typical in late adulthood (choice A can be eliminated). Item III is false: difficulty in recognizing a familiar face amidst a crowd of unfamiliar faces is a task of recognition, which is not an aspect of cognition thought to naturally decline as a factor of age (choice D can be eliminated and choice C is correct).

3. **C** Alzheimer's dementia (AD) is characterized by repid declines in memory and cognitive functioning, and while the exact mechanism is not known, the presence of neurofibrillary tangles in the brain is characteristic of the disease (choice C is correct). Neurons of the hippocampus appear to be some of the first neurons affected in the brain, leading to a decrease (not increase) in hippocampal activity, which helps to explain why one of the first signs of AD is memory dysfunction (because memories are not being properly consolidated from short-term memory to long-term memory, as the hippocampus is compromised). Difficulty initiating movement and a reduction of dopamine-producing neurons in the brain are both characteristic of Parkinson's disease, not AD (choices A and B are wrong).

4. **C** Integrity vs. despair is the final of eight stages in Erikson's model of psychosocial development and it represents the final life crisis, which is whether or not an individual can look back over they lives and feel as though they have accomplished what they wanted to, or if they feel a sense of hopelessness and despair about their lives (choice C is correct). Identity vs. role confusion is the stage that occurs during adolescent when individuals are clarifying who they are through social interactions and trying on new identities (choice A is wrong). Generativity vs. stagnation is the stage right before the final stage of integrity vs. despair when an individual in middle adulthood either feels a sense of accomplishment regarding their lives, or feels as though they are not contributing to society in a meaningful way (choice B is wrong). Intimacy vs. isolation is the stage that occurs during early adulthood when individuals are first engaging in intimate relationships and trying to figure out to develop healthy relationships (choice D is wrong).

5. **A** The researchers appear to be most interested in investigating the links between cognitive processing speed decline and internal clock slowing, as evidenced by spontaneous tapping tests compared to the memory and processing tests. Therefore, it would be logical to try to further understand the mechanisms behind both declines in speed (choice A is correct). This research focuses mostly on the internal clock slowing as it relates to the age-related decline in cognitive processing speed, so linking it to an investigation of memory recall would be an unlikely direction for future study for these researchers (choice B is wrong). For similar reasons, it is unlikely the researchers would be interested in studying links between a decline in cognitive processing speed and memory recognition, especially since recognition does not normally decline with age (choice C is wrong). Slowed reaction times are symptomatic of declines in cognitive processing speed so these researchers would not be likely to want to further explore the links between them based on the results of this research (choice D is wrong).

Passage 33

1. **D** Figure 1 shows the data for ASC, while Figure 2 shows the data for academic achievement. In Figure 1, the line corresponding to students who dropped a track in 10th grade (drop-track 1) shown an initial increase at the 10th grade marker and then a steady decrease beginning in 11th grade. In Figure 2, the line corresponding to this group of students shows a steady decrease in academic achievement beginning in 10th grade. Thus, by the time a student from this group reaches 12th grade, ASC and achievement show a similar pattern of change (I is true; choice B is wrong). While the data from the figures shows that stable-track students show a steady decrease in ASC along with a steady increase in achievement scores, it is impossible to conclude that the mechanism underlying this pattern is a deliberate attempt to compensate for low ASC by improving achievement scores. In fact, neither variable may be a cause of the other at all (II is false: choices B and C are

wrong). The data does show that, for students in the stable track and those who drop a track in 11th grade, an increase in ASC corresponds to a decrease in achievement scores, while a decrease in ASC corresponds to an increase in achievement scores at any given measurement point. Whenever a decrease in one variable corresponds to, or predicts, an increase in another variable, the pattern is referred to as a negative correlation (III is true; choice D is correct).

2. **C** While the first study described in the passage measured the ASC of students from different tracks, the participants remained in the same tracks throughout the course of the study. This provides a comparison of two groups (a low-track group and a high-track) group, and it is appropriately considered a between-groups design. In the second study, however, participants changed from a high track to a low track, which allows a comparison of the effects of placement in different tracks on the same individuals. This is called a within-group design, because the effects of different levels of the independent variable (track) are observed within a given group (choice C is correct). As noted, both the first and second studies compared different groups (choice B is wrong). Also, both studies entailed measurement of participants at multiple points over time and are thus considered longitudinal designs (choice A is wrong). A cross-sectional design entails the one-time measurement of multiple groups of differing ages rather than measurement of groups of the same age over multiple points in time. Neither study employed a cross-sectional design (choice D is wrong).

3. **A** Crystallized intelligence is the term for previously acquired knowledge, such as basic facts or vocabulary (choice A is correct). The ability to reason with known facts is termed Fluid intelligence, and is independent of crystallized intelligence (choice B is wrong). Crystallized intelligence can change in that it is dependent upon learned facts, and people generally keep adding to their knowledge base as they are exposed to new information (choice C is wrong). Crystallized intelligence is independent of physical attributes, and is only dependent on physical ability to the extent that it permits or inhibits the ability to respond to questions (choice D is wrong).

3. **A** Figure 1 shows the data pertaining to the students ASC. The line representing stable-track students shows the same or lower ASC score than students who dropped a track in 10th or 11th grade. The term reference group is used to described the group of individuals a person identifies with and to whom a person compares him/herself .Thus, in comparison to students remaining in a high track, students moving from a relatively high-achieving reference group to a relatively low-achieving reference group do not experience a negative impact on their ASC (choice A is correct). While students who dropped a track at the beginning of 11th grade report similar ASC scores by the end of 12th grade as those who dropped a track at the beginning of 10th grade, those who dropped a track at the beginning of 11th grade exhibit a steeper decline in ASC scores. Therefore, the rate of change in ASC is not the same for these two groups of students (choice B is wrong). It is also evident from Figure 1 that the increase in ASC points was greater for students who dropped a track later in high school than for those who dropped a track earlier in high school. Specifically, Drop-Track 2 ASC jumped from approximately 4.5 to 6.5 points, which is a two-point difference, while Drop-Track 1 ASC jumped from 5 to 6 points, which is a one-point increase (choice C is wrong). None of the groups exhibited a continuous increase in ASC. The stable-track group exhibited a continuous decrease in ASC, while the other groups exhibited a temporary increase followed by a decrease in ASC (choice D is wrong).

4. **B** BFLPE refers specifically to the impact of tracking on students' self-concept. If self-concept scores were found to predict achievement test scores, a compelling argument could be made for the importance of understanding what contributes to the BFLPE so that the relationship between the two variables could be further explored and achievement test scores could be poten-

tially improved (choice B is correct). While a finding that educational outcomes are unrelated to the way in which students view their ranking among their peers would not render the BFLPE irrelevant or meaningless, such a finding would not support further research on BFLPE (choice A is wrong). BFLPE does not address the quality of students' peer interactions, nor does it examine the effect of class size on students' self concept (choices C and D are wrong)

5. **C**   In order to achieve a meaningful comparison of results from multiple studies, several aspects of the studies need to remain constant. Regarding the issue of tracking and students' self concept, the definition of tracking (grouping patterns and associated reference groups), the definition of ASC, and the age of the samples need to be consistent across studies in order to accurately compare results. For instance, tracking based on subjective teacher impressions is not the same as tracking based on standardized tests (choice A is true and therefore wrong). In addition, different definitions of ASC reflect different psychological constructs that may not be able to be meaningfully compared (choice B is true and therefore wrong). Finally, tracking may differentially impact students at different points in their cognitive and psychosocial development (choice D is true and therefore wrong). However, disparate scores on ASC measures is precisely the variable under study, and, assuming a consistent definition of ASC, this would not explain discrepant findings across studies (choice C is false and therefore correct).

6. **B**   The explanation of BFLPE stated in the first paragraph is that "when relatively low-achieving students compare themselves to other students within the same general achievement level, they feel more capable than when comparing themselves to a broader spectrum of students, including some with significantly higher achievement capabilities." In other words, students assess their own academic ability and rank based on the abilities and ranks of others. This notion of self-assessment relative to others represents the core of Festinger's social comparison theory, and the above explanation of BFLPE thus represents the application of Festinger's theory to the school context (choice B is correct). The above explanation of BFLPE does not suggest that students in different tracks do not reach the same stages of cognitive development (choice A is wrong). While Bandura's notion of self-efficacy is related to the broader construct of ASC, the above explanation does not imply that self-efficacy or ASC is necessarily relevant to academic outcomes. It merely offers a hypothesis as to why ASC tends to increase when students drop tracks (choice C is wrong). Finally, while BFLPE refers to a tendency for students in different tracks to have different levels of ASC, the tendency to conform may still be evident in many other aspects of students' lives. Furthermore, nothing in the above explanation contradicts Asch's observation of people's tendency to conform (choice D is wrong).

Passage 34

1. **C**   The glass ceiling a concept that describes an invisible barrier that women have trouble surpassing during their careers. It is thought to be an effect of subtle sexism in which women are not thought to be a good fit for leadership positions (choice C is correct). The wage gap is one aspect of occupational sex-segregation, but instead of describing a limit on how high the a woman can advance in an organizational hierarchy, it describes the fact that women are paid significantly less for the same work than men are (even controlling for outside factors) (choice A is wrong). Stratification is a macrosocial concept that describes forms of inequality and how they come to be entrenched in society (choice B is wrong). Downward mobility is a term that describes a decrease in socioeconomic class. In the information given in the question stem, women are not downwardly mobile, merely stagnant (choice D is wrong).

2. **A**   Sleep spindles are bursts of 12-14 Hz waves on an EEG and they are characteristic of stage 2 sleep (choice A is correct). Stage 3 sleep is characterized by delta waves, which indicated deep sleep (choice B is wrong). Stage 1 sleep is characterized by theta waves on the EEG and slow rolling eye movements (choice C is wrong). REM sleep is characterized by rapid eye movements and waves on the EEG that resemble brain waves from when individuals are awake (choice D is wrong).

3. **B**   The symptoms listed above are indicative of generalized anxiety disorder (choice B is correct). Panic disorder is characterized by panic attacks; there is no information about panic attacks given in the question stem (choice A is wrong). Acute stress disorder is similar to PTSD, and occurs over a short time course (less than a month). Information given in the question stem indicates that at least one of the patient's symptoms is long term (choice C is wrong). Obsessive-compulsive disorder is characterized by repetitive, intrusive thoughts and/or uncontrollable compulsions (choice D is wrong).

4. **C**   Learned helplessness is a condition of passivity that a person adopts in response to a situation s/he has learned that s/he cannot control (choice C is correct). Internal locus of control is used to describe someone who feels that her decisions and reactions are under her control; this is the opposite of the scenario presented (choice A is wrong). Low self-esteem describes one's evaluation of one's self worth. This evaluation may or may not reflect the reality of one's ability (choice B is wrong). Self-efficacy describes a person's belief in her ability to do something; while the woman in the question stem does not believe she can change her situation, self-efficacy does not explain the reason for the woman's passivity (choice D is wrong).

5. **C**   Teacher expectancy theory describes the way a teacher's racial, class and gender stereotypes can pervade their expectations for their students, such that teachers expect more out of some students and less out of others—this is not based on the students themselves, but rather on the teachers (choice C is correct). A self-fulfilling prophecy can be the outcome of teacher expectations; when a student realizes what a teacher expects out of him, he is likely to perform in a way that matches those expectations (choice A is wrong). Prejudice is also a related concept. While it describes the aspect of teacher expectancy theory that is not rooted in actual experience, but merely in stereotypes, it does not explain the process by which the teacher comes to make those stereotypes material in a particular group of children (choice B is wrong). Stratification is a macrosocial concept that describes forms of inequality and how they come to be entrenched in society (choice D is wrong).

6. **A**   Cultural capital refers to non-financial assets that promote social mobility, and education is one of the classic examples of cultural capital (choice A is correct). Social capital is the ability to leverage social ties and turn them into opportunities for social mobility (choice B is wrong). Meritocracy describes a social system in which merit is rewarded and everyone is on an equal playing field in terms of resources (this system is a yet unreached ideal) (choice C is wrong). Privilege describes a system of unearned benefits one receives because of some personal attribute outside of one's control, such as race, gender, ability, nationality, etc. While the girls were already privileged to be in a school system that had the resources to sponsor this special program, privilege does not precisely explain the future effects of the enrichment course as well as cultural capital does (choice D is wrong).

Passage 35

1. **C** The Five Factor Model can be remembered using the OCEAN acronym: Openness to Experience, Conscientiousness, Extraversion, Agreeableness, Neuroticism. Thus, Amenableness is NOT a factor of the model (choice C is correct). Neuroticism, Openness to Experience, and Extraversion are all factors of the FFM (choices A, B, and D are wrong).

2. **D** A true experiment requires random assignment of subjects to groups in order to control for all factors. However, personality factors cannot (obviously) be assigned to participants, thus, this study would have to be correlational, and is therefore NOT a true experiment, but a quasi-experiment (choice D is correct; choice A is wrong).

3. **C** Table 1 shows that Education is negatively correlated (b= −0.30) with relationship dissolution; thus, increased education does NOT predict relationship dissolution (I is false, eliminate choices B and D). Neuroticism is positively correlated (b= 0.11) with relationship dissolution, as seen in Table 1, (II is true). High openness to experience is also correlated (b= 0.25) with relationship dissolution (III is true, eliminate choice A; choice C is correct).

4. **B** According to the American Psychological Association, personality is the individual differences in characteristic patterns of thinking, feeling and behaving (choice B is correct). While there is a belief that there is a biological basis to personality, it does not predetermine a person's behavior in isolation from psychological factors (choice A is wrong). Personality has also been defined as being *enduring*, thus personality factors are NOT ephemeral (choice C is wrong). The definition of personality includes more than simply the behavior of a person; it also includes his/her feelings and thoughts as well (choice D is wrong).

5. **D** First, remember that Z-scores are standardized scores in which zero is equal to the mean, and a z-score of 1 is equal to 1 standard deviation above the mean, while a −1 would be one standard deviation below the mean. Based on the information presented in figure 1, it is clear that an individual 1.5 standard deviations below the mean in Agreeableness would have the greatest likelihood of relationship dissolution, as he/she would have approximately a 20% probability of relationship dissolution (choice D is correct). The other choices have a lower probability of dissolution; a person with a Neuroticism score 1 deviation above the mean would have approximately a 14% chance of relationship dissolution (choice A is wrong). A person scoring one standard deviation below the mean on Conscientiousness would have approximately a 10% chance of having his or her relationship dissolve (choice B is wrong), while a person scoring one and a half standard deviations above the mean of Openness would have approximately a 15% chance of relationship dissolution (choice C is wrong).

Passage 36

1. **D** The resource model of attention states that humans have a limited amount of resources for attention. Thus, if one wants to multitask, and the attentional needs exceed available resources, these tasks cannot be completed simultaneously (choice D is correct). The spotlight theory of attention is related more to visual attention and refers to the idea of where one focuses attention in one's visual field, as opposed to where one moves his or her eyes (choice A is wrong). That humans fill in missing information is related to the priming effect where if people are "primed"

or exposed repeatedly to particular sensory data, they are more likely to notice it. For example, if one is primed to be aware of monsters, he or she may be more likely to fill in the blank with "ster" if presented with "mon----" (choice B is wrong). The idea that humans selectively filter out unnecessary information is part of the Broadbent Filter Model of Selective Attention, which states that sensory information enters a buffer and is then either filtered out or passed through to higher areas of processing based on various characteristics. Some sensory input decays while other data moves on to short-term and even long-term memory (choice C is wrong).

2. **B** Using additional words instead of shapes as the distracting element would have made the task of memorizing these words significantly harder, since the additional words would have interfered with the initial memorization task and required more resources (choice B is correct). While the color change would have added to task similarity, a factor in divided attention, the shape and color differences would still be different enough that the task would not be significantly harder (choice A is wrong). Changing the shapes from circles to abstract but still distinct objects would also not increase task difficulty since the words and shapes would still be quite dissimilar (choice C is wrong). A switch to alternating colors might initially make the task more difficult until the pattern was learned and then the task difficulty would be about the same as in the original case (choice D is wrong).

3. **A** Writing a paper while listening to instrumental music is a multitasking situation, and these tasks are dissimilar enough that one should not interfere with the other since they require different resources—one verbal and the other auditory. This is similar to the situation in the above research, because one task—listening to music—could even provide an attentional boost factor, which would therefore demonstrate results very similar to those in Figure 1 (choice A is correct). The bystander effect predicts that when an individual needs help and there are many people (bystanders) present, that individual is actually less likely to receive help, as all of the bystanders believe that someone else will step in, so no one actually ends up helping. While an interesting phenomenon in social psychology, the bystander effect does not have anything to do with multitasking or attention (choice B is wrong). The Stroop effect occurs when we are presented with color words which are in a different ink color than the written word—in other words, the word "black" would be presented in red ink—and have a harder time saying the ink color because of the interference from the printed word. This attention switching phenomenon greatly reduces our speed and accuracy at the task, which is the opposite of the results in Figure 1 (choice C is wrong). Studying in a calm environment with sound-canceling headphones is not an example of multitasking scenario, but rather of selective attention (choice D is wrong).

4. **C** The cocktail party effect occurs when one is suddenly able to hear one's name or another piece of information of personal importance from previously unattended to channels (choice C is correct). Treisman's attenuation model tries to account for selective attention by explaining that the brain "turns down the volume" on unwanted or unnecessary sensory data. This would not explain why one would hear one's name in a crowded, noisy stadium (choice A is wrong). The Broadbent filter model suggests that unwanted or unnecessary sensory input is filtered out before it can be stored in short-term memory. This would also not explain why one would hear one's name in a crowded stadium (choice B is wrong). Selective priming is when one encounters particular sensory data very frequently or is expecting that particular data. While one does encounter one's name frequently, one would not expect to hear it at a stadium, so this choice does not fully explain why one would be able to pick out one's name in a noisy stadium (choice D is wrong).

5. **C** Anne Treisman developed the attenuation model for selective attention, which would explain the research above as the words and circles both entering the sensory store and going through an attenuating filter. At that point, all of this sensory information hits a bottleneck, where the volume turns up on the words (which are supposed to be attended to) and down on the circles, so that the words can be stored in working memory, and then later recalled (choice C is correct). Words and circles entering a central executive into a phonological loop, a visuospatial sketchpad, and episodic buffer before arriving at memory describes Baddeley's Model of Working Memory, not Treisman's model of attention (choice A is wrong). Words and circles going through a selective filter describes the selective filter theory of selective attention, not Treisman's model of attention (choice B is wrong). A pathway in which words and circles enter a sensory store, proceed to a phonological filter and then reach working memory is actually a combination of Baddeley's model and the selective filter model and does not exist (choice D is wrong).

6. **A** Task difficulty is one of three factors associated with performance on multitasking according to the resource model. If the task was too difficult, the FA group might have scored higher (choices B is wrong), but if the task was too easy, it should not have impacted the scores of the DA group (choice A is correct). Again, if the second task was too similar to the first, the FA group might also have scored higher than the DA group (choice C is wrong). Similarly, if the second task required way too much practice, the FA group might have scored higher than the DA group (choice D is wrong).

Passage 37

1. **B** Prejudice is the biased thoughts or ideas that individuals have about other people (choice B is correct). Discrimination is known to be the result of prejudice, since it involves the unjust actions towards others; the veterans' responses convey their thoughts as opposed to actual actions (choice A is wrong). Institutional discrimination is the unjust treatment of others by large organizations (choice C is wrong). Stereotype threat occurs when the individual is afraid of being negatively stereotyped, which is irrelevant to the question stem (choice D is wrong).

2. **A** The passage explains that the more stable the individual's group affiliation, the higher degree of ethnic tolerance; this is considered a positive correlation. The more content the individual is with their life, the less likely they would express ethnic hostility, which is considered a negative correlation (choice A is correct; choices B, C, and D is wrong).

3. **C** External control is most analogous to social control because they both refer to how individuals' beliefs and behavior could be influenced and controlled by social systems (choices A and B can be eliminated). Superego influences the ego into following moral beliefs as opposed to only rational beliefs, which makes superego control most analogous to conscience control. Rational self-control is most analogous to ego control because the ego is known to use rational reasoning to control one's consciousness (choice D can be eliminated and choice C is the correct answer).

4. **C** Item I is true: External control is being applied in this scenario since the individual originally became affiliated because he felt pressured and influenced by society to do so (choice D can be eliminated). Item II is false: The scenario did not indicate that the individual solely used logic and reasoning to affiliate himself with the Democratic Party (choice B can be eliminated). Item III is true: The individual independently embraced the ideals of the Democratic Party without fear of disapproval by his peers, which is implementing conscience control (choice A can be eliminated and choice C is, therefore, the correct answer).

5. **D** According to Figure 1, there were 73 participants under the section "no mobility" and "Anti-Black Stereotyped," which is the highest amount of participants categorized out of the three types of social mobility (choice D is correct). Participants who experienced no mobility actually had the highest concentration of ethnic stereotypes (46%, 54%) compared to those who experienced downward mobility and upward mobility (choice A is wrong). Looking under the "total participants" section, more participants had hostile opinions towards Blacks (33%) than Jews (24%; choice B is wrong). Participants who experienced upward mobility (62%, 40%) were more likely to express ethnic tolerance than those who experienced downward mobility (16%, 19%; choice C is wrong).

Passage 38

1. **A** The universal emotions include happiness, sadness, surprise, disgust, fear, and anger; these emotions are thought to be expressed by all people across all cultures, so this is an example of a trait with cross-cultural universality (choice A is correct). Not all cultures (or individuals) bond with only one other person monogamously, or promote that type of pair-bonding. In some cultures it is the norm to pair or mate with multiple partners (choice B is wrong). Social norms for making eye contact vary greatly across cultures; though it is true that most normally-developing infants will begin making eye contact with caregivers at a very early age, the social norms for when it is appropriate to make eye contact dictate that as we age, our propensity for eye contact is determined more by culture (choice C is wrong). Intelligence is a multi-faceted trait that is the result of many genes and environmental factors; this would not be the best example of a trait that is thought to demonstrate cross-cultural universality (choice D is wrong).

2. **B** The passage states that an exaptation is an adaptation that has been "re-designed" to solve a different evolutionary problem. If feathers originally evolved for warmth, but have since adapted to aide in flight, they are an example of an exaptation (choice B is correct). If feathers have been shifted to a new evolutionary use, adaptation would not the best answer because an adaptation is defined in the passage as a trait, which shows complexity and a specific functionality, designed to solve an ancestral problem; in this example, that problem would be warmth (choice A is wrong). The adaptation is neither a by-product nor a random variation, based on the definitions in the passage (choice C and choice D are wrong).

3. **D** For this except/not/least question, eliminate any answer choices that would be applicable to the theory of parental involvement, which states that if there is asymmetry in parental involvement, the more involved sex will be more sexually selective; a study of parental involvement not related to sex differences could also fall under this rubric (choice C is wrong). Willingness to give and its relationship to sexual selection is an aspect of the theory (choice B is wrong). Male willingness to provide for a child depending on the physical similarity to a photograph is also concerned with parental involvement and sexual selection (choice A is wrong). Only choice D is not involved in sexual selection and parental involvement (choice D is correct).

4. **A** The heart has a very specific function, circulating blood, and is poorly adapted to broadening to other problems. Therefore, answer choices that include domain-general can be eliminated (choice B and choice D are wrong). The heart is also still adapted to its original function, and has not shifted to adapt to new evolutionary problems (choice A is correct and choice C is wrong).

5. **B** The question stem states that group selection occurs when evolutionary constraints result in survival being dependent on differences between groups of organisms rather than between individual organisms within a group. The correct answer should involve a function that advances the probability of a group of organisms surviving. Language is a function that facilitates communication among individuals within a group and increases likelihood of group survival through increased cohesion (choice B is correct). Muscle mass could evolve outside of group constraints due to individual advantages (choice A is wrong). Epidermal tissue likewise offers individual advantages (choice C is wrong) and intelligence would benefit an individual organism in sexual and natural selection irrespective of group mechanisms (choice D is wrong).

Passage 39

1. **A** Monozygotic twins have identical genotypes while dizygotic twins share about 50% of their genetic makeup (choice D is wrong, choice A is correct). While studies using monozygotic twins do help elucidate the effect of genes on shared traits, because MZ twins also share a great deal of their environment, MZ twin studies can also help determine the impact of the environment on shared traits (choice B is wrong). It is impossible for researchers to completely control for environmental differences between twins, as it is possible to have slight variations in the prenatal environment (even with MZ twins, sometimes one twin receives more nourishment than the other, or one might become infected with a virus in utero while the other does not, etc.), and postnatally, there is even more potential variation in MZ twins' environment, even though it may be very similar (choice C is wrong).

2. **A** Item I is true: In trying to discern a genetic link, looking at the closest genetic relatives—the biological siblings and parents—and their peer-relationships, might give some insight into inherited traits and patterns, such as a quick temper or an overly nervous disposition (choice B can be eliminated). Item II is false: while academic difficulties might be related to peer-relationship difficulties, studying academic difficulties will not help clarify the genetic component of peer-relationship difficulties (choice C can be eliminated). Item III is false: while understanding the teachers' role also adds information to the environmental dimension, it will not help clarify the role of genetics in peer-relationship difficulties (choice D can be eliminated and choice A is correct).

3. **C** The biopsychosocial model of disease predicts that many human diseases are caused by a complex combination of genetics or biological traits, psychological factors, and environmental influences. Therefore, according to this model, both nature and nurture are important elements in the development of disease (choice C is correct). While it is true that, according to the Diagnostic and Statistical Manual of Mental Illness, psychological disorders are, by definition, both diagnosable and treatable, this is not what the biopsychosocial model of disease suggests (choice A is wrong). According to the biopsychosocial model of disease, there are many factors that potentially contribute to disease. Genetics is often an underlying factor in many diseases, but necessarily all diseases (choice B is wrong). The biopsychosocial model of disease does not predict that social factors become more relevant to the onset of disease as individuals age (choice D is wrong).

4. **C** Because adoption creates two groups—genetic relatives and environmental relatives—it creates a unique opportunity for researchers to compare adopted individuals to both groups and further clarify the impact of genetics and environment (choice C is correct). Since adoption studies clarify genetic relatives and environmental relatives, these studies do not make it harder to con-

trol for genetic factors (choice A is wrong). As noted above, adoption studies focus on both the genetic and environmental aspects, not simply the genetic angle (choice B is wrong). Although adoption studies add additional factors to the research, they are not confounding variables that would adversely affect any other variables (choice D is wrong).

5.   **A**   Twins who acted aggressively with peers on occasion, but without displaying a consistent pattern over time would be an argument against a genetic link in peer relationship difficulties since children do get into fights with other children on occasion (choice A is correct). A consistent pattern of relationship difficulties in both twins, rather than just one, would be one argument in favor of a genetic link (choices B is wrong). Stability and consistency in the pattern of aggression and peer relationship difficulties over time, as displayed in the research results, is more evidence for a genetic link (choice C is wrong). Had the incidents of peer relationship difficulties occurred in an unstable environment, rather than the stable environment as was the case in the research, the environment could be implicated as a factor. However, relationship difficulties in spite of a stable environment further support the genetic link (choice D is wrong).

Passage 40

1.   **A**   According to Maslow's hierarchy of needs, one must first take care of one's safety needs, and then can progress to needs for love and belonging. Next is the need to achieve, which is then followed by the need to self-actualize (choice A is correct). While one must take care of safety needs first, self-actualization cannot occur until needs for love and achievement are satisfied (choice B is wrong). A person cannot satisfy the need for love and belonging before establishing safety. Then that person can satisfy needs for achievement and then self-actualization (choice C is wrong). Self-actualization is the final stage, so that would never occur before the needs for safety, love, and achievement, respectively are filled (choice D is wrong).

2.   **B**   The self-serving bias occurs when people attribute their own successes to intrinsic qualities—for example, motivation to succeed—while attributing failures, such as inability to motivate others or to be motivated, to external causes. Students in the study seem to locate positive motivation within themselves, while the teachers locate that same motivation of students as within the *themselves*, as factor of their teaching ability. So both groups are attributing the students' "success" (in this study, success can be seen as motivation) with their own intrinsic qualities (choice B is correct). The fundamental attribution error is a tendency to underestimate the situation and overestimate one's personality, character, or abilities when making attributions about someone else's behavior. For example, if someone behaves in a certain way, attributing that behavior to their personality (e.g. he acted that way because he is mean) would be an example of the fundamental attribution error (choice A is wrong). The optimism bias is a belief that bad things only happen to other people, which does not explain the findings in this study (choice C is wrong). The just world phenomenon describes the situation when people believe that the world is fair place and people get what they deserve, which also does not explain the findings in this study (choice D is wrong).

3.   **C**   Using descriptive questions, a technique often employed in qualitative research and useful in quantitative research, can help provide researchers with a better understanding of complex human interactions since the participants may provide important data the researchers would not have anticipated and thus not have included in a survey (choice B can be eliminated). Item II refers to adding more detailed options to the survey to get at the details of the student-teacher

relationship by solely quantitative means (choice A can be eliminated). While more detail in how much participants agree or disagree with statements can add a modicum of information to the study, it does not give researchers any additional informational on the nature of the student-teacher interactions that lead or do not lead to motivation. Rather, it only tells them more about the intensity of the participants' beliefs (choice D can be eliminated and choice A is correct).

4. **C** Homeostasis is the point at which human bodies are thought to be in balance. According to drive reduction theory, it is suggested that there is a set point for each individual human body that puts it into homeostasis, but homeostasis itself is a state and not a theory for motivation (choice C is correct). Incentive theory suggests that humans need some external stimuli as a motivator for behavior—to either encourage or discourage particular actions (choice A is wrong). Instinct is based the idea that certain behaviors are unconscious and inherent in particular species—human as well as nonhuman—and motivate behavior without conscious input (choice B is wrong). Drive reduction theory proposes that humans have particular needs—many physiological, such as hunger or thirst—that force a person into particular behaviors, such as eating or drinking, in order to reduce those needs and bring the body into balance (choice D is wrong).

5. **C** Puberty causes changes in secondary (not primary) sex characteristics during adolescence (choice C is correct). The brain, including the prefrontal cortex, is still developing throughout the teenage years, so high school students' decisions may not always be the wisest or most well-thought out (choice A is wrong). According to Erikson's stages of development, adolescence is a time of "identity versus role confusion," where teenagers are trying to sort out their identities from the roles they have been assigned by parents, teachers, siblings, friends, and society (choice B is wrong). Because the limbic system develops more rapidly during adolescence than the prefrontal cortex, emotions may run high during the teenage years (choice D is wrong).

Passage 41

1. **D** There are multiple descriptions used to discuss stress. First, stress can be described as acute or chronic in nature. The former is the most common form of stress and such stress is the result of experiences in the recent past and near future; acute stress is short-term stress, though it can become problematic in the long-term when its occurrence is too frequent or intense. The later is more dangerous for the person experiencing it and such stress occurs through the accumulation of difficult experiences; chronic stress is long-term stress. Birth is better described as an acute stressor – even though its effects can contribute to severe chronic stress such PPD – because labor is a short-term experience, often lasting less than 20 hours for the first, second, and third stages combined (choice A is wrong). Furthermore, birth occurrences are not excessive as there is at least nine months between labor experiences assuming full-term pregnancies. PPD can be described as a chronic effect of an acute stressor. Next, there are three main categories of stressors to be familiar with for the MCAT: (1) catastrophes are large-scale events that are often unpredictable and dangerous to the large amounts of people experiencing such events, like natural disasters; (2) significant life changes are also rather large-scale events but the subsequent stress is relative to the person experiencing the event, like marriage; and (3) daily hassles are small-scale common occurrences where the subsequent stress is again relative to the person experiencing the event, like with the irritation of lost belongings. Traumatic birth might have significant consequences for those involved, but it is it not quite catastrophic and it is more accurate to consider the birth process to be a significant life change (choice D is correct and choices B and C are wrong).

2. **D** The concept of the sick role was developed by American sociologist Talcott Parsons. According to Parsons, when an individual is ill (such as with PPD), she takes on the sick role in society; this role includes rights and obligation. One obligation is that the individual should have a desire to get better (choice D is correct). According to sick role theory, illness is a form of social deviance (choice A is wrong). According to Parsons, when one takes on the sick role, one of their rights is to be exempt from normal social functioning for a period of time (choice B is wrong). Sick role theory does not make any predictions about childhood occurrences impacting someone later in life, though this would be something Freud would likely suggest (choice C is wrong).

3. **A** Paragraph 2 provides descriptions of the participant groups and the time periods. Figure 1 presents the research findings helpful in answering this question; according to the title, the percentages in the figure for each group represent the proportion of people who would meet the clinical criteria for a PPD diagnosis. Item I is true: PPD was observed most often at the first time period, 10-14 days postpartum (choice C is wrong). Item II is true: PPD was observed most often among those in the GAD group, indicated by the fact that the percentages for this group are higher than for the other three groups at all three time periods (choice B is wrong). Item III is false: Those with both GAD and SAD experienced PPD at a rate that was lower than those with GAD only, and slightly higher than those with SAD only; therefore, the rate of PPD for those with both GAD and SAD is not most similar to those with GAD only. If anything, the rate of PPD for those with both GAD and SAD is actually more similar to those with SAD only (choice A is correct and choice D is wrong).

4. **A** Roles can be sources of tension for people in various situations. Role conflict is applicable to the situation described in the question (choice A is correct). People with multiple statuses might experience role conflict when these statuses conflict based on the expectations present in their communities. Mothers, for example, are often both parents and partners, though this is not the case for all families (e.g., single mothers). The normative behaviors associated with these roles often conflict. Mothers are often expected to attend to the needs of both their children and their partners and this can be difficult due to time constraints; for example, a mother might need to cancel a date night to care for a sick child, an unexpected situation that creates role conflict. Role exit happens in the case of disengagement from a role that is important to a person's sense of self; for example, a mother might experience role exit as a result of birth because she exits the role of a pregnant woman (choice B is wrong). Role strain happens in the case of a single status that has conflicting expectations associated with it; for example, a mother might experience role strain due to the struggle between the expectation to show compassion to her children while also being expected to discipline them for poor behavior (choice C is wrong). Role tension is a more general term and there are three forms – role conflict, role exit, and role strain – as described above (choice D is wrong).

5. **C** A person with generalized anxiety disorder (GAD) experiences chronic nervousness and tension (choice C is correct), but does *not* experience panic attacks (the presence of panic attacks would indicate a diagnosis of panic disorder; choice A is wrong). The symptom of psychosis is characteristic of a psychotic illness, such as schizophrenia; psychosis is not a characteristic of any anxiety disorder (choice B is wrong). A past trauma that causes a variety of symptoms (included anxiety) would fall under the post-traumatic stress disorder category, not GAD (choice D is wrong).

Passage 42

1. **A** A self-fulfilling prophecy occurs when a prediction about what will happen directly or indirectly causes itself to become true, due to positive feedback between belief and behavior. In other words, due to the prediction about a future event, behavior changes to actually make that prediction come true. When Shirley tells herself that she is no good at math, her behavior functions to actually make that prediction come true: She doesn't study and spends her time doing things other than prepare for her test. She fails her test and her prediction about her abilities was confirmed. Shirley's self-fulfilling prophecy came true (choice A is correct). However, when Marco makes the prediction that the day will be terrible, his experience proves otherwise when he gets to school. His prediction did not come true, and he was not operating under the self-fulfilling prophesy (choice B is wrong). Similarly, Robert's belief that he is good at physics was not confirmed. His behavior was to not study for his Physics test, due to his belief that he *was* good at Physics and ends up failing his test; this does not demonstrate a self-fulfilling prophecy (choice C is wrong). Finally, Felicia not being confident about her abilities in Biology makes her doubt her performance on the exam. She studies and gets a good grade on the Biology exam. Even though she prophesied that she would do poorly on the exam, her prediction did not come true due to her diligence with studying for the test (choice D is wrong).

2. **B** Figure I displays the correlational relationship between Self-Judgment and Stereotype Threat at the time of the pre-group training; this figure demonstrates a strong correlational relationship between Stereotype Threat and Self-Judgment. As Stereotype threat increases, Self-Judgment also increases. This is an example of a positive correlational relationship (choice B is correct). Figure 2 (not Figure 1) looks at the relationship between mindfulness and stereotype threat; Figure 2 appears to indicate that mindfulness and stereotype threat are inversely correlated—as mindfulness increases, stereotype threat decreases (choice A is wrong). This study did not examine the effects of stereotype boost, and it is not possible to make any assumptions about stereotype boost just from the information provided in Figure 1 (choice C is wrong). Furthermore, that passage does not provide a hypothesis (though it could be inferred that the hypothesis is that mindfulness training will decrease stereotype threat, so the null hypothesis would be that there is no reduction in stereotype threat with mindfulness training); regardless, Figure 2 (not Figure 1) depicts the relationship between mindfulness training and stereotype threat (choice D is wrong).

3. **D** An example of Stereotype Threat will include a person from a type of group that has a stereotype associated with it. If Stereotype Threat is present, a negative stereotype associated with the group member will produce lowered levels of performance in that individual. In choice D, Jennifer keeps her opposing opinions to herself at a family function. This is not an example of stereotype threat, because Jennifer's group membership is not impairing her functioning due to a stereotype about Democrats. She simply keeps her opinions to herself out of respect for the family. Further, people with strong views politically may have the stereotype of speaking up, rather than staying quiet, which does not function as Stereotype Threat if Jennifer stays quiet (choice D is correct). In choice A, Gina is operating under the stereotype that women perform more poorly on tests of spatial ability than men. Even though she is a smart, well-educated woman, she performs poorly at this task with her teammates watching, including Zachary (choice A is wrong). In choice B, the black students performed poorly on a test that specifically was told to measure ability. These individuals were operating under stereotype threat that black student do more poorly than white students on tests of ability. This is Stereotype threat because the black students performed just as well on the test when it was not labeled as an aptitude test (choice

B is wrong). Likewise, in choice C, Ned was operating under the stereotype that white people perform worse on aptitude tests than East Asian individuals, and he also performed more poorly than his actual aptitude level (choice C is wrong).

4. **B** In Figure 2, the measurements taken at the Pre-Group Training show that both groups, the experimental and the control group, demonstrated similar levels of Stereotype Threat in response to the priming. However, in the Post-Group Training, there is now a significant difference between the level of Stereotype Threat for each group. The treatment condition received the independent variable of Mindfulness training, and the Treatment group is displaying lower levels of Stereotype Threat compared to the control group. This gives evidence to the effectiveness of the independent variable, Mindfulness, in effectively lowering levels of Stereotype threat (choice B is correct). Therefore, it would be incorrect to say that Mindfulness was not effective at reducing levels of Stereotype Threat (choice A is wrong). It would also be incorrect to say that there is no relationship between Mindfulness and Stereotype Threat, as a clear reduction in Stereotype Threat levels is present in Figure 2 (choice C is wrong). Stereotype Threat was not reduced in the Neutral group training activity control group as it was for the Mindfulness training treatment group, as shown in Figure 2 (choice D is wrong).

5. **C** The experimental study is presented in the data of Figure 2, in which the participants were randomly assigned to the treatment group or the control group. The dependent variable is the outcome or experimental variable that is not manipulated by the researchers. The outcome variable in the experimental study was the level of Stereotype Threat (choice C is correct). Self-Judgment was not a variable measured for the experimental study, and was instead included in the correlational analysis with Stereotype Threat shown in Figure 1 (choice A is wrong). Mindfulness was the independent variable in the experimental study, the variable that the experimenters manipulated by randomly assigning individuals into the Mindfulness or the control group (choice B is wrong). Self-Fulfilling Prophecy is a related concept to Stereotype threat, but is not included in the measurement of this study (choice D is wrong).

Passage 43

1. **A** The weak DSH hypothesis suggests that different combinations of alleles have the potential to amplify sensitivity to parental hostility; therefore a child's behavior has the potential to be affected by hostile interactions with their parent, regardless of the genetic makeup of that child. Couple this with Mary Ainsworth's strange situation experiments, which suggested that children who had insensitive and unresponsive caregivers were more likely to develop an insecure attachment, and the most logical conclusion is that those children raised in hostile households would be more likely to demonstrate an insecure attachment (choice A is correct). Ainsworth's experiments did not look at sensitivity to cortisol (choice B is wrong), nor did they examine social learning (choice C is wrong). While it is possible that insecurely attached infants might avoid romantic relationships as adults, this is also not something that Ainsworth concluded from her strange situation experiments (choice D is wrong).

2. **B** The passage states that saliva samples were analyzed for the presence of alleles, or alternative gene states. The process of examining which genes an individual carries is known as genotyping (choice B is correct). Phenotypes are the observable traits expressed by the genotype, or genetic information, of the individual (choice B is wrong). Human genome mapping refers to the broad

endeavor of discovering the vast network of genes that comprise the totality of genetic information common to the human species (choice C is wrong). Trait detection is not a formal term associated with the study of genetics (choice D is wrong).

3. **D** Genes are located in pairs along the strands of a chromosome. Different gene states, or alleles, exhibit different types of relationships with other alleles in a given gene pair. Dominant alleles are those that express themselves whenever they are present, such as the allele for brown eyes, while recessive alleles are those that are invariably overridden when the second member of the allele pair is dominant. Only if both members of a gene pair are recessive do they express themselves, as is the case for the allele for blue eyes. The plasticity index described in the passage does not indicate whether the alleles associated with plasticity are dominant or recessive in nature (choices A and B are wrong). The passage states that the researchers used the sum of alleles to represent the plasticity index, which suggests that plasticity is the product of multiple genes. Whenever a trait is attributed to multiple genes or alleles, those genes are considered to have a cumulative relation to the phenotype, or trait, in question (choice D is correct). The term autosomal refers chromosomes, not genes. Specifically, it refers to the 22 out of 23 chromosomes that are not responsible for determining a person's sex (choice C is wrong).

4. **C** The diathesis-stress model posits that some people are genetically predisposed to certain physical or psychological vulnerabilities, though the actual activation of those vulnerabilities may depend on environmental circumstances or experience. However, while the diathesis stress model focuses only on negative gene x environment interactions, the differential susceptibility hypothesis (DSH) proposes that some people may possess a general sensitivity to both positive and negative environmental influences. Hence, the DSH represents an expansion, or augmentation, of the diathesis stress model (choice C is correct). Cognitive-behavioral models are used to described the relationship between people's thoughts and behaviors and is not directly relevant to genetics or the DSH (choice A is wrong). Although the question stem assumes applicability of the DSH to men and women, it is not limited to either sex. Similarly, the DSH is not limited to the 23rd chromosome that contains the genetic information that guides one's biological sex (choice B is wrong). The DSH implies that certain genotypes may reduce or prevent a gene x environment interaction, but this merely serves to qualify a broad assumption of gene x interaction rather than replace it (choice D is wrong).

5. **D** The last paragraph of the passage differentiated between two versions of the DSH. In the strong version, plasticity completely controls sensitivity to hostility or positive engagement, while in the weak version, plasticity merely amplifies sensitivity. The difference between the two is illustrated in a case where a person has no plasticity at all. According to the strong version, plasticity is completely responsible for sensitivity, so a total absence of plasticity would render the individual impervious, or unaffected, by environmental hostility or positive engagement. Alternatively, the weak version would predict that the person may still be sensitive to hostility or positive engagement, albeit less so than someone with some degree of plasticity. If so, the two versions are mutually exclusive (I and II cannot both be true). The two graphs in Figure 1 show that the higher the plasticity score, the steeper the slope of the line. This indicates that higher plasticity resulted in lower and higher degrees of hostility and positive engagement having more extreme effects on targets' romantic relationships. In the case of a plasticity score of 0, the line is completely horizontal, which indicates that regardless of the degree of parental hostility or positive engagement, the target exhibited the same degree of hostility and positive engagement in his/her relationship with a romantic partner. Thus, parental interaction does not affect, either positively or negatively, those with zero plasticity. Accordingly, the strong DSH is confirmed (II is true and I is false by definition; therefore choices A and C are wrong). As noted, the slope of the phenotype, which, in this case, is the observable trait of hostility or positive engagement, increases as a function of a higher plasticity index (III is true; therefore choice B is wrong and choice D is correct).

6. **A** Monozygotic twins are the result of a split of a single zygote, or egg-sperm combination. Thus, they share identical genetic information. In contrast, dizygotic twins are the result of two independent fertilizations of two eggs, so they do not share identical genetic information. If twins with identical genetics and who were raised in different parenting environments have similar traits, it would seem that genetics alone, not environment, predict later relationship dynamics (choice A does NOT support the notion that parent-child interactions predict later relationship dynamics and is therefore correct). If monozygotic twins raised in different environments show different relationships traits despite identical genetics, the assertion in the question stem is supported (choice B supports the notion and is therefore wrong). Findings that dizygotic twins raised in similar parenting environments, albeit by different parents, exhibit relationship qualities similar to those of the parents that raised them suggest that parent-child interactions are predictive of later relationship dynamics (choices C and D support the notion and are there

Passage 44

1. **D** The passage states that people with TS also report problems with anxiety and mood disorders (conversion disorder is a somatoform disorder so choice C is wrong). The remaining disorders have all been reported in those with TS, but the discussion of tics, especially the notion of urges, in paragraph reflects the presence of obsessive-compulsive disorder (OCD; choice D is correct and choices A and B are wrong). The repetitive behaviors (tics) are sometimes associated with the intrusive thoughts characteristic of OCD and can lead to ritualistic behaviors. For example, a fear of dirt and germs (an obsession) that leads to repetitive hand-washing (a compulsion).

2. **B** The frontal lobes, positioned at the foremost region of the cerebral cortex, are considered the seat of emotions and are divided into three areas: the prefrontal cortex, the premotor area, and the motor area (choice A is wrong). The prefrontal cortex is critical for emotional experiences (choice B is correct). The prefrontal region of the frontal lobes is associated with the reduction of emotional feelings, such as fear, and methods of emotional regulation and stress relief can therefore activate its processes. The premotor and motor areas are involved in the control of muscle movement, particularly voluntary movement, as suggested by their names (choices C and D are wrong). The precentral cortex is not an actual area, but the precentral gyrus is the location of the primary motor cortex. These regions are detailed; when discussing emotion, for the MCAT, it is most important to be familiar with the role of the prefrontal cortex in emotions, as well as executive functions, decision making, and temperament.

3. **B** Estimates suggest that about 26% of Americans suffer from diagnosable psychological disorders at any given time; therefore, this choice is closest to 1 in 4 Americans, which is 25% (choice B is correct). However, serious psychological disorders are less common with estimates suggesting prevalence rates around 6% in the U.S. Nonetheless, mental illness is an important part of our culture and, in particular, our model of healthcare.

4. **C** According to the Kinsey scale of sexual behavior, sexual orientation is thought to lie along a scale or spectrum, with exclusive heterosexual behavior on one end, and exclusive homosexual behavior on the other end. However, sexual orientation is not a psychological disorder (choice C is correct). The latest revision of the Diagnostical and Statistical Manual of Mental Disorders characterizes autism as a spectrum disorder (choice A is wrong), mood disorders (ranging from extreme depression to extreme mania) along a spectrum (choice B is wrong), and schizophrenia and other psychotic disorders along a spectrum (choice D is wrong).

5. **A** Paragraph one of the passage states that TS and other neuroemotional disorders are distinguished from neurocognitive and neurodegenerative disorders. Cognitive decline in memory, perception, and problem-solving are characteristic of neurocognitive disorders, which include dementia, delirium, amnestic, and other cognitive disorders such as Alzheimer's disease (choices C and D are wrong). Progressive loss of the function or structure of neurons is characteristic of neurodegenerative disorders, such as amyotrophic lateral sclerosis, Huntington's disease, and Parkinson's disease (choice B is wrong). Therefore, using the process of elimination (POE), self-injurious behavior (SIB) is the correct answer (choice A is correct). For example, SIB is one of the current focuses in neuropsychiatric research at the New England Primate Research Center (NEPRC) at Harvard Medical School. SIB involves intentional injury of the body tissue, often without suicidal intentions. ADHD is another common example of a disorder in this category.

Passage 45

1. **A** The study described in the passage attempted to apply the SDT dimensions to social identity. Specifically, the researchers wanted to know if the various SDT motivation types yield positive and negative consequences regarding social identity processes in the same way that they yield diverse consequences in behavior. The assumption of such a study is that the operational definitions of "positive" and "negative" as applied to behavior also apply to social identity processes (choice A is correct). Social identity theory proposes that a person's affiliation with a given group influences his/her attitudes towards members of the same group and towards those belonging to different groups. In general, social identity theory predicts that people will adopt attitudes that favor the group with which they affiliate. To say that social identity theory is a corollary of SDT means that if SDT is true, then social identity theory must also be true. This equation is not correct, because the two theories address different concepts, i.e. SDT addresses the results of certain types of motivations, and social identity theory addresses the attitudes people form as a function of group identity. Thus, the pattern of consequences of self-determined versus non-self-determined motivations as predicted by SDT does not necessarily imply that people form attitudes favorable to their group (choice B is wrong). The application of SDT to social identity explores the possibility that SDT dimensions predict positive or negative consequences of social identity. Neither identity strength nor quality of identity is an SDT dimension and would not be expected to yield positive or negative consequences. In fact, the study treats quality of identity as a positive consequence (choice C is wrong). While the researchers' exploratory hypothesis was that the outcomes of social identification are predicted by dimensions of SDT, the question stem asks for an a priori assumption upon which the study was based (choice D is wrong).

2. **C** Correlations between variables are represented with a number between -1 and 1. Positive numbers represent a positive correlation in which an increase in one variable is associated with an increase in the other variable, while negative numbers represent a negative correlation in which an increase in one variable is associated with a decrease in the other variable. Table 1 shows that Psychological Wellbeing is negatively correlated with the SDT dimension of amotivation (-.18*), which suggests that a high Psychological Wellbeing score would be associated with a low amotivation score (choice C is correct; choice B is wrong). Psychological Wellbeing is negatively correlated with introjected regulation, albeit to an insignificant degree (choice A is wrong), and it is positively correlated with integrated regulation (choice D is wrong).

3. **D** Ostracization occurs when an individual harshly denigrates a member of the same in-group when that member behaves in a manner that is inconsistent with the values of the group. In so doing, a person attempts to maintain his/her in-group's positive image. Even without consulting Table 1, it follows that one's treatment of another student as an outcast represents a negative consequence of social identity similar to school superiority, which would thus be predicted by a high score on a non-self-determined motivation. The only answer choice that meets these criteria is a high introjected regulation score (choice D is correct; choices A, B, and C are wrong).

4. **A** Validity refers to the accuracy of measures and data interpretation. If variance, or discrepancy from the mean, of the variables in the study was associated primarily with the strength, or degree, of students' school identities rather than with the types of motivations, the correlations between SDT motivation types and positive or negative consequences would be misleading. Therefore, it would be critical to first ascertain the amount of variance that could be attributed to, or associated with, identity strength and only then to determine if the remaining variance associated with each motivation variable is significant or not (choice A is correct; choice C is wrong). Integrated regulation and in-group bias are both variables that are the subject of the study, so it would not be critical to account for the variance due to these variables prior to proceeding with correlational analysis (choices B and D are wrong).

5. **C** According to Table 1, external regulation is positively correlated with a consequence of school superiority. Since acknowledgment of another school's superiority would contradict this attitude, Linda would likely attribute the competing school's victory to situational factors, such as the turf or the weather, than to that team's inherent athletic superiority. An individual's attribution of the successes of a group to situational rather than internal factors is known as the ultimate attribution error (choice C is correct). In contrast, the self-serving bias applies to one's attributions about the successes of oneself or that of other individuals, not groups (choice D is wrong). External regulation is not negatively correlated with identity quality (choice A is wrong), though it is significantly positively correlated with in-group bias (choice B is wrong).

NOTES

NOTES

NOTES